English Letters	**Meaning**
n_1, n_2, n	Number of observations in a group (or cell)
O_k, O_{jk}	Observed frequencies for χ^2 statistics
$p(\ ), p, p\text{-value}$	Probability
p	Population proportion; stretch size
P	Sample proportion
PR	Percentile rank
q	Probability of a failure, $1 - p$; Studentized range statistic
q_{crit}	Critical value from the Studentized range distribution
Q_1	First quartile, 25th percentile
Q_3	Third quartile, 75th percentile
R	Number of rows in a contingency table; multiple correlation coefficient
R^2	Square of the multiple correlation coefficient
r	Pearson's correlation coefficient
r^2	Square of r
r_S	Spearman rank order correlation coefficient
$\overset{*}{s}{}^2, \overset{*}{s}{}^2_X$	Sample variance of X
$\overset{*}{s}$	Sample standard deviation of X
$\overset{*}{s}{}^2_Y$	Sample variance of Y
$\overset{*}{s}_Y$	Sample standard deviation of Y
$\overset{*}{s}{}^2_{\text{explained}}$	Sample variance of Y explained by regression
$\overset{*}{s}{}^2_{\text{not explained}}$	Sample variance of Y not explained by regression
s^2	Unbiased sample variance of X
s	Square root of the unbiased sample variance of X
$s^2_{Y \cdot X}$	Sample variance of Y around the regression line
$s_{Y \cdot X}$	Standard error of estimate
s^2_d	Sample variance of d's
$s_{\overline{X}_1 - \overline{X}_2}$	Sample standard deviation of $\overline{X}_1 - \overline{X}_2$
s^2_{pooled}	Sample variance of observations within groups (ANOVA)
$s^2_{\overline{X}}$	Sample variance of $\overline{X}_j$ values
SS	Sum of squares
T score	A standard score with mean 50 and standard deviation 10
T_1, T_2, T_+, T_-, T_j	Various rank sums
T	Wilcoxon's statistic
t	Student's t statistic
UH	Upper hinge
U_1, U_2, U	Various U statistics for the Mann-Whitney test
X	An observed score
$\overline{X}$	X-bar, sample mean of X
$\overline{X}_j, \overline{X}_k, \overline{X}_{jk}$	Various sample means used in ANOVAs
$\overline{X}_1 - \overline{X}_2$	Difference of sample means from two groups
X_{50}	Sample median
Y	An observed score on the criterion variable
Y'	Predicted score on Y
$\overline{Y}$	Sample mean of Y
z, z_X	z score (standard score) for X
$\bar{z}$	Sample mean of z
z_P	z score for a proportion
$z_{\overline{X}}$	z score for $\overline{X}$
z_Y	z score for Y

Second Edition

Introductory Statistics for the Behavioral Sciences

Second Edition

Introductory Statistics for the Behavioral Sciences

Larry E. Toothaker
Lise Miller

University of Oklahoma

Brooks/Cole Publishing Company

I(T)P™ An International Thomson Publishing Company

Pacific Grove • Albany • Bonn • Boston • Cincinnati • Detroit • London • Madrid • Melbourne
Mexico City • New York • Paris • San Francisco • Singapore • Tokyo • Toronto • Washington

Sponsoring Editor: *Jim Brace-Thompson*
Marketing Team: *Gay Meixel and Romy Fineroff*
Marketing Representative: *Jennifer Jewett*
Editorial Assistant: *Dorothy Kormos*
Production Editor: *Laurel Jackson*
Production Assistant: *Dorothy Bell*
Manuscript Editor: *Carol Reitz*

Permissions Editor: *Cathleen S. Collins*
Interior and Cover Design: *Katherine Minerva*
Interior Illustration: *MacArt Design*
Art Editor: *Lisa Torri*
Typesetting: *Weimer Graphics, Inc.*
Cover Printing: *Color Dot Graphics, Inc.*
Printing and Binding: *Quebecor Printing Hawkins*

For more information, contact:

BROOKS/COLE PUBLISHING COMPANY
511 Forest Lodge Road
Pacific Grove, CA 93950
USA

International Thomson Publishing Europe
Berkshire House 168-173
High Holborn
London WC1V 7AA
England

Thomas Nelson Australia
102 Dodds Street
South Melbourne, 3205
Victoria, Australia

Nelson Canada
1120 Birchmount Road
Scarborough, Ontario
Canada M1K 5G4

International Thomson Editores
Campos Eliseos 385, Piso 7
Col. Polanco
11560 México D. F. México

International Thomson Publishing GmbH
Königswinterer Strasse 418
53227 Bonn
Germany

International Thomson Publishing Asia
221 Henderson Road
#05-10 Henderson Building
Singapore 0315

International Thomson Publishing Japan
Hirakawacho Kyowa Building, 3F
2-2-1 Hirakawacho
Chiyoda-ku, Tokyo 102
Japan

Printed in the United States of America
10 9 8 7 6 5 4 3 2 1

Library of Congress Cataloging-in-Publication Data

Toothaker, Larry E.
    Introductory statistics for the behavioral sciences / Larry E.
Toothaker, Lise Miller.—2nd ed.
        p.   cm.
    Includes bibliographical references (p.   –   ) and index.
    ISBN 0-534-20262-4 (alk. paper)
    1. Statistics.   I. Miller, Lise, [date]–   . II. Title.
QA276. 12. T66 1996
001.42'2—dc20   95-15104
                                                 CIP

Brief Contents

Part I   Topics and Tools for Description and Inference   1

1   Introduction   3

2   Research and Research Design   35

3   Describing Data for a Single Variable: Pictorial Descriptions   67

4   Describing Data for a Single Variable: Summary Measures   103

5   Measures of Relative Standing and the Normal Distribution   137

6   Describing Data for Two Variables: Correlation   167

7   Describing Data for Two Variables: Regression   197

8   Probability   241

9   Sampling Distributions   269

10   Introduction to Hypothesis Testing   307

11   Types of Error and Power   337

Part II   Inferential Statistical Methods   367

12   Statistics for Evaluating One-Sample Experiments   369

13   Statistics for Evaluating Two-Sample Experiments   405

14   One-Way Analysis of Variance   449

15   Multiple Comparison Procedures   483

16   Two-Way Analysis of Variance   513

17   Repeated Measures ANOVA   547

18   Nonparametric Methods: χ^2 Tests   575

19   Nonparametric Methods: Rank Tests   599

20   Review and Choice of Statistical Method   627

Contents

Part I   Topics and Tools for Description and Inference   1

1   Introduction   3

Research Example 1   4
1.1   How Researchers Draw Conclusions   5
1.2   College Decisions: Data and Statistics in Your Daily Life   6
1.3   The World around You: Data and Statistics   8
1.4   The Need for Statistics; or, Why Study Statistics?   12
1.5   Statistics in Research   13
1.6   Overview of Statistics   14
1.7   Preview of Inferential Statistics   20
1.8   Use of This Text   25
1.9   Help for You   26
1.10 Summary and Study Tips   29
      Exercises   30

2   Research and Research Design   35

Research Example 2   36
2.1   Introduction   37
2.2   Research   37
2.3   Variables   41
2.4   Types of Relationships   48
2.5   Types of Research   50
2.6   Data in Research   55
2.7   Summary, Study Tips, and Computers   59
      Exercises   62

3   Describing Data for a Single Variable: Pictorial Descriptions   67

Research Example 3   67
3.1   Overview and Introduction   69

3.2   Pictorial Descriptions: Frequency Distributions   73
3.3   Pictorial Descriptions: Stem and Leaf Displays   78
3.4   Pictorial Descriptions: Graphs   81
3.5   Misleading Graphs   86
3.6   Description with Statistics   89
3.7   Summary, Study Tips, and Computation   91
       Exercises   98

4   Describing Data for a Single Variable:
       Summary Measures   103

       Research Example 4   104
4.1   Introduction   105
4.2   Summation Notation: A Tool Necessary for Sample Statistics   106
4.3   Describing the Central Tendency of Data   108
4.4   Sample Mode   109
4.5   Sample Median   110
4.6   Sample Mean   112
4.7   Describing the Variability of Data   116
4.8   Ranges   118
4.9   Absolute Deviation   119
4.10 Sample Variance   120
4.11 Sample Standard Deviation   123
4.12 Five-Number Summaries and Box-Plots   126
4.13 Summary, Study Tips, and Computation   129
       Exercises   134

5   Measures of Relative Standing and the
       Normal Distribution   137

       Research Example 5   137
5.1   Introduction   139
5.2   Standard Scores   139
5.3   Normal Distributions   144
5.4   Other Standard Scores   153
5.5   Percentiles   154
5.6   Summary, Study Tips, and Computation   158
       Exercises   164

6   Describing Data for Two Variables: Correlation   167

       Research Example 6   168
6.1   Introduction   168
6.2   Linear Relationships   169
6.3   Pearson Correlation Coefficient: A Measure of the Degree of
       Linear Relationship   170

6.4   Properties of *r*   173
6.5   Computational Formula for *r*   176
6.6   Factors to Consider in Using *r*   179
6.7   Correlation and Causation   184
6.8   Summary, Study Tips, and Computation   185
        Exercises   192

7   **Describing Data for Two Variables: Regression   197**

Research Example 7   198
7.1   Introduction: Regression and Linear Prediction   199
7.2   Using and Interpreting the Regression Equation   202
7.3   Least Squares and the Best-Fitting Line   206
7.4   Standard Error of Estimate   210
7.5   Partitioning Total Variability   213
7.6   Regression: Enhancing Your Understanding   215
7.7   Multiple Regression and Other Topics   220
7.8   Summary, Study Tips, and Computation   226
        Exercises   234

8   **Probability   241**

Research Example 8   242
8.1   Introduction   244
8.2   Definitions   245
8.3   Sampling: With or without Replacement   253
8.4   Probability Distributions: Discrete (Binomial) and
        Continuous (Normal) Variables   256
8.5   Probability and Statistics   262
8.6   Summary, Study Tips, and Computation   264
        Exercises   266

9   **Sampling Distributions   269**

Research Example 9   270
9.1   Introduction and Review   271
9.2   Three Different Types of Distributions   273
9.3   Population Distribution   274
9.4   Sample Distribution   276
9.5   Sampling Distribution   277
9.6   Sampling Distribution of $\overline{X}$ as an Example   282
9.7   Sampling Distributions of Other Statistics   288
9.8   Estimation: Means of Sampling Distributions and Unbiased Estimates   292
9.9   Estimation: Confidence Interval for the Population Mean   298
9.10   Summary, Study Tips, and Computation   302
        Exercises   303

10   Introduction to Hypothesis Testing   307

Research Example 10   308
10.1   Introduction   309
10.2   Overview: Integration of Probability, Sampling Distributions, and Decision Making   310
10.3   Rat Shipment Example   312
10.4 $z_{\bar{x}}$: Example of a Test Statistic   314
10.5   Null and Alternative Hypotheses   318
10.6   Significance Level   320
10.7   Directional and Nondirectional Hypotheses   320
10.8   One- and Two-Tailed Tests, Critical Values, Rejection Values, and Decision Rules   322
10.9   Logic of Hypothesis Testing   329
10.10   Summary, Study Tips, and Computation   332
Exercises   334

11   Types of Error and Power   337

Research Example 11   338
11.1   Overview: Types of Error, Power, and Variables That Influence Power   339
11.2   Two Potential Decisions and Associated Errors   341
11.3   Power   347
11.4   Variables That Influence Power   348
11.5   Computing Power and Sample Size   355
11.6   Summary, Study Tips, and Computation   360
Exercises   361

Part II   Inferential Statistical Methods   367

12   Statistics for Evaluating One-Sample Experiments   369

Research Example 12   370
12.1   Overview: Available Statistical Procedures   371
12.2   One-Sample *t*-Test: A More Practical One-Sample Test   371
12.3   Confidence Interval for the Population Mean   379
12.4   Test of a Hypothesis about a Population Correlation   383
12.5   Large-Sample Test of a Hypothesis about a Population Proportion   389
12.6   Summary, Study Tips, and Computation   395
Exercises   400

13   Statistics for Evaluating Two-Sample Experiments   405

Research Example 13   406
13.1   Overview: Two-Sample Experiments and Tests for Means   407

13.2   Two Independent Samples: Means   410
13.3   Two Dependent Samples: Means   426
13.4   Comparison of Independent and Dependent Sample Cases   433
13.5   Two Independent Samples: Proportions   435
13.6   Summary, Study Tips, and Computation   439
       Exercises   445

14   **One-Way Analysis of Variance   449**

       Research Example 14   450
14.1   Introduction   451
14.2   Logic of ANOVA   455
14.3   ANOVA: Partitioning of Variability   460
14.4   ANOVA F Test   466
14.5   Summary, Study Tips, and Computation   474
       Exercises   478

15   **Multiple Comparison Procedures   483**

       Research Example 15   483
15.1   Introduction   484
15.2   Error Rates and Statistics   486
15.3   Tukey, Fisher-Hayter, and Ryan MCPs   490
15.4   Unequal Sample Sizes   497
15.5   Orthogonal Contrasts   500
15.6   Summary, Study Tips, and Computation   505
       Exercises   511

16   **Two-Way Analysis of Variance   513**

       Research Example 16   514
16.1   Introduction   515
16.2   ANOVA: Partitioning of Variability   523
16.3   ANOVA F Tests   528
16.4   ANOVA Computation   531
16.5   Summary, Study Tips, and Computation   538
       Exercises   542

17   **Repeated Measures ANOVA   547**

       Research Example 17   547
17.1   Introduction   549
17.2   Characteristics of Repeated Measures Designs   550
17.3   Simple Repeated Measures Design   553
17.4   Groups by Trials Repeated Measures Design   559
17.5   Assumptions   564

17.6   Summary, Study Tips, and Computation   565
          Exercises   571

18   Nonparametric Methods: χ^2 Tests   575

Research Example 18   576
18.1   Introduction to Nonparametric Methods   577
18.2 χ^2 Tests: Qualitative Data   581
18.3   Chi-Square Test for Goodness of Fit   582
18.4   Chi-Square Test for Contingency Tables   587
18.5   Summary, Study Tips, and Computation   591
          Exercises   595

19   Nonparametric Methods: Rank Tests   599

Research Example 19   600
19.1   Rank Tests: General Comments   601
19.2   Mann-Whitney U Test: Two Independent Samples   603
19.3   Wilcoxon Test: Two Dependent Samples   606
19.4   Kruskal-Wallis Test: J Independent Samples   609
19.5   Friedman Test: J Dependent Samples   611
19.6   Spearman Correlation Coefficient   615
19.7   Summary, Study Tips, and Computation   618
          Exercises   622

20   Review and Choice of Statistical Method   627

Research Example 20   627
20.1   Introduction   629
20.2   Overview of Statistical Procedures   630
20.3   Choice of Statistic   632
20.4   Beyond These Statistics   638
          Exercises   638
          Appendix A   Tables   643
          Appendix B   Review of Basic Mathematics   659
          Answers to Selected Exercises   667
          References   695
          Index   699

Preface

Characteristics of the Course

Introductory Statistics for the Behavioral Sciences, Second Edition, is a basic survey of statistical methods usually taught in an introductory course in applied statistics. This course could be taught in any social or behavioral science department (such as psychology, education, or sociology) or in a mathematics department (in a course designed for behavioral or social science majors).

Characteristics of This Text

The text covers topics usually taught in a one-semester course, but it could also be used with supplementary material in a two-semester sequence of courses. Not all the material in this book can be presented in one semester. For example, in our classes, we teach selected parts of most chapters, omitting some of Chapters 5, 8, 12, 13, 18, and 19, and all of Chapter 17. However, other instructors might teach everything through the two-sample *t*-tests (Chapter 13).

The text approaches statistical topics with the aim of achieving conceptual understanding rather than emphasizing rote computation, yet without neglecting the computational aspects of each topic. Understanding why, when, and where a particular method is used is as important as knowing how to perform computations. Although the latter is taught in this text, it is not emphasized. The need for conceptual understanding to accompany computational accuracy is evidenced daily in the misuse of statistics in wide-ranging applications, from media commercials to top-level professional journals in behavioral and other applied sciences. At all levels, users of statistics usually understand how to compute the values of the statistics but routinely blunder by using the wrong method for the problem, by using poor methods, by misinterpreting the results, or by incorrectly citing some statistical principle. All these problems stem from and are exacerbated by the lack of conceptual understanding of statistics. Given the proliferation of powerful computers and computer programs to accurately compute statistics, it is even more important that we build correct conceptual understanding to guide and accompany this power. A computer's output cannot be better than the data and instructions fed to it; the principle of GIGO (garbage in, garbage out) applies.

Important Features of This Text

To help you understand more clearly how statistics are used in research, we have started each chapter with a *Research Example*. These examples draw from a wide range of disciplines (psychology, communications, medicine, sociology, public health, and education) to offer a broad-based experience in the use of statistics. (You can focus more on your particular interests in future courses, such as experimental psychology or research methods in your area.) As much as possible, these examples are drawn from actual published research to show you how the statistics you are learning are used in the real world.

Certain data sets are used in several places in the text. For example, you might see some data first in Chapter 2 where we discuss types of research; again in Chapter 4, in the discussion of descriptive statistics; and then again in Chapter 13, when two-sample *t*-tests are covered. We do this both to show you the continuity among different topics in statistics and to present a realistic picture of data analysis. Whenever possible, these data sets are also real, so some of them are fairly large.

Periodically in the text, a *Quick Quiz* appears so that you can check your progress in understanding the concepts presented. The Quick Quizzes serve as midchapter exercises and will be most helpful if you attempt to answer the question yourself before looking at the answer. At the end of each chapter, we have included *Study Tips*, which give you the benefit of other students' experiences.

For most of the statistics given in the text, we present two *formulas*: one is *definitional* (conceptual), and the other is *computational*. The definitional formula is presented to help you conceptually understand the statistic and is usually given in a verbal form. You don't have to understand the computational formula in great depth, but you should realize that it is the best formula to use for computing the statistic or for programming computers to do the calculating.

To accompany the conceptual emphasis of the text, we deal with computational aspects of the various methods by accurate presentation of formulas, decision rules, and so on, and by examples of computer runs (programs and output) from common statistical packages (SAS and SPSS). Computer sections are always optional, but they offer a fairly easy entry into computer usage. End-of-chapter exercises are organized by chapter sections. Your best strategy for these exercises is to work on the appropriate ones after you finish reading each section.

The first chapter contains a *seven-point outline* of topics that are common to all inferential statistical methods. This outline is a preview of much of the text. However, you are not expected to comprehend these topics completely in the first chapter. Rather, the preview is intended to focus your attention on the seven topics and to give you a means of organizing the material in Chapters 1 through 11. Students have found this preview a helpful first step in outlining the material in the first one-half to two-thirds of the course. Some instructors may choose to skip this material as a preview and assign it as a review when Chapter 9 or Chapter 10 is begun.

Acknowledgments

No work of this magnitude is done alone. We have labored together, and a shared burden is easier to carry. Additionally, there were those who encouraged the starting of this text. Others helped to carry it to its completion, and the result is the product of a team effort. The first person who was key to this effort is Nietzie Toothaker, wife of the first author, who provided support throughout the project, beginning with reading early versions of the manuscript of the first edition. Other first-edition help was given by Lori Toothaker (now Warnick), Brady Toothaker, Martha Banz, Bridgette Perry, other graduate students, and Charles Harding (who helped minimize the cost of photocopying the preliminary version for use in classroom testing). Students in various statistics classes (Fall 1984 for the first edition; Summer and Fall 1994 and Spring 1995 for this edition) helped by using this text in a preliminary version. One of those students, Valerie Spiegle, provided a copy of the journal article used in Research Example 20. Colleagues who made helpful contributions to one or both of the editions include Dr. W. Alan Nicewander, Dr. Jorge Mendoza, and Dr. Joseph Rodgers; they provided valuable assistance as sounding boards on technical and teaching matters. The reviewers of the second edition offered many useful suggestions. These reviewers include Terry Ackerman, University of Illinois; Nancy S. Anderson, University of Maryland at College Park; Bryan C. Auday, Gordon College; Dennis Cogan, Texas Tech University; G. William Hill IV, Kennesaw State College; Kermit Hoyenga, Western Illinois University; Martin Johnson, Missouri Western State College; Paul Koch, St. Ambrose College; Valerie C. McKay, California State University at Long Beach; Paul Nelson, Kansas State University; Reuben Rusch, State University of New York at Albany; Craig L. Smith, Vanderbilt University; Philip Tolin, Central Washington University; Eric Turkheimer, University of Virginia; and John Vicedomini, University of Oregon.

As this edition goes into print, we are already looking ahead to the third edition and seeking ways to improve this text. If you, the student, have ideas for study tips, better exercises, and so on, or if you, the teacher, have ideas on better ways to present material in this text, please write to us at the University of Oklahoma, Department of Psychology, 455 W. Lindsey, Room 705, Norman, OK 73019 (e-mail address: Ltoothaker@oupsy.uoknor.edu). After all, improving people's understanding of statistics is a major reason we wrote this book.

From Larry E. Toothaker: I want to express my thankfulness to my Lord. Without His leading, this text would not have been written. "Commit your works to the Lord, and your plans will be established" (Proverbs 16:3).

From Lise Miller: I am grateful to Larry Toothaker, for his patience, respect, guidance, and belief in me; to the faculty of the OU Psychology Department, for supporting me and allowing my graduate work to be delayed by this project; and to my family, especially my parents, both of whom taught me the beauty of the written word. My father showed me the value of disciplined work habits and encouraged me to hone my mind; my mother demonstrated the gentle grace of the heart. Finally, to students who use this text, I'd like to say that being a scientist doesn't require a cold heart. Do what you love and follow your passion. To paraphrase *A Course in Miracles*, only love is real; herein lies peace.

Larry E. Toothaker
Lise Miller

Second Edition

Introductory Statistics for the Behavioral Sciences

I

Part One

Topics and Tools for Description and Inference

The focus of the first part of this text is on tool building. Before you can use statistics to make decisions, you need some basic tools of the trade. Such tools include descriptive statistics, probability, and estimation. You also need to learn some concepts that relate to the statistics themselves: sampling variability of statistics, distributions of statistics, and theoretical reference distributions. Finally, the basic steps and language of hypothesis testing compose the final tool necessary for statistical decision making.

1

Introduction

How do you decide whether an educational program increases test scores? Is an average gain of five points a big increase or a chance fluctuation? People use statistics to answer such questions. Statistics may be numerical summary measures that describe information, or they may be procedures used to decide whether changes in numbers are caused by more than chance. This chapter gives examples of statistics you see every day and introduces the idea of using statistical procedures in scientific settings. You'll need to start picking up the vocabulary of statistics in this chapter because it is the foundation of everything else in the book.

Research Example 1

1.1 **How Researchers Draw Conclusions**

1.2 **College Decisions: Data and Statistics in Your Daily Life**

Description and decision making

Relevance and usefulness

Risks

1.3 **The World around You: Data and Statistics**

Health

Government

Business

Education

Sports

1.4 **The Need for Statistics; or, Why Study Statistics?**

Better consumer

Better reader

Better researcher

1.5 **Statistics in Research**

1.6 **Overview of Statistics**

Populations

Samples

Sampling

Two areas of statistics

1.7 **Preview of Inferential Statistics**

Descriptive statistics

Probability

Estimation

Sampling variability

Distributions

Theoretical reference distribution

Hypothesis testing

1.8 Use of This Text
  Organization
  Key terms and concepts
  Realistic data sets
  Computation and exercises
  Appendixes, symbol glossary, and list of formulas
1.9 Help for You
  You can do it
  Math anxiety
  Study strategies
  Test-taking strategies
1.10 Summary and Study Tips
  Chapter summary
  Study tips
Exercises

Research Example 1

Do you demand immediate satisfaction? Or are you able to delay gratification—that is, able to surrender an immediate reward for the sake of some benefit or goal in the future?

This fascinating area of research, called *delay of gratification,* has been summarized by Mischel, Shoda, and Rodriguez (1989), especially as it relates to children. Mischel and his colleagues studied children's preference for immediate smaller rewards versus delayed larger rewards. The choice to delay gratification is called *preference-to-delay.* Research shows that preference-to-delay increases as the size of the delayed reward increases, and it drops as the delay time increases. Preference-to-delay also goes up as the child gets older and is higher for more intelligent children. Studies show that children who are able to resist temptation have higher preference-to-delay. As social responsibility and achievement goals increase, so does preference-to-delay.

Shoda, Mischel, and Peake (1990) added to this body of research by demonstrating that under certain conditions, delay of gratification in children about $4\frac{1}{2}$ years old is significantly related to late adolescent cognitive and academic competence. That is, the children who had greater preference-to-delay as preschoolers had higher cognitive and academic achievement as teenagers.

The original research had individual children in a schoolroom where they initially played with toys and were told that they could play with them again later. Each child was then seated at a table where there was a bell and some objects, such as marshmallows, pretzels, toys, or poker chips. These items were presented as a pair of choices, such as one marshmallow versus two marshmallows. Researchers played a game with each child in which the child was to choose which of the pair he or she preferred. The children were told they could have the preferred item if they waited until the researcher returned to the room. If they wanted, they could signal the researcher to come back early by ringing the bell, at which time they would get the less preferred item. The variable of interest is the length of time in seconds that the child would delay (up to 15 minutes).

The original researchers included several variables in the study to test their impact on the delay of gratification (delay time in seconds). The first variable was rewards, visibly exposed versus obscured. The second variable was ideas given to the child about how to cope with the delay time (suggested ideation) versus no ideas given (spontaneous ideation). Four groups were made by combining the two levels of each variable: (1) rewards exposed/spontaneous ideation, (2) rewards obscured/spontaneous ideation, (3) rewards exposed/suggested ideation, and (4) rewards obscured/suggested ideation. Children were randomly assigned to one of the four groups. Only the rewards exposed/spontaneous ideation group had significantly shorter average delay times.

The really intriguing aspect of this research came more than 10 years later when the researchers collected follow-up information. Parents rated the children's cognitive ability, ability to cope, and self-control skills. The researchers also obtained verbal and quantitative SAT scores and a range of personality items. The results showed, for only the rewards exposed/spontaneous ideation group, that delay of gratification (measured more than a decade earlier) is related to a host of variables measured at the later time. For example, delay time is significantly related to parental ratings of self-control (a positive relationship), distractibility when trying to concentrate (a negative relationship), and academic ability (a positive relationship). Delay time also is significantly related to whether the adolescent "uses and responds to reason" (a positive relationship) and "tends to go to pieces under stress" (a negative relationship). Delay time also has a significant positive relationship to both verbal and quantitative SAT scores.

Why do these results hold for only the rewards exposed/spontaneous ideation group? Think about it for a minute. The children are not given any ideas, so they must come up with strategies to delay and use them on their own. The rewards are in front of them, so they are not helped by "out of sight, out of mind"; again, they must cope on their own. This combination elicits the behavior that is indicative of the individual differences in children's ability that carry over into adolescence.

So, can you delay gratification by turning off the TV and studying for your statistics course? Just the fact that you are a college student is a good predictor of a positive answer to this question. Think about it.

1.1 How Researchers Draw Conclusions

People who drink just two or three caffeinated beverages a day could face withdrawal symptoms more severe than the flu.

Placing babies on their backs at bedtime accounted for a decrease in the rate of sudden infant deaths in Avon County, England.

Southern males—but not Southern females—are more likely to use tobacco products than are people from other areas of the United States.

White suicide rates are higher in cities where more airtime is given to country music.

Students who are allowed to write questions for an exam report fewer symptoms of exam stress, but their test scores are unaffected.

People whose jobs require them to judge whether someone is telling the truth may not do that any better than anyone else. Only Secret Service personnel are better at catching a liar than are judges, police officers, psychiatrists, and even employees of the CIA and FBI.

Conclusions such as these are reported commonly in newspapers and on television. But you may wonder, How do they know that? Where did they get that conclusion?

Take the first example. Let's say you have read about or experienced withdrawal symptoms when you quit drinking beverages with caffeine. You decide to figure out how much caffeine intake is required to lead to withdrawal symptoms when caffeine intake is cut off. How are you going to do it? You could ask your friends to complete a questionnaire and list how many caffeinated drinks they have each day. You could also ask them to list symptoms, such as headaches, sluggishness, and depression, they may have suffered when they've stayed away from coffee, tea, and colas. The problem is that your friends might be similar to you, and their experience might not reflect what happens to people in general. Your friends might also want to please you and tell you what you want to hear so that you can publish a study and be famous.

Maybe you could set up a study in which people of different races, ages, and socio-economic backgrounds are represented. Perhaps you could get them to agree to drink only the beverages you give to them, and you could disguise the containers so they don't know whether they have caffeine. You could control which people get coffee and cola that contain caffeine and which ones get decaffeinated beverages. Later, you could switch them from drinks with caffeine to decaffeinated drinks. You could ask everyone to keep a diary of his or her physical and mental health, and you could look at whether symptoms appeared soon after you cut off someone's caffeine.

The advantage of the latter approach is clear: You can say what happens to people in general, and you can say that their symptoms are probably the result of your manipulation of their beverages. But before you can draw your conclusion, you have to measure the symptoms somehow. You could count them or give them some kind of rating—more points for more severe symptoms. Then what do you do with the numbers? Is someone with a symptom rating of 45 suffering a lot more than someone with a rating of 40, or could that be a minor difference? If it is a significant difference, then how do you draw that conclusion from the numbers?

That's what this book is about. Statistics aren't just percentages and averages. Statistics also are procedures. They are part of a dynamic process of going from an idea about a phenomenon to a conclusion by examining the numbers. Statistics are used to describe a phenomenon and to make decisions about the significance of the phenomenon.

The rest of the examples are described elsewhere in the book. Before learning how researchers make decisions based on the numbers in their studies, let's look at how statistics affect your life.

1.2   College Decisions: Data and Statistics in Your Daily Life

Description and Decision Making

As a college student, you obviously have a lot of information to cope with every day, such as when your first class starts and what you are asked to learn in class. You also have decisions to make, such as what time to get up in order to get to class on time. Routine decisions don't require you to process much information. Other decisions are bigger and need more information, more processing of the information, and more time to accomplish these tasks.

As an example of a nonroutine decision, suppose you are applying for admission to graduate school. For each department you consider, you have to gather information to help you make your decision. Such information might include entrance requirements, research areas of the faculty, graduate assistantship stipends, and characteristics of the community. Such information could be considered **data,** defined as facts or figures. Other data might include the grade point averages (GPAs) of all students admitted in the last five years and the number of students who graduate. You need to examine and explore the data to look for patterns that will help you in your decision. Perhaps you'll find that a certain school admits a high percentage of its applicants but graduates only a small percentage of them.

In addition, you may have some statistics, such as the average GPA of students admitted in the past five years or the percentage of students who graduate. **Statistics** are numerical summary measures computed on the data. Statistics, an integral part of data analysis, are computed to represent the data and thus to reveal something about them. You need to be aware, however, that sometimes statistics may conceal or even misrepresent important information about a phenomenon. Additionally, you need to be open to seeing unexpected patterns in the data, which is most likely to happen if you examine the data using appropriate displays or pictures (see Chapter 3).

Notice that you can use data and statistics to serve two purposes: to describe or to make decisions. The average GPA of admitted students is one way to describe each department you are considering, and it also may help you choose a particular graduate program. As you will see later, though, the average GPA may be influenced by one extreme GPA that can be discovered only if you look at the data, all of the original GPAs.

Data
Information expressed as facts or figures

Statistics
Numerical summary measures computed on data from a sample; numerical characteristics of a sample

Relevance and Usefulness

Some data and statistics may not be relevant to a particular decision. If you are going into counseling psychology, information about a cognitive psychology program may not pertain to your career goals. Some information may be in error, which makes it useless. Some faculty members listed in the brochure may have left by the time you arrive, or graduate assistantship stipends may have increased since the department printed its information packet.

One question about any data or statistics is: Are the data or statistics in a useful form? To answer this question, you need to understand the statistics. For example, what is meant by *average*? Is the "average" in "grade point average" the **mean**? The mean is defined as the arithmetic average (see Chapter 4). Or is it some other measure? If a report uses statistics that you don't understand or if the data are not relevant, then you need to either gather relevant data or learn about these new statistics.

Mean
Arithmetic average; the sum of the scores divided by the number of scores

Risks

Sometimes you have to make decisions in spite of ambiguous data, so some risk is involved. For example, one risk in choosing a graduate school is that faculty members who were crucial to your decision may leave the department. Or you may think that you are not good enough to get into a good program and thus not even apply. You have to take the data, the statistics, and the risks into account in making any decision.

Clearly you must be able to process information (data) in your world in order to make decisions. You also need to understand the statistics you encounter.

1.3   The World around You: Data and Statistics

You encounter data and statistics every day. You see data on television or in the newspaper; on a more personal level, you see data in the form of test scores and tuition expenses. In your college courses, you are likely to encounter data in the form of research results, such as attitudes of patients toward counseling psychologists who have used various types of counseling techniques. As stated earlier, you can use these data and statistics to accomplish one or both of these functions: (1) to describe, which includes exploring and examining some event or phenomenon, and (2) to infer, make decisions, or evaluate what you described.

Each day you are likely to see statistics in the areas of health, government, business, education, and sports.

Health

How many helpings of fruits and vegetables do you eat each day? The news article in Box 1.1 is an example of how health statistics find their way into the popular media. This article is packed with statistics, such as averages, percentages, and probabilities.

In reading the article, did you find the concept of average used to describe how many servings of fruits and vegetables were eaten? The goal of the program was to get Americans to increase their consumption from 3.5 servings on the average to 5 servings. At the time the article was written, only 23% of people ate five or more servings of fruits and vegetables per day. What was the probability that an American believed that eating fruits and vegetables would help prevent cancer? The answer was four out of ten, or a probability of .40 (see Chapter 8). Statistics would have been used to draw the conclusion that women are more likely than men to think that they should increase their consumption of fruits and vegetables. Did you see the mention of the relationship between children's consumption of fruits and vegetables and the same behavior in adult life? What decision could you make based on this information?

Government

Statistics are found in all areas of government. You can find statistics about taxes, unemployment, crime, the census, and so on. This may be the first year you will have to file your own income tax report with the IRS, so you might like to know where your money is being used. Examine the chart in Figure 1.1 to see how federal tax money was used in 1992. Perhaps the use of tax money is an issue in a congressional race in your state. You may decide whom to vote for based on graphs that show how money was used and the candidates' stands on these issues. It's important to know how to interpret graphs such as this one (see Chapter 3).

Box 1.1   Five Apples a Day Keep Cancer Away

The following article appeared in the *Oklahoma Daily* on July 2, 1972:

WASHINGTON—Most Americans could significantly cut their risk of cancer by adding a green salad and a glass of juice to their daily diet, the National Cancer Institute said Wednesday.

Kicking off a five-year, $33 million program to get people to eat five servings of fruits or vegetables daily, the institute said a new survey shows that most adults already eat an average of three and one-half.

"An apple a day keeps the doctor away," was good advice, said Bernadine Healey, director of the National Institutes of Health. "We're extending that."

A glass of orange juice in the morning, a lettuce and tomato salad at noon, apple or carrots for a snack and broccoli or another vegetable at dinner would put a person over the quota, said Health and Human Services Secretary Louis Sullivan.

"Let me stress, five-a-day is a minimum," he said. "If you can eat up to nine servings a day, all the better."

The government will provide $18 million in grants to local and state organizations with projects to promote the message, Sullivan said.

The Produce for Better Health Foundation, an industry group, will spend $15 million more in advertising and store promotions, said Bruce Obbink, president of the foundation.

It is the largest-ever government and food industry nutrition program.

Many studies show that nutrients in fruits and vegetables protect against cell damage that leads to cancer, said Dr. Peter Greenwald, director of cancer prevention at the National Cancer Institute.

He emphasized that the five-a-day plan is based on findings that people are better protected if they eat a wide variety of fruits and vegetables.

Studies of populations around the world show that the more fruits and vegetables consumed, the lower the cancer rate, Greenwald said.

The cancer institute's survey of 2,837 Americans over age 18 showed that Hispanics eat fewer fruits and vegetables than do blacks and whites.

The survey said only 23 percent of all adults eat five or more servings a day.

Other findings:

• People with less than a high school education eat about half a serving less per day than those with more education.

• Adults aged 18 to 34 eat about three servings of fruits and vegetables a day while those 65 and older consume four on average.

• Although men consume more food than do women, men eat fewer servings of fruits and vegetables—three a day, compared to four for women.

• Women are more likely to think they should increase their fruit and vegetable consumption than are men.

• Four in 10 Americans believe that eating fruits and vegetables will help prevent cancer, five in 10 think it will help prevent heart disease, and six in 10 believe it will help maintain weight.

• In general, about a quarter of Americans usually eat vegetables cooked in fat and about a fifth usually add fat, such as butter, cream or cheese sauce, when a vegetable is served.

• People who ate lots of fruits and vegetables as children continue to eat lots of them as adults.

• Generally, Americans consume more vegetables than fruits, but seem to like fruit better.

The most popular fruit and vegetable dishes: green salad; orange or grapefruit juice; potatoes; string beans; peas; corn; tomatoes; bananas; and other fruit juices.

Source: Associated Press (1992).

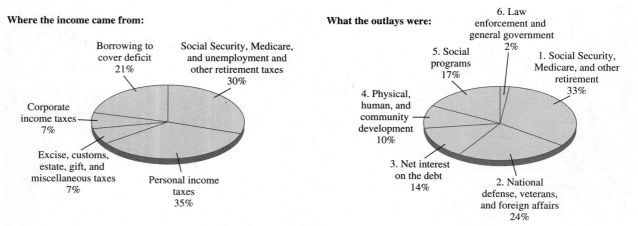

Figure 1.1
Federal money: Income and outlays, 1992. *Source: U.S. Department of the Treasury.*

Business

Business is another area where statistics influence your daily life, and this use is conspicuous in advertising. Statistics in advertising campaigns attempt to persuade you that a certain product is best. But is 34% fewer cavities enough to be meaningful? Does one car have much better mileage than other small cars?

Read the article in Box 1.2 as an example of problems with use of research and statistics in advertising. Knowing how advertisers try to influence your decisions can turn you into a more careful consumer. We certainly don't want you to have a negative attitude toward statistics, however. Statistics can be used correctly, even in advertisements.

In many industries, statistics describe various figures or values that are needed to make decisions. Investment analysis and the stock market are examples. Any annual report of a corporation includes numerous summary statistics and graphs. For example, Figure 1.2 shows the graph of a life insurance company's total incomes for several years.

Education

You probably keep close track of how you are doing in school. Your grade point average, a list of characteristics of the freshman class of 1995, and an average score for a professor on a teaching evaluation are all examples of statistics in education. Many instructors use statistics to decide where to draw the boundaries between grades, such as between an A and a B. In one course, the instructor may decide that C is the "average" grade and base the other grades around the mean. Another may decide to assign grades on the basis of percentage of total points.

Sports

Any sports fan can tell you some statistics about a favorite athlete or team. Media organizations rank football and basketball teams. Numerical values are kept for each player in almost every sport. For example, consider a baseball pitcher's earned-run

Box 1.2 Shadow of a Doubt

The following article appeared in the August, 1992, issue of *Consumer Reports:*

Dodge dealers in the New York City area recently aired a series of TV commercials boasting that more than 70 percent of the owners of *Toyota Corollas, Honda Civics, Ford Escorts,* and *Chevrolet Cavaliers* actually preferred the new *Dodge Shadow,* according to "100 [people] surveyed." Since our own surveys of CONSUMER REPORTS subscribers have shown that owners of *Civics* and *Corollas* are more satisfied with their cars than are owners of *Dodge Shadows,* the commercial piqued our interest. The reasons for the difference between our survey results and those reported in the *Dodge* commercial became clear after Chrysler Corp. described the survey's methodology to us.

A survey firm retained by Chrysler chose owners of 1988 to 1991 *Civics, Corollas, Cavaliers,* and *Escorts* to participate in an experiment. The willing respondents—about 25 for each competitor—were given an opportunity to inspect a '92 *Dodge Shadow* and a '92 version of the car they already owned. They were also allowed to take the *Dodge*—but not the other car—out for a spin. After the look-see, the 100 people were asked if they thought the *Dodge* was better or worse than their current car. Seventy-three percent reportedly said the *Dodge* was better.

Does that mean that most *Civic* and *Corolla* owners would prefer a new *Dodge Shadow* to a new *Civic* and *Corolla,* as the commercial implied? Probably not. Here's why.

First, of course, since the respondents were allowed to test-drive only the *Dodge,* not a new version of the model they owned, they were actually comparing a new car with a used one. For balance, we would like to have seen what owners of an older *Dodge Shadow* thought of their car after driving a new *Corolla, Civic, Escort,* and *Cavalier.*

Second, combining the opinions of owners of four different cars hides any distinctions among them. *Honda Civic* and *Toyota Corolla* owners, for example, might have preferred their own car to the *Dodge Shadow,* while *Ford Escort* and *Chevrolet Cavalier* owners might have strongly opted for the *Dodge.* One can't know from the reported result.

Finally, it's hard to believe that the respondents couldn't have guessed what the test was all about (and perhaps have wanted to please its sponsor), since they'd been promised $60 apiece to do a test that involved driving just one manufacturer's car.

Source: Consumers Union of U.S., Inc. (1992).

average, a basketball player's free-throw percentage, and a football running back's average number of yards gained per play. These statistics not only describe athletes' performances but also are used in making decisions, such as whether a college team will recruit an athlete.

The use of statistics in sports has become more sophisticated in research on sports medicine and biomechanics. For example, videotapes of expert racquetball players have been computer-analyzed to break down their motions into finite parts. The computer then generates stick figures that are used to teach the optimal form for a given stroke.

In summary, data and statistics come out of research and you can hardly consider any aspect of your life without seeing their impact. Even the chair you use at a computer may have been designed to protect against carpal tunnel syndrome in your wrists. Let's use the next section to explore the relationship between research and statistics.

Quick Quiz
List three examples of statistics that you encountered today.

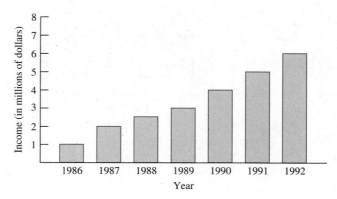

Figure 1.2
Total incomes of Bogus Life Insurance Company from 1986 to 1992

1.4   The Need for Statistics; or, Why Study Statistics?

Before reading this text, you probably thought of statistics as numbers. You surely have heard the word *statistics* used that way in sports and government. Now your concept of statistics should be expanding to include the computation of statistics and the reasoning process behind description and inference. The word *statistics* also indicates a scholarly discipline. Statistics as a science includes thousands of people dedicated not only to the use and teaching of these two areas, but also to the development and perfection of new statistical methods for description and inference.

We can answer the question Why study statistics? by pointing to three areas in which knowledge of statistics will help you.

Better Consumer

You need to study statistics to understand all the data and statistics in your everyday life. Learning more about statistics will improve your ability to deal with the data around you and help you make more informed decisions. You may be misled by important-sounding research, such as that in Box 1.2. To be candid, however, we know you do not need most of this text for this goal, even though advertisements are becoming more statistically elegant.

Better Reader

The second goal of this text is to make you capable of understanding research articles in your area of study. As you progress in your studies, you will find increasing reference to research. You often will find research results reported in the form of statistics. For example, what is meant by the statement, "The groups were significantly different, Mann-Whitney $U = 17$, $p < .05$"? By the end of this text, this statement will be completely understandable to you.

Table 1.1

Exam stress data: Number of symptoms for perceived control and no control groups

Perceived Control	No Control
12	9
12	12
8	9
5	11
12	11
5	15
11	14
12	7
7	11
15	11
11	9
6	17
12	14
11	17
8	11
11	13
12	19
11	14
13	11
11	13
13	12
12	14
7	7
13	11
9	16
7	15
5	13
15	13
7	10
7	16

Exam stress data

A data set that is used throughout the text; it consists of the numbers of symptoms for two groups of students: perceived control and no control

Better Researcher

For some of you, a third goal of this text is to enable you to use statistics correctly in your own research. Most areas in the behavioral sciences need statistics to help in the description or decision-making process of the research. Some of you will actually do research, perhaps even in an undergraduate course. What you have learned from this book should give you a good foundation for using statistics correctly in analyzing your data.

1.5   Statistics in Research

Our primary concern in this text is the use of statistics in behavioral science research. Most research projects give results in a written report. Some reports are published in professional journals, books, and technical reports. These reports also may be summarized in newspapers and magazines or on television. For example, the research on country music and white suicide rates (see the research example in Chapter 6) was reported in *Newsweek*. Regardless of where it is published, almost every research project uses statistics to summarize and organize data and to make decisions from the data.

Do you get exceptionally nervous before a test? Psychologists have done a lot of research on stress, including exam stress. DasGupta (1992) randomly assigned 30 students to each of two conditions that differed with respect to their perceived control over a test-taking situation. The *perceived control* (PC) participants were told to write questions for an upcoming test in their introductory psychology class, and they were told that the questions might be used on the test. The *no control* (NC) participants also were asked to submit questions, but they were told only that this task would help them study for the test. The actual test contained questions that were similar to 82% of the questions from the PC group and 87% of the NC group. The researcher measured for each participant the number of symptoms indicated on a form of the *Stress Self-Assessment Checklist* (Neidhardt, Weinstein & Conry, 1985), an average stress frequency rating, and performance on the in-class test. The **exam stress data** in Table 1.1 are simulated to replicate the results on the number of symptoms.

The following are direct quotes from DasGupta (1992) showing how results, statistics, and conclusions are typically reported in applied journals. You should not expect to understand everything here, but by the time you finish this text, you will understand it all.

The NC group reported a greater number of symptoms ($M = 12.50$) than the PC group ($M = 10.00$), $t(58) = 3.28$, $p = .002$.

While the NC group did report a higher frequency of stress than the PC group, this difference did not reach significance, $t(58) = 1.46$, $p > .1$. The two treatment groups did not differ in terms of their test performance ($p > .1$).

. . . Student participation in the process of evaluation may indeed increase their sense of control and prevent the negative experience that is often attached to tests and exams. . . .

The symbol M stands for the sample mean ($\overline{X}$ is used in this text), t is a statistic used to compare the group means, and p is the probability of getting a t statistic at least as extreme as the reported *t*. All of these terms and symbols are explained later in the text. For now, simply take this example as illustrative of how statistics are presented in a research report.

Quick Quiz

Did perceived control make a difference in exam stress?

Answer

Perceived control over the test-taking situation resulted in significantly fewer symptoms, but not significantly less stress or better performance.

1.6   Overview of Statistics

You should see now that you can use statistics to describe the world and to make decisions about it. To lay a foundation for studying statistics, you need to learn some important terms that are used repeatedly throughout the text.

Populations

At the beginning of this chapter, we discussed withdrawal from drinking caffeinated beverages. One approach to studying caffeine withdrawal was to examine the phenomenon by surveying your friends about any withdrawal effects they have had. What is the problem with this approach? Your conclusions are limited to your group of friends; you can't generalize to the rest of the world. So your conclusions won't help doctors and mental health practitioners recognize symptoms that could go along with quitting caffeine consumption.

When there is a large group about which you want to draw a conclusion, you have identified a population. The **population** is the target group, the group of subjects about whom the researcher wants to make a decision. The process of making a decision about a target group based on a small group of subjects is called **inference.**

Silverman, Evans, Strain, and Griffiths (1992) conducted a careful study of caffeine withdrawal effects. What was their target group? The target group could have been the 62 participants in the study, or all adults in the United States who drink caffeinated beverages, or all adults from our culture and cultures similar to ours. More than likely, the target group for this study was larger than just the 62 people in the study. In fact, most researchers in this area want their inferences to apply to some group close to that given in the last answer: all adults, with some restrictions. After all, researchers usually want to learn something that can help a large number of people, not just their friends or the 62 people in the study.

You define the population by deciding what group to target for the inferences and by listing the common characteristics of all subjects in this group. Then you choose some measure or score of interest, such as a ranking of the severity of symptoms. In statistics, a population is usually discussed in terms of a target group of scores rather than the participants themselves.

Regardless of whether you're interested in caffeine withdrawal, test anxiety, or delay of gratification, you won't be able to study everyone who falls within your defined population because most populations share three properties: They are usually *large, unobtainable,* and *hypothetical.* In most behavioral science research, the population

Population
A target group of participants about which the researcher will make decisions

Inference
Process of making decisions about the population based on a small group of participants

may be as *large* as "all adults." Other examples of large populations are the population of the United States, all white rats, and all sixth-grade students in a state. Some populations may be small, such as all exceptionally bright sixth-grade students able to attend college even though they are only 11 or 12 years old. Generally, however, researchers deal with large populations.

For large populations, the second property is obvious: they are *unobtainable.* Even the U.S. census, which tries to measure characteristics of the entire population, confronts an unobtainable population; by the time the census is finished, the population has changed. Most small populations are unobtainable too, because researchers are interested in future participants who have not yet been identified. For example, consider a talent search program that identifies exceptionally bright sixth-grade students able to attend college at 11 or 12 years old. They can identify only current bright sixth-graders, and they are interested in all such students in the future. Some future participants are just starting school, so this population is unobtainable.

The last property of populations is that some are *hypothetical,* and this will take more effort to understand. Many populations are hypothetical in the sense that even if the population were available, the researcher could not give everyone in the population the conditions of the experiment. Suppose all $4\frac{1}{2}$-year-old children were available for the delay of gratification research. The researcher would not even consider manipulating rewards (visible versus obscure) for the population and then observing a small number of participants selected from this population. Rather, the researcher first would choose a group of participants and then manipulate the visibility of rewards for them. Those participants are assumed to behave as if they came from the population of all $4\frac{1}{2}$-year-old children who received visible or obscured rewards. Of course, some populations are not hypothetical in that the researcher can select from the desired population. For example, if a researcher is interested in gender effects, both male and female participants can be selected. In this case, the male and female populations are not hypothetical.

Entire populations usually aren't used because of cost. Research requires money, resources, and time. Researchers sometimes have to pay people as an inducement to participate in a study. Materials used in the research also may be expensive, such as medical tests that caffeine researchers might run to double-check whether a participant followed instructions on the intake of certain foods and beverages. Sometimes a study consumes a lot of time, such as when each participant must be tested individually over several weeks. If the cost is high, then the number of participants in the study needs to be restricted.

Quick Quiz

What population was of interest to the researchers in Research Example 1 on delay of gratification?

    Answer

The researchers wanted to generalize their conclusions to all people. In fact, extensions of this research have been done in other cultures and with other ages.

Samples

Because populations are often large and unobtainable, they generally cannot be observed or measured. Another way to discover their characteristics is to take representative samples. Samples are used in the process of making decisions about populations.

Sample
Subgroup of the population; small group of participants from which the researcher makes decisions about the population

A **sample** is some subgroup or part of the population; it is the small group of participants used in the actual research. For example, the caffeine researchers ran newspaper advertisements and posted notices on bulletin boards in the Johns Hopkins University area to recruit volunteers. They were looking for people 18 to 50 years old who had at least a high school education, had no history of psychiatric disorders, met certain health standards, and consumed no more than 600 mg of caffeine a day. So what was the population that interested the researchers? You might say they were interested in making inferences about healthy adults who consume caffeine. The sample had 62 participants who met the researchers' requirements and agreed to participate. The sample is usually discussed in terms of scores (data) selected from the population of scores, so the caffeine researchers evaluated various scores that reflect the participants' physical and mental well-being.

Quick Quiz

What was the sample in Research Example 1 on delay of gratification?

Answer

The original sample was $4\frac{1}{2}$-year-old children. Later, the follow-up studies obtained data from many of those same people as teenagers.

Parameters
Numerical characteristics of a population

You make inferences from the statistics—the numerical characteristics of the sample—to their unobtainable counterparts in the population. The numerical characteristics of a population are called **parameters.** For example, the people in the caffeine study had a mean caffeine intake of 235 mg daily. If the researchers were interested in all healthy adults who drink caffeine, what is the average caffeine intake for that population? It is not known. The population is unobtainable and so are the parameters, the numerical characteristics of the population. However, statistics are obtainable and computed on the observations from the sample. We infer from the sample and statistics to what we don't have: the population and parameters. We tell our students that if populations and their parameters were obtainable, then there would be no need for statistics and the title for this course would be "Parameters."

The symbols used for statistics are usually letters from the English alphabet with some special markings, such as an X with a bar over it for the sample mean, $\bar{X}$. The symbols used for parameters are letters from the Greek alphabet—for example, μ (pronounced "mu" as in *mute*) for the population mean. For most behavioral science studies, parameters are unobtainable, so we do not give any formulas to compute them. See Figure 1.3 for an illustration of a population, a sample, a parameter, and a statistic.

Quick Quiz

Fill in the blank in this analogy: Statistics are to parameters as ——————— are to populations.

Answer
Samples

Sampling

You use a sample because you cannot obtain a population. But the sample needs to be representative of the population so that your inference is meaningful. If your sample

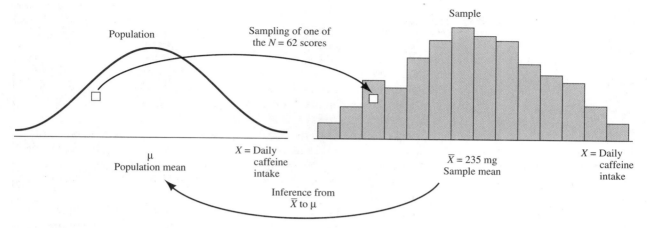

Figure 1.3

Illustration of population, sample, parameter, and statistic. The small square illustrates a score selected for the sample. Here μ is a population parameter, and $\overline{X}$ is a sample statistic. Descriptive statistics such as $\overline{X}$ describe the sample. Inferential statistics are used to infer from the sample statistic $\overline{X}$ to the population parameter μ.

includes only females in their 20s, you cannot make a general statement about how all healthy adults will react to a cutoff of caffeine intake. You also hope to have statistics that are representative of the parameters in the population. Because you cannot make statements about the population parameters with complete certainty, you must make statements about your sample statistics in terms of probability. The use of probability in your statements relies on the selection process. The selection process is called **sampling.** Your inferences will be only as good as your sampling. The basic idea behind sampling is to build a solid foundation for making an inference from a sample to a population. Let's consider two strategies for sampling: random sampling and stratified random sampling.

Sampling

Process of selecting a sample from a population

Random sampling is a procedure in which the selection of any one observation from a population is independent of (not related to) the selection of any other observation from the same population. A bias in sampling is anything that causes the sampling of one observation to be dependent on the sampling of another observation.

Random sampling

Process of selecting a sample such that the selection of one observation is independent of the selection of any other observation

For example, there is a human bias toward what is called *evenness* in selecting what you'd think is a random sample. If asked to pick ten people at random from a room of 100 people, most of you would tend to scatter your choices around the room, rarely selecting any two people who are together and never selecting three together. That is, if one person is selected, you will most likely *not* select the person next to him or her, so in fact the selection of the second (or third) person is dependent on the selection of the first. In random sampling, the selection of any observation does not depend on the selection of any other observation. If there are no biases that introduce dependence in the selection process, then you have random sampling.

The use of sampling in the behavioral sciences includes both independence of the selections (random sampling) and equal probability of events being selected. Equal probability is not necessary for the definition of random sampling. Many of the statistics in this text are based on random sampling. Box 1.3 is a discussion of the procedure of random sampling.

Box 1.3   Random Sampling

Random sampling is the selection of any one observation from a population such that its selection is independent of the selection of any other observation. Although this definition of random sampling is simple, actual random sampling is not. The real problem is the first task—to identify every member of the population and assign each a number. Given that most populations are large, unobtainable, and possibly hypothetical, this task is usually impossible. Second, you must choose the sample size, the number of participants in the sample. You will need to draw that many members' numbers from the population. But those numbers need to be chosen randomly, so you need a source for numbers that are in random order. Unique random numbers may come from a table of random numbers, such as Table A.1, or they can be generated by a computer program. Select that many unique numbers, up to your sample size, and then contact the participants represented by these numbers to try to get them to participate in your research.

Suppose that the population for the study of Table 1.1 was not all college students but all 1700 students enrolled in a large introductory course in a given semester. The class roster is a list of all students in the course, not allowing for late additions or early dropouts, and you assign them each a unique number from 1 to 1700. To select 40 unique random numbers from 1 to 1700 from Table A.1, you begin by entering the table at any arbitrary point. Then you move in any direction and get a string of random digits that can be divided into four-digit segments, such as 15633849249041590061. The four-digit segments are 1563, 3849, 2490, 4159, and 0061. You discard any numbers larger than 1700 (such as 3849, 2490, and 4159) as well as any duplicates, and you continue to select numbers in this way until you have 40 unique numbers ranging from 1 to 1700. You then have 40 names to contact.

Now the fun begins. First, try to contact the 40 students; second, get them to consent to participate; third, arrange a time when their schedule matches the times you are running the research; and fourth, get them to show up for the appointment. Of course, all of this assumes they are still in the course. Practical experience says that out of the 40 original names, you might end up with 15 to 20 actual people who participate in the research. So you must take more than 40 names in the original sampling.

Most researchers are interested in a more broadly defined population and are not willing to put up with the inconvenience of random sampling. So what do researchers actually do? They draw samples of convenience, or what we call *judgment samples.* That is, they obtain participants in some fair, legal, and moral way that is convenient, and then they judge whether the sample deviates from what could be expected by random sampling. This is not to say that researchers do not have some sampling plan. It merely says that the plan does not use random sampling. A common method of obtaining human participants is to ask for volunteers. The most obvious question to ask in the judgment phase is: Do the volunteers differ from nonvolunteers? Remember that these volunteers have not been randomly selected from a population of volunteers. The adequacy of judgment sampling varies, depending on the actual research area. All things considered, judgment samples can be sufficient, but without random sampling the representativeness of the sample is only as good as your judgment.

Stratified random sampling
Random sampling within defined segments of the population

A second sampling strategy is called **stratified random sampling.** Here is an example. When doing research on attitudes of college students toward the quality of their college, a researcher takes random samples of first-, second-, third-, and fourth-year students. The population has been stratified by class, and then random samples are taken from each class. In contrast, a random sample from the entire student body would not guarantee equal or proportional representation of each class.

Quick Quiz

What are the key words in the definition of random sampling?

       Answer

       Selection and independence

Two Areas of Statistics

In the same way that the study of antibiotics is only a part of the science of medicine, summary statistics from the sample are only a part of the science of statistics. Data analysis involves examining and exploring data, including pictorial description and summary descriptive statistics, as well as confirming relationships with inferential methods. These processes involve the computation of descriptive and inferential statistics.

Descriptive statistics

Statistical procedures used to describe a sample

    Descriptive statistics are measures used to describe some phenomenon, such as the sample mean $\bar{X}$. This area of descriptive statistics is primarily concerned with describing some characteristics of the sample. Most research yields enough data that organization and summary are needed, so descriptive statistics are usually computed, even in the simplest studies. For example, the mean caffeine intake of 235 mg daily is a descriptive statistic. Examining and exploring data can include pictorial plots and graphs. An exploration of the caffeine consumption of all 62 participants in the Johns Hopkins study would reveal that most of them consumed between 100 and 399 mg of caffeine a day, and the average was 235 mg daily; only one participant was in the 500–600 mg range.

Inferential statistics

Statistical procedures used to make decisions about a population based on results from a sample

    The second major area of statistics is inferential statistics. **Inferential statistics** are measures used to infer from a sample to a population; you use statistics to estimate parameters of the population and to make decisions. Inferential statistics are used to support, never prove, what you believe about relationships observed in data. The inferential statistic may be computed like the descriptive statistic, but a different process is used to make an inference.

    Consider the analogy that an inferential statistic is to behavioral sciences as the microscope is to biology; both allow us to infer relationships not visible with the naked eye. Probability operates in both sides of this analogy. The microscope lets you see blood cells, but you still have to decide whether they are typical or atypical (such as in testing for mononucleosis), and there is some probability of deciding incorrectly. In a similar fashion, statistics let you set relationships among variables, but you still have to use probability to make decisions about relationships. When you explore the data to discover relationships, you need to confirm what you believe to be true about these relationships. For example, the researchers in Research Example 1 on delay of gratification found many relationships between delay time and personal characteristics. Delay time and achievement were positively related but only for preschoolers who had visible rewards and no coping ideas given.

Chance

Occurrence of a certain result without apparent cause

    Inferential statistics are used to make decisions by helping you separate **chance** from nonchance results. Throughout this text, a chance result means an outcome without apparent cause. That is, a chance result occurs in the absence of any known reason why the result should turn out one way or the other. Note that statistics do not eliminate uncertainty; they just allow you to say how likely it is that chance alone is operating.

Using probability helps you decide whether chance or real differences produced the statistic.

Many behavioral scientists want to infer relationships among variables, and they need inferential statistics. For example, in the caffeine withdrawal study, 52% of participants reported moderate or severe headaches during the time the researchers secretly had taken away their caffeine. Without an inferential statistic, you cannot tell whether or not this percentage indicates a relationship between headaches and caffeine withdrawal.

1.7   Preview of Inferential Statistics

In this preview, you'll read about seven topics common to all inferential methods. We discuss inferential methods and use a research project to illustrate the seven topics. Keep in mind that this preview is presented to give you a better idea of what inferential statistics are all about. Each topic is covered in greater detail later in the book. Some students have found it helpful to outline the material in the first 11 chapters in terms of these seven points. This is an excellent method of studying for a midterm or final examination.

Any inferential statistical method contains the following:

1. Use of some descriptive statistic in the actual computation of the inferential statistic (Chapters 3, 4, 6, and 7)
2. Use of probability in the decision process (Chapter 8)
3. Potential for estimation of population parameters (Chapter 9)
4. The fact that statistics have sampling variability (Chapter 9)
5. The fact that statistics have distributions (Chapter 9)
6. Use of a theoretical reference distribution to approximate the distribution of the statistic (Chapters 5 and 9)
7. Two hypotheses, two types of potential errors in testing hypotheses, and the ability to control the probability of making these errors (Chapters 10 and 11)

Let's examine these topics briefly, using the following example. Will a comprehensive change in life-style reverse the progression of heart disease? A study (Ornish et al., 1990) designed to address this question included these life-style changes: reduction of fat intake to 10% or less of total calories; moderate, supervised exercise; stress management; and cessation of smoking. After meeting various entry criteria, 94 participants with serious heart disease were randomly assigned to one of two groups: a group with these life-style changes or a group called the usual care comparison group. Patients in the comparison group were asked to make a diet change that included reduced intake of fat and cholesterol, exercise moderately, and stop smoking. When presented with the choice to participate or not, 28 agreed out of the 53 assigned to the life-style change group and 20 agreed out of the 41 assigned to the usual care comparison group. One outcome variable of interest was the percentage reduction in coronary artery blockages as measured by a cardiac positron emission tomography (PET) scan (see Ornish et al., 1990). One other variable of interest was the change in the total cholesterol level. People participated in the study for at least one year.

Suppose that the mean levels of total cholesterol at start-up and at 12 months were as given in Table 1.2. After 12 months, both groups had reduced levels of total choles-

Table 1.2
Mean levels of total cholesterol (in mg/dL)

Group	Mean at Start-up	Mean at 12 Months	Reduction
Life-style change	227	172	55
Comparison	245	232	13
Difference	18	60	42

terol. The comparison group had an average reduction of 13 mg/dL, and the life-style change group had an average reduction of 55 mg/dL. Is the difference of 42 mg/dL significant?

The life-style/heart study is used to illustrate each of the seven topics common to all inferential methods. Don't feel that you must completely understand everything about each topic right now. We use some numbers without explaining how they were obtained. You'll learn to calculate them in later chapters.

Descriptive Statistics

Descriptive statistics were introduced earlier, but not much was said about the relationship between descriptive statistics and inferential statistics. The relationship is quite simple: Some descriptive statistic is used in the actual computation of each inferential statistic. Some summary measure is computed on the sample data and is then used to find the inferential statistic. In the life-style/heart study, the average of the total cholesterol amounts was computed for each group. These averages, or means, are descriptive statistics and were then used in computing the difference of the mean reductions, $55 - 13 = 42$. Then this difference of means would be used in computing the final inferential statistic.

Probability

Probability
Relative frequency of occurrence

Probability can be defined as the relative frequency of occurrence, or a proportion. A proportion is defined as some fraction out of a whole, expressed as a decimal. The probability of getting a head when tossing a fair coin is $1/2 = .5$; of the two possible outcomes, one of them is a head, so the relative frequency of occurrence is 1/2. To illustrate how probability is used to make decisions, let's use a coin example.

Suppose you were asked to wager $100 on a single toss of a coin you had never seen before. What would you want to know about this coin? You would want to know whether it is a fair coin. If it is fair, a head occurs in about 50% of the tosses of this coin and a tail turns up in the other 50%. How would you assess the fairness of this coin? You would examine it to be sure it has both a tail and a head and that it has not been altered in any way. You could take the coin, toss it a certain number of times, and record the frequency of heads and tails. If you tossed the coin ten times and obtained ten heads, what do you think about the fairness of the coin? Of course, you think it is not fair, but biased. How did you make this decision? Whether or not you realize it, you used probability to make your decision.

You know that *if the coin is fair,* then the probability of getting ten heads in ten tosses by chance alone is very small. (In fact, it is 1/1024). It is so unusual to get ten heads in ten tosses of a fair coin by chance alone that you doubt the premise of "fair coin."

Now suppose you tossed the coin and got six heads and four tails in the ten tosses. What do you think about the fairness of the coin? You think that the coin is most likely fair because six or more heads in ten tosses is likely to happen by chance alone. (In fact, the probability is .377). It appears that this is a usual event for a fair coin and that only chance is operating (there is no bias). With a fair coin, you are as likely to lose your $100 as you are to win.

The coin-tossing example should give you an intuitive feel for how decisions are made by using probability. To consider how probability is used in decision making in research, let's return to the life-style/heart study. The average reduction in the total cholesterol level was computed for each group: 13 for the usual care comparison group and 55 for the life-style change group, so the difference is 42. Two possibilities exist: The treatments are equally effective, or one is better than the other. If the two treatments are equally good, then the difference of 42 is due to chance. If one treatment is truly better than the other, then it is not a chance result that the difference of 42 occurred. Probability is used to decide between these two options.

Suppose that the probability is .0192 of getting a difference of means of 42 or larger by chance alone if the two treatments are equally effective. The small probability of .0192 means that the 42 is unusual *if the two treatments are equally effective,* so most likely they are not equally effective. Notice that a small probability makes you doubt the "if" portion of the statement, or the hypothetical portion. This decision is similar to what you did with the coin. When the probability is small, chance results are not likely, and you doubt the hypothetical portion of a statement. For example, you doubt "if the coin is fair" or "if the two treatments produce the same results in the population." With a probability close to .5, you do not doubt the hypothesis; instead, you decide that the results are likely due to chance.

Quick Quiz

Suppose that the mean total cholesterol reductions were 17 and 13 and the difference was $17 - 13 = 4$. If you found that the probability of getting 4 or more by chance alone if the two treatments are equally effective was .41, then what would you decide?

Answer

Because .41 is not a small probability, you should decide that the 4 is a chance difference between equally effective treatments.

Estimation

Estimation
Calculation of an approximate value of a parameter

Any time a researcher computes a sample statistic, there is the potential for estimating the corresponding population parameter. **Estimation** is the calculation of an approximate value of a parameter (numerical characteristic of a population). Populations are usually large, unobtainable, and often hypothetical, so population parameters also are unobtainable. But sample statistics can be computed and used to approximate, or estimate, population parameters. In the life-style/heart study, you're interested in the difference between the population mean reductions in the total cholesterol levels for the two treatments, but these parameters cannot be obtained. You can estimate the population means and the difference between them by using the sample mean reductions, 55 and 13, and the difference between them, 42. Estimation may not be your primary goal, but the potential for estimation is present in every inferential method.

Sampling Variability

Variability
The spread or dispersion of scores

Sampling variability of statistics
Tendency of statistics to differ from one another

Will everyone in your statistics class get the same score on the first exam? Of course not. The scores will differ from one another. This is the idea behind variability. **Variability** refers to the spread or dispersion of scores. You can think of variability as the tendency for scores to differ from one another. **Sampling variability of statistics** refers to the tendency of *statistics* to differ from one another. For example, the mean reduction in the total cholesterol level for the life-style change group was 55. If you ran the study again with another sample, you might get a mean reduction of 52 for the life-style change group. Statistics will vary from sample to sample.

Initially, this concept of the sampling variability of statistics is difficult to grasp. You say to yourself, "I have just computed the mean reduction for the group that had the life-style change treatment, and that mean is 55. The value 55 cannot have any variability in it." Well, you are right and you are wrong. The mean reduction of 55 is a constant for the sample of people who had the life-style change treatment. But if the researchers ran the experiment again and obtained a mean reduction in the total cholesterol level for the new sample of people with the life-style change treatment, would they get exactly 55 again? No, but they probably would get some fairly close value. That is, sampling variability of statistics means that there is variability from sample to sample in statistics computed on samples from the same population. Another way to think of this variability is that any one of the sample means—say, 55—is unlikely to be exactly equal to the population mean; that is, it is likely to vary from the population mean because of the individual scores that happen to be in the sample. Statistics have sampling variability, considered as variability from sample to sample or as variability from the population parameter.

Distributions

Distribution
Set of values associated with elements of the sample or population and dispersed through some space, like a number line

Sampling distribution
Hypothetical distribution of the values of a statistic if it were computed repeatedly with similar samples

The people in your statistics class will get a variety of scores on the first exam. The scores will differ from one another; that is, they will have variability. How might you look at all the scores at once? You could draw a number line and draw one box for each person's score. Some test scores likely will occur more than once; perhaps five people will get 80% on the test. Other scores might occur just once—that hardworking person who gets 100%. Those boxes on the number line can be considered a distribution. A **distribution** is a set of values, each associated with an element of the sample or population, that are organized in some way. Consider the life-style/heart example. You know that the average reduction in the total cholesterol level for the sample of people who had the life-style change treatment was 55. Not every replication of this study would result in a mean reduction of 55. There is a reduction value associated with every potential study, and the values can be organized from, say, -25 (a gain) to 137 along the number line (see Figure 1.4).

As you learned earlier, statistics have variability. If the researchers did the life-style/heart study again, most likely the average reduction would be slightly different. They could run the study 100 times and calculate 100 means. Just as you put each cholesterol reduction in a distribution, you could put those 100 averages in a distribution. The distribution of a statistic is called a **sampling distribution.** Sampling distributions are hypothetical in that they are the distributions of statistics that would be formed *if* you repeatedly took samples of a certain size from a population and computed a statistic for each sample. Sampling distributions also are hypothetical in that they are considered

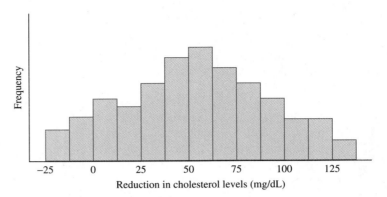

Figure 1.4
Cholesterol reduction values

to be formed from *infinitely* many statistics from infinitely many samples in this hypothetical repeated sampling process.

Theoretical Reference Distribution

Theoretical reference distribution
Mathematical expression of all possible existing values

Because the sampling distribution is hypothetical, you actually never need to build a sampling distribution; instead, you approximate it by using a known tabled distribution called a **theoretical reference distribution.** A theoretical reference distribution is a mathematical expression of all possible values that exist, rather than a distribution of observed values, as in a sample. An example is normal distributions (see Chapter 5). A theoretical reference distribution is theoretical because it is not obtained from experimentation or sampling but from a precise mathematical equation that defines the distribution. One area of concern is the fit of this theoretical distribution to the sampling distribution you would obtain if you carried out a particular sampling procedure. We rely on certain theorems and the results of research that tell us that sampling distributions have known shapes or can be closely approximated by known theoretical distributions. For the life-style/heart study, you would refer an inferential statistic based on the differences between the sample mean reductions to one of these known theoretical distributions. For this distribution, a table (covered in Chapter 13) can be used to obtain the probability of the statistic. This probability would be used to make a decision about using the life-style change treatment.

Hypothesis Testing

Hypothesis
Testable guess or tentative proposition set forth to explain some data

A **hypothesis** is a testable guess or tentative proposition given to explain some data. It also is a conjectural statement of the relationship between two or more variables. A hypothesis cannot be proved or disproved because you use probability to make a decision about it. Among its other characteristics, a hypothesis incorporates the theory, precedes the data collection, is in testable form, and is a bridge between theory and data.

Hypothesis testing (see Chapter 10) is the focus of this preview of statistics. Hypothesis testing is where decision making in the inferential process is formalized. On the basis of the computed inferential statistic and the probability obtained when the statistic is referred to a theoretical distribution, you can make a decision about hypotheses. Given that there are generally only two hypotheses, a small probability will lead to a decision in favor of one hypothesis, whereas a large probability will lead to a decision in favor of the other hypothesis. This decision is a "test" of a hypothesis.

In testing the hypothesis, two decisions can be made, so there are two types of potential errors: false alarms and misses. If a person decides that the life-style change treatment is effective when it really is not, then that person has gone to some trouble and expense to change his or her life-style when it was not effective. This incorrect decision is a false alarm. Similarly, a decision not to change one's life-style when it is, in fact, effective leads to the other type of error, a miss. Results from this incorrect decision could include the person's having a heart attack. In the life-style/heart study, the researchers found that a life-style change resulted in not only greater reduction in the cholesterol level but also less chest pain and decreased coronary artery blockage and increased blood flow to the heart.

These seven topics common to all inferential statistical methods provide some structure for the next ten chapters of this text. Whenever you feel the need to see the big picture or wonder where some topic fits into the whole scheme of statistics, return to this section and review these seven points.

Quick Quiz

Which of the seven areas common to all inferential methods is concerned with using a statistic as an approximate value of a population parameter?

Answer

Estimation

1.8 Use of This Text

Organization

Each chapter of this book begins with a research example to illustrate some of the concepts in that chapter. An introduction precedes the main content of each chapter. As you have seen, "Quick Quizzes" are scattered throughout the chapter so you can check whether you are understanding the material. If any of the questions stump you, go back and reread the difficult material and make a note to ask your instructor about it. Each chapter concludes with a summary, key terms, study tips, computation (in most chapters), and exercises.

Key Terms and Concepts

The summary section includes a list of key terms and concepts introduced in the chapter. This list can be a helpful study guide. You should be able to define each item in the list and have some idea of how it relates to the chapter's material.

Realistic Data Sets

Realistic data sets are used throughout the text. Whenever one of these data sets is introduced, it is labeled in the margin so that you can find it easily for use in later chapters. The lead-in research examples are usually drawn from actual published research.

Computation and Exercises

The summary and computation section introduces you to existing computer programs from two widely used packages of statistical programs, SAS and SPSS. You can learn how to use these programs by examining examples given for some of the statistical methods introduced in each chapter. All of the necessary commands are given for simple introductory use of these programs, as well as example output, or results, for each program. Further practice of the statistics, computer programs, or both is provided in the exercises at the end of each chapter. You'll notice section numbers next to the exercises, so if you need help answering a question, you can look back to the specific part of the chapter.

Appendixes, Symbol Glossary, and List of Formulas

Tables for using the statistical methods are given in Appendix A, followed by a review of basic mathematics (Appendix B). Next comes Appendix C, "Answers to Selected Exercises." A glossary of statistical symbols is provided inside the front cover. Most computational formulas given in the text are also listed inside the back cover. Familiarize yourself now with the general layout of the text so you can use it effectively.

1.9   Help for You

You Can Do It

Studying statistics should be a positive experience, something you might be surprised to find yourself actually enjoying. It might help you to realize the following:

1. You have intuitive math knowledge that you can learn to trust.
2. Each of you absorbs concepts differently. Some people learn mathematically, some spatially, some graphically, and some verbally. If at first you don't understand something, wait a page or two, or try looking at the content from another perspective; look for a figure associated with the concept.
3. Respect your own curiosity and even your own mistakes. Realize that you are probably making mistakes already made by a genius in statistics.

Go after this subject matter intending to master it and enjoy it. You will be pleasantly surprised at how you can apply many of the principles in your daily life. You probably have heard someone say, "I know just enough math to balance my checkbook." But you are unlikely to ever hear anyone happily admit, "I know just enough about reading to fill out a job application." You can become just as comfortable with managing numbers as you are with organizing ideas for a written report.

Math Anxiety

To some of you, this text and the course in which you are enrolled seem like the beginning of the "valley of despair." You have briefly examined the text and have reacted to the formulas and the fact that statistics is a branch of mathematics with what we call *symbol shock*. We understand your fear and apprehension. Perhaps it will help you to know that everyone feels some degree of fear and apprehension over this topic (even we were afraid in our first statistics courses). Two excellent books that can help you in this area are Hackworth (1992) and Tobias (1978). Check your school library. Much of the next section is drawn from these helpful books.

The first step in coping with anxiety is to become aware of your problem. You also have to realize that your fear of math and your negative experiences with mathematical subjects do not necessarily have a cause-and-effect relationship (at least not in the direction you might think). Some of your negative experiences may have come from your fear. Your problem might not be ability, but rather an accumulation of years of interaction of fears and failures. Your discomfort with math has grown to anxiety and avoidance. Realize, therefore, that *your anxiety is learned, and thus it can be unlearned.*

To accompany this, you have an increasing awareness of the importance of math. For most behavioral science majors, math has grown in importance as the use of statistics and computers has increased. Now you find yourself in a statistics course, required for many of you, and you are experiencing the same old anxiety or fear that you have had before. What do you do? Find one or both of the books by Hackworth and Tobias and read them. They give a much broader perspective on the issue.

Hackworth's book helps you understand math anxiety and begin to work through the issues. It lets you deal with your anxiety gradually and gives you tasks to learn systematically how to control your learning environment.

Some of Tobias's suggestions for overcoming math anxiety are to seek outside help and begin to help yourself. Outside help from counselors, math teachers, or both might lead to some of the following ways of combating your anxiety: math anxiety workshop groups, talking about math, diagnosis of the depth of the problem, or immersion (practice in math). You also may need to practice before the experience (and during it, since you are in this course now) and follow suggestions for reading mathematical subjects. Use pencil and paper to sketch what is presented, take notes, underline, ask questions, and go slowly.

Obviously, reading a statistics textbook is not like reading a novel. The pace is much slower, and comprehension of one subject may depend on understanding an earlier subject. The subjects are in sequence and need to be studied in the same way that you climb a ladder: one step at a time. Because of this, it is important for you not to miss class. If you do, be sure to get lecture notes from another student and make a special effort to catch up. If you are having trouble understanding a particular subject, seek help early, no more than one or two lectures later if your solo efforts to understand have not helped.

If you realize that your mathematics background is weak, work through the review of basic mathematics in Appendix B. This review will rehearse you on the basic mathematics necessary for this text.

Most people consider math courses to be much different from other classes. Actually, math and many other areas of study force you to think in a straight line. When you are writing an English paper, you have to know where to start, how to order the information, and where you are going with the ideas. The work requires a linear thought process; you have to follow a train of logic from the beginning of the paper to the end. The same is true with mathematical problem solving. The same is even true of music. Ask a music student about the mathematical aspects of music. What other classes require a linear thought process?

Study Strategies

Coon (1980) presented three different general aids for studying: the SQ3R method (Robinson, 1941), LISAN (Carman & Adams, 1972), and memory devices. First, let's consider the SQ3R method.

SQ3R

In the SQ3R method for studying and reading, the letters in its title stand for the steps in effective study:

1. *Survey.* Take a quick survey of the chapter, reading section and topic headings and the summary statement at the end of the chapter. Try to gain an overall perspective of the chapter.
2. *Question.* Form a question for each topic heading to increase your concentration and focus on the material.
3. *Read.* Read is the first *R*. Read only from one topic heading to the next. Then go to the next *R*.
4. *Recite.* Recite means to answer your question, writing it down in some brief notes or saying it over to yourself. Be sure you have included the major points under each topic. When you are finished with a topic, go back to step 2 (question) for each topic until you have finished the chapter.
5. *Review.* Review the completed chapter. Methods of review include going over your notes, reciting the answers again, and asking someone to quiz you about the topics.

LISAN

LISAN stands for the five steps in a listening/note-taking plan:

1. *L = lead (don't follow).* Try to anticipate where the instructor is going. Reading the assignment before class helps a lot.
2. *I = ideas.* Any lecture topic is composed of important ideas. What are the primary and secondary (supporting) ideas for each lecture?
3. S = *signal words.* Listen for key words that signal the direction of the lecture. "Three characteristics of the mean are . . ." (here come some ideas about the mean). "The most important . . ." (a primary idea). "Therefore . . ." (a conclusion).
4. *A = actively listen.* Make sure you can hear and see the teacher's presentation. Be on time and ask questions. Bring your book and have it open to the topic area of the lecture (compare it to what is being said).
5. *N = note taking.* Be selective in your notes. Listen to everything, but don't write everything down. Write down the primary and secondary ideas and whatever extra you need to help piece them together. For definitions not in the book, write down every word (ask the instructor to repeat if necessary).

Memory Devices

You can remember what is important to you and what you make an effort to memorize. Here are some devices that researchers in memory have found to be effective:

- *Recitation.* Repeat out loud what you have learned from your reading.
- *Overlearning.* Continue to study after you have learned the material. This helps overcome the effect of test anxiety.

- *Selection.* Memorize primary and secondary ideas, not the entire text. Similarly, don't underline everything in the text.
- *Spaced practice.* Schedule your study time so you space your study for this course throughout the week. Don't try to study all of the assignment in one 3-hour session.
- *Organization.* Outline chapters, lectures, the first half of the book, the material covered since the last quiz. Separating the material into chunks helps you memorize.
- *Serial position.* You make the greatest number of errors on the middle of any set of material. Give special attention to the middle material (in sequence) to be included on a test.
- *Sleep.* When you are asleep, interference with what you have studied right before sleeping is minimal. And you need a good night's sleep before a test.
- *Review.* If you have done all these other steps, reviewing the material merely ties it together right before a test. Don't count on review as the only method of memory.

Test-Taking Strategies

If you have prepared for a test using the preceding guidelines, you will be ready for it. Here are some ideas for keeping your anxiety in check during that crucial hour in which you are tested:

1. Make sure you take all the materials you need: plenty of paper, pencils, pens, calculator—whatever is required.

2. When you are handed the test, scan the entire test to see what types of questions are involved.

3. Look for the easiest questions, the ones you are sure you know how to answer. This will give you confidence that you will succeed. Do the true–false or multiple choice items first. Eliminate multiple-choice options that you are sure are wrong; then choose the best answer from those remaining.

4. Before spending too much time on a difficult problem, make sure it is worth it in terms of points. If you spend a lot of time on a difficult two-point question, you may not leave yourself enough time for an easier ten-point problem.

5. If an item is unclear to you, raise your hand and ask the instructor to clarify it. The teacher may say something that will trigger your memory of the specific topic.

6. Most important, when the test is returned, make sure you understand every item you missed. Make an appointment to talk to your teacher if you need extra explanation of a difficult topic. In statistics, the information presented earlier in the semester is used again and again, so you need a solid understanding of what has already been covered.

1.10   Summary and Study Tips

Chapter Summary

We have discussed data and statistics as they affect your daily life. Statistics are also found in most research projects. Studying statistics helps to make us better consumers, better readers, and better researchers. A population is the target group for your inferences, and a sample is a subgroup of a population. Statistics as a science is divided into descriptive and inferential statistics. Statistics enable you to describe and to separate chance from nonchance results. The seven topics common to all inferential statistical methods are descriptive statistics, probability, estimation, sampling variability, distributions of statistics, theoretical reference distributions, and hypothesis testing.

The following key terms are introduced in this chapter:

Data
Statistics
Mean
Exam stress data
Population
Inference
Sample
Parameters
Sampling
Random sampling
Stratified random
  sampling
Descriptive statistics
Inferential statistics

Chance
Probability
Estimation
Variability
Sampling variability
  of statistics
Distribution
Sampling distribution
Theoretical reference
  distribution
Hypothesis
Seven topics common
  to all inferential
  methods

Study Tips

The goal of your studying at this point should be to memorize the definitions of the terms introduced in this chapter because these terms are used throughout the book. A good way to memorize definitions is to use flashcards. You also should review Section 1.9 and see which study methods appeal to you. Notice the distinction between recognition and recall; you may recognize the term *variability* from this chapter, but unless you can recall the definition and write it down without looking it up, you haven't learned it.

Exercises

Section 1.1

1. Suppose that instead of using your friends in a study of caffeine, you posted notices asking for volunteers to be in the study. You used newspaper ads, bulletin boards, letters to civic groups, and other means to recruit volunteers. Then you simply asked them to list the effects they have noticed related to caffeine.
   a. What problems might this approach have with regard to people telling you what you want to hear?
   b. Suppose you ran a second study in which you controlled the caffeine in beverages. What disadvantages would the volunteer study have compared to this second study?

Section 1.2

2. Suppose you have been arrested for driving under the influence of alcohol. Give examples of data that might be used by the prosecutor in the effort to convict you. Now suppose you have been convicted. As part of your sentence, you have to take classes that give factual information about the consumption of alcohol. What statistics would be cited on drinking and driving?
3. You will have to deal with data and statistics as you make your decision about what job to accept after

graduation. In fact, you may have to make decisions about one job at a time, such as whether to accept a current job offer or wait for a potentially better offer.
   a. What types of data will you encounter?
   b. What statistics will have an impact on your decision?
   c. What risks are involved with each decision?

Section 1.3

4. List as many statistics as you can find in Box 1.1.
5. List the statistics you find in Box 1.2.

Section 1.4

6. Do the following:
   a. List some areas of your life where you might need to be a better consumer and thus where statistics might be able to help you.
   b. Name other courses you have taken or expect to take in which statistics could play a crucial role.
   c. Ask professors from other departments whether they had to take a statistics course as part of their graduate training.

Section 1.5

7. Consult the DasGupta (1992) study on exam stress given as an example of research.

a. List all the statistics given to you.

b. How are these statistics used in drawing conclusions?

c. Discuss this study with respect to being free from biases and participants' telling the researchers what they want to hear.

Section 1.6

8. Why do researchers use samples? Why do researchers compute statistics? Answer these questions in the context of the life-style/heart study by Ornish and colleagues (1990).

9. If your statistics class is a sample and you are part of a research project on teaching statistics, what defines the population?

10. In the study of caffeine withdrawal, what would be the population if your sample contained only your friends?

11. You have been assigned to randomly select 20 people from a college class of 100 students. The 20 people will participate in a study on caffeine withdrawal.

a. If the sample consists of the 20 randomly selected people, what are the characteristics of the population? What kinds of hypotheses might the researchers test?

b. Suppose you are given an alphabetical list of the 100 people in the class. A friend tells you that a random sample can be drawn by choosing every fifth person on the list. Is your friend right or wrong, and why?

c. Describe how you might use a random-number table to draw the sample.

12. The Gallup Poll is conducted regularly by asking questions of U.S. residents 18 years of age and over. About 1800 people are selected, and percentages are reported for their opinions about public issues, such as candidates at election time.

a. What is the population?

b. What is the sample?

c. If 65% of the people in the sample say they support Candidate X, what inference is made about the population?

d. Is 65% a statistic or a parameter?

e. Why are only 1800 people surveyed?

f. If another polling organization telephoned every tenth person in a phone book, would that be a random sample? What would be the population?

13. One television rating organization supplies a "diary" for each household, in which the programs watched by any member of the household are recorded for

one week. About 1200 households are recruited by telephone.

a. What is the population?

b. Do all households with televisions have telephones?

c. Is the actual sampled population the same as the targeted population?

d. What is the sample?

e. What effect will unlisted numbers have on this research?

14. What biases exist in using telephone directories to sample residents in the Los Angeles area to find out the percentage of a national television audience that watches an educational program on Latino culture?

15. What biases exist in Congressman Blooper's argument in favor of the withdrawal of troops from Country X based on 300 of the 450 letters received expressing this opinion?

16. What biases exist in an advice columnist's asking readers to write their opinions on in-law problems?

17. In each of the following, indicate whether the bold-face value is a statistic or a parameter.

a. The quarterback for State U threw 15 completed passes out of 30 attempts in the game against Upstate U, for a **50% completion rate.**

b. The average IQ score on the Wechsler Adult Intelligence Scale-Revised is **100.**

c. If indeed **57%** of the voters favor Candidate Y, it is not too surprising for a poll to find that **59%** of those asked would vote for Candidate Y if the election were held today.

d. Fifteen female college students averaged **22** on the self-acceptance scale when the norm is **20.**

Section 1.7

18. In a study of Sudden Infant Death Syndrome (SIDS) in Avon County, England, Wigfield and colleagues (1992) focused on the variable of the sleeping position of infants. The traditional placement of infants is on their stomachs, largely because of concern for the baby choking if he or she should vomit while asleep on the back. Recent attention to sleeping position has identified it as a potential factor in SIDS. The Wigfield article found that the rate of death from SIDS was considerably lower if babies up to one year of age were placed on their backs to sleep.

a. What is the sample? What is the population?

b. What do we call the rate of death from SIDS for babies placed on their backs for Avon County? For the entire country of England?

19. In a study of rates of tobacco use in various parts of the United States, Shopland, Niemcryk, and Marconi (1992) found that overall, 32.8% of the 105,225 adults surveyed use at least one form of tobacco. Overall, 39.7% of the males and 26.6% of the females use tobacco. However, in the South, 44.6% of the males and 27.9% of the females are tobacco users. The researchers concluded that the tobacco use rate among Southern males was significantly higher than that for males overall.

a. What is the population? What is the sample?

b. Give an example of a descriptive statistic from this research.

c. What do we call the type of statistic used to draw the conclusion about tobacco use by Southern males as compared to use in the entire United States?

20. Ekman and O'Sullivan (1991) concluded that Secret Service employees are better at catching a liar than are people in other occupations. The study says that if there are no population differences in people's ability to catch a liar, then the probability of their statistic is less than .05.

a. A probability of less than .05 is small. What premise does this small probability lead you to doubt?

b. If you were to compare Secret Service personnel, judges, and psychiatrists, what populations are of interest to you?

21. Consider an over-40 male trying to make a decision about taking one aspirin as a preventive measure against heart attacks. His doctor has said that he doesn't have heart problems at this time but has told him about a study sponsored in part by Bristol-Myers, the makers of Bufferin aspirin. The participants were 22,071 male doctors over 40; they were randomly assigned to two groups. Men in one group took one aspirin every other day, and men in the other group took an identical-looking pill that had no aspirin in it (a placebo). The mechanism by which aspirin was supposed to reduce heart attacks is by interfering with blood clot formation, but it has the side effect of making the stomach more acidic.

a. What would you expect to happen to the incidence of heart attacks in the one-aspirin group?

b. What would you expect to happen to the incidence of hemorrhagic strokes (bleeding into the brain)?

c. What would you expect to happen to the incidence of gastric and duodenal ulcers?

d. What would you expect to happen to the overall incidence of deaths from all causes?

e. What characteristics about doctors would make you concerned with the generalizability of the results of the study?

22. Silberstein and Parsons (1981) compared 25 female alcoholics with 25 female nonalcoholics to investigate the relationship between mental–psychological impairment and alcoholism. They collected scores for each participant in both groups for many variables. Among those variables that differed was time to complete the Halstead Tactual Performance Test, which involves placing irregular shapes in a form-board while blindfolded. The mean for the alcoholic group was 23.03 minutes, whereas the mean for the nonalcoholic group was 15.65 minutes, for a difference of 7.38 minutes. Now, 7.38 could be a real difference, or it could be due to chance alone. If there are no population differences in mental functioning, the probability of getting a difference of 7.38 by chance alone is less than .005.

a. What descriptive statistics were computed in this study?

b. Consider the population of alcoholic females. Is it large? Unobtainable? Hypothetical?

c. Do you doubt the hypothesis of "no population differences in cognitive impairment"?

23. Refer to the article in Box 1.1 as you answer these questions.

a. What process of decision making was used when the researchers drew the conclusions listed in the article under "Other findings"?

b. How does the article describe the sample? What is the population?

c. After reading Chapter 1, what would you say about the accuracy of the phrase "studies of populations around the world"?

d. What do you think the researchers' hypothesis was?

24. In the life-style/heart study by Ornish and colleagues (1990), 94 participants who met various entry criteria were randomly assigned to the life-style change or to the usual care comparison group. When presented with the choice to participate or not, 28 agreed of the 53 assigned to the life-style change group, and 20 agreed of the 41 assigned to the usual care comparison group. This means that (28/53) 100 = 53% agreed in the life-style group, and (20/41)100 = 49% agreed in the comparison group.

a. What do you think about this difference in the

percentages of participation? How does this affect the population to which the study can be inferred?

b. What if the researchers had gotten agreement from the 94 people to participate in the study under the condition that they might be randomly assigned to either of the two groups, and *then* randomly assigned those who agreed to the two groups? Would this have been better than the way they did the study? What problems might this have given the two groups?

25. The National Assessment of Educational Progress (NAEP) achievement tests are given to fourth-, eighth-, and twelfth-graders every year. The summary of the results is called the "Nation's Report Card." Now other countries are using versions of the NAEP test, and entire nations' educational systems are being compared based on the results.

a. In the United States, what is the sample? What is the population?

b. In other countries, what is the sample? What is the population?

c. Some people use the results from the NAEP test to conclude that the U.S. school system is worse than other countries' systems. How are the U.S. public schools different from schools in other countries? You may need to ask a professor about schools in other countries or seek information from your library.

2

Research and Research Design

Now that you have been introduced to the use of statistics in your daily life, let's take a closer look at how researchers use statistics. What is meant by *research*? Is research the same as science? You'll see that research involves the uncovering of brand-new information about the world, which you can't do by just going to the library. You'll learn when you can make causal conclusions, what researchers do to ensure that their results are valid, and how to get the numbers used in calculating statistics. Crucial vocabulary, to be used frequently in future chapters, is introduced.

Research Example 2
2.1 Introduction
2.2 Research
    Comparative versus absolute
    Research and science
    Example
2.3 Variables
    Independent variable
    Dependent variable
    Extraneous variable
    Operational definition
2.4 Types of Relationships
    Causal relationship
    Predictive relationship
2.5 Types of Research
    True experiment
    Observational research
    Quasiexperimental designs
2.6 Data in Research
    Data
    Quantitative and qualitative data
    Scales of measurement
2.7 Summary, Study Tips, and Computers
    Chapter summary
    Study tips
    Computers
Exercises

Research Example 2

Centerwall (1992) studied the impact on viewers of television violence, citing many research reports on the subject. The common thread in much of this research is that watching television, especially violent television, is connected to later physical aggression and involvement in violent crime. Think about what causes violent behavior. Try to think of some plausible rival hypotheses to the statement: Watching violent television causes violent behavior.

Do you think socioeconomic status or innate aggressiveness also might have an impact on whether someone behaves violently? Other variables might include intelligence, exposure to parental violence, other violence in the home, neighborhood (or place of residence), and school performance. These were mentioned in the studies reviewed by Centerwall.

Any research project that examines the impact of television on violent behavior must account for as many of these variables as possible. If these variables are not accounted for, then any conclusion about the impact of television may be questioned.

For example, one study examined a small Canadian town that did not get television until 1973 because of signal reception problems. First- and second-grade students were measured in an objective way for two years for their rates of noxious physical aggression, defined as hitting, shoving, and biting. These children were compared to same-age children in two similar communities that already had television. Which variables were controlled in this study? Comparing similar towns controlled for the socioeconomic status of the community, the racial makeup of the community, and neighborhood influences. Observing the same children for two years controlled for the socioeconomic status of individuals, innate aggressiveness, intelligence, race of individuals, prior exposure to parental violence, prior other violence in the home, and school performance. That is, if Johnny is being observed, he is the same person at the start of the study and at the end of the study two years later. Some things about him have changed, to be sure, but he is about the same on most variables, so they have been accounted for. Results showed that the rates of physical aggression did not change significantly over time in the two similar communities, but they increased by 160% among the children who were first exposed to television.

Other studies cited in Centerwall (1992) found the following results:

• From 22% to 34% of young male felons who had been imprisoned for committing violent crimes reported that they had consciously imitated crime techniques seen on television.

• Infants who saw on television the adult behavior of working a toy had a 65% success rate for imitating adult behavior and working the toy, versus 20% for infants who did not see the behavior on television.

• The average aggressiveness as measured by observation of spontaneous, natural behavior for children exposed to media violence significantly increased in controlled short-term studies.

• Following 875 boys from ages 8 to 30 showed that television violence viewed at a young age significantly predicted the seriousness of crimes for which they were later convicted as adults, even when innate aggressiveness, intelligence, and socioeconomic status at age 8 were controlled.

• The homicide rate among white South Africans increased from 2.5 per 100,000 in 1974 to 5.8 per 100,000 in 1987 (a 130% increase) after television was introduced in 1975. The variables that didn't affect the homicide rate were changes in age distribution, urbanization, economic conditions, alcohol consumption, capital punishment, civil unrest, and availability of firearms.

Also in this area is the classic study of imitation by Bandura, Ross, and Ross (1963). Preschool children were randomly assigned to one of four groups: real-life models showing aggressive behavior toward an inflated large doll, humans on film showing the same behavior, cartoon characters showing the same behavior, and a group that watched an adult who sat quietly ignoring the inflated doll and available instruments of aggression. Children in the aggression groups imitated many aggressive behaviors they had seen, whereas children in the fourth group rarely demonstrated such behavior. The random assignment controlled for the variables that might interfere with the variable under study: aggression or nonaggression by models. You'll study research methods such as these in this chapter.

2.1   Introduction

Imagine that you want to figure out which jobs train people to be good at catching a liar. How will you find the answer? You could lie to everyone you know and keep track of who can detect when you are lying. But this approach has several drawbacks, not the least of which is that you could lose friends. Your approach also has the same problem we confronted when we first discussed caffeine withdrawal in Chapter 1: If you study only your friends and acquaintances, you cannot say how people in general will react. You also may not be acquainted with people in certain occupations, such as polygraph operators or the Secret Service, who may be better at judging by appearances whether someone is telling the truth.

People in certain fields—the legal system, for instance—should be better than the general public at catching a liar. To find out which occupations train people to be good at telling whether someone is truthful, we have to take an organized approach: research.

Researchers start with an intriguing question and look for clues in published reports. Then, if no one has already found the answer, they do research and analyze the results to bring new knowledge into the world. Research is the context in which data are generated and statistics are used.

2.2   Research

Research is more than just serious or studious inquiry into some subject. You may do a research paper for a course where you spend time at the library, search for several references, and write a paper that brings together information or discusses an issue. These things are part of research, but not all of it. When we say *research,* we mean careful, critical, thorough investigation or experimentation with a goal of changing or adding to existing facts. After all, the information you find in the library originates someplace; it is the result of research. So research does involve studious inquiry, library work, and report writing, but it is broader than that.

Original research?

Research
Structured problem solving

Research could be called *structured problem solving* (Helmstadter, 1970). For a study to be *structured,* it must use one of several specific methods. It must deal with a *problem,* defined as some unsolved issue faced by society. And it must attempt to find the *solution* to the problem. In the liar example, the problem is to determine whether people in certain jobs are better than the general public at catching a liar. You now know you cannot find a solution by taking an unorganized approach of lying to people; you need to structure your problem solving.

One key feature of the "problem" part of research is the way the problem is stated. It should be stated so that empirical testing of some hypothesis is possible. If not, then you will fail to solve the problem. You need to restate the problem so hypotheses can be tested and a solution found. Perhaps you need to limit your study of liar catching to a few occupations, such as Secret Service personnel, judges, and psychiatrists. Then you can test a hypothesis about which of these groups of people are better at detecting lies.

Comparative Versus Absolute

Research can be classified in many ways. One basic classification is whether the research is absolute or comparative. **Absolute research** is done to measure some phenomenon. What is the distance from Star A to Star B in the Milky Way galaxy? What percentage of young male felons say they have consciously imitated crime techniques learned from television (Research Example 2)? What percentage of first-year college students in 1995 scored higher than 700 on the verbal part of the Scholastic Aptitude Test (SAT)? These questions are answered by absolute research.

Absolute research
Research with the purpose of measuring some phenomenon

Comparative research involves some comparison of groups, usually groups in the same study. How do Astronomer X's distances between six stars compare with those measured by Astronomer Y? Does the average aggressiveness score for children exposed to media violence increase in controlled short-term studies? Do judges catch more lies on videotape than Secret Service personnel or psychiatrists? Comparison of groups is found in most modern research.

Comparative research
Research that compares the results from two or more groups

For a longer example of comparative research, consider the Salk polio vaccine. Some of your parents may have participated in the largest and most expensive medical experiment in history. Researchers field-tested the Salk poliomyelitis vaccine in 1954 on more than 1.8 million children in grades 1–3 (Meier, 1978).

Early in polio research, scientists discovered that a virus caused polio. Even though polio was rare, the polio virus was common. Polio was more common in families with good hygiene and was virtually unknown in poorer countries. It seemed that people who had poor hygiene were exposed to polio early in life and built up immunity to the disease by contracting a mild case of it. The body became immune after developing antibodies while fighting a mild case of polio. Similarly, a vaccine's effectiveness relies on the body building up antibodies as it fights a mild case of the disease or a similar disease induced by the vaccine injected into the body.

One issue in the polio study was that parents had to give consent for their children to participate in research on the vaccine. Lower-income parents consent less often than do higher-income parents. Thus, if two groups were formed, consent to the vaccine and no consent, a bias would exist against the vaccine because children more likely to get polio would be in the consent group.

Preceding this study was considerable discussion of the merits and ethics of any research involving human life. The low incidence of polio in the population (about 60,000 in 1952 and about 35,000 in 1953) necessitated using a large number of children. The total research program had several parts. The main experiment used children whose parents gave consent, slightly more than 400,000. The research also involved 350,000 children whose parents did not give consent.

Two features characterized the experimental part of the research: use of *randomization* and a *placebo* group. *Randomization,* a term thoroughly defined later in this chapter, is a way of assigning subjects to groups in order to control variables such as age, socioeconomic status, and bias on the part of the researchers. The placebo group would not get vaccine but would get a neutral preparation of salt solution that looked exactly like the vaccine. To achieve the best results, more than 400,000 school children whose parents gave consent were randomly assigned to either the Salk vaccine group or the placebo group. The bottles of vaccine and salt solution were numerically coded, so only the research team in charge of the project knew which children were in which group. The children, their parents, those injecting the children, and the doctors examining the children for polio did not know the details of the experiment.

When the results were in, the experimental group (Salk vaccine) showed a rate of 28 cases per 100,000 children, with no fatalities. The placebo group (salt solution) showed a rate of 70 cases per 100,000 children, with 2 fatalities per 100,000. The no-consent group showed a rate of 48 cases per 100,000 children, with no fatalities. Statistical examination of the results confirmed what appears strikingly obvious: Vaccine made a difference that would be called *significant* (having a low probability of happening if the vaccine and the placebo were equally effective). The results were so successful that the vaccine was released for widespread use. But the vaccine was not perfect, and the process was halted temporarily for more evaluation. Better vaccines have since replaced the Salk type, but the experiment yielded useful information.

This experiment is an excellent example of how research can affect your everyday life. Without this research, polio vaccine would not have achieved widespread use and polio might still be a health menace.

Research and Science

Science
Area of knowledge organized for the purpose of discovering and establishing general laws

Research is a part of the broader concept of science. **Science** can be thought of generally as an area of organized knowledge or, more specifically, knowledge organized for the purpose of discovering and establishing general laws. Structured problem solving (research) is used within science to further knowledge and refine this knowledge in the form of general laws. The goals of science are to explain, understand, predict, and attribute causation for the natural events in the world around you. Research is the major tool to accomplish these goals.

Usually there are several possible explanations for the relationships between variables in a study. Research allows you to examine these explanations and eliminate, or at least reduce the probability of, some of them. So, for an observed phenomenon, research is a process of finding plausible rival explanations and systematically working to eliminate some of them or establish others. Research is usually done by using one of the structured systems called **scientific methods.** Most of these methods have a sequence of fairly general steps for proceeding through the research. One sequence is given here:

Scientific methods
Structured systems to
perform research

1. Encounter and identify the problem.
2. Formulate hypotheses and define variables.
3. Think through the consequences of the hypotheses.
4. Design and run the study, collect data, compute statistics, and test hypotheses.
5. Draw conclusions.

Although statistics play an obvious role in step 4, two major points need to be emphasized. First, there is more to research and the steps of scientific methods than just statistics. Sometimes students rush into step 4 without the necessary thinking that is part of steps 1–3. Realize that the use of statistics is just a part of scientific methods. If a researcher has failed to think through a problem carefully before running a study, no statistical procedure in the world will make the results useful. The old computer phrase "garbage in, garbage out" applies here.

Paradoxically, the second major point is that the influence of statistics pervades all research and the steps of scientific methods. Problems, hypotheses, consequences, design, and conclusions need to be considered with statistics in mind. That is, statistics are not isolated from the rest of research, but integrated into all parts of research and all areas of research—psychology, medicine, marketing, engineering, education, and so on. Finally, most research is an ongoing process in which the last step of one project leads to the first step of the next project. Figure 2.1 shows this cyclic nature for the steps listed above and the imitated aggression example below.

Example

The Bandura, Ross, and Ross (1963) study in Research Example 2 illustrates the steps of scientific methods. The study was one in a series done by Bandura and his colleagues (see Bandura & Walters, 1963) on the role of models in imitative behavior. Imitation plays an important role in passing on information in most cultures, perhaps more than spoken information. Thus, the question about learning aggression from models was the problem identified by Bandura. Next, the researchers formulated hypotheses about how children's behavior toward an inflated clown doll would be affected by witnessing aggressive acts. The researchers identified variables such as whether a child was exposed to a real person or a film of a person committing an aggressive act, and the number of aggressive acts the children initiated. They designed and ran their study with these hypotheses and variables in mind, collected the data on the aggressive acts, computed statistics, and tested their hypotheses. The researches concluded that children in the aggression groups initiated many aggressive acts, whereas the children in a nonaggression group rarely did.

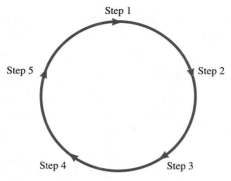

Figure 2.1

Steps of scientific methods and the research on imitated aggression (from Bandura, Ross & Ross, 1963): *Step 1. Encounter and identify the problem:* Do children learn aggressive behavior by imitating adults? *Step 2. Formulate hypotheses:* One hypothesis says that children who see aggression in adult models will exhibit about the same aggressive behavior as those children who see no aggression in adult models. The second hypothesis says that there are differences in aggressive behavior. *Step 3. Think through the consequences of the hypotheses:* If the first hypothesis is true, average aggression scores for the adult-model-aggression groups will be about the same as those for the adult-model-no-aggression group. *Step 4. Design and run the study, collect data, compute statistics, and test hypotheses:* Decide on the different aggression model groups, how many children are in each group, how to measure aggressive behavior in the children and so on. Run the study, measure aggressive behavior, and so on. *Step 5. Draw conclusions:* Higher average aggression scores occur in the model-aggression groups as compared to the control group (no aggression), so conclude that children can learn aggression by imitating adult models.

Quick Quiz

What is the difference between science and research?

Answer

Science is an area of organized knowledge, in which people conduct research, which is structured problem solving. Research is part of science.

2.3   Variables

Variable
Quantity or property that is free to take on different values

Continuous variable
Variable that theoretically can take on infinitely many values

Discrete variable
Variable that can take on only a finite number of values

Some of the most important parts of any study are the variables involved. A **variable** is defined as a quantity or property that is free to take on different values. A variable also can be a symbol that stands for this quantity or property. A variable can take on values that are numerical (number of liars detected out of ten) or nonnumerical (*P* and *A,* standing for presence and absence of a lie). A variable can be continuous or discrete. A **continuous variable** theoretically can take on infinitely many values between any two points. For example, height is a continuous variable because there are infinitely many values between 5 ft 6 in. and 5 ft 7 in. A **discrete variable** can take on only a finite number of values between any two points. For example, the number of liars detected out of ten is a discrete variable because only the value 2 is between the points 1 and 3. You do have to measure continuous variables in a discrete fashion. The person's height might be 5 ft 6.2573 in., but you measure height discretely, usually to the nearest

Unit of measurement
Unit of precision used in measuring a variable

4 inches, cup, miles, etc.

Units of analysis
The objects on which statistics are computed

inch, at 5 ft 6 in. Although infinitely many values exist between 5 ft 6 in. and 5 ft 7 in., you measure continuous variables discretely and thus approximately.

When you decide how to measure a continuous variable, you have to select the **unit of measurement,** or the unit of precision used in measuring. For example, if a person's height is measured to the nearest inch, then the unit of measurement is the inch. However, the height of buildings might be measured to the nearest foot, so the foot becomes the unit of measurement. Because continuous variables are measured discretely and approximately, you use the unit of measurement to establish limits for the true value of the variable.

Another related concept is the **unit of analysis,** the object on which the statistical analysis is computed. For example, would the liar study focus on how well an individual could detect liars and get a score for each individual, or would the job group as a whole be the unit to be analyzed? In most studies, the subject or individual is the unit of analysis. In some studies, statistics are computed to obtain norms, or standards, on some variable. In these studies, it is the group statistic, or norm, that is the focus of attention. The answer to the question, For what do I have a score? usually gives the unit of analysis. Be careful not to confuse unit of measurement and unit of analysis. For example, if you were studying the height of college students, the unit of measurement might be inches and the unit of analysis would be the individual subject.

In contrast to a variable, a *constant* is a value that does not vary. Examples of constants are the integer 2 and the ratio of the circumference of any circle to its diameter, which is $\pi = 3.14159$.

Let's see how variables played a role in the life-style/heart study by Ornish and colleagues (1990) from Chapter 1. This study examined the total cholesterol level as one of its variables. The initial cholesterol level of the participants was a variable, and 185, the cholesterol level of one participant in the study, was a value of this variable. The cholesterol level of each person was a variable because not only did cholesterol levels vary from participant to participant, but also the researchers took into account the participants' cholesterol levels at both the beginning and the end of the study. A reduction of 10 points on the cholesterol scale has a different meaning for someone with an initial level of 185 than for someone with an initial level of 250. The unit of analysis was the individual participant, and the unit of measurement was milligrams per deciliter (mg/dL).

Independent Variable

Independent variable
Variable whose values are changed by the researcher

Manipulation
Intervention on the part of the researcher to change the values of the independent variable

In every study, there are several types of variables. The **independent variable** has values that are changed by the researcher. Changing the values of the independent variable is called **manipulation,** or *intervention*. The values or *levels* of the independent variable usually are used to define groups of participants, where the participants in that group receive that level of the independent variable. (An exception to this is in designs called *repeated-measures designs*; see Chapter 17.)

In the imitated aggression study (Bandura, Ross & Ross, 1963), the independent variable was aggressive behavior by models. Levels of this variable were real-life adult models showing aggressive behavior toward an inflated large doll, adults on film showing the same behavior, cartoon characters showing the same behavior, and an adult sitting quietly ignoring the inflated doll and available instruments of aggression. These levels were used to define four groups of subjects.

For another example, let's consider a study of the effectiveness of subliminal self-help tapes in improving memory. The researcher prepares two types of tapes, one with a subliminal message and one without. Then the researcher can test the memory ability of the two groups. The independent variable is the presence or absence of subliminal messages on the tapes. The group that receives the subliminal messages is called an **experimental group,** or **treatment group,** because the participants receive the level of the independent variable that defines the experiment. The absence of subliminal messages defines the control condition, and the group that has this condition is called a control group. A **control group** is identical to the experimental group except for the manipulated condition. In the imitated aggression study, the group that saw the adult exhibiting no aggression was a control group.

Experimental group, treatment group

Group of participants who receive the level of the independent variable that defines the experiment

Control group

Group of participants who are identical to the experimental group except for the absence of the manipulated condition

A control group is designed to help rule out plausible rival explanations. Consider a study of the percentage of neurotics who are cured following Freudian psychotherapy (Eysenck, 1967). The only way to tell whether the therapy was effective was to have a control group. In fact, the percentages of neurotics who are cured after Freudian psychotherapy did not differ from the percentages of spontaneous remissions (cures with no intervention).

Quick Quiz

Consider the Salk vaccine research. (a) What was the independent variable? (b) Was there a control group? (c) Would a group that was simply not vaccinated have been a control group?

Answers

(a) The independent variable was presence or absence of vaccine. (b) Yes; the group that got the salt solution vaccine was the control group. Those participants were in the absence of vaccine condition. (c) No; a group that was not vaccinated would not be a control group because they would not have visited the vaccination site or received a "vaccine" as did the experimental group. If comparisons were made between the experimental group and this "not vaccinated" group, conclusions about differences due to the vaccine being valid because the differences could be caused by other factors such as not being vaccinated, even with salt solution.

Dependent Variable

Dependent variable

Behavior of the participant that is observed and measured by the researcher

The **dependent variable** is the participant's behavior that is observed and measured by the researcher. Its values are the *scores* for each participant in the study. Another definition of the dependent variable is the variable affected or changed by the independent variable. In the imitated aggression study, the dependent variable was the number of imitative aggressive behaviors. The symbol X is often used to stand for the dependent variable, especially in later chapters when particular values of the dependent variables are discussed. In Chapter 1 the symbol $\overline{X}$ was used as the sample mean of the values of the dependent variable.

To help you understand the relationship between independent and dependent variables, examine Figure 2.2. The independent variable comes first in time and influences the dependent variable, which comes second in time.

In the study on using subliminal self-help tapes to improve memory, what came first? The independent variable, which was the presence or absence of subliminal messages on memory improvement. What came second? The dependent variable, the number of items correctly recalled in a standard memory task.

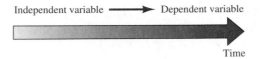

Figure 2.2
Time line showing the independent variable first in time and the dependent variable second in time

Extraneous Variable

Extraneous variable
Any variable that is not an independent or dependent variable but that might have an effect on the dependent variable

Control
To make the groups under study as comparable as possible on an extraneous variable

Confounding
Confusion of the effect of an independent variable with that of an extraneous variable

A third type of variable is the **extraneous variable.** An extraneous variable is any variable that is not manipulated as an independent variable or measured as a dependent variable but that might have a potential effect on the dependent variable. Because extraneous variables might affect the dependent variable, they are competitors to the independent variable. The researcher thus wants to reduce their influence on the dependent variable. Most researchers want to **control** extraneous variables. Here *control* means to make the groups under study as comparable as possible on the extraneous variable. In fact, a researcher's goal should be to make the groups as comparable as possible in all aspects except the variable being manipulated (independent variable).

If extraneous variables are not controlled, they could account for any significant differences in the dependent variable. This confusion of the effect of an independent variable with that of an extraneous variable is called **confounding.** For example, in the use of subliminal self-help tapes, if the researcher did not control for participants' innate memory capability, then that innate capability might be confounded with any treatment effect. That is, if the subliminal message group had better memories at the outset compared with the control group, then the researcher might not be able to tell whether the tapes or better initial memories caused more items to be recalled. One way to control prior ability is to give participants a pretest and use the gain in memory from pre- to posttest as the dependent variable. By measuring the same participants repeatedly, researchers can avoid the variability that is introduced when different participants are measured each time.

In the imitated aggression study, examples of extraneous variables are gender, age, innate aggressiveness, and home background. These extraneous variables are potential sources of confounding if they are not controlled. This list of extraneous variables is not exhaustive, and you can easily add to it. Any study has many extraneous variables, some of which are controlled by the researcher.

Here are three ways to control extraneous variables:

1. Randomize participants to groups.
2. Keep all participants constant on the extraneous variable.
3. Include the extraneous variable in the design of the experiment.

**Randomizing participants
to groups**
Randomly assigning participants to the levels of the independent variable such that the probability of any possible arrangement of the subjects is constant

Randomizing participants to groups means to randomly assign participants to conditions, which are the levels of the independent variable. This is different from random sampling, which has to do with how the participants are selected. The purpose of random sampling is to reduce bias in generalizations, whereas the purpose of randomizing participants to groups is to control extraneous variability. Extraneous variables are controlled by equalizing the chance that any level of the extraneous variable

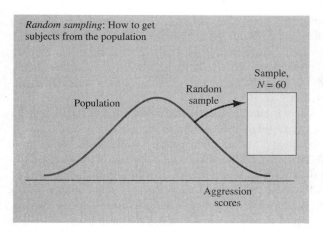
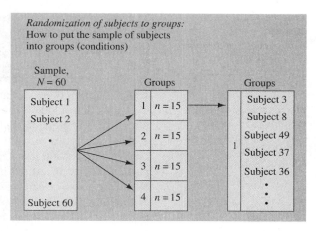

Figure 2.3
Random sampling compared with randomization of subjects to groups

will be in any group. Randomization will not guarantee that the extraneous variable is the same for each group; it only keeps the chance for any level of the extraneous variable constant for all groups. For example, if gender were considered an extraneous variable in the imitated aggression study, then randomization of children to groups would keep the chance of any particular male/female split constant for both groups. This is not to say that the number of males would be the same for each group. Randomization essentially reduces the *chances* of an extreme split in the number of males/females in each group.

Of course, any extraneous variable that has many values, such as IQ, also can be controlled by randomization. Groups should be comparable in terms of the average IQ score, and randomization of participants to groups keeps the chance of any IQ distribution the same for all groups. Small differences in average IQ are not unusual.

Proper randomization of participants to groups (see Hader, 1973) is done as follows:

1. Number all participants who will be in the experiment, using the numbers from 1 to the total number of participants.
2. Use a table of random numbers such as Table A.1 in Appendix A to select enough unique random numbers to fill each of the groups except the last group. (See Box 1.3 for an explanation of the random-number table.)
3. Put the remaining participants in the last group, which is not necessarily the control group.

In the imitated aggression study, suppose there were a total of 60 children, or 15 per group. You would start by numbering the children from 1 to 60, and then select 15 random numbers ranging from 1 to 60 from Table A.1. The children associated with these 15 numbers would be assigned to one of the four groups. The remaining 45 not selected for the first group would be available for the second group, and so on. The last 15 would go into the fourth group. You can use this method for randomly assigning participants to any number of groups. Examine Figure 2.3, which illustrates the randomization of participants to groups and contrasts it with random sampling.

Keeping participants constant
Control of an extraneous variable by using only one of its levels in the study

Include the extraneous variable in the design
Control of an extraneous variable by using all of its levels in the study

Keeping participants constant on an extraneous variable is accomplished by using, say, only males, thus controlling gender as an extraneous variable. However, if you use this approach, you cannot generalize the results of the study to females. If a researcher were comparing athletes and nonathletes on their attitudes toward women, using only white males as participants would keep the participants constant on the potential extraneous variables of gender and race.

The final method of control is to **include the extraneous variable in the design.** In the imitated aggression study, you could include gender in the design by increasing the number of groups to eight and having a male group and a female group for each of the four aggression levels. A study's outcome also could be affected by whether the participants are measured in the morning, afternoon, or evening. By including time of day in the study, researchers can deal with this extraneous variable. Although any given extraneous variable may be included in the design, you still must rely on random assignment of participants to groups to control other extraneous variables.

Another impact on the dependent variable can come from either participants or observers/researchers who know to which groups the participants were assigned. Participants might knowingly or unknowingly alter their performance on the dependent variable if they know they are in a treatment group as opposed to a control group. Such knowledge and influence on the dependent variable are called **subject bias.** For example, if you know that you are in an experiment designed to improve memory by using subliminal self-help tapes, you memory might change simply because you know you are in the experimental group and you try harder.

Subject bias
Influence on the dependent variable of the participants' knowledge of the levels of the independent variable

Observer bias
Influence on the dependent variable of the observer's (researcher's) knowledge of the levels of the independent variable

If the observer or researcher influence scores on the dependent variable, the result is called **observer bias.** For example, the researcher who administers a memory test in the self-help tape study might be more encouraging to the group that heard the subliminal messages, and thus those participants might do better because of confidence instilled by the researcher.

Single-blind experiment
Experiment constructed to eliminate subject bias

Double-blind experiment
Experiment constructed to eliminate both subject and observer bias

If an experiment is constructed to eliminate subject bias by not letting the participant know the details of the experiment, the experiment is said to be a **single-blind experiment.** If an experiment is constructed to eliminate both subject and observer bias by not letting either the participant or the observer know the details of the experiment, the experiment is said to be a **double-blind experiment.** In the self-help tape study, if the assistant researcher who gave out the tapes and scored the pre- and posttests for memory did not know which participant was in which group, then the study was double-blind. The caffeine withdrawal study cited in Chapter 1 was a double-blind experiment; the participants were given capsules containing a powder that might have been a substance commonly found in food, such as caffeine, or that might have been a placebo. The people who gave the capsules to the participants handled coded pills and didn't know what treatment condition the participants were in.

Quick Quiz

(a) Was the Salk vaccine experiment a single- or double-blind experiment? (b) How were extraneous variables controlled?

Answers

(a) The experiment was double-blind to control subject and observer biases. (b) Other extraneous variables were controlled by randomizing participants to treatment conditions.

To give you practice identifying the types of variables, let's examine another study. Suppose that someone is concerned about caffeine's influence on the performance of air traffic controllers. A researcher designs a study where half of the subjects will be given an orange-flavored breakfast drink with caffeine, and the other half will be given an identical drink without caffeine. Performance on an auditory vigilance task is assumed to be similar to one of the tasks performed by air traffic controllers. The influence of caffeine depends on body weight and previous caffeine habit. Now, answer each of these questions about this study:

1. What is the independent variable?
2. What is the dependent variable?
3. Are there any extraneous variables, and if so, what are they?
4. If there are extraneous variables, how would you control them?
5. What label is given to the group that gets the drink without caffeine?

Now for the answers.

1. The independent variable is the presence or absence of caffeine.
2. The dependent variable is the score on the auditory vigilance task, such as the number of correct identifications of preselected sequences of sounds.
3. The extraneous variables mentioned are subject body weight and previous caffeine habit.
4. Giving the amount of caffeine as a function of body weight, such as "quantity of caffeine per kilogram of body weight," would control for body weight. Previous caffeine habit could be controlled by randomizing subjects to groups or including "caffeine habit" in the design (high or low, depending on coffee, tea, and cola soft drink consumption).
5. The answer is "control group."

Operational Definition

Operational definition
Precise definition of how the researcher will observe and measure a concept

Some variables can be independent, dependent, or extraneous, depending on how they are defined in a given study. The **operational definition** is the definition of a concept that describes the precise way the researcher will observe and measure it. Some variables are restricted in terms of what type they may be. For example, size of reward in a learning study is usually defined as an independent variable and sometimes as an extraneous variable, but rarely as a dependent variable.

Let's consider how the variable anxiety could be any one of three types of variables. First, consider a study where the researcher induces anxiety in the participants. This makes anxiety an *independent* (manipulated) *variable*. One such study was designed to examine the effects of drive on performance. The low-drive condition had college students working alone on difficult math problems, whereas the high-drive condition had the students working with two people looking over their shoulders. The high-drive condition was assumed to increase anxiety, so anxiety was manipulated. The dependent variable was performance on the math problems. Results are plotted in Figure 2.4 as average scores for each group. The horizontal axis shows the levels (low and high) of the independent variable (drive/anxiety), and the vertical axis shows the dependent variable (number of correct problems). The average for the participants in the low-

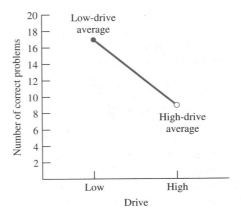

Figure 2.4
Average number of correct problems for low- and high-drive conditions with difficult problems

drive condition was 16.6, and the average for the high-drive condition was 8.2. These averages are plotted as dots connected with a solid line to show the relationship between drive/anxiety and number of correct responses.

In a second study in which the researcher examines the effects of two teaching methods (independent variable) on performance on the final examination (dependent variable), anxiety is an *extraneous variable.* As a potential competitor with teaching methods, anxiety may be controlled to some extent by keeping the testing situation similar for both classes.

A third study is interested in the effects of the color of wall paint (independent variable) in an office on the anxiety of workers. Here, anxiety is the *dependent* (measured or observed) *variable* and may be defined by using some measure such as the Taylor Manifest Anxiety Scale.

In any given study, you have to see what questions are being asked and how the variables are being used and measured before you can operationally define any variable as independent, dependent, or extraneous.

Quick Quiz

In the Bandura study on children and imitated behavior, what kind of variable was aggression?

Answer

Because of the emphasis on imitation, aggression was two kinds of variables, each connected to an operational definition. It was an independent variable because the researchers manipulated whether or not a child was in a group that witnessed an aggressive act. Aggression also was a dependent variable because the researchers measured the number of aggressive acts initiated by the children in the various groups.

2.4   Types of Relationships

Let's consider two other topics that are closely related to types of variables: relationships between variables and classification of research. We will soon return to the topic of types of variables to define and illustrate two additional types.

Given the goals of science to *explain, understand, predict,* and *attribute causation,* researchers must focus on relationships between variables and how knowledge of one variable helps to explain, understand, or predict another variable. For example, does knowledge of the level of drive/anxiety help you to explain, understand, or predict performance? Note that in Figure 2.4 the difficulty is controlled by keeping that variable constant for all participants: They all get high-difficulty tasks. High drive/anxiety on difficult tasks reduces performance. So you would say, yes, knowledge of the level of drive/anxiety does help you to explain, understand, or predict performance if you know the difficulty of the task. This study examined the relationship between the variables of anxiety and performance with task difficulty controlled.

Causal Relationship

All research projects examine relationships between variables. In any given research project, the relationship between any two variables will be one of two types. The relationship between drive/anxiety and performance is a causal relationship. The key feature of a **causal relationship** is that one of the variables (the independent variable) is manipulated by the experimenter. This manipulation causes a resulting change in the participant's behavior or performance (the dependent variable).

Thus, a causal relationship is between an independent and a dependent variable. When a causal relationship exists, you can say that the independent variable *causes* change in the dependent variable. In the study of Figure 2.4, changes in drive/anxiety (independent variable) cause changes in performance (dependent variable). Note that changes in an independent variable, which is manipulated by the researcher, cause changes in the dependent variable—*not* the reverse. A decrease in performance doesn't cause the drive/anxiety group to change because drive/anxiety is under the researcher's control. A causal relationship is the strongest relationship that can exist between two variables because it best helps us explain, understand, and predict. The inference from a causal relationship is called a *causal inference,* or a *cause-and-effect statement.*

Causal relationship
Relationship that exists when a researcher can assert that the independent variable caused the observed changes in the dependent variable; manipulation of the independent variable is a key feature of this relationship

---

Quick Quiz
Was there a causal relationship in the Salk vaccine research?
Answer
Yes; the experimenters manipulated whether children received the Salk vaccine or a placebo. The experimenters could say that the Salk vaccine caused a reduced incidence of polio.

Suppose a researcher wants to examine the influence of anxiety on the performance of difficult tasks using two groups of students. The participants in one group were selected because they had high scores on a measure of anxiety called the Taylor Manifest Anxiety Scale. The participants in the second group had low scores on the same scale. Would this study show a causal relationship? No, because the researcher did not manipulate anxiety. The type of relationship here is predictive.

Predictive relationship
Relationship that exists when a researcher can assert only that a change in one variable predicts a change in another variable

Predictive Relationship

When you do not manipulate one of the variables, you have the other type of relationship—a **predictive relationship.** A predictive relationship is weaker than a causal relationship because you can say only that when the first variable changes, there are

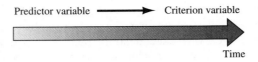

Figure 2.5
Time line showing the predictor variable first in time and the criterion variable second in time

---

Predictor variable

Variable in a predictive relationship that is analogous to the independent variable; the researcher predicts *from* this variable

Criterion variable

Variable in a predictive relationship that is analogous to the dependent variable; the researcher predicts *to* this variable

changes in the second variable. This type of relationship is often examined with statistical methods generally called *correlational methods* (see Chapters 6 and 7). A predictive relationship has no manipulation by the researcher of the first variable and no cause-and-effect statement, but only a predictive statement. The types of variables are the **predictor** and **criterion** variables. The predictor variable is the variable from which you are predicting, and the criterion variable is the result of the prediction. The time of occurrence between these variables usually differs, with the predictor variable preceding the criterion variable (see Figure 2.5).

One example of a predictive relationship is the classic relationship between smoking and lung cancer. It has been known for years that the likelihood of a person getting lung cancer can be predicted from the amount of his or her cigarette smoking. That is, lung cancer is observed with lower incidence in people who do not smoke and is observed with higher incidence in people who do smoke. Essentially, the more cigarettes a person smokes, the higher is the likelihood of developing lung cancer. The amount of cigarette smoking is the predictor variable, and the incidence of lung cancer is the criterion variable. The tobacco industry always points out that smoking behavior is beyond the control of the researcher and is not manipulated, so there can be no cause-and-effect statement such as "Smoking causes lung cancer." In predictive relationships, there is always the possibility of a third variable, an extraneous variable, sometimes called a *lurking variable,* as the causative agent. For example, heredity is commonly mentioned in the smoking and lung cancer relationship, which could cause both a desire to smoke and a predisposition to lung cancer. All of these variables are beyond actual experimentation or manipulation in humans for ethical reasons.

The two types of relationships between variables lead to two broad classes of research.

Quick Quiz
In Research Example 2, what kind of relationship existed between homicide rates among white South Africans and the introduction of television?

Answer
Predictive relationship

2.5   Types of Research

When research was introduced in Section 2.2, it was classified as absolute or comparative. Research can also be classified as true experiments, observational research, or quasiexperimental research.

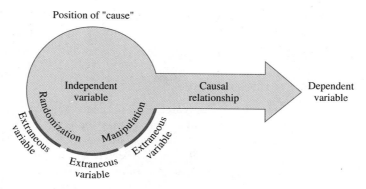

Figure 2.6
Key features of a true experiment: Manipulation and randomization act as shields against extraneous variables.

True Experiment

True experiment
Research that uses an independent variable and a dependent variable and controls extraneous variables by randomization; causal relationships can be asserted when a true experiment is conducted

The first type of research is associated with causal relationships and with independent and dependent variables; it is called *controlled experiment* or the *true experiment*. The **true experiment** is characterized by manipulation of an independent variable and by control of extraneous variables, including random assignment of participants to levels of the independent variable. It is only from the true experiment that you can make cause-and-effect statements because the independent variable is manipulated. Control of various extraneous variables ensures that the cause-and-effect statements are effective for only the independent variable. In the imitated aggression study, the researchers manipulated the aggressive behavior of the adult models and randomly assigned children to groups to control extraneous variables. So the researchers could say that aggression in the models caused more aggressive acts by the children.

Examine Figure 2.6 to see the key features of a true experiment. Because of manipulation and randomization and other ways of controlling extraneous variables, the extraneous variables are most likely excluded from the causal relationship between the independent and dependent variables. Manipulation and randomization act as shields against the influence of extraneous variables. You can think of manipulation and randomization as being like football linemen protecting the quarterback by keeping out competitors. They keep extraneous variables from interfering with the inference of the independent variable being in a causal relationship with the dependent variable. You are trying to find out what would cause the variation in the dependent variable. The independent variable is a potential "cause," but so are the extraneous variables, unless they are kept (shielded) from the position of "cause."

A true experiment can be done in a laboratory setting, as in the air traffic controllers study, or "in the field," in a real-world setting. Field research using a true experiment could be done to test whether making eye contact increases helping behavior. You can pretend to be conducting a survey with someone and then "accidentally" drop papers to see whether the person being interviewed will help. Before encountering someone to interview, you can randomly decide whether the participant will be in the group that does not get any eye contact from you. With the other participants, you can make extensive eye contact. The dependent variable is the extent to which participants help you pick up the papers. The study would be conducted on the street of a college campus, in a real-world setting, and thus this research would be considered a field experiment.

Observational Research

Observational research
Research that can assert only predictive relationships because of the absence of manipulation and randomization

The second type of research is associated with predictive relationships and is called **observational research.** Other names for observational research are *correlational research, natural experiment, sampling designs,* and *nonmanipulative research.* There is no good title for this type of research, but we use *observational research.* Do not confuse this type of research with observation as a method of collecting data, which can be used in true experiments or observational research. Observational research is characterized by lack of manipulation, no randomization of subjects to groups, and minimal control of extraneous variables. There is no independent variable because there is no manipulation; thus, there is no ability to detect a causal relationship. The type of relationship that results is predictive, and the types of variables are the predictor and criterion variables. Remember that a predictive relationship exists when changes in the first variable (predictor) are followed by changes in the second variable (criterion).

Consider a study on the difference between mountain climbers and a control group of similar-age students on a scale that measures sensation seeking. Do you understand why the research is observational? The researcher has not manipulated the subjects into the two groups, and one variable merely predicts the other. Here it is not obvious which variable is the predictor and which is the criterion. Does sensation seeking lead one to become a mountain climber? Or the reverse?

Let's return to the example about which occupations teach people to detect liars. You would like to find out whether judges, psychiatrists, or Secret Service personnel are best at catching a liar. This is an example of observational research because the researcher cannot randomly assign someone to an occupation. People in each occupation group can be shown 1-minute videotape segments of ten people, five of whom are lying, telling how they feel about a film. Then the viewers are asked to indicate whether the person in the videotape was telling the truth. The predictor variable is occupation, and the criterion variable is the accuracy score, or the percentage of correct responses. Simulated data for this study (discussed in Research Example 4) are given in Table 2.1. Examine the **liar data** to see if you think there are differences in the three groups. Later, you will see how statistics are used to answer the research question.

Liar data
A data set used throughout the text; it consists of deception accuracy scores for three professions: Secret Service agents, judges, and psychiatrists

Because observational research is characterized by observing natural changes rather than changes manipulated by the researcher, a causal relationship cannot be determined by observational research. Many variables other than the predictor variable are also free to change and could be confounded with the predictor variable in causing the changes in the criterion variable. That is, there are many plausible explanations for the observed phenomena. The shields of manipulation and randomization crucial to the true experiment are missing, so the extraneous variables can enter the position of "cause." Figure 2.7 shows the key features of observational research.

For example, you think that smoking is the cause of lung cancer, but many other variables are uncontrolled. Without manipulation by the researcher, you do not know which variables are contributing to lung cancer. The smoking and lung cancer issue never will be settled completely because it would be unethical to perform a true experiment using these variables with human participants. However, results from true exper-

Table 2.1
Liar Data: Deception accuracy scores (percent correct)

Secret Service Personnel		Judges		Psychiatrists	
60	50	50	60	60	60
60	40	60	40	90	60
70	50	50	50	60	40
50	40	60	50	70	60
70	50	70	40	60	70
60	70	50	70	50	40
70	70	60	70	50	50
70	70	50	50	50	50
60	60	40	50	60	60
60	60	70	70	70	60
40	70	50	60	60	60
80	60	70	50	60	50
70	80	40	80	60	40
90	60	90	70	50	80
80	80	50	70	70	60
60	50	60	50	30	40
80	60	40	30	60	80
90		60		50	

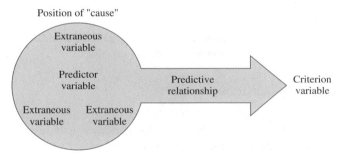

Figure 2.7
Key features of observational research: No shields

iments with other primates show that a causal relationship between smoking and lung cancer does exist in these species.

Let's look at another example of observational research. Let's say you examine the relationship between the length of babies at birth and their later adult height. Can adult height be predicted from baby length? The **baby length/adult height data** in Table 2.2 are analyzed by computer in Section 6.8 of Chapter 6. It turns out that you must also consider the person's gender if you want to establish a good predictive relationship. The columns headed "Baby" show the baby lengths, the columns headed "Adult" list adult heights, and the columns headed "Gender" give the subjects' genders. (Question marks indicate missing data.) Any given row of three columns (for example, 18.0   70.0   ?) lists the values of these three variables for one of the 39 subjects. This

Baby length/ adult height data
A data set used throughout the text; it consists of baby length, adult height, and gender of 39 college students

Table 2.2
Baby length/adult height data: Baby length, adult height, and gender of 39 college students

Baby (in.)	Adult (in.)	Gender*	Baby (in.)	Adult (in.)	Gender*
18.0	70.0	?	20.0	70.0	M
18.0	69.0	M	21.5	65.0	F
20.0	69.0	M	20.5	73.0	M
21.0	67.0	F	23.0	67.0	F
20.0	67.5	F	21.0	62.0	F
19.5	64.0	F	19.0	64.0	F
22.0	67.5	F	17.0	62.0	F
21.0	71.0	M	19.0	60.5	F
20.5	70.0	M	19.0	66.0	M
19.0	69.0	?	20.0	68.5	F
19.0	64.0	F	21.0	72.0	M
20.0	63.0	F	23.5	69.0	F
20.0	66.0	F	19.5	69.5	M
20.5	63.5	F	20.0	62.5	F
21.0	71.0	M	22.0	67.0	F
21.0	65.5	F	20.5	65.0	?
21.0	68.0	F	20.0	63.5	F
20.5	67.0	F	20.5	67.0	F
20.5	67.0	M	21.5	58.1	F
19.0	60.0	?			

*A question mark indicates that the gender was not reported.

research has no manipulation of the predictor variable (baby length), no randomization, and minimal control of extraneous variables.

Quasiexperimental Designs

Many research designs fall short of the true experiment, and researchers must then try to remove the plausible rival explanations of extraneous variables. For example, a two-group study without randomization of subjects to groups, but with manipulation, requires that outcomes be considered in terms of the strength of the causal statement. Some outcomes yield stronger possibilities of causal inference than others. An example of such a design is two intact classes of students, where one class is given an experimental teaching method and the other class gets a control teaching method. Subjects are not randomly assigned to classes, but the researcher can manipulate the independent variable, teaching methods. Designs like this are called **quasiexperimental designs.** It might help you to think of a continuum of types of research with observational research on one end of the scale and true experiments on the other end. Quasiexperimental designs are somewhere between these two ends.

Evaluation of quasiexperimental designs involves the use of two or more types of validity. Cook and Campbell (1979) state that validity refers "to the best available approximation to the truth . . . of propositions." **Internal validity** refers to whether the causal inference from variable *A* to variable *B* is valid, given the way the variables were manipulated or measured. Internal validity is the validity of the manipulation of the independent variable; it asks whether the relationship to the dependent variable is causal. Much of the topic of research design is concerned with properly dealing with threats to internal validity. For example, randomization of subjects to levels of the independent variable precludes many threats to internal validity in a true experiment.

Quasiexperimental designs Designs in which the researcher can manipulate the independent variable but cannot randomly assign participants to groups

Internal validity Truth of the causal inference from the independent variable to the dependent variable

Table 2.3

Variables, relationships between variables, and types of research

True Experiment	*Observational Research*	*Quasiexperimental Designs*
1. Manipulation of an independent variable	1. Observation of predictor and criterion variables	1. Manipulation of an independent variable
2. Randomization of subjects to levels of the independent variable	2. No manipulation	2. No randomization of subjects to levels of the independent variable
3. Other optional methods to control extraneous variables	3. Minimal control of extraneous variables	3. Some control of extraneous variables
4. Causal relationship between the independent variable and the dependent variable	4. Predictive relationship between the predictor variable and the criterion variable	4. Degree to which you can attribute a causal relationship depends on consideration of possible outcomes

External validity
Truth of the generalizability of the results of a study

Another type of validity is **external validity,** which refers to the generalizability of the causal inference from A to B. If A causes B for sixth-graders, does A cause B for college students? If A causes B in a laboratory setting, will A cause B in a field experiment? External validity asks whether the results of our research will generalize to other subjects, settings, or times.

Table 2.3 is a summary of variables, types of relationships between variables, and types of research. Note that all types of research have extraneous variables, but each deals with them differently.

2.6 Data in Research

Data

In Chapter 1, *data* was defined as facts or figures. Data must be in some useful form. Information in verbal form may be useful for description and decision making at one level, but it is not amenable to be used in many statistics. For example, the data in Table 2.2 include values of the variable gender. These values are M, F, and ?, with the last symbol standing for gender not reported. These values are not amenable for computing the sample mean, where you add the values and divide by the number of values. The operation of addition has no meaning on symbols such as M and F. Statistics are primarily computed on data that have numerical values. For example, the baby-length values are numbers, and you can compute the average of those values.

All types of research generate data. Data can be numbers or other symbols, such as F. True experiments generate data because participants give values for the dependent variable. However, data can also be values collected on various preliminary measurements taken on variables other than the dependent variable in a true experiment. For example, in the life-style change/heart study, the independent variable had the values life-style change and usual care. Each participant had a value for total cholesterol before the experiment started. Each participant also had a value on the independent variable indicating group membership, in addition to the various dependent variables, such as total cholesterol level and blood flow improvement.

Observational research typically generates numerical data for the criterion variable. But data can be values collected for the predictor variable, and they can be numerical data. For the liar data, the predictor variable was occupation, and each participant had one data point such as "judge," indicating group membership, in addition to a deception accuracy score. For the baby length/adult height data, the predictor variable baby length and the criterion variable adult height both generated numerical data.

Quantitative and Qualitative Data

Data can be of different types, depending somewhat on the scale of measurement, and the type of the data can influence your choice of statistical procedure. General guidelines can help you select the right statistical method for each type of data.

Quantitative data are observations expressed in numerical form—that is, numerical values. Because this is the way you have been led to think about data so far, this definition should be no surprise. Values of the dependent variable in the study of drive/anxiety in Figure 2.4 are quantitative because the number of items correct is expressed as a number. However, what about the gender variable in the baby length/adult height data in Table 2.2? Values for gender are M, F, and ?. These values are qualitative data.

Qualitative data are observations expressed as labels or names, or observations that possess some characteristic, or observations assigned to one of several categories. Any method for labeling the gender of the subjects in the baby length/adult height study suffices, such as M for male and F for female. Numbers could also be used to label or name values on this variable, such as 2 for male and 1 for female. A third approach would be to group the subjects into two categories, male and female, and count the frequency in each category. Studies that yield qualitative data often present results as frequencies or percentages.

Scales of Measurement

Whether the data collected in a study are quantitative or qualitative depends to a great extent on how the variable is measured. Measurement is simply the act of determining the quantity of, or assigning numbers to, values of a variable. Take height as an example. John Doe's height is a value on the variable height. To measure his height as 67 in., or 1.702 meters (m), is to determine the quantity of his particular value of the variable height. The number 67 is assigned to his value of height. Another example of measurement is the assignment of 2 and 1 to males and females, respectively, in the baby length/adult height study.

Scales of measurement can be generated by asking to what degree the numbers produced by the measurement process capture the four properties of identity, order, distance (or equal intervals), and a true zero point. *Identity* refers to maintaining the distinction between different values. *Order* refers to the sequence (rank) of values. *Distance* refers to the positive difference between values, especially when those differences are a constant. *A true zero point* means the absolute absence of the variable measured. Allowable numbers for a scale of measurement preserve the properties of that scale.

When the measurement process results in a scale that has only the property of identity, the numbers really do not have quantity or magnitude, and the scale is called a **nominal scale of measurement.** Such data do not possess order; that is, a large number does not represent more of the variable than a small number. Nominal data also do not have meaningful distances between numbers. Finally, nominal data do not have a point on the scale that represents the absence of the variable; there is not a true zero point. Assigning 2 to males and 1 to females in the baby length/adult height data is just a labeling process; the 2 and 1 do not represent any quantity. The 2 reveals the identity

---

Quantitative data
Observations that are numerical values

Qualitative data
Observations that are expressed as labels or names

Nominal scale of measurement
Type of measurement process that yields data that have only identity; the data are qualitative

Table 2.4
Nominal scale property: Identity

Variable: Gender	Values		
	M	F	
Allowable	2	1	
Allowable	0	1	
Allowable	12	73.2	
Nonallowable	0	0	Reason: no identity
Nonallowable	1	1	Reason: no identity

of the value of the variable, and all students who have a 2 have the identity "male." Another example of the nominal level of measurement is football players' numbers. The numbers on football jerseys do not have a magnitude but are used to label or identify or even to classify the players. Thus, a player with 72 on his jersey is not any better than someone with 55, but 72 is different from 55. On some football teams, 72 is a tackle and 55 is a center, illustrating the use of the numbers in classifying. The nominal scale of measurement generates data that are qualitative. See Table 2.4 for examples of allowable and nonallowable assignment of numbers for a nominal scale of measurement.

The remaining three scales of measurement all generate quantitative data. Numbers produced in an **ordinal scale of measurement** have the identity and order properties. These numbers have quantity, but they do not give information on the distance between values on the scale; nor do they have a true zero point. The lack of information on the distance between values on the scale is sometimes called lack of equal intervals because an equal distance between the numbers does not represent an equal distance on the variable. For example, football team rankings of 1, 2, 3, and so on do not mean that the difference in ability between the first- and second-place teams is the same as the difference in the ability between the second- and third-place teams. The distances between the numbers are equal to one, but this does not mean that differences in ability or quality are equal. The ordinal scale yields numbers that have order or can be ranked. Another classic example is Mohs' scale for the hardness of rocks: If one rock scratches another, the first rock is ranked as harder than the second. Other examples are professorial ranks, military ranks, and the rank order of paintings by a judge of a painting contest. Table 2.5 lists allowable and nonallowable assignments of numbers for an ordinal scale of measurement.

Ordinal scale of measurement
Type of measurement process that yields data that have identity and order

Table 2.5
Ordinal scale properties: Identity and order

Variable: Football Rankings	Values			
	Team A	Team B	Team C	
Allowable	1	2	3	
Allowable	93	99	100	
Nonallowable	7	7	7	Reason: no identity
Nonallowable	2	1	3	Reason: wrong order (correct order is not preserved)

Table 2.6
Interval scale properties: Identity, order, and distance

Variable: Temperature	Values			
	Day 1	*Day 2*	*Day 3*	
Allowable (°C)	36	26	16	Distances = 10°C
Allowable (°F)	96.8	78.8	60.8	Distances = 18°F
Nonallowable	10	10	10	Reason: no identity
Nonallowable	50	70	60	Reason: wrong order
Nonallowable	40	20	10	Reason: distances not constant

Interval scale of measurement
Type of measurement process that yields data that have identity, order, and equal distance between numbers on the scale

The next level is the **interval scale of measurement.** Numbers in interval measurement have the properties of identity, order, and distance. These data have not only quantity and order but also equal intervals between the numbers on the scale. Many variables used in behavioral science research are in this level of measurement. Temperature is the classic example of an interval scale. Temperature values have quantity, and the intervals between numbers that appear equal do indeed represent equal differences in temperature. The difference between 10° and 20°C is the same as the difference between 20° and 30°C. Missing in interval scales is a true zero point, which is a value of the variable that usually equals zero and means the actual absence of the variable measured. A temperature of 0°C does not mean the absence of temperature, but rather the freezing point of water. Table 2.6 gives allowable and nonallowable assignments of numbers for an interval scale of measurement.

Ratio scale of measurement
Type of measurement process that yields data that have identity, order, equal distance, and a true zero point

Numbers produced in a **ratio scale of measurement** have all four properties: identity, order, distance, and a true zero point. Most ratio scales are physical measurements, such as height, weight, and length, or the difference between any two interval scale measures. An example of the difference between two interval scale measures is the time it takes to complete a task. The elapsed time is simply the difference between the ending time and the beginning time. Other examples of ratio scales are number of errors, number of trials to solution, and number of words recalled in a memory experiment. Remember that the requirement is for zero on the scale to mean the absence of the variable measured, not "do you ever find a level of the variable with the value of zero?" Thus, height is measured on a ratio scale because 0 in. means the absence of height, in spite of the fact that no person will ever be 0 in. tall. Another way to tell that something is being measured on a ratio scale of measurement is to see whether negative values are allowed. If the scale of measurement has an absolute zero, then it won't have negative values.

Table 2.7
No true zero point: Temperatures

Temperature	Day 1	Day 2
°C	20	40
°F	68	104

One characteristic of data from ratio scales is that they can be compared in a ratio function, such as "twice as long" or "half as tall." Scores from other scales cannot be compared in this fashion because of the absence of a true zero point. A good example is the temperature on two days measured in degrees Celsius and degrees Fahrenheit as given in Table 2.7. From the Celsius scale you might be tempted to say that day 2 was twice as warm as day 1, whereas the Fahrenheit scale tells you that day 2 was 1.53 times as warm as day 1. Obviously, something is wrong here. The amount of heat in day 1 and day 2 has not changed; only the scales of measurement have. The Celsius and Fahrenheit scales have different points labeled 0, and neither is a true zero point. Examine the properties of ratio scales in Table 2.8.

Table 2.8
Ratio scale properties: Identity, order, distance, and a true zero point

Variable:	*Values*			
Height	*Person 1*	*Person 2*	*Person 3*	
Allowable (ft)	5	6	7	
Allowable (in.)	60	72	84	
Allowable (m)	1.52	1.83	2.13	
Nonallowable	5	5	5	Reason: no identity
Nonallowable	6	7	2	Reason: wrong order
Nonallowable	10	13	14	Reason: distance not constant
Nonallowable	4	6	8	Reason: height of person 1 is not 50% of the height of person 3, but $(5/7)(100) = 71.43\%$

Most of this text deals with statistical procedures appropriate for quantitative data. Quantitative data may come from any of the scales of measurement, but they typically come from the ordinal, interval, and ratio scales. Chapter 18 presents some special-purpose statistical procedures appropriate for qualitative data (nominal scale). Chapter 19 presents such procedures for quantitative ordinal data.

Quick Quiz

Look at your driver's license and categorize the data on it as qualitative or quantitative. If an item is quantitative, identify the scale of measurement.

Answer

Your name, sex, street, and Social Security number are all qualitative data. Age, height, weight, and house or apartment number are quantitative. The first three have ratio scales of measurement, and the last has ordinal.

2.7   Summary, Study Tips, and Computers

Chapter Summary

Research can be classified as absolute or comparative and is part of the bigger concept called science. Scientific methods have orderly steps for proceeding through research, and statistics is part of these steps. Variables are important to research. They can be classified as discrete or continuous. The five types of variables are independent (manipulated), dependent (measured), extraneous (controlled), predictor (usually occurs in time before the criterion variable), and criterion (follows the predictor variable). Various procedures control extraneous variables, including randomizing subjects to groups, keeping subjects constant on the extraneous variable, and including the extraneous variable in the design. Single-blind studies remove subject bias, and double-blind studies remove both subject and observer bias. Depending on the study, a variable might be operationally defined as any one of the five types.

A causal relationship exists between an independent and a dependent variable because the researcher manipulates the independent variable and randomizes the subjects to groups. A predictive relationship occurs between a predictor and a criterion variable. True experiments contain manipulation of an independent variable, randomization of subjects to groups, other optional methods of controlling extraneous variables, and a causal relationship between independent and dependent variables. Observational research is characterized by predictor and criterion variables, no manipulation, minimal control of extraneous variables, and a predictive relationship between the predictor and criterion variables. Quasiexperimental designs involve manipulation of an independent variable, no randomization of subjects to groups, and some control of extraneous variables; the possibility of causal inference depends on ruling out rival explanations. Data can be qualitative or quantitative and measured on nominal, ordinal, interval, or ratio scales.

The following key terms are introduced in this chapter:

Research
Absolute research
Comparative research
Science
Scientific methods
Variable
Continuous variable
Discrete variable
Unit of measurement
Units of analysis
Independent variable
Manipulation

Experimental group
Control group
Dependent variable
Extraneous variable
Control
Confounding
Randomizing participants
    to groups
Keeping participants
    constant
Include the extraneous
    variable in the design

Subject bias
Observer bias
Single-blind experiment
Double-blind experiment
Operational definition
Causal relationship
Predictive relationship
Predictor variable
Criterion variable
True experiment

Observational research
Quasiexperimental design
Internal validity
External validity
Quantitative data
Qualitative data
Nominal scale
Ordinal scale
Interval scale
Ratio scale

Study Tips

More definitions are introduced in this chapter. Learn these definitions so that you are firmly grounded in the basic concepts before you are required to do computations. If you have skipped the quick quizzes, go back over them. See if you can answer the questions without looking in the text.

The most frequent student errors are (1) confusing independent and dependent variables (*Hint:* Think of the time line) and (2) *assuming* a study is a true experiment.

Computers

Some calculators are really simplified computers. They have all the common aspects of a computer—an input device, an output device, a memory, a component that does the arithmetic operations—and they can be programmed. Thus, computers and sophisticated calculators are similar, differing mainly in price. Computers range from large to small, fast to slow, and expensive to affordable.

Large (fast; expensive) computers are called *mainframe computers* and are typically owned by governments, universities, and large companies. The components of a mainframe computer might fill a medium-sized room. Midsize computers are called *minicomputers* and are typically owned by the same organizations that own mainframe computers as well as smaller businesses, including banks. Their components might be the size of a large desk. Small (slow relative to mainframes but fast enough for any statistical computations; affordable) computers are called *personal computers* (PCs). They are used by all the above organizations plus individuals. Some of you may own a PC, either a desktop or a portable computer, sometimes called a laptop or a notebook computer.

Typically you think of only the physical components of the computer, called the *hardware.* Equally important to any computer system are the programs written to run the computer, called *software.* Because computer programs run the computers and get them to do what you want, they obviously have to be written in a language the computer can understand. Some computer languages are easy to learn and use and can be adapted easily to different computers. Others are more difficult and machine-specific. You do not have to learn any computer language to use the computer sections of this text. Rather, you can learn how to run computer programs that other people have written.

Proliferation of computers has made computation of statistical procedures easy. Collections of computer programs for statistical procedures, called *statistical packages,* have been written, and all you have to do is learn how to use them. Some are available only on mainframe computers; others are available for PCs.

Excellent statistical packages such as SAS and SPSS allow the user of statistics and computers easy access to a wide variety of statistical procedures with all the speed of computer analysis. Of course, you still need a course in statistics and a text such as this to learn statistical concepts, including when to use such procedures. Thus, a statistics text should show you how to compute statistical procedures using these modern tools. Most researchers use computerized statistical analysis in their data analysis, and so should you, the statistics student. In keeping with this philosophy, throughout the text examples are given of the use of computer programs from the statistical packages SAS and SPSS. These appear in the last section of each chapter, and they include illustrations of necessary input statements as well as output from the computer programs.

If you plan to do considerable research and data analysis beyond that done in this course, you might want to read the manual for the computer package your computer center supports, because the instructions given here are limited in scope and simplified. However, what is given is sufficient for this text, and you need to refer to other sources only if you want to proceed beyond this text.

Your Computer System

You need to get answers to the following questions either from your instructor in the course or from your computer center personnel. What statistical packages are supported on your system? What means of input are available (terminal), and what means of output are available (printer, terminal, or both)? Where are they located, and when are they available for student use? Also, is instruction available on using these devices? How does a person get a project account number? What lines are used to get into the statistical package? That is, what system lines are necessary to use the statistical package?

Statistical Package Jobs

Once you know the what, when, where, and how of your computer system, you need to know something about the job to be submitted. Every job is a collection, in order, of lines that can be either data or commands to the computer or the program. Commands get the computer's attention, get you into the statistical package, tell the package what you want to do, and input the data to the package. Thus, every job will contain the following:

1. System control commands ("Hello, computer, I'd like to do some work now.")
2. Statistical package commands ("Package, would you please run these statistics on the data, which are coming next?")
3. Data lines
4. Statistical package commands ("Package, would you do this additional work?")
5. More system control commands, if any ("Good-bye for now, computer.")

The examples in the remaining chapters include all the lines (commands and data) necessary to do the analysis. When you get ready to run these examples, you need to have the computer system questions answered and you need to refer occasionally to this section. Remember, this is going to be simple and very specific to the statistics in this text, so do not panic. Computers are not things to fear, but machines that can greatly enhance your ability to deal with data. Relax and enjoy!

EXERCISES

Section 2.2

1. For each of the following, decide whether the research is comparative or absolute.
   a. Dr. M measured the white male suicide rate for City A.
   b. A study was done to see whether Treatments C and D differ for Illness Y.
   c. The DasGupta (1992) exam stress study from Chapter 1.
   d. The finding from Box 1.1 that four in ten Americans believe that eating fruits and vegetables will help prevent cancer.
   e. The Silberstein and Parsons (1981) study in Exercise 22 of Chapter 1. The study looked at the relationship between mental-psychological impairment and alcoholism for 25 alcoholics and 25 nonalcoholics.

2. Return to the life-style/heart study by Ornish and colleagues (1990) from Chapter 1. Describe the five steps of scientific methods in the context of that study.

Sections 2.3–2.5

3. A mathematics professor thinks that college algebra should be a prerequisite for the statistics course. To support her position, she examines the statistics grades of a recent class and finds that the average grade for those who had taken college algebra is higher than that for those who had not taken college algebra. She claims that this proves that taking college algebra causes higher grades.
   a. Is her claim accurate? Explain.
   b. What are some possible extraneous variables? Have these been controlled?
   c. What type of variable is taking algebra, independent or predictor?
   d. What type of variable is statistics grade, dependent or criterion?

4. Studies on family life show that children feel more secure in structured (organized, disciplined) homes than in unstructured (permissive) homes. Can you conclude that structure causes more feelings of security? What potential confounding exists?

5. Research has been done to investigate the effectiveness of vitamin C in preventing colds. Half of 200 adult participants were randomly assigned to a placebo control group, and the other half to a group that received large daily doses of vitamin C. Participants did not know which pill they were receiving. Both groups were checked for illness every month during a recent winter. At the end of the winter, the percentage of participants who had not had a cold was recorded for each group.
   a. Is this a true experiment?
   b. What is the independent variable?
   c. What is the dependent variable?
   d. Name some extraneous variables. Are these controlled? If so, how?
   e. What is the sample? What is the population?
   f. What statistic is given in this description?

6. A researcher wants to compare an individual-based programmed instruction (self-paced) approach with a standard teaching method in descriptive statistics. Students in a statistics class are measured on their statistics knowledge and divided into two groups. Both groups learn through their respective methods for 6 weeks, and then all students are retested on their statistics knowledge. The researcher is interested in the change in knowledge, or the difference between the before and after measures.
   a. What questions would you ask before you could tell whether this was a true experiment?
   b. If your questions are answered and you feel it is a true experiment, what is the independent variable? Dependent variable?

7. Suppose you find that for 4000 twelfth-graders, males get an average of 53.9 and females get an average of 60.1 words per minute on a test of clerical speed and accuracy.
   a. Is this a true experiment or observational research?
   b. Suppose that the probability of this difference is .003 if there are no differences between males and females in the population. Can you say that gender differences cause differences in clerical speed and accuracy?
   c. What possible plausible explanations can you think of other than gender differences?

8. Consider the caffeine withdrawal study in Section 1.1 of Chapter 1, where some people got beverages with caffeine and others got decaffeinated beverages. They were asked to keep a diary of their physical health, including symptoms such as headaches and sleeplessness.
   a. Is this a true experiment or observational research?
   b. What is the independent variable?

c. How is extraneous variability controlled?

d. What is the dependent variable?

9. See the life-style/heart study by Ornish and colleagues (1990) given in Chapter 1.

    a. Is this a true experiment or observational research?

    b. What is the independent variable?

    c. How is extraneous variability controlled?

    d. What is the dependent variable?

10. See the DasGupta (1992) study on exam stress given in Chapter 1 as an example of research.

    a. Is this a true experiment or observational research?

    b. What is the independent variable?

    c. How is extraneous variability controlled?

    d. What is the dependent variable?

11. From Exercise 22 in Chapter 1, Silberstein and Parsons (1981) compared 25 female alcoholics to 25 female nonalcoholics to investigate the relationship between mental–psychological impairment and alcoholism.

    a. Is this a true experiment or observational research?

    b. Can you say that alcoholism caused the differences they found between these two groups?

    c. What plausible explanations can you think of other than alcoholism?

    d. What is the population?

12. Wigfield and colleagues (1992) studied whether sudden infant death syndrome (SIDS) rates were affected by babies being placed on their stomachs or backs at bedtime.

    a. Is this a true experiment or observational research?

    b. What is the predictor variable?

    c. How is extraneous variability controlled?

    d. What is the criterion variable?

13. What if the Bandura, Ross, and Ross (1963) study had not randomly assigned preschool children to groups? Suppose instead that they had to use four intact groups of children, such as preschool classes, but they could randomly assign one of the three treatments or the control to each group.

    a. Is this a true experiment or observational research?

    b. What label, or type of design, would you give to this research?

14. Consider an experiment on the relationship between neatness of essay examinations and grades (Marshall & Powers, 1969). All other variables were held constant, except for neatness, by having the same paper prepared in four ways: typed, neat handwriting, average handwriting neatness, and poor handwriting. The papers were graded by 420 prospective high school teachers, with each grader grading one paper within one of the four ways of preparation. Graders were instructed to grade on content alone and disregard everything else. Grades could range from a low of 1 to a high of 9. The content of the papers was constant for all four groups, each grader graded only one paper, and all graders were given the same instructions. The only difference between papers in the four groups was the way they were graded. Average grades were 5.15 (typed), 5.66 (neat handwriting), 5.02 (average handwriting neatness), and 5.25 (poor handwriting). Only the means for neat handwriting and average handwriting differed significantly.

    a. What is the manipulated variable?

    b. Does the description of the study indicate random assignment of graders to ways of paper presentation?

    c. How is extraneous variability controlled?

    d. Does this fit exactly our description of a true experiment?

    e. What label, or type of design, is applied to such research?

15. Let's think again about the over-40 male trying to make a decision about taking aspirin as a preventive measure for heart attacks (Exercise 21 in Chapter 1). In a study sponsored in part by an aspirin maker, 22,071 male doctors over age 40 were randomly assigned to take either one aspirin every other day or an identical-looking pill that had no aspirin in it (a placebo). Aspirin is supposed to reduce heart attacks by interfering with blood clot formation, but it has the side effect of making the stomach more acidic.

    a. Was this a true experiment? That is, did the research have randomization of subjects to groups and manipulation of an independent variable?

    b. What extraneous variables were present in the research? How were they controlled?

    c. Critically examine the research with respect to its *external validity*.

16. Suppose a researcher observed that 67% of the neurotic patients who went to a clinic reported that they had no symptoms within 12 months of beginning treatment. A second researcher at another clinic randomly assigned subjects to either a therapist or a waiting list. Both groups reported a decreasing number of symptoms during an 8-week session. Also, the researcher reported no differences between the two groups at the end of the 8-week session.

a. Is the first study an example of absolute or comparative research? The second study?

b. In the second study, what method of control of extraneous variables is used? Is the second study a true experiment?

c. In the second study, could the reporting of symptoms be a form of therapy that in itself reduces the number of symptoms reported? If this is true, does this problem threaten internal or external validity?

17. In the Salk vaccine study, the experimental group had a rate of 28 cases of polio per 100,000, and the placebo control group had a rate of 70 cases per 100,000.

a. What was the population? Are you part of the population?

b. What was the sample for this part of the research?

c. If the probability for the differences in the rates between the placebo control and the experimental group was $p = .001$, what conclusions can be drawn?

d. Why couldn't the researchers have given a group of children the vaccine and compared the 1954 number of children with polio with that of 1953 (about 35,000)? Or 1952 (about 60,000)?

e. What does the rate of 48 cases per 100,000 for the no-consent group tell you about the bias introduced by consent and how it is related to income?

Section 2.6

18. You are attending a track meet at your university. It's 79° outside, with a northerly wind of about 15 mph. Your best friend is wearing jersey number 52 and finishes second in the 100-m dash. Another friend must clear ten hurdles in her race and finishes with a time of 16.56 s.

a. Give an example of the nominal scale of measurement.

b. Give an example of the ordinal scale of measurement.

c. Give an example of the interval scale of measurement.

d. Give an example of the ratio scale of measurement.

e. Which variables are discrete? Continuous?

19. For each of the following variables, is the scale of measurement nominal, ordinal, interval, or ratio?

a. The milligrams of vitamin A in a packaged food product

b. The types of roaches found in someone's dormitory room

c. The position of State U's football team in the conference standings

d. The total points scored by a statistics student during her semester class

e. Your responses to this exercise

f. Ability in mathematics as measured by a standardized test

g. House addresses on a city street

20. Schwab and Schwab (1981) compared U.S. and Japanese married couples on expected and actual roles within marriage. They used the Marital Roles Inventory (MRI), which has the subjects rank-order 11 roles from 1 = most important to 11 = least important. They wanted to explore the relationships between expected and actual roles and to examine any differences in those relationships across cultures.

a. Is this a true experiment or observational research?

b. What type of relationship exists between expected and actual roles?

c. Are the data for a subject on expected roles quantitative or qualitative?

d. What is the level of measurement for scores on the MRI?

21. Categorize the following variables as continuous or discrete and qualitative or quantitative. Also give the scale of measurement for each variable.

a. Political party

b. Gender

c. Cultural origin

d. Color

e. Birth order

f. Rank of your preferences of cola brands

g. Order of Indy 500 finishers as a measure of speed

h. Hardness of pencil leads

i. Family size

j. Number of successful free throws in a basketball game

k. Height

l. Reaction time as a measure of speed of neuroprocessing

22. See the liar study covered in this chapter.

a. Are the deception accuracy scores (in Table 2.1) quantitative or qualitative? What scale of measurement is used?

b. Is the variable occupation quantitative or qualitative? What scale of measurement is used?

23. See the delay of gratification study in Research Example 1.

a. Is this a true experiment or observational research?

b. What type of variable is delay time? Is it quantitative or qualitative?

c. What is the scale of measurement for delay time?

d. List any possible extraneous variables.

24. Consider the article in Box 1.1 of Chapter 1.

a. What kind of research is represented by most of these studies?

b. Under "Other findings" in the second column, what confounding variables could be involved in the finding that cancer rates are lower in countries where more fruits and vegetables are consumed?

c. What kind of variable is number of fruits and vegetables consumed? Is it quantitative or qualitative? What is the scale of measurement?

d. What kind of variable is cancer rate? Is it quantitative or qualitative? What is the scale of measurement?

3

Don't worry about frequency distributions

Describing Data
for a Single Variable:
Pictorial Descriptions

Building on your knowledge from Chapter 2 on the role of statistics in research, you now begin to see what researchers do with numbers. The data that help scientists make decisions about research questions need to be summarized, and pictorial displays quickly explain a set of data. You may have heard of bar graphs and pie charts; you will see those in this chapter, along with some forms of pictorial description that may be unfamiliar to you: frequency distributions, stem and leaf displays, scatterplots, frequency polygons, and histograms. You can discover patterns in data that help explain a phenomenon.

Research Example 3
3.1 Overview and Introduction
  Overview
  Introduction
3.2 Pictorial Descriptions: Frequency Distributions
  Frequency distributions
  Relative frequency distributions
  Cumulative frequency distributions
3.3 Pictorial Descriptions: Stem and Leaf Displays
3.4 Pictorial Descriptions: Graphs
  Bar graph and histogram
  Frequency polygon
  Pie chart
  Scatterplot
  Beyond these displays and graphs
3.5 Misleading Graphs
3.6 Description with Statistics
3.7 Summary, Study Tips, and Computation
  Chapter summary
  Study tips
  Computation
Exercises

Research Example 3

When researchers perform studies, they are looking for answers to questions: Do people who quit drinking caffeinated beverages suffer from headaches and other withdrawal symptoms? Which occupations are best at catching liars? After researchers have collected data—number and severity of withdrawal symptoms

67

experienced, number of lies detected—they need to look at the data for patterns that can lead to answers to their research questions.

Many graphical techniques for describing data are available. The following examples illustrate how graphs can be used to convey information.

Our first example in Figure 3.1 is a histogram from *USA Today*. This graph shows the percentage of cigarette smokers who would quit if the price of cigarettes reached various levels. You may notice that the smokers in the $3 category are included in all higher categories. So the graph is portraying the increase in percentages from one category to the next. The biggest jump is between $3 and $4. An additional 14% of smokers said they would quit if the cost of a pack reached $4. All the subsequent increases add up to 13%.

The second example in Figure 3.2, also from *USA Today,* is a pie chart from a Gallup Poll conducted for the National Cattlemen's Association on people's prefer-

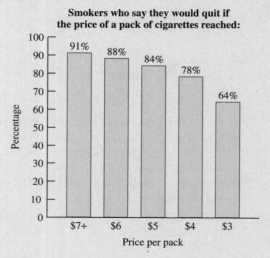

Figure 3.1
Cigarette smoking: Cost per pack to quit. *Source: Data from the Gallup Organization for SmithKline Beecham.*

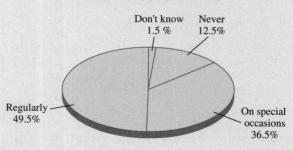

Figure 3.2
When do people grill? *Source: Data from the Gallup Poll for the National Cattlemen's Association.*

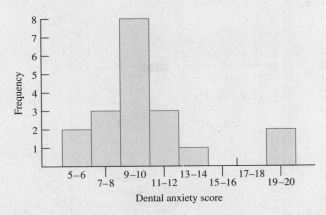

Figure 3.3
Histogram of dental anxiety scores for $N=19$ females

ences on when to cook out. In the original drawing in *USA Today,* the "pie" was drawn as a slab of meat on a grill. Almost half of those polled said they cook out regularly, and another third said they cook out on special occasions—probably good news for the beef industry.

The final example in Figure 3.3 is also a histogram. This graph contains data from a study of dental anxiety by Arntz, van Eck, and Heijmans (1990), which will be discussed in Chapter 6. The bars show the number of female subjects whose dental anxiety scores fall within one of eight intervals on the Dental Anxiety Scale, which ranges from 4 to 20, with high scores indicating high anxiety. Most of the scores are 9–10, but two scores are in the highest interval. Could these extreme scores have affected the results of the study? Note that the lowest observed score is a 5, although the scale allows for a score as low as 4.

Graphs like these give a quick descriptive picture of research results. They sometimes show you unexpected patterns. Every time you collect data, you have an opportunity to look for those patterns with graphs such as the ones we discuss in this chapter.

3.1   Overview and Introduction

Overview

Suppose you have the fictitious data set in Table 3.1 that includes a midterm score, overall GPA, and major for 42 students in a class. What can you do to describe these data? Is there any structure or pattern in the data? What can you learn from these data? Could some of the types of visual displays in Research Example 3 be used here?

You can't get a quick, meaningful idea of patterns in these data from their current form. The following are some visual displays that could be used to pictorially describe these data. You'll learn more about each kind of graph later.

Frequency Distribution.   Table 3.2 shows frequency distributions of the GPAs for the psychology and engineering majors. Frequency distributions tell only how many scores are in each interval, not the scores themselves. Note that Tables 3.2 and 3.3 do not include the five students who are undecided about their major.

Table 3.1
Fictitious data set

Subject	Midterm	GPA	Major	Subject	Midterm	GPA	Major
1	89	3.20	psychology	22	79	2.71	psychology
2	92	3.45	engineering	23	90	3.55	psychology
3	71	3.11	psychology	24	73	3.01	undecided
4	65	2.73	psychology	25	75	2.97	psychology
5	75	2.99	engineering	26	81	2.76	engineering
6	81	3.29	psychology	27	69	2.31	psychology
7	94	3.87	psychology	28	98	3.87	engineering
8	97	3.57	psychology	29	92	3.45	psychology
9	87	3.13	engineering	30	82	3.07	engineering
10	77	3.02	undecided	31	79	2.72	psychology
11	62	2.45	psychology	32	64	2.63	psychology
12	69	2.33	psychology	33	89	3.14	undecided
13	71	2.97	psychology	34	74	2.78	engineering
14	76	2.69	engineering	35	87	3.12	engineering
15	73	2.80	undecided	36	92	3.34	psychology
16	91	3.12	psychology	37	71	2.56	undecided
17	87	3.02	psychology	38	76	2.67	psychology
18	83	3.11	engineering	39	81	2.89	psychology
19	75	3.04	engineering	40	73	2.67	psychology
20	71	2.76	engineering	41	82	2.96	engineering
21	79	2.97	psychology	42	97	3.69	psychology

Table 3.2
Frequency distributions of GPAs

GPA Interval	Psychology Frequency	Engineering Frequency
3.76–4.00	1	1
3.51–3.75	3	0
3.26–3.50	3	1
3.01–3.25	4	5
2.76–3.00	4	5
2.51–2.75	6	1
2.26–2.50	3	0
	Total 24	13

Stem and Leaf Display.   Table 3.3 shows stem and leaf displays of midterm scores for the psychology and engineering majors. Stem and leaf displays give a good overall picture of the distribution of data while preserving each data point.

Bar Graph and Histogram.   Figure 3.4 is a bar graph of the number of students with GPAs over 3.0 for the three categories of majors. Figure 3.5 shows histograms of midterm scores for the psychology and engineering majors.

Frequency Polygon.   Figure 3.6 is a frequency polygon of midterm scores for psychology majors.

Table 3.3
Stem and leaf displays of midterm scores

Psychology *Midterm Scores*			*Engineering* *Midterm Scores*	
9.	7 7		9.	8
9*	0 1 2 2 4		9*	2
8.	7 9		8.	7 7
8*	1 1		8*	1 2 2 3
7.	5 6 9 9 9		7.	5 5 6
7*	1 1 3		7*	1 4
6.	5 9 9			
6*	2 4			

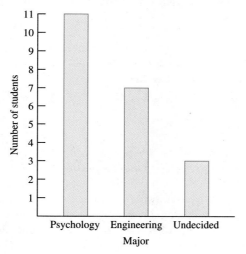

Figure 3.4
Bar graph showing the number of students with grade point averages over 3.0, by major

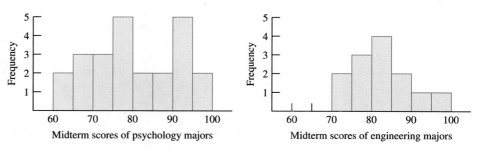

Figure 3.5
Histograms of midterm scores

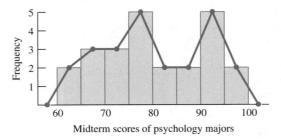

Figure 3.6
Frequency polygon for midterm scores of psychology majors

Pie Chart.   Figure 3.7 is a pie chart of the number and percentage of the three categories of majors.

Scatterplot.   Figure 3.8 shows a scatterplot of two variables, GPAs and midterm scores. Each dot represents two numbers for one student: the student's GPA is on the horizontal axis or *X* axis, and the midterm score is on the vertical axis or *Y* axis. The student with a midterm score of 98 and a GPA of 3.87 is noted on the plot.

Introduction

Have you ever been in a class where a few brilliant students got high scores on an exam, while many people struggled to make a passing grade? The average score for the class may seem high, like 78%. A teacher who doesn't examine the distribution of the scores may not notice that the exam was too difficult for most students.

When you are examining a batch of data, such as the midterm scores in Table 3.1, you can look for patterns that may tell you something about the phenomenon—how well a class performed on a test, for instance. Researchers do the same thing with their data.

After running a scientific study, one of a researcher's first tasks is to try to describe the data. This must be done whether the data came from a true experiment or from observational research. Three principles guide us: simplicity, thoroughness, and accuracy.

The goal of pictorial description is to take the raw data and organize them so that you can describe all of the data as a group, rather than as individual scores. "Simple"

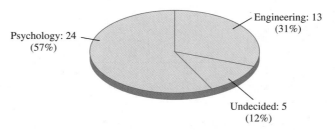

Figure 3.7
A pie chart of the number and percentage of majors

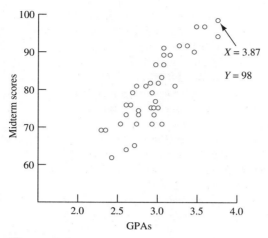

Figure 3.8
Scatterplot of GPAs and midterm scores for all students

description means the data are condensed to a less cumbersome and more easily comprehended picture, and "thorough" means all scores are represented. You want to learn something about all of the data without having to study a list of scores. At the same time, you don't want to misrepresent the data; this is what we mean by "accurate." The goal is to reduce a large amount of data to a simple picture and a few statistics that contain as much information as possible.

Just as there are many ways of viewing a mountainside, there is no single best picture of data. You may have to try different vantage points—different kinds of graphs—before you find the best view. When you look at a mountain, you notice its shape. The same is true with a graph. Graphs will help you understand the shape of the distribution of data. Are many scores clustered at the lower end of the scale with just a few high numbers? Visual displays are superior to statistics in describing the shape or pattern of the data. We focus now on various ways to pictorially describe data.

Quick Quiz

What is the goal of a pictorial description of data?

       Answer

To give a simple, thorough, and accurate summary of the data so that a large number of scores are summarized in an understandable form and so that the researcher can see patterns in the distribution of scores.

3.2 Pictorial Descriptions: Frequency Distributions

Frequency Distributions

Suppose you are interested in the data on heights (to the nearest half inch) of college students given in Table 2.2 because you want to compare your own height with other students' heights. It would take you a long time to compare your height to every single score. So you need to organize the data into a picture that is thorough, simple, and accurate. You can start by ranking the heights from shortest to tallest. This provides some organization but no summary. It also mixes the heights of males and females. Ordering the male and female heights separately, as in Table 3.4, provides more organization and some summary. But if you group the data in some way, you can simplify the picture even more. One approach is to group the scores separately for males and females by some intervals—for example, 58 to 59.0, 59.5 to 60.5, and so on—and then count the frequency in each grouping.

__Frequency distribution__

Distribution that pairs the value of *X* with its frequency in the sample

A **frequency distribution** is simply a pairing of the value of each score, *X*, with how frequently that *X* occurs in the sample. (Whenever we talk about the "frequency" of an event, we mean "how often the event occurs.") Sometimes the "value of *X*" is a range or an interval of values. The frequency distributions of adult heights for male and female college students are given in Table 3.5. With the data in frequency distribution form, you can make some interesting comparisons between the heights of male and female students and your own height. For example, it is now obvious that the average height of males is greater than that of females because the male distribution is centered on a higher height than is the female distribution. Where is your height in the appropriate distribution?

Table 3.4
Adult heights to nearest 0.5 in.

Males (in Order)				Females (in Order)		
73.0	69.0			69.0	67.0	63.5
72.0	67.0			68.5	67.0	63.5
71.0	66.0			68.0	66.0	63.0
71.0				67.5	65.5	62.5
70.0				67.5	65.0	62.0
70.0				67.0	64.0	62.0
69.5				67.0	64.0	60.5
69.0				67.0	64.0	58.0

Table 3.5
Frequency distributions of heights of a sample of college students

Males		Females	
Interval (in.)	Frequency	Interval (in.)	Frequency
73.0–74.0	1		
71.5–72.5	1		
70.0–71.0	4		
68.5–69.5	3	68.5–69.5	2
67.0–68.0	1	67.0–68.0	8
65.5–66.5	1	65.5–66.5	2
		64.0–65.0	4
		62.5–63.5	4
		61.0–62.0	2
		59.5–60.5	1
		58.0–59.0	1
	Total 11		Total 24

Real limits

The score value plus or minus one-half the unit of measurement

Apparent limits

Highest and lowest actual score values that could be contained in the interval

Interval width

Difference between the upper and lower real limits of the interval

One piece of information you need before you start to build frequency distributions is that the **real limits** of a score value are equal to the value plus or minus one-half of the unit of measurement. For example, the real limits for a height of 5 ft 6 in. are 5 ft 5.5 in. and 5 ft 6.5 in. because the unit of measurement is 1 in. Real limits show the continuity of the frequency distribution and are used to obtain interval width.

Some rules for forming frequency distributions are as follows:

1. The intervals are of equal width.
2. Intervals are listed even when the frequency is zero, unless they are on either the top or bottom of the scale.
3. The intervals do not overlap.
4. The **apparent limits** of an interval are the highest and lowest actual score values that could be contained in the interval.
5. The real limits of an interval are the upper real limit of the highest value and the lower real limit of the lowest value that could be in the interval.
6. The **interval width** is the difference between the upper and lower real limits of the interval.
7. The interval width should be chosen so there are 10 to 20 intervals.

Let's look at the height example to see how to start forming a frequency distribution. If you divide the difference between the high and low scores by the interval width, you get the approximate number of intervals. Here you had a high score of 73 and a low score of 58, so the difference is $73 - 58 = 15$. Let's try an interval width of 1.5 in. When you divide 15 by 1.5, you find that there are $15/1.5 = 10$ intervals. Depending on where you start, you will have 10 or 11 intervals. Start with the lowest score, 58, and build the intervals up until you get an interval that includes the highest score, 73. Remember that the interval width of 1.5 is the difference in the real limits, so apparent limits of the bottom interval are 58–59, but the real limits are 57.75–59.25. The separate distributions for males and females make the picture less simple, but they do give useful information.

Other rules about constructing frequency distributions could be given, but they would unnecessarily complicate things. As the researcher, you can choose the interval width and the number of intervals arbitrarily to best describe your data. Common sense tells you not to choose a large or a small number of intervals. If there are too many intervals, all the scores are stretched out, and the distribution looks flat. If there aren't enough intervals, the scores pile up together. A frequency distribution with a large number of intervals gives a picture that is accurate but not simple. Choosing a small number of intervals gives a distribution that is simple but not accurate. The rule of thumb of choosing between 10 and 20 intervals is only a rough guideline. Choose the number of intervals that allow you to see a pattern in your data.

Baseline/posting data

Data set used throughout the text; it consists of speeds (km/h) of 90 vehicles during the baseline and posting periods

As another example, researchers studying behavior modification wondered whether driving speeds in a Canadian city would be reduced if the percentage of drivers who did not speed on the previous day was posted (Van Houten, Nau & Marini, 1980). They measured the speed of vehicles several times in the day with concealed radar to establish a baseline, and they calculated the percentage of vehicles that were traveling within the legal speed limits. Then the next day they posted the percentage of drivers who did not speed, and again they measured the speeds of all vehicles. Examine the data of Table 3.6, which gives **baseline/posting data;** that is, simulated data for 90 vehicles for the baseline period and for the period when the percentage not speeding was posted. The speed limit was 50 kilometers per hour (km/h).

Table 3.6
Baseline/posting data: Speeds (km/h) of 90 vehicles during baseline period and posting period

Baseline					Posting				
46	78	48	49	59	46	64	49	49	49
79	76	76	77	58	78	49	64	71	68
74	75	75	61	64	47	48	65	64	51
51	51	51	50	65	47	49	66	59	53
61	73	73	73	65	76	48	53	63	52
72	50	51	72	60	74	69	53	59	62
70	52	59	53	65	48	50	52	54	55
52	71	71	71	64	49	51	53	54	55
53	53	59	69	62	62	63	63	55	61
54	68	69	69	61	54	54	54	50	51
63	55	54	55	63	55	53	53	53	51
68	54	69	55	63	53	67	67	51	51
54	55	66	67	61	66	51	50	60	60
55	62	57	57	61	61	52	65	60	56
66	66	59	57	66	61	56	57	65	57
67	57	67	64	61	56	57	57	57	57
62	56	63	58	61	57	57	57	56	57
62	67	56	59	60	58	59	59	59	59

How would *you* construct a frequency distribution of these data? As you choose an interval width, keep in mind how many intervals you will obtain using that width. After you have done your work on these baseline data, look at Table 3.7.

To show you how arbitrary choices can affect the picture of the data, Table 3.7 gives three different interval widths: 1, 3, and 8. The data for the baseline period are grouped, with an interval width of 1 yielding 34 intervals, an interval width of 3 yielding 12 intervals, and an interval width of 8 yielding 5 intervals. Notice that the frequency distributions show the contrast between simplicity (distribution c) and accuracy (distribution a). The best distribution is b, which has 12 intervals. From b, you can see that most speeds are between about 54 and 68, with a few more extreme speeds at the high end of the distribution. If you had selected an interval width in the range of 2 to 4, you would have built an adequate frequency distribution for these data.

Quick Quiz
(a) How many intervals should appear in a frequency distribution? (b) What is meant by *frequency*?
  Answers
  (a) A good rule of thumb is 10 to 20 intervals. (b) Frequency means how often an event occurs.

Relative Frequency Distributions

Relative frequency distribution
Distribution that pairs a value of X with its proportion or percentage of frequency in the sample

Another type of frequency distribution is the **relative frequency distribution.** Relative frequency distributions give a proportion or percentage for the frequency of each X or interval of X values. The *proportion* is the fraction of the total X values that have a certain characteristic. To calculate the proportion for an interval, divide the frequency for that interval by the total frequency for the entire distribution. The *percentage* for

Table 3.7
Frequency distributions of baseline speeds (km/h)

(a)			(b)			(c)	
Interval	*Frequency*		*Interval*	*Frequency*		*Interval*	*Frequency*
79	1		78–80	2		78–85	2
78	1		75–77	5		70–77	15
77	1		72–74	6		62–69	28
76	2		69–71	8		54–61	31
75	2		66–68	10		46–53	14
74	1		63–65	10			90
73	3		60–62	13			
72	2		57–59	11			
71	3		54–56	11			
70	1		51–53	9			
69	4		48–50	4			
68	2		45–47	1			
67	4			90			
66	4						
65	3						
64	3						
63	4						
62	4						
61	7						
60	2						
59	5						
58	2						
57	4						
56	2						
55	5						
54	4						
53	3						
52	2						
51	4						
50	2						
49	1						
48	1						
47	0						
46	1						
	90						

an interval is simply the proportion multiplied by 100. For example, if you build a frequency distribution from the data in Table 3.6 with an interval width of 2, you find that 10% of the vehicles had speeds of 60–61 km/h (9/90 = .10, .10 × 100 = 10%). The relative frequency distributions for the speeds in both the baseline and posting periods from Table 3.6 are given in Table 3.8 using proportions. Relative frequency distributions are helpful in comparing two or more distributions that have different total numbers of observations.

If you add the relative frequencies in the bottom seven intervals, 46 to 59.9, you find 40% of the baseline drivers and 70% of the posting period drivers. Does it appear to you that posting the percentage of drivers who did not speed on the previous day had some effect on vehicle speed?

Table 3.8
Relative frequency distributions of speeds (km/h)

		Baseline					Posting		
Interval	Frequency	Frequency/ Total	=	Relative Frequency	Interval	Frequency	Frequency/ Total	=	Relative Frequency
78–79	2	2/90	=	.02	78–79	1	1/90	=	.01
76–77	3	3/90	=	.03	76–77	1	1/90	=	.01
74–75	3	3/90	=	.03	74–75	1	1/90	=	.01
72–73	5	5/90	=	.06	72–73	0	0/90	=	.00
70–71	4	4/90	=	.04	70–71	1	1/90	=	.01
68–69	6	6/90	=	.07	68–69	2	2/90	=	.02
66–67	8	8/90	=	.09	66–67	4	4/90	=	.04
64–65	6	6/90	=	.07	64–65	6	6/90	=	.07
62–63	8	8/90	=	.09	62–63	5	5/90	=	.06
60–61	9	9/90	=	.10	60–61	6	6/90	=	.07
58–59	7	7/90	=	.08	58–59	7	7/90	=	.08
56–57	6	6/90	=	.07	56–57	14	14/90	=	.16
54–55	9	9/90	=	.10	54–55	9	9/90	=	.10
52–53	5	5/90	=	.06	52–53	11	11/90	=	.12
50–51	6	6/90	=	.07	50–51	10	10/90	=	.11
48–49	2	2/90	=	.02	48–49	9	9/90	=	.10
46–47	1	1/90	=	.01	46–47	3	3/90	=	.03
Total	90			1.00	Total	90			1.00

Quick Quiz

How is a relative frequency distribution different from a frequency distribution?

Answer

A frequency distribution pairs an interval with how often scores occur within the interval. A relative frequency distribution pairs each interval with the proportion or percentage of the total data set associated with values in that interval.

Cumulative Frequency Distributions

Cumulative frequency distribution
Distribution that pairs the value of *X* with its cumulative frequency

Cumulative frequency distributions give, for each interval, the accumulation of the frequency up to and including that interval. Cumulative distributions also can be created by using percentages or proportions; then they are called *cumulative relative frequency distributions.* Returning to the height example, we give cumulative distributions for the heights of female students from Table 3.4 in Table 3.9. If you are a female between 64.0 and 65.4 in. tall, then about 50% of the females in this sample were your height or shorter. Cumulative relative frequency distributions can give the percentage (cumulative relative frequency times 100) below a given data value.

For a summary of the rules for making frequency distributions, see Box 3.1.

3.3   Pictorial Descriptions: Stem and Leaf Displays

Exploratory data analysis (see Tukey, 1977) has provided stem and leaf displays, an easy and informative way to arrange data. Look back at Table 3.3, which shows stem and leaf displays for the midterm scores of psychology and engineering majors. The original midterm scores are two-digit numbers. Notice that each score has been divided

Table 3.9
Cumulative frequency distributions of female heights

Interval (in.)	Frequency	Cumulative Frequency	Frequency/Total = Relative Frequency	Cumulative Relative Frequency
73.0–74.4	0	24	.000	1.000
71.5–72.9	0	24	.000	1.000
70.0–71.4	0	24	.000	1.000
68.5–69.9	2	24	.083	1.000
67.0–68.4	8	22	.333	.917
65.5–66.9	2	14	.083	.583
64.0–65.4	4	12	.167	.500
62.5–63.9	4	8	.167	.333
61.0–62.4	2	4	.083	.167
59.5–60.9	1	2	.042	.083
58.0–59.4	1	1	.042	.042
	Total 24			

into two digits, with the first digit to the left of the vertical line and the second digit to the right. The numbers to the right of the vertical line are the leaves, and the leaves share a stem, the number in the left column. The symbols that accompany the first digit are explained soon. All of the original scores are displayed. On the psychology students' stem and leaf display, the top line shows that there were two scores of 97; the next line represents the scores 90, 91, 92, 92, and 94.

Stem and leaf displays are built with the following steps:

Stem and leaf display
Arrangement of data that uses the first digit(s) of a score as a base (stem) and the last digit as an extension of that base (leaf)

1. Choose how to split each data point into the stem and the leaf. You might use the first one or two digits of each data point to form the stem and the last digit to form a leaf on that stem. For example, with the speed data, all the scores are between 40 and 79 km/h, so the stems could be 4, 5, 6, and 7, with the leaves being the values of the second digits.

Box 3.1   Rules for Creating Frequency Distributions

1. Decide whether any grouping needs to be done (males/females, experimental/control group, and so on).
2. Put the data in order (slowest to fastest, highest to lowest test scores, and so on).
3. Decide on the interval width to use (width of 5, giving 95–100, 90–94, 85–89, . . . , for a group of test scores, for instance).
4. Count how many scores are in each interval.
5. Arrange the intervals and frequencies in a frequency distribution.
   a. To make a relative frequency distribution, divide each frequency by the total number of observations. This number is the proportion of the scores that are in that interval.
   b. To make a cumulative frequency distribution, add the frequencies that are in or below a certain interval. This number shows how many scores are found up to and including a particular interval.
   c. To make a cumulative relative frequency distribution, divide each cumulative frequency from part b by the total number of observations.

Table 3.10

Stem and leaf displays of baseline speeds (km/h)

Order as Recorded		Rank Order	
Stem	Leaf	Stem	Leaf
7	89667455333220111	7	011122333455566789
6	145150549289913389367121666774 1231270	6	0011111112222333344455566667777889999
5	98110012932339454545455779776869	5	0011112233344445555566777 78899999
4	689	4	689

2. Make a column with the largest stem on the top and the smallest stem on the bottom. The smallest baseline score in Table 3.6 is 46, which has a stem of 4 and a leaf of 6. Note that some sources orient the stem with the smallest on the top; we decided to put the largest stem on the top to be consistent with frequency distributions and with SAS computer output.

3. For each data value, write down the leaves. Table 3.10 shows how stem and leaf displays can be arranged for the baseline speed data.

One important issue in building stem and leaf displays is to decide on the number of stems. In Table 3.10, we have chosen four stems. We could also use two stems for each digit, marked by an asterisk (*) for leaves 0–4 and a period (.) for leaves 5–9. Thus, we use each digit twice as a stem. This was the approach in Table 3.3, the stem and leaf displays on psychology and engineering majors' midterm scores. Another choice is five stems per digit, marked by an asterisk for leaves 0 and 1, T for leaves 2 (**T**wo) and 3 (**T**hree), F for leaves 4 (**F**our) and 5 (**F**ive), S for leaves 6 (**S**ix) and 7 (**S**even), and a period for leaves 8 and 9. Here we use each digit five times as a stem, with leaves grouped into 0–1, 2–3, 4–5, 6–7, and 8–9. Table 3.11 shows this approach for the baseline speeds. A good guideline for choosing the total number of stems is the one used to determine the total number of intervals for frequency distributions: 10 to 20.

The stem and leaf display gives the most information when the leaves are arranged in rank order for each stem, but it is easier to record the leaves as you come to each score. One timesaver is to first record the leaves as you get to each score, and then rewrite the stem and leaf display with the leaves in order within each stem.

Note that the stem and leaf display in Table 3.11 is the same arrangement of the baseline data as the frequency distribution in Table 3.7. Frequency distributions and stem and leaf displays each have their advantages as descriptive tools. The stem and leaf display shows all the original data intact and gives an improved visual image over that of the frequency distribution. Frequency distributions give the frequency of the scores in each interval, which is helpful for drawing other graphs of the data.

Often it is useful to combine two stem and leaf displays into one display called a *back-to-back stem and leaf display*. Both stem and leaf displays share a common stem, with the leaves from one display extending to the right and the leaves from the other display extending to the left. This type of display is useful for comparing data from two similar data sets. Table 3.12 contains a back-to-back stem and leaf display for the baseline and posting speeds.

What do you see in the back-to-back stem and leaf display? Does the baseline or posting period have more high speeds? With the speed limit of 50 km/h, are most drivers still speeding? Did the intervention of posting the percentage speeding from the previous day reduce the speeds?

Table 3.11

Stem and leaf display of baseline speeds (km/h), five lines per stem (in rank order)

Baseline Stem	Leaf
7.	89
7S	667
7F	455
7T	22333
7*	0111
6.	889999
6S	66667777
6F	444555
6T	22223333
6*	001111111
5.	8899999
5S	667777
5F	444455555
5T	22333
5*	001111
4.	89
4S	6

Table 3.12

Back-to-back stem and leaf display of baseline and posting speeds (km/h), five lines per stem (in rank order)

Baseline Leaf	Stem	Posting Leaf
89	7.	8
667	7S	6
455	7F	4
22333	7T	
0111	7*	1
889999	6.	89
66667777	6S	6677
444555	6F	444555
22223333	6T	22333
001111111	6*	000111
8899999	5.	8999999
667777	5S	66667777777777
444455555	5F	444445555
22333	5T	22233333333
001111	5*	0001111111
89	4.	888999999
6	4S	677

See Box 3.2 for a summary of how to make a stem and leaf display.

3.4 Pictorial Descriptions: Graphs

Bar Graph and Histogram

Once you have a frequency distribution, the next natural step is to complete this pictorial description by drawing a graph of the data. A bar graph or histogram is essentially the frequency distribution of the data turned on its side. You also can turn a stem and leaf display on its side and look at the distribution.

In bar graphs and histograms, the horizontal axis shows intervals, and the vertical axis shows the frequency. A vertical "bar," or rectangle, sits on the X axis at a certain

---

Box 3.2 Rules for Creating a Stem and Leaf Display

1. Decide how to break up the scores into a stem and a leaf.
2. Decide how many stems you want: one, two, or five stems per digit. (Do you need 9*, 9., 8*, 8. or perhaps 9*, 9T, 9F, 9S, 9.?)
3. Write the stems in a column, with the largest number at the top.
4. Record the leaves next to the appropriate stems.
5. Rewrite the stem and leaf display so that the leaves on each stem are in numerical order.
6. Decide whether you have enough stems to reveal a pattern in your data, or whether you have so many stems that the numbers are too spread out to show clusters of scores.

Bar graph
Graph of the data where the score or category is paired with a bar that represents the frequency of that score or category; it is used with qualitative data; the bars don't touch

Histogram
Graph of the data where the bars for scores or intervals are connected; it is used with quantitative data

interval and goes up to the height that represents the frequency, or sometimes the percentage, within that interval. For a bar graph that is pleasing to the eye, the vertical axis should be approximately 75% of the length of the horizontal axis. Another recommendation is to include the zero point on the vertical axis. Sometimes graphs are presented with the bars running horizontally.

When the bars don't touch, this graph is called a **bar graph.** Bar graphs are appropriate for displaying frequencies from qualitative data. The categories have no quantitative meaning, so the bars don't touch. You saw a bar graph in Figure 3.4, the number of students with grade point averages over 3.0, categorized by major.

A **histogram** is much like a bar graph except that the bars touch. You should use a histogram for frequencies from quantitative data, such as the midterm exam scores. Figure 3.9 shows histograms based on the frequency distributions in Table 3.5 of the heights of male and female college students.

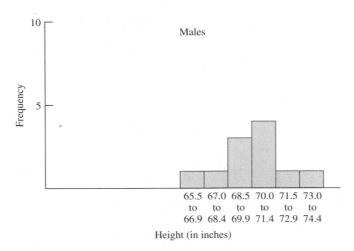

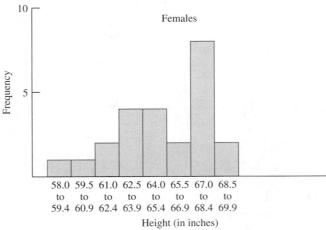

Figure 3.9
Histograms of the heights of male and female college students from Table 3.5

Quick Quiz

Using the midterm data in Table 3.1, (a) draw a bar graph showing the frequency of psychology, engineering, and undecided majors, and (b) draw a histogram showing the frequency of scores within the intervals 60–69, 70–79, 80–89, and 90–99.

Frequency Polygon

Frequency polygon
Graph in which a smooth line connects the top of the bars in a histogram

The third type of graph is a **frequency polygon,** which is a smooth line that connects the midpoints of the intervals at the top of the bars of a histogram, and then connects the line to the *X* axis at both ends of the graph at the middle of the next intervals. Figure 3.10 is a frequency polygon for the female height data in Table 3.4. This type of graph makes sense only when the variable plotted on the *X* axis is quantitative.

Pie Chart

Pie chart
Graph drawn as a circle with segments representing variables as percentages or proportions of the distribution

Qualitative

You saw a **pie chart** in Figure 3.2 for the percentages of people who cook out at certain times. The pie chart is useful in showing how a total quantity (budget, sales, land, number of people, and so on) is divided into subgroups. In the cookout example, the pie chart illustrates the percentages of people who responded to the various options of a multiple-choice question. Both frequencies and percentages are given in Figure 3.11.

See Box 3.3 for rules on constructing bar graphs, histograms, frequency polygons, and pie charts.

Scatterplot

Scatterplot
Graph that plots two variables as the axes and points that represent a pair of scores on the variables

In a **scatterplot,** you plot scores for each subject on two variables. One variable is represented on the horizontal axis and the other on the vertical axis. Each subject's pair of scores appears as a point. Figure 3.12 shows the scatterplot for the midterm

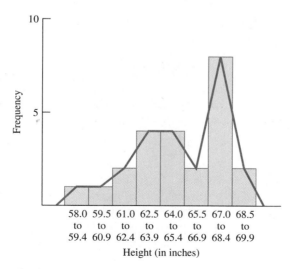

Figure 3.10
Frequency polygon of female heights from Table 3.5

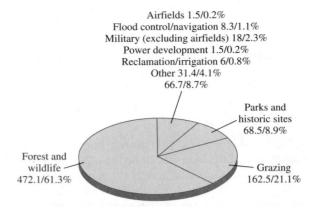

Airfields 1.5/0.2%
Flood control/navigation 8.3/1.1%
Military (excluding airfields) 18/2.3%
Power development 1.5/0.2%
Reclamation/irrigation 6/0.8%
Other 31.4/4.1%
66.7/8.7%

Parks and
historic sites
68.5/8.9%

Forest and
wildlife
472.1/61.3%

Grazing
162.5/21.1%

Figure 3.11
Pie chart of federal land use, million acres/%. *Source: Statistical Abstract of the United States (1980)*

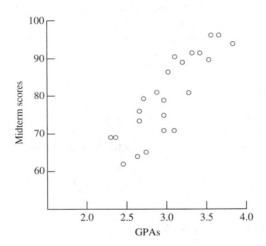

Figure 3.12
Scatterplot of GPAs and midterm scores for psychology majors

scores and GPAs of psychology majors from Table 3.1. How does this scatterplot differ from the one in Figure 3.8? A scatterplot can give you an idea of what happens to scores on one variable as scores on the other variable increase. For example, for psychology majors, does a high GPA tend to be associated with a high midterm score? Scatterplots will be used in Chapters 6 and 7.

See Box 3.4 for rules on constructing scatterplots.

Box 3.3 Rules for Creating Bar Graphs, Histograms, Frequency Polygons, and Pie Charts

Bar Graphs

1. Determine whether you have a qualitative variable (such as categories of heavy smokers, light smokers, former smokers, and lifetime nonsmokers). If so, you can represent the data with a bar graph.
2. Count the number of observations within each category.
3. Draw a Y axis tall enough to accommodate the largest frequency and an X axis long enough to allow one bar for each category. Label the axes.
4. Draw a bar for each category, with the height determined by the frequency. The bars should not touch.

Histograms

1. Determine whether you have a quantitative variable.
2. Decide how many intervals (number of bars) you will have. Data can be transferred from a frequency distribution or a stem and leaf display to a histogram.
3. Count the number of scores in each interval.
4. Draw a Y axis for frequency and an X axis for the intervals. Label them.
5. Draw a bar for each interval, with the height determined by the frequency. The bars should touch.

Frequency Polygons

1. Once you have drawn a histogram, draw a dot in the middle of the top of each bar.
2. Draw straight lines to connect the dots.
3. Connect the line to the X axis at both ends at the middle of the next intervals.

Pie Charts

1. You can use the information from a bar graph.
2. Calculate the percentage of scores that fall into each category. Compute the degrees of the circle to be associated with each category. For example, if the percentage for a category is 25%, then 25% of the total 360 degrees is 90 degrees. You can use a protractor to convert the degrees to the size of the wedge.
3. Draw a circle, and draw the appropriately sized wedge associated with each percentage. Label each wedge with the name of the variable, and give the frequency out of the total number of observations or the percentage or both.

Quick Quiz

How is a scatterplot different from the other kinds of pictorial description in this chapter?

Answer

A scatterplot pairs scores on two variables for each subject, such as GPA and midterm grade. The other forms of pictorial description give an indication of the frequency for one variable.

Box 3.4   Rules for Creating Scatterplots

1. Determine whether you have scores on two variables that you might be interested in observing together in one graph (reaction time and total number of items correct on a speeded quiz, number of grams of fat consumed and scores on an alertness scale, and so on).

2. Decide which variable will go on the Y axis and which will go on the X axis. If you think that knowing someone's score on one variable will help you predict his or her score on the second variable, the second variable should go on the Y axis.

3. Plot each pair of scores. Find the value of the X score, and then move vertically from that point until you reach the level associated with the Y score. Put a dot at that point.

Beyond These Displays and Graphs

With the advent of the computer came sophistication in drawing graphs. We have merely introduced the subject of pictorial description by giving a few basic methods. An interesting extension of bar graphs (or histograms) is used in the area of quality control. Pareto charts are used to show defects in a product (for example, a car) graphed by type and then presented for different units, such as week or month. The bar graph can be modified in a Pareto chart to include the cumulative percentage of defects, or to show breakdowns within type of defect by some other unit, such as the different plants that make the product. These charts can be used in a larger scheme developed by Pareto to reduce the number of defects.

Another extension of graphing is three-dimensional displays. Such innovations greatly increase the usefulness of graphs but also increase the complexities and problems of graphing. Some of these show up as we discuss misleading graphs.

3.5   Misleading Graphs

In Chapter 1 our reasons for studying statistics included being a better consumer of media and advertisements and a better reader of research articles. Understanding pictorial descriptions can keep you from being misled by graphs and charts (see Huff, 1954).

The biggest danger lies in the violation of the accuracy principle. Graphs may be inaccurate in many ways, including distortions of the axes, manipulation of the area of the bars or the height of the bars, changes in the color of the bars, and mislabeling of the axes. Distortions of the axes can include compression or expansion of one or both axes, absence of a zero point, and unequal intervals on the horizontal axis. These errors can be accidental, but sometimes they may be done deliberately when someone tries to use data to make an argument more convincing. For example, Table 3.13 gives the percentages of the voting-age population who voted in various national election years. Someone arguing for stability of voting behavior might graph the data as in Figure 3.13, whereas someone arguing for an alarming decline might use Figure 3.14. Try to detect how many different inaccuracies are illustrated in the figures.

As computerized graphing techniques get more sophisticated and user-friendly, subtle problems arise. For example, some popular media like to use figures other than

Table 3.13

Percentages of voting-age population casting votes

1960	1964	1968	1972	1976	1980	1984	1988	1992
62.8	61.9	60.9	55.5	54.3	51.8	53.1	50.1	55.2

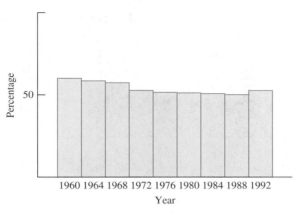

Figure 3.13

Data from Table 3.13 plotted to show stability of voting behavior

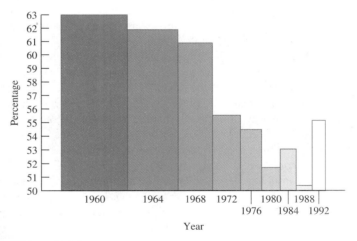

Figure 3.14

Data from Table 3.13 plotted to show decline of voting behavior

bars for their bar graphs and histograms. In a graph that shows the number of new homes started in different years, they might use different sizes of houses for the bars. The problem comes when more than one dimension of the house is changed because a 50% increase in the number of homes will look like much more than that if three dimensions—width, depth, and height—are all increased by 50%. Scientific bar graphs and histograms should show the "bars" changed in only one dimension.

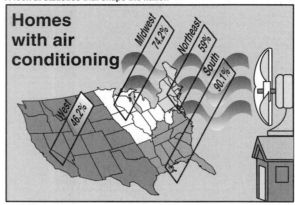

USA SNAPSHOTS®
A look at statistics that shape the nation

Homes with air conditioning

Midwest 74.2%
Northeast 59%
South 90.1%
West 46.2%

Figure 3.15
Which region has the highest percentage of homes with air conditioning? *Source: Data from the U.S. Census Bureau.*

Another problem can occur when bars are placed on a three-dimensional surface, such as a map of the United States. Part of the country may be shown as being "deeper" in the picture or farther away from the viewer. If so, the size of the bar corresponding to the farther-away region may be distorted. *USA Today* uses graphs every day and the creators of its graphs are aware of this problem. Figure 3.15 is a bar graph of the percentage of U.S. homes that have air conditioning. Four regions have a bar drawn to show the percentage of air-conditioned homes. In the original graph, color was used to define the states in the same region. Notice that *USA Today* realized the possibility of misperception of the height of the bars because the surface of the country is shown in three dimensions. So the creators of this graph included the percentages inside each bar; this way, you can tell that the South has the highest percentage of air-conditioned homes. The bottom of the South's bar is lowest vertically and the top of the bar is higher on the page than only the West's bar, which represents the lowest percentage of air-conditioned homes. If *USA Today* had not given the percentages, you might have had trouble judging which region had the highest percentage of air-conditioned homes.

Even well-drawn graphs may misrepresent information. You need to think about what someone is trying to make you believe in a particular graph. Imagine you are applying for a job after graduation with Company X, and the starting salary is $18,000. You think you could find a job with higher initial pay, but the recruiter says other companies can't match Company X's record at steadily increasing salaries during the first years on the job. She shows you a scatterplot like Figure 3.16 that plots years with the company on the *X* axis and salary (in thousands of dollars) on the *Y* axis. Study the scatterplot and write down some questions about it.

Here are some questions you may have about the graph:

1. There are 14 dots on the scatterplot. Does this represent just 14 people? If so, here are some more questions:
   a. Do all of the people represented work at the same job? How much promotion is possible in terms of job responsibilities and job titles? Does the increase in salary accompany such increases in responsibility?

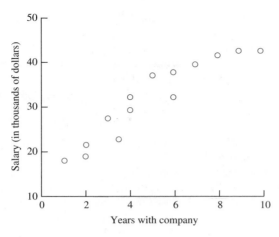

Figure 3.16
Scatterplot of years with the company (*X* axis) and salary (*Y* axis)

b. What was the initial salary of the 10-year employees on the graph? Did they start at $18,000 a decade ago? If so, does that mean the top salary 10 years from now will still be about $45,000?

c. The graph seems to flatten out at about $45,000 after about 8 years on the job. Do people leave the job at that point, or is that the most they can earn?

d. If these 14 people are all working at the same job, are they *all* of Company X's employees in this position? In other words, have any data been omitted? Were these numbers selected to show the greatest increase in salary?

2. Does each dot represent an average salary for a certain number of years on the job? If so, then here are some more questions:

a. Why do there appear to be two dots for some numbers on the *X* axis? For example, for four years on the job, there appear to be a dot at about $30,000 and another dot at about $33,000. What does that mean?

b. How many people's salaries went into computing each average? For instance, are there 50 people working at $18,000 and just a handful of people earning $45,000?

c. Are people with different jobs included in this graph?

You probably can think of many more questions. Graphs are useful for summarizing information, but *be sure you know what is being summarized*. As you draw graphs, follow the rules given for each type of display and use common sense. You still will have considerable flexibility in drawing graphs. Draw your graphs with a proper balance of thoroughness and simplicity, keep them accurate, and they will give a good pictorial description of your data.

3.6 Description with Statistics

The process of description is multifaceted. You can describe data with pictures and with descriptive statistics. Graphs allow you to see the distribution of your data, and descriptive statistics summarize the data. Before going on to Chapter 4, which covers descriptive statistics, we present an overview of four characteristics than can be measured by statistics or visually displayed in graphs.

1. *Central tendency*—a typical or representative score, a score that represents the middle of the distribution
2. *Variability*—the spread or dispersion of the scores
3. *Skewness*—departure from symmetry (symmetry is when the right half of the distribution is a mirror image of the left half)
4. *Kurtosis*—peakedness relative to certain bell-shaped curves known as normal distributions

Central tendency
Location of the center (middle) of a distribution of scores

When distributions differ with respect to a measure of **central tendency,** the locations of the distributions differ. For example, psychology and engineering majors differ on their midterm exam scores. The average midterm score for psychology majors is 80.125, whereas the average score for engineering majors is about 81.77. If you use the mean (average) as a measure of the center of the distribution, you could say the center of the distribution of engineering students' scores is slightly higher than the center of the psychology students' distribution.

Variability
Dispersion or spread of a distribution of scores

Distributions differ in their **variability** when the scores are more spread out in one distribution than in the other. For example, the midterm scores for psychology majors are more spread out than are those for engineering majors. Examine the stem and leaf displays in Table 3.3 to see this difference in variability.

Skewness
Departure from symmetry in a distribution

The language used in connection with **skewness** (departure from symmetry) reports zero skewness if the distribution is symmetric. Skewness shows up in two aspects of the distribution: the majority of the scores are bunched on one side of the distribution while a few extreme scores are scattered out on the other side. You can get a skewed distribution from an experiment where subjects are timed on completing an activity. Most people may have a reaction time of 1 s or less, but one or two subjects may take much longer to respond. The distribution of the response times is skewed by those aberrant scores. The way skewness is labeled depends on the rightmost or leftmost extreme scores, called the *tails* of the distribution. You have positive skewness if the right or *positive* tail contains the extreme scores and negative skewness if the left or *negative* tail contains the extreme scores. The extreme scores cause the skewness, so the distribution is labeled according to where the extreme scores are located. The distributions in Figure 3.17 illustrate skewness.

Kurtosis
Peakedness of a distribution relative to a normal distribution

Kurtosis refers to the peakedness of the distribution relative to something called a *normal distribution,* which is introduced in Chapter 5. A distribution with high kurtosis has a high peak of scores in the center, with fairly thick tails. A distribution with

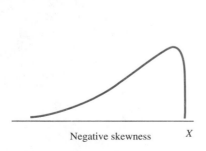
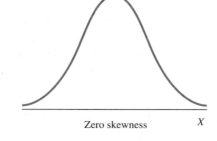
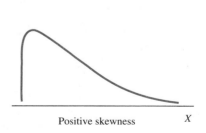

| Negative skewness X | Zero skewness X | Positive skewness X |

Figure 3.17
Different types of skewness

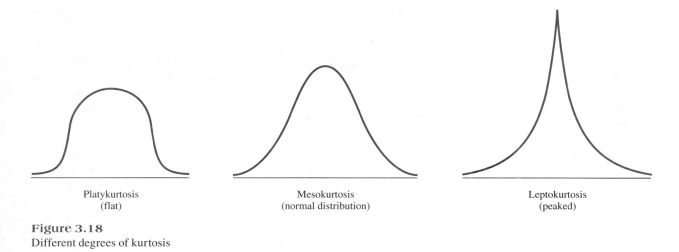

Figure 3.18
Different degrees of kurtosis

low kurtosis has the scores more evenly spread out, with a fairly flat lump of scores in the center. Figure 3.18 shows distributions that have three different degrees of kurtosis.

Measures of skewness and kurtosis are now available in many packages of statistical programs, but many researchers don't report these measures. We'll talk later about skewness and its effect on statistics. Formulas for measuring skewness and kurtosis are not given here (see Ferguson & Takane, 1989).

Quick Quiz

What four major characteristics of data can be measured by statistics or visually displayed in graphs?

Answer

(1) Central tendency—the center of a distribution of scores. (2) Variability—how the scores are spread out. (3) Skewness—departure from symmetry. (4) Kurtosis—the peakedness of the distribution relative to a normal distribution.

3.7   Summary, Study Tips, and Computation

Chapter Summary

When you have data on one variable, you can describe these data by using one or more pictorial descriptions. Pictorial descriptions include frequency distributions, stem and leaf displays, and various types of graphs. Any description of the sample data should be simple, thorough, and accurate. Additionally, you can describe data using summary measures for central tendency, variability, skewness, and kurtosis.

The following key terms are introduced in this chapter:

Frequency distribution	Bar graph
Real limits	Histogram
Apparent limits	Frequency polygon
Interval width	Pie chart
Relative frequency distribution	Scatterplot
Cumulative frequency distribution	Central tendency
Stem and leaf display	Variability
	Skewness
	Kurtosis

Study Tips

You should be able to recognize various kinds of graphs and pictorial displays of data. Look in a publication like *Newsweek* or *USA Today* and find some graphs. Do they meet the guidelines of being simple, thorough, and accurate? Do you know a better way to display the data?

You may be approaching your first test in your statistics course. Here is a good way to study for the test (you may not believe it works until you have tried it): Find someone in your class who is willing to work with you. You will write test questions, and so will your "study buddy." Then you'll take each other's tests. Writing the questions forces you to figure out which material is the most important and what the answers are. Explaining the answers to your study buddy will reinforce your knowledge. Seeing the other person's test questions will show you another person's idea of what material is important and may help you identify your weak spots. Get together with your study buddy at least a week before the test. You can do it if you break down the material into bite-sized chunks.

The most frequent student errors are: (1) violating one or more of the rules for forming frequency distributions, (2) confusing histograms and bar graphs, (3) confusing the meaning of notations for stems, such as 7F, and (4) inaccurate counting for any of these methods (for example, counting the wrong number of scores in an interval).

Computation

The role of the computer in pictorial description is to provide speed and flexibility. Once data are keyed into the computer, an available statistical package can give numerous frequency distributions and a variety of graphs with only slight changes in instructions.

The examples of lines given here for the SAS procedures and SPSS commands follow the general format given in Section 2.7, so you might want to review that section now. For each statistical method, you are given a sample set of lines including data, as well as the output for each job. Notice that the actual lines are in all capital letters. If any line needs explanation, the explanation is enclosed in parentheses after the line and is set in a different typeface. This explanation is not to be entered into the computer; it is for your instruction only.

SAS Examples

Once you get beyond the system's lines, all SAS *statements* end with a semicolon. There is no fixed place on the line where the SAS statement must fit, but the blanks between words are important and the ending semicolon is crucial (do not put semicolons in the actual *data* lines). Also note that whenever a variable name is needed, you must choose a name that is up to eight characters long, begins with a letter, and does not contain any special characters or blanks. The figure that follows each example shows the output that SAS gives for that job. The numbers in the figures refer to key aspects of the output that are explained in the list following each figure.

(SAS system's lines)

DATA CHART;   (the first SAS statement, beginning the data step, to create a data set named CHART)
INPUT YEAR PERC;   (statement to input the year and the percentage of registered voters voting)
CARDS;   (statement that tells the program you are using batch input for the following data)
1960 62.8   (data from Table 3.13)
1964 61.9
1968 60.9
1972 55.5
1976 54.3
1980 51.8
1984 53.1

```
1988 50.1
1992 55.2
PROC PRINT;    (beginning of PROC step, statement to request the inputted data to be printed)
PROC CHART;    (statement to have the CHART procedure run on the data)
VBAR YEAR/TYPE = PERCENT MIDPOINTS = 1960 1964 1968
1972 1976 1980 1984 1988 1992 SUMVAR = PERC;    (statement that years are on the horizontal axis and percentage is
                                                  on the vertical axis)

TITLE 'CHART OF PERCENTAGE VOTING BY YEAR';    (title to be printed with the statistics)
(system's line)
```

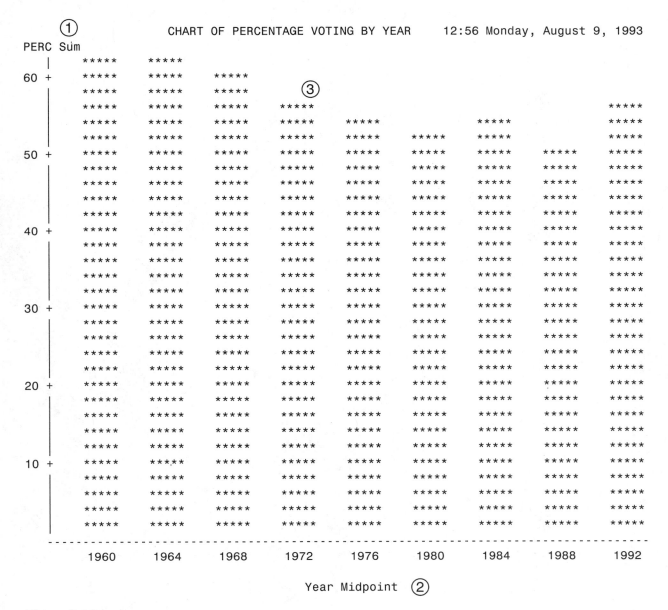

Figure 3.19
SAS output from PROC CHART

For PROC CHART, the SAS output in Figure 3.19, a bar graph for percentage voting by year, shows the following:

1. Percentage is the vertical axis, labeled PERC, which was the variable name used in the INPUT and VBAR statements in the program.
2. The horizontal axis is labeled YEAR Midpoint because the bar for the midpoint of the year interval is plotted. Note that the midpoints were specified in the VBAR statement.
3. For 1972, the percentage voting is 55.5. PROC CHART uses multiple asterisks to draw the bar to the appropriate height.

(SAS sytem's lines)
```
DATA PLOT;
INPUT SEX$ HEIGHT FREQ;    (input the sex, height interval, and frequency for the interval from the data in Table 3.4; note that the
                            interval width is 1 and the lower apparent limit is used here to represent the interval)
CARDS;
M 73 1 M 72 1 M 71 2 M 70 2 M 69 3 M 67 1 M 66 1 F 69 1
F 68 2 F 67 7 F 66 1 F 65 2 F 64 3 F 63 3 F 62 3 F 60 1
F 58 1
PROC PRINT;
PROC PLOT;    (statement to run PLOT procedure)
PLOT FREQ*HEIGHT=SEX/HPOS=50 VPOS=20;    (statement to request frequency as the vertical axis and height as the
                                          horizontal axis, using sex as the plot character, and requesting that the
                                          horizontal axis fit in 50 spaces and the vertical axis fit in 20 lines)

TITLE 'PLOT OF FREQ BY HEIGHT FOR SEX';
```
(system's line)

OBS	SEX	HEIGHT	FREQ
1	M	73	1
2	M	72	1
3	M	71	2
4	M	70	2
5	M	69	3
6	M	67	1
7	M	66	1
8	F	69	1
9	F	68	2
10	F	67	7
11	F	66	1
12	F	65	2
13	F	64	3
14	F	63	3
15	F	62	3
16	F	60	1
17	F	58	1

Figure 3.20
SAS output from PROC PLOT

(continued)

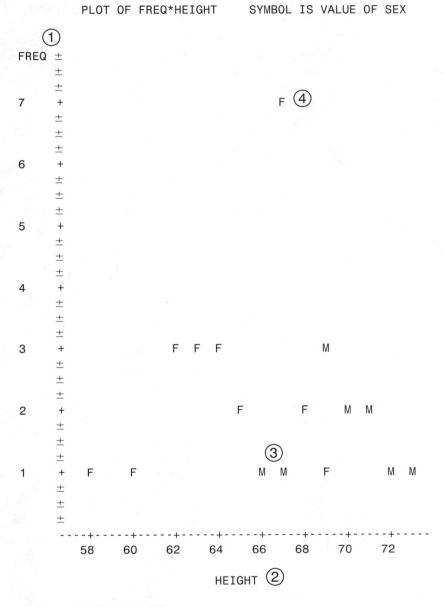

Figure 3.20 (continued)

.For PROC PRINT, the SAS output in Figure 3.20, a plot (which could be used to draw a histogram) of the frequencies of heights for females and males, shows the following:

1. Frequency is the vertical axis, labeled FREQ, which was the variable name used in the INPUT statement.

2. The horizontal axis is labeled HEIGHT, the variable name used in the INPUT statement.
3. The symbol used is the value of the variable SEX (M or F). For this particular case, the height of 66 has a frequency of 1 for both male and female, so only one character is printed and the output tells us that one observation is hidden.
4. For height = 67, the male frequency is 1 and the female frequency is 7, so the M is plotted at 1 and the F at 7, both over height = 67.

SPSS Example

SPSS has a variety of commands and subcommands by which you choose the statistical procedures to be computed. Some of the subcommands are placed after a slash and can be on a following line. Be sure you do not split words or commands when continuing to another line. As with SAS, variable names may be up to eight characters long and must begin with a letter. Here SPSS is used to give a frequency distribution, a histogram, and a stem and leaf display of the midterm scores for the psychology majors from Table 3.1.

```
(SPSS system's lines)
SET WIDTH 80
DATA LIST FREE/MIDTERM    (FREE is the label for the type of format that allows data to be entered on the line with blanks
                           separating data points, MIDTERM is the name of the dependent variable)

BEGIN DATA
89 71 65 81 94 97 62 69 71 91 87 79 79 90 75 69 92 79
64 92
76 81 73 97
    (these are the scores on the variable MIDTERM for 24 psychology majors)
END DATA
FREQUENCIES VARIABLES=MIDTERM/HISTOGRAM    (this command tells the program you want frequencies computed on
                                            the variable called MIDTERM and that you want a histogram)

EXAMINE VARIABLES=MIDTERM/PLOT=STEMLEAF
FINISH    (a command to let the program know that you are finished giving it commands and data)
(system's line)
```

The SPSS output in Figure 3.21 includes a frequency distribution, a histogram turned on its side, and a stem and leaf display. Note the following:

1. Under the label Value are the actual values of the variable MIDTERM in the DATA LIST. The values range from 62 to 97 and are given for the histogram and the frequency distribution.
2. A column of frequencies and the total frequency.
3. The relative frequency.
4. The cumulative relative frequency.
5. The command FREQUENCIES uses asterisks (ten for each frequency) to draw the bars. There were three values of 79.
6. Stems of 6* to 9. arranged from top to bottom.

MIDTERM

Value Label ①	Value	② Frequency	③ Percent	Valid Percent	④ Cum Percent
	62.00	1	4.2	4.2	4.2
	64.00	1	4.2	4.2	8.3
	65.00	1	4.2	4.2	12.5
	69.00	2	8.3	8.3	20.8
	71.00	2	8.3	8.3	29.2
	73.00	1	4.2	4.2	33.3
	75.00	1	4.2	4.2	37.5
	76.00	1	4.2	4.2	41.7
	79.00	3	12.5	12.5	54.2
	81.00	2	8.3	8.3	62.5
	87.00	1	4.2	4.2	66.7
	89.00	1	4.2	4.2	70.8
	90.00	1	4.2	4.2	75.0
	91.00	1	4.2	4.2	79.2
	92.00	2	8.3	8.3	87.5
	94.00	1	4.2	4.2	91.7
	97.00	2	8.3	8.3	100.0
	Total	24	100.0	100.0	

```
Count   Midpoint   One symbol equals approximately .10 occurrences

  0      ①  59 I
  0          61 I
  1          63 I*********
  2          65 I********************
  0          67 I
  2          69 I********************
  2          71 I********************
  1          73 I*********
  1          75 I*********
  1          77 I*********
  3          79 I****************************** ⑤
  2          81 I********************
  0          83 I
  0          85 I
  1          87 I*********
  1          89 I*********
  2          91 I********************
  2          93 I********************
  1          95 I*********
  2          97 I********************
  0          99 I
             +----+----+----+----+----+----+----+----+----+----+
             0         1         2         3         4         5
                            Histogram frequency
```

Figure 3.21
SPSS output from FREQUENCIES and EXAMINE

(continued)

```
    MIDTERM

Valid cases:          24.0   Missing cases:        .0   Percent missing:      .0

Mean        80.1250   Std Err     2.2184   Min     62.0000   Skewness     .0168
Median      79.0000   Variance  118.1141   Max     97.0000   S E Skew     .4723
5% Trim     80.1759   Std Dev    10.8680   Range   35.0000   Kurtosis  -1.2216
                                           IQR     19.7500   S E Kurt     .9178

                        ⑥
Frequency      Stem & Leaf
    2.00        6  * 24
    3.00        6  . 599
    3.00        7  * 113
    5.00        7  . 56999
    2.00        8  * 11
    2.00        8  . 79
    5.00        9  * 01224
    2.00        9  . 77

Stem width:       10.00
Each leaf:         1 case(s)
```

Figure 3.21 (continued)

Exercises

Section 3.1

1. Compare and contrast each of the following pairs with respect to how well they meet the three principles of simplicity, thoroughness, and accuracy.

   a. Frequency distribution versus stem and leaf display
   b. Histogram versus stem and leaf display
   c. Frequency distribution versus histogram

Section 3.2

2. For this exercise use the number of anxiety symptoms in Table 1.1.

   a. Build separate frequency distributions for the perceived-control and no-control groups. Use the same intervals for the two distributions. Compare the two frequency distributions and summarize what you learned about the number of anxiety symptoms for the two groups.

   b. Build a relative frequency distribution for perceived control.

   c. Build a cumulative frequency distribution for perceived control.

   d. Build a cumulative relative frequency distribution for perceived control.

   e. Summarize what you learned in parts b–d about the number of anxiety symptoms in the perceived-control group.

3. For this exercise use the deception accuracy scores in Table 2.1.

   a. Build separate frequency distributions for Secret Service personnel, judges, and psychiatrists. Use the same intervals for the three distributions. Compare the three frequency distributions and summarize what you learned about the deception accuracy scores for the three groups.

   b. Build a relative frequency distribution for the Secret Service.

c. Build a cumulative frequency distribution for the Secret Service.

d. Build a cumulative relative frequency distribution for the Secret Service.

e. Summarize what you learned in parts b–d about deception accuracy scores for the Secret Service.

Section 3.3

4. Use the GPA data from Table 3.1.

a. Build a stem and leaf display for psychology majors.

b. Build a stem and leaf display for engineering majors.

c. Put the two stem and leaf displays from parts a and b together into a back-to-back stem and leaf display.

d. Summarize what you have learned about the GPA data for these two majors. How have the stem and leaf displays helped you describe these data?

5. Use the number of anxiety symptoms in Table 1.1 for this exercise.

a. Build a stem and leaf display for the perceived-control group.

b. Build a stem and leaf display for the no-control group.

c. Put the two stem and leaf displays from parts a and b together into a back-to-back stem and leaf display.

d. Summarize what you have learned about the number of anxiety symptoms for these two groups. How have the stem and leaf displays helped you describe these data? Compare what you have done in this exercise with your results in Exercise 2. Which do you like better, frequency distributions or stem and leaf displays?

6. For this exercise use the deception accuracy scores in Table 2.1.

a. Build a stem and leaf display for the Secret Service group.

b. Build a stem and leaf display for the judges group.

c. Put the two stem and leaf displays from parts a and b together into a back-to-back stem and leaf display.

d. Summarize what you have learned about the deception accuracy scores for these two groups. How have the stem and leaf displays helped you describe these data? Compare what you have done in this exercise with your results in Exercise 3.

Section 3.4

7. Use the adult height data in Table 2.2.

a. Draw a bar graph of the number of people taller than 67 in. for males and females.

b. Because the total number of males is smaller than the total number of females, would it be more accurate to redraw the bar graph using the proportion of people out of the total for each gender? Draw this bar graph with the height of the bar being the proportion of people taller than 67 in. for males and females. Would you change any conclusions comparing the heights of males and females from those you made from the bar graph in part a?

8. Draw histograms of the baseline and posting data from Table 3.6, using an interval width of 2 and starting with the lowest interval 46–47. Can you get the same information from these as you can from the back-to-back stem and leaf display in Table 3.12?

9. Draw a histogram from the stem and leaf display of baseline speeds in Table 3.11. You should get exactly the same graph as you drew in Exercise 8 for the baseline speeds. Note that you can easily build a histogram from a stem and leaf display. If you had the histogram first (but not the raw data), could you build a stem and leaf display?

10. Draw frequency polygons for the baseline and posting data in Table 3.6, starting with the histograms you drew in Exercise 8.

11. See the GPA data in Table 3.1 and the bar graph in Figure 3.4.

a. Draw a pie chart of the number of students with GPAs of 3.0 or higher as they are distributed among the three majors.

b. Draw a pie chart of the number of students with GPAs less than 3.0 as they are distributed among the three majors.

c. Compare the pie charts in parts a and b.

12. See the speed data in Table 3.6 and the back-to-back stem and leaf display in Table 3.12.

a. For the baseline data, draw a pie chart showing three categories: the number obeying the speed limit of 50 km/h (or driving slower), the number going more than 50 but less than 60, and the number going 60 or faster.

b. Draw a similar pie chart for the posting data.

c. Do the pie charts give a good visual comparison of the impact of the posting?

13. Use the data in Table 2.2 for this exercise.

a. For females, draw a scatterplot of baby length (on the *X* or horizontal axis) and adult height (on the *Y* or vertical axis).

b. Make a similar scatterplot for males, using the same axis as in part a.

c. Compare the scatterplots in parts a and b. Do longer babies tend to grow up to be taller adults?

d. If you overlay the two plots (place one paper on top of the other, hold them up to a light, and align the axes), does it appear that the relationship between baby length and adult height is as strong for both groups combined as it is for each separately? What is the principle factor in this difference?

14. You are given the birthdates of 50 famous people. What kinds of pictorial description can you use to describe the distribution? What is the best interval for a frequency distribution?

15. An area of research known as interpersonal attraction uses the bogus stranger paradigm in some of its research. First, an attitude survey is given to a group of potential participants. These attitudes include how they feel about certain current topics, such as how the president is doing. Second, participants are selected to participate in the research, and for each participant selected, a unique listing of attitudes is constructed. This unique list (called the *bogus stranger's attitude survey*) contains attitudes that agree (or disagree) with the participant's own attitudes for a certain percentage of the items on the survey. Differing levels of agreement (percentage of similarity) is one of the major manipulations in this type of research. Participants are randomly assigned to a level of similarity. Next, participants are scheduled in the experiment, given the bogus stranger's attitude survey, and asked to rate the stranger on a scale that measures how much they would like to work with the stranger on some project. The rating scale is called the *Interpersonal Judgment Scale (IJS),* and it is a measure of attraction toward the stranger, with a high score meaning high attraction.

a. Describe the sample and the population.

b. Is this a true experiment or observational research? State your reasons.

c. What type of variable is percent of similarity? Explain.

d. What type of variable is the IJS score? Explain.

e. What is the scale of measurement for IJS scores?

f. Build a frequency distribution for each of the two groups of **attraction data** given here.

Attraction data
A data set used throughout the text; it consists of attraction scores for 72 participants

Attraction data: Scores on IJS for 36 subjects in each group

80% Similar				80% Dissimilar			
10	10	10	12	8	8	9	6
13	9	10	10	12	12	7	8
11	10	12	10	7	4	11	10
9	9	8	12	5	10	6	10
12	12	11	12	5	8	7	8
12	11	10	12	5	6	10	5
8	6	10	12	8	5	6	8
9	8	13	7	7	5	8	8
12	10	12	12	4	6	4	6

g. Now construct a stem and leaf display for each group. Does this help you compare the two groups?

h. Draw a histogram for each group.

i. Draw frequency polygons for each of the histograms in part h.

16. From the data given here, plot both the average speed and the average miles per gallon by year on the same

Motor vehicle speed on level, straight, rural interstate highway, off-peak hours (data for Exercise 16)

Year	1960	1965	1970	1972	1973	1974	1975	1976	1977	1978
Number of Vehicles Recorded (thousands)	NA	NA	200	160	181	203	102	515	500	468
Average Speed (mph)	54.8	60.6	63.8	64.9	65.0	57.6	57.6	58.2	58.8	58.8
Domestic Motor Fuel Consumption										
Average Miles per Gallon	14.28	14.15	13.58	13.67	13.29	13.65	13.74	13.93	14.15	14.26

Source: U.S. Bureau of the Census, 1980.

graph so that the lines are reasonably close together without touching. Does there seem to be a relationship between these variables?

Section 3.6

17. Label each of the following distributions as positively skewed, negatively skewed, or symmetric:
    a. Scores of sixth-graders on a college-level test
    b. Scores for your class if you were given the final examination this week
    c. Scores of your class on a spelling test for sixth-graders
    d. The age (in months) of children in the third grade in a local school
    e. The number of personal computers purchased by year over the last 20 years

Section 3.7

18. Use SAS PROC CHART or SPSS FREQUENCIES to graph the posting data from Table 3.6. Compare your output to what you drew in Exercise 8.

19. Use SAS PROC UNIVARIATE or SPSS EXAMINE to build stem and leaf displays for the GPA data from Table 3.1. For SAS, if you add the statements "PROC SORT; BY x;" before "PROC UNIVARIATE;" and use "BY x;" (where "x" is the variable name you give to major) after "PROC UNIVARIATE" then SAS will create three separate stem and leaf displays and give you a comparative display of all three together.

4

Describing Data for a Single Variable: Summary Measures

In Chapter 3 you learned how to describe data from one variable using pictures. We listed four characteristics of a sample that can be described by graphs or statistics. Two of these characteristics are key to this chapter: central tendency and variability. You'll learn to compute statistics that describe the middle of a distribution, or its *central tendency,* and the spread of the data, or its *variability.* Both of these characteristics of data are extremely important throughout this text.

Research Example 4
4.1 Introduction
4.2 Summation Notation: A Tool Necessary for Sample Statistics
4.3 Describing the Central Tendency of Data
4.4 Sample Mode
    Definition
    Characteristics
4.5 Sample Median
    Definition
    Characteristics
4.6 Sample Mean
    Definition
    Characteristics
    Comparison of the mean, median, and mode
    Population mean
4.7 Describing the Variability of Data
4.8 Ranges
4.9 Absolute Deviation
4.10 Sample Variance
    Derivation and definition
    Characteristics
    Computational formula
    Squared units of measure
4.11 Sample Standard Deviation
    Definition
    Characteristics
    Population variance
    Beyond these measures of central tendency and variability
4.12 Five-Number Summaries and Box-Plots
    Five-number summary
    Box-plots

4.13 Summary, Study Tips, and Computation
Chapter summary
Study tips
Computation
Exercises

Research Example 4

Most reports on scientific studies present some descriptive statistics, often measures of central tendency and variability. These measures usually are reported for every variable used in the study in order to help the reader understand the data. Because the original scores are rarely reported, sample measures of central tendency and variability are reported to represent the data simply, thoroughly, and accurately. Let's see how one scientific journal article presented descriptive statistics.

Ekman and O'Sullivan (1991) examined the ability of people in different occupations to detect lying. Subjects were from seven occupations: Secret Service personnel, federal polygraphers, robbery investigators, judges, psychiatrists, a group they called *special interest* (people from various other professions interested in being able to detect liars), and, for comparison with prior research, college students. Table 4.1 contains sample size, gender, age, and job experience for each group. The researcher's article used the symbol *M* for the sample mean and the symbol *SD* to stand for standard deviation, a measure of variability.

Each subject watched a videotape of 1-minute interviews with each of ten women who were either lying or telling the truth. Each subject saw each interview and then had 30 seconds to record his or her decision as to whether the woman in the interview was lying. In fact, exactly five of the women were lying and five were telling the truth. The ten answers for each subject were then combined into a deception accuracy score that could range from 10 to 100, reflecting the percentage of the guesses that were correct. Table 4.2 shows the sample means and standard deviations for the deception accuracy scores for the seven groups. Only the Secret Service group scored significantly different from chance (a score of 50) and significantly better than the other groups.

Table 4.1
Sample size, gender, age, and job experience in observer groups

Observer group	N	Women (%)	Age (in Years) M	Age (in Years) SD	Job Experience (in Years) M	Job Experience (in Years) SD
Secret Service	34	3	34.79	5.96	9.12	6.69
Federal polygraphers	60	8	39.42	6.76	6.54	6.19
Robbery investigators	126	2	39.21	8.26	14.77	7.15
Judges	110	11	52.64	9.37	11.50	7.77
Psychiatrists	67	3	54.24	10.28	23.63	10.28
Special interest	73	53	43.33	13.44	10.76	9.89
College students	39	64	19.90	1.74	—	—

Source: Ekman and O'Sullivan (1991).

Table 4.2

Deception accuracy means and standard deviations in observer groups

Observer group	M	SD
Secret Service	64.12	14.80
Federal polygraphers	55.67	13.32
Robbery investigators	55.79	14.93
Judges	56.73	14.72
Psychiatrists	57.61	14.57
Special interest	55.34	15.82
College students	52.82	17.31

These tables are typical of results presented as descriptive statistics in journal articles. When you are finished with this chapter, these statistics will be more understandable.

4.1 Introduction

Imagine that you want to research whether preschool children imitate aggressive behavior. You believe children have changed since the 1960s, when Bandura, Ross, and Ross (1963) did their classic study, which was discussed in Chapter 2. You think children won't mimic adults who punch an inflated clown doll. You obtain permission from parents whose children attend a local day care center and you randomly assign the children to two groups. The adult day care worker supervising one group punches the doll, and the supervisor of the other group ignores the doll. Over a week's time, you and an assistant record the number of aggressive acts by each child in each group.

What can the numbers of aggressive acts tell you about imitated aggression among preschoolers? Think about ways to describe the data.

For each group, you could describe the data by building a frequency distribution, histogram, or stem and leaf display. These would give a picture of your results. You can inspect your histograms to see where the distributions for the two groups are centered. You also can see how spread out the numbers are. But these pictorial displays do not *measure* the central tendency and variability of your data.

Descriptive statistics summarize sample data. That's why these measures are called *summary characteristics,* or *summary measures.* When you describe your data's central tendency, you want to include a typical score that helps you see where the distribution is located: Do the values tend to be high or low? On the average, do children in the group that observed the adult punching the doll have more aggressive acts? A measure of central tendency should show you the location of the approximate "middle" of the distribution—that is, where the middle is located on the number line.

What about the spread of the scores? You can see them in your histogram or stem and leaf display, but in scientific reports, researchers give statistics that summarize the variability of their data. You can compute one number that lets you see how the distribution is spread out. Do the values tend to be tightly bunched or widely scattered? Perhaps the children who saw the adult punching the inflated doll have a wide variety of scores, with some children showing many aggressive acts and others retreating from any interaction with their playmates. Not only are the measures of variability useful for describing the distribution, but they are also used later in computing inferential statistics for decision making.

Before we can discuss how to obtain summary measures, you need to learn about summation notation. Some students may appreciate the way we have broken this material on summation notation into small steps. If you have math anxiety, this material will help you become familiar with new symbols and operations. If you already understand summation notation, you can skip to Section 4.3.

Quick Quiz

How are descriptive statistics different from pictorial descriptions, like frequency distributions?

Answer

Descriptive statistics are numerical summaries of distributions of data and give a measure of certain characteristics, such as central tendency and variability.

4.2   Summation Notation: A Tool Necessary for Sample Statistics

Summation is a necessary tool for computing summary measures. Summation includes a notation system and rules for the use of this system; it allows you to more easily and efficiently express yourself when discussing statistics. See Box 4.1 for a discussion of summation rules.

Condensed into its simplest form, summation notation uses several symbols:

1. Σ (capital Greek sigma, read as "sum of") stands for the summation operation.
2. X stands for scores.
3. N stands for the number of scores, also called the **sample size.**

Sample size
Number of scores in the sample, symbolized by N

These symbols are used together as

$$\Sigma X = \text{sum of } X = \text{sum of } N \text{ values of } X \tag{4.1}$$

You need to remember that ΣX simply means to add all N scores in the sample.

For the observations in Table 4.3, find ΣX. You should get $\Sigma X = 7 + 5 + \cdots + 11 = 64$. What is N? It's the sample size, or $N = 10$, because there are ten observations in this sample.

One important calculation is the summation of the squares of values, ΣX^2, read as "sum of the squares of X." That is, you square each observation and then sum the squares. If you have $X_1 = 2$, $X_2 = 3$, and $X_3 = 5$, then

$$\Sigma X^2 = X_1^2 + X_2^2 + X_3^2 = 2^2 + 3^2 + 5^2 = 4 + 9 + 25 = 38$$

Table 4.3

7	8
5	9
6	4
4	3
7	11

Another important use of summation is in the square of the sum of a set of values, $(\Sigma X)^2$, which is read as "sum of X quantity squared." This is *not* the same as ΣX^2, which we just examined. In $(\Sigma X)^2$, you compute the sum first and then you square that single number. Using the values above, you get

$$(\Sigma X)^2 = (2 + 3 + 5)^2 = 10^2 = 100$$

Box 4.1 Summation Rules

The first summation rule involves summing N values of a constant, or adding a constant N times:

Rule 1. $\sum a = Na$

where a is a constant. In essence, you are using multiplication as a shortcut for addition. If you have eight values of a constant—say, 4—you might at first say, "Four plus 4 plus 4 and so on." Most people simply say, "Oh, I have eight 4's, so the answer is 8 times 4, or 32." This rule says that the sum of a constant is N times the constant.

The second rule in using summation notation is concerned with the sum of N values of a variable, where each is multiplied by a constant:

Rule 2. $\sum aX = a\sum X$

where a is a constant. If everyone in your statistics class had their scores multiplied by 3, what would be the sum of the new scores in relation to the sum of the old scores? Everyone's score was multiplied by 3, so 3 is common as a multiplicative factor and the new sum must be 3 times the old one. This rule says the sum of a constant times a variable is the constant times the sum of the variable.

The third rule states that the sum of a quantity of a variable and a constant is the sum of the variable plus N times the constant:

Rule 3. $\sum (X + a) = \sum X + \sum a = \sum X + Na$

where a is a constant. When adding these values, you have the sum of N values of a variable plus the sum of N values of the constant, or, from the first summation rule, the sum of the variable plus N times the constant. If your professor added 10 to the scores on your next test for all the students in your class, then the sum of the new scores can be obtained from the old sum and the number of students times 10.

The final rule is expressed in a general form, and then a specific example is given. In contrast to the earlier rules, this rule is not in equation form, but in a verbal form.

Rule 4. If the sum of a function is given, the function is to be calculated for the specified values of X and then the summation is to be completed. If the function of a sum is given, the summation is to be completed first and then the function is to be evaluated for the entire sum. Parentheses can be used to separate the function from the summation.

For example, consider $\sum X^2$ and $(\sum X)^2$. $\sum X^2$ is the sum of a function, and $(\sum X)^2$ is a function of a sum. Clearly, $\sum X^2$ does not equal $(\sum X)^2$.

From this example it is obvious that $\sum X^2 = 38$ does not equal $(\sum X)^2 = 100$. Both $\sum X^2$ and $(\sum X)^2$ can appear in the same formulas, and if you confuse them, your answer will be wrong. This is the most frequent computational mistake made by beginning statistics students. Remember: Operations inside parentheses come first. In $(\sum X)^2$, do the calculation in the parentheses *first* (summation) and then square that total. If there are no parentheses, as in $\sum X^2$, square each number and then add them up. You will see these two formulas many times in this text, and you must always distinguish between them. Mark this place in your book and review it regularly.

Compute $\sum X^2$ from the data given in Table 4.3, with $N = 10$ scores. You should get $\sum X^2 = 466$. Taking $\sum X = 64$ from the same data, you get $(\sum X)^2 = 64^2 = 4096$. Do you see that $(\sum X)^2$ is the square of a single number, whereas $\sum X^2$ is the sum of the squares of N numbers? You are performing the same operations in each, summing and squaring. These formulas differ in not only *how many times* you perform an operation but also *when* you do the operation. In getting $\sum X^2$, you are first squaring N numbers and *then* summing these squared numbers. In getting $(\sum X)^2$, you are first summing N numbers and *then* squaring one number. You may think we are overemphasizing the differences between these operations. From our teaching experience, we know this heavy emphasis is necessary. In spite of all this attention, an alarmingly high percentage of students still confuse these two formulas. You could be the next one to make this mistake—unless you take this warning to heart.

More explanation of summation is given in Chapter 14, where the use of two summation signs is considered. The exercises at the end of this chapter give you some additional practice in summation work.

Quick Quiz

Calculate $\sum X$, $(\sum X)^2$, and $\sum X^2$ for the following set of numbers: 7, 1, 9, 20.

Answer

$\sum X = 37, (\sum X)^2 = 1369,$ and $\sum X^2 = 531$

4.3   Describing the Central Tendency of Data

Measures of central tendency describe the location, or "middle" or center, of a distribution of scores. There are three measures of central tendency in this section, and each has the same function: to show the central tendency or location of a distribution of scores—that is, to find a typical score. Look at the data for the heights of females from Table 3.4, reproduced here as Table 4.4. From the data, you might guess that a typical height is 64 to 65 in. Rather than use this inexact guess, let's look at exact measures of central tendency.

In choosing a single typical measure to represent all of the scores, some random error occurs in that representation. That is, the single measure of central tendency does not equal every score in the sample and may not exactly equal even one score. Suppose that the average height of females for the sample in Table 4.4 is 64.96 in. Although 64.96 in. is typical of the female heights, it does not represent any of the actual heights because no one's height is listed as 64.96 in. You can think of the heights being randomly distributed around 64.96 in. For those five heights that are 67 in., the error, sometimes called a *deviation score,* is 2.04 in., obtained by $67 - 64.96 = 2.04$. For the one 63-in. height, the error (deviation) is $63 - 64.96 = -1.96$ in. The average of 64.96 in. is too large in representing some scores and too small in representing others. The idea of a measure of central tendency being in error is inherent to the concept of getting one score to represent all of the data.

Most statistics texts describe three sample measures of central tendency: mode, median, and mean. We will define these measures in increasing order of importance and frequency of use in the behavioral sciences. Pay attention to the characteristics of each measure of central tendency; one measure might be good in one situation, whereas you might need a different statistic for another data set. You need to know when to use one instead of another.

Table 4.4

Heights (in.) of a sample of $N = 24$ female college students

69.0	67.0	63.5
68.5	67.0	63.5
68.0	66.0	63.0
67.5	65.5	62.5
67.5	65.0	62.0
67.0	64.0	62.0
67.0	64.0	60.5
67.0	64.0	58.0

Quick Quiz

(a) What is the purpose of measures of central tendency? (b) Is there one single measure of central tendency that should always be used?

Answers

(a) Measures of central tendency are used to describe the middle or the location of a distribution of scores. A measure of central tendency also may be thought of as a typical score. (b) There isn't a single best measure of central tendency; one research situation may require a measure that might not be used for another data set.

4.4   Sample Mode

Definition

Mode
Most frequent score

The **mode** is *the most frequent score* if one exists. Note that the mode has no formula, only this verbal definition. The procedure for finding the mode is simple: Just find the most frequently occurring score. For the data in Table 4.5, use the frequency of each score to find the mode. The mode is 53 because there are three values of 53. As another example, what is the mode for the female heights in Table 4.4? The mode is 67.0 in. because there are five heights of this value and this is the highest frequency for all heights.

Characteristics

The mode is best used for qualitative data. For the imitated aggression study, you may want to describe the racial makeup of the sample. Suppose there were 28 white, 19 African American, 7 Asian American, 4 Latino, and 2 Native American children in your study. The mode for race is "white." The mode is the only measure of central tendency available for this variable. Recall that the scale of measurement for qualitative data is the nominal scale.

You might not want to use the mode because of problems with finding only one mode. Some distributions have multiple modes, and others do not have any mode. For example, the heights of the males from Table 3.4, reproduced here as Table 4.6, have three modes—71, 70, and 69—each with a frequency of 2. The mere notion of a distribution with three modes (a trimodal distribution) goes against the idea of central tendency. You are looking for a typical score, not two or three typical scores. Thus, the mode is useful only in unimodal distributions. Sometimes the mode is not in the middle of the distribution. The mode also is based on only one value in the distribution and ignores all other scores. Because the mode doesn't summarize all of the available information, it is usually not used as a typical value.

One slight advantage of that mode is that it is the only measure of central tendency that is always one of the actual scores, if a mode exists. Another advantage is that the mode is the best guess for the most probable score for any subject. And, as we already said, the mode is the only measure of central tendency for some qualitative (nominal scale) data. If you are marketing a product and want to identify the average consumer likely to buy your product, you need to identify this frequently occurring purchaser according to some characteristic. For example, you may find that the typical consumer is a young female, and "female" is not a quantitative variable.

In summary, the following are characteristics of the mode:

1. Is not easily expressed in a formula
2. Has the problem of possibly having two or more values in a data set

Table 4.5

X	Frequency
55	2
54	2
53	3
52	2
51	1
	N = 10

Table 4.6
Heights (in.) of a sample of male college students

73.0	70.0	69.0
72.0	70.0	67.0
71.0	69.5	66.0
71.0	69.0	

3. Contains little of the available information in the data
4. Is always one of the actual scores
5. Is the best guess for the most probable score
6. Is suitable for qualitative (nominal scale) data

Ordinarily, the mode is not chosen as a descriptive statistic because it is rarely (if ever) used in inferential methods.

Quick Quiz

For the following data set, give two reasons that you would not want to use the mode as a measure of central tendency: 61, 62, 68, 69, 52, 89, 52, 61, 52, 89, 60, 89.

Answers

This data set has two modes or most frequently occurring scores: 52 and 89. Both modes are extremes and don't tell us anything about the middle, or central tendency, of the data set.

4.5 Sample Median

Definition

Median
Middle value in the distribution; 50% of the scores are above it (and below it), symbolized by X_{50}

The **median** is the middle value in a distribution in terms of the rank order of the data. A verbal definition is that the median is *the middle of the ordered scores*. Like the mode, the median is defined only verbally, not with a formula. It is the score that has 50% of the N scores (in order) in the sample both below it and above it—hence, the notation X_{50}. We first order the N scores and then find the middle value.

Consider the following example. You are given the following IQ scores for a group of students:

101   105   98   95   104

To find the median, you first put the scores in order:

95   98   101   104   105

Now find the middle score. You should get 101 as the median.

Suppose you overlooked one student's IQ score of 103 and now you are refiguring the median. Putting the scores in order, you get:

95   98   101   103   104   105

Now, the middle score isn't as easy to find because you have an even number of scores. In this case, you take the middle two scores and average them. So the median is 102.

Median position
Position of the middle of the scores in order, $(N + 1)/2$

Note that the **median position,** the position of the middle value, is $(N + 1)/2$. In the first IQ example you had five scores, so the median position is $(5 + 1)/ = 3$, and the IQ score with the rank of 3 is 101.

For values of N that are even, the convention is to take the average of the two middle scores. That is, compute the middle of the distance between the score below the median position and the score above the median position, when the scores are in order. For our second IQ example, you had six scores, so the median position is $(6 + 1)/2 = 3.5$. With a rank of 3.5, the median lies halfway between the third and fourth scores.

The data from Table 2.1, reproduced here as Table 4.7, are fictitious data similar to those produced in the study described in Research Example 4 on detecting liars. Each group has 35 deception accuracy scores. For now, compute X_{50} for only the Secret

Service data. Here's how to proceed: $N = 35$, so the median position is $(35 + 1)/2 = 18$. Put the 35 scores for the Secret Service in order. Now count in from either top or bottom to the 18th score in order: It should be 60, so $X_{50} = 60$.

Quick Quiz

(a) Find the median for the data in Table 4.8. (b) Find X_{50} for the 11 male heights in Table 4.6.

Answers

(a) With $N = 10$ scores, the median position is $(N + 1)/2 = 11/2 = 5.5$. There are five scores with values of 53 or less and five with values of 54 or more, so the median must lie between 53 (the score below median position 5.5) and 54 (the score above median position 5.5). By convention the median is one-half of the way between 53 and 54, or $X_{50} = 53.5$. (b) You should get a median position of 6, so $X_{50} = 70.0$ because it is the sixth score in order.

Table 4.7

Deception accuracy scores (percentage correct)

Secret Service Personnel	Judges	Psychiatrists
60	50	60
60	60	90
70	50	60
50	60	70
70	70	60
60	50	50
70	60	50
70	50	50
60	40	60
60	70	70
40	50	60
80	70	60
70	40	60
90	90	50
80	50	70
60	60	30
80	40	60
90	60	50
50	60	60
40	40	60
50	50	40
40	50	60
50	40	70
70	70	40
70	70	50
70	50	50
60	50	60
60	70	60
70	60	60
60	50	50
80	80	40
60	70	80
80	70	60
50	50	40
60	30	80

Source: Ekman and O'Sullivan (1991).

Characteristics

The median depends not on the value of every score but on the *frequency* of the scores. In the example from Table 4.8, if the highest score had been 98 instead of 58, the median would still be 53.5. The median is recommended for quantitative data when the distribution is skewed, especially if this skewness is the result of a few extreme scores. These few extreme scores have no effect on the median.

A final characteristic of the median is that it minimizes the sum of the absolute deviations:

$\sum |X - X_{50}|$ is a minimum

(If you are unfamiliar with those vertical bars, they symbolize "absolute value," which means you drop any negative signs and deal with only positive values.) For any set of data, if you take difference scores, or deviations, from any number other than the sample median, you get a larger sum of the absolute values of the deviations than you do for the median.

In summary, the characteristics of the median are:

1. Depends on the frequencies of the scores, not on the values of every score
2. Is recommended for quantitative data when the distribution is skewed (when there are extreme scores)
3. Minimizes $\sum |X - X_{50}|$

Table 4.8

X	Frequency	Cumulative Frequency
58	1	10
57	1	9
56	1	8
55	1	7
54	1	6
53	1	5
52	1	4
51	0	3
50	1	3
49	1	2
48	0	1
47	1	1
	10	

A "mean" kid?

4.6   Sample Mean

Definition

Mean

Arithmetic average, symbolized by $\overline{X}$

Almost everyone has calculated a **mean,** or arithmetic average of a data set. It is the easiest measure of central tendency to define by mathematical formula and therefore the easiest to use in inferential statistical methods. The mean is defined as the *sum of the scores divided by the sample size.* It is symbolized by $\overline{X}$ (read as "X bar"), where

$$\overline{X} = \frac{\sum X}{N} \tag{4.2}$$

The mean fits most people's commonsense definition of "average," and although the notation in formula 4.2 may be new to you, you've probably figured your average score for a class. Adding your scores and dividing by the number of scores to determine your grade is an example of obtaining the sample mean. Suppose the data in Table 4.9 are the nine scores you have earned in a class. What is the mean? Remember that $\sum X$ means the sum of X (the scores), and N is the sample size (number of scores). The sum of the grades is $\sum X = 801$ and $N = 9$. The value of the mean is

$$\overline{X} = \frac{\sum X}{N} = \frac{801}{9} = 89$$

If these grades are the number of points out of a possible 100 and a strict A–B cutoff of 90 is used, then these nine grades average to a B.

Return to Table 4.7 and compute $\overline{X}$ for the deception accuracy scores for the Secret Service. Remember that $N = 35$. You should get $\sum X = 2240$ and $\overline{X} = 64.0$.

Table 4.9

Class grades

91
93
90
89
90
90
77
90
91

Characteristics

The sample mean is the balance point, or center of gravity, of the distribution. The mean is like the fulcrum on a seesaw: If the frequency of each score is like the weight of a person and is placed the correct distance from the mean, the seesaw will balance perfectly. Consider Figure 4.1. For these data, $\overline{X} = 44/11 = 4$. To see how $\overline{X}$ balances the distribution, first take the product of each frequency and the distance X is from $\overline{X} = 4$. Now sum the product of these frequencies and distances for each side of the distribution. The fact that the sum of distances is the same for both sides shows that the seesaw will balance.

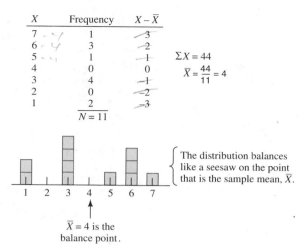

Figure 4.1
$\overline{X}$ is the balance point in a distribution.

The second characteristic of the sample mean is merely a mathematical restatement of the first. The sample mean $\overline{X}$ is the only measure of central tendency for which the sum of the deviation scores (errors) equals zero. Here, the deviation scores show the sign of the difference. Expressed in a formula,

$$\Sigma(X - \overline{X}) = 0 \tag{4.3}$$

This is easily seen in Figure 4.1 by adding the deviation scores, or $3 + 2 + 2 + 2 + 1 - 1 - 1 - 1 - 1 - 3 - 3 = 0$. Because $\Sigma(X - \overline{X})$ is always zero, the average deviation $\Sigma(X - \overline{X})/N$ is also always zero. Remember that any measure of central tendency (used as representative of the scores) is considered to be in error as a representative of any individual score. Error is illustrated in the deviation score $X - \overline{X}$. If you consider these deviation scores as errors, then this characteristic of $\overline{X}$ shows you that $\overline{X}$ keeps the average error at zero. You'll see this characteristic and the final characteristic of the mean later in this chapter.

The sample mean $\overline{X}$ is the point about which the sum of the squared deviations is a minimum. That is, the choice of $\overline{X}$ as the measure of central tendency minimizes the sum of the squared deviation scores. The mean is subtracted from each score, the difference is squared, and then these quantities are summed. This quantity is typically called the **sum of squares** and is abbreviated *SS* (*SS* is used extensively in later chapters). Expressing this characteristic in summation notation gives

$$\Sigma(X - \overline{X})^2 \text{ is a minimum} \tag{4.4}$$

Sum of squares
Sum of squared deviations of scores from the mean, $\Sigma(X - \overline{X})^2$, abbreviated *SS*

Least-squares criterion
Choice of a statistic so that a sum of squares is minimized; $\Sigma(X - \overline{X})^2$ is minimized by $\overline{X}$

[handwritten: Don't worry about now, will cover it later.]

This characteristic of $\overline{X}$ minimizing the sum of the squared deviations is called the **least-squares criterion** (*least* for minimizing, *squares* for the sum of the *squared* deviations). Thus, $\overline{X}$ fits the least-squares criterion by minimizing $\Sigma(X - \overline{X})^2$. For a concrete illustration of this characteristic, use the data in Figure 4.1 to get deviations from the mean, $\overline{X} = 4$, and deviations from the mode, or 3. The sum of the squared deviations from $\overline{X} = 4$ is

$$3^2 + 2^2 + 2^2 + 2^2 + 1^2 + (-1)^2 + (-1)^2 + (-1)^2 + (-1)^2 + (-3)^2 + (-3)^2$$

$$= 9 + 4 + 4 + 4 + 1 + 1 + 1 + 1 + 1 + 9 + 9 = 44$$

whereas the sum of the squared deviations from mode $= 3$ gives

$$4^2 + 3^2 + 3^2 + 3^2 + 2^2 + 0^2 + 0^2 + 0^2 + 0^2 + (-2)^2 + (-2)^2$$

$$= 16 + 9 + 9 + 9 + 4 + 4 + 4 = 55$$

Here $\Sigma(X - \text{mode})^2$ is greater than $\Sigma(X - \overline{X})^2$. The mode was arbitrarily chosen for this example; any value other than the mean gives a larger sum of squared deviations than the mean gives.

Finally, the mean is affected by extreme scores. The value of $\overline{X}$ is pulled toward the values of the extreme scores because all scores go into the computation of $\overline{X}$. So a high score inflates $\overline{X}$, just as the average of your test scores will go up if you ace the midterm exam.

In summary, note these characteristics:

1. The mean is the balance point of the distribution.
2. $\Sigma(X - \overline{X}) = 0$
3. $\Sigma(X - \overline{X})^2$ is a minimum.
4. The mean is affected by extreme scores.

Comparison of the Mean, Median, and Mode

Table 4.10 summarizes these three measures of central tendency and should facilitate your comparisons.

Given these characteristics, you would choose $\overline{X}$ as a sample measure of central tendency if you want the average signed (plus or minus) error to be zero or if you want to minimize the sum of the squared deviation scores. Another reason for using the sample mean is its extensive use in inferential methods, where you want to maintain consistency in using descriptive and inferential statistics.

Table 4.10
Summary of central tendency measures

Measure	Definition	Characteristics
Mean	$\Sigma X/N$	$\Sigma(X - X) = 0$, $\Sigma(X - X)^2$ is minimum, most affected by extreme scores
Median	Middle value	Not easily expressed in a formula, not affected by extreme scores, minimizes $\Sigma|X - X_{50}|$
Mode	Most frequent score	Not easily expressed in a formula, can have two or more values in a data set

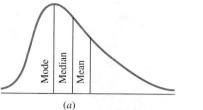
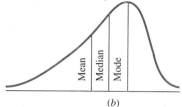

Figure 4.2

Relationships among the mean, median, and mode for (*a*) positively skewed and (*b*) negatively skewed distributions

As a descriptive statistic, the mean can be less desirable because it is so affected by extreme scores, more so than the median or the mode. For example, if you have four scores of 1, 2, 2, and 3, then mode $= X_{50} = \bar{X} = 2$. However, if the fourth score, X_4, is 11 rather than 3, then mode $= X_{50} = 2$ but $\bar{X} = 4$. Figure 4.2 shows the relationships among the mean, median, and mode for skewed distributions.

Consider the grade data in Table 4.9 and the influence of the single low grade of 77. The mean is $\bar{X} = 89$. The median is $X_{50} = 90$. The difference between the values of $\bar{X}$ and X_{50} is small but important. Yet the mean is the only measure of central tendency that accounts for every score.

When you have extreme scores, such as in a skewed distribution, the median is usually recommended over the mean if all you need is a descriptive statistic. You can report both the mean and the median for skewed distributions. If inferential methods are to be computed, then you probably would choose the mean as your descriptive statistic. For a discussion of this problem and the use of truncated samples (samples with extreme scores ignored), see Dixon and Massey (1983, p. 380).

If a distribution is symmetric, then the mean and the median are equal. What if you have one or more unknown extreme scores? You cannot compute the mean. For example, if you are measuring how long it takes for a subject to complete a task in a memory study, but some subjects fail to complete the task in the allotted 20 minutes, you have to decide what to do. You could discard the slow subjects from the research, give them a score of 20, or indicate that their score is greater than 20 (>20). The score of 20 is likely to make the distribution skewed, which favors the median, but the mean could be computed. However, >20 is an unknown extreme score, and so the median is preferred because the mean cannot be computed.

You should use the mode only if you want to have the best guess for the most probable score or if you have qualitative data.

Quick Quiz

Consider the following scores for the number of aggressive acts by ten children in the imitated aggression study: 2, 2, 1, 0, 3, 2, 8, 11, 1, 2. Compute the median and the mean, and discuss why they are different.

Answer

If you put the scores in order and average the middle two values, the median is 2. By summing the scores and dividing by 10, you find the mean is 3.2. The mean is higher because two extreme scores, 8 and 11, affect the average. In fact, the mean is higher than most of the scores in the sample.

Population Mean

Population mean
Parameter of the population indicating the center (middle) of the population distribution, symbolized by μ and estimated by the sample $\overline{X}$

Central tendency also exists in populations. The **population mean** is the parameter (numerical characteristic) of the population that indicates the middle of the population distribution. It indicates the location of the population and may be used as typical, or representative, of the scores in the population. For example, the population of the data in Table 4.2 for judges is the deception accuracy scores for all the judges in, say, the United States.

The symbol for the population mean is μ (pronounced "mew" as in the first two letters of the word *mute*). It was chosen because it is the Greek letter m, for *mean*. Even though its value is generally unknown, μ exists as a measure of the population central tendency. Because you cannot obtain the population mean, you estimate it with the sample mean. (However, if you have a small population where all the scores are obtainable, then you can compute the population mean using the formula for the sample mean.)

4.7   Describing the Variability of Data

In Chapter 3 you read that three principles should guide a pictorial description of data: It should be simple, thorough, and accurate. The mean, median, and mode are all simple. But are you *thoroughly* and *accurately* describing the data if your description stops there?

Several distributions can have the same mean but still be different. For instance, suppose you are a high school counselor and you notice a tendency toward depression among students after the holidays. You want to find out whether males and females have the same depression levels. You find a questionnaire that measures depression where each question requires a rating of 1 to 5: 1 means almost never, 3 means sometimes, and 5 means almost always. Suppose an average score of 3 shows a normal teenage depression level, and both males and females in your study have an average response of 3. Does this mean that depression in males and females is the same? You need to look at your data carefully. The females' responses might cluster around 3, with a few responses of 2 or 4, whereas the males may have responded either 1 or 5 and never 3. These two groups may have the same mean, but the spread of the scores is different in an important way. Perhaps they come from populations like those in Figure 4.3. Those extreme responses may indicate that some males in the study are having emotional problems.

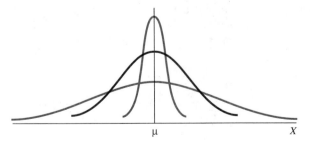

Figure 4.3
Distributions with the same mean but different measures of variability

Table 4.11
Tactual performance test scores, time (min)

Alcoholics					Nonalcoholics				
34	26	18	26	9	15	2	23	7	18
28	14	33	43	50	13	9	23	8	16
26	10	21	33	24	27	28	12	4	28
28	1	30	25	27	12	18	18	14	6
19	10	20	14	7	15	15	31	15	15
Mean = 23.04					Mean = 15.68				
Scores range from 1 to 50					Scores range from 2 to 31				

Variability
Tendency for scores to depart from some measure of central tendency

The spread or dispersion of the scores is **variability.** Variability is the tendency for scores to differ from other scores in a distribution. It also is the tendency for scores to depart from the mean or other measure of central tendency. In the same way that the sample mean $\bar{X}$ is a single measure that depicts the central tendency of all N scores in a sample, you now want a single measure that depicts the variability of the scores.

Female alcoholic and nonalcoholic data
A data set used throughout the text; it consists of time scores on the Tactual Performance·Test

Consider Table 4.11, which contains **female alcoholic and nonalcoholic data.** These are scores on the Tactual Performance Test, the time that it takes blindfolded subjects to fit irregular shapes into a formboard (based on Silberstein & Parsons, 1981). Not only do the scores for the two groups differ in central tendency, but also the scores for the 25 nonalcoholics are less variable, or more tightly clustered around the middle, than the scores for the 25 alcoholics. Figure 4.4 shows a plot of the data from Table 4.11. How can you measure this variability? To answer this question, let's look at the next list.

These are desirable characteristics of a statistic that measures variability:

1. The statistic should indicate when the variability is zero. Specifically, if the scores are all the same, then the variability is zero and the statistic that measures variability should have a value of zero.

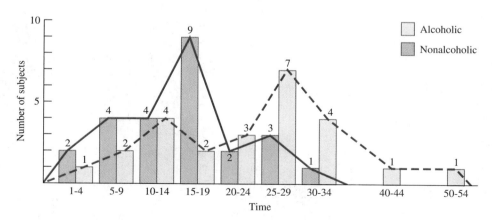

Figure 4.4
Time on tactual performance test for female alcoholics and nonalcoholics

2. The statistic should increase when the variability increases. For the data in Table 4.11, the value of the statistic should be larger for alcoholics than for nonalcoholics.

3. The statistic needs to measure variability in spite of the size of a measure of central tendency. The statistic should measure just the spread of scores, not the data's location on the number line. You don't want the statistic to reflect the fact that the alcoholics have a higher middle than the nonalcoholics.

Now let's look at measures of variability.

Quick Quiz

How is variability different from central tendency?

Answer

Central tendency refers to the location of the distribution, or a typical or middle score. Central tendency is measured by the mean, median, and mode. Variability is the spread of the scores in a distribution, or the scores' tendency to differ from the middle of the distribution.

4.8   Ranges

Range
Measure of variability in the sample; it is the high score minus the low score

Half-range
A range of half of the data

Lowrange
The range of the lower half of the data; the median minus the lowest score

Midrange
The range of the middle half of the data

Highrange
The range of the higher half of the data; the high score minus the median

Hinge
Median of the upper or lower half of the data

Hinge position
Position of a value that is a middle score for the upper or lower half of the data

The first measure of variability is the simplest. The **range** gives some indication of the variability of a sample and is simply *the highest score minus the lowest score.* For the alcoholic data in Table 4.11, the high score is 50 and the low score is 1, so the range is $50 - 1 = 49$. The range is not used much, possibly because it is more variable from sample to sample than other measures. The range depends on only two of the N scores for its computation. If either the high or low score is extreme, the range is inflated. However, the range can give a quick idea of the variability of the data and is easily computed.

You also can compute **half-ranges,** which take into account the range of half of the data at a time. You'll use half-ranges at the end of this chapter when two new graphs are introduced. There are three half-ranges: the **lowrange,** which is the median minus the lowest score (the range for the bottom half of the data); the **midrange,** which is the range for the middle 50% of the scores; and the **highrange,** which is the highest score minus the median (the range for the top half of the data). You might see the midrange referred to as the *interquartile range, midspread,* or *H-spread.*

Let's use the data for the alcoholic group in Table 4.11 to illustrate the half-ranges. Put all of the scores in order ($N = 25$) and find the median. Do you get $X_{50} = 25$? Calculate the lowrange and the highrange. You should get $25 - 1 = 24$ for the lowrange, and the highrange $= 50 - 25 = 25$.

Calculating the midrange is a little trickier because you need to identify which scores are the **hinges,** or the medians of the upper and lower halves of the data. You start with the median position, which is $(N + 1)/2$. To find the hinges, drop any decimals and use just the integer portion of the median position. For the alcoholic data, the median position is $(25 + 1)/2 = 13$, so there aren't any decimals to drop. Now we need to find the **hinge position,** or the position of the values that are midway through the upper half and lower half of the data. We use a formula similar to the one used to find the median position. Instead of N, use [median position], which is the symbol for the integer portion of the median position. The formula is

$$\text{Hinge position} = \frac{[\text{median position}] + 1}{2}$$

For the alcoholic data, the hinge position is $(13 + 1)/2 = 7$. To find the lower hinge, count to the seventh score from the bottom. You should find the lower hinge is 14. To find the upper hinge, count down from the top and find the score that is in the seventh position from the top. Did you get 28? Now you have the information you need to calculate the midrange. Subtract the lower hinge from the upper hinge: $28 - 14 = 14$. This is the midrange.

4.9   Absolute Deviation

Let's use the definition of variability as "the tendency of scores to depart from a measure of central tendency." Measures of variability may use the median as the point from which scores depart. You can obtain a measure of how far any given score deviates from the median by simply computing the deviation score, $X - X_{50}$. You might be tempted to do this for all of the scores in the sample, and then find an average or middle of the deviation scores. You are on the right track, but remember that 50% of the X values above the median give positive deviation scores and 50% of the X's below the median give negative deviation scores. Some of these positive and negative deviation scores will cancel each other out to give an inaccurate measure of variability. How can you eliminate the problem of positive and negative deviation scores canceling each other out?

One way to eliminate the sign of the deviation score is to use absolute values. The average of these absolute values is the **mean absolute deviation:**

Mean absolute deviation
Mean of the absolute values of deviation scores from the median

$$\text{Mean absolute deviation} = \frac{\sum |X - X_{50}|}{N} \qquad (4.5)$$

But just as extreme scores affect the sample mean, big absolute deviations influence the mean of the absolute deviations. So the logical solution is to find the median of these absolute deviations. The **median absolute deviation** (*MAD*) is a measure of variability that is not influenced by extreme deviation scores. To get the *MAD*, order the absolute values of the deviations and find the middle value. If there are two middle values, average them.

Median absolute deviation
Middle of the absolute values of deviation scores from the median, symbolized as *MAD*

For example, for the following data, what are the values of the mean absolute deviation and the median absolute deviation?

X	$X - X_{50}$	$|X - X_{50}|$
1	-2	2
2	-1	1
3	0	0
7	4	4
10	7	7

The median of the X values is 3, the sum of the $|X - X_{50}|$ values is 14, and the mean absolute deviation is $14/5 = 2.8$. The median absolute deviation is 2, the middle of the five deviations.

These are good measures of variability because they have a value of zero when there is no variability, they increase when variability increases, and they measure variability in spite of the size of the median. The main characteristic of the mean absolute deviation and the median absolute deviation is their connection to X_{50} as a measure of central tendency. Note that the mean absolute deviation is a minimum as it is defined with the deviations being taken around X_{50}. The measures of variability described next are used more often because of their connection with the frequently used $\overline{X}$.

4.10   Sample Variance

Derivation and Definition

As scores deviate from a measure of central tendency, the positive and negative deviation scores can cancel each other out. Using absolute values eliminates negative signs. Another way to remove the sign of deviation scores is to square each deviation score before summing, resulting in $\sum(X - \overline{X})^2 = SS$, the sum of squares. Is the sum of squares a good measure of variability? It does equal zero when there is no variability in the scores. SS also goes up as variability increases. But you cannot use SS directly as a measure of variability because it increases as the number of scores increases. That is, as N increases, the value of $\sum(X - \overline{X})^2$ increases as long as the same population is being sampled.

You could divide SS by N and obtain a measure of variability that is not an increasing function of N. So $\sum(X - \overline{X})^2/N$ is an average of the squared deviation scores. How is it an average? In the formula $\overline{X} = \sum X/N$, the raw scores are added up and divided by N. Similarly, in the formula $\sum(X - \overline{X})^2/N$, the squared deviation scores are added up and divided by N. This newly derived statistic is called the **sample variance** and is symbolized by $\overset{*}{s}{}^2$. A verbal definition of $\overset{*}{s}{}^2$ is *the average squared deviation from $\overline{X}$*. Here is the definitional formula, which should *not* be used to compute the variance because it usually leads to too many computational mistakes:

Sample variance
Measure of variability in the sample; it divides the sum of squares by N, symbolized by $\overset{*}{s}{}^2$

$$\overset{*}{s}{}^2 = \frac{\sum(X - \overline{X})^2}{N} = \frac{SS}{N} \tag{4.6}$$

This is one formula for sample variance. A computational formula for $\overset{*}{s}{}^2$ is given later.

Another measure of variability, which is slightly different, is given by the definitional formula

$$s^2 = \frac{\sum(X - \overline{X})^2}{N - 1}$$

which is covered in Chapter 9. Note that $\overset{*}{s}{}^2$ is always smaller than s^2. Some people call s^2 the *unbiased variance estimate*. The "star" notation for sample variance, $\overset{*}{s}{}^2$, is used to distinguish it from the unbiased variance estimate, s^2. A former student says he used the phrase, "un-starred, unbiased" to help him distinguish between these two measures. There is no agreement among statisticians about the notation of these two sample variances. We have introduced both sample variances and have chosen the notation that we think is most helpful to you.

Let's return briefly to the idea of $\overline{X}$ being representative of X. Its error in being representative of a score can be seen in the deviation score, $X - \overline{X}$. So the sample variance $\overset{*}{s}{}^2$ is a measure of the variability of error.

Characteristics

The sample variance $\overset{*}{s}{}^2$ has a value greater than zero unless all the X values are equal, in which case there is no variability and $\overset{*}{s}{}^2 = 0$. As variability increases, $\overset{*}{s}{}^2$ increases. Additionally, $\overset{*}{s}{}^2$ is a minimum as it is defined with the deviations being taken around $\overline{X}$. Any other choice of a measure of central tendency results in a larger value of the *SS*, as shown earlier, and a larger $\overset{*}{s}{}^2$.

Most people who are first encountering the variance have a "so what" feeling. You have calculated the average of your scores in a class, but it's highly unlikely that you have measured how spread out your scores are. Because the measure is abstract, students have difficulty relating $\overset{*}{s}{}^2$ to the original data. You may feel unsure about what $\overset{*}{s}{}^2$ means. Do you have a lot of variability or a little variability if $\overset{*}{s}{}^2 = 180$? This value means little to anyone who is unfamiliar with the variables in the study. For IQ scores, you would know that $\overset{*}{s}{}^2 = 180$ is small only if you know it should be about 225.

Computational Formula

The definitional formula for $\overset{*}{s}{}^2$ is formula 4.6, which should never be used to actually compute $\overset{*}{s}{}^2$. Computation of $\overset{*}{s}{}^2$ by the definitional formula is cumbersome, time-consuming, and potentially inaccurate. Inaccuracies can enter the formula because you have to square the deviation scores, which are rarely whole numbers and usually have many decimal places. Rounding in the middle of the computation of $\overset{*}{s}{}^2$ results in wrong final answers. Instead, we advise that you use the following computational formula for $\overset{*}{s}{}^2$:

$$\overset{*}{s}{}^2 = \frac{N\Sigma X^2 - (\Sigma X)^2}{N^2} \tag{4.7}$$

An alternative computational formula is

$$\overset{*}{s}{}^2 = \frac{\Sigma X^2 - \dfrac{(\Sigma X)^2}{N}}{N} \tag{4.8}$$

which has two divisions instead of one, as in formula 4.7.

Although we are focusing on $\overset{*}{s}{}^2$, we have mentioned the unbiased variance estimate s^2, so here is its computational formula:

$$s^2 = \frac{N\Sigma X^2 - (\Sigma X)^2}{N(N-1)}$$

These computational formulas may look difficult, but they are composed of pieces that are already familiar to you: N, ΣX, and ΣX^2. Remember the warning you were given in Section 4.2 about ΣX^2 and $(\Sigma X)^2$? Here is the first of several applications, so don't confuse these two expressions.

Table 4.12 contains data from Table 4.5 and computation of the sample variance $\overset{*}{s}{}^2$ using formula 4.7, which is most efficient for calculator work or computer programming and minimizes the chance of a mistake. First, square each score, X^2. Second, obtain the sum, ΣX, and the sum of the squares, ΣX^2. Third, put the sum, the sum of the squares, and N into formula 4.7 and compute $\overset{*}{s}{}^2$. The various steps of the computations are shown in Table 4.12. The value of $\overline{X}$ is 53.2, and $\overset{*}{s}{}^2 = 1.56$. Practice using

Table 4.12
Calculation of $\overset{*}{s}{}^2$ from data in Table 4.5

X	X^2
55	3025
55	3025
54	2916
54	2916
53	2809
53	2809
53	2809
52	2704
52	2704
51	2601
$\Sigma X = 532$	$\Sigma X^2 = 28{,}318$

$$\overline{X} = \frac{\Sigma X}{N} = \frac{532}{10} = 53.2$$

$$\overset{*}{s}{}^2 = \frac{N\Sigma X^2 - (\Sigma X)^2}{N^2} = \frac{10(28{,}318) - (532)^2}{10^2}$$

$$= \frac{283{,}180 - 283{,}024}{100} = \frac{156}{100}$$

$$= 1.56$$

the computational formula by computing $\overset{*}{s}{}^2$ for the heights of college males given in Table 4.6. Do you get $\overset{*}{s}{}^2 = 3.79$? Now try the computation for the performance scores of the alcoholics given in Table 4.11. You should get $\overset{*}{s}{}^2 = 128.48$.

Compute $\overset{*}{s}{}^2$ on the deception accuracy scores for the Secret Service in Table 4.7. Important pieces of information are $N = 35$, $\Sigma X = 2240$, and $\Sigma X^2 = 149{,}200$. You should get $\overset{*}{s}{}^2 = 166.86$.

Squared Units of Measure

As a descriptive measure of variability, the sample variance has the positive characteristics listed earlier. But $\overset{*}{s}{}^2$ has one major fault: The sample variance is not in the same units of measure as the original scores. For example, the heights of males in Table 4.6 are in inches. A score of 70 is 70 in., the mean is 69.77 in., but the variance is 3.79 squared inches (in.^{2}). The obvious solution is to take the square root of $\overset{*}{s}{}^2$ and get a statistic expressed in the original units of measure. Doing this gives the next measure of variability, which is easier to relate to the original data.

Quick Quiz
What do you know if you calculate $\overset{*}{s}{}^2 = -68.07$?
            Answer

You have made a computational error. The sample variance is in squared units of measure, so it cannot be negative.

4.11 Sample Standard Deviation

Definition

The standard deviation is a measure of variability that is in the original units of measure, or the units of measure of the original scores. The **standard deviation** is simply the square root of the variance:

Standard deviation
Measure of variability in the sample; it is the square root of the sample variance, symbolized by $\overset{*}{s}$

$$\overset{*}{s} = \sqrt{\overset{*}{s}^2} = \sqrt{\frac{\Sigma(X - \overline{X})^2}{N}} \qquad (4.9)$$

for a definitional formula, and

$$\overset{*}{s} = \sqrt{\overset{*}{s}^2} = \sqrt{\frac{N\Sigma X^2 - (\Sigma X)^2}{N^2}} \qquad (4.10)$$

for a computational formula. A verbal definition for the standard deviation is *the square root of the sample variance*. Like $\overset{*}{s}^2$, $\overset{*}{s}$ is greater than zero unless all the X values are equal, $\overset{*}{s}$ increases as variability increases, and $\overset{*}{s}$ is a minimum when $\overline{X}$ is used as the measure of central tendency. In short, the standard deviation has the desirable properties of the variance without the disadvantage of being in squared units. From the male height data of Table 4.6 where $\overset{*}{s}^2 = 3.79$ in.^{2}, the value of $\overset{*}{s}$ is 1.95 in. For the deception accuracy scores of Table 4.7, what do you get for the standard deviation for the data in the Secret Service group? The answer is $\sqrt{\overset{*}{s}^2} = \overset{*}{s} = \sqrt{166.86} = 12.92$.

Characteristics

Let's relate the standard deviation to the mean and the position of a score in a distribution. The standard deviation can be used to indicate the position of any score relative to the mean; that is, a score is a certain number of standard deviations greater or less than the mean. A male college student with height $X = 72$ in. has a score that is about one standard deviation above the mean because $\overline{X} + \overset{*}{s} = 69.77 + 1.95 = 71.72$.

Use Table 4.13 to compare the sample measures of variability. All of them have a minimum of zero and increase as variability increases. If you add a constant to every score, or multiply every score by a constant, you change the scale of X. Box 4.2 shows the effect of changing the scale.

Quick Quiz

Assume you have observed a group of ten children in an imitated aggression study, counted the number of aggressive acts by each child, and obtained these scores: 0, 1, 1, 2, 2, 2, 2, 3, 8, 11. Compute the range, the sample variance $\overset{*}{s}^2$, and the sample standard deviation $\overset{*}{s}$.

Answer

Range = 11, $\overset{*}{s}^2 = 10.96$, and $\overset{*}{s} = 3.3105891$.

Table 4.13
Summary of variability measures

Measure	Definition	Characteristics
Range	High score − low score	Variable from sample to sample, depends on only two scores
Mean absolute deviation	$\Sigma \lvert X - X_{50} \rvert / N$	Is used with X_{50}
Median absolute deviation (*MAD*)	Middle value of $\lvert X - X_{50} \rvert$	Is used with X_{50}, not sensitive to extreme deviations
Variance	$\overset{*}{s}{}^2 = \Sigma(X - \bar{X})^2/N$	Is used with $\bar{X}$, in squared units of measure
Standard deviation	$\overset{*}{s} = \sqrt{\overset{*}{s}{}^2}$	Same as variance, except in original units of measure

---

Box 4.2   Change of Scale

Changing the scale of X means adding a constant to every score or multiplying every score by a constant. Of course, subtracting a constant is just adding a negative constant, and dividing by a constant is just multiplying by the reciprocal of the constant. Realistic applications of change of scale include changing feet to inches, changing minutes to seconds, changing kilometers per hour to miles per hour, asking what the average age of a given group will be in 5 years, and equating test scores. The principles presented here not only use some of the summation rules (see Box 4.1) but also bring about greater understanding of the various descriptive statistics.

The effects of changes of scale on measures of central tendency are illustrated for the sample mean; the same principles hold for the mode and the median. Table 4.14 lists the formulas that relate the new statistics to the statistics before the change of scale. The changes involve adding a constant a to every score and multiplying every score by a constant.

Table 4.14
Changes of scale on statistics

Change	$\bar{X}$	$\overset{*}{s}{}^2$	$\overset{*}{s}$	Range
$X_{new} = X + a$	$\bar{X}_{new} = \bar{X} + a$	$\overset{*}{s}{}^2_{new} = \overset{*}{s}{}^2$	$\overset{*}{s}_{new} = \overset{*}{s}$	$\text{Range}_{new} = \text{range}$
$X_{new} = aX$	$\bar{X}_{new} = a\bar{X}$	$\overset{*}{s}{}^2_{new} = a^2 \overset{*}{s}{}^2$	$\overset{*}{s}_{new} = \lvert a \rvert \overset{*}{s}$	$\text{Range}_{new} = \lvert a \rvert \text{ range}$

To illustrate these principles, add 10 to every score in Table 4.15. Also multiply every score by 2. Now compute the new $\bar{X}$, $\overset{*}{s}{}^2$, $\overset{*}{s}$, and the range for $X + 10$ and $2X$.

Remember that the measures of central tendency are supposed to be representative of all scores in the sample. The sample mean should be a typical score. Thus, if something happens to every score in the sample, it should also happen to the typical score. Hence, it should not be surprising to find that if you form $X + a$, the new mean is $\bar{X} + a = \bar{X} + 10 = 4 + 10 = 14$; or if you form aX, $a\bar{X} = 2\bar{X} = 2(4) = 8$ is the new mean.

Adding a constant to every score in the sample has no effect on the sample variance. Adding a constant simply shifts the distribution to the left or right on the scale and does not spread or condense the scores. For example, in Table 4.15 the range in the scores X is $7 - 1 = 6$, and the range in the scores $X + 10$ is $17 - 11 = 6$. The spread, or variability, of the scores does not change, so none of the measures of variability changes.

Table 4.15

X	X + 10	2X
7	17	14
6	16	12
6	16	12
6	16	12
5	15	10
3	13	6
3	13	6
3	13	6
3	13	6
1	11	2
1	11	2
$\sum X = 44$	$\sum X = 154$	$\sum X = 88$
$\sum X^2 = 220$	$\sum X^2 = 2200$	$\sum X^2 = 880$
$\overline{X} = \dfrac{44}{11} = 4$	$\overline{X} = \dfrac{154}{11} = 14$	$\overline{X} = \dfrac{88}{11} = 8$
$\overset{*}{s}{}^2 = \dfrac{11(220) - 44^2}{11^2}$	$\overset{*}{s}{}^2 = \dfrac{11(2200) - 154^2}{11^2}$	$\overset{*}{s}{}^2 = \dfrac{11(880) - 88^2}{11^2}$
$= \dfrac{484}{121}$	$= \dfrac{484}{121}$	$= \dfrac{1936}{121}$
$= 4$	$= 4$	$= 16$
$\overset{*}{s} = \sqrt{\overset{*}{s}{}^2} = 2$	$\overset{*}{s} = 2$	$\overset{*}{s} = 4$
Range $= 7 - 1 = 6$	Range $= 17 - 11 = 6$	Range $= 14 - 2 = 12$

Multiplying every score in the sample by a constant does change the sample variance. The new variance is the old variance multiplied by the square of the constant. This makes sense when you realize that the formulas for $\overset{*}{s}{}^2$ square the scores; thus, aX becomes $a^2 X^2$. Just so you will realize that the scores are more spread out when you multiply by $a = 2$, note that the range of the $2X$ is $14 - 2 = 12$, larger than the original range of 6.

The effect of changing the original scale on the standard deviation is readily obtained from the same effect on the variance. The new standard deviation is the old standard deviation multiplied by the absolute value of the constant. If the constant is negative, $|a|$ must be used to get $\overset{*}{s}_{\text{new}}$ because the standard deviation can never be negative.

Population Variance

Population variance and standard deviation
Measures of variability in the population, symbolized by σ^2 and σ, respectively

Finally, just as there is a population measure of central tendency μ, there are population measures of variability. These measures are called the **population variance and population standard deviation,** and they are symbolized by σ^2 and σ (read as "sigma squared" and "sigma"), respectively. For example, in the population of deception accuracy scores for judges, there is some variability. The value of σ^2 for these scores is probably unknown, but σ^2 for this population does exist. If the population is small and all of the scores are obtainable, then the population variance can be computed using the formula for $\overset{*}{s}{}^2$.

Students are often confused when they first encounter the words *variance* and *standard deviation* because these names are used for both sample and population measures of variability. Confusion also results from the symbols used, with students typically reversing the sample and population symbols. Remember, regular letters are used to represent data, *X,* and regular letters symbolize statistics ($\overline{X}$, $\overset{*}{s}{}^2$, and $\overset{*}{s}$). Population parameters are always represented by Greek characters, such as μ and σ^2.

Beyond These Measures of Central Tendency and Variability

There are many sample measures of central tendency and variability; only a few of them are covered in this chapter. For example, a whole class of measures of central tendency is based on trimming extreme scores (outliers) from the top and bottom of the data and then computing a mean on the remaining scores. These *trimmed means* are usually characterized by the percentage of the sample that is trimmed from the top and bottom, such as a 10% trimmed mean, which trims 10% of the top scores and 10% of the bottom scores.

The concept of variability is used repeatedly in this text, and not necessarily associated with the computation of a sample statistic. There is variability in data, but there also is variability in statistics. If you run two identical studies on imitated aggression, they probably won't get the same values for the average number of aggressive acts. You'll also read about variability being accounted for or explained. For instance, many factors influence how many aggressive acts children commit; there is variability among children in terms of their aggression. How much of the variability among children's aggression can be explained by the amount of television they watch? These are some of the ways you'll see variability discussed later.

4.12   Five-Number Summaries and Box-Plots

In Chapter 3 you saw that stem and leaf displays are useful tools to visually describe data. Such displays show all of the original data while giving a visual image of the distribution. Two new ways to describe the data are *five-number summaries* and *box-plots.* We weren't able to introduce these graphs earlier because you needed to know about the median and half-ranges. Many steps and some new terms are used in the construction of these graphs. It may seem confusing at first, but we give all of the information in sequence with examples, so you should be able to back up and retrace your steps if you get lost.

Let's use as an example the posting speeds of vehicles in the behavior-modification study from Chapter 3. Part of the stem and leaf display from Table 3.12 is reproduced as part of Table 4.16.

Five-Number Summary

Five-number summary
Five points in the data: low score, lower hinge, median, upper hinge, and high score, plus distances and half-ranges

The **five-number summary** is composed of (1) five numbers, (2) some distances, and (3) the half-ranges. The five numbers are the *low score (LO),* the *lower hinge (LH),* the *median (X_{50}),* the *upper hinge (UH),* and the *high score (HI).* Remember, the hinges are the medians of the lower and upper halves of the data.

For the speed data, $N = 90$, so the median position is $(N + 1)/2 = (90 + 1)/2 = 45.5$. The integer part of the median position is $[45.5] = 45$, and so the hinge position

Table 4.16
Posting speeds (km/h)

Stem	Leaf	Box-Plot
7.	8	*
7S	6	*
7F	4	
7T		
7*	1	
6.	89	
6S	6677	
6F	444555	
6T	22333	
6*	000111	
5.	8999999	
5S	666677777777777	
5F	444445555	
5T	22233333333	
5*	0001111111	
4.	888999999	
4S	667	

is ([median position] + 1)/2 = (45 + 1)/2 = 23. Now we use the hinge position to find the hinges. The lower hinge (*LH*) is the 23rd score from the bottom, and the upper hinge (*UH*) is the 23rd score from the top. From Table 4.16, if you count up from the bottom 23 scores, you get *LH* = 52. If you count down from the top 23 scores, you get *UH* = 61. The value of X_{50} is 56, the average of the 56 in the 45th position and the 56 in the 46th position. Because the *LO* is 46 and the *HI* is 78, the five numbers are (remember, $LO\text{–}LH\text{–}X_{50}\text{–}UH\text{–}HI$):

$$46 \quad 52 \quad 56 \quad 61 \quad 78$$

To complete the five-number summary, you need to include the distances and the half-ranges. The **distances** are simply the four differences between the neighboring five numbers in the five–number summary. For example, the first distance is $LH - LO$, or $52 - 46 = 6$. The half-ranges are the lowrange $= X_{50} - LO$, midrange $= UH - LH$, and highrange $= HI - X_{50}$. The five numbers, distances, and half-ranges are summarized as:

Distances
Differences between contiguous values in the five numbers

Five numbers	*LO*		*LH*		X_{50}		*UH*		*HI*
Distances		$LH - LO$		$X_{50} - LH$		$UH - X_{50}$		$HI - UH$	
Half-ranges			$X_{50} - LO$		$UH - LH$		$HI - X_{50}$		

Note that symmetry in the data results in equal distances on either side of the median and in the low- and highranges. The five-number summary for the speed data is:

46		52		56		61		78
	6		4		5		17	
		10		9		22		

Table 4.17

Deception accuracy scores for the Secret Service group

Stem	Leaf
9	00
8	00000
7	000000000
6	00000000000
5	00000
4	000

From the stem and leaf display in Table 4.16, you can see that there are some extreme scores in the positive direction, which indicates positive skewness. In this five-number summary, the $17 \neq 6$ and $22 \neq 10$ show the positive skewness that is evident in the stem and leaf display.

Let's do another example. For the deception accuracy scores of the Secret Service group, placed in a stem and leaf display in Table 4.17, compute the five-number summary.

Because there are 35 scores, the median position is 18, and the hinge position is $(18 + 1)/2 = 9.5$. You count up from the bottom to the 9th and 10th scores, and the average of them is the lower hinge. Count down from the top to the 9th and 10th scores, and the average of them is the upper hinge. You should get $LO = 40$, $LH = 60$, $X_{50} = 60$, $UH = 70$, and $HI = 90$. The five-number summary is:

40		60		60		70		90
	20		0		10		20	
		20		10		30		

Because the lowrange, 20, is not equal to the highrange, 30, the five-number summary shows some positive skewness, consistent with the stem and leaf display.

Box-Plots

Box-plot

Graph that uses a box of hinges and median to show the middle part of the data and uses lines extending from the box to indicate variability of the tails of a distribution

Using the five-number summary as a basis, we can construct a **box-plot.** You might use the box-plot as an additional visual display to give a graphical summary that leaves out some of the detail in the stem and leaf display. For a given distribution of data, it shows how spread out the middle is, using the box, and the length of the tails, using lines called whiskers. It emphasizes the tails and extremes of the data. See Table 4.16 for an example of a box-plot.

The box is formed with the hinges (*LH* and *UH*) as the ends and the median as a line through the middle. Because $UH - LH$ is the midrange that contains one-half of the data, one-half of the scores are in the box. Because the median is the middle, one-quarter of the scores are in the box on either side of the line for the median. The box-plot may be oriented either horizontally or vertically. If the box is placed vertically, the high scores are on the top; if horizontally, the high scores are to the right.

Inner fence

The point that is more extreme than a hinge by $1.5 \times$ midrange

Now the whiskers can be defined. We use the midrange and hinges from the five-number summary, along with some new terms: inner fences and adjacent values. **Inner fences** are points, one above the median and one below the median, that are more extreme than the hinges by 1.5 times the midrange. Inner fences are used to find the adjacent values to which you will draw the whiskers. The lower inner fence is

$$LH - 1.5 \times \text{midrange}$$

and the upper inner fence is

$$UH + 1.5 \times \text{midrange}$$

For the speed data in Table 4.16, the midrange is 9, so $1.5 \times 9 = 13.5$, and the inner fences are $52 - 13.5 = 38.5$ and $61 + 13.5 = 74.5$.

Adjacent value
An actual data value closest to the inner fence but not outside it

Adjacent values are the values of the data that are closest to the inner fences but not outside them. For the speed data, 46, the smallest value, is the adjacent value at the bottom of the data. Note that 46 is not outside (smaller than) 38.5, the inner fence. At the top of the data, 74 is the adjacent value because it is not outside (larger than) 74.5, the inner fence.

Whisker
A line drawn from the hinge to the corresponding adjacent value

Whiskers are drawn from the hinges to the corresponding adjacent values: from 52 to 46 and from 61 to 74. Any value outside the adjacent values is marked individually, is said to be *outside,* and is called an **outlier.** For the speed data, the values of 76 and 78 are outliers and are marked individually. The box-plot for the speed data is given in Table 4.16, where the outliers were marked with asterisks. The box-plot calls attention to both the positive skewness by showing a longer whisker on the top, and the outliers by giving them special marks.

Outlier
Any value outside an adjacent value

Draw a box-plot for the deception accuracy scores of the Secret Service group in Table 4.7. The box is a rectangle from 60 to 70 on the ends. The midrange is 10, so $1.5 \times 10 = 15.0$, and the inner fences are $60 - 15 = 45$ and $70 + 15 = 85$. The adjacent values are 50 at the bottom of the data and 80 at the top of the data. Whiskers now can be drawn from the 60 at the bottom end of the box to 50 (adjacent value) and from the 70 at the top end of the box to 80. Outliers marked with asterisks are the three values of 40 and the two values of 90.

Quick Quiz

Use the data in Table 4.4 to construct a five-number summary of female college students' heights.

Answer

	7.25		3.75		3.75	
	5.25	2		1.75		2
58	63.25		65.25		67	69

number summary is:

$LO = 58$ and $HI = 69$. The median position is $(24 + 1)/2 = 12.5$, so the median is 65.25, the average of the scores in the 12th and 13th positions. To find the hinge: $([12.5] + 1)/2 = (12 + 1)/2 = 6.5 =$ hinge position. LH is the average of the 6th and 7th scores from the bottom, or 63.25. UH is the average of the 6th and 7th scores from the top, or 67. The complete five-

---

4.13   Summary, Study Tips, and Computation

Chapter Summary

When you have data on one dependent or criterion variable, you can describe these data by using one or more summary measures. Of the measures of central tendency (mode, median, and mean), the mean is chosen most frequently to be representative of the data. Sample statistics that describe variability are various ranges, the variance, and standard deviation, with the standard deviation having the advantage of being in the units of measure of the original scores. Population parameters include the mean, variance, and standard deviation. The five-number summary gives additional summary measures, and the box-plot gives an additional visual plot.

The following key terms are used in this chapter:

Summation notation	Midrange
Sample size, N	Highrange
ΣX	Hinges
ΣX^2 and $(\Sigma X)^2$	Hinge position
Central tendency	Mean absolute deviation
Deviation score	Median absolute deviation
Mode	Sample variance, s^{*2}
Median	Standard deviation, s^{*}
Median position	Population variance, σ^2
Mean, $\overline{X}$	Five-number summary
Sum of squares	Distances
Least-squares criterion	Box-plot
Population mean, μ	Box
Variability	Inner fences
Range	Adjacent values
Half-ranges	Whiskers
Lowrange	Outlier

Study Tips

Now you are computing statistics. The concepts you are learning will help you understand whatever you are putting into your calculator. For some of you, the reverse is true: Doing computations will help you understand the concepts. If you don't understand the difference between the various measures of central tendency, compare their characteristics and then dream up a set of numbers and compute the mean, median, and mode. Do the characteristics hold up?

If you are having trouble with the computations, make an appointment with your instructor. Ask for another explanation or computational example. If you have the money to hire a tutor, ask your teacher to recommend someone. Look back in the textbook and your class notes to the place where you lost track of what was going on; that will help your teacher explain the material to you. You may even want to write question marks in the margins of your notebook during a lecture so that you will know where you got lost.

Students' most frequent errors are: (1) not putting the X values in order before finding X_{50}, (2) thinking that the following equations have the same meaning: $\Sigma(X - \overline{X}) = 0$ and $\Sigma(X - \overline{X})^2$ is a minimum, and (3) confusing ΣX^2 and $(\Sigma X)^2$.

Computation

The role of the computer in description is to provide speed and accuracy. Most statistical packages have programs or procedures that compute all the statistics presented here. For example, SAS has the MEANS and UNIVARIATE procedures, and SPSS has the EXAMINE command, each of which computes descriptive statistics. These programs are illustrated in this section. Pocket calculators also help keep computations accurate and speed up the process, especially those that have special function keys to give the mean, variance, or standard deviation with only the push of one key following data entry. Calculators that use single–button computation of variances and standard deviations may not use the same formulas for both. Some use variance $s^{*2} = SS/N$ and compute the standard deviation as $\sqrt{SS/(N - 1)} = \sqrt{s^2}$. Even with these modern conveniences, you should learn the hand computational formulas because you will need to use them as a check of your calculator or computer work. Computers and calculators rarely make a mistake, but they compute statistics for whatever data are entered, even if there is a mistake in what was entered. So this computational check is necessary.

The examples of lines given here for the SAS procedures and SPSS commands follow the general format from Section 2.7. You might want to review that section and the computational section of Chapter 3 before proceeding with these examples. As before, the figures following each job show the actual computer outputs.

SAS Example

(SAS system's lines)

`DATA MEANS;`   (beginning of the DATA step, statement to create a data set named MEANS)

`INPUT SCORE$ X;`   (statement to input a label for each score and the value of the variable X)

`CARDS;`   (statement that signals the end of the data step)

`SCORE1 55`   (data from Table 4.5)

`SCORE2 55`

`SCORE3 54`

`SCORE4 54`

`SCORE5 53`

`SCORE6 53`

`SCORE7 53`

`SCORE8 52`

`SCORE9 52`

`SCORE10 51`

`PROC PRINT;`   (beginning of PROC step, statement to request the input data to be printed)

`PROC MEANS;`   (statement to have the MEANS procedure run on the data)

`VAR X;`   (statement to tell which variable you want MEANS to use)

`PROC UNIVARIATE PLOT;`   (statement to have the UNIVARIATE procedure run on the data, including plotting a stem and leaf display and a box-plot)

`VAR X;`

`TITLE 'STATISTICS FOR TABLE 4.5 DATA';`   (title to be printed with the statistics)

(system's line)

For PROC MEANS, the SAS output in Figure 4.5 gives:

1. The name of the variable X, as given in the INPUT statement.
2. The sample size, which the program counts on its own.
3. The sample mean $\bar{X}$.
4. The sample standard deviation, which is the square root of the unbiased sample variance s^2, which is not the same as $\overset{*}{s}{}^2$. From Table 4.12, $\overset{*}{s}{}^2 = 1.56$, but $s^2 = 1.73$. Note that $\overset{*}{s}{}^2 = \overset{*}{s}(N-1)/N$. Note that this is not $\overset{*}{s}$, but s.
5. The minimum (smallest) value of X.
6. The maximum (largest) value of X.

```
STATISTICS FOR TABLE 4.5 DATA

Analysis Variable: X ①
```

N	Mean	Std Dev	Minimum	Maximum
10 ②	53.2000000 ③	1.3165612 ④	51.0000000 ⑤	55.0000000 ⑥

Figure 4.5

SAS output from PROC MEANS

Variable=X ①

Moments				Quantiles(DEF=5)			
				⑨			
② N	10	Sum Wgts	10	100% Max	55	99%	55
③ Mean	53.2	Sum	532 ⑥	75% Q3	54	95%	55
④ Std Dev	1.316561	Variance	1.733333 ⑦	50% Med	53	90%	55
⑤ Skewness	−0.08764	Kurtosis	−0.75127 ⑧	25% Q1	52	10%	51.5
USS	28318	CSS	15.6	0% Min	51	5%	51
CV	2.474739	Std Mean	0.416333			1%	51
T:Mean=0	127.7823	Pr>|T|	0.0001	Range	4		
Num ^= 0	10	Num > 0	10	Q3-Q1	2		
M(Sign)	5	Pr>=|M|	0.0020	Mode	53		
Sgn Rank	27.5	Pr>=|S|	0.0020				

```
              Stem Leaf                         #        Boxplot
              55 00                             2           |
              54                                            |
              54 00                             2        +-----+
              53                                          |   |
              53 000                            3        *--+--*
              52                                          |   |
              52 00                             2        +-----+
              51                                            |
              51 0                              1           |
                 ----+----+----+----+
```

Figure 4.6
SAS output (partial) for PROC UNIVARIATE

For PROC UNIVARIATE, the SAS output in Figure 4.6 gives:

1. The name of the variable X, as given in the INPUT statement
2. The sample size
3. The sample mean, $\overline{X}$
4. The sample standard deviation, s
5. A skewness coefficient
6. The sum of the scores, ΣX
7. The unbiased sample variance, s^2
8. A kurtosis coefficient
9. The maximum, third quartile (Q3, similar to and sometimes the same as the upper hinge), median, first quartile (Q1, similar to and sometimes the same as the lower hinge), and the minimum

Obviously, PROC UNIVARIATE computes many other statistics, as well as plotting a stem and leaf display and a box-plot. Note the large number of decimal places given for the values in these outputs. You can decide how many significant digits to keep.

SPSS Example

(SPSS system's lines)

```
SET WIDTH 80
DATA LIST FREE/SCORE Y     (FREE is the label for the type of format that allows data to be entered on the line with blanks
                           separating data points, SCORE is an ID number for each value of Y, Y is the name of the
                           dependent variable)

BEGIN DATA
1 55 2 55 3 54 4 54 5 53 6 53 7 53 8 52 9 52 10 51
EXAMINE VARIABLES=Y/PLOT=BOXPLOT     (command that tells the program you want descriptive statistics and a box-plot
                                     computed on the variable Y)

FINISH     (a command to let the program know that you are finished giving it commands and data)
```
(system's line)

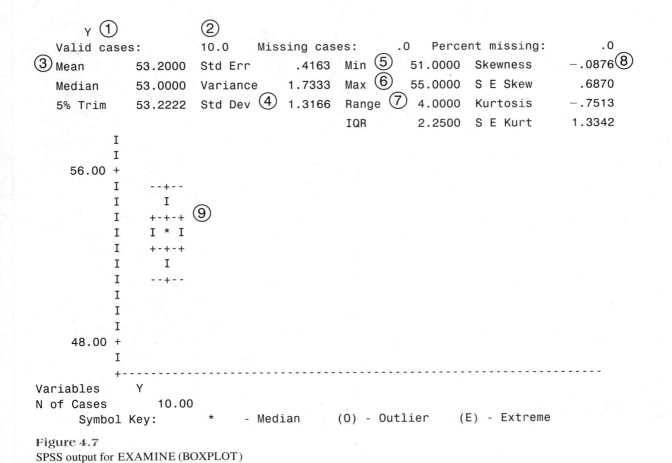

Figure 4.7
SPSS output for EXAMINE (BOXPLOT)

For the EXAMINE command, the SPSS output in Figure 4.7 gives:

1. The name of the variable, Y
2. The sample size, N
3. The sample mean, $\overline{X}$
4. The sample standard deviation, s
5. Minimum (smallest) value of X

6. Maximum (largest) value of X
7. The sample range
8. Sample kurtosis and skewness measures
9. The box-plot

Exercises

Section 4.2

1. For $X_1 = 1$, $X_2 = 3$, and $X_3 = 3$, find ΣX, $(\Sigma X)^2$, and ΣX^2.
2. For the following data set, find ΣX, $(\Sigma X)^2$, and ΣX^2: 4, 19, 6, 12, 17, 9, 15, 9, 12, 10.

Sections 4.3–4.6

3. Calculate the mode, median, and mean for the following data: 9, 1, 7, 9, 6, 19, 21, 81. Which is the best descriptive measure of central tendency?
4. If you wanted to find a typical value for eye color in your statistics class, you would count how many people have blue eyes, how many have brown eyes, and how many have green eyes. What measure of central tendency can be obtained for these data?
5. Suppose you have data from seven males and females on a Postholiday Depression Scale, which ranges from 1 to 5. Using the accompanying data, discuss why researchers need more descriptive statistics than just measures of central tendency.

| Females: | 2 | 3 | 3 | 3 | 3 | 3 | 4 |
| Males: | 1 | 1 | 1 | 3 | 5 | 5 | 5 |

6. Consider the article in Box 1.1 in Chapter 1. What measures of central tendency might be used to describe the most popular fruits and vegetables in the United States?
7. How can the mean, median, and mode be used to describe the performance of a punter on a college football team? What are the advantages and disadvantages of each measure?
8. Obtain $\overline{X}$ for the heights of males given in Table 4.6.
9. Crude measures of central tendency can be obtained directly from a frequency distribution or graph by using the midpoint of an interval to stand for each of the scores in that interval. Use Table 3.9 to answer these questions:
   a. Which measure of central tendency is easiest to obtain from the frequency distribution? What is its value?
   b. In what interval is the median?
10. What is the best measure of central tendency for the following?
    a. A timed measure where most subjects take 6 to 10 s but a very few subjects take as long as 50 s
    b. Heights of first-grade boys
    c. A standardized achievement test
    d. A marketing survey on the most preferred numbers for football jerseys
11. What measure of central tendency is appropriate for each of the following?
    a. How a student performed in classes over the first three years of college
    b. A description of the race and gender of the typical shopper in a store
    c. Typical annual contributions by individuals to United Way
    d. The values of homes in a neighborhood
12. a. What average measure of speed are you using if

you drive just fast enough that the number of vehicles you pass equals the number that pass you?

b. If you are driving on a slightly hilly interstate with your cruise control set on 65 mph, your average speed should be 65. Comment on the values of your speed sampled at 30 1-minute intervals as compared to those of a loaded semi that is also averaging 65 mph.

13. Comment on the statistics student who tried to cross on foot a river that had an average depth of 2 ft.

Sections 4.7–4.11

14. Calculate the range, the variance $\overset{*}{s}{}^{2}$, and the standard deviation $\overset{*}{s}$ for the data in Exercise 1.

15. For each of the two data sets, calculate the range and $\overset{*}{s}$.

Data set 1: 10, 11, 20, 29, 30

Data set 2: 10, 19, 20, 21, 35

Compare the two measures. Why is the range for Data set 2 larger than for Data set 1, while the standard deviation is smaller?

16. Compute the mean $\overline{X}$ and standard deviation $\overset{*}{s}$ for these sets:

Set A: 7, 5, 3, 2, 4

Set B: 107, 105, 103, 102, 104

Set C: 70, 50, 30, 20, 40

a. Compare the three means and the three standard deviations. Does adding 100 to the scores in Set A to get the scores in Set B change the mean? How?

b. Does the standard deviation change? How?

c. When you form the scores in Set C by multiplying the scores in Set A by 10, does the mean change? How? Does the standard deviation change? How?

d. What is the median of the scores in Set A? In Set B?

e. What is the range of the scores in Set A? In Set C?

17. For the accompanying data from Table 1.1 (number of anxiety symptoms) for two groups of students, compute the following statistics for each group: $\overline{X}$, $\overset{*}{s}{}^{2}$, $\overset{*}{s}$, X_{50}, and range.

Number of symptoms for perceived-control and no-control groups

Perceived Control	No Control
12	9
12	12
8	9
5	11
12	11
5	15
11	14
12	7
7	11
15	11
11	9
6	17
12	14
11	17
8	11
11	13
12	19
11	14
13	11
11	13
13	12
12	14
7	7
13	11
9	16
7	15
5	13
15	13
7	10
7	16

18. For the data from Table 4.7 (deception accuracy scores) for three groups of subjects, compute the following statistics for each group: $\overline{X}$, $\overset{*}{s}{}^{2}$, $\overset{*}{s}$, X_{50}, and range. (You computed the first four of these statistics for the Secret Service group elsewhere in the chapter.)

19. Use the numbers 0, 0, 1, 1, 2, 2.

a. Create a data set consisting of two of these numbers such that your data set has the greatest possible variance.

b. Choose two numbers that have the smallest variance. What is the value of $\overset{*}{s}{}^{2}$ for these two numbers?

20. Bourne and Archer (1956) compared subjects who had a rest period of 15 s between trials with those who had 45 s between trials. The task at each trial was 30 s of keeping a pointer on a moving target, and the score for each subject was the percentage of time on target. Those who had 15 s of rest were the massed practice group, and those who had 45 s of rest were the spaced practice group. The following simulated data are similar to the data obtained on trial 17 from that study. Compute $\overline{X}$, $\overset{*}{s}{}^{2}$, and $\overset{*}{s}$ for both groups.

Spaced		Massed	
26	26	13	7
25	27	12	8
30	33	10	13
32	29	12	17
33	30	11	7

21. Suppose you use a new computerized instrument to measure attentiveness and get $\overline{X} = 3$ min 40 s for time on target. The instrument allows subjects to practice for 30 s; then it gives an attentiveness task and measures the time on target. Later the company informs you that the time reported for each subject included the 30 s of practice time. What is the true value of $\overline{X}$ for the actual test time without the practice time included?

22. If 1 mile (mi) = 1.6093 km and if the average speed of vehicles is 50 km/h, what is the average in miles per hour?

Section 4.12

23. Compute the five-number summary and draw a box-plot for the data for each group in Exercise 17. Do you learn anything new about the data compared to what you discovered from the stem and leaf display in Exercise 5 of Chapter 3?

24. Compute the five-number summary and draw a box-plot for the data for each group in Table 4.7. Do you learn anything new about the data compared to what you discovered from the stem and leaf display in Exercise 6 of Chapter 3?

Section 4.13

25. Submit the data of Table 4.7 to SAS using PROC UNIVARIATE PLOT or to SPSS using EXAMINE. Compare your results to the box-plots you did by hand in Exercise 24.

5

Measures of Relative Standing and the Normal Distribution

You have learned how to describe data for one variable with pictures and summary measures. Now you will learn how to describe the relative position of each score in the distribution. Relative standing in a distribution is measured with standard scores, such as the z score. Another key topic is the use of a theoretical distribution, the normal distribution. Try to integrate your knowledge of central tendency and variability with the idea of relative position.

Research Example 5
5.1 Introduction
5.2 Standard Scores
    Formula for z scores
    Characteristics of z scores
5.3 Normal Distributions
    Definition
    Parameters and notation
    The standard normal distribution
5.4 Other Standard Scores
    General equation
    Specific examples
5.5 Percentiles
    Percentile ranks: Computation
    Computation of a score with a given percentile rank
    Relationship of percentile ranks and z scores
5.6 Summary, Study Tips, and Computation
    Chapter summary
    Study tips
    Computation
Exercises

Research Example 5

You probably are familiar with standardized tests of general intelligence, such as the Wechsler Adult Intelligence Test-Revised (WISC-R) and the Stanford-Binet Intelligence Scale. Almost every U.S. school child takes standardized tests, such as the Stanford Achievement Test, Iowa Tests of Educational Development, or California

Achievement Tests. You took a standardized test when you applied for college (the Scholastic Aptitude Test or the American College Testing Battery), and you will take another if you go on to higher education (Graduate Record Examination, Law School Admission Test, Medical College Admission Test).

Interpreting standardized test scores is easier if you understand the terms *norms* and *percentile*. A norm is a numerical characteristic of performance, such as an average, for some group of people who took the test when it was first developed or on some subsequent occasion. Some testing corporations norm their tests regularly. A percentile is a number from 1 to 100 that indicates the percentage of scores below yours on that administration of the test. You might have had a 700 on the SAT verbal and a percentile of 92.

Some researchers study gender differences in standardized tests. Feingold (1988) surveyed literature showing that females generally have higher scores in tests of verbal ability and males score higher in tests of quantitative and spatial ability. Feingold studied the norming results for several years on the PSAT (Preliminary Scholastic Aptitude Test) and the SAT (Scholastic Aptitude Test). These two tests use equivalent items and content but are given to different groups. The PSAT is currently taken by high school juniors, including students who may not go to college. The SAT is taken by students who are aspiring to go to college. Early in its existence, the PSAT was taken by both juniors and seniors; the SAT is taken by both juniors and seniors.

Feingold reports the gender differences in the norms by using effect size, the difference in the averages divided by a pooled standard deviation. He calls these effect sizes *d*'s. These values are negative if the difference shows higher female performance and positive if the difference shows higher male performance. SAT norms are based on essentially the population of those who took the tests, whereas PSAT norms are based on representative samples of high school students. Table 5.1 shows the results.

Feingold (1988) points to these results and others to illustrate declining gender differences. Think about the PSAT and SAT results. Why are they different? For example, SAT 1983 norms show a male advantage for verbal (a slight female advan-

Table 5.1

Cognitive gender differences (*d*'s) on the PSAT and SAT by test, grade, and year of norms

Test and Year	Verbal		Math	
	Juniors	Seniors	Juniors	Seniors
PSAT				
1960	−.12	−.03	.34	.49
1966	−.08	−.02	.24	.32
1974	.01	NA	.17	NA
1983	−.02	NA	.12	NA
SAT				
1960	NA	−.06	NA	.51
1967[a]	−.05	−.01	.37	.38
1974	−.02	.04	.42	.42
1983	.11	.08	.42	.42

Source: Feingold (1988).

NA = not available

[a]1966 norms for SAT examinees were not published.

tage on the PSAT) and a much bigger male advantage for math than on the PSAT. Remember that the SAT students are those who aspire to go to college. The self-selection process of the SAT probably accounts for much of the difference.

5.1   Introduction

By now you may have taken the first test in your statistics course. Let's say you got a 50. What is your immediate reaction?

You probably are disturbed to see a score of 50, but then you remember that the test was worth just 60 points. Now how do you feel about your performance? Think about what you need to know to judge your performance.

Most likely you want to know how your classmates did. You want to know whether a 50 is a good score or a poor score compared to the rest of the class. You know how to summarize sample data by using pictorial displays and statistics. These statistics were developed to describe and summarize the observations in a sample. Your teacher might be able to provide your class with measures of central tendency that summarize everyone's performance on the test. Let's say your instructor says the mean on the exam was a 54. Now you know your score was below the mean. Is that enough information for you to judge how well you did on the test?

Remember what you learned in Chapter 4 about variability. Two samples can have the same mean but still be quite different in how the scores are spread out. You need to know how spread out the exam scores were in order to judge whether you did well on the test. Suppose your teacher said there was a lot of variability in the scores. If scores are quite spread out, then several scores around the mean could be passing grades. If the scores were tightly clustered around the mean, any departure from the mean could hurt your grade. You might even want to see a stem and leaf display of everyone's scores to see whether there are any extreme scores, such as 60s, that are inflating the mean.

The statistics $\overline{X}$ and $\overset{*}{s}$ can be used to describe the entire sample. Sometimes you want to describe an individual score, such as your exam score, within a sample. This chapter shows you how to use $\overline{X}$ and $\overset{*}{s}$ to describe individual scores in a sample rather than to describe an entire sample.

5.2   Standard Scores

Relative standing
Position of a score within a distribution relative to other scores or to a numerical characteristic from the distribution

How do you help a friend interpret a test score of 650 on the verbal part of the SAT? What percentage of the adult population has IQ scores higher than 130? What is the meaning of a percentile rank of 97.5 on some standardized test? These questions are related to the idea of describing a single value in terms of its relative standing in a distribution. **Relative standing** means the position of a score relative to other scores or to statistics computed on the sample. Measures of relative standing are not statistics in the true sense of the word because they do not give a characteristic of the sample. Measures of relative standing give a characteristic of an individual score and, as such, are transformations of the original data.

To illustrate the need for measures of relative standing, consider what happened to one of us as an undergraduate.

139

In the first semester of my junior year, I was taking a calculus course and a course in chemistry. The calculus professor had a tendency to give easy examinations, but the chemistry tests were very difficult. As a result, many of us got very high scores in calculus but low scores in chemistry. I can remember one calculus examination that had a mean of 95 out of 100, with a standard deviation of 2. I earned a 98 to just barely get an A, and anyone with lower than 91 got an F! Here every point was very expensive, being worth one-half of a standard deviation. However, the typical chemistry test had a mean of about 60 with a standard deviation of 10. On these tests, my 70s earned me B's. Points on chemistry tests were less expensive, being worth one-tenth of a standard deviation. When I wrote home about my grades, these scores made some sense because the higher calculus score earned higher grade. Consider another less fortunate student in my class. He earned a 92 for a D in calculus and a 65 for a C in chemistry and had to try to explain these scores to his folks! The problem lies in trying to interpret the raw test scores. Without any information on the characteristics of the distributions, it appears that 92 would be a better score than 65.

The moral of this story is that you cannot compare raw scores from different distributions. You need to interpret the scores in terms of the means and standard deviations of their respective distributions. Essentially, each score must be evaluated in terms of its relative standing, or position, in the distribution; then these relative standings can be compared. For the other student, which of the two test scores indicated better performance? The chemistry score, of course. Why is the chemistry score better than the calculus score? You will probably say, "Because it is 0.5 standard deviation above the mean and the calculus score is 1.5 standard deviations below the mean." You have evaluated each score by asking, In standard deviation units, how far is the score from the mean? Doing this for each score in its respective distribution gives you measures of relative standing called z scores. Think of the z as coming from the word *standardize,* which is what you are doing. You are taking scores from different distributions and standardizing them so that you can compare them. You couldn't compare the 92 in calculus to the 65 in chemistry, but you can compare the scores' relative positions in their distributions.

Formula for *z* Scores

To arrive at a formula for z scores, review what you did when you evaluated the chemistry score. The other student scored 65 on a test with $\overline{X} = 60$ and $\overset{*}{s} = 10$. When you said that 65 was 0.5 standard deviation above the mean, you were saying that the difference between 65 and 60 is equal to $0.5\overset{*}{s}$, because 5 divided by 10 gives 0.5. So to find out how many standard deviations a score is from the mean, subtract the mean from the score and divide by the standard deviation.

$$z = \frac{X - \overline{X}}{\overset{*}{s}} \tag{5.1}$$

z score
Something minus its mean divided by its standard deviation, symbolized by z

A general verbal definition for a **z score** *is something minus its mean divided by its standard deviation.* The "something" can be an original raw score or, as you will see later, a statistic.

This formula is appropriate for describing the relative position of an original raw score in a sample. It can also be used to compare two or more scores from the same or different distributions. For example, you can compare your score on the first quiz in a given course to another person's score on that quiz or to your performance on the second quiz. So z scores computed for each raw score allow you to compare relative performances. To describe a score in a population, the following formula is used:

$$z = \frac{X - \mu}{\sigma} \tag{5.2}$$

Characteristics of z Scores

Notice that z scores are expressed in terms of standard deviations. An IQ score with $z = 1.5$ is 1.5 standard deviations above the mean. A person's height that has $z = -2.7$ is 2.7 standard deviations below the mean. Not only does a z score give the distance of the score from the mean in standard deviation units, but also the sign of the z score tells the direction of the score from the mean.

When you compute z scores for all raw scores in a sample, you are transforming each X to a z. The transformed scores, the z values, have a new mean and standard deviation. The mean of the z scores is $\bar{z}$, and

$$\bar{z} = 0 \tag{5.3}$$

The variance of a set of z scores is 1, so the standard deviation is also 1:

$$\overset{*}{s}{}^{2}_{z} = 1 \tag{5.4}$$

Thus, the mean of a set of z scores is 0 and the variance and standard deviation of a set of z scores are 1 unless all the raw scores are equal. When all the raw scores, or X values are equal, z technically is undefined because $\overset{*}{s} = 0$ and division by zero is not allowed. Box 5.1 has a more detailed explanation of the mean and standard deviation of z scores, including derivations of formulas 5.3 and 5.4.

Now, examine the data in Table 5.2 and compute a z score for each X. First, compute $\bar{X}$ and $\overset{*}{s}$ for the X values and then use formula 5.1 to compute the z values. Even though all of the work is done in Table 5.2, you will get the most benefit from this exercise if you do the computations yourself and just use the results in the table to check your work. After the z scores are found, the mean and the variance of the z scores can be computed to illustrate that these values are 0 and 1, respectively.

A final characteristic of z scores is that the transformation to z scores does *not* change the shape of the distribution of the scores. If the distribution of X is positively skewed, then the distribution of z scores computed from the X's is also positively skewed. Figure 5.1 is a graph of the data from Table 5.2 for both raw scores and z scores. Both distributions are positively skewed, and only the central tendency and variability of the z's differ from those of the X's.

The transformation from X to z changes only the mean and the variance, not other aspects of the shape of the distribution. It is especially important to realize that computing z scores does not change the shape of the distribution to a normal (bell-shaped) distribution, about which you'll learn shortly. Somehow many students get the mistaken idea that the z transformation is a normalizing transformation. Remember that not all z's have a normal distribution and that the z transformation changes only the mean and variance of the distribution.

Box 5.1   Mean and Variance of *z* Scores

When you compute z scores for all of the raw scores in a sample, you are essentially changing the scale of the scores. The transformation of X to z is done for every score by subtracting the constant $\overline{X}$ and then dividing by the constant $\overset{*}{s}$. Because the scale is being changed, both the mean and the standard deviation of the z scores will be different from those for X. To find the mean and standard deviation of z scores, you can use the principles of the influence of change of scale on the mean, variance, and standard deviation (given in Box 4.2) as well as the summation rules in Box 4.1.

The mean of the z scores, $\overline{z}$, can be shown to be 0:

$$\overline{z} = \frac{\sum z}{N} = \frac{\sum[(X - \overline{X})/\overset{*}{s}]}{N}$$

$$= \frac{1}{\overset{*}{s}} \frac{\sum(X - \overline{X})}{N}$$

$$= \frac{1}{\overset{*}{s}} \frac{0}{N}$$

$$= 0$$

Do you see where you used the definition of z, the summation rule that gives $\sum aX = a\sum X$, and the property of $\overline{X}$ that gives $\sum(X - \overline{X}) = 0$? If not, go back through the above equations and try to see where each principle is used.

The variance of a set of z scores is 1, so the standard deviation is also 1. By starting with the definitional formula for the variance from Chapter 4, the following derivation shows that $\overset{*}{s}{}^2_z = 1$:

$$\overset{*}{s}{}^2_z = \frac{\sum(z - \overline{z})^2}{N} = \frac{\sum(z - 0)^2}{N} = \frac{\sum z^2}{N}$$

$$= \frac{\sum[(X - \overline{X})/\overset{*}{s}]^2}{N} = \frac{[\sum(X - \overline{X})^2/\overset{*}{s}{}^2]}{N}$$

$$= \frac{(1/\overset{*}{s}{}^2)\sum(X - \overline{X})^2}{N} = \frac{(1/\overset{*}{s}{}^2)N\overset{*}{s}{}^2}{N}$$

$$= \frac{N}{N}$$

$$= 1$$

Do you see where you used $\overline{z} = 0$, the definition of z, and the definitional formula for $\overset{*}{s}{}^2$ to get $N\overset{*}{s}{}^2 = \sum(X - \overline{X})^2$? If you cannot see where these expressions are used, go through the derivation until you understand how the result was obtained.

Table 5.2
Computation of z scores

X	X^2	z	z^2
3	9	-1	1
3	9	-1	1
3	9	-1	1
3	9	-1	1
5	25	0	0
5	25	0	0
5	25	0	0
7	49	1	1
7	49	1	1
9	81	2	4
$\Sigma X = 50$	$\Sigma X^2 = 290$	$\Sigma z = 0$	$\Sigma z^2 = 10$

$$\bar{X} = \frac{50}{10} = 5$$

$$\overset{*}{s}{}^2 = \frac{10(290) - 50^2}{10^2} = \frac{2900 - 2500}{100} = \frac{400}{100} = 4$$

$$\overset{*}{s} = \sqrt{4} = 2$$

$$\bar{z} = \frac{\Sigma z}{N} = \frac{0}{N} = 0$$

$$\overset{*}{s}{}^2_z = \frac{10(10) - 0}{10^2} = \frac{100}{100} = 1$$

$$\overset{*}{s}_z = \sqrt{1} = 1$$

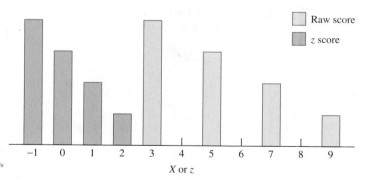

Figure 5.1
Data from Table 5.2 as raw scores and as z scores

Quick Quiz

What is the shape of any distribution of *z* scores?

Answer

The shape of the distribution of *z* scores is the same shape as the distribution of the original scores.

5.3   Normal Distributions

Definition

Normal distributions
Family of theoretical distributions that are symmetric, smooth, unimodal, and bell shaped; defined by parameters μ and σ^2

The word *normal* is used differently in statistics than you use it on a daily basis (or as you *normally* use it). When we talk about **normal distributions,** we are referring to a family of theoretical distributions. Normal distributions are symmetric, continuous, and unimodal and are usually described as being bell-shaped. Normal distributions have scores that range from negative infinity to positive infinity, so the tails of the curve never touch the horizontal axis (see Figure 5.2). In every normal distribution, the mean, median, and mode are all equal.

Normal distributions are important in statistics because of their wide range of applicability. They are good approximations for two types of distributions: the distributions of some variables, such as IQ and height, and the sampling distributions of some statistics, such as $\bar{X}$. You'll learn about sampling distributions when you move from descriptive statistics to inferential statistics. Normal distributions are good examples of theoretical reference distributions, mentioned in Chapter 1. They also play an important role as the assumed distributions for scores used in some statistics and for errors in measurement theory. You may encounter normally distributed errors in a course on tests and measurements.

Theoretical reference distributions such as normal distributions are defined from precise mathematical formulas. The formula that defines the family of normal distributions is given in Box 5.2. You might want to examine it just to reinforce the ideas that the curve is determined by a mathematical equation and that there are many different normal distributions, centered on different values on the number line and with different variances.

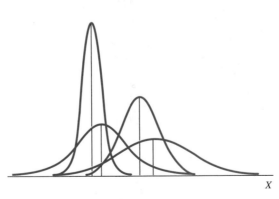

X

Figure 5.2

Different normal distributions (vertical lines show the means)

Box 5.2   Normal Distributions

Because there is a family of normal distributions, each with a unique pair of parameters, μ and σ^2, it helps to see how these parameters define a given normal distribution. The formula that defines the family of normal distributions is

$$Y = \frac{1}{\sigma\sqrt{2\pi}} e^{-(1/2)[(X - \mu)^2/\sigma^2]}$$

where

Y = height of the curve at X
X = variable with values from positive infinity to negative infinity
π = constant with approximate value of 3.1416
e = constant with approximate value of 2.7183
μ = mean of the distribution
σ^2 = variance of the distribution

Examine the components of the formula to fix in your mind which ones vary from distribution to distribution. The values of e, π, and 2 are constants, whereas X, μ, and σ^2 are variables. Once you choose values for μ and σ^2, the only variable for a given distribution is X. So the choice of μ and σ^2 uniquely determines which normal distribution you have.

Parameters and Notation

As you recall, a parameter is a numerical characteristic of a population. Normal distributions are theoretical distributions that have two parameters or numerical characteristics: μ (population mean) and σ^2 (population variance). Figure 5.2 shows several normal distributions with different values of μ and σ^2. The vertical lines indicate the means of the normal distributions. Once μ and σ^2 are specified, you have the information you need to completely determine a particular normal distribution. A unique normal distribution is determined for any given μ and σ^2. The values of $\mu = 100$ and $\sigma^2 = 225$ completely specify a certain normal distribution. Because there are infinitely many values of μ and σ^2, there are infinitely many normal distributions. That's why we have talked about a family of distributions called *normal* rather than just "the" normal distribution.

For $\mu = 100$ and $\sigma^2 = 225$, the normal distribution approximates the distribution of IQ scores. You have to specify a completely different μ and σ^2 for the distribution of heights of American men. An especially useful normal distribution has $\mu = 0$ and $\sigma^2 = 1$.

The Standard Normal Distribution

Any given μ and σ^2 define a specific bell-shaped curve. Half of the scores in the distribution are above μ and half are below μ. In fact, we can cut up the distribution into smaller parts around μ and find the exact fraction or proportion of scores that are in any section of the distribution. Then the proportions can be put in a table. Now, with these infinitely many normal distributions, do we need infinitely many tables, one for each pair of μ and σ^2? Or is there some transformation that does not change the shape of the distribution but gives a known mean and variance?

You can transform X to z, which has a distribution with mean 0 and variance 1, without changing the shape of the data. If X is distributed normally with mean μ and variance σ^2, then z is normally distributed with mean 0 and variance 1. Because you are transforming any normal distribution to a standard distribution, the normal distribution with mean 0 and variance 1 is called the **standard normal distribution.** The standard normal distribution is available in table form and is used to find the proportions of scores in any part of any normal distribution.

Standard normal distribution
Normal distribution with $\mu = 0$ and $\sigma^2 = 1$

Notice, however, that we talk about transforming *normally distributed X* values. What will be the shape of the distribution of z values? The same as the distribution of the X's; in this case, the normal shape doesn't change. This is where students can get confused about the shape of the z distribution. Look back at the last quick quiz. The answer hasn't changed just because the X's are now normally distributed.

The standard normal distribution is used to find the proportion of cases in certain regions of a normal distribution. For example, your friend with the SAT verbal score of 650 might want to know what proportion of people who took that test had scores higher than hers. Once you are familiar with the standard normal distribution, you can answer questions about the proportion of cases in any normal distribution.

As you work with the standard normal distribution, think of the proportion of cases and the area under the curve as interchangeable concepts. The total area under the curve is 1, and the total of all proportions is 1, because area and proportion of cases are synonymous in theoretical distributions such as a normal distribution. Because a proportion is a relative number, it must be greater than or equal to zero and less than or equal to one. Relating proportions to area, you cannot have negative area, but you can have zero area or any area up to the total of 1. Note that you can have negative z values, but areas associated with these negative z's are always positive or zero.

Use of Table A.2

Table A.2 in Appendix A gives proportions of cases, or areas, for the standard normal distribution. These proportions are arranged in sets of three columns: the first column lists z scores, the second column contains the proportion of scores between the z in column 1 and the mean, and the third column gives the proportion of scores larger than the z in column 1. Only the upper half of the distribution is given in Table A.2 because any normal distribution is symmetric. Each half of the distribution has a total proportion of .5000—half of the scores are above the mean and half are below the mean. Negative z scores are in the lower half of the distribution, which is a mirror image of the upper half. You can find the area associated with a negative z score by ignoring the negative sign and looking at the entry for the corresponding positive z score. The entry in column 2 plus the entry in column 3 at any given z always equals .5000. Examine Figure 5.3 to get a sense of how Table A.2 is organized. From the graphs of the distribution at the top of the columns, notice that the area in column 3 is a "tail" proportion and the area in column 2 is a "middle" proportion.

When you are working with z scores and Table A.2, there are two key principles: the total area equals one and symmetry. Here are some suggestions to help you work the problems:

1. Draw a rough picture of the distribution; put the mean at 0 and any relevant z score in its approximate location.

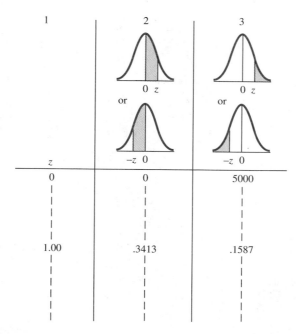

Figure 5.3
Organization of Table A.2, standard normal distribution

2. Locate the area desired for the answer.
3. Decide whether the area is small or large—that is, whether the area is less than .50 or larger than .50.
4. Decide whether the area is a tail area or a middle area.
5. If the z score is negative, use symmetry to find the corresponding area in the upper half of the distribution.
6. If the area is formed by the sum of separate areas, decide which parts are added.

Let's examine three general types of problems about proportions of the standard normal distribution. If you want to understand the standard normal distribution, get your pencil and paper and work through these examples. In each type of problem, follow the preceding six steps to obtain the answer.

Problem Type One.   Find the proportion of z values that are less than or equal to a (this proportion is called a cumulative proportion). If a is negative, then the answer can be read directly from Table A.2, column 3, because normal distributions are symmetric. If a is positive, then add the entry from column 2 to .5000.

For example, suppose you want to find the proportion of z's that are less than or equal to -1.35. First, draw a rough picture of the distribution (mean $= 0$) including $z = -1.35$, and shade in the area that represents "less than or equal to -1.35." Your picture should look like Figure 5.4. Get a general idea of the area you want to find and then look up 1.35 in Table A.2. You should realize that the desired answer is a small value and because of symmetry is the same as the proportion of z's that are greater than or equal to 1.35. This proportion is given in column 3 as .0885.

As another example, find the proportion of z values that are less than or equal to 1.35. The answer is obtained by using column 2 to get .4115 and then adding it to

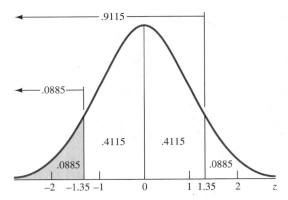

Figure 5.4
Proportion of z's less than or equal to a

.5000 to get .9115. An alternative approach is to subtract .0885 from 1.00 (total area) to get .9115.

Problem Type Two.   Find the proportion of z values that are greater than or equal to a. If a is negative, then you need to add the entry from column 2 to .5000 to get the answer. If a is positive, read the answer directly from column 3.

As examples, find the proportion of z's greater than or equal to 0.23 and the proportion of z's greater than or equal to -0.23, using Figure 5.5 and Table A.2. You should get .4090 for the proportion of z's greater than or equal to 0.23 and .5910 for the proportion of z's greater than or equal to -0.23.

Problem Type Three.   Find the proportion of z values that are between a and b, where $a < b$. This type of expression is evaluated as the proportion of z's less than or equal to b minus the proportion of z's less than or equal to a—that is, the difference between two cumulative proportions.

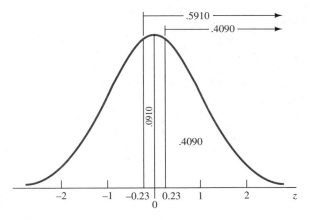

Figure 5.5
Proportion of z's greater than or equal to a

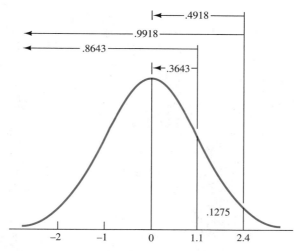

Figure 5.6
Proportion of z's between a and b

Find the proportion of z's between 1.1 and 2.4. Note the word *between*. Because you have z's *between* 1.1 and 2.4, you want the area under the curve *between* these two z's. Figure 5.6 shows the appropriate areas and values. First find the proportion of z's less than or equal to 2.4 as .9918. Then find the proportion of z's less than or equal to 1.1 as .8643. The difference is .9918 − .8643 = .1275. You probably noticed that for this example you can shorten the computation by taking the difference of the two proportions in the upper tail without adding .5000 to each, or .4918 − .3643 = .1275.

If one z score is negative and one is positive, you can easily add two table entries from column 2 (middle proportions). For example, the proportion of z's between −1 and 1 is .3413 + .3413 = .6826.

Quick Quiz
What is the proportion of z values between −1.96 and 1.96?

Answer

Draw a picture and use Table A.2. The answer is .95.

Transforming to the Standard Normal Distribution

If you are reasonably comfortable with using Table A.2, you can find proportions of the area in any normal distribution. If not, go to Exercise 9 at the end of the chapter and practice; then return here. You use z scores to transform any given normal distribution to the standard normal distribution, and then use Table A.2 to find the proportions of interest.

Again, remember that transforming to z scores does not change the shape of the distribution. When the shape of the distribution is unchanged, the proportions in the distribution of X are accurately represented by the proportions in the distribution of z. Because the proportion of z values that are greater than or equal to 1 is .1587 in the standard normal distribution, the proportion of values that are more than 1 standard deviation above the mean in any normal distribution is .1587.

Suppose X is distributed normally with $\mu = 100$ and $\sigma^2 = 225$ and you want to find the proportion of X's that are greater than or equal to 115. First you need to find the standard deviation by taking the square root of 225, getting $\sigma = 15$. Then you transform $X = 115$ to z by:

$$z = \frac{X - \mu}{\sigma} = \frac{115 - 100}{15} = \frac{15}{15} = 1$$

Now the proportion of X's that are greater than or equal to 115 is equal to the proportion of z's that are greater than or equal to 1, or .1587. In this last step you simply use Table A.2.

If the X above is IQ with $\mu = 100$ and $\sigma = 15$, what percentage of the population has higher scores than 115? Conversion from proportion to percentage involves multiplying by 100, so $.1587 \times 100 = 15.87\%$ is the answer. What percentage of the population scores higher than 130? Stop here and calculate. Transforming to z gives $z = 2$. The proportion of X's that are greater than or equal to 130 is equal to the proportion of z's that are greater than or equal to 2, or .0228, so the anwer is 2.28%. Figure 5.7 shows a distribution with these areas for X distributed normally with $\mu = 100$ and $\sigma^2 = 225$.

Suppose a certain school district claims that the average IQ of its students is 115 with a standard deviation of 15 IQ points. If the IQ of these students is normally distributed, what percentage of the students are expected to have an IQ of 90 or less? Transforming to z gives

$$z = \frac{X - \mu}{\sigma} = \frac{90 - 115}{15} = \frac{-25}{15} = -1.67$$

The proportion of IQs that are less than or equal to 90 is equal to the proportion of z's that are less than or equal to -1.67, or .0475 from Table A.2. The answer is that 4.75% of the students have IQs of 90 or less.

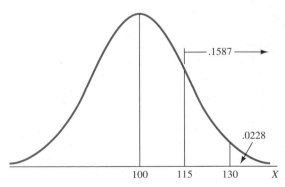

Figure 5.7
Distribution and areas for X having a normal distribution ($\mu = 100$, $\sigma^2 = 225$) for $X = 115$ and $X = 130$

What percentage of the students are expected to have IQ scores between 95 and 135? The relevant z scores are

$$z = \frac{95 - 115}{15} = \frac{-20}{15} = -1.33$$

and

$$z = \frac{135 - 115}{15} = \frac{20}{15} = 1.33$$

The cumulative proportion for 95 is the proportion of IQs that are less than or equal to 95, which equals the proportion of z's that are less than or equal to -1.33, or .0918. The cumulative proportion for 135 is the proportion of IQs that are less than or equal to 135, which equals the proportion of z's that are less than or equal to 1.33, or .4082 + .5000 = .9082. The difference .9082 − .0918 = .8164 gives the proportion of IQs between 95 and 135. In percentage form, the answer is that 81.64% of the students are expected to have IQs betwee 95 and 135. The proportion .8164 also could be obtained from symmetry: .4082 + .4082 = .8164. Figure 5.8 shows the areas and values of IQ.

Be sure to use the correct distribution to answer questions about proportions or percentages. In the last example, the distribution of IQ scores was not assumed to be the usual distribution of IQs with 100 for the mean, but a normal distribution with a higher mean of 115. Think about comparing your height to a population average. If you're female, you need to compare your height to some distribution of female heights. You may be the average height for a female, but if you use the norms for males, you've got the wrong reference distribution.

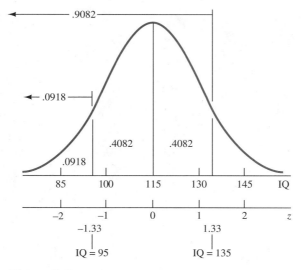

Figure 5.8
Normal distribution for IQ ($\mu = 115$, $\sigma^2 = 225$); area between 95 and 135 is .8164

Scores in Normal Distributions

You have used the standard normal distribution to find proportions or percentages for given scores in some normal distribution. What if you have a percentage or proportion and you want to find the score that has that value? Table A.2 can be used for this task. Simply enter the table at the proportion and find the corresponding *z*.

For example, what *z* score has a proportion of .07 in the upper tail of the distribution? Enter column 3 at .07, find .0708 as the closest proportion, and from column 1, read *z* = 1.47 as the answer.

Once you have a *z* score, you have to solve for the correct value of *X* by taking *z* times the standard deviation and adding the mean. The IQ score that cuts off 7% of the distribution in the upper tail is:

$$1.47(15) + 100 = 122.05$$

because an IQ of 122 is about 1.47 standard deviations above the mean. Figure 5.9 shows areas in the normal distribution with a mean of 100 and a variance of 225.

Remember, the *z* score transformation does not change the shape of the distribution, so this section on the use of the standard normal distribution is appropriate only for variables where the original raw score *X* is normally distributed.

Quick Quiz

Suppose your IQ score is 110. The mean is 100 and the variance is 225 for the population, and we assume that IQ is normally distributed. Calculate the *z* score for your IQ and find the proportion of people whose IQ is greater than or equal to yours.

Answer

.2514.
Your z score is 0.67. The proportion of people who have IQs greater than or equal to yours is

---

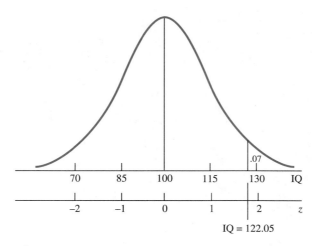

IQ = 122.05

Figure 5.9
Normal distribution for IQ ($\mu = 100$, $\sigma^2 = 225$); IQ score that cuts off 7% in the tail is 122.05

5.4 Other Standard Scores

General Equation

Because z scores have negative signs for scores that are less than the mean and because z scores usually have fractional parts expressed in decimal form, test results often are reported in some other standard score form. These other standard scores are easily obtained from z scores and are related to z scores by the following general equation. If the new standard score is to have mean MU and standard deviation STD, then the new standard score is defined as:

$$\text{New standard score} = (STD)(z) + MU \tag{5.5}$$

Specific Examples

For example, raw scores from the Wechsler Adult Intelligence Scale-Revised are standardized by transforming them to IQ scores with mean 100 and standard deviation 15. Substituting $MU = 100$ and $STD = 15$ into formula 5.5 gives

$$IQ = (15)(z) + 100$$

Someone who has a raw score that corresponds to $z = 1$ has IQ $= 115$.

The Scholastic Aptitude Test is standardized to have mean 500 and standard deviation 100, or

$$SAT = (100)(z) + 500$$

Someone who has an SAT score of 650 has a z score of 1.5; that is, 650 is 1.5 standard deviations above the mean. If SAT scores are normally distributed, what percentage of the scores are below 650? Or, a slightly different question, what percentage correctly fills in the blank in this statement: "This person is in the top _____% of the distribution"? You should get 93.32% and 6.68% for your answers.

Another standard score is obtained when you use mean 50 and standard deviation 10. It is sometimes called a **T score,** or

T score
Standard score that has a mean of 50 and a standard deviation of 10

$$T = (10)(z) + 50$$

Someone who has a z score of 1.4 has $T = 10(1.4) + 50 = 64$. The Self-Acceptance (SA) scale of the California Personality Inventory (CPI) uses T scores to report results. Another classic personality measure, the Minnesota Multiphasic Personality Inventory (MMPI), also reports results on separate scales in terms of T scores.

These other standard scores—for example, T scores—are interpreted similar to z scores. Any standard score describes the relative position of a score in a distribution. The z score gives the position of the raw score in terms of the mean and standard deviation; it is the distance from the mean in standard deviation units. However, because these other standard scores are one step removed from z scores, they are a little more difficult to interpret because you need to remember the mean and standard deviation. For example, what does an SAT score of 450 mean? You have to recall that the mean is 500 and the standard deviation is 100 to say that 450 is 0.5 standard deviation below the mean. With z scores, the interpretation is direct: -0.5 means 0.5 standard deviation below the mean.

Quick Quiz
If T scores have mean of 50 and standard deviation of 10, and you have $z = -2.00$, then you have $T = $ _____.

Answer

$T = (10)(z) + 50 = (10)(-2.00) + 50 = -20.00 + 50 = 30$

5.5   Percentiles

Did you take the SAT or ACT to get into college? Maybe you've taken the TOEFL to be able to study in the United States. The results presented to you included a percentile.

Although a standard score gives the position of a score relative to the mean in standard deviation units, it does not give information about the score relative to the rest of the scores in the distribution. Unless you have a normal distribution, knowing that a raw score of 12 has $z = 1.1$ does not tell you what percentage of the scores are less than 12. The **percentile rank** of a score is the percentage of the distribution that lies below the score; it gives direct information about a score's position relative to the rest of the scores.

Percentile rank
Percentage of a distribution lying below the score of interest

In Chapter 4, you learned that the median has 50% of the scores below it, so the median has a percentile rank of 50. The cumulative relative frequency discussed in Chapter 3 gives the percentile rank of a score when you multiply it by 100. From the cumulative relative frequencies for female heights given in Table 3.9 and reproduced here as Table 5.3, we find that a height of 68.25 in. has a percentile rank of 91.7 because the cumulative relative frequency is .917 for the interval from 67.0 to 68.0.

Table 5.3
Cumulative frequency distributions of female heights (in.)

Interval	Frequency	Cumulative Frequency	Relative Frequency	Cumulative Relative Frequency
73.0–74.0	0	24	.000	1.00
71.5–72.5	0	24	.000	1.00
70.0–71.0	0	24	.000	1.00
68.5–69.5	2	24	.083	1.00
67.0–68.0	8	22	.333	.917
65.5–66.5	2	14	.083	.583
64.0–65.0	4	12	.167	.500
62.5–63.5	4	8	.167	.333
61.0–62.0	2	4	.083	.167
59.5–60.5	1	2	.042	.083
58.0–59.0	1	1	.042	.042

Percentile Ranks: Computation

For grouped data, you can compute the percentile rank (*PR*) for any score *X* by using:

$$PR = \frac{f_\Delta (X - LL) + \Delta f_{LL}}{N\Delta} (100) \tag{5.6}$$

where

PR = desired percentile rank for score *X*
f_Δ = frequency in the interval containing *X*
X = score for which you desire the percentile rank
LL = lower real limit of the interval containing *X*
Δ = interval width = upper real limit − lower real limit
f_{LL} = frequency below the interval
N = total sample size

For example, what is the percentile rank for $X = 67$ from Table 5.3? Here $X = 67$ is in the interval 67.0–68.0. The frequency in the interval is $f_\Delta = 8$, the lower real limit is $LL = 66.75$, the interval width is $\Delta = 1.5$, the frequency below the interval is $f_{LL} = 14$, and $N = 24$. Therefore,

$$PR = \frac{f_\Delta (X - LL) + \Delta f_{LL}}{N\Delta} (100)$$

$$= \frac{8(67 - 66.75) + 1.5(14)}{24(1.5)} (100)$$

$$= \frac{23}{36} (100)$$

$$= 0.6389 (100)$$

$$= 63.89$$

So $X = 67$ has a percentile rank of 63.89, or 64. Thus, 63.89% of the scores are below $X = 67$.

For scores that are normally distributed, percentile ranks can be obtained from proportions in Table A.2. Find the z score for *X* and the proportion of scores that are less than *X*, and then convert the proportion to a percentage. For the person with an SAT score ($\mu = 500$, $\sigma = 100$) of 650,

$$z = \frac{650 - 500}{100} = \frac{150}{100} = 1.5$$

Because the proportion of z values that are less than 1.5 is .4332 + .5000 = .9332, the proportion of *X*'s that are less than 650 is .9332 and the percentile rank of 650 is 93.32.

Quick Quiz

Find the percentile rank of an IQ score of 117. (Remember that IQ scores are normally distributed with $\mu = 100$ and $\sigma = 15$.)

Answer

80'L8

Computation of a Score with a Given Percentile Rank

Approaching the percentile rank question from the opposite direction, you might want to find the score that has a given percentile rank. Use

$$X = LL + \frac{\Delta[(PR/100)N - f_{LL}]}{f_\Delta} \tag{5.7}$$

where all the components are defined as in the computation of percentile ranks (see formula 5.6). For $PR = 40\%$, the score that has the 40th percentile rank from Table 5.3 is

$$X = 63.75 + \frac{1.5[(40/100)(24) - 8]}{4}$$

$$= 63.75 + \frac{1.5(9.6 - 8)}{4}$$

$$= 63.75 + 0.60$$

$$= 64.35$$

Thus, $X = 64.35$ is the score that has 40% of the distribution below it.

For a normally distributed variable, you can use Table A.2 without using formula 5.7. What score has the percentile rank of 67 among SAT scores? To answer this question, you have to enter Table A.2 and find the z that has a cumulative proportion of .67. Any cumulative proportion over .50 is made up of two parts—.50 plus an entry from column 2. So .67 is .50 + .17, and .17 comes from column 2 for $z = 0.44$. The desired SAT score is 0.44 standard deviation above the mean, or

$$SAT = 500 + 0.44(100) = 500 + 44 = 544$$

An SAT score of 544 has a percentile rank of 67.

One note of realism needs to be added here. We have oversimplified the case of standardized test scores such as the SAT. Scores on standardized tests always need to be interpreted in terms of a correct reference group. Although the mean of all SAT scores is 500 and the standard deviation is 100, the SAT is usually interpreted for a more specific reference group. Results are usually given along with a percentile rank for that specific administration of the test. A 650 scored on a test given in 1994 might have a different percentile rank than that of 650 on a test given in 1995. Some standard-

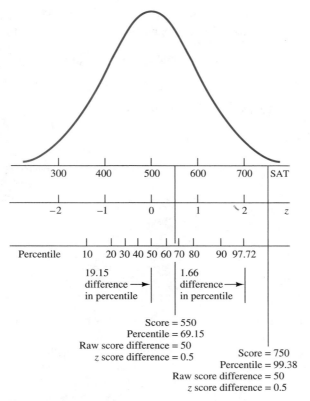

Figure 5.10
Difference between z scores and percentiles for the normal distribution: 550 compared to 500 and 750 compared to 700

ized tests even refer to a distribution of students in a specific area of study, such as psychology. The specific reference group for your GRE score might be "psychology majors who took the GRE in October 1998."

Relationship of Percentile Ranks and z Scores

Percentile ranks give another descriptive view of a single score and its relative position in a distribution. However, differences in percentile ranks do not give proportional differences in raw scores. For scores near the mean, differences in percentile ranks are large for small raw-score differences. For extreme scores, differences in percentile ranks are small for large raw-score differences.

For example, the differences in the percentile ranks of 550 and 500 (with $\mu = 500$ and $\sigma = 100$) is $69.15 - 50 = 19.15$, but the difference in the percentile ranks of 750 and 700 is only $99.38 - 97.72 = 1.66$. Figure 5.10 shows this relationship between percentile ranks and z scores. Because of this distortion, some preference is given to z scores. Finally, z scores not only describe the relative position of a score in a distribution, but also provide a connection to inferential statistics, as you will see in Chapters 9 and 10.

Quick Quiz

If GRE scores are normally distributed and for a particular administration of the test have $\mu = 520$ and $\sigma = 110$, what GRE score has a percentile rank of 95?

Answer

700.95, or about 701

5.6   Summary, Study Tips, and Computation

Chapter Summary

Two options exist to describe individual scores in the sample or population: standard scores and percentile ranks. Computation of z scores gives the position, or relative standing, of a score with respect to the mean in terms of standard deviations. And z scores have a mean of 0, a standard deviation of 1, and the same shape distribution as the distribution of X. The use of z scores or any of the other standard scores allows the comparison of different raw scores from the same or different distributions. The family of normal distributions has parameters μ and σ^2 that uniquely define each distribution. The standard normal distribution has $\mu = 0$ and $\sigma^2 = 1$, and its proportions, given in Table A.2, can be used to compute proportions for any normal distribution using the z transformation. Other standard scores, such as T scores, can be used if you want to avoid negative standard scores. The percentile rank of a score gives the percentage of the population or sample that falls below that score; it is used to describe a score's relative position with respect to all the other scores in the distribution.

Key terms in this chapter are:

Relative standing	Normal distributions
z score	Parameters μ and σ^2
Standard normal distribution	T score
	Percentile rank

Study Tips

How are you doing in your statistics class? Are your scores above average? These questions are about your relative standing, the main idea introduced in this chapter. Memorize the formula for z scores and understand how it reflects relative standing. You can calculate z scores regardless of what the distribution looks like. Be sure you understand that a normal distribution is only one kind of distribution, and that Table A.2 shows proportions for the standard normal distribution. Practice using the table. Do all of the problems in the text and be sure you understand how you got the answer.

You need to understand the concept of areas in a distribution because future chapters discuss how to decide whether the results of a research project are typical or unusual, just as your test scores in this course are either close to the class average or far above it.

Students' most frequent errors are: (1) in z, dividing by s^{*2}, (2) confusing z (which can be negative) and proportion (which can't), and (3) getting a proportion greater than one or less than zero.

Computation

Computation in this chapter is relatively simple. The emphasis is on the computation of z scores and the use of the normal distribution. Computation of percentile ranks or the reverse operation of finding a score that has a given percentile rank is not emphasized, simply because these operations are done only occasionally in data analysis by research scientists.

Most statistical packages have the capability of computing at least some of the procedures in this chapter. SAS has the STANDARD procedure, which standardizes variables to a new mean and/or standard deviation; it can be used to compute z and other standard scores. The SAS UNIVARIATE procedure can be used to find a limited number of percentiles and a cumulative percentage for a frequency distribution, but it does not compute percentile ranks for a given score. Examples of each of these SAS procedures are given below, with the attraction data from Exercise 15 in Chapter 3. For SPSS, you can get z scores using the option /SAVE as a subcommand to DESCRIPTIVES, but you have to ask for them to be printed using PRINT and EXECUTE.

SAS Example

(SAS system's lines)

```
DATA STAND;
INPUT X SIM$ @@;    (here you input the attraction score and the classification of similarity; the $ after SIM tells the computer that
                     SIM is a character variable, and the @@ allows multiple sets of observations per line)
SX = X;    (this establishes the new standardized variable)
CARDS;
10 S 13 S 11 S 9 S 12 S 12 S 8 S 9 S 12 S 10 S 9 S 10 S
9 S 12 S 11 S 6 S 8 S 10 S 10 S 10 S 12 S 8 S 11 S 10 S
10 S 13 S 12 S 12 S 10 S 10 S 12 S 12 S 12 S 12 S 7 S
12 S 8 D 12 D 7 D 5 D 5 D 5 D 8 D 7 D 4 D 8 D 12 D 4 D
10 D 8 D 6 D 5 D 5 D 6 D 9 D 7 D 11 D 6 D 7 D 10 D 6 D
8 D 4 D 6 D 8 D 10 D 10 D 8 D 5 D 8 D 8 D 6 D
PROC PRINT;
PROC SORT;
BY SIM;
PROC STANDARD MEAN=0 STD=1 OUT=NEW;    (statement to do the standardization with selected mean and standard deviation;
                                        OUT=NEW creates a new data set for the results)
BY SIM;    (statement that tells the program that the data are to be standardized within each similarity group)
VAR SX;    (statement that tells the program that the variable to be standardized is SX)
PROC PRINT;    (statement to get the results printed; the PROC standard does not automatically print)
BY SIM;
TITLE 'Z SCORES';
PROC MEANS;
BY SIM;
PROC STANDARD MEAN=500 STD=100 OUT=NEWER;
BY SIM;
VAR SX;
PROC PRINT;
BY SIM;
TITLE 'OTHER STANDARD SCORES';
PROC MEANS;
BY SIM;
```

(system's line)

Z SCORES

---------------- SIM=D ------------------------- SIM=S ---------

OBS	X ①	SX ②	OBS	X	SX
1	4	−1.4907	37	6	−2.5922
2	4	−1.4907	38	7	−2.0089
3	4	−1.4907	39	8	−1.4257
4	5	−1.0359	40	8	−1.4257
5	5	−1.0359	41	8	−1.4257
6	5	−1.0359	42	9	−0.8425
7	5	−1.0359	43	9	−0.8425
8	5	−1.0359	44	9	−0.8425
9	5	−1.0359	45	9	−0.8425
10	6	−0.5811	46	10	−0.2592
11	6	−0.5811	47	10	−0.2592
12	6	−0.5811	48	10	−0.2592
13	6	−0.5811	49	10	−0.2592
14	6	−0.5811	50	10	−0.2592
15	6	−0.5811	51	10	−0.2592
16	7	−0.1263	52	10	−0.2592
17	7	−0.1263	53	10	−0.2592
18	7	-0.1263	54	10	−0.2592
19	7	−0.1263	55	10	−0.2592
20	8	0.3285	56	11	0.3240
21	8	0.3285	57	11	0.3240
22	8	0.3285	58	11	0.3240
23	8	0.3285	59	12	0.9073
24	8	0.3285	60	12	0.9073
25	8	0.3285	61	12	0.9073
26	8	0.3285	62	12	0.9073
27	8	0.3285	63	12	0.9073
28	8	0.3285	64	12	0.9073
29	9	0.7832	65	12	0.9073
30	10	1.2380	66	12	0.9073
31	10	1.2380	67	12	0.9073
32	10	1.2380	68	12	0.9073
33	10	1.2380	69	12	0.9073
34	11	1.6928	70	12	0.9073
35	12	2.1476	71	13	1.4905
36	12	2.1476	72	13	1.4905

Figure 5.11
SAS output for PROC STANDARD

(continued)

VARIABLE	N	MEAN	STANDARD DEVIATION	MINIMUM VALUE	MAXIMUM VALUE	STD ERROR OF MEAN	SUM	VARIANCE
------------------------------------- SIM=D ---------------------------								
x③	36	7.2778	2.1988	4.0000	12.0000	0.3665	262.000	4.8349
SX ④	36	0.0000	1.0000	−1.4907	2.1476	0.1667	0.000	1.0000
------------------------------------- SIM=S ---------------------------								
X	36	10.4444	1.7146	6.0000	13.0000	0.2858	376.000	2.9397
SX	36	0.0000	1.0000	−2.5922	1.4905	0.1667	0.000	1.0000

OTHER STANDARD SCORES

-------------- SIM=D ------------------------- SIM=S ---------

OBS	X	SX ⑤	OBS	X	SX
1	4	350.932	37	6	240.781
2	4	350.932	38	7	299.105
3	4	350.932	39	8	357.429
4	5	396.410	40	8	357.429
5	5	396.410	41	8	357.429
6	5	396.410	42	9	415.754
7	5	396.410	43	9	415.754
8	5	396.410	44	9	415.754
9	5	396.410	45	9	415.754
10	6	441.889	46	10	474.078
11	6	441.889	47	10	474.078
12	6	441.889	48	10	474.078
13	6	441.889	49	10	474.078
14	6	441.889	50	10	474.078
15	6	441.889	51	10	474.078
16	7	487.367	52	10	474.078
17	7	487.367	53	10	474.078
18	7	487.367	54	10	474.078
19	7	487.367	55	10	474.078
20	8	532.846	56	11	532.402
21	8	532.846	57	11	532.402
22	8	532.846	58	11	532.402
23	8	532.846	59	12	590.727
24	8	532.846	60	12	590.727
25	8	532.846	61	12	590.727
26	8	532.846	62	12	590.727
27	8	532.846	63	12	590.727
28	8	532.846	64	12	590.727

Figure 5.11 (continued)

(continued)

29	9	578.324	65	12	590.727
30	10	623.802	66	12	590.727
31	10	623.802	67	12	590.727
32	10	623.802	68	12	590.727
33	10	623.802	69	12	590.727
34	11	669.281	70	12	590.727
35	12	714.759	71	13	649.051
36	12	714.759	72	13	649.051

```
                  OTHER STANDARD SCORES

VARIABLE   N    MEAN   STANDARD  MINIMUM MAXIMUM STD ERROR  SUM   VARIANCE
                       DEVIATION  VALUE   VALUE   OF MEAN

--------------------------------- SIM=D ----------------------------

X  ⑥     36   7.2778    2.1988    4.000  12.000   0.3665    262.00   4.8349
SX       36 500.0000 100.0000  350.932 714.759  16.6667  18000.00 10000.00


--------------------------------- SIM=S ----------------------------

X        36  10.4444    1.7146    6.000  13.000   0.2858    376.00   2.9397
SX       36 500.0000 100.0000  240.781 649.051  16.6667  18000.00 10000.00
```

Figure 5.11 (continued)

For PROC STANDARD, the SAS output in Figure 5.11 gives:

1. The original raw scores X in order from low to high within each similarity group, D and S.
2. The new variable, called SX, which is z. The X values are standardized for each similarity group separately. Note that the z scores are formed by using $z = (X - \overline{X})/s$.
3. PROC MEANS is given for variable X.
4. PROC MEANS is given for variable SX, showing the mean of 0 and variance and standard deviation of 1.
5. Here the variable SX is formed by transforming X to have a mean of 500 and a standard deviation of 100.
6. PROC MEANS for variable SX shows the mean to be 500 and the standard deviation to be 100.

SPSS Example

(SPSS system's lines)

```
SET WIDTH 80
DATA LIST FREE/MIDTERM    (statement to input the midterm scores for psychology majors, Table 3.1)
```

```
BEGIN DATA
89 71 65 81 94 97 62 69 71 91 87 79 79 90 75 69 92 79
64 92 76 81 73 97
END DATA
DESCRIPTIVES VARIABLES=MIDTERM/SAVE
PRINT/MIDTERM ZMIDTERM    (ZMIDTERM is the name SPSS gives to the z scores it computed on midterm scores)
EXECUTE
FINISH
(system's line)
```

```
  Number of valid observations (listwise) =        24.00
                                                   Valid
① Variable      Mean    Std Dev   Minimum    Maximum   N  Label
   MIDTERM      80.12     10.87     62.00      97.00   24

   7  PRINT /MIDTERM ZMIDTERM  ②
   8  EXECUTE
   89.00       .81662
   71.00      -.83962
   65.00     -1.39170
   81.00       .08051
   94.00      1.27668
   97.00      1.55272
   62.00     -1.66774
   69.00     -1.02364
   71.00      -.83962
   91.00      1.00064
   87.00       .63259
   79.00      -.10351
   79.00      -.10351
   90.00       .90863
   75.00      -.47157
   69.00     -1.02364
   92.00      1.09265
   79.00      -.10351
   64.00     -1.48371
   92.00      1.09265
   76.00      -.37955
   81.00       .08051
   73.00      -.65559
   97.00      1.55272
```

Figure 5.12
SPSS output for DESCRIPTIVES (z scores)

The SPSS output showing the z scores is given in Figure 5.12. Note the following:

1. The DESCRIPTIVES gives some descriptive statistics.
2. Because we asked for both MIDTERM and ZMIDTERM scores to be printed, we got both: 89 has a z score of 0.81662.

Exercises

Section 5.2

1. For a standardized test: $\mu = 83$, $\bar{X} = 79.5$, $\sigma^2 = 49$, $\overset{*}{s}{}^2 = 36$, and $X_{50} = 80$. If your score is $X = 90$, choose the pieces you need and put them together in the formula, but do not do the computation, to find:
   a. Your z in the sample
   b. Your z in the population
2. Joe took a standardized test for which the norms are $\mu = 24$ and $\sigma^2 = 4$. His score was $X = 22$. When he computed his z score, he got $z = (22 - 24)/4$. Knowing that he is not doing as well in statistics as you are, Joe asked you to check his work. What do you have to say to him?
3. For the Wechsler Adult Intelligence Scale (WAIS), the mean is 100 and standard deviation is 15.
   a. What IQ score has $z = 2$?
   b. If WAIS IQ = 123, what is z?
4. For the Self-Acceptance (SA) scale of the California Personality Inventory (CPI), $\mu = 19$ for males, with $\sigma^2 = 4$. Find z for SA = 26.
5. For the exam stress data in Table 1.1 and Exercise 17 in Chapter 4, the perceived control group had $\bar{X} = 10.0$ and $\overset{*}{s}{}^2 = 8.5333$. Compute the z score for the student who has $X = 12$.
6. A subset of data from the Secret Service group in the liar detection study is: 60, 60, 70, 50, 70, 60, 70, 70, 60, 60.
   a. Computer $\bar{X}$.
   b. Computer $\overset{*}{s}{}^2$.
   c. Compute the z score for the person who has $X = 60$.
   d. If you computed all ten z scores, what would be the mean of these ten z scores?
   e. If you computed all ten z scores, what would be the variance of these ten z scores?
7. Use the grades in the table.
   a. Compute the $\bar{X}$ and $\overset{*}{s}$.
   b. Compute the z score for each X.
   c. Compute the mean and variance of these z scores.

Class grades
91
93
90
89
90
90
77
90
91

8. Suppose you calculate z scores for a subscale of a personality test.
   a. What is the shape of the distribution of the z scores?
   b. What is the mean of the z scores?
   c. What is the standard deviation?
   d. Are we guaranteed that 50% of the z scores are above the mean? Explain.

Section 5.3

9. Use Table A.2 to find the proportion of cases in the standard normal distribution that fit each description. In each part, draw a standard normal curve, put 0 (the mean) and any numbers in the problem on the horizontal line for the z's, and shade in the desired area.
   a. Less than or equal to -1.65
   b. Less than or equal to 1.23
   c. Less than or equal to -1.96
   d. Less than or equal to 3.00
   e. Larger than 1.96
   f. Larger than 2.58
   g. Larger than 2.33
   h. Larger than 0.30
   i. Larger than -0.55
   j. Larger than -1.71
   k. Between -1.65 and 1.65
   l. Between -1.27 and 1.27

m. Between -1.80 and 1.35

n. Between 0.42 and 1.82

o. Between 1.11 and 2.79

p. Between -1.43 and -0.19

q. Larger than 2.58 or less than -2.58 (*Hint:* Be careful; this is a new type.)

10. Use Table A.2 to find the value of the z score that satisfies each condition. In each case, draw a standard normal curve, put in 0 (the mean), and shade in the approximate area from the problem. This will help you approximate the value of the appropriate z.

    a. The z that has 67% of the scores above it

    b. The z that has 19% of the scores below it

    c. The z that has 13% of the scores above it

11. The WAIS IQ is normally distributed, with $\mu = 100$ and $\sigma = 15$.

    a. What percentage of the population has an IQ greater than or equal to 130?

    b. If WAIS IQs that are less than or equal to 85 define the educable mentally handicapped, what percentage of the population fits this definition?

    c. If an educator states that someone should have a WAIS IQ over 110 before applying to a particular college, what percentage of the population qualifies?

    d. What WAIS IQ score cuts off 10% of the scores in the upper tail of the distribution?

12. A manufacturer of batteries for watches claims that the average lifetime of a particular type of battery is 9000 hours, with a standard deviation of 500 hours. Your watch has that type of battery and it has failed after you have owned it for only 296 days. Battery lifetimes can be assumed to be normally distributed.

    a. What percentage of such batteries are expected to fail in 296 or fewer days?

    b. What else should you consider before you complain about the lifetime of your battery?

13. If SAT scores ($\mu = 500$, $\sigma = 100$) are normally distributed, what percentage of the population has scores between 390 and 520?

14. The following sample was drawn randomly from a population with $\mu = 50$ and $\sigma^2 = 100$.

    46 50 34 41 47 53 48 43 55 56 54 54 54 59 68
    68 54 42 44 60 52 53 44 24 51 68 44 32 50 51

    a. Draw a histogram of the data.

    b. Calculate $\overline{X}$.

    c. Calculate $\overset{*}{s}{}^2$.

d. Comment on the difference between $\overline{X}$ and μ.

e. Comment on the difference between $\overset{*}{s}{}^2$ and σ^2.

f. Describe the skewness of the sample using the histogram you drew in part a. Also describe any other notable features of the shape of the sample distribution—smooth or lumpy, continuous or discrete, and so on.

g. One additional piece of information about the population: It is normally distributed. Comment on the difference between your description of shape in part f and the normally shaped population.

h. How do you account for the differences you noted in parts d, e, and g?

15. Suppose a certain manufacturer of electric light bulbs claims that the average lifetime of its 60-watt (W) bulbs is 1000 h with a standard deviation of 75 h.

    a. If the lifetimes of these bulbs are normally distributed, what percentage of the bulbs are expected to fail when they are used for 800 h or less?

    b. What percentage of the bulbs are expected to last between 900 and 1100 h?

16. Suppose a relatively tall young man wants to know the proportion of males who are his height or taller. His height is 6 ft, or 72 in., and the heights of males are approximately normally distributed with a mean of 69 in. and a standard deviation of 3 in.

    a. What is the answer to his question?

    b. How would the answer change if the question were restricted to male college basketball players?

17. Suppose a manufacturing process produces a part that is normally distributed with an average length of 2 in. and a standard deviation of 0.05 in.

    a. What proportion of these parts are between 1.95 and 2.05 in. long?

    b. What proportion of these parts are longer than 2.10 in.?

    c. If you found a part that had a length of 2.20 in., would you think something was wrong with the manufacturing process? Explain.

    d. What values of length make up 50% of the parts?

Section 5.4

18. Suppose you obtain a raw score of 17 on the SA scale of the CPI ($\mu = 19$, $\sigma = 4$). What score would be reported for you on the scale with $\mu = 50$ and $\sigma = 10$?

Section 5.5

19. a. Calculate the percentile rank of $X = 65$ for the data in Table 5.3.

   b. Calculate the percentile rank of $X = 62$ for the data in Table 5.3.

20. a. What value of X is at the 70th percentile for the data in Table 5.3?

   b. What value of X is at the 30th percentile for the data in Table 5.3?

21. A job placement test yields normally distributed scores that have a mean of 34 and a standard deviation of 4.

   a. What is the score above which lies 20% of the distribution?

   b. What percentage of the scores are below 27?

   c. What scores include the middle 75% of the distribution?

   d. In a group of 50 job applicants, what score cuts off the top ten applicants?

22. a. For a distribution of X values of 32, 41, 44, 47, and 56, what score has a percentile rank of 80? What is the z score of 47?

   b. For a distribution of X values of 32, 34, 44, 54, and 56, what score has a percentile rank of 80? What is the z score of 54? What is the z score of $X = 47$?

23. Suppose the Okeedohkee Test Company makes the following claims about test scores for its IQUQ test. Comment on the accuracy of each claim.

   a. Because they use z scores to report results, these z's are normally distributed.

   b. The mean z is 1.00.

   c. The variance of the z's is 0.

   d. In the population, 20% of the subjects have scores above $z = 1.00$.

6

Describing Data for Two Variables: Correlation

You know how to describe the central tendency and variability of data for one variable. Now you will learn how to describe the tendency for scores on two variables to "go together," "occur in parallel," or be related. Correlation measures the degree of linear relationship between two variables. The statistic for correlation includes the idea of relative standing in its definitional formula.

Research Example 6
6.1 Introduction
6.2 Linear Relationships
6.3 Pearson Correlation Coefficient: A Measure of the Degree of Linear Relationship
    Definition of r
    Different degrees and types of linear relationship
6.4 Properties of r
    Two variables
    Boundaries on r
    Linear only
    r^2 = proportion of variability explained
    When is r undefined?
    r is dimensionless
    r and change of scale
6.5 Computational Formula for r
    Computing r
    Example
    Population correlation coefficient
6.6 Factors to Consider in Using r
    Restriction of range
    Combined data
    Extreme scores (outliers)
6.7 Correlation and Causation
    Correlation does not imply causation
    Example
    Causation, true experiments, and r
6.8 Summary, Study Tips, and Computation
    Chapter summary
    Study tips
    Computation
Exercises

Research Example 6

Are white suicide rates related to the amount of airtime given to country music? This is the question addressed by Stack and Gundlach (1992) as they looked for a possible link between country music airtime and suicide rates in 49 metropolitan areas.

When two variables are studied together, researchers consider whether there is some association between them. Does a high score on one variable necessarily yield a high (or low) score on the other? In this example, do cities with much airtime devoted to country music have high suicide rates, whereas cities with little airtime for country music have low suicide rates? One way of deciding whether airtime or suicide rates are high is to calculate their relative position. Based on what you learned in Chapter 5, you can take the airtime data and calculate the z score for each city, and then do the same thing for the white suicide rate. If the relationship or association between the two variables is positive, then a city's z score on airtime is similar to its z score on white suicide rate. In this example, a positive relationship between country music airtime and the white suicide rate means that a metropolitan area with a high z score on country music airtime has a similarly high z score on white suicide rates. If the relationship is negative, then a high z score on one variable is paired with a low z score on the second variable.

For 49 metropolitan areas, Stack and Gundlach recorded the number of suicides per 100,000 people for both whites and blacks and the proportion of radio airtime devoted to country music. Among the extraneous variables that they controlled were poverty, whether or not the metropolitan area was in the Southern United States, divorce rates, and gun availability. They found a positive relationship between the proportion of radio airtime devoted to country music and white suicide rates. The strength of the relationship was measured with a statistic called the *Pearson correlation coefficient,* symbolized by *r.* This statistic ranges from -1 for the strongest negative relationship to $+1$ for the strongest positive relationship. For their data, Stack and Gundlach computed $r = .54$. Even when the extraneous variables are controlled, this positive relationship persists.

As you recall from Chapter 2, you cannot say what causes an event unless you have a true experiment. Stack and Gundlach therefore avoid talking about a causal relationship, but they did discuss possible explanatory schemes, such as the impact of music on mood. They also found that the Southern region and divorce rates were positively related to white suicide rates. None of the variables was significantly related to black suicide rates, which are called an "understudied phenomenon" by Stack and Gundlach.

6.1   Introduction

You probably have an intuitive idea of what *correlation* means. A synonym you may think of is *parallel,* a good word to keep in mind as you learn about correlation in statistics. Two events can occur simultaneously—that is, in parallel—without one event causing the other. Research Example 6 is a good illustration; cities with much airtime devoted to country music have higher white suicide rates, and cities with little country music airtime have lower white suicide rates. Airtime and suicide rates are happening in parallel, but we cannot point to a cause. Does the popularity of country music influence the suicide rate? And if so, should there be warning labels on those sad country songs? Could it be that high suicide rates influence people to listen to sad songs? Or is an unidentified third factor responsible for both phenomena?

When researchers are interested in the relationship between two variables, it is not enough to consider the variables one at a time. Measures of central tendency and variability can be computed for country music airtime and for suicide rates of the 49 metropolitan areas. But those statistics don't show the connection between the two variables. To see how country music airtime and suicide rates are jointly distributed, you could draw a scatterplot with one variable on the *X* axis and the second variable on the *Y* axis. This would give you a picture of the relationship between the two variables.

Relationships between variables can be found in observational research or in a true experiment. Most of the time, however, correlations are in observational research because relationships between variables, such as country music airtime and suicide rates, are just being discovered. After a parallel relationship has been identified, researchers then conduct true experiments so they can control extraneous variables and make statements about causation. Sometimes true experiments cannot be done. Can you imagine randomly assigning cities to an amount of country music airtime?

6.2   Linear Relationships

To describe the degree of linear relationship between two variables, we compute *r,* or the Pearson correlation coefficient, which is a kind of average. In Chapter 7, you'll learn more about describing two variables' linear relationship by computing a linear prediction equation. Once you had a prediction equation for the country-music/suicide data, you could enter a new city's country-music airtime into the equation and compute a predicted score for the white suicide rate. The area concerned with prediction from one variable to another is called *regression.*

Notice the word *linear.* This chapter deals with only linear, or straight-line, relationships between two variables. The Pearson correlation coefficient measures only the degree to which a straight line can be fit through the data points. Other variables might cycle up and down; for example, a person's activity level varies as her blood sugar level fluctuates throughout the day, but an extremely high blood sugar level will trigger an insulin dump, which severely depresses activity. Pearson's *r* does not measure such cyclic relationships. Think of Pearson's *r* as being "blind" to anything but straight-line relationships. If income goes up as a person works more years with a company, then Pearson's *r* can "see" this linear relationship. For the cyclical relationship between blood sugar and activity levels, the correlation coefficient won't "see" anything and will be around zero, saying, "There's no linear relationship to report."

Quick Quiz

Why is the word *linear* important when discussing correlation?

   Answer

                            variables.

The Pearson correlation coefficient measures only the degree of linear relationship between two

---

6.3   Pearson Correlation Coefficient: A Measure of the Degree of Linear Relationship

You may think it's interesting but useless to know that there's a correlation between the amount of country music airtime and white suicide rates. Many factors affect suicide rates, and your personal well-being may be untouched by the kind of music you listen to. But this research accomplishes a goal of science—to explain and understand the world.

To see how understanding an event can improve people's lives, let's look at something that affects many people: eating disorders. Part of a clinical psychologist's job is to help a client understand why he or she reacts in certain ways, and this may involve much discussion about family history. Researchers at Yale University have found a correlation between teenage girls' beliefs about weight control and their mothers' attitudes. Pike and Rodin (1991) concluded that a mother's concern about her own and her daughter's weight and appearance places the daughter at risk of developing an eating disorder. A therapist who can raise a client's awareness about this risk can help the client counteract the familial influence and develop new attitudes about eating.

Definition of *r*

Correlation
Degree of linear relationship between two variables

Pearson correlation coefficient
Statistic used to measure correlation, symbolized by *r*

Correlation is defined as the degree of linear relationship between two variables. The **Pearson correlation coefficient** *r* is the statistic used as a measure of correlation, where

$$r = \frac{\Sigma z_X z_Y}{N} \tag{6.1}$$

Here z_X is the z score on a subject's value of X, z_Y is the z score on the same subject's value of Y, and N is the number of subjects as well as the number of pairs of scores. The verbal definition of *r* is the *average product of z scores*. Thus, *r* fits the notion of an "average" that has been used for $\overline{X}$ and s^{*2}. Another formula that can help you conceptually understand *r* is

$$r = \frac{\Sigma(X - \overline{X})(Y - \overline{Y})}{\sqrt{[\Sigma(X - \overline{X})^2][\Sigma(Y - \overline{Y})^2]}} = \frac{\Sigma(X - \overline{X})(Y - \overline{Y})}{\sqrt{(SS_X)(SS_Y)}} \tag{6.2}$$

Because *r* measures the degree to which two variables, X and Y, are linearly related, let's examine data with differing degrees of linear relationship and see how the value of *r* is affected for each data set.

Different Degrees and Types of Linear Relationship

Linear relationships come in many different *degrees,* ranging from zero to weak to perfect, but the only two *types* of linear relationship are positive and negative. Table 6.1 shows five different sets of data. Each data set has five pairs of scores with similar values of X and Y, but each set has a different degree or type of linear relationship. For each set of data, the z scores are shown for each variable, and the value of *r* is computed.

Table 6.1
Correlations for five data sets

Set a		Set b		Set c		Set d		Set e	
X	Y	X	Y	X	Y	X	Y	X	Y
1	3	1	7	1	4	1	4	1	6
2	4	2	6	2	3	2	7	2	5
3	5	3	5	3	5	3	5	3	4
4	6	4	4	4	7	4	3	4	7
5	7	5	3	5	6	5	6	5	3

$\overline{X} = 3 \qquad \overline{Y} = 5$

$\overset{*}{s}{}_X^2 = 2 \qquad \overset{*}{s}{}_Y^2 = 2$

$\overset{*}{s}_X = \overset{*}{s}_Y = \sqrt{2} = 1.414$

z_X	z_Y	z_X	z_Y	z_X	z_Y	z_X	z_Y	z_X	z_Y
−1.414	−1.414	−1.414	1.414	−1.414	−0.707	−1.414	−0.707	−1.414	0.707
−0.707	−0.707	−0.707	0.707	−0.707	−1.414	−0.707	1.414	−0.707	0
0	0	0	0	0	0	0	0	0	−0.707
0.707	0.707	0.707	−0.707	0.707	1.414	0.707	−1.414	0.707	1.414
1.414	1.414	1.414	−1.414	1.414	0.707	1.414	0.707	1.414	−1.414

$z_X z_Y$		$z_X z_Y$		$z_X z_Y$		$z_X z_Y$		$z_X z_Y$	
2		−2		1		1		−1	
0.5		−0.5		1		−1		0	
0		0		0		0		0	
0.5		−0.5		1		−1		1	
2		−2		1		1		−2	

$\Sigma z_X z_Y = 5$	$\Sigma z_X z_Y = -5$	$\Sigma z_X z_Y = 4$	$\Sigma z_X z_Y = 0$	$\Sigma z_X z_Y = -2$
$r = \dfrac{5}{5} = 1$	$r = -\dfrac{5}{5} = -1$	$r = \dfrac{4}{5} = .8$	$r = \dfrac{0}{5} = 0$	$r = -\dfrac{2}{5} = -.4$

Scatterplots of the data sets are shown in Figure 6.1. The same numbers are used for X and Y in each set; they are just rearranged. The means and variances are the same, making the z score and r computation simple.

Remember that a z score is calculated by subtracting the mean from the score and then dividing by the standard deviation. For example, set a has $\overline{X} = 3$ and the standard deviation $\overset{*}{s} = \sqrt{2}$. The score $X = 2$ has -0.707 for its z score because $z = (X - \overline{X})/\overset{*}{s} = (2 - 3)/\sqrt{2} = -0.707$.

Positive linear relationship
High scores on X paired with high scores on Y, and low scores on X paired with low scores on Y

Set a shows a perfect **positive linear relationship,** where all the points are on a straight line that slopes upward (from the lower left to the upper right) and where $r = 1$. The degree of the relationship is perfect and the type is positive.

The statistic r is a positive number where there are positive relationships and a negative number where there are negative relationships. This is best shown by examining the plots of the z scores for the pairs of scores in Figure 6.1. Notice that for sets a and c the scores with negative z scores on X also have negative z scores on Y, and the product of the z scores is positive. So the scores below the mean on each variable yield positive products of z scores. Similarly, the scores above the mean have positive z scores on both X and Y, so the product is also positive. The average of these positive products

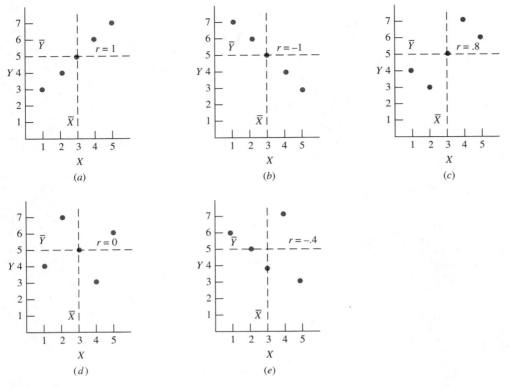

Figure 6.1
Scatterplots of data from Table 6.1

of z scores gives a positive value of r. Positive relationships are sometimes called *direct relationships.*

For sets *b* and *e*, there are negative values of r so the type of relationship is negative. The scores below the mean on variable X have negative z scores and are paired with values of Y that are above the mean and have positive z scores. The product of the z scores is negative, as is the product of the z's for the scores above the mean for variable X and the scores below the mean for variable Y. The average of these negative products of z scores gives a negative value of r. Negative relationships are sometimes called *inverse,* or *indirect, relationships.* Set *b* illustrates a perfect **negative linear relationship,** where all the points are on a line that slopes downward (from the upper left to the lower right).

Perfect relationships such as those in sets *a* and *b* never occur in real behavioral science data. Set *c* shows a high positive, but not perfect, linear relationship with $r = .8$. Set *d* has a zero linear relationship with $r = 0$. Finally, set *e* illustrates a moderately negative linear relationship with $r = -.4$. Even though the values of r for sets *c–e* are typical of behavioral science data, these simplistic data sets are not realistic because of the small N and the one-digit numbers for X and Y. Real-world experiments typically have moderate to large sample sizes with data that contain multiple digits and sometimes decimal places. The resulting values of r are not exactly -1 or $+1$, but are somewhere in between, like .54 or $-.26$.

Negative linear relationship
High scores on X paired with low scores on Y, and low scores on X paired with high scores on Y

An example of $r = -1.0$

Quick Quiz

Most people feel anxiety about giving a speech. What kind of relationship may exist between the speaker's anxiety and the number of people in the audience?

Answer

Most people become more anxious as the size of their audience increases, so anxiety goes up as the audience number. This is a positive relationship.

6.4   Properties of *r*

Two Variables

For each subject or other entity in a study, there is a pair of scores. Both variables involved in the linear relationship must yield quantitative data and should be measured on an interval or ratio scale. Chapter 19 includes a statistic used to examine relationships between two variables measured by ordinal scales.

Boundaries on *r*

The second property of *r* is that its values are in the range $-1.00 \leq r \leq 1.00$. Note that *r*'s that have the same value but different signs show the same *degree* of linear relationship, but different *types* of linear relationship. The Pearson *r* for country music airtime and white suicide rates is $r = .54$, which indicates a positive linear relationship.

Quick Quiz

For $r = .57$, $r = -.10$, $r = .42$, $r = -.57$, and $r = .07$: (a) Which *r*'s show the same type of relationship? (b) Which *r*'s show the same degree of linear relationship?

Answers

(a) $r = .57$, $r = .42$, and $r = .07$ all show positive relationships. Negative relationships are shown by $r = -.10$ and $r = -.57$. (b) The values of $r = .57$ and $r = -.57$ show the same degree of linear relationship.

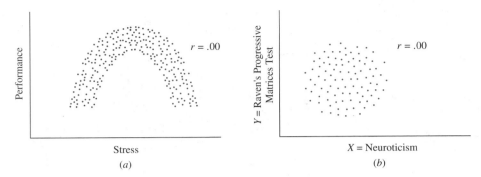

Figure 6.2

(*a*) Curvilinear relationship between stress and performance, $r = 0$. (*b*) No linear relationship between X and Y, $r = 0$.

Linear Only

We have emphasized the third property of r; it measures only the degree of *linear* relationship. Other relationships may exist—for instance, the cyclic relationship mentioned earlier between blood sugar and behavior levels—but the statistic r is insensitive to nonlinear relationships. Any relationship that is curvilinear is not detected by r. A classic example of a curvilinear relationship is between stress and performance. Slight stress may make people work harder, but as stress increases, people peak in performance, and increased stress merely reduces performance. See Figure 6.2, part (*a*). The value of r for this relationship is zero because the data have no linear relationship.

Statements about r must include the word *linear* in discussing the degree of relationship. This caution is best shown when r equals zero: Either there is no relationship or there is a relationship that r is not designed to measure. When there is no relationship between X and Y, the scatterplot of the pairs of scores is roughly a circle. See Figure 6.2, part (*b*). To be safe, when $r = 0$, you should always say there is no *linear* relationship.

Quick Quiz

You conduct a study of age and exam stress, thinking that older students are more experienced and will be less anxious about taking an exam. You compute $r = -.23$. What type of linear relationship is indicated by your statistic? What does that mean about age and exam stress?

Answer

A negative linear relationship is indicated, meaning that as age goes up, exam stress decreases.

---

r^2 = Proportion of Variability Explained

When you obtain a value for r, such as $r = .54$ for the country music/suicide rates example, you might have some problem deciding whether the degree of relationship is low or high. It certainly is not zero, and it is not a perfect positive relationship of $r = 1$.

The major problem in interpreting r is that the values of r are not on a linear scale. That is, $r = .8$ does not indicate a degree of relationship that is twice as strong as that indicated by $r = .4$.

Proportion of variability of Y that is explained by X
The definition of r^2

To be able to interpret r correctly, first you must square the value of r. When you square r, you obtain a measure of the **proportion of variability of Y that is explained by X**. For $r = .54$, you get $r^2 = (.54)^2 = .2916$ as the proportion of variability of white suicide rates that is explained by the amount of country music airtime. The statistic r^2 is sometimes called the *strength of association,* or the *coefficient of determination.* It is important for you to realize that r^2 is just a number that characterizes the joint distribution of two variables, not some mystical property. Think of r^2 as a more interpretable form of r. Many factors may explain what creates the variability in suicide rates; one factor is country music airtime. If r^2 is multiplied by 100, we get the percentage of variability of Y that is explained by X. Note that the word *explained* is used interchangeably with *accounted for* or *predicted,* but not *caused.* Squaring r doesn't allow you to suddenly talk about one variable *causing* a change in another variable.

Quick Quiz

(a) For $r = .8$, you get $r^2 =$ _____, which is defined as _____.

(b) For $r = .4$, $r^2 =$ _____, which is defined as _____.
    Answer

Y explained by X.
(a) .64: the proportion of variability of Y explained by X (b) .16: the proportion of variability in

---

Two values of r do not give information about their relative strength because r is not on a linear scale. You can use the r^2 values to compare the relationships. To compare $r = .8$ and $r = .4$, square each one and look at the r^2 values: .64 and .16. The $r = .8$ indicates a relationship that is four times as strong as the relationship indicated by $r = .4$, because $.64 = 4 \times .16$. Note that the proportion of variability of Y that is explained by X is less than the absolute value of r. What appears to be a fairly large r may explain a relatively small proportion of variability. A value of r of $-.5$ has $r^2 = .25$; only one-fourth, or 25%, of the variability of Y is explained by X, while three-fourths, or 75%, is not explained.

One of the most frequent mistakes made by students is to take the value of r directly and use it as a measure of the proportion of variability of Y explained by X. Do not make this mistake; always square r when you are asked for the proportion or percentage of variability of Y explained by X.

Even though r^2 is more easily interpreted than r, you still have no clear way to decide whether r^2 is high or low. You know what to conclude when $r = 0$, -1, or $+1$, but what about other values? The answer is part of inferential statistics and is covered in Chapter 12. For now, a crude idea of "large r" is any r^2 greater than .50.

When Is r Undefined?

If either of the variables has zero variance, then r is undefined. That is, if $s^{*2}_X = 0$ or if $s^{*2}_Y = 0$, then r cannot be computed because the z scores cannot be computed. Computation of z scores asks you to divide by the standard deviation, but dividing by zero is

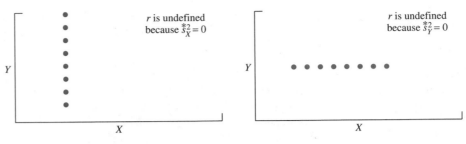

Figure 6.3
Here r is undefined

an arithmetic operation that is not allowed, or is undefined. If all the X's or all the Y's in a given set of data are identical, then r is undefined. Figure 6.3 shows two sets of data for which r is undefined because of a zero variance for X or Y.

r Is Dimensionless

The statistic r has no unit of measure. You have seen that r^2 is a proportion, and thus r is the square root of a proportion. A proportion has no unit of measure. For example, if you ask what proportion of a person's income is spent on food and you get .34 as the answer, the .34 has no unit of measure. The reason is that .34 might be obtained by dividing \$340 by \$1000, and then the unit of measure, dollars, cancels out. Thus, an r of .87 is simply $r = .87$, not .87 "somethings."

r and Change of Scale

The last property of r is that its value does not change when the scale with which X or Y is measured is changed, as long as the change is linear in nature. That is, if you add (or subtract) a constant to every X or Y, or if you multiply (or divide) every X or Y by a constant, then the value of r does not change. If the value of r between country music airtime and white suicide rates is .54, the value for r is still .54 if airtime is calculated in hours instead of minutes. Because the change from minutes to hours is simply to divide X in minutes by 60, r does not change.

6.5   Computational Formula for r

Computing r

The definitional formula for r given in formula 6.1 and the additional conceptual formula 6.2 are tedious to use for anything but tiny sample sizes, and you will have a greater tendency to make mistakes with them because of all the decimal places in the z scores. Instead, use this computational formula for r:

$$r = \frac{N\Sigma XY - (\Sigma X)(\Sigma Y)}{\sqrt{[N\Sigma X^2 - (\Sigma X)^2][N\Sigma Y^2 - (\Sigma Y)^2]}} \tag{6.3}$$

Table 6.2
Use of computational formula for r

X	Y	XY	X^2	Y^2
1	4	4	1	16
2	3	6	4	9
3	5	15	9	25
4	7	28	16	49
5	6	30	25	36
$\Sigma X = 15$	$\Sigma Y = 25$	$\Sigma XY = 83$	$\Sigma X^2 = 55$	$\Sigma Y^2 = 135$

$$r = \frac{N\Sigma XY - (\Sigma X)(\Sigma Y)}{\sqrt{[N\Sigma X^2 - (\Sigma X)^2][N\Sigma Y^2 - (\Sigma Y)^2]}} = \frac{5(83) - (15)(25)}{\sqrt{[5(55) - (15)^2][5(135) - (25)^2]}}$$

$$= \frac{415 - 375}{\sqrt{(275 - 225)(675 - 625)}} = \frac{40}{\sqrt{(50)(50)}} = \frac{40}{50} = .80$$

Of course, formulas 6.1, 6.2, and 6.3 give the same answer for any given set of data if all of the work is done correctly. Although formula 6.3 looks large and foreboding, it is actually mostly made up of pieces you have seen before. The denominator is simply the square root of the product of the numerators of the computational formulas for the sample variances (see formula 4.7) of variables X and Y. The numerator contains the sums of the scores for each of the two variables, N (the number of pairs), and the sum of the product of the scores. Only one of these pieces is new to you. The sum of the product of the scores is obtained by multiplying each X by each Y for each pair and then summing these N products.

Table 6.2 shows the computation of r for data set c in Table 6.1. As you can see, the same result, $r = .8$, is obtained by using the computational formula and the definitional formula, but without the problem of all the decimal places in the z scores.

Example

Dental anxiety data
A data set used throughout the text; it consists of dental anxiety scores, age, and gender

Let's look for a relationship between two variables and then compute r. Suppose you suspect that people become less anxious about going to the dentist as they get older. In other words, as age goes up, dental anxiety goes down. To study the relationship between age and dental anxiety, you have 40 people answer four questions about dental anxiety. Scores on each question range from 1 to 5. The dental anxiety score is obtained by summing the responses to the four questions. High numbers mean high anxiety. To show you what you might obtain, look at the **dental anxiety data** in Table 6.3. These are actual data from a dental anxiety study conducted by Arntz, van Eck, and Heijmans (1990), which is discussed in Research Example 7. Note that the data for one subject has the age missing, so r is computed with $N = 39$ subjects. In the calculations, X = age and Y = dental anxiety.

As you saw in Chapter 3, a scatterplot can give an idea of what happens to scores on one variable as scores on the other variable increase. To see what happens to dental anxiety as age increases, draw a scatterplot using the data set in Table 6.3. Put age on the X axis and anxiety on the Y axis. Your picture may look like Figure 6.4.

For the entire data set, the correlation coefficient is $r = -.18$; that is, the degree of linear relationship between age and dental anxiety is $-.18$. When you compute $r^2 = (-.18)^2 = .03$, you find that only slightly more than 3% of the variability in dental

Table 6.3
Dental anxiety data: Dental anxiety, age, and gender

Age	Gender	Anxiety Score
25	M	5
29	M	5
30	M	6
45	M	9
26	F	9
40	M	10
45	F	10
71	M	10
44	F	5
41	M	10
33	M	7
—	F	8
41	F	8
44	M	7
27	F	19
39	F	10
33	F	19
21	F	14
33	M	8
50	F	7
39	F	10
28	M	9
35	M	5
41	F	10
41	M	11
45	M	10
30	F	10
17	M	9
22	F	12
18	F	9
32	F	6
18	F	12
29	F	10
29	M	8
28	M	10
23	F	11
18	M	11
39	M	6
46	F	7
27	M	6

$\sum X = 1322$ $\sum Y = 360$ $N = 39$

$\sum X^2 = 49,372$ $\sum Y^2 = 3706$ $\sum XY = 11,970$

$$r = \frac{N\sum XY - (\sum X)(\sum Y)}{\sqrt{[N\sum X^2 - (\sum X)^2][N\sum Y^2 - (\sum Y)^2]}}$$

$$= \frac{39(11,970) - (1322)(360)}{\sqrt{[39(49,372) - (1322)^2][39(3706) - (360)^2]}}$$

$$= \frac{466,830 - 475,920}{\sqrt{(177,824)(14,934)}} = \frac{-9090}{\sqrt{2,655,623,616}}$$

$$= \frac{-9090}{51,532.74314} = -.1764$$

$$= -.18$$

Source: Arntz (1990).

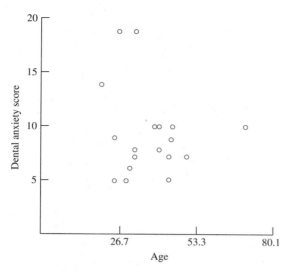

Figure 6.4
Scatterplot of age and dental anxiety score

anxiety is explained by age. The relationship is negative but not very strong. Another way of saying this is that *r* is not much different from zero. For this set of data, with males and females together, the degree of linear relationship is fairly low.

Quick Quiz

Suppose you use definitional formula 6.1 for *r*, and obtain *r* = .34. If you use the computational formula 6.3, what value do you get for *r*?

Answer

.34, with rounding error. Remember that computational formulas are easier, and definitional formulas should not be used because they are more time-consuming and usually lead to more errors. Definitional formulas should help you with conceptual understanding.

Population Correlation Coefficient

Population correlation coefficient

Population measure of the degree of linear relationship between two variables, symbolized by ρ

As you know, the sample mean $\overline{X}$ estimates the population mean, symbolized by μ. Similarly, *r* is a sample correlation that estimates the unobtainable population correlation coefficient, symbolized by ρ (Greek rho, pronounced "row"). The **population correlation coefficient** ρ is a measure of the degree of linear relationship in the population. For example, there is a population correlation coefficient for the degree of linear relationship between country music airtime and white suicide rates. You cannot obtain its value, but you can take a sample and compute a sample value, *r* = .54, as an estimate of ρ.

6.6   Factors to Consider in Using *r*

Correlation coefficients are used for purposes other than simply showing the degree of relationship between two variables. Another purpose is to measure the consistency and

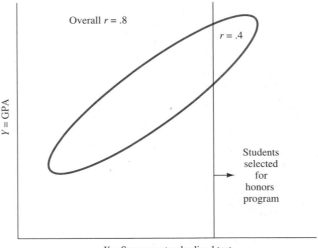

Figure 6.5
Restriction of range and effect on *r*

accuracy of standardized tests. Reliability, or consistency in measurement, can be measured by computing *r* for two measures on the same variable, with some time lapse between the two measurements. It also can be measured by computing *r* for two halves of a test (called a *split-half reliability*). High values of *r* indicate high reliability. The validity of a new test can be measured by computing *r* for the new test and for an accepted standard in the area. For example, if you developed a new intelligence test, you might measure its validity by computing the correlation between the new test and the Stanford-Binet or Wechsler test. Reliability and validity are topics covered in more advanced courses. Regardless of the purposes for using *r*, you need to take into consideration the effects of restriction of range, combined data, and extreme scores. These factors can inflate or reduce the value of the correlation coefficient.

Restriction of Range

The problem of restriction of range is fairly common. Suppose a researcher used the scores on a standardized test to select students to participate in an honors program and later computed the correlation between their standardized test scores and college GPAs. Examine Figure 6.5 to see whether you recognize the problem.

The value of *r* for all the students is reasonably high at *r* = .80 (64% of the variability in one variable is explained by the other). When the researcher used a high score on the standardized test to choose honors students, the selected group consisted of students who had similar scores on the standardized test. So the value of *r* for the select group is low at *r* = .40 (only 16% of the variability is explained). Whenever you compute *r* for a full group and then again for a subgroup formed by restricting the range on one variable, you can expect to obtain different values of *r*.

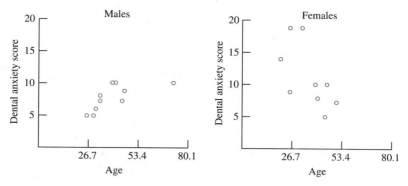

Figure 6.6
Scatterplots of age and dental anxiety score by gender

Combined Data

The dental anxiety data in Table 6.3 give a good illustration of the problem of combined data. Look back at Figure 6.4. It's hard to tell anything from this picture. But from the data in Table 6.3, it appears that most young females have higher dental anxiety scores than older females. Perhaps the relationship between age and dental anxiety depends on whether you are studying males or females. Draw two new scatterplots, one for the males and another for the females. Your pictures may look something like Figure 6.6.

What do you notice? The scatterplot for males shows a positive relationship; as age goes up, dental anxiety goes up. The scatterplot for females shows a negative relationship; as age goes up, dental anxiety goes down.

The correlation between dental anxiety and age for all 39 subjects is $r = -.18$. But if you separate subjects by gender, you find much different values for r: for males $r = .24$, for females $r = -.44$. (To practice computing r, see if you get these answers for the males and females.) There is a positive relationship for the males' ages and dental anxiety scores ($r^2 = .06$) and a negative relationship for the females' data ($r^2 = .19$). For all subjects, the negative relationship of $r = -.18$ is between the r's computed for males and females separately (with $r^2 = .03$). There isn't a "right" answer for the correlation; you learn more about your data as you explore them and try different graphs and statistics. Figure 6.7 shows the pairs of scores plotted as M's for males and as F's for females.

To see how correlation can go up when groups are combined, consider Figure 6.8. Because the number of words correct in a vocabulary test is unrelated to height at any given age, the separate values of r for first- and sixth-grade students are low, but the overall degree of correlation is $r = .86$. Both height and vocabulary increase with age.

Sometimes researchers see the same problem when they select groups from the high and low extremes of a scale. Suppose subjects who score high or low on a scale of introversion–extraversion are chosen for a study. The researcher looks at the effect of caffeine stimulation on performance on a tracking task. The correlation for these

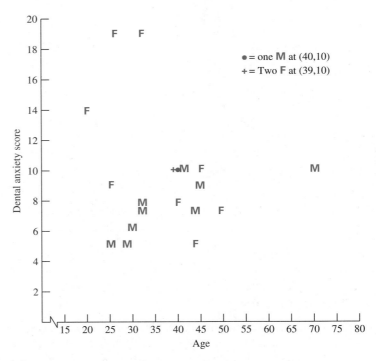

Figure 6.7
Joint scatterplot of males' and females' ages and dental anxiety scores

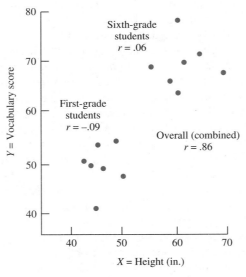

Figure 6.8
Correlation in combined groups

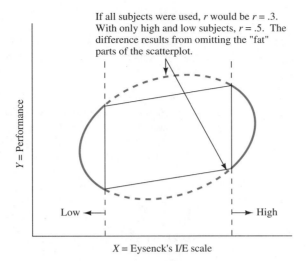

If all subjects were used, r would be $r = .3$.
With only high and low subjects, $r = .5$. The
difference results from omitting the "fat"
parts of the scatterplot.

Y = Performance

Low ← ⊢   ⊢ → High

X = Eysenck's I/E scale

Figure 6.9
Correlation when subjects are selected by extreme scores

subjects is higher than the r that would be obtained if the middle scoring subjects were included. Figure 6.9 shows the scatterplot for this situation.

Extreme Scores (Outliers)

The correlation coefficient should be used with caution whenever you have an extreme score on one or both variables. An extreme score on X or Y or both yields a scatterplot that looks as though it will have a value of r much different from the actual value. Figure 6.10 shows several situations with extreme scores and the influence on r. The extreme score can lower, raise, or even change the sign of the value of r, compared with the r for the rest of the data.

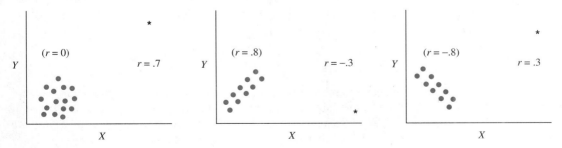

Figure 6.10
Scatterplots with extreme scores (* = single extreme score, r in parentheses is the value of r without *, the other r includes *)

Quick Quiz
Suppose you could measure the number of hairs on the heads of 100 adults of various ages. Then you computed a correlation of $r = -.12$ between age and hairs. (a) What does $r = -.12$ mean? (b) What factors could influence the statistic?

Answer

(a) Negative linear relationship (b) The statistic might be influenced by an outlier (your data may include one older balding person whose scores are driving the correlation), combined groups (as they age, females tend to keep their hair more than males do, which tempers the correlation), or restriction of range (you may have a sample of only older people, which may affect the correlation).

6.7   Correlation and Causation

Correlation Does Not Imply Causation

A frequent mistake for statistics students or the careless researcher is to make causal statements based on nonexperimental research. Many times these statements are based on a correlation coefficient. Keep in mind that correlation does not imply causation. The statistic $r = .8$ does not mean that X causes Y or that Y causes X. In fact, $r = .95$ or even higher does not imply causation between the two variables. Either X or Y could cause the other, but both could be caused by a third variable, Z. This third variable is called a *lurking variable* (Box, 1966) because it is always lurking behind the scenes and you rarely know its identity. You seldom know the causal agent behind a correlation coefficient.

Example

Consider the study of the relationship between white suicide rates and the amount of airtime given to country music. Because this was observational research, the published report made only relational statements about these two variables. The researchers know that $100r^2 = (100)(.54)^2 = 29.16\%$ of the variability in white suicide rates is explained by the amount of country music airtime (or vice versa). There appears to be a relationship between these two variables, with the possibility of the causal agent being some lurking variable, such as mood, which the researchers suggested.

Causation, True Experiments, and r

Causal inferences can come only from true experiments in which the researcher manipulates an independent variable and randomly assigns subjects to groups. Of course, if you have a true experiment with a quantitative independent variable, then you can compute the value of r between the independent and dependent variables, and you may make causal statements. However, the ability to make causal statements comes from the fact that you have a true experiment, not from the calculation of r. For an excellent discussion of this issue using the variables smoking and lung cancer, see Moore and McCabe (1993, p. 198ff).

Quick Quiz

Suppose your new roommate tells you that no one is allowed to smoke in your shared apartment because "second-hand smoke causes cancer." In light of your knowledge of statistics, how might you respond?

Answer

A causal statement can be made only when a true experiment has been performed. Because of ethical considerations, no one will ever randomly assign some people to live in smoky, potentially dangerous surroundings and then wait to see whether they get cancer. Causal statements cannot be based on observational research, so only a predictive relationship may be discussed.

6.8   Summary, Study Tips, and Computation

Chapter Summary

Correlation is the degree of linear relationship between two variables and is measured by the descriptive statistic r. Properties of r include the following: X and Y must yield quantitative data, the range of r is $-1.00 \leq r \leq 1.00$, r is for linear relationships only, r is undefined if s_Y^{*2} or s_X^{*2} equals zero, r has no unit of measure, and r is not changed by a change in scale of X or Y or both. You must square r to correctly interpret it, obtaining the proportion of variability of Y explained by X. Problems in using r include restriction of range of one of the variables, the effect of combining groups, and the effect of extreme scores, or outliers. Correlation does not imply causation.

Key words and symbols for this chapter are:

Linear	Positive relationship
Scatterplot	Negative relationship
Correlation	r^2
r	ρ

Study Tips

Even for students who are comfortable with numbers, the formula for r is intimidating. Some exercises at the end of this chapter are designed to ease your concerns about the symbols in the formula; you already have used most of those symbols in previous chapters.

To help you understand the factors that affect r, take a data set with an X, Y pair for each subject, such as the midterm and GPA scores given at the beginning of Chapter 3. (You don't have to use all of the data; practice with half of the numbers.) Draw a scatterplot and compute r. Then draw a vertical line somewhere through your scatterplot and compute r for only part of your data. Does your value of r change? Now, write an explanation of what happened and why. This requires *recall*, which is much different from *recognition*. It takes better understanding of a topic to be able to explain it (recall it) than to recognize a symbol when you see it.

Students' most frequent errors are: (1) in computing r, in the denominator, doing some operation $(+-/)$ other than multiply on the two big pieces in parentheses, and (2) using r instead of r^2 as the proportion of variability of Y explained by X.

Computation

Computation of a single correlation coefficient does not require the use of a computer. However, not only does the computer do this chore, which is more difficult than computing the mean, but also it computes correlations for all possible pairs of variables in a given data set. Let's see how to do scatterplots. Then have the computer compute one value of r, such as that between baby length and adult height. Where *data* appears, use the data given in the first example in this section.

SAS Examples

(SAS system's lines)

```
DATA CORR;
INPUT BABY ADULT SEX$ @@;
```

```
CARDS;
18.0 70.0 ? 18.0 69.0 M 20.0 69.0 M 21.0 67.0 F 20.0 67.5 F 19.5 64.0 F 22.0 67.5 F
21.0 71.0 M 20.5 70.0 M 19.0 69.0 ? 19.0 64.0 F 20.0 63.0 F 20.0 66.0 F 20.5 63.5 F
21.0 71.0 M 21.0 65.5 F 20.0 70.0 M 21.5 65.0 F 20.5 73.0 M 23.0 67.0 F 21.0 62.0 F
19.0 64.0 F 17.0 62.0 F 19.0 60.5 F 19.0 66.0 M 20.0 68.5 F 21.0 72.0 M 23.5 69.0 F
19.5 69.5 M 20.0 62.5 F 22.0 67.0 F 20.5 65.0 ? 21.0 68.0 F 20.5 67.0 F 20.5 67.0 M
19.0 60.0 ? 20.0 63.5 F 20.5 67.0 F 21.5 58.0 F
PROC PLOT;
PLOT ADULT*BABY=SEX
```
 (the start of the PLOT statement; asks for a plot of the variables ADULT and BABY with the character to be plotted being the value of the variable SEX)

```
/VREF=69.77 64.96
```
 (an option of the PLOT statement asking for horizontal lines to be drawn at 69.77 and 64.96, the mean on *Y* for males and females, respectively)

```
HREF=20.09 20.52
```
 (vertical lines are to be drawn at 20.09 and 20.52, the means on *X* for males and females, respectively)

```
HPOS=70;
```
 (option to ask for the horizontal axis to be limited to 70 positions)

```
TITLE 'SCATTERPLOT OF BABY LENGTH AND ADULT HEIGHT BY SEX';
```
(system's line)

For the output from this job using PROC PLOT, see Figure 6.11.

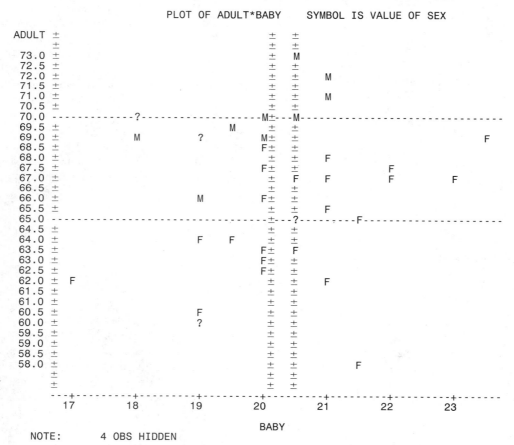

Figure 6.11
SAS output showing a scatterplot with horizontal and vertical lines giving the male and female means on the two variables

(SAS system's lines)

```
DATA CORR;
INPUT BABY ADULT SEX$@@;
CARDS;
'data '
PROC PRINT;
PROC CORR;    (this procedure computes correlations for all the participants for all possible pairs of variables in the data set; here we have
                 only BABY and ADULT as numeric variables, so it computes only one r)
PROC SORT; BY SEX;    (sorts the data by the variable sex)
PROC CORR; BY SEX;    (computes separate correlations for males and females)
```

(system's line)

Correlation Analysis

2 'VAR' Variables: BABY   ADULT

Simple Statistics

Variable ①	N	Mean	Std Dev	Sum	Minimum	Maximum
BABY	39	20.256410	1.292039	790.000000	17.000000	23.500000
ADULT	39	66.423077	3.461325	2590.500000	58.000000	73.000000

② Pearson Correlation Coefficients / Prob > |R| under Ho: Rho=0 / N = 39

	BABY	ADULT
BABY	1.00000 0.0	0.17811 ③ 0.2780
ADULT	0.17811 0.2780	1.00000 0.0

-- SEX=? --

Correlation Analysis

2 'VAR' Variables: BABY   ADULT

Simple Statistics

Variable	N	Mean	Std Dev	Sum	Minimum	Maximum
BABY	4	19.125000	1.030776	76.500000	18.000000	20.500000
ADULT	4	66.000000	4.546061	264.000000	60.000000	70.000000

Figure 6.12 (continued)
SAS output from PROC CORR

(continued)

```
Pearson Correlation Coefficients / Prob > |R| under Ho: Rho=0 / N = 4
```

	BABY	ADULT
BABY	1.00000	−0.39124
	0.0	0.6088
ADULT	−0.39124	1.00000
	0.6088	0.0

```
------------------------------------ SEX=f -----------------------------------------
```

Correlation Analysis

2 'VAR' Variables: BABY   ADULT

Simple Statistics

Variable	N	Mean	Std Dev	Sum	Minimum	Maximum
BABY	24	20.520833	1.386889	492.500000	17.000000	23.500000
ADULT	24	64.958333	2.765929	1559.000000	58.000000	69.000000

```
Pearson Correlation Coefficients / Prob > |R| under Ho: Rho=0 / N = 24
```

	BABY	ADULT
BABY	1.00000	0.43944
	0.0	0.0317
ADULT	0.43944	1.00000
	0.0317	0.0

```
------------------------------------ SEX=m -----------------------------------------
```

Correlation Analysis

2 'VAR' Variables: BABY   ADULT

Simple Statistics

Variable	N	Mean	Std Dev	Sum	Minimum	Maximum
BABY	11	20.090909	0.943880	221.000000	18.000000	21.000000
ADULT	11	69.772727	2.041613	767.500000	66.000000	73.000000

Figure 6.12 (continued)

(continued)

```
Pearson Correlation Coefficients / Prob > |R| under Ho: Rho=0 / N = 11
```

	BABY	ADULT
BABY	1.00000	0.54370
	0.0	0.0838
ADULT	0.54370	1.00000
	0.0838	0.0

Figure 6.12 (continued)

For PROC CORR, the SAS output in Figure 6.12 shows the following:

1. For each of the variables, BABY and ADULT, the value of N, mean, standard deviation (s), sum, minimum, and maximum are given.
2. This heading shows that the table that follows has correlation coefficients with probabilities used in hypothesis testing (see Chapter 12) under each r. There are $N = 39$ pairs of scores.
3. The value of r for BABY and ADULT is given as .17811. Note that each variable correlates perfectly ($r = 1.0$) with itself.

Similar output follows for each group under the variable SEX: ? , f, and m.

SPSS Example
(SPSS system's lines)
```
SET WIDTH 80
DATA LIST FREE/STRESS PERFORM
BEGIN DATA
10 20 11 21 9 20 15 40 17 45 50 20 48 20 51 21 42 40 45 45 40 60 41 59 39 60 40 40 40
50 20 60 21 59 19 60 20 40 21 50 30 90 30 88 28 91 25 80 27 82 37 71 38 70 36 72 34 80
35 82 15 26 14 25 16 25 15 34 16 37 23 71 24 70 22 72 24 77 25 75 45 26 46 25 44 25 45
34 46 37 31 87 30 86 31 86 34 87 36 85 29 87 30 88 31 86 30 77 32 80
END DATA
PLOT PLOT=PERFORM WITH STRESS     (this command tells the program that we want a scatterplot of the variables PERFORM
                                   and STRESS)

FINISH
```
(system's line)

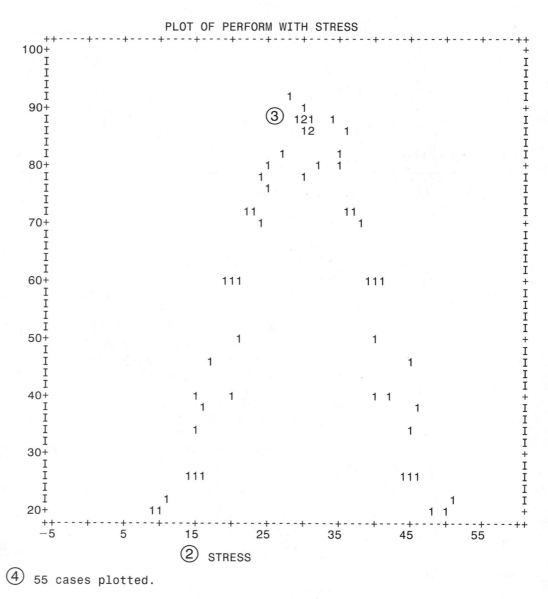

Figure 6.13
SPSS output for PLOT

For the PLOT command, the SPSS output for Figure 6.13 shows the following:

1. A scatterplot of stress and performance, with performance labeled PERFORM on the vertical axis.
2. Stress labeled STRESS on the horizontal axis.
3. The symbol 2 used when two values overlap.
4. The sample size N as the number of cases plotted.

```
(SPSS system's lines)
SET WIDTH 80
DATA LIST FREE/BABY ADULT
BEGIN DATA
18.0 70.0 18.0 69.0 20.0 69.0 21.0 67.0 20.0 67.5 19.5 64.0 22.0 67.5 21.0 71.0 20.5
70.0 19.0 69.0 19.0 64.0 20.0 63.0 20.0 66.0 20.5 63.5 21.0 71.0 21.0 65.5 20.0 70.0
21.5 65.0 20.5 73.0 23.0 67.0 21.0 62.0 19.0 64.0 17.0 62.0 19.0 60.5 19.0 66.0 20.0
68.5 21.0 72.0 23.5 69.0 19.5 69.5 20.0 62.5 22.0 67.0 20.5 65.0 21.0 68.0 20.5 67.0
20.5 67.0 19.0 60.0 20.0 63.5 20.5 67.0 21.5 58.0
END DATA
CORRELATION VARIABLES=BABY ADULT/PRINT TWOTAIL SIG
```
(computes *r* for the variables listed, BABY and ADULT, and asks for two-tailed probabilities used later in hypothesis testing)

```
FINISH
```
(system's line)

```
        - -   Correlation Coefficients   - -

              BABY        ADULT

BABY        1.0000        .1781   ①

            (   39)     (   39)   ②
            P= .         P= .278


ADULT        .1781       1.0000
            (   39)     (   39)
            P= .278      P= .

(Coefficient / (Cases) / 2-tailed sig)  ③
"  .  " is printed if a coefficient cannot be computed.
```

Figure 6.14
SPSS output for CORRELATION

For the CORRELATION command, the SPSS output in Figure 6.14 shows the following:

1. The value of *r* for BABY and ADULT. Note that each variable correlates perfectly (*r* = 1.0) with itself.
2. The value of *N* for each pair of variables.
3. The labeling key showing that the correlations (*r*) have *N* (in parentheses, called Cases) below the *r*'s and probability values below the *N*'s. The probabilities can be used in hypothesis testing (see Chapter 12).

Exercises

Section 6.2

1. At a college football game, the following variables were observed:

   Sale of cold soft drinks   Quality of opponent
   Sale of hot drinks   Sale of umbrellas
   Sale of peanuts   Attendance
   Inches of rain   Temperature
   Quality of home team

   Create all the possible pairs of variables.
   a. Which variables would you expect to be positively related?
   b. Which variables would you expect to be negatively related?
   c. Which variables would you expect to be unrelated?
   d. Would any two variables have a curvilinear relationship?

2. In the game of bowling, consider the variables number of pins knocked down and speed of the ball.
   a. Are the two variables positively related?
   b. How is number of pins knocked down related to the time it takes the ball to go down the alley?

Section 6.3

3. For each of the following pairs of variables, indicate whether *r* would be positive, negative, or about zero.
   a. People's weight and salary
   b. The age and height of a tree
   c. The age of your TV set and its value (excluding antiques)
   d. The number of alcoholic drinks consumed and the ability to drive a car
   e. Age and height of adults
   f. Age and height of children
   g. The number of murders in a city and the weight of its telephone book

Section 6.4

4. Research has shown that the shyness of female college students (*N* = 56) is related to their mother's acceptance of them (both measures were self-reports) with *r* = −.32.
   a. Explain what the negative value of *r* means in terms of these variables.
   b. What percentage of variability in the measure of shyness is explained by the measure of mother's acceptance?

5. Arcuri and Lester (1990) found that, for police officers who moonlighted (*N* = 28), the number of hours worked at other jobs was related to their self-report stress scores, *r* = .45.
   a. What percentage of variability in the stress scores is explained by the number of hours worked at other jobs?
   b. What possible extraneous variables could also account for variability in stress scores?
   c. Comment on this quote regarding the association between the two variables as evidenced by the value of *r*: "the present data do not allow a choice to be made among the cause-and-effect possibilities in this association."

Section 6.5

6. For the following parts of the formula for the correction coefficient *r*, name another formula, if any, that

you have seen so far in this book that used the same part:

a. N
b. ΣX
c. ΣY
d. ΣX^2
e. ΣY^2
f. $(\Sigma X)^2$
g. $(\Sigma Y)^2$
h. $N\Sigma X^2 - (\Sigma X)^2$
i. $N\Sigma Y^2 - (\Sigma Y)^2$
j. (something minus something) divided by the square root of something
k. ΣXY

7. Using the following data set:

Pair	1	2	3	4	5
X	7	8	2	11	10
Y	22	19	20	21	18

a. Draw a scatterplot of the data.
b. Compute $(\Sigma X)^2$ and $(\Sigma Y)^2$.
c. Compute ΣX^2 and ΣY^2.
d. Compute N.
e. Compute ΣXY.

8. You have obtained data about the suicide rates and the amount of country music airtime in five cities in your state.
a. What does X represent? What does Y represent?
b. You have calculated the following pieces of the formula for r:

$$\Sigma X = 110$$

$$\Sigma Y = 77$$

$$\Sigma X^2 = 2430$$

$$\Sigma Y^2 = 1207$$

$$\Sigma XY = 1695$$

Complete the calculation of r.
c. What type of linear relationship appears to exist for your data set?

9. You have completed a study of preschoolers' aggressiveness and television watching habits. Parents of ten preschoolers have kept a diary of how much time their child watched television for one week. During the same week, you and a coresearcher watched the ten children through a mirrored glass at their preschool and calculated an aggression score for each child. The score was based on the number of times the child pushed another child or otherwise acted aggressively. Here are the results from your study (X = number of hours of television, Y = aggression score, *Child* = the number used to identify each child):

Child	1	2	3	4	5	6	7	8	9	10
X	26	28	24	18	19	36	12	21	28	33
Y	4	2	0	5	5	4	6	3	2	0

a. Draw a scatterplot of the data.
   Check your work at each of these steps toward computing r:
b. Compute the means for X and Y.
c. Compute X^2 and Y^2 for each child.
d. Compute s^{*2} for X and Y.
e. Compute the XY product for each child.
f. Find the other pieces needed for the formula for r: N, $(\Sigma X)^2$ and $(\Sigma Y)^2$ (see part b), ΣX^2 and ΣY^2 (see part c), and ΣXY (see part e).
g. Put together the pieces and compute r.
h. Did your results turn out as Bandura might have predicted? If you obtained a negative value for r, what does that mean about the relationship between amount of television watched and aggressiveness among preschoolers?
i. Let's say you expected a positive value of r, but your statistic is negative. You go back to the parents' diaries of television habits to look for a reason. You find that the children who watched the most television also were avid viewers of Barney, the friendly purple dinosaur who advocates moral behavior. How might you design a study to investigate whether Barney is having an effect on children?

10. *Locus of control* refers to the placement of control of reinforcement in one's world. *Internal* control refers to the belief that events are dependent on a person's own behavior, while *external* control refers to the belief that events are not entirely dependent on personal behavior but are the result of some outside influence (others, luck, and so on). Rotter (1966) developed the I/E (internal/external) scale to measure the locus of control. Suppose a researcher asked students to answer the questions in this scale as they thought a typical student at their university might answer them. Also suppose that 6 months earlier

these same students had answered the questions in the scale for themselves. The following data were collected:

Student	A	B	C	D	E	F	G	H
I/E (self)	14	17	25	11	9	17	19	20
I/E attributed to other	18	17	22	19	10	18	18	16

a. Compute the mean and standard deviation for both variables.
b. Plot the pairs of scores in a scatterplot. Does it appear that I/E (self) and I/E attributed to other are related?
c. Compute *r*. Are these two variables related?

11. Use the following data:

Pair	A	B	C	D	E
X	1	7	6	5	2
Y	2	4	3	3	1

a. Draw a scatterplot of these data and then compute *r*.
b. Change the value for E and Y from 1 to 5, make a scatterplot of the data, and then compute *r*. Does the change in *r* surprise you?

12. Does $r = .11$ necessarily show that there is little or no relationship between the two variables? Could there possibly be a high degree of relationship? Explain.

13. Which value of $r = .3$, $r = .1$, and $r = -.4$ shows the strongest relationship? Explain.

Section 6.6

14. Use these data:

Pair	1	2	3	4	5
X	15	20	17	19	39
Y	10	7	11	9	5

a. Form a scatterplot of the data.
b. Estimate the value of *r* visually.
c. Compute *r* and compare it to your guess in part b.
d. How would *r* change if the last *Y* score were changed to 25?
e. Compute *r* on only the first four pairs of scores; compare this value of *r* to those found in parts c and d. How does one pair of scores influence *r*?

15. A company gives a placement test battery to 60 job applicants and finds a correlation between two of the variables to be .73. They select ten of these people to hire, and after 6 weeks on the job they give only these ten people the same battery of tests. Now the correlation is .31. Could the 6 weeks on the job be the only influence on *r* (other than chance fluctuations), or is there another possible explanation?

Section 6.7

16. For a group of distance runners, a track coach observes $r = .25$, where X = number of hours of sleep and Y = number of miles run in practice in a week. Can she argue that X causes Y, so everybody should sleep more? Explain.

17. Use the following data:

Pair	1	2
X	1	2
Y	4	7

a. Find *r*.
b. Change $X = 2$ to $X = 100$ and recompute *r*.
c. Change $X = 1$ to $X = 100$ and recompute *r*.
d. What conclusions can you draw about the possible values of *r* if $N = 2$?
e. Can you compute *r* for these data?

Pair	1	2
X	1	1
Y	4	7

What condition must be placed on your conclusions in part d?

18. Consider these data for the average speed of a sample of vehicles on level interstate highway and the average miles per gallon of all vehicles operated in the United States.

Year	1960	1965	1970	1972	1973	1974	1975	1976	1977	1978
Average Speed	54.8	60.6	63.8	64.9	65.0	57.6	57.6	58.2	58.8	58.8
Average Miles per Gallon	14.28	14.15	13.58	13.67	13.29	13.65	13.74	13.93	14.15	14.26

a. Draw a scatterplot of the average speed (in miles per hour) and average mileage (in miles per gallon).

b. Calculate r for all 10 years.

c. Calculate r for the first 5 years.

d. Calculate r for the last 5 years.

e. Intuitively, for a given vehicle on a given day, is speed positively or negatively related to miles per gallon? Then what is happening with the data in the table? What are some possible confounding variables?

19. Use SAS or SPSS to do any of the computational exercises above. Then compare your hand computations to the computer output.

7

Describing Data for Two Variables: Regression

Chapter 6 showed you how to describe the degree of linear relationship between two variables. Now we move to the topic of regression. Regression allows you to write a linear prediction equation. You can take a new subject's score on one variable and put it into the prediction equation to come up with a predicted score on the other variable.

Research Example 7

7.1 Introduction: Regression and Linear Prediction
  Correlation versus prediction
  Prediction
  Equation for a straight line

7.2 Using and Interpreting the Regression Equation
  Linear only
  Limited generalization
  Example
  Scatterplots
  Error defined and illustrated

7.3 Least Squares and the Best-Fitting Line
  Least-squares criterion
  Computational formulas for b and a
  Example

7.4 Standard Error of Estimate
  Variability of errors
  Definition of $s_{Y \cdot X}$
  Computational formula for $s_{Y \cdot X}$

7.5 Partitioning Total Variability
  Example: Variance explained and variance not explained

7.6 Regression: Enhancing Your Understanding
  Relationship of regression to correlation
  Confidence limits
  Relationship of regression to ANOVA

7.7 Multiple Regression and Other Topics
  Prediction equation
  Standardized variables
  Multiple correlation
  Overlap problem
  Best equation
  Beyond multiple regression

7.8 Summary, Study Tips, and Computation
Chapter summary
Study tips
Computation
Exercises

Research Example 7

You were introduced in Chapter 6 to the study by Arntz, van Eck, and Heijmans (1990) on dental anxiety. The researchers had several hypotheses about the relationship between predictions of pain, actual experienced pain, and memory of pain.

The study's participants, 20 male and 20 female volunteers, had an average age of 33.9 (age ranged from 17 to 71, with one person's age missing), and they were all treated twice. The average time between treatments was 10.4 days, with a range from 1 to 37 days. The treatments, consisting of typical dental work, were potentially painful. Before each treatment, the participants answered questions about their anxiety, fear, and predicted pain. They used a 100-mm line to rate their feelings. For instance, the scale for predicted pain ranged from 0 = "not at all painful" to 100 = "the worst pain imaginable," and each person made a mark on the line to indicate the rating. Immediately after each treatment, each participant rated the actual experienced pain on the same scale. Five months after the second treatment, 31 participants responded to a follow-up survey about memories of pain on the same scale. The researchers wanted to know which variables influenced memories of pain. Do people remember their predictions of pain or their actual experience of pain?

Arntz, van Eck, and Heijmans found that original predicted pain (prediction before the first treatment) was the best predictor of memories of pain 5 months after the second treatment. The linear prediction equation based on $N = 31$ follow-up respondents is

$$Y' = 6.8280 + 0.3895(\text{PREPAIN1})$$

where PREPAIN1 is the predicted pain score before the first treatment and Y' is a predicted score for the memory of pain. For this equation, $r^2 = .447$, so 44.7% of the variability in the memories of pain is explained by PREPAIN1.

Suppose you form a prediction equation with the following predictors: PREPAIN1 (predicted pain before treatment 1), PREPAIN2 (predicted pain before treatment 2), EXPPAIN1 (actual experienced pain after treatment 1), EXPPAIN2 (actual experienced pain after treatment 2), AGE, DAST (total score on the Dental Anxiety Scale), and SEX. For the 30 follow-up respondents whose ages were known, the multiple linear prediction equation with all seven predictors is:

$$Y' = 6.0419 + 0.0273(\text{EXPPAIN1}) + 0.1200(\text{EXPPAIN2})$$
$$+ 0.2967(\text{PREPAIN1}) + 0.2144(\text{PREPAIN2})$$
$$- 0.00256(\text{AGE}) - 0.4741(\text{DAST}) + 3.2379(\text{SEX})$$

with $R^2 = .571$, or 57.1% of the variability in the memories of pain explained by all seven variables.

That's a complicated equation. There is, however, a two-predictor equation that may be the "best" equation in the sense of explaining the most variability in memories of pain with the fewest predictors. The multiple linear prediction equation with the two best predictors for $N = 30$ is

$$Y' = 5.6364 + 0.2829(\text{PREPAIN1}) + 0.1925(\text{PREPAIN2})$$

with $R^2 = .545$, or 54.5% of the variability in the memories of pain explained by PREPAIN1 and PREPAIN2. Do you really need to add five more variables to explain just 2.6% more variability? In this chapter you will learn these additional regression analyses.

These data suggest that memories of dental pain are largely influenced by predictions of pain that patients made before the treatments. That is, memories are most influenced by the cognitive processes that go on before the dental work itself is done. These predictions of pain are even better predictors of memories of pain than the actual experienced pain. Do we remember what we want to remember rather than the truth?

7.1 Introduction: Regression and Linear Prediction

Correlation versus Prediction

Correlational studies generally consider only the degree of linear relationship between two variables, such as age and dental anxiety. You can take the idea a step further, however. If you know about the trend toward increased dental anxiety as men get older, you can predict a certain man's dental anxiety at various ages. If you have a scatterplot of men's ages and dental anxiety scores, you might have a handful of people at a given age—say, 38—with a variety of dental anxiety scores. Which dental anxiety score is the best guess for someone who is 38? Probably an anxiety score in the middle of that range of dental anxiety scores for 38-year-old men.

What if, instead of looking at the data, you have a line that represents the best guesses for anxiety scores at all ages for which you have data? Then you could pick an age and look for the dental anxiety score that falls on the prediction line. Or you could ask a new dental patient his age and predict his dental anxiety by using a line that best fits the data.

Regression
Area of statistics where a researcher is concerned with predicting one variable from another

Finding the best-fitting line for data involves more than looking at the data and drawing. The numbers in a data set are used to create a mathematical expression for the prediction line. (In fact, the math results in a kind of *average* line, one that balances some data points above it and other data points below it.) The area of statistics concerned with predicting one variable from another is **regression.**

Quick Quiz

A friend tells you that his weight is correlated with the weather: As the temperature rises, his weight goes down, and as the temperature drops, his weight rises. Suppose you measure the temperature and his weight once a month for a year and compute the correlation coefficient, *r*. What do you expect to find if he is correct about his weight and temperature?

Answer

You might find a negative *r*, reflecting a negative linear relationship between the two variables.

Prediction

Prediction problems usually involve a separation in time between observations on the two variables, but correlation problems often do not. The amount of violent television watched may be measured over several months or years, and the related aggressive behavior may be observed later in life. In most prediction studies, scores are obtained on both variables from an existing group of participants. The regression (prediction) equation is formed from these pairs of scores and is used for predicting only linear relationships between two variables.

You may think it's frivolous to form a prediction equation for age and dental anxiety. After all, you already know how afraid you are (or aren't) about a trip to the dentist. But regression is also used in many real-life situations. For example, administrators of some graduate school programs use linear prediction (regression) equations to assist in admissions decisions. They use predictors such as the Graduate Record Examination (GRE) score, undergraduate grade point average (GPA), and quality of the undergraduate program. They want to predict success in their graduate program for each applicant, with the graduate GPA as a measure of success. A person with a high predicted graduate GPA is more likely to be admitted.

Equation for a Straight Line

Let's start with simple linear prediction. "Simple" means that you use only one predictor and one criterion variable. Only linear relationships are considered for several reasons, the most obvious being simplicity of the mathematics and interpretation. Linear relationships are also used because sometimes they serve as good approximations to realistic data sets, even when the relationship is nonlinear.

Prediction equation
$Y' = bX + a$

The formula for the **prediction equation** is

$$Y' = bX + a \tag{7.1}$$

where Y' = **predicted score** on the criterion variable

Predicted score
Predicted value of Y
for a given value of X,
symbolized by Y'

X = score on the predictor variable
b = slope of the line
a = Y intercept of the line

In the example of dental anxiety and age, Y' is the predicted dental anxiety score (criterion variable) based on the equation with X = age as the predictor variable. The other two components of formula 7.1, slope and Y intercept, need further explanation.

Slope

Slope
The rise of a line divided by the run, symbolized by b

The **slope** of the line, b, has the verbal definition *rise over run*—that is, the rise divided by the run, or the change in the vertical distance divided by the change in the horizontal distance:

$$b = \frac{\text{rise}}{\text{run}} = \frac{\text{change in vertical distance}}{\text{change in horizontal distance}}$$

Figure 7.1 shows the slope of a line in terms of the rise and the run. Think of the steepness of a hill as its slope: the more steep the hill, the higher the slope. A steep hill

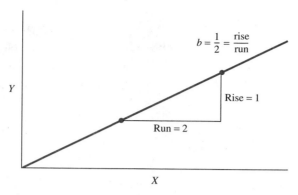

Figure 7.1
Slope = b = rise divided by run

has a large change in vertical distance for a given change in horizontal distance. In simple terms, you go "up" more rapidly than you go "over." A gentle hill has a small slope because the change in vertical distance is small relative to the change in horizontal distance. If the land is flat, the slope is zero because there is no change in vertical distance as the horizontal distance changes. The correlation and the slope always have the same sign. Any time the value of r is positive, the value of b, the slope of the line, is also positive. If $r = 0$, the slope also equals zero. Figure 7.2 shows four lines with different slopes.

Notice the line that has a negative slope. This is because the change in the vertical distance is negative; that is, the vertical change decreases as the horizontal distance changes in a positive direction. When there is negative slope, you are going downhill rather than uphill.

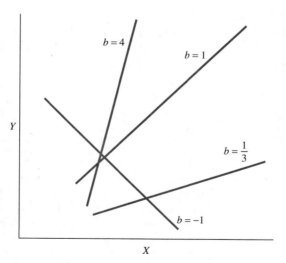

Figure 7.2
Four lines with different slopes

Y intercept
Point where the line
intersects the Y axis,
symbolized by a

Y Intercept

The **Y intercept** of the line, a, is the point where the line intersects the Y axis, or the value of Y' when $X = 0$. When $X = 0$ in formula 7.1, you get

$$Y' = bX + a$$
$$= b(0) + a$$
$$= 0 + a$$
$$= a$$

Thus, a, the Y intercept, is verbally defined as *the value of the predicted score for Y when X = 0.* The lines in Figure 7.2 have different values of a because each line would intersect the Y axis at a different point.

Quick Quiz

You decide to measure the classic relationship between job stress and performance. You obtain self-reported stress scores from 20 members of a large office staff and a supervisor's rating of their performances that day. You compute $r = .01$ and decide there must be something wrong with your calculations because it's clear from your scatterplot that performance goes up and then down in relation to increased stress. What's wrong here?

Answer

Your only conclusion can be that there is no *linear* relationship between the variables. The statistic r does not tell you about curvilinear relationships, such as the one discovered here.

7.2   Using and Interpreting the Regression Equation

Linear Only

In regression the relationship between the predictor variable X and the criterion variable Y must be linear or well approximated by a straight line. Other methods instead of linear correlation and regression are better to use if the relationship is nonlinear. A linear regression equation underestimates a nonlinear relationship. However, as mentioned earlier, many relationships between variables in the behavioral sciences are linear.

Limited Generalization

A linear regression equation is found by using the data from only one sample. You cannot generalize the results beyond the actual values of X used in computing b and a. You are limited to generalizations within the range of the X scores in your sample. Early research on the relationship between stress and performance showed a linear relationship for low levels of stress. Researchers speculated that increased stress would result in increased performance, but in reality performance decreased at higher levels of stress. The true relationship between stress and performance is curvilinear. If a prediction were based on the early equations and the researchers predicted performance for a stress level higher than any score in the original sample, they would incorrectly conclude that a high level of stress results in high performance. In the female dental anxiety study, the participants' ages were 21 to 50, so you could not use these data to generalize about the relationship between age and dental anxiety for women over 50.

Another limitation on generalizations is restriction of range. Similar to the problems that restriction of range gives to computing r (see Chapter 6), you can generalize your prediction only to the range of the X variable used in forming the regression equation.

A third limitation is that the b and a are sample statistics and as such are subject to sampling variability. If you draw another sample from the same population, you will get different values for b and a. Increasing the sample size will increase the stability of b and a, but this also increases the cost of the research.

Quick Quiz

To study the drowsiness effects of a certain cold remedy, you are working with doctors at a research hospital. The doctors have observed that small doses of the medication slightly increase people's drowsiness. At medium doses, drowsiness increases considerably. But higher doses of the medication seem to make people quite jumpy and unable to rest. Should you recommend the use of linear regression to measure the relationship between dosage and drowsiness?

Answer

No, because the relationship appears to be curvilinear, not linear, which is what the regression equation is designed to handle.

Example

The values of b and a completely specify the equation for the line $Y' = bX + a$. That's why they are sometimes called *regression constants*. If you know that $b = 2$ and $a = 1$, not only can you draw the line with slope 2 and Y intercept 1, but also you know that the prediction equation is $Y' = 2X + 1$. If you have an X value of 40, you know that the value of Y' is

$$Y' = 2X + 1$$
$$= 2(40) + 1$$
$$= 80 + 1$$
$$= 81$$

We could insert any value of X and get its corresponding value of Y', the predicted value of Y.

Suppose someone has a broken pipe at home and calls a plumber to fix it. The plumber charges a flat "per job" fee of \$30 in addition to \$35 per hour or any part thereof. The charges of the plumber may be expressed as a linear equation with $a = \$30$ and $b = \$35$, or $Y' = \$35X + \$30$. If the plumber works for 2 h, the charge for the labor portion of the bill is:

$$Y' = \$35X + \$30$$
$$= \$35(2) + \$30$$
$$= \$70 + \$30$$
$$= \$100$$

Scatterplots

Notice that the equation for the plumber's wages yields a perfectly straight line. All values of Y are on the line $Y' = bX + a$ because there is a perfect linear relationship between hours and wages. Most variables, however, are not perfectly related, and the scatterplot shows a cluster of scores that do not form a straight line. Where do we draw the line?

A line must be computed to fit the data as well as possible. When you use the line $Y' = bX + a$ to approximate or fit the data, most scores are not on the line. Some scores are close to the line; others are farther away. Figure 7.3 shows the scatterplots of the five data sets from Table 6.1 with the line $Y' = bX + a$ included. For the perfect relationships in sets *a* and *b,* all scores are on the line. For the other data sets, not all scores are on the line, so the observed Y is not equal to the predicted score Y'. This gap between Y and Y' is called *error.*

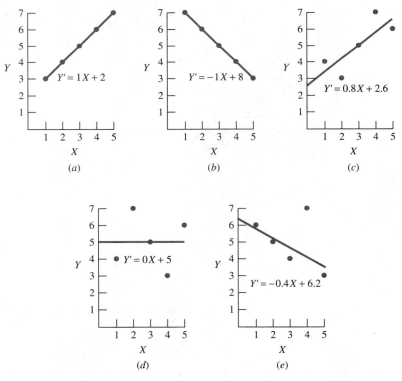

Figure 7.3
Regression lines and scatterplots for data from Table 6.1

Error Defined and Illustrated

Error
Difference between the observed Y and Y', symbolized by $e = Y - Y'$

Error is symbolized as e and defined simply as

$$e = Y - Y' \tag{7.2}$$

or the difference between the observed Y and the predicted Y'. Sometimes the word *residual* is used instead of *error*. The actual observed Y score differs from the predicted score Y'. In other words, we predicted Y' and the actual score is Y, so we made an error in our prediction.

The concept of error as a deviation score (difference score) was introduced when we used a measure of central tendency (for example, $\bar{X}$) to represent all the scores. Error was defined as $X - \bar{X}$. Here error is a similar deviation score—the observed score Y minus the predicted score Y'. As you might expect, the error should be as small as possible so the predictions are better.

Figure 7.4 shows a plot of the original data for X and Y from data set c along with the regression line. The error for each (X,Y) point is indicated by an arrow. For example, the (X,Y) pair of $(1,4)$ is above the regression line, so the error is positive, $Y - Y' = 4 - 3.4 = 0.6$. Remember, we are interested in using the line to predict Y, so error is the deviation of Y from the line.

Table 7.1 gives data set c and shows the computation of Y' and error e for each data point. Table 7.1 also lists the values of ΣX^2, ΣY^2, and ΣXY, which are used later. The values of b and a are given without showing you how to compute them. You will learn the computational formulas in the next section. For now, just use the given values of b and a to understand errors and predicted scores.

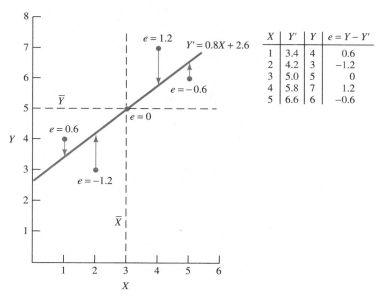

X	Y'	Y	$e = Y - Y'$
1	3.4	4	0.6
2	4.2	3	−1.2
3	5.0	5	0
4	5.8	7	1.2
5	6.6	6	−0.6

Figure 7.4
Error and the regression line for data set c

Table 7.1
Calculation of Y' and e for data set c

X	Y	$Y' = bX + a$ $= 0.8X + 2.6$	$e = Y - Y'$	X^2	Y^2	XY
1	4	$Y' = 0.8(1) + 2.6$ $= 0.8 + 2.6$ $= 3.4$	$e = 4 - 3.4$ $= 0.6$	1	16	4
2	3	$Y' = 0.8(2) + 2.6$ $= 1.6 + 2.6$ $= 4.2$	$e = 3 - 4.2$ $= -1.2$	4	9	6
3	5	$Y' = 0.8(3) + 2.6$ $= 2.4 + 2.6$ $= 5.0$	$e = 5 - 5.0$ $= 0$	9	25	15
4	7	$Y' = 0.8(4) + 2.6$ $= 3.2 + 2.6$ $= 5.8$	$e = 7 - 5.8$ $= 1.2$	16	49	28
5	6	$Y' = 0.8(5) + 2.6$ $= 4.0 + 2.6$ $= 6.6$	$e = 6 - 6.6$ $= -0.6$	25	36	30
$\Sigma X = 15$	$\Sigma Y = 15$		$\Sigma e = 0$	$\Sigma X^2 = 55$	$\Sigma Y^2 = 135$	$\Sigma XY = 83$

Return to Figure 7.4 and find each (X, Y) pair, each Y', and each error. Make sure you can see the connections among these components of linear regression.

Notice that the sum of the values of e equals zero. This is not a coincidence; it's true for any set of data if Y' is computed with the correct choice of b and a. Notice that the best line also goes through the point $(\overline{X}, \overline{Y})$ on the graph. There are many lines for which the sum of the errors is zero, and all of them go through the point $(\overline{X}, \overline{Y})$ on the graph. But we need to define b and a so that the errors sum to zero *and* the line minimizes the error. Let's look at the computational formulas for b and a.

Quick Quiz

Suppose we have a regression equation between age and dental anxiety. What do you call the difference between the actual dental anxiety score (Y) and the predicted dental anxiety score from the equation (Y')?

Answer

Error, e

7.3   Least Squares and the Best-Fitting Line

Least-Squares Criterion

When we talk about the "best-fitting" line, several criteria could be used to define which line is "best." The criterion usually used in regression is to minimize the sum of the squared errors:

$$\Sigma e^2 = \Sigma(Y - Y')^2 \text{ is a minimum}$$

Least-squares criterion
Choice of statistics so as to minimize a sum of squares; Σe^2 is minimized by the correct choice of b and a

The formulas that are given for b and a define Y' such that the sum of the squared errors is smaller than for any other line. For this reason, the criterion of minimizing the sum of the squared errors is called the **least-squares criterion.** You saw in Chapter 4 that $\overline{X}$ met the least-squares criterion because it minimized $\Sigma(X - \overline{X})^2$. Now b and a must define Y' so that the least-squares criterion—to minimize $\Sigma(Y - Y')^2$—is met. The line Y' is a kind of average line through the data, so the least-squares criterion here is similar to what you learned in Chapter 4. Return to Figure 7.4 to understand the idea of the errors being minimized by the line in terms of "least squares."

Computational Formulas for *b* and *a*

The computational formula for b has familiar pieces. The numerator is the same as the numerator in the formula for r, and the denominator of b is the same as the numerator of $\overset{*}{s}{}^2$ of the X values. The slope b is computed from

$$b = \frac{N\Sigma XY - (\Sigma X)(\Sigma Y)}{N\Sigma X^2 - (\Sigma X)^2} \tag{7.3}$$

The Y intercept a is computed from

$$a = \overline{Y} - b\overline{X} \tag{7.4}$$

In using formula 7.4 to compute a, you must use the unrounded value for b. Because b is multiplied by $\overline{X}$, rounding errors in b can lead to large mistakes in a. Another formula for the slope that some students find helpful is

$$b = \frac{\Sigma(X - \overline{X})(Y - \overline{Y})}{\Sigma(X - \overline{X})^2} = \frac{\Sigma(X - \overline{X})(Y - \overline{Y})}{SS_X} \tag{7.5}$$

For data set c in Table 7.1 the slope b is computed as

$$b = \frac{N\Sigma XY - (\Sigma X)(\Sigma Y)}{N\Sigma X^2 - (\Sigma X)^2} = \frac{5(83) - (15)(25)}{5(55) - (15)^2}$$

$$= \frac{415 - 375}{275 - 225} = \frac{40}{50} = 0.80$$

and the Y intercept a as

$$a = \overline{Y} - b\overline{X} = 5 - 0.8(3) = 5 - 2.4 = 2.6$$

So the regression constants for data set c are $b = 0.8$ and $a = 2.6$.

Figure 7.5 shows plots of the least-squares line for data set c and two other lines that have errors that sum to zero but are not the least-squares line. Line 2 obviously is not a

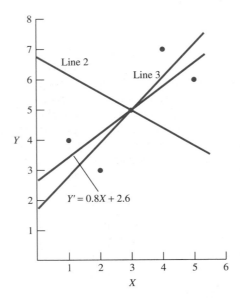

Figure 7.5
Three lines with errors that sum to zero

good fit to the data and has a large value of Σe^2. Line 3 might appear to be the best fit, but its Σe^2 is larger than the Σe^2 for the least-squares line.

You now have $Y' = bX + a$ as the best-fitting line for a set of data given the least-squares criterion. You could form a second regression line that fits the data given the least-squares criterion by predicting X from Y. But most researchers prefer to use Y for the criterion variable and X for the predictor variable, so we follow that convention in this text.

Example

Let's use a realistic data set to find a regression equation. Consider the dental anxiety/age example from Chapter 6. The size of the correlations of dental anxiety with age depends on gender: for men $r = .24$ and for women $r = -.44$. The different values of r for men and women suggest that we should compute separate regression equations. Table 7.2 shows the computations of the regression constants necessary for forming the prediction equations for dental anxiety of men and women.

The regression equation for predicted dental anxiety score for men is $Y' = 0.04$ (age) $+ 6.65$, and for women is $Y' = -0.16$ (age) $+ 15.71$. The negative value of b for women indicates the negative relationship between dental anxiety and age indicated earlier by the negative r. The Dental Anxiety Scale ranges from 4 to 20, with higher scores indicating higher anxiety. Knowing your age, you can use the appropriate regression equation to find your own Y'. Does your Y' approximate what you think is your actual dental anxiety?

Quick Quiz

Jane calculated her predicted dental anxiety Y' to be 15.77. Her actual dental anxiety score is 14. John found his predicted dental anxiety score to be 5.65. His actual dental anxiety score is 9. Compare the errors for these two people.

Answer

For Jane's data, $e = Y - Y' = 14 - 15.77 = -1.77$. For John's data, $e = 9 - 5.65 = 3.35$. The equation for women overpredicted her dental anxiety, and the equation for men underpredicted his.

Table 7.2

Prediction equations for men and women, using age to predict dental anxiety

$X = Age$	$Y = Dental$ $anxiety$	X^2	Y^2	XY
		Men		
25	5	625	25	125
29	5	841	25	145
30	6	900	36	180
45	9	2025	81	405
40	10	1600	100	400
71	10	5041	100	710
41	10	1681	100	410
33	7	1089	49	231
44	7	1936	49	308
33	8	1089	64	264
28	9	784	81	252
35	5	1225	25	175
41	11	1681	121	451
45	10	2025	100	450
17	9	289	81	153
29	8	841	64	232
28	10	784	100	280
18	11	324	121	198
39	6	1521	36	234
27	6	729	36	162
$\Sigma X = 698$	$\Sigma Y = 162$	$\Sigma X^2 = 27{,}030$	$\Sigma Y^2 = 1394$	$\Sigma XY = 5765$

$$\bar{X} = 34.9 \qquad \bar{Y} = 8.1$$

$$\overset{*}{s}{}_X^2 = 133.49 \qquad \overset{*}{s}{}_Y^2 = 4.09$$

$$b = \frac{N\Sigma XY - (\Sigma X)(\Sigma Y)}{N\Sigma X^2 - (\Sigma X)^2} = \frac{20(5765) - (698)(162)}{20(27{,}030) - (698)^2}$$

$$= \frac{11{,}530 - 113{,}076}{540{,}600 - 487{,}204} = \frac{2224}{53{,}396}$$

$$= 0.0416511 = 0.04$$

$$a = \bar{Y} - b\bar{X} = 8.1 - 0.0416511(34.9)$$

$$= 6.646378 = 6.65$$

$$Y' = 0.04X + 6.65$$

(continued)

Table 7.2 (continued)

Prediction equations for men and women, using age to predict dental anxiety

X = Age	Y = Dental anxiety	X^2	Y^2	XY
		Women		
26	9	676	81	234
45	10	2025	100	450
44	5	1936	25	220
41	8	1681	64	328
27	19	729	361	513
39	10	1521	100	390
33	19	1089	361	627
21	14	441	196	294
50	7	2500	49	350
39	10	1521	100	390
41	10	1681	100	410
30	10	900	100	300
22	12	484	144	264
18	9	324	81	162
32	6	1024	36	192
18	12	324	144	216
29	10	841	100	290
23	11	529	121	253
46	7	2116	36	322
$\Sigma X = 624$	$\Sigma Y = 198$	$\Sigma X^2 = 22{,}342$	$\Sigma Y^2 = 2312$	$\Sigma XY = 6205$

$$\overline{X} = 32.8 \qquad \overline{Y} = 10.4$$

$$s_X^{*2} = 97.29 \qquad s_Y^{*2} = 13.09$$

$$b = \frac{19(6205) - (624)(198)}{19(22{,}342) - (624)^2}$$

$$= \frac{117{,}895 - 123{,}552}{424{,}498 - 389{,}376} = \frac{-5657}{35{,}122}$$

$$= -0.1610671 = -0.16$$

$$a = 10.421053 - (-0.1610671)(32.842105)$$

$$= 15.710837 = 15.71$$

$$Y' = -0.16X + 15.71$$

Source: Arntz (1990).

7.4   Standard Error of Estimate

Variability of Errors

In real data, observed pairs of scores rarely fall on the regression line Y'. The difference between Y and Y' is called *error,* which is positive for some scores and negative for others. Because the sum of the errors is zero, the average error is also zero. How can you tell whether there is a lot of error—a "loose" prediction—or whether the data points are fairly close to the prediction line?

Before we answer that question, let's review information about sample variance. For a set of numbers, you are interested in their spread or dispersion around the mean (as you are interested in the spread of errors around the regression line). You tried to measure the dispersion by taking each score, subtracting the mean to form a difference score, and then adding up the difference scores. But that sum is always zero because the numbers below the mean balance out the numbers above the mean. The solution was to square each difference score and then average the squared differences. The result was the sample variance.

Do you see the connection to the errors in regression? The errors, like the difference scores about $\overline{X}$, sum to zero. Maybe you can square the errors and measure the variability of the errors in regression. This variability will be small if the line does a good job of predicting Y. Error is $Y - Y'$, so any measure of the variability of the errors also measures the variability of the observed scores around the regression line.

Definition of $s_{Y \cdot X}$

Standard error of estimate
Standard deviation of errors in regression; also the standard deviation of Y scores around the regression line

The **standard error of estimate** is verbally defined as *the standard deviation of the errors in linear regression;* it serves as a measure of the variability of the errors. The standard error of estimate is also the standard deviation of Y around the regression line Y', as can be seen in the following definitional formula:

$$s_{Y \cdot X} = \sqrt{\frac{\Sigma(e - \bar{e})^2}{N - 2}} = \sqrt{\frac{\Sigma e^2}{N - 2}} = \sqrt{\frac{\Sigma(Y - Y')^2}{N - 2}} \tag{7.6}$$

where $e = Y - Y'$ and $\bar{e}$ = mean of $e = 0$. The symbol $s_{Y \cdot X}$ is used to distinguish the standard error of estimate from the standard deviation $\overset{*}{s}$, or, more specifically, the standard deviation of Y, $\overset{*}{s}_Y$, or the standard deviation of X, $\overset{*}{s}_X$. The $Y \cdot X$ as the subscript of $s_{Y \cdot X}$ stands for the prediction of Y from X. Can you see the similarity between this formula and the formula for $\overset{*}{s}^2$? The $N - 2$ in the denominator of $s_{Y \cdot X}$ makes it a better estimate of a population standard deviation of errors than if you used N to average the squared errors. You will learn more about this in Chapter 9.

What happens to the value of the standard error of estimate as r gets stronger? To find the answer, let's compare this measure of variability around the regression line to a measure of variability of the Y values (around the mean of Y). If you used the average of the Y's as the best guess of the criterion variable, the variance of the Y's would be the errors, and the prediction line would be the horizontal line at $\overline{Y}$. Now, imagine a scatterplot that shows a strong positive correlation, with a horizontal line at $\overline{Y}$ and an uphill regression line through the points. You could look at the errors around $\overline{Y}$ or the errors around Y'. There will be more variability around the line for $\overline{Y}$ than around the regression line. So the value of $s_{Y \cdot X}$ is dependent on the value of r; the stronger the correlation, the lower the value of $s_{Y \cdot X}$. Figure 7.6 shows scatterplots for data sets c and d and gives the respective values of the standard error of estimate for each.

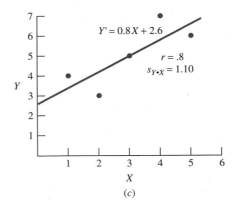

X	Y	Y'	e	e²
1	4	3.4	0.6	0.36
2	3	4.2	−1.2	1.44
3	5	5.0	0	0
4	7	5.8	1.2	1.44
5	6	6.6	−0.6	0.36

$$\Sigma e^2 = 3.6$$

$$s_{Y \cdot X} = \sqrt{\frac{\Sigma e^2}{N-2}} = \sqrt{\frac{3.6}{5-2}}$$
$$= \sqrt{1.2} \quad = 1.0954$$
$$= 1.10$$

$Y' = 0.8X + 2.6$

$r = .8$

$s_{Y \cdot X} = 1.10$

(c)

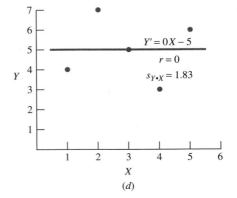

X	Y	Y'	e	e²
1	4	5	−1	1
2	7	5	2	4
3	5	5	0	0
4	3	5	−2	4
5	6	5	1	1

$$\Sigma e^2 = 10$$

$$s_{Y \cdot X} = \sqrt{\frac{\Sigma e^2}{N-2}} = \sqrt{\frac{10}{5-2}}$$
$$= \sqrt{3.33} \quad = 1.8257$$
$$= 1.83$$

$Y' = 0X - 5$

$r = 0$

$s_{Y \cdot X} = 1.83$

(d)

Figure 7.6
Relationship of r to $s_{Y \cdot X}$

Computational Formula for $s_{Y \cdot X}$

Definitional formula 7.6 for $s_{Y \cdot X}$ allows us to visualize that $s_{Y \cdot X}$ fits the verbal definition given for the standard error of estimate. However, like all definitional formulas,
formula 7.6 is difficult to use in practice and can lead to incorrect answers because of
rounding along the way. The computational formula is

$$s_{Y \cdot X} = \sqrt{\frac{N}{N-2}} (\overset{*}{s}_Y)\sqrt{1 - r^2} \tag{7.7}$$

or, using s_Y instead of $\overset{*}{s}_Y$,

$$s_{Y \cdot X} = \sqrt{\frac{N-1}{N-2}} (s_Y)\sqrt{(1 - r^2)}$$

It may be hard to see the connection between the computational and the definitional formulas of $s_{Y \cdot X}$, but formula 7.7 is considerably easier to use. It also makes the association between r and $s_{Y \cdot X}$ more apparent.

For example, the standard error of estimate for the males in the age/dental anxiety problem is given as

$$s_{Y \cdot X} = \sqrt{\frac{20}{20 - 2}}(2.02237)\sqrt{1 - (0.2379517)^2}$$

$$= (1.0540926)(2.02237)(0.943379)$$

$$= 2.01106 = 2.01$$

The value of 2.01 is exactly what you would have gotten if you had computed $s_{Y \cdot X}$ from the definitional formula 7.6, but this way is simpler and more accurate.

Quick Quiz

Suppose you read about two identical studies on the correlation between the amount of television violence watched by children and the level of aggression in the children. Both studies found $r = .42$. Study A reported $s_{Y \cdot X} = 2.21$, and Study B had $s_{Y \cdot X} = 5.52$. Without knowing the regression equations, can you say which study has a better prediction?

Answer

Study A has a better prediction because there is less variability around the regression line.

7.5   Partitioning Total Variability

You can look at whether $s_{Y \cdot X}$ is smaller than $\overset{*}{s}_Y$ and decide whether the regression line provides a better prediction than the mean of Y. But this approach can present an incomplete or even incorrect picture of the improvement in the prediction when Y' is used. One part of the problem is that the definitional formulas for $s_{Y \cdot X}$ and $\overset{*}{s}_Y$ have different denominators, $N - 2$ and N. Think about your goal of explaining why people are anxious about dental visits. There is variability in dental anxiety, and one factor that might explain this variability is age. You need a way to partition the total variance ($\overset{*2}{s}_Y$) into variance due to error and variance due to the linear prediction, where the variances use the same denominator. Then you can see if the error variance is small relative to the total variance.

Example: Variance Explained and Variance Not Explained

You know that r^2 is the proportion of variability in Y that is explained by X. We will use r^2 to partition variability into explained and unexplained portions. For women's dental anxiety, $r = -.44$ and $r^2 = .19$. You can say the variable age explains .19 of the variability in women's dental anxiety; that is, .19 is the proportion of variability in women's dental anxiety that is explained by age. You could convert the proportion to a percentage and say that 19% of the variability in women's dental anxiety is accounted for by age. What about the other 81% of the variability in women's dental anxiety? It is not explained by age.

Now, you actually can take the total observed variance of Y and partition it into two pieces: the part explained by X and the part not explained by X. Multiply s^{*2}_Y by r^2 for the variance explained by X. Multiply s^{*2}_Y by $1 - r^2$ to get the variance not explained by X. Thus, you have the formula

$$s^{*2}_Y = s^{*2}_Y r^2 + s^{*2}_Y (1 - r^2)$$

(7.8)

Total = explained + not explained

Variance explained and variance not explained

Total variance of Y can be partitioned into a piece due to linear prediction and a piece due to error

This is the total variance partitioned into **variance explained** by linear prediction and **variance not explained.** The variance not explained also can be considered the variance due to error. For women's dental anxiety and age,

$$13.09 = 13.09(.19) + 13.09(1 - .19)$$

$$13.09 = 2.4871 + 10.6029$$

The numerical value 2.4871 is the amount of the variance in women's dental anxiety that is explained by a linear relationship with age, whereas 10.6029 is the amount of the variance that is due to error, or unexplained.

Another way to show the same partitioning of total variance from definitional formulas is

$$\frac{\Sigma(Y - Y')^2}{N} = \frac{\Sigma(Y' - \bar{Y})^2}{N} + \frac{\Sigma(Y - Y')^2}{N}$$

(7.9)

or

$$s^{*2}_Y = s^{*2}_{explained} + s^{*2}_{not\ explained}$$

Note that $s^{*2}_{not\ explained}$ does not have the same formula as the square of the standard error of estimate, $s_{Y \cdot X}$. Conceptually, both $s^{*2}_{not\ explained}$ and $s^2_{Y \cdot X}$ are measures of error variance, but $s^2_{Y \cdot X}$ is a better estimate of population error variance. However, when total variance is partitioned, it is easier to use $s^{*2}_{not\ explained}$.

Figure 7.7 illustrates this partitioning by showing how total variability is broken into two parts for the (X, Y) pair $(27, 19)$ from the women's dental anxiety data set in Table 7.2. Be sure you can see how the total variability of $Y - \bar{Y} = 19 - 10.4 = 8.6$ is broken into variability explained of $Y' - \bar{Y} = 11.36 - 10.4 = .96$ and variability not explained of $Y - Y' = 19 - 11.36 = 7.64$. For the women's data, where $s^{*2}_Y = 13.09$ and $r = -.44$, $r^2 = .19$ of the variance is explained, giving an amount explained of about 2.49, as shown earlier. The variance not explained, 10.6, is the variance of error when women's dental anxiety is predicted from age. Note that you have reduced the variance from 13.09 to 10.6 by using a linear prediction equation Y' instead of $\bar{Y}$. Deciding whether the reduction in variance is significant is explained in Chapter 12.

Quick Quiz

What are the nonoverlapping parts in simple linear regression?

Answer

The variability in the criterion variable Y is divided into the part that is explained by the predictor variable X and the part that is not explained by the predictor.

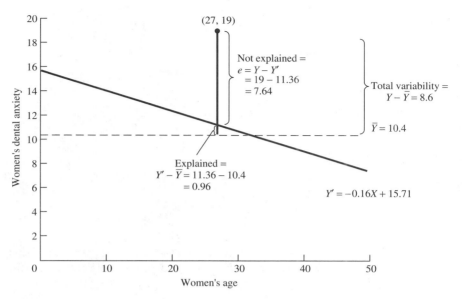

Figure 7.7
Total variability = explained + not explained, $Y - \bar{Y} = (Y' - \bar{Y}) + (Y - Y')$ for data point $(X, Y) = (27, 19)$ in women's dental anxiety data set in Table 7.2 ($b = -0.16$, $a = 15.71$)

7.6   Regression: Enhancing Your Understanding

The following topics are important for an overall perspective of regression, and they can help you relate regression to other statistical methods.

Relationship of Regression to Correlation

You already are aware of certain relationships between correlation and the linear regression equation, such as that the sign of r is the same as the sign of b and that if r is zero, then b is also zero. Another relationship is given in an alternative computational formula for b if r is already known:

$$b = r\frac{\overset{*}{s}_Y}{\overset{*}{s}_X} \tag{7.10}$$

or, using s values instead of $\overset{*}{s}$ values,

$$b = r\frac{s_Y}{s_X}$$

The use of formula 7.10 results in an alternative formula for Y' that can be obtained by taking

$$Y' = bX + a$$

and

$$a = \bar{Y} - b\bar{X}$$

and forming

$$Y' = bX + \bar{Y} - b\bar{X}$$

Substituting for b gives

$$Y' = r\frac{\overset{*}{s}_Y}{\overset{*}{s}_X}X + \bar{Y} - r\frac{\overset{*}{s}_Y}{\overset{*}{s}_X}\bar{X}$$

or $Y' = \bar{Y} + r\dfrac{\overset{*}{s}_Y}{\overset{*}{s}_X}(X - \bar{X})$ (7.11)

which is easier to use as a formula for the predicted criterion variable Y' if r is known. Similarly, if b is known, then r is easily obtained by

$$r = b\frac{\overset{*}{s}_X}{\overset{*}{s}_Y}$$ (7.12)

or using s values instead of $\overset{*}{s}$ values

$$r = b\frac{s_X}{s_Y}$$

Another useful expression for r is given in terms of formulas 7.6 and 7.8, where

$$\overset{*2}{s}_Y r^2 = \frac{\Sigma(Y' - \bar{Y})^2}{N} = \overset{*2}{s}_{explained}$$

Then it can be shown that

$$r^2 = \frac{\Sigma(Y' - \bar{Y})^2}{\Sigma(Y - \bar{Y})^2}$$ (7.13)

which is simply a way of illustrating that r^2 is the proportion of variability in Y that is explained by linear prediction. Thus, the correlation can be expressed as

$$r = \pm\sqrt{\frac{\Sigma(Y' - \bar{Y})^2}{\Sigma(Y - \bar{Y})^2}}$$ (7.14)

If both variables are in z score form, there is another helpful relationship between correlation and regression. If you have z_X and z_Y for all pairs of scores and you have computed either b from the z scores or r, then you have actually obtained *both* b and r because

$$b_{z\text{ scores}} = r$$ (7.15)

Of course, r computed on the z scores is exactly the same as r computed on the raw scores because a change in scale does not change r.

Confidence Limits

Confidence limits

Bounds on Y' that include a desired percentage of Y scores

Another topic in regression is the practical application of **confidence limits,** also called *confidence bounds.* You want to obtain limits, or bounds, on a predicted score Y' that include a desired percentage of the actual observed scores Y. Suppose you know the parents of a newborn baby boy who was 20 in. long at birth. In your enthusiasm for the subject of statistics, you tell them about prediction equations and how adult height can be predicted from baby length. They ask you to compute their son's predicted adult height, which you do by using values computed in the SAS example for Chapter 6. First, compute b using the s version of formula 7.10 and the values for r and the standard deviations for baby length and adult height. You should get $b = 1.176$, or 1.18. Next, $a = \bar{Y} - b\bar{X} = 46.1453$, or 46.15. So the baby's predicted height is

$$Y' = 1.18X + 46.15$$

With $X = 20$, you obtain

$$Y' = 1.18(20) + 46.15 = 69.75$$

The predicted adult height of their son is 69.75 in., or 5 ft 9.75 in. Being curious parents and not knowing much about statistics, they want to know whether their son's height will be exactly 69.75 in. You tell them about the concept of error and that their son's adult height will be close but probably not exactly equal to 69.75 in. They want to know whether you can give them some limits around 69.75 in. that most likely will include their son's height.

Using the standard error of estimate and the normal distribution, you can find approximate limits around the predicted score, 69.75. Because error exists in the prediction, you know that there is a distribution of adult heights for 20-in.-long male babies and that this distribution is centered, in the sample, at 69.75 in. You also know that the standard deviation of the observed scores around the regression line is the standard error of estimate. Using the s version of formula 7.7 and values from the SAS example in Chapter 6, the standard error of estimate is

$$s_{Y \cdot X} = \sqrt{\frac{N-1}{N-2}}(s_Y)\sqrt{(1-r^2)} = \sqrt{\frac{10}{9}}(2.041613)\sqrt{1-(.5437)^2}$$

or

$$s_{Y \cdot X} = 1.81$$

The sample distribution of male adult heights for 20-in. male babies is centered at 69.75 with a standard deviation of 1.81. The idea is to find values 1.96 standard deviations above the line (Y') and 1.96 standard deviations below the line. If you assume that height is normally distributed in the population, then 95% of the heights are included in an interval of

$$Y' - 1.96s_{Y \cdot X} \qquad \text{to} \qquad Y' + 1.96s_{Y \cdot X} \tag{7.16}$$

For this problem,

Lower limit = 69.75 − 1.96(1.81)   Upper limit = 69.75 + 1.96(1.81)

= 66.20   = 73.30

You can tell your friends that in 95% of cases, the range from 66.20 to 73.30 in. includes the actual adult height for male babies who were 20 in. long. They can be 95% confident that their son's height will be between these two values. (You might notice that this is a fairly broad range of values—from about 5 ft 6 in. to almost 6 ft 2 in.) If you want to change the confidence from 95% to 99%, you would have to use a value from the standard normal distribution, Table A.2 in Appendix A, of 2.57 in place of 1.96. In a similar manner, you could choose any confidence you desire and find the value from Table A.2 that has (1 − confidence)/2 in each tail of the distribution. Notice that increasing the confidence increases the width of the interval.

The use of confidence limits in regression assumes that the population distribution of Y around the regression line is normal and has the same variance for every X. These are referred to as the assumptions of **normality and homoscedasticity** (equality of variances). Figure 7.8 shows what is meant by these two assumptions. The concepts covered in Chapters 9 and 12 under the topic of confidence intervals are similar to those in this section. They allow us to compute confidence limits in regression that are more exact than those given here.

Normality and homoscedasticity
For each X, we assume that the distribution of Y around the regression line is normal with equal variance

Relationship of Regression to ANOVA

Regression is related not only to correlation, but also to the analysis of variance (ANOVA). Because this chapter could be used *after* Chapter 14 (on one-way ANOVA), we briefly discuss this relationship.

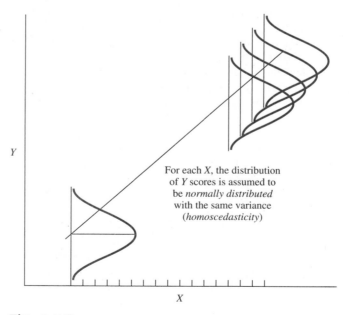

For each X, the distribution of Y scores is assumed to be *normally distributed* with the same variance (*homoscedasticity*)

Figure 7.8
Assumptions of normality and homoscedasticity in regression

Regression and ANOVA both partition variance. In one-way ANOVA, total variability is partitioned into parts called *sum of squares between groups* and *sum of squares within groups*. Both regression and ANOVA use the idea of breaking apart total variance into nonoverlapping parts. ANOVA and regression are based on a common model, called the *general linear model* (GLM). The GLM is an advanced topic beyond the scope of this text (see Winer, Brown, & Michels, 1991).

We can modify the scatterplot of *X* and *Y* data to organize the *X* values into groups as is done in ANOVA, further showing the relationship between regression and ANOVA. For example, Figure 7.9 shows two scatterplots, one for an observational research study and another for a true experiment on caffeine withdrawal symptoms. Suppose you first run the observational research, in which you determine how much caffeine 60 people consumed each day. Then you instruct the participants to stop

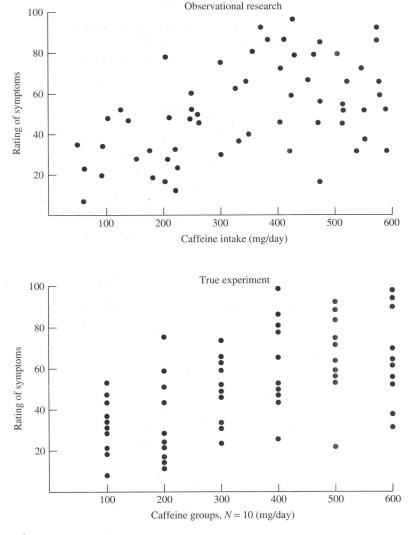

Figure 7.9
Relationship of regression and ANOVA

drinking caffeinated beverages. Two days later, you have them rate their physical health and symptoms to see whether there is a linear relationship between how much caffeine they consumed and their rating of symptoms. Now, suppose you design another study in which participants are randomly assigned to levels of caffeine consumption, which you control by providing them with cola bottles that don't show how much caffeine is contained. After some time, you switch all the participants to decaffeinated colas. Two days later, you have them rate their symptoms. Your results may look like the second scatterplot in Figure 7.9.

In the first scatterplot in Figure 7.9, the ratings of symptoms are scattered throughout the range of values for caffeine intake. In the second scatterplot, the ratings of symptoms are clustered at the values of caffeine intake chosen by the researcher.

7.7   Multiple Regression and Other Topics

Multiple linear regression
Use of two or more predictors for Y in one prediction equation

As a final topic, let's briefly consider **multiple linear regression.** The mathematics of multiple linear regression and the formulas for the regression constants are not covered here. We will strive for conceptual understanding and leave the computation to SAS or SPSS.

Prediction Equation

Multiple linear regression is a natural extension of simple linear regression. The idea is to use two or more predictors, X values, for the single criterion variable, Y, but to use them together in the same prediction equation. For p predictors, the equation for the observed score on the criterion variable, Y, is

$$Y = \beta_0 + \beta_1 X_1 + \beta_2 X_2 + \cdots + \beta_p X_p + e \qquad (7.17)$$

The prediction equation for Y' is

$$Y' = \beta_0 + \beta_1 X_1 + \beta_2 X_2 + \cdots + \beta_p X_p$$

Remember, p stands for the number of predictors. We have, then,

$$Y = Y' + e$$

and

$$e = Y - Y'$$

as in simple linear regression. Note that the regression weights, $\beta_0, \ldots, \beta_p$, are given as population parameters, each of which is estimated in the sample by a corresponding statistic, $b_0, \ldots, b_p$.

In simple linear regression, the slope and the Y intercept are determined in accord with the least-squares criterion, which you first saw as a characteristic of the sample mean. No value different from $\overline{X}$ gives a smaller number for the sum of the squared deviations from it; that is, $\Sigma(X - \overline{X})^2$ is a minimum. The simple regression line is a kind of average line through the data, the sum of the squared errors is a minimum, and no other line gives a smaller value for $\Sigma(Y - Y')^2$.

In multiple regression, the graph is again a kind of average, but now two or more axes are predictors of the criterion Y. Another similarity with simple linear regression is that the multiple regression equation is defined by an intercept and several slopes, the b values, which weight each variable, just as the slope weighted the single predictor in simple regression. As in simple regression, these b's are derived and computed so that Σe^2 is a minimum (the least-squares criterion again). The prediction equation has one Y intercept, β_0, but a separate β for each predictor. The size of each b depends not only on the strength of a given predictor, but also on the size of the standard deviation of the corresponding variable.

For example, consider the multiple linear regression equation from Research Example 7. The regression equation included the following predictors: PREPAIN1 (predicted pain before treatment 1), PREPAIN2 (predicted pain before treatment 2), EXPPAIN1 (actual experienced pain after treatment 1), EXPPAIN2 (actual experienced pain after treatment 2), AGE, DAST (total score on dental anxiety scale), and SEX. The multiple linear regression equation with all seven predictors was

$$Y' = 6.0419 + 0.0273(\text{EXPPAIN1}) + 0.1200(\text{EXPPAIN2})$$
$$+ 0.2967(\text{PREPAIN1}) + 0.2144(\text{PREPAIN2}) - 0.00256(\text{AGE})$$
$$- 0.4741(\text{DAST}) + 3.2379(\text{SEX})$$

The numerical values in this equation are the b's, or the regression weights for the predictors. The error for any person is the difference between the remembered pain Y and the predicted score Y' for remembered pain. This prediction is found by plugging his or her numerical values of EXPPAIN1, EXPPAIN2, and so on into the above equation.

Standardized Variables

Standardized regression coefficient

Regression coefficients or weights that have been computed when all of the variables have been standardized as z scores

If you standardize all of the variables before computing multiple regression, you will get a different set of regression weights. This means you compute z scores for Y and all of the X values and then compute the regression coefficients. Each **standardized regression coefficient,** with the notation β', will have different numerical values than the β for each X:

$$z_Y = \beta_0' + \beta_1' z_1 + \beta_2' z_2 + \cdots + \beta_p' z_p + e$$

Because all of the z scores for the different variables now have the same mean (0) and standard deviation (1), the variables are in comparable units of measure. The sizes of the standardized regression coefficients can give some indication of the relative importance of the different variables. A one-unit change in one variable is the same as a one-unit change in any other variable in terms of its impact on z_Y.

For the memories of pain problem, the multiple linear regression equation with standardized regression coefficients is

$$z_Y' = 0.0327(z_{\text{EXPPAIN1}}) + 0.1187(z_{\text{EXPPAIN2}}) + 0.5136(z_{\text{PREPAIN1}})$$
$$+ 0.4116(z_{\text{PREPAIN2}}) - 0.0018(z_{\text{AGE}}) - 0.0963(z_{\text{DAST}})$$
$$+ 0.1000(z_{\text{SEX}})$$

The standardized regression weight for b_0, the Y intercept, is always zero, so it is not given in the equation. [It is zero because the line goes through the point $(\overline{X}\,\overline{Y})$, and the mean for any set of z scores is zero.] From this equation, it appears that the predictions of pain, PREPAIN1 and PREPAIN2, are the best predictors of memories of pain. When these people remembered the pain involved in a dental experience, they seem to have relied on their original predictions of the pain more than on their actual experience.

Multiple Correlation

Multiple correlation coefficient

The correlation between Y and Y' from multiple regression, symbolized by R

Just as there is a correlation coefficient r for simple linear regression, there is a correlation coefficient for multiple regression. The **multiple correlation coefficient** R is defined as

$$R = r_{YY'} \qquad (7.18)$$

that is, the Pearson correlation coefficient r between the observed scores on the criterion variable, Y, and the predicted scores, Y'. The range of values for R is $0 \le R \le 1.00$, so it can never be negative. An important use of R is that R^2 is the proportion of the variability of Y explained by $X_1, \ldots, X_p$ in the multiple linear relationship. This is the same idea expressed as r^2 giving the proportion of the variability of Y explained by X in simple linear regression. For the "memories of dental pain" problem of Research Example 7, the value of R^2 for all seven predictors was .570815; that is, about 57% of the variability in the memories of pain is explained by the best linear combination of the seven predictors.

The b's used to estimate the β's in Y' are computed using least squares, which takes into account all of the idiosyncrasies in the data. Because of this problem, R^2 can be too large when it is used as an estimate of the population multiple correlation. The following formula takes into account the computed R, N, and p to give a better estimate of the population multiple correlation coefficient. This formula is commonly called the *shrinkage formula* for multiple R^2 because it reduces the numerical value from that of R^2.

$$\text{Estimated } R^2 = 1 - \frac{(1 - R^2)(N - 1)}{N - p - 1} \qquad (7.19)$$

For the memories of dental pain problem, $R^2 = .570815$ reduces to

$$\text{Estimated } R^2 = 1 - \frac{(1 - R^2)(N - 1)}{N - p - 1}$$

$$= 1 - \frac{(1 - .570815)(30 - 1)}{30 - 7 - 1}$$

$$= .4343$$

Overlap Problem

One problem that occurs in multiple regression is overlap among the p predictors. The predictor variables explain some of the same variability of Y, and they are correlated among themselves. Some authors call this problem *multicollinearity*, or *multiple de-*

pendence. If you want to predict graduate GPA, the predictors undergraduate GPA and verbal GRE are themselves correlated. Undergraduate GPA explains some of the variability in graduate GPA, and verbal GRE explains some of the variability in graduate GPA, and the two predictors may be explaining some of the same variability. See Figure 7.10 for a graphical explanation of overlap.

Figure 7.10 illustrates the percentage of variability using Venn diagrams. In Venn diagrams, one circle represents the total variability of Y and other circles represent the total variability of the X values. To the extent that the variability of Y is explained by an X, the circles overlap. Figure 7.10 shows pairs of circles for one predictor with $r = 1$, $r = .8$, $r = .4$, and $r = 0$. Notice that r^2 is the proportion of the area of each circle that is held in common by both circles, and $1 - r^2$ is the proportion of the area of each

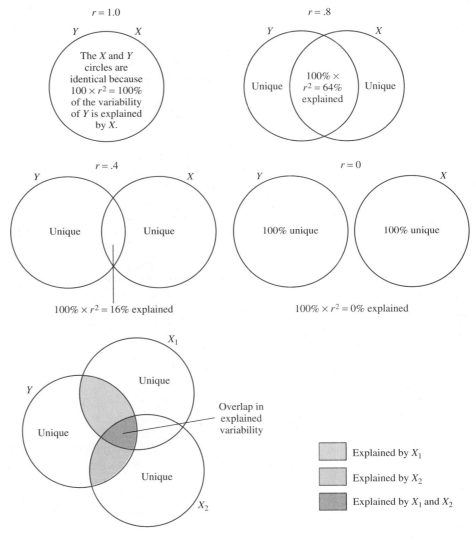

Figure 7.10
Venn diagrams showing percentage of variability explained

circle that is unique to that circle. You also can see that r^2 shows the proportion of the variability of X that is explained by Y; that is, for $r = .8$, $r^2 = .64$ is the proportion of the variability of X that is explained by Y and the proportion of the variability of Y that is explained by X. The area shared by both circles helps to illustrate this last point. The final set of Venn diagrams shows two predictors and illustrates the idea of overlap of the predictors. The multiple R^2 is the total area of the circle for Y that is overlapped with one or both of the X's.

You can tell that there is an overlap problem when you try to add up the r^2 values of the predictors with Y. This sum is not the same as R^2. That is, because each predictor variable may be explaining some variability that is explained by another predictor, adding together the separate r^2 values gives a larger value than R^2. For example, in Research Example 7, PREPAIN1 had $r^2 = .4375$ and PREPAIN2 had $r^2 = .3566$ as the best two single predictors of memories of dental pain. When these are combined in a two-predictor equation, $R^2 = .5446$, considerably less than $.4375 + .3566 = .7941$.

After a few predictors are in the equation, adding more predictors does not vastly increase R^2 because of the overlap among the predictors. Consequently, the prediction equation should include the fewest predictors while explaining as much variability in Y as possible. You want to find the best equation.

Best Equation

Consider taking a picture from a mountain. The picture is of a beautiful valley below the mountain, and everyone knows that the very best picture can be taken from the very top of the mountain. However, it takes considerable effort to reach the top, including some technical rock climbing with ropes and danger. You are the photographer, and you hike up an easy trail for one hour and find a spot from which to take your picture. Then you realize that you could hike another hour and get a better picture. From the second point, you would have to go on without a trail for another two hours to a third point. Then there is, yet farther up, a fourth point from which to take the picture, at the base of the cliff that requires the technical climb to the top. Each point farther up the mountain will give a better picture, but at what cost? How much better will your picture get for the effort expended to reach the next point? The goal is to balance the effort expended and the quality of the picture.

In a similar way, you want to find the best equation, one that gives a balance between the number of predictors used and the variability of Y explained. Another way to say this is to balance the parsimony and the quality of the fit. A small number of predictors gives parsimony, but larger numbers of predictors improve the fit of the equation to the data. So your goal is to both minimize p and maximize R^2. To minimize p alone is easy: Take the best single-predictor equation. To maximize R^2 is easy: Take the equation with all p predictors. But somewhere in between one and p is the ideal number of predictors and the best equation. Just as there may be different trails to the best picture-taking point, there are different ways to find this best equation.

Suppose you have $N = 50$ graduate students who have been admitted to a program and have reached the third year of graduate work. For each of the 50 students, graduate GPA $= Y$ and $p = 5$ predictors: $X_1 =$ undergraduate GPA, $X_2 =$ verbal GRE, $X_3 =$ quantitative GRE, $X_4 =$ rating of letters of reference, and $X_5 =$ rating of quality of undergraduate program. You don't have to include all of the predictors in the final equation used for predictions. You could use, say, only four of the predictors, or maybe as few as two. There are many possible prediction equations. You could form five equations that have only one predictor, ten equations with two predictors, ten with three predictors, five with four predictors, and one with all five predictors. Which of these equations is the best? Remember, you want the prediction equation to have the fewest predictors while explaining as much variability in Y as possible. If one of the two-predictor equations accounts for, say, 41% of the variability of Y, are you wasting your time to add a third predictor that accounts for only an additional 6% of the variance?

There are many rules on when to stop adding variables to the equation. Only the simplest stopping rule is given here. The MS_e **stopping rule** says to find the equation with the smallest MS_e, which is defined as the variance of the errors and is related to the standard error of estimate. The equation with the smallest MS_e gives the best prediction. MS_e is given by

$$MS_e = \frac{SS_e}{df_e} \tag{7.20}$$

where $SS_e = \Sigma e^2$ and $df_e = N - p - 1$. Most computer programs that compute multiple regression give these values. Table 7.3 gives an example where a three-predictor equation using X_3, X_4, and X_5 yields the minimum MS_e of 4.2.

The preceding material is often called *stepwise multiple regression*. The goal of stepwise multiple regression is to find the best equation, the one that gives that balance of minimizing the number of predictors and maximizing the R^2. Unfortunately, any computer program that computes stepwise multiple regression has limitations. First, it has to implement some stopping rule, not necessarily the one you would choose. Second, it usually limits output to only one of the equations for each value of p—for example, one one-predictor equation, one two-predictor equation, and so on—and you might want to examine more than one equation for a given number of predictors. Finally, because of the programming of only one stopping rule, the computer program might not actually find the best equation. For example, some programs find the best one-predictor equation and then add to it the second variable that has the highest gain in R^2 *given the variable in the first equation*. In Table 7.3, X_3 is the best single predictor, and X_4 adds the most to R^2 for the best two-predictor equation. But it doesn't have to be that way: What if neither X_5 nor X_1 was the best single predictor but, taken together, they do a better job than the two-predictor equation that contains X_3 and X_4? Most

MS_e stopping rule
In multiple regression, find the model with the smallest MS_e

Table 7.3
MS_e stopping rule for multiple regression

Number of Predictors	R^2	MS_e	Predictors	
1	.30	5.1	X_3	$N = 50$
1	.26	8.1	X_1	Max $p = 5$
1	.25	11.2	X_4	
2	.41	4.6	$X_3 X_4$	
2	.40	4.8	$X_3 X_1$	
2	.32	5.0	$X_5 X_1$	
3	.47	4.2	$X_3 X_4 X_5$	
3	.46	4.3	$X_3 X_4 X_1$	
3	.42	4.5	$X_3 X_5 X_1$	
4	.49	4.30	$X_3 X_4 X_5 X_1$	
4	.485	4.36	$X_3 X_4 X_2 X_5$	
4	.48	4.40	$X_3 X_4 X_2 X_1$	
5	.491	4.40	$X_3 X_4 X_5 X_1 X_2$	

computer programs would miss it and tell you that the X_3 and X_4 equation is best. In Section 7.8, we show how to use SAS to find the best equation.

Beyond Multiple Regression

Because this section is meant only to introduce the topic of multiple regression, you might need a list of other sources for further study. Lewis-Beck (1980), Achen (1982), Berry and Feldman (1985), Schroeder, Sjoquist, and Stephan (1986), Darlington (1990), Aiken and West (1991), and Winer, Brown, and Michels (1991) are all good sources for more information on regression, and many of them include multiple regression. You also need to know that equations and methods exist for curvilinear regression. Most of the sources listed here give at least some coverage to those methods.

Quick Quiz

A friend who is studying to become a psychiatrist tells you that he has been studying the linear relationships between depression and exercise, and between depression and fruit intake. He says that according to studies he has run, there is a negative linear relationship between exercise and depression, with $r = -.39$. That is, as people spend more time exercising, their depression levels drop. He also says fruit intake is negatively related to depression, with $r = -.32$. He says his two variables account for about 25% of the variability in depression levels for the people in his study. What questions do you have for him?

Answer

You might ask him if he did a multiple regression or simply added together his r^2 values. If he added his r^2 values, then he isn't taking into account the probable correlation between his predictors. They might be explaining the same variability. Fruit also may not be important; it could be that clinically depressed people just eat more of everything when they are less depressed.

7.8   Summary, Study Tips, and Computation

Chapter Summary

Regression is concerned with predicting a criterion variable Y from a predictor variable X and with establishing a prediction, or regression, equation. In the formula for a straight line, $Y' = bX + a$, the slope b and the Y intercept a determine the line. Regression deals with variables that are not perfectly related, so not all scores fall on the line; there is error $e = Y - Y'$. The least-squares principle is used to give the best-fitting line by the proper computation of b and a so that the sum of the squares of e is a minimum. The standard error of estimate $s_{Y \cdot X}$ measures the variability of the errors and is the standard deviation of the observed Y values around the regression line. You can partition the total variance into variance explained by linear prediction and variance due to error to see whether linear prediction reduces the variance over predicting with $\bar{Y}$. Factors in the use of regression include linearity and limited generalizations. Other regression topics are the relationship to correlation, confidence limits, the relationship to ANOVA, and multiple regression.

The following are key words and symbols from this chapter:

Regression	Confidence limits
Prediction equation	Homoscedasticity
Y' = predicted score	Multiple linear regression
b = slope	Standardized regression
a = Y intercept	coefficient
e = error	Multiple correlation
Least-squares criterion	coefficient
$s_{Y \cdot X}$	MS_e stopping rule
Partition of variance	

Study Tips

The computations involved in regression sometimes make students unable to see the forest for the trees. If you are confused about what you are trying to accomplish by computing a regression line, back off from the problem and think about the variables involved. What are you trying to predict? What is the meaning behind the criterion and predictor variables? If you can write a de-scription of the problem you are working on in everyday language, then you truly understand it. Try writing an explanation of what you are doing for someone who doesn't know statistics—say, a friend, a parent, or a sibling. That might help you see the areas where you are lacking some understanding.

The most frequent errors students make in simple re-gression are (1) rounding the value of b before computing a and (2) getting the wrong sign when computing e.

Computation

Regression lends itself to the use of the computer not only because the computations are more extensive than those we have encountered before, but also because so many different types of computations can be done on any given data set. For example, all the computations done in this chapter on the memories of dental pain were done on the computer. Two of the SAS procedures are new to you: PROC REG and PROC RSQUARE. You used PROC CORR in Chapter 6. PROC REG is a procedure to compute regression and must be used to get standardized regression weights. PROC RSQUARE can compute all possible multiple regression equations for 1 to p predictors, but we restrict it to giving the best three equations for each number of predictors. We use PROC RSQUARE as the principal tool for finding the best mul-tiple regression equation. We use only one data set, the dental anxiety data, to run all of these PROCs. The SPSS command to run regression is REGRESSION.

SAS Examples

(SAS system's lines)

```
DATA DENTAL;
INPUT S$ SEX AGE DAST PREPAIN1 EXPPAIN1 PREPAIN2 EXPPAIN2
REMPAIN;   (line to input all the scores for person S, where the scores are as explained in Research Example 7; for sex, 1 = male and
           0 = female; the researchers had follow-up data on only 31 of the original 40 participants, but note that S12 did not give
           her age, so some of the analyses use all 31 participants and some use only 30)
CARDS;
S2   1 29   5  1  1   1  1   1
S3   1 30   6  1  1   1  1   0
S6   1 40  10  9  1   8 29  23
S8   1 71  10 10  2   3  3  10
S10  1 41  10 21 15  11  1  22
S11  1 33   7 26 12   1  1   4
S14  1 44   7 26  1  25  1  31
S19  1 33   8  9  1   1  2   9
S22  1 28   9 24  2   7  2   5
S25  1 41  11 50  1   4  1  17
S28  1 17   9 24 17  17 17  23
```

```
S34  1 29   8 12   1   7   1 12
S35  1 28  10 79   2   4  12 20
S37  1 18  11   6   3   2   4 12
S38  1 39   6 35  28  11   1 30
S40  1 27   6   2  10   2  18  1
S7   0 45  10 80  19  24  17  6
S9   0 44   5 11   6   1   1  4
S12  0  .   8  7   5  11   8  1
S13  0 41   8 24  97  29  46 15
S15  0 27  19  1   1  93  30  3
S16  0 39  10 20   1   1   1 25
S17  0 33  19 98   1  99   5 49
S18  0 21  14 99  44  97  48 82
S20  0 50   7  7  10  15   1 22
S21  0 39  10 45  21  82   1 22
S24  0 41  10 49   3  14   1 20
S29  0 22  12  3  13  68  61 23
S30  0 18   9 30  39  44  14 24
S32  0 18  12 10   5   2   1  6
S33  0 29  10  6   2   9   4 11
PROC PRINT;
PROC CORR;    (computes all possible Pearson correlations among the variables in the data set)
PROC REG;    (computes regression, used with a required model statement)
MODEL REMPAIN=PREPAIN1;    (statement to give the equation for REG; here it is the simple regression equation predicting
                            memories of pain from predicted pain time 1, resulting in the computation of b and a; note that
                            the model statement is in the form criterion variable = predictor variable)
PROC REG;    (used for multiple regression with all seven predictors of memories of pain, asks for standardized regression coefficients
             with the option following the / at the end of the model statement)
MODEL REMPAIN=EXPPAIN1 EXPPAIN2 PREPAIN1 PREPAIN2 AGE DAST SEX/STB;
PROC RSQUARE SELECT=3 MSE B;    (procedure to compute the three multiple regressions by using SELECT=3, with the highest
                                 R² for each number of predictors from one to six, and to give the multiple regression for
                                 seven predictors; it gives R², the mean square error, by using MSE, and the regression
                                 weights by using B; note that the MODEL statement contains all seven predictors)
MODEL REMPAIN=EXPPAIN1 EXPPAIN2 PREPAIN1 PREPAIN2 AGE DAST SEX;
(system's line)
```

For PROC CORR, the SAS output in Figure 7.11 gives:

1. Some simple statistics.

2. All possible Pearson r's for the variables in the data set. The r's are reported in a correlation matrix, a systematic arrangement of the statistics that shows every variable on the top and left side, with the r's for every combination in the body of the matrix.

3. For each combination, the first number is r, the second number is the two-tailed probability, and the third number is N.

The SAS System

Correlation Analysis

9 'VAR' Variables: SEX AGE DAST PREPAIN1 EXPPAIN1 PREPAIN2 EXPPAIN2 REMPAIN EXPTOT

① Simple Statistics

Variable	N	Mean	Std Dev	Sum	Minimum	Maximum
SEX	31	0.516129	0.508001	16.000000	0	1.000000
AGE	30	33.833333	11.576085	1015.000000	17.000000	71.000000
DAST	31	9.548387	3.294831	296.000000	5.000000	19.000000
PREPAIN1	31	26.612903	28.210728	825.000000	1.000000	99.000000
EXPPAIN1	31	11.774194	19.417706	365.000000	1.000000	97.000000
PREPAIN2	31	22.387097	31.103780	694.000000	1.000000	99.000000
EXPPAIN2	31	10.774194	15.997312	334.000000	1.000000	61.000000
REMPAIN	31	17.193548	16.438612	533.000000	0	82.000000
EXPTOT	31	22.548387	31.126450	699.000000	2.000000	143.000000

The SAS System

Correlation Analysis

② Pearson Correlation Coefficients / Prob > |k| under Ho:
Rho=0 / Number of Observations

	SEX	AGE	DAST	PREPAIN1	EXPPAIN1	PREPAIN2	EXPPAIN2	REMPAIN	EXPTOT
SEX	1.00000 ③	0.03914	−0.39380	−0.21121	−0.30544	−0.53414	−0.31742	−0.21993	−0.35368
	0.0	0.8373	0.0284	0.2540	0.0947	0.0020	0.0819	0.2345	0.0510
	31	30	31	31	31	31	31	31	31
AGE	0.03914	1.00000	−0.20523	0.00967	−0.04036	−0.20217	−0.27305	−0.09012	−0.16565
	0.8373	0.0	0.2766	0.9596	0.8323	0.2840	0.1443	0.6358	0.3817
	30	30	30	30	30	30	30	30	30
DAST	−0.39380	−0.20523	1.00000	0.41979	−6.06625	0.72287	0.34203	0.41708	0.13446
	0.0284	0.2766	0.0	0.0187	0.7233	0.0001	0.0597	0.0196	0.4708
	31	30	31	31	31	31	31	31	31
PREPAIN1	−0.21121	0.00967	0.41979	1.00000	0.21482	0.46835	0.11946	0.66842	0.19541
	0.2540	0.9596	0.0187	0.0	0.2458	0.0079	0.5221	0.0001	0.2921
	31	30	31	31	31	31	31	31	31

Figure 7.11
SAS output from PROC CORR

(continued)

EXPPAIN1	−0.30544	−0.04036	−0.06625	0.21482	1.00000	0.27798	0.54066	0.29807	0.90171
	0.0947	0.8323	0.7233	0.2458	0.0	0.1300	0.0017	0.1034	0.0001
	31	30	31	31	31	31	31	31	31
PREPAIN2	−0.53414	−0.29217	0.72287	0.46835	0.27798	1.00000	0.52975	0.59812	0.44568
	0.0020	0.2840	0.0001	0.0079	0.1300	0.0	0.0022	0.0004	0.0120
	31	30	31	31	31	31	31	31	31
EXPPAIN2	−0.31742	−0.27305	0.34203	0.11946	0.54066	0.52975	1.00000	0.34850	0.85123
	0.0819	0.1443	0.0597	0.5221	0.0017	0.0022	0.0	0.0547	0.0001
	31	30	31	31	31	31	31	31	31
REMPAIN	−0.21993	−0.09012	0.41708	0.66842	0.29807	0.59812	0.34850	1.00000	0.36506
	0.2345	0.6358	0.0196	0.0001	0.1034	0.0004	0.0547	0.0	0.0435
	31	30	31	31	31	31	31	31	31
EXPTOT	−0.35368	−0.16565	0.13446	0.19541	0.90171	0.44568	0.85123	0.36500	1.00000
	0.0510	0.3817	0.4708	0.2921	0.0001	0.0120	0.0001	0.0435	0.0
	31	30	31	31	31	31	31	31	31

Figure 7.11 (continued)

```
Model: MODEL1
Dependent Variable: REMPAIN  ①
```

Analysis of Variance

Source	DF	Sum of Squares	Mean Square	F Value	Prob>F
④ Model	1	3622.03624	3622.03624	23.421	0.0001
Error	29	4484.80247	154.64836		
C Total	30	8176.83871			

③ Root MSE	12.43577	R-square	0.4468 ②	
Dep Mean	17.19355	Adj R-sq	0.4277	
C.V.	72.32811			

Parameter Estimates

Variable	DF	Parameter Estimate	Standard Error	T for H0: Parameter=	Prob > [T]
INTERCEP	1 ⑤	6.827965	3.19454330	2.206	0.0354
PREPAIN1	1 ⑥	0.389495	0.08148181	4.840	0.0001

Figure 7.12
SAS output from PROC REG

For PROC REG, the SAS output in Figure 7.12 gives an analysis of the simple linear regression problem to obtain the prediction equation in the form of b and a. Consider the following:

1. REMPAIN is labeled as the dependent variable, when it is really the criterion variable.
2. The value of r^2 is given.
3. The Root MSE is actually $s_{Y \cdot X}$, the standard error of estimate.
4. Because PREPAIN1 is the predictor variable, the values of df, SS, F, and $PR > F$ given for PREPAIN1 can be used later in hypothesis testing. There is some similarity between this output and that for the ANOVA in Chapters 13 and 15 (see also Chapter 11 for hypothesis testing using r).
5. The estimate for INTERCEPT is the Y intercept $a = 6.827965$.
6. The estimate for SLOPE is $b = 0.389495$. The values of b and a are the statistics of primary interest in this output. Note the large number of decimal places given so you can decide how many significant digits to keep.

The SAS System

Model: MODEL1
Dependent Variable: REMPAIN

Analysis of Variance

Source	DF	Sum of Squares	Mean Square	F Value	Prob>F
① Model	7	4472.83137	638.97591	4.180	0.0046
Error	22	3363.03529	152.86524		
C Total	29	7835.86667			

Root MSE	12.36387	R-square	0.5708 ②	
Dep Mean	17.73333	Adj R-sq	0.4343	
C.V.	69.72106			

Parameter Estimates

Variable	DF	Parameter Estimate	Standard Error	T for H0: Parameter=0	Prob > |T|	Standardized Estimate
INTERCEP	1 ③	6.041862	14.06152056	0.430	0.6716	0.00000000
EXPPAIN1	1	0.027313	0.16624945	0.164	0.8710	0.03274737
EXPPAIN2	1	0.119988	0.20594804	0.583	0.5661	0.11870685
PREPAIN1	1	0.296695	0.09809154	3.025	0.0062	0.51356515
PREPAIN2	1 ④	0.214382	0.13155476	1.630	0.1174	0.41163735
AGE	1	−0.002561	0.21034108	−0.012	0.9904	−0.00180336
DAST	1	−0.474065	1.15108567	−0.412	0.6844	−0.09627861
SEX	1	3.237856	5.70561404	0.567	0.5761	0.09994875

Figure 7.13
SAS output from PROC REG

For PROC REG, the SAS output in Figure 7.13 gives the analysis for the multiple regression using seven predictors. Consider the following:

1. The Model includes all seven predictors.
2. The R^2 for this model is 0.5708, which means about 57% of the variability in pain memories (the criterion variable) is accounted for by the seven predictors. Note the "Adj R-sq," which is the adjusted R^2 with value 0.4343 computed earlier.
3. The estimate for the intercept is b_0 with value 6.041862.
4. The estimates for the weights for the seven predictors b_1–b_7 are given as the numerical values 0.027313 through 3.237856.

The SAS System

N = 30   Regression Models for Dependent Variable: REMPAIN

Number in Model	① R-square	② MSE	Parameter Estimates ③ Intercept	EXPPAIN1	EXPPAIN2	PREPAIN1	PREPAIN2	AGE	DAST	SEX
1	0.43747068	157.42517	7.3145	.	.	0.3821	.	.	.	.
1	0.35655565	180.06943	10.6533	.	.	.	0.3110	.	.	.
1	0.16775301	232.90630	−1.6271	.	.	.	.	.	2.0167	.
④ 2	0.54462124	132.15879	5.6364	.	.	0.2829	0.1925	.	.	.
2	0.51231541	141.53450	4.7937	.	0.2784	0.3636	.	.	.	.
2	0.46218709	156.08260	6.2339	0.1341	.	0.3627	.	.	.	.
3	0.55784776	133.25561	4.7557	.	0.1391	0.2960	0.1491	.	.	.
3	0.55307546	134.69389	5.0896	0.0801	.	0.2772	0.1812	.	.	.
3	0.55214655	134.97384	10.3966	.	.	0.2902	0.2369	.	−0.6219	.
4	0.56444760	136.51722	9.2492	.	0.1343	0.3024	0.1922	.	−0.5831	.
4	0.56411839	136.62041	2.4663	.	0.1434	0.2952	0.1761	.	.	3.0959
4	0.56232733	137.18179	2.1504	0.0988	.	0.2743	0.2137	.	.	3.8487
5	0.57028808	140.29855	6.8921	.	0.1386	0.3014	0.2168	.	−0.5641	2.9896
5	0.56749626	141.21007	1.9347	0.0604	0.1014	0.2867	0.1854	.	.	3.6232
5	0.56452954	142.17869	9.7884	.	0.1322	0.3030	0.1921	−0.0135	−0.5906	.
6	0.57081225	146.21991	5.9372	0.0272	0.1205	0.2966	0.2145	.	−0.4729	3.2444
6	0.57028859	146.39832	6.9370	.	0.1384	0.3015	0.2168	−0.00107	−0.5647	2.9866
6	0.56750626	147.34623	1.7592	0.0601	0.1023	0.2866	0.1857	0.00475	.	3.6335
7	0.57081515	152.86524	6.0419	0.0273	0.1200	0.2967	0.2144	−0.00256	−0.4741	3.2379

Figure 7.14
SAS output from PROC RSQUARE

For PROC RSQUARE, the SAS output in Figure 7.14 gives three regression equations for p (number of predictors in the equation) ranging from one to six and the regression equation for seven predictors. The output includes:

1. The value of R^2 for each equation.
2. The *MSE* for each equation.
3. The parameter estimates, the b values for those predictors included in any given equation. It always gives the estimate of the intercept, a "." if a variable is not included in that equation but a numerical value for the b if a variable is included.
4. From this line you can see that this equation has the smallest *MSE* (132.15879) of all the equations. $R^2 = .54462124$ and the equation would be given by

$$Y' = 5.6364 + 0.2829(\text{PREPAIN1})$$
$$+ 0.1925(\text{PREPAIN2})$$

where Y' is the predicted score for the criterion variable, REMPAIN.

SPSS Example

Multiple regression and correlation can be done in several ways. The simplest is to change the ENTER method to read ENTER (first predictor variable) TO (last predictor variable), such as ENTER PREPAIN1 TO PREPAIN2. See the SPSS Base System User's Guide (1990) in your computer center for more information.

```
(SPSS system's lines)
SET WIDTH 80
DATA LIST FREE/BABY ADULT
BEGIN DATA
18.0 70.0 18.0 69.0 20.0 69.0 21.0 67.0 20.0 67.5 19.5 64.0
22.0 67.5 21.0 71.0 20.5 70.0 19.0 69.0 19.0 64.0 20.0 63.0
20.0 66.0 20.5 63.5 21.0 71.0 21.0 65.5 20.0 70.0 21.5 65.0
20.5 73.0 23.0 67.0 21.0 62.0 19.0 64.0 17.0 62.0 19.0 60.5
19.0 66.0 20.0 68.5 21.0 72.0 23.5 69.0 19.5 69.5 20.0 62.5
22.0 67.0 20.5 65.0 21.0 68.0 20.5 67.0 20.5 67.0 19.0 60.0
20.0 63.5 20.5 67.0 21.5 58.0
END DATA
REGRESSION DEPENDENT=ADULT/METHOD=ENTER BABY
```
(computes a simple regression analysis with the criterion/ dependent variable ADULT, and enters the variable BABY as a predictor)

```
FINISH
```
(system's line)

For the REGRESSION command, the SPSS output in Figure 7.15 shows the following:

1. The Pearson r
2. The standard error of estimate, $s_{Y \cdot X}$
3. The Y intercept, a
4. The slope, b

```
* * * * M U L T I P L E   R E G R E S S I O N  * * * *
```

Listwise Deletion of Missing Data

Equation Number 1   Dependent Variable..   ADULT
Block Number 1. Method: Enter   BABY

Variable(s) Entered on Step Number
   1..   BABY

Multiple R   .17811①
R Square   .03172
Adjusted R Square   .00556
Standard Error   3.45170②

Analysis of Variance
                    DF   Sum of Squares   Mean Square
Regression   1   14.44334   14.44334
Residual   37   440.82589   11.91421

F =   1.21228   Signif F =   .2780

----------------- Variables in the Equation ------------------

Variable   B   SE B   Beta   T   Sig T
BABY   ④.477162   .433376   .178115   1.101   .2780
(Constant) ③56.757478   8.796030   6.453   .0000
End Block Number   1   All requested variables entered.

Figure 7.15
SPSS output for REGRESSION

Exercises

Caution: Do not round any computation until the final answer. Also, use only unrounded answers when computing from one statistic to the next (for example, using b to compute a).

Sections 7.1–7.3

1. Your friend Dan says he can't study well unless he has soft drinks with caffeine in them. He says his amount of studying increases with the amount of caffeine he consumes, but if he drinks too much caffeine, he gets jittery and can't sit still to study. If you wanted to use statistics to measure the relationship between Dan's caffeine intake and amount of studying, would you use linear regression? Explain.

2. For the plumber with a flat per-job fee of $30 and an hourly rate of $35, how much will a 5-h job cost in labor?

3. You know that a line has slope 2 and Y intercept 10.
   a. Is the correct prediction equation $Y' = 2X + 10$, $Y' = 10X + 2$, or $Y' = 2(10) + X$?
   b. What is the predicted Y for $X = 5$?
   c. What is the error for $X = 5$ if the actual Y value is 19?

4. We are given that $b = 0.52$ and $a = -1.243$ for a study on dental anxiety and time required in the waiting room.
   a. Sketch a graph of the regression line.
   b. Write the prediction equation.

c. Suppose time in the waiting room is linearly related to dental anxiety. For the data on which your prediction equation is based, is *r* positive or negative? What does that mean in terms of the variables?

5. Use these data:

Pair	1	2	3	4	5
X	7	8	2	11	10
Y	22	19	20	21	18

a. Draw a scatterplot of the data.
b. Compute *r* (use formula 6.3 in Chapter 6).
c. Compute *b* and *a*, and write the regression equation. (Remember, do not round *b* before you compute *a*.)

6. You have data on the suicide rates and the amount of country music airtime in five cities in your state.
a. What does *X* represent? What does *Y* represent?
b. Calculate *b* and *a* from the following pieces of the formulas:

$$\Sigma X = 110$$

$$\Sigma Y = 77$$

$$\Sigma X^2 = 2430$$

$$\Sigma Y^2 = 1207$$

$$\Sigma XY = 1695$$

7. *Locus of control* refers to the placement of control of reinforcement in one's world. *Internal* control means that a person believes that events are dependent on one's own behavior, whereas *external* control refers to the belief that events are not entirely dependent on personal behavior but are the result of some outside influence (others, luck, and so on). Rotter (1966) developed the I/E (internal/external) scale to measure locus of control. Suppose a researcher asked students to answer the questions in this scale as they thought a typical student at their university might answer them. Also suppose that 6 months earlier these same students had answered the questions in the scale for themselves. The following data were collected:

Student	A	B	C	D	E	F	G	H
I/E (Self)	14	17	25	11	9	17	19	20
I/E Attributed to Other	18	17	22	19	10	18	18	16

a. Compute the mean and standard deviation for both variables.
b. Plot the pairs of scores in a scatterplot. Does it appear that self I/E and I/E attributed to other are related?
c. Compute *b* and *a*, and write the regression equation. Are these two variables related?
d. Draw the regression line in your scatterplot. Start with the value of *a* on the *Y* axis (*X* = 0) as one point. Use the value of *b* to get a second point by going up *b* units from the (0,*a*) point (or down if *b* is negative) and over to the right one unit on *X*. Now connect the two points with the line that is the regression line.

8. You have completed a study of preschoolers' aggressiveness and television watching habits. Parents of ten preschoolers have kept a diary of how much time their child watched television for one week. During the same week, you and a co-researcher watched the ten children through a mirrored glass at their preschool and calculated an aggression score for each child. The score was based on the number of times the child pushed another child or otherwise acted aggressively. Here are the results from your study (*X* = number of hours of television, *Y* = aggression score, *Child* = the number used to identify the child):

Child	1	2	3	4	5	6	7	8	9	10
X	26	28	24	18	19	36	12	21	28	33
Y	4	2	0	5	5	4	6	3	2	0

a. Draw a scatterplot of the data.
b. Compute *r* (use formula 6.3 in Chapter 6).
c. Compute *b* and *a*, and write the regression equation.
d. Now draw the regression line in your scatterplot. Start with the value of *a* on the *Y* axis (*X* = 0) as one point. Use the value of *b* to get a second point by going up *b* units from the (0, *a*) point (or down if *b* is negative) and over to the right one unit on *X*. Now connect the two points with the line that is the regression line.
e. For a child who watches 16 h of television each week, how many aggressive acts could a parent expect the child to commit in preschool?
f. If the child who watches 16 h of television each week actually commits four aggressive acts, what is *e*?

Data for Exercise 11

Year	1960	1965	1970	1972	1973	1974	1975	1976	1977	1978
Average Speed	54.8	60.6	63.8	64.9	65.0	57.6	57.6	58.2	58.8	58.8
Average Miles per Gallon	14.28	14.15	13.58	13.67	13.29	13.65	13.74	13.93	14.15	14.26

9. Use the following data:

Pair	A	B	C	D	E
X	1	7	6	5	2
Y	2	4	3	3	1

   a. Make a scatterplot of these data and then compute b and a. Write the regression equation and draw in the line in a manner similar to Exercise 8, part d.
   b. Change the value for E and Y from 1 to 5, and redo everything in part a. Does the change in the regression line surprise you?

10. Use these data:

Pair	1	2	3	4	5
X	15	20	17	19	39
Y	10	7	11	9	5

   a. Make a scatterplot of the data.
   b. Estimate where you think the regression line will go, and sketch in your estimated line in some other color than what you used for the scatterplot.
   c. Compute b and a, write the regression equation, and draw in the line in a manner similar to Exercise 8, part d. How close is your estimated line to the actual regression line?
   d. How would the regression line change if the last Y score were changed to 25? Do the computations for b and a.
   e. Compute b and a on only the first four pairs of scores; compare this line to those found in parts c and d. How does one pair of scores influence the regression line? What impact would a larger N have on your answer to this last question?

11. Consider the data shown above on the average speeds of a sample of vehicles on level interstate highway and the average miles per gallon of all vehicles operated in the United States.

   a. Make a scatterplot of the average speed (in miles per hour) and average mileage (in miles per gallon).
   b. Find the regression line for all ten years.
   c. Find the regression line for the first five years.
   d. Find the regression line for the last five years.
   e. Intuitively, for a given vehicle on a given day, is speed positively or negatively related to miles per gallon? Then what is happening with the data in this exercise? What possible confounding variables exist?

12. Suppose you have collected data on monthly advertising budgets and monthly total sales for some furniture stores. (See table below.)

   a. Find b and a, and write the regression equation.
   b. Find $Y' =$ predicted sales and $e = Y - Y'$ for each store.
   c. Compute Σe. Comment on the value you find.
   d. If another store in the area had an advertising budget of $3000, what would you predict for its total sales?

Sections 7.4–7.5

13. Researchers have found that it is possible to predict future drug use from attitudes toward cigarette smoking (Smith, Schwerin, Stubblefield & Fogg, 1982). A score on attitude toward cigarette smoking (CIG) was taken in seventh grade, and a self-report measure on drug use (DRG) was taken in twelfth grade. The scoring of the attitude toward cigarette smoking is such that a high score indicates a favorable attitude toward smoking. The self-report measure simply asked the number of times students had used illicit drugs (for example, mari-

Data for Exercise 12

Store	A	B	C	D	E	F
Advertising Budget	$4500	$1500	$2400	$1100	$9000	$2000
Total Sales	$70,000	$37,000	$97,000	$59,000	$247,000	$123,000

Data for Exercise 13

Subj	CIG	DRG	Subj	CIG	DRG	Subj	CIG	DRG	Subj	CIG	DRG
1	1.139	0	11	1.772	16	21	1.351	0	31	1.485	11
2	1.447	22	12	1.441	0	22	1.678	22	32	1.220	0
3	1.627	21	13	1.121	0	23	1.547	19	33	1.872	32
4	1.609	0	14	1.556	0	24	1.502	12	34	1.071	0
5	1.260	0	15	1.431	0	25	1.780	31	35	1.586	22
6	1.289	3	16	1.733	5	26	1.152	0	36	1.462	4
7	1.790	0	17	1.363	0	27	1.657	9	37	1.704	7
8	1.373	3	18	1.657	0	28	1.306	0	38	1.451	0
9	1.284	0	19	1.470	0	29	1.832	7	39	1.704	4
10	1.313	0	20	1.328	1	30	1.502	3	40	1.315	0

juana or cocaine). The data at the top of the page came from 40 students.

a. Find b and a, and write the regression equation.

b. Compute r and $s_{Y \cdot X}$.

c. What percentage of the variability of Y is accounted for by the linear prediction from X?

d. Comment on the large number of zeros for DRG and the ability to predict for any given subject.

14. Suppose we have the following IQ scores for fathers and their sons:

Pair	A	B	C	D	E
X = father IQ	119	109	127	121	140
Y = son IQ	110	115	130	129	130

a. Compute $\bar{Y}$, $\bar{X}$, $\overset{*}{s}{}^2_X$, and $\overset{*}{s}{}^2_Y$.

b. Compute r.

c. Compute b and a.

d. For father A, obtain Y', the predicted son's IQ. Compare Y' to Y for son A. What is $Y - Y'$?

e. Compute $e = Y - Y'$ for all five pairs. Now compute Σe. Is Σe what you expected?

f. Compute $Y - \bar{Y}$ for all five pairs. Is the absolute value of $Y - \bar{Y}$ larger than the absolute value of $e = Y - Y'$ for every pair? Now compute Σe^2 and $\Sigma (Y - \bar{Y})^2$. What principle or criterion does this illustrate?

g. Compute $\Sigma Y'$ and $\bar{Y}' = \Sigma Y'/N$. Compare $\bar{Y}'$ to $\bar{Y}$.

h. Obtain a predicted Y for $\bar{X}$. Is it equal to $\bar{Y}$? Should it be?

i. Obtain $s_{Y \cdot X}$ using formula 7.6 and then formula 7.7. Are the results the same within rounding error?

15. The data at the bottom of the page are scores from 15 students on Y (ACT composite scores) and X (number of semester hours of science courses in 3 yr of high school):

a. Form a scatterplot with Y as the vertical axis and X as the horizontal axis. Draw what appears to be the best-fitting line to predict Y (ACT score) from X (science hours).

b. Compute b and a, and draw in the line $Y = bX + a$. How closely does it fit the line you drew in part a?

c. Compute r. What percentage of variability in Y is explained by X?

d. Compute $s_{Y \cdot X}$ and compare it to $\overset{*}{s}_Y$.

16. Let us hypothesize that job-centered leadership style (Y) can be predicted by field independence (X) as measured by the embedded figures test (based on Erez, 1980). Job-centered leadership style can be measured by a scale of initiating structure (the degree to which a leader deals with a group working to attain a goal by assigning tasks, scheduling, taking control, and criticizing). The embedded figures test asks the participant to find which of five simple geometric figures are embedded in a complex design. The following results are available: $\bar{X} = 10.64$, $\overset{*}{s}{}^2_X = 5.67$, $\bar{Y} = 70.16$, $\overset{*}{s}{}^2_Y = 7.23$, $N = 45$, and $r = -.47$.

Data for Exercise 15

Pair	1	2	3	4	5	6	7	8	9	10	11	12	13	14	15
Y	23	27	30	19	18	21	17	21	27	29	25	22	26	25	24
X	15	18	18	12	9	9	6	12	15	12	12	12	15	12	18

Data for Exercise 18

Student	1	2	3	4	5	6	7	8	9	10	11	12	13
Y	100	45	60	120	30	45	60	75	90	90	130	90	45
X	88	72	91	95	69	79	78	83	85	78	96	93	90

a. Write the regression equation to predict job-centered leadership style from field independence.

b. If you interview a person with an embedded figures test score (X) of 18, what would you predict for his or her score on initiating structure (Y)?

Section 7.6

17. A researcher predicts that amount of exercise is related to overall health. We have X = number of minutes of exercise per week, Y = number of visits to physicians per year, and $\overline{X} = 32.1$, $\overset{*2}{s}_X = 5.1$, $\overline{Y} = 8.3$, $\overset{*2}{s}_Y = 4.1$, $N = 85$, and $r = -.32$.

a. Use the information to form a regression equation that predicts health from exercise.

b. Find the predicted number of visits to physicians for the time spent exercising of 110.

c. Compute the standard error of estimate.

d. Assuming the numbers of visits to physicians per year are normally distributed, compute 95% confidence limits for the predicted value in part b. How do you interpret this interval?

18. We are given data (shown at the top of the page) for percentage correct on a quiz (Y) and amount of time (in minutes) spent studying for the quiz (X):

a. Write the equation to predict performance from time studying.

b. Find the predicted percentage correct on the quiz for time spent studying of 110.

c. Compute the standard error of estimate.

d. If quiz percentages are normally distributed, compute 95% confidence limits for the predicted value in part b. How do you interpret this interval?

19. Suppose you are given the information on mother-daughter pairs that for X = mother's IQ and Y = daughter's IQ, $\overline{X} = 103$, $\overline{Y} = 118$, $\overset{*}{s}_X = 15$, $\overset{*}{s}_Y = 19$, $N = 200$, and $r = .51$.

a. Form a regression equation that predicts daughter's IQ from mother's IQ.

b. Find the daughter's predicted IQ for her mother's IQ of 110.

c. Compute the standard error of estimate.

d. Assuming IQs to be normally distributed, compute 95% confidence limits for the predicted value in part b. How do you interpret this interval?

20. You have examined some factors that affect the number of hours college students devote to studying. You found a negative correlation of .52 for hours worked on part-time jobs and hours spent studying. If the variance in study hours is $\overset{*2}{s}_Y = 26.12$, complete the following table:

	Explained by Work Hours	Not Explained by Work Hours	Total
Proportion of Variance in Study Hours			
Amount of Variance in Study Hours			

21. You are applying for graduate school and have already taken the Graduate Record Exam (GRE) admissions test. You didn't score as well as you had hoped you would on the verbal section, and you plan to take the GRE again. You are in the process of deciding which schools to apply to, and your verbal score of 530 may not be high enough for your top choice. You heard about a study involving the prediction of second-time GRE scores based on first-time GRE scores. Suppose the study says that for the verbal part of the GRE, the standard error of estimate is $s_{Y \cdot X} = 70$ for $N = 62$ participants. The study gives a prediction equation of $Y' = 0.8X + 114$.

a. Calculate a predicted score based on how you did on the GRE verbal test the first time.

b. You want to find out how close your second verbal score might be to the predicted score, so calculate the confidence limits on the prediction.

c. If your top choice for graduate school requires at least a 600 on the verbal test, are you wasting your time by taking the test again, or does the prediction indicate you could make the grade?

Section 7.7

22. In a study of aggression among children, you decide to look at variables that might predict which children become the most aggressive. You ask parents of 35 8-year-olds to complete a questionnaire and to permit you to observe their children on a playground. The parents are asked questions on four variables:

X_1 = How many hours of television does your child watch per week?

X_2 = How many children are living in the same home?

X_3 = On a scale of 1 to 10, how assertive are you, the parent (1 = not assertive enough, 10 = very assertive)?

X_4 = Rate your child's ability to cooperate with others, using a scale of 1 to 10 (1 = extremely cooperative, 10 = extremely uncooperative).

After observing the children, you and a colleague come up with a measure of aggressiveness and assign each child an aggression score (Y). You think television will be the best predictor of aggression scores, but you think competition with siblings also will be important. You run a multiple regression and obtain the results listed in the table. Use the MS_e stopping rule to identify the "best" equation. What does it mean in terms of those variables?

Number of Predictors	R^2	MS_e	Predictors
1	.26	9.1	X_1
1	.20	9.3	X_2
1	.18	14.3	X_3
2	.39	5.9	X_1X_2
2	.32	6.6	X_2X_3
2	.29	8.0	X_3X_4
3	.43	7.2	$X_2X_3X_4$
3	.42	7.3	$X_1X_2X_4$
3	.41	7.5	$X_1X_2X_3$
4	.44	7.3	$X_1X_2X_3X_4$

23. In an initial study of factors that influence college students to keep a drunk person from driving, you

survey 118 members of a freshman psychology course about how willing they are to intervene and keep someone from driving. You ask them to rate (1 to 10 scale) their willingness to intervene and to rate 12 factors according to whether they are unimportant (1) to very important (10) to their decision to stop the drunk driver. Among the factors you ask about are how long they have known the driver, how badly the driver needed help, number of previous interventions like this, number of previous conversations with others about intervention, number of previous conversations with the driver about intervention, how old the driver was, and how able they were to take control of the situation.

a. What are the predictor variables? The criterion variable?

b. Suppose you run a multiple regression analysis and find that an equation with three variables— how long the participants had known the driver, previous conversations with others about intervention, and how badly the driver needed help— leads to $R^2 = .285$. What does this mean in terms of variability explained?

c. You decide to look at the R^2 for the complete equation with all 12 factors in it. You find $R^2 = .312$. How should you decide which equation is the "best"?

24. You want to predict adult height from baby length, but you suspect that the gender of those in the survey might be an important influence. (Note that this data set is similar to that used in the SAS examples in Chapter 6, but that participants with "unknown" gender have been dropped.) When all the participants were examined together, baby length was not highly correlated with adult height, $r = .23$, or slightly more than 5% of the variability in adult height was explained by baby length. However, when participants were separated into males and females and correlations were computed separately, you obtained $r = .54$ for males and $r = .44$ for females. The higher correlations for males and females separately show that the gender of the participant is an important variable in predicting adult height. Thus, you would like to form a multiple regression equation that includes both baby length and gender as predictors and have one equation to predict adult height. To use gender as a variable in the computer program, it must be quantified by arbitrarily

assigning males = 2 and females = 1. Here, B stands for baby length, A stands for adult height, and G stands for gender.

B	A	G	B	A	G	B	A	G
18.0	69.0	2	21.0	71.0	2	21.0	72.0	2
20.0	69.0	2	21.0	65.5	1	23.5	69.0	1
21.0	67.0	1	20.0	70.0	2	19.5	69.5	2
20.0	67.5	1	21.5	65.0	1	20.0	62.5	1
19.5	64.0	1	20.5	73.0	2	22.0	67.0	1
22.0	67.5	1	23.0	67.0	1	21.0	68.0	1
21.0	71.0	2	21.0	62.0	1	20.5	67.0	1
20.5	70.0	2	19.0	64.0	1	20.5	67.0	2
19.0	64.0	1	17.0	62.0	1	20.0	63.5	1
20.0	63.0	1	19.0	60.5	1	20.5	67.0	1
20.0	66.0	1	19.0	66.0	2	21.5	58.0	1
20.5	63.5	1	20.0	68.5	1			

a. Enter the data in a SAS (or SPSS) program.
b. For SAS, use PROC CORR (in SPSS, add to the REGRESSION command the option /DESCRIPTIVES=CORR) to get descriptive statistics including all possible correlations.
c. Use PROC REG as discussed above (in SPSS, use the REGRESSION command with ENTER BABY TO GENDER as mentioned earlier) to find the weights for the multiple regression. Write the prediction equation with the numerical values of the weights.

25. Marital satisfaction is determined by many factors. Suppose you want to assess the role each of several predictors plays in influencing marital satisfaction. The variables you think may be predictors are number of years married (M), number of months the two knew each other before marriage (K), general life satisfaction (G), total family income in thousands (I), satisfaction with sex life on a scale from 1 to 7 (S), whether the person surveyed is the husband or the wife (HW), and number of children (C). You find scales to measure marital satisfaction (MS) and gen-

eral life satisfaction (scores can be from 1 to 50), and you write items for a survey for the other variables. The following data are gathered from 20 married adults, but none of them are married to each other (you surveyed only one partner from any given marriage). Here, 2 stands for husband and 1 stands for wife for the variable HW.

Subject	M	K	G	I	S	HW	C	MS
1	12	23	19	43	5	2	2	34
2	9	8	24	49	3	1	3	28
3	17	60	31	55	5	1	3	39
4	25	11	25	78	5	2	2	35
5	3	18	21	27	4	2	0	30
6	11	4	29	63	3	2	4	30
7	8	12	23	45	4	1	2	32
8	21	17	35	92	4	2	3	38
9	12	21	41	67	4	1	3	40
10	9	6	23	27	3	2	3	28
11	13	15	34	36	5	2	4	35
12	15	8	38	34	2	2	4	25
13	12	7	31	29	4	1	1	27
14	14	12	34	28	5	2	3	34
15	11	10	37	67	4	1	0	35
16	22	11	42	65	3	2	2	33
17	17	15	32	45	4	1	1	32
18	13	24	34	54	4	2	1	36
19	19	32	36	34	5	2	2	37
20	12	17	40	54	3	1	3	36

a. Enter the data in a SAS program.
b. Use PROC CORR to get descriptive statistics including all possible correlations.
c. Use PROC RSQUARE with the options discussed above to find the "best" prediction equation with the MS_e stopping rule. What proportion of variance in marital satisfaction is explained by the predictors in your "best" equation? Write the prediction equation with the numerical values of the weights.

8

Probability

We have focused our attention on ways to describe data: for one variable—central tendency and variability—and for two variables—correlation and regression. Now we turn to another of the seven topics common to all inferential methods: probability. The use of probabilities in drawing inferences makes this topic important as a basis for the next several chapters.

Research Example 8
8.1 Introduction
8.2 Definitions
    Card example
    Sample space
    Elementary event
    Event
    Probability
    Conditional probability
    Independence
    Multiplication (And) rule
    Mutually exclusive
    Addition (Or) rule
    Coin example
    Juror example
8.3 Sampling: With or without Replacement
    Sampling with replacement
    Sampling without replacement
    Real-world research
8.4 Probability Distributions: Discrete (Binomial) and Continuous (Normal) Variables
    Discrete variables: Relative frequency distributions
    Binomial: Definition
    Continuous variables: Normal distribution
    Normal approximation to the binomial

8.5   Probability and Statistics
     Inferential statistics
     $\overline{X}$ as an example
     $\overline{X}$ and probability
8.6   Summary, Study Tips, and Computation
     Chapter summary
     Study tips
     Computation
    Exercises

Research Example 8

Some research reports include percentages in the results. For example, consider the article "Geographic and Gender Variations in Total Tobacco Use" (Shopland, Niemcryk & Marconi, 1992). Shopland and colleagues reported data from a 1985 survey called the *Current Population Survey,* which included a series of questions on tobacco use. This nationwide survey recorded responses for $N = 105,225$ individuals aged 20 or older, with the results broken down by gender and by state and thus geographic region. Table 8.1 shows one of the tables from Shopland, Niemcryk, and Marconi (1992).

In the entire sample, almost 40% of the men and more than 26% of the women used at least one tobacco product in 1985. When you compare the columns for "at least one tobacco product" to those for "cigarette," you can see that use of other forms of tobacco is low for men ($39.67 - 32.66 = 7.01\%$) and even lower for women ($26.59 - 25.81 = 0.78\%$).

Some of the more interesting results are by geographic regions, but only for men (the geographic differences for women are much smaller). For men 20 or older, the South reports the highest percentage, with 44.56% using at least one tobacco product, whereas the West reports the lowest, 34.43%.

When the data are broken down by states, West Virginia tops the list for men at 56.66%, with Utah the lowest at 23.07%. Other states in the top ten in order are Mississippi (54.34%), Alaska (51.16%), Kentucky (50.01%), Arkansas (49.77%), North Carolina (48.78%), Georgia (47.06%), Oklahoma (46.35%), Tennessee (46.27%), and Alabama (46.24%).

In this chapter, you will learn about the importance of probability in statistics and research. Because probability can be defined as *relative frequency,* any percentage can be expressed as a probability by simply dividing it by 100, or moving the decimal point two places to the left. Thus, the probability of any given man in the entire country using at least one tobacco product is .3967. Notice how these probabilities change depending on geographic region or state. If you restrict your sample to the South, the probability is .4456; for West Virginia, .5666. If you examine only women aged 20 or older, the probability of using at least one tobacco product is .2659. Probabilities like these in restricted samples are called *conditional probabilities.*

Learning about probability in this chapter will bring you one step closer to completing coverage of the seven topics common to all inferential methods.

Table 8.1

Percentages of tobacco use in persons 20 years of age or older, by gender and geographic location

	Men							Women		
	None	Cigarette	Snuff	Chewing Tobacco	Cigar	Pipe	At Least One Tobacco Product	None	Cigarette	At Least One Tobacco Product
United States (105,225)	60.32	32.66	1.84	3.95	2.14	2.40	39.67	73.41	25.81	26.59
Northeast (26,186)	63.12	31.00	0.94	1.48	3.15	2.57	36.89	74.00	25.77	26.01
New England (9,434)	64.34	30.25	0.42	0.74	3.67	2.79	35.66	72.25	27.58	27.75
Middle Atlantic (16,752)	62.71	31.26	1.11	1.73	2.98	2.49	37.30	74.59	25.16	25.40
North Central (26,154)	60.45	32.20	2.07	3.43	2.29	3.01	39.55	72.54	27.33	27.46
East North Central (16,388)	60.07	32.83	1.70	2.90	2.53	3.20	39.94	71.31	28.55	28.70
West North Central (9,766)	61.34	30.70	2.95	4.69	1.72	2.54	38.66	75.40	24.51	24.60
South (31,646)	55.44	36.04	2.48	6.22	1.89	2.17	44.56	72.11	26.03	27.89
South Atlantic (18,014)	56.53	35.89	1.64	5.35	2.12	2.23	43.46	71.79	26.19	28.20
East South Central (4,985)	51.49	37.33	2.57	9.58	1.65	2.12	48.51	71.77	25.95	28.22
West South Central (8,647)	55.99	35.54	3.82	5.65	1.66	2.11	44.01	72.84	25.82	27.16
West (21,239)	65.57	29.19	1.41	3.34	1.29	1.82	34.43	76.28	23.47	23.72
Mountain (8,854)	62.20	29.92	2.36	5.61	1.46	2.04	37.81	75.44	24.27	24.57
Pacific (12,385)	66.81	28.92	1.05	2.51	1.23	1.73	33.18	76.58	23.18	23.42

Note: Percentages are based on the number of men and women participants within the individual geographic categories.
Source: Shopland, Niemcryk, and Marconi (1992).

8.1   Introduction

When researchers are studying a phenomenon, such as different people's ability to catch a liar, one group sometimes stands out from the others. Research Example 4 concerned a study by Ekman and O'Sullivan (1991), in which the group of Secret Service employees detected more liars than the other groups did. The researchers had to answer this question: If the groups are all the same, how likely is it for the Secret Service group to have this higher score? If the likelihood of the result is high—around .5, or a 50–50 chance—then the Secret Service group really isn't different from the others. But given that the groups are the same, what if the likelihood of the Secret Service's result is extremely small? What if it's a one in a thousand occurrence?

Researchers in the social sciences and other disciplines are interested in more than just means, standard deviations, and correlation coefficients. They want to know the likelihood, or *probability,* of their results.

Chapter 1 listed seven topics common to all inferential statistical methods. One was the use of probability in making decisions. Probability was defined as the relative frequency of occurrence, or:

$$\text{Probability} = \frac{\text{number of outcomes of interest}}{\text{total possible number of outcomes}}$$

Let's see how to apply this simple definition to weather forecasting. A more exact definition of probability is given later.

In a weather forecast you might hear the statement, "Tomorrow, the chance of rain will be 20%." This statement is based on the relative frequency definition of probability. Out of the previous, say, 100 days that had the same meteorological characteristics predicted for tomorrow, rain occurred on 20 of those days. So 20/100 is the probability of rain tomorrow, which leads to the "20% chance" statement. Do you see how this statement about probability in weather forecasting could help you make decisions? A 20% chance of rain for tomorrow might sound unlikely enough for you to decide to leave your umbrella at home.

Probability affects your decision making in many areas of everyday life, but you rarely even realize that you are using it. Sometimes you know that probability is being used, but the probabilities are subjective guesses that are not computed in any precise way. These types of probabilities are **subjective probabilities.**

In this text, probability is discussed in terms of its use in decision making about populations and their parameters. Probability as it is used outside the applied inferential process is not covered. The interested student is advised to refer to Moore and McCabe (1993).

Subjective probabilities
Arbitrary guesses at probabilities, not computed in any precise way

---

Quick Quiz

How would you use probability to decide which topics you want to study most carefully for your next statistics test? What kind of probability would you use?

Answer

You want to put the most emphasis on the material that the instructor is most likely to put on the test; that is, if the probability is high that the teacher will ask you to compute a regression equation, you should study that topic. If the probability is low that you will need to know the formula for the correlation coefficient, you will not memorize it. These are examples of subjective probabilities.

8.2   Definitions

Any discussion of probability must begin with essential definitions, some of which may not seem to be immediately relevant. To provide relevancy we first introduce an example, then give the definitions, and illustrate the definitions with the example. Two additional examples are given after all the definitions are discussed in detail in terms of the first example.

Card Example

Consider drawing one card from a well-shuffled standard deck of 52 cards. What is the probability that the card will be the jack of diamonds? What is the probability of the card being a jack? If you draw a jack and then draw a second card, what is the probability that the second card will be a jack?

Sample Space

Sample space
Group of data points representing all possible outcomes of an experiment; a population

The **sample space** is a group of data points that represent all possible outcomes of an experiment. A population is an example of a sample space.

For the card example, the sample space is the deck of 52 cards. The 52 cards represent all possible outcomes of the drawing of one card. Another way of thinking about it is that the 52 cards represent the population from which you will sample one card at random.

Elementary Event

Elementary event
A single member of the sample space

An **elementary event** is a single member, element, or point in the sample space. An outcome of an experiment is an elementary event.

Any one card in the deck is an elementary event, such as the jack of diamonds. The jack of diamonds is one of 52 possible outcomes.

Event

Event
Any group of elementary events

An **event** is any group of elementary events. All you have to do to form an event is to collect some elementary events.

In the card example, "jack" is an event because you could collect the elementary events of the jacks of diamonds, hearts, clubs, and spades. What is another illustration of an event? "Any spade" or "any card less than a 7" or any number of others.

Probability

Probability
Where A is an elementary event, the probability of A, denoted by $p(A)$, is 1 divided by the total number of possible outcomes

Where A is an elementary event in a sample space of equally probable elementary events, the **probability** of A, symbolized as $p(A)$, is

$$p(A) = \frac{1}{\text{total number of possible outcomes}} \tag{8.1}$$

This fits our earlier definition of probability because there is only one outcome of interest.

Probability of an event
The number in the event divided by the total number of possible outcomes

The **probability of an event** is simply the number of equally probable elementary events in the event divided by the total number of possible outcomes, or

$$p(\text{event}) = \frac{\text{number in event}}{\text{total number of possible outcomes}} \tag{8.2}$$

In most research in the behavioral sciences, it is assumed that all individuals have an equal chance of being selected to participate in the research. That is, these individuals are assumed to be equally probable elementary events. Random sampling is tied to the notion of equal probability, but it is not identical. Random sampling is independent selection that reduces the chances of systematic bias in the selection process, whereas equal probability deals with the elementary events themselves. In the card example, there are 52 cards, each of which is equally likely to be selected from a well-shuffled deck.

Theoretical probability
A probability that is based on a model or theory

Empirical probability
A probability that is based on the experience of empirical sampling

Probabilities can be defined by using formulas 8.1 and 8.2 from either a theoretical approach or an empirical approach, depending on the setting. A **theoretical probability** is based on a model or theory that gives it its value. A theoretical probability is not based on actual experience. For example, the probability of drawing a jack is 4/52 because of the theory of equal probability based on the deck being well shuffled. On the other hand, **empirical probability** is based on the experience of empirical sampling. If you drew one card from the deck, noted its value, replaced it in the deck, shuffled the deck, and continued this experiment 52 times, then you might obtain 3 jacks. The empirical probability of a jack is 3/52, and the theoretical probability of a jack is 4/52.

In practice, the observed proportion of occurrences for any event or elementary event may not equal the theoretical probability. However, as the number of trials for which sampling is done approaches infinity, the observed proportion (empirical probability) for any event or elementary event approaches the theoretical probability. For example, if you ran only 13 experiments, it is possible that you obtained no jacks. If you ran 520 experiments, 42 jacks would not be unlikely. This important concept bears repeating: As the number of experiments increases, the empirical probability approaches the true theoretical probability.

By definition, probability ranges from zero to one. Zero is the probability of an impossible event, and one is the probability of an event that has all the elements in the sample space. For example, there is no joker in a standard 52-card deck, so the probability of drawing a joker is zero. The probability of the card being a diamond, heart, club, or spade is one because every card in the deck is one of these suits.

Probability ranges from 0 to 1.

zero being impossible, 1 being in all likelihood.

Quick Quiz
Let's say there are 50 people in your statistics class and your teacher decides to randomly select one person to answer aloud the first question on a test. What is the probability that you will be chosen (assuming everyone shows up for the test)? What happens to the probability if half of the class drops out before the exam is given?

Answer

The probability is 1/50 because each student is one elementary event out of the total number of 50 possible elementary events. The probability that you will be put on the spot goes up as the number of people in the class decreases.

Conditional Probability

Conditional probability
A probability of one event
that is dependent on another
event, symbolized by $p(A|B)$

In some cases, the probability of one event depends on some other event. **Conditional probability** is a special type of probability that takes into account this dependence. It is defined as

$$p(A|B) = \frac{\text{number in } A \text{ and } B}{\text{total number of outcomes in } B} \tag{8.3}$$

where $A|B$ is read "A given B."

Conditional probability takes into account the influence that one event has on another. It is the probability of an event given that some condition exists. Knowing that the condition exists might change the probability. If you draw a jack and then draw another card without replacing the jack, what is the probability that the second card is a jack? This probability is 3/51 because there are 3 jacks remaining in the redefined sample space of 51 cards. The idea of redefining the sample space greatly helps some students understand conditional probability. Another way of thinking about it is to consider this as a subgroup of your original population. Here, the subgroup is the set of 51 cards that remains after one jack is drawn.

Independence

Independence
A is independent of B if the
occurrence of B does not
change the probability of A

Independence means that the occurrence of one event does not change the probability of occurrence of another event. Stated in terms of conditional probability, events A and B are independent if

$$p(A|B) = p(A) \tag{8.4}$$

The definition of the independence of A and B makes sense if you realize that condition B doesn't change the probability of A. If you put back the first card and reshuffle the deck of 52 cards, then the probability of a jack on the second draw given a jack on the first draw is still 4/52. Because the probability of a jack on the second draw is the same as the probability of a jack on the first draw, the two draws are independent (only if you put back the first card and reshuffle the deck). If the probability of an event is not changed when you restrict your attention to some subgroup, isn't the event independent of the variable that defines the subgroup? Asking a question about independence leads you to compare the probability and the conditional probability of an event. If they are equal, then the two events in question are independent. The events "jack on the first draw" and "jack on the second draw" when the first card is not returned and the deck is not reshuffled are not independent because 4/52 is not equal to 3/51.

Quick Quiz

Suppose your statistics teacher decides that anyone who got an A on Exam 1 is excused from having to answer a question aloud before Exam 2. Fifty people took the test, and you are among the seven people who got an A. What is the probability that your friend Steve, who got a B on Exam 1, will be chosen? What kind of probability is this?

Answer

Steve's probability of being chosen is 1/43. This is a conditional probability; the sample space has been restricted to the 43 people who did not get an A on Exam 1.

". . . don't understand probability at all."

Multiplication (And) Rule

Multiplication (And) rule
The probability of *A* and *B* is the product of $p(A)p(B)$ if *A* and *B* are independent; if *A* and *B* are not independent, it is the product of a probability and a *conditional* probability

If *A* and *B* are independent events or elementary events, then the **multiplication (And) rule** states

$$p(A \text{ and } B) = p(A)p(B) \qquad (8.5)$$

If *A* and *B* are not independent, then the multiplication rule is

$$p(A \text{ and } B) = p(A|B)p(B) = p(A)p(B|A) \qquad (8.6)$$

The inclusion of "(And)" in the title of the rule is to help you remember to use it for the probability of the joint occurrence of two events, an "And" type of question. Because this is the probability of a joint occurrence, it is sometimes called a **joint probability.** Generally, to find the probability of something in the form of "this *and* that," use the multiplication rule. Think of this rule as requiring two facts to be true simultaneously. The probability of getting a single card that is both a diamond *and* a face card is an example. Be sure that you distinguish between the equations for independent events and those for dependent events. For independent events, multiply a probability by a probability. For dependent events, multiply a probability by a *conditional* probability.

Joint probability
Probability of a joint occurrence, $p(A \text{ and } B)$

As an example of dependent events, consider the probability of getting a single card that is both a diamond and a face card (including aces). Figure 8.1 shows how the product of the probability and the conditional probability gives the correct answer. First, the probability of face card is 16/52. Then the probability of a diamond given that you have a face card is 4/16. So the probability of a card being a diamond and a face card is 4/16 of 16/52, which equals 4/52. Note that you can get the same answer by switching the "diamond" and "face card" in the equation. Simply counting the 4 diamonds that are face cards out of the 52 cards in the deck verifies our answer.

For independent events, consider the probability of drawing a jack, replacing the card, shuffling the deck, and drawing a second jack. This probability is 4/52 times 4/52 because the two events are independent.

Mutually Exclusive

Mutually exclusive
Events *A* and *B* are mutually exclusive when they do not have any elementary event in common

When events *A* and *B* do not have any elementary event in common, when *A* and *B* cannot occur simultaneously, or when $p(A \text{ and } B) = 0$, events *A* and *B* are **mutually exclusive.**

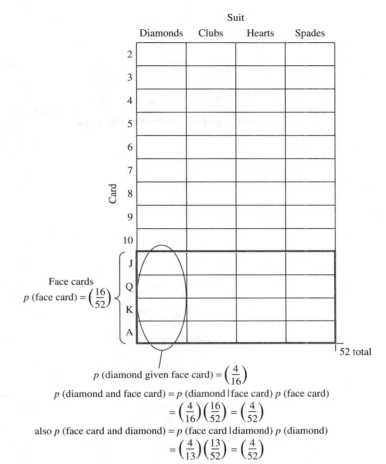

Figure 8.1
The multiplication (And) rule is sometimes the product of a probability and a conditional probability

The events jack and queen are mutually exclusive because a card cannot be both a jack and a queen. Jack and diamond are not mutually exclusive because the jack of diamonds is a common elementary event.

Addition (Or) Rule

Addition (Or) rule
Probability of A or B is
$p(A) + p(B) - p(A$ and $B)$

If A and B are events or elementary events, then the **addition (Or) rule** states

$$p(A \text{ or } B) = p(A) + p(B) - p(A \text{ and } B) \tag{8.7}$$

If A and B are mutually exclusive, then this simplifies to

$$p(A \text{ or } B) = p(A) + p(B) \tag{8.8}$$

Generally, this statement means to include all the cases that are in one event or the other. Usually the word *or* is the cue for the use of this rule. You will include an event if it meets one condition *or* the other condition; *A* is true or *B* is true. Sometimes the *or* is implied. The probability of drawing a card smaller than a 4 means a 3 or a 2 (mutually exclusive). You get this probability by adding the separate probabilities, 4/52 + 4/52 = 8/52. Remember to note whether the events are mutually exclusive. Mutually exclusive events allow simple addition of the probabilities.

Figure 8.2 illustrates this rule. Suppose you are playing a card game, you need to draw either a jack or a diamond to win, and you are using a new 52-card deck. What is the probability of drawing a jack or a diamond? The probability of a jack is 4/52, the probability of a diamond is 13/52, and the probability of the jack of diamonds is 1/52. You want to count all the jacks and all the diamonds, but you don't want to count the jack of diamonds twice. So the correct probability is *p*(jack) + *p*(diamond) − *p*(jack and diamond), or 4/52 + 13/52 − 1/52 = 16/52.

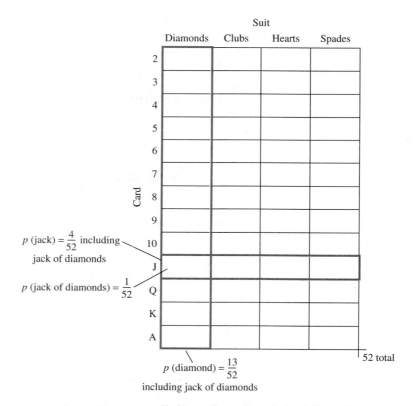

$$p \text{ (jack or diamond)} = p \text{ (jack)} + p \text{ (diamond)} - p \text{ (jack and diamond)}$$
$$= \frac{4}{52} + \frac{13}{52} - \frac{1}{52}$$
$$= \frac{16}{52}$$

Figure 8.2
The addition (Or) rule: *p*(jack) + *p*(diamond) − *p*(jack and diamond)

Coin Example

Now let's take another example. Suppose you toss a fair coin twice. What is the probability of a head on the first toss and a tail on the second toss? An experiment in which you toss two fair coins once would give the same results. Experiments in the behavioral sciences sample N subjects and measure them once, thus more closely fitting the second statement of this coin experiment.

The sample space is TT, TH, HT, and HH, where T = tails and H = heads. An elementary event is HT. "H on toss 2" is an event because it contains the elementary events TH and HH, those with a head on the second toss. Any other group of elementary events in this example is also an event.

Probabilities for this example are theoretical, based on the theory of a fair coin with two sides. Any actual coin experiment might yield results that deviate from the theoretical probabilities. For example, if you actually tossed a fair coin ten times, would you expect exactly five heads? No, you might get a number close to five, maybe three or four or six. If the number of trials is increased from ten to 100, the observed proportion of heads should be closer to .50, maybe 46/100 for a given 100 trials. For 1000 trials, 485/1000 would not be unusual for a fair coin. As the number of trials increases, the proportion of heads approaches .50.

An extension of the multiplication (And) rule gives the probability of more than two independent events occurring together (jointly). It is simply the product of all the probabilities. The probability of 10 heads on ten tosses of a fair coin is 1/1024. The probability of ten heads, or HHHHHHHHHH, is the probability of a single head, 1/2, ten times. To explain why you take the product of the probabilities, consider only two tosses of a fair coin. If you obtain two heads, you say the probability of two heads is 1/4, or 1/2 times 1/2. Of the potential outcomes on the first toss, one-half of them have H. Then H on the second toss leads to one-half of the original one-half, or one-fourth. The logical extension of this for ten heads is that $p(\text{ten heads}) = (1/2)^{10}$, which comes from one-half (toss 10) of the one-half (toss 9) of the one-half (toss 8), and so on, of the one-half that gave H on the first toss. Figure 8.3 shows how the product of the ten one-halves gives the correct answer of 1/1024.

Quick Quiz

Let's say you maintain your A average in statistics by getting an A on Exam 2. Your teacher announces that anyone who got an A on both tests is freed from having to answer questions aloud for the rest of the term. What rule would you use to calculate the probability of being freed from oral questions?

Answer

Use the multiplication rule to find the probability of being freed (an A on Exam 1 *and* an A on Exam 2).

Juror Example

Is the probability of receiving an award in a civil suit dependent on the authoritarianism of the jurors? To answer this question, suppose a researcher developed a verbal scale to measure authoritarianism (based on Kirby, 1971). This scale consisted of several questions that could be asked of potential jurors to determine authoritarianism, which might be related to how jurors make decisions. The next step was to compare the verbal

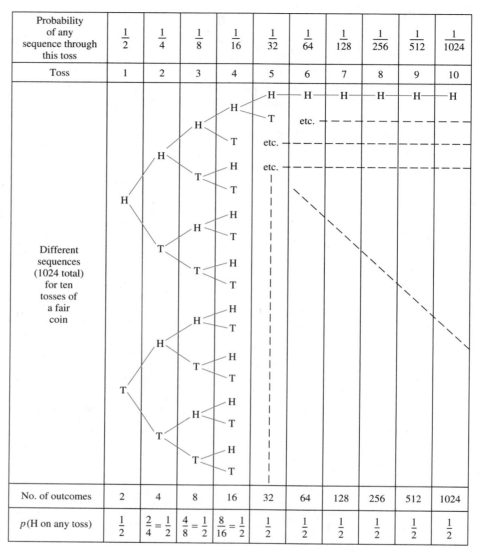

Probability of any sequence through this toss	$\frac{1}{2}$	$\frac{1}{4}$	$\frac{1}{8}$	$\frac{1}{16}$	$\frac{1}{32}$	$\frac{1}{64}$	$\frac{1}{128}$	$\frac{1}{256}$	$\frac{1}{512}$	$\frac{1}{1024}$
Toss	1	2	3	4	5	6	7	8	9	10
No. of outcomes	2	4	8	16	32	64	128	256	512	1024
p(H on any toss)	$\frac{1}{2}$	$\frac{2}{4}=\frac{1}{2}$	$\frac{4}{8}=\frac{1}{2}$	$\frac{8}{16}=\frac{1}{2}$	$\frac{1}{2}$	$\frac{1}{2}$	$\frac{1}{2}$	$\frac{1}{2}$	$\frac{1}{2}$	$\frac{1}{2}$

Figure 8.3
Probability of ten heads $= 1/2^{10} = \frac{1}{1024}$ (ten tosses of a fair coin)

scale to an existing written scale on authoritarianism, such as the authoritarian or F scale (Adorno, Frenkel-Brunswick, Levinson & Sanford, 1950). It was found to be highly related to the F scale. The researcher then tested the scale in a mock trial setting to see whether there were differences between authoritarians and nonauthoritarians (egalitarians) in the frequency with which they assess damages in a civil suit involving an automobile accident. To test these differences, 48 people were classified as authoritarian or egalitarian by the verbal scale and were randomly assigned to four 12-person juries. After hearing the evidence and the summation of a fairly neutral or questionable case, the jurors were asked to fill out a ballot indicating the amount of monetary award

Table 8.2

Jurors classified as to award and authoritarian or egalitarian

	Authoritarian	Egalitarian	Totals
Gave an award	18	13	31
Gave no award	2	15	17
Totals	20	28	48

they would give. The ballots were classified as to whether they gave any award and whether the juror was authoritarian or egalitarian, resulting in the data in Table 8.2. Based on these data, what do you think about the original question? Is the probability of receiving an award dependent on the authoritarianism of the jurors?

Consider the issue of theoretical versus empirical probabilities in this example. Theory might say that the probability of a juror giving an award in a neutral case is $1/2 = .50$ because one of the two possible decisions, or outcomes, is to give an award. However, you have empirically found 31 of the 48 jurors giving an award, or $31/48 = .65$ as the probability of an award. In this example, the probabilities in Table 8.2 are all empirical.

An example of a joint probability is p(award and authoritarian) = 18/48. A probability such as p(award) = 31/48 is called a **marginal probability** because it depends on only the frequencies in the margins (table row or column totals). Conditional probabilities redefine the sample space to one of the marginal conditions, such as authoritarian. One conditional probability is p(award|authoritarian) = 18/20.

Conditional probability takes into account the influence of one event on another. Does the probability of the jurors giving an award depend on authoritarianism? The value of p(award|authoritarian) is $18/20 = .90$. This conditional probability is computed by finding the number of authoritarians who gave a reward and then dividing by the number of authoritarians. You have essentially redefined the sample space to be authoritarians and then computed the probability of an award in the new sample space. Authoritarians is a subgroup of the population of jurors. The value of p(award|egalitarians) is $13/28 = .46$, which is considerably different from .90. Could the defense lawyer use the verbal authoritarians scale to select the jury members at the beginning of the trial? In this example, p(award) = 31/48, or 65, but p(award|authoritarian) = .90, so giving an award and authoritarianism are not independent.

Table 8.3 summarizes all three examples by illustrating each definition for each example.

Marginal probability
A probability that depends on only the frequencies in the margins (rows or columns) of a table

8.3   Sampling: With or without Replacement

When sampling was introduced in Chapter 1, we considered some basic issues such as definitions of random sampling, a sample, and a population. We now address yet another issue: sampling with or without replacement and its impact on probability.

Sampling with replacement
Each elementary event that is sampled is replaced in the sample space (population)

Sampling with Replacement

One crucial question that must be raised in problems involving probability is whether the sampling is done with or without replacement. **Sampling with replacement** means

Table 8.3
Probability definitions and juror, card, and coin examples

Definition	Juror Example	Card Example	Coin Example
Sample space	All jurors	All 52 cards	HT, TH, HH, TT
Elementary event	Some juror who awarded $300	Jack of diamonds	HT
Event	Jurors who gave an award	Any jack	H on toss 2
p(elementary event)	p(any juror) = 1/48	p(jack of diamonds) = 1/52	p(HT) = 1/4
p(event)	p(award) = 31/48 = .65	p(any jack) = 4/52	p(H on toss 2) = 2/4
$p(A|B)$	p(award|authoritarian) = 18/20 = .90	p(jack on draw 2|jack on draw 1) = 3/51	p(H on toss 2|H on toss 1) = 1/2
Independence	p(award|authoritarian) = .90 ≠ p(award) = .65, so award and authoritarian are not independent	3/51 ≠ 4/52, so jacks on two draws are not independent unless all 52 cards are reshuffled	p(H on toss 2|H on toss 1) = p(H on toss 2), so H on toss 2 is independent of H on toss 1
Multiplication (And) rule	p(award and authoritarian) = p(award|authoritarian) × p(authoritarian) = (18/20)(20/48) = 18/48	p(jack on draw 2 and jack on draw 1) = (3/51)(4/52)	p(H on toss 2 and H on toss 1) = (2/4)(2/4) = 1/4
Mutually exclusive	Award and no award are mutually exclusive because each juror must give or not give an award.	Jack and queen are mutually exclusive because jack and queen cannot occur simultaneously.	H and T on one toss are mutually exclusive because H and T cannot occur simultaneously.
	Award and authoritarian are not mutually exclusive because they have elementary events in common.	Jack and diamond are not mutually exclusive because they have an elementary event in common.	H on toss 1 and T on toss 2 are not mutually exclusive because HT is the common elementary event.
Addition (Or) rule	p(award or authoritarian) = .65 + .42 − .38 = .69	p(jack or diamond) = 4/52 + 13/52 − 1/52 = 16/52	p(H on toss 1 or T on toss 2) = 1/2 + 1/2 − 1/4 = 3/4

that after you sample an elementary event, you put it back into the sample space, or population. The sample space is not changed for subsequent samples.

An example of sampling with replacement is the card example when you replace the card and reshuffle the deck. Drawing a card from the deck, replacing the card, shuffling the deck, and drawing another card leave the number of elementary events in the sample space the same for draw 2 as it was for draw 1. The sample space is not changed.

Sampling with replacement usually is done with independent events, which allows use of the simpler multiplication rule.

Sampling without Replacement

Sampling without replacement
Each elementary event that is sampled is not replaced in the sample space (population)

Sampling without replacement means that after you sample an elementary event, you do not put it back into the sample space. Because the elementary events are not replaced, the sample space, or population, changes at each sampling.

Consider this example of sampling without replacement. You sampled one card from a 52-card deck and asked the probability of the card being the jack of diamonds. If the first card was a jack, what is the probability that a second card is a jack? Because you did not replace the first jack and shuffle the deck, the sampling is without replacement. For the second sampling, there are now 51 cards in the deck, so the sample space has changed.

Sampling without replacement almost always implies that different events will be dependent. This dependence comes from the change in the sample space and the subsequent difference between the probability and the conditional probability. Because of the dependence in sampling without replacement, you use the version of the multiplication rule that multiplies a conditional probability and a probability.

Real-World Research

Most research in the behavioral sciences samples without replacement. For example, consider the exam stress study introduced in Chapter 1. After a college sophomore was sampled for that experiment, the researcher did not sample him or her again for the same or even similar research. In research that surveys households, once a home is surveyed for attitudes on some issue, it won't be contacted again. The actual practice of most applied researchers is to do sampling without replacement; however, most statistical methods (models) assume sampling with replacement. That is, the probabilities used to make decisions from inferential statistical methods typically require sampling with replacement for their validity. The research and the statistics seem to be at odds with respect to the type of sampling. What is the solution to this dilemma?

The resolution of the apparent conflict between the practices of researchers and the probabilities of statistical methods lies in a compromise. For most populations sampled, the actual computed probabilities for sampling with and without replacement are very similar because the populations are large. The actual probabilities for sampling without replacement are well approximated by those for sampling with replacement. The agreement gets even closer as the size of the population (sample space) increases. Because you typically assume the populations to be large, you can use the statistical methods with confidence that the probabilities are accurate. You can use all of the available statistical methods and the simpler computations of probabilities associated with sampling with replacement.

To illustrate the closeness of probabilities from sampling with and without replacement, consider the card example. Granted, the card example is not typical of behavioral science research, but it does give easily computed probabilities for both types of sampling. Given sampling without replacement, what is the probability of obtaining two jacks? Using the multiplication rule, you get

$$p(\text{two jacks}) = \left(\frac{3}{51}\right)\left(\frac{4}{52}\right) = .0045$$

Using the simpler version of the multiplication rule to get $p(\text{two jacks})$ for sampling with replacement gives

$$p(\text{two jacks}) = \left(\frac{4}{52}\right)\left(\frac{4}{52}\right) = .0059$$

Thus, .0059 from the simpler computation given sampling with replacement is a good approximation to the exact .0045. The closeness of these two values illustrates the closeness of agreement between probabilities from sampling with and without replacement.

Quick Quiz

Suppose your statistics teacher decides to randomly sample one student every class period to answer a question aloud. It is Day 15 and you have not been called on. Which would you prefer the teacher to be using—sampling with or without replacement?

Answer

If you want to avoid being called on to answer orally, you would hope the teacher is sampling with replacement.

8.4 Probability Distributions: Discrete (Binomial) and Continuous (Normal) Variables

Probability distribution
Distribution where each value of X is paired with its probability

When you consider all the outcomes from an experiment and their associated probabilities, you have a **probability distribution.** An example of a probability distribution is the speeds of 90 vehicles and their associated relative frequencies. Another example is the normal distribution of heights of all U.S. men. First, we consider probability distributions for discrete variables.

Discrete Variables: Relative Frequency Distributions

An example of a probability distribution was given in Chapter 3. The relative frequency distribution of the speeds of 90 vehicles during the baseline period in the speed control research is actually a probability distribution. Table 8.4 shows a probability distribution for the frequencies of baseline speeds in Table 3.8. The probability column in this table would be the relative frequency column in Table 3.8 if you computed relative frequencies for this distribution. This underscores the idea that probabilities are relative frequencies. Note that the sum of the probabilities is one, which is true for all discrete probability distributions.

You can use some of the probability rules to answer questions about this distribution. For example, what is the probability that a vehicle was going at the speed limit of 50 km/h or slower? Because this is an "or" question, you need to use the addition rule. If

Table 8.4
Frequency distribution and probability distribution of baseline speeds

Speed Interval	Frequency	Probability $= \dfrac{Frequency}{Total}$
78–80	2	.0222
75–77	5	.0556
72–74	6	.0667
69–71	8	.0889
66–68	10	.1111
63–65	10	.1111
60–62	13	.1444
57–59	11	.1222
54–56	11	.1222
51–53	9	.1000
48–50	4	.0444
45–47	1	.0111
Total	90	1.00

Table 8.5
Probability distribution for number of heads in two tosses of a fair coin

Event	Number of Heads	Frequency	Probability = $\frac{Frequency}{Total}$
2 heads	2	1	1/4 = .25
1 head, 1 tail	1	2	2/4 = .50
2 tails	0	1	1/4 = .25
		Total = 4	Total = 1.00

you assume sampling without replacement, then a vehicle can fit into only one interval and the events are mutually exclusive, which allows you to use the simple addition rule. To obtain p(speed less than or equal to 50), you need to add two separate probabilities: p(speed 48–50) and p(speed 45–47). The answer is .0444 + .0111 = .0556, with the apparent discrepancy due to rounding error.

Consider the earlier example of the number of heads in two tosses of a fair coin. Number of heads is a discrete variable. You can get two, one or no heads in two tosses. Of the four outcomes in the sample space, one gives two heads, so p(two heads) = 1/4. Both HT and TH give one head, so p(one head) = 2/4. The value of p(no heads) = 1/4 comes from TT. The probability distribution is given in Table 8.5. You can add these probabilities to answer questions such as, What is the probability of getting one or more heads in two tosses of a fair coin? This particular probability distribution is an example of a *binomial distribution*.

Quick Quiz

The probability of two heads in Table 8.5, .25, was obtained because two heads is one of four outcomes, 1/4 = .25. Given that two heads is HH or H and H, what rule of probability could be used to get the same answer, .25?

Answer

The multiplication (And) rule: H on toss 1 has probability 1/2, H on toss 2 also has 1/2, so "H and H" has probability (1/2)(1/2) = 1/4.

Binomial: Definition

Binomial distribution

Probability distribution of the number of successes in sampling with replacement from a population with only two values (success and failure)

One useful application of many of the concepts in probability is the **binomial distribution.** The binomial is a probability distribution of a discrete variable. If you independently sample with replacement a sample of size N from a population (sample space) that has only two values, the number of one of those values in the N observations is a binomial variable. The value of interest is typically called a "success" and the other value a "failure." For example, success could be an H on a fair coin, or a multiple-choice item being correct, or an ESP experimenter making the correct choice, or one chimpanzee in a pair getting a grape in a study on dominance.

Each of these examples defines an original population (sample space) that has only two possible values (outcomes, or elementary events). They also involve sampling from the population (sample space) N times, so the sample size is N. On each selection from the population (sample space), you draw one of the two possible values—for example, head or tail. If $N = 2$, you sample twice and obtain either H or T each time. The number of successes in a sample of size N, or in N trials, is a binomial variable.

Binomial Probabilities

Computing probabilities for a binomial distribution can be time-consuming for N's that are not small. Not only is the formula for the probabilities complex (see Box 8.1), but also a probability has to be computed for each possible value of number of successes from zero to N. That is, the probability of five successes on $N = 10$ coin flips is different from the probability of ten successes on $N = 10$ coin flips. If you know N and p, the probability of one success (in the population, or sample space), you can use Table A.3 in Appendix A, which lists probabilities for a limited number of binomial distributions. Probability values are provided for $X =$ number of successes from $N = 2$ to $N = 10$. Notice in Table A.3 that the probability of one success is given across the top row. For a coin flip, $p = .5$, but for another variable, the probability can be anything between zero and one. Knowledge of N and p completely specifies a binomial distribution, so N and p are the parameters of the binomial distribution. Probability values for larger values of N can be obtained by using the normal approximation, given later in this section.

Example

If you toss a fair coin twice, the number of heads is a binomial variable. Table 8.5 gives the probabilities for the binomial distribution with $N = 2$ and $p = .5$. The value of N is 2 because you toss a fair coin twice (or two fair coins once). The value of p is .5

Box 8.1   Binomial Distribution

Computation of probabilities for the binomial distribution requires knowledge of the parameter N, the sample size or number of trials, and p, the probability of success on one trial. The equation for the probability of r successes in N trials is:

$$p(r \text{ successes}) = \frac{N!}{r!(N-r)!}p^r q^{N-r}$$

where $N!$ is read as "N factorial" and has value $N! = N(N-1)(N-2) \cdots 1$, or the successive products of N to one, and where $q = 1 - p$. Note that $0!$ is always taken to one.

Assume $N = 10$ and $p = .25$; then $q = 1 - .25 = .75$. The probability of $r = 8$ successes is

$$p(8 \text{ successes}) = \frac{10!}{8!(10-8)!}(.25)^8(.75)^{10-8}$$

$$= .00039$$

The factorial part of the equation is considerably simplified by writing out the numerator factorial in terms of the denominator factorials:

$$\frac{10!}{8!(10-8)!} = \frac{10(9)(8!)}{8!2!} = \frac{10(9)}{2!} = \frac{90}{2(1)} = 45$$

and canceling appropriate terms, such as the $8!$ in this example.

Table 8.6
Binomial probabilities for $N = 10$ and $p = .25$

X = Number of Successes	Probability
10	.000001
9	.00003
8	.00039
7	.00309
6	.01622
5	.05840
4	.14600
3	.25028
2	.28157
1	.18771
0	.05631

because there are only two outcomes and the coin is fair, making the probability of H in the population (sample space) .5.

Suppose you take a quiz that has ten multiple-choice items, each with four responses. The probability of guessing and getting an item correct is $p = 1/4 = .25$ because one out of the four responses is correct. And $N = 10$ because there are ten items. See Table 8.6 for probabilities computed from Box 8.1 for $N = 10$ and $p = .25$.

Figure 8.4 shows this binomial distribution. What is the probability of getting a score of 8 or higher by just guessing? That is, what is the probability in the upper tail of values of 8 or higher? Use the addition rule to get

$$p(8 \text{ or higher}) = p(8) + p(9) + p(10) = .000421$$

Examine Figure 8.4 to find this upper-tail area.

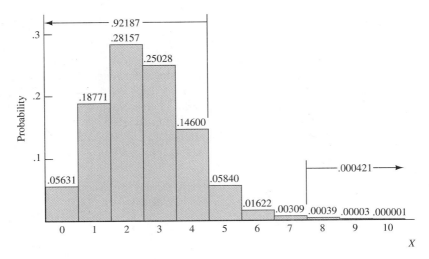

Figure 8.4
Binomial distribution with $N = 10$ and $p = .25$ showing $p(X < 5)$ and $p(X \geq 8)$

What is the probability of getting a score less than 5 by guessing alone? This value is

$$p(\text{less than 5}) = .92187$$

We added the probabilities for certain values of X to get .92187, but which values? The values of X are 4, 3, 2, 1, and 0. Again, examine Figure 8.4 to see how you obtained this probability, which includes values in the lower tail of the distribution.

Quick Quiz
Use Table A.3 to find the probability of $X = 2$ successes when $N = 9$ and the probability of one success is .15.

Answer

.2597

Continuous Variables: Normal Distribution

The normal distribution covered in Chapter 5 is a theoretical distribution often used as a probability distribution for some continuous variables. To find the probability for this type of variable, you cannot use formulas 8.1 and 8.2. Instead, you must use a modification of those formulas that uses area instead of number of events or outcomes. In a distribution for a continuous variable, probability is defined as:

$$p = \text{some proportion of area under the curve} \tag{8.9}$$

When you found proportions of scores in certain intervals in normal distributions in Chapter 5, you were doing the same task as in finding probabilities. For example, for the standard normal distribution, the proportion of z scores between -1 and 1 is .6826. The probability of a z being between -1 and 1 is also .6826 because probability is a proportion in a normal distribution.

Example

Consider the distribution of the heights of men. If the heights are normally distributed with a mean of 69 in. and a standard deviation of 3 in., what is the probability of selecting one man at random whose height is greater than 74 in.? First you need to compute $z = (74 - 69)/3 = 1.67$. Now you can ask: What is the probability that z is greater than 1.67? Table A.2 gives the proportion of z's greater than 1.67 as .0475. So the probability that z is greater than 1.67 as .0475, and the probability of selecting one man at random who is taller than 74 in. is also .0475. Figure 8.5 shows this probability.

Two points need to be emphasized:

1. You always work with intervals when finding probabilities in the normal distribution. This is true for any distribution of a continuous variable. The probability of a single point makes no sense for a continuous variable because there is no area under the curve at one point.

2. You treat the total area under the curve as one (unity) to correspond to the fact that the sum of the probabilities is one for discrete variables.

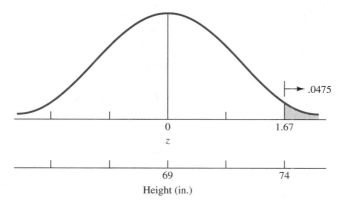

Figure 8.5
Area in the tail of the standard normal distribution, $z = 1.67$, height $= 74$ in.

Work with inferential statistics and their sampling distributions involves discrete or continuous variables. So finding areas, or probabilities, in distributions of these variables is important.

Normal Approximation to the Binomial

Even though the binomial distribution is a probability distribution for a discrete variable, it can be reasonably well fit by a continuous normal distribution. If N is sufficiently large and p is close to .5, then the binomial distribution can be approximated with the normal distribution with mean Np and variance Npq. Samuels and Lu (1992) give improved rules for sample size requirements for this approximation. A shortened version of their requirements is listed in Table 8.7. Note that if p is greater than .50, use $q = 1 - p$ to enter the table. Also, f is the observed frequency of the event in question.

If you want to know the probability that a score on a $N = 36$ item multiple-choice test with $p = .25$ will be 19 or higher by just guessing, can you use the normal approximation to the binomial? From Table 8.7 with $p = .25$, you need f to be 19 or more. Since the example has $f = 19$, you can use the approximation. The binomial can be approximated by a normal distribution with $\mu = 36(.25) = 9$ and $\sigma^2 = 9(.25)(.75) = 6.75$. The probability may be calculated by using a z score of

Table 8.7

Requirements for adequacy of the normal approximation to the binomial (using the moderate rule from Samuels & Lu, 1992)

p Minimum	Required f
.05	48
.10	40
.15	33
.20	25
.25	19
.30	14
.35	8
.40	5
.45	5
.50	5

$$z = \frac{X - Np}{\sqrt{Npq}}$$

which is distributed approximately as the standard normal distribution. For the $N = 36$, $p = .25$ binomial, the probability that X will be 19 or higher by guessing alone requires the calculation of z for $X = 19$. The value is

$$z = \frac{19 - 36(.25)}{\sqrt{36(.25)(.75)}} = \frac{19 - 9}{\sqrt{6.75}} = 3.85$$

From Table A.2, we find that the probability of getting a z score greater than or equal to 3.90 is .00005. Thus, the probability of getting 19 or more items correct merely by guessing on a 36-item (four-response) multiple-choice test is about .00005.

8.5   Probability and Statistics

Inferential Statistics

The use of any inferential statistic in this text assumes random sampling with replacement from large or infinite populations with equally probable elementary events. However, real research usually samples without replacement, sometimes from a small population. Even without meeting all the assumptions, the resulting probabilities in the distributions of the statistics are close to what they should be. Because most distributions of statistics are approximated by continuous theoretical distributions, of which normal distributions are examples, probabilities for statistics are discussed in terms of areas under a theoretical distribution.

You might be asking, Why should I be interested in how probability is used in inferential statistics? Remember that probability is used to make decisions. In Section 8.1 you saw that the researchers in the liar study were interested in knowing how likely it is for the Secret Service group to detect a certain number of liars. Using probability, you can choose between two theories. If an outcome is unlikely (low probability) under theory 1, then the outcome doesn't support that theory. If the results have high probability given theory 2, then the data support theory 2. In the case of the liar research, one theory would say that the career groups are all the same. If so, how likely is the Secret Service's performance? If the Secret Service outcome has a low probability, you would doubt that the career groups are all the same. Perhaps the data support an alternative idea, that the Secret Service employees are better than anyone else at detecting a liar.

In terms of understanding how researchers draw conclusions, you must see that all inferential statistics use probability to make decisions.

$\overline{X}$ as an Example

Even though distributions of statistics (sampling distributions) are not thoroughly covered until the next chapter, we illustrate here how probability is used in such distributions. We build the sampling distribution of the sample mean $\overline{X}$ for a population with only three score values. Even with this simplistic setting, you can learn how probability concepts apply to distributions of statistics.

The population consists of only the scores 1, 2, and 3, each with equal frequency. Sampling randomly with replacement, we draw out samples of size $N = 2$. What different values of X can you put together, and what are the resulting values of $\overline{X}$? Also, what is the probability of each of these $\overline{X}$ values? Figure 8.6 shows the population and all possible samples for $N = 2$, along with the probabilities for each $\overline{X}$.

Did you recognize that the multiplication (And) rule was used to compute the probability of each $\overline{X}$? For example, the probability of $\overline{X} = 1.0$ comes from the fact that $\overline{X} = 1.0$ is composed of $X_1 = 1$ and $X_2 = 1$. So

$$p(\overline{X} = 1.0) = p(X_1 = 1 \text{ and } X_2 = 1) = p(X_1 = 1)p(X_2 = 1) = (1/3)(1/3) = 1/9$$

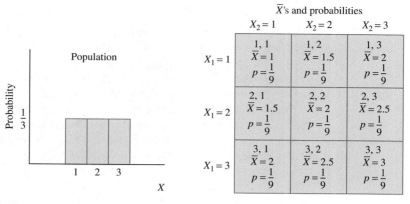

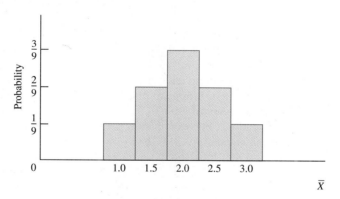

Figure 8.6
Population of three scores and resulting possible $\overline{X}$'s, $N = 2$

Figure 8.7
Distribution of $\overline{X}$ from population of Figure 8.6

The next step is to collect these values of $\overline{X}$ into a distribution. To do this, you use the addition (Or) rule. For example, there are two different ways to get $\overline{X} = 1.5$: from $X_1 = 1$ and $X_2 = 2$ and from $X_1 = 2$ and $X_2 = 1$. To get the probability of $\overline{X} = 1.5$ for the first or the second sample, you add the two probabilities to get $1/9 + 1/9 = 2/9$. The other probabilities are found in a similar manner. The multiplication (And) rule and the addition (Or) rule give the correct probabilities for each value of $\overline{X}$. Even if N is larger than 2 and the population has more than three values with unequal probabilities, this approach gives the correct probabilities for $\overline{X}$. Figure 8.7 shows the distribution of the $\overline{X}$'s and their associated probabilities.

With a large population and more values of X possible in the population, the distribution of $\overline{X}$ becomes less discrete. The larger sample size (N) helps to smooth out the curve.

$\overline{X}$ and Probability

Now let's illustrate each of the basic definitions with the sampling distribution of $\overline{X}$. This illustration should help you understand how probability is used in sampling distributions of statistics. In a sampling distribution, the sample space is all possible values of the statistic. In the sampling distribution of $\overline{X}$, the sample space is made up of all $\overline{X}$ values that could be computed on samples of a given size N from a given population.

The statistics themselves are the elementary events, and any grouping of the statistics is an event. The $\overline{X}$'s are elementary events in the sampling distribution of $\overline{X}$, and an example of an event is all $\overline{X}$'s larger than some value. From the data in Figure 8.6, $\overline{X} = 1.5$ is an elementary event, and all $\overline{X}$'s larger than 2.5 is an event.

Because random sampling is assumed, the elementary events or statistics in the sampling distribution are independent. Events, or intervals of statistics, also are independent. Any $\overline{X}$ in the sampling distribution of $\overline{X}$ is independent of every other $\overline{X}$.

Intervals of values of statistics are almost always mutually exclusive in sampling distributions because the intervals are chosen to be nonoverlapping. The events "$\overline{X}$ less than or equal to 1.5 ($\overline{X} \leq 1.5$)" and "$\overline{X}$ greater than or equal to 2.5 ($\overline{X} \geq 2.5$)" are mutually exclusive because the intervals do not overlap. Because of this choice of intervals, the probability of any $\overline{X}$ being in both intervals is zero, or the events have a joint probability of zero.

In sampling distributions you obtain the probability of the statistic being in one or the other of nonoverlapping intervals by using the addition (Or) rule and adding the separate probabilities.

Because of the simplicity of this example and the resulting $\overline{X}$'s, a false impression has been presented. It appears that the distribution of a discrete variable can be used for the sampling distribution of $\overline{X}$, when, in fact, continuous distributions are used for most applications. For example, in normal distributions, you are not able to compute the probability of a given $\overline{X}$, but you can compute the probability of an interval of $\overline{X}$ values. So you look for the proportion of the area under the curve for an interval of $\overline{X}$'s, and this ties the concept of probability to the concept of relative frequency. Even for the discrete distribution in Figure 8.7, the probability of $\overline{X}$ being larger than 2.5 is the proportion of the area under the curve for that interval.

Determining the probability of the Secret Service's performance is even more complicated than that. For now, just remember that the researchers had to use probability to decide whether the Secret Service personnel did better than the other groups or were close enough to be considered like the rest. The next chapter explains more about how to compute probabilities for $\overline{X}$.

8.6   Summary, Study Tips, and Computation

Chapter Summary

Probability is used in many areas of our everyday life. By using the concepts of sample space, elementary event, and event, we give some rigor to the definition of probability as relative occurrence. The probability of an equally probable elementary event is 1 divided by the total number of possible outcomes. The probability of an event is the number of equally probable elementary events in the event divided by the total number of possible outcomes. Other terms and rules were defined and used in three examples.

There are differences between sampling with and without replacement, but researchers can use the statistics that rely on sampling with replacement because of similar probabilities for the two sampling types. Probability distributions for discrete and continuous variables consist of the outcomes from an experiment and their associated probabilities. Probability distributions for continuous variables require defining probability as some proportion of the area under a curve.

The binomial distribution is an example of a probability distribution for a discrete variable. The normal distribution is an example of a probability distribution for a continuous variable. Finally, probability is integrated with statistics by considering each probability concept in the sampling distribution of $\overline{X}$.

Key terms used in this chapter are:

Sample space	Addition (Or) rule
Elementary event	Marginal probability
Event	Sampling with
Probability	replacement
Conditional probability	Sampling without
Independence	replacement
Multiplication (And) rule	Probability distribution
Joint probability	Binomial distribution
Mutually exclusive	

Study Tips

Section 8.2 may have more definitions than any other single section of the book, and you must memorize them in order to have a good grasp of probability. Some students read the first few definitions and think they're pretty easy. Go back and read Section 8.2 and make an arrow next to the first definition that seems difficult. That's the point where you may need to slow down in your studying and recognize that the material is harder than the first definition.

Many students get confused between the multiplication (And) rule and the steps used to find independence. As you memorize the formula for the multiplication rule, remind yourself that you are multiplying the conditional probability of one event by the unconditional probability of a different event—$p(A|B)p(B)$. In finding independence, you are looking at the unconditional and conditional probabilities *of the same event:* Is $p(A)$ equal to $p(A|B)$?

You might survey your friends and family on some topic. Ask men and women whether they prefer chocolate or vanilla ice cream, or whether they support some presidential policy. The practice using the definitions and rules in this chapter in your analysis.

The most frequent errors made by students are: (1) confusing the multiplication rule and independence (see above); (2) confusing joint probability and conditional probability, especially in tables of frequencies (*Hint:* does the question have the word *and* or *given*?); and (3) in computing probability using the addition (Or) rule, subtracting some probability other than the joint probability, $p(A \text{ and } B)$.

Computation

Anyone who has the ability to program a computer can use it to perform the computations in this chapter. However, most of you only know how to use existing packages of computer programs, so you have to compute these probabilities by hand or with a calculator. It is helpful to know that the computer will calculate the probability of most inferential statistics. As you progress through the chapters, the computer routines illustrated usually compute the probability of the desired inferential statistic. This probability usually appears in the form of one of these examples: $p = .007$ (the probability equals .007), Prob $< .01$ (the probability is less than .01), Prob $> F$ (the probability of the statistic being larger than F, used as a heading of a column), Prob $> |t|$ (the probability of the statistic being larger than the absolute value of t), or Prob $> |r|$ (the probability of the statistic being larger than the absolute value of r). These last two examples give two-tailed probabilities. One- and two-tailed probabilities of statistics are covered in more detail in Chap-ter 10.

Exercises

Sections 8.1–8.2

1. You are looking for a good used car to buy.
   a. Give an example of how you might use probability to decide between two models.
   b. What kind of probability is this?
   c. What do you think of the sales pitch: "90% of our customers who trade in their old used car for one of our previously owned cars say they are extremely satisfied"?
2. Suppose someone is interested in the grades earned by the 1300 students enrolled in introductory psychology and finds the following distribution of grades:

Grade	Frequency
A	140
B	300
C	550
D	220
F	90
	1300

   a. What is the sample space?
   b. What is an elementary event?
   c. Give an example of an event.
   d. For any student selected at random, what is the probability that her or his grade will be an A?
   e. What is the probability of getting a grade of B or better? What rule did you use?
   f. Are the events A and F mutually exclusive?
3. From a well-shuffled deck of 52 cards, what is the probability of drawing the following:
   a. A 7
   b. A spade
   c. The queen of spades
   d. A queen or a spade
4. Suppose that an anxiety measure classifies subjects into one of four levels of severity of anxiety. The classification of 100 subjects gives the following results:

Level	Number in Level
1	44
2	20
3	19
4	17
	100

   a. What is the probability of a subject being classified in level 1? Level 4?
   b. What is the probability of a subject being classified in level 1 or level 2?
   c. If you classified another 50 subjects, how many would you expect to be in level 2?
   d. Suppose you selected two subjects at random. What is the probability that subject 1 and subject 2 would be classified in level 2?
   e. Are the probabilities in this problem empirical or theoretical?
5. The following data came from two different slot machines:

	Machine A	Machine B
Paid	23	11
Did not pay	271	339

   Do these data support the idea that payoff is independent of the machine? Show calculations to justify your answer.
6. The probability of misclassifying a subject on psychological factor A is .20, and the probability of misclassification on factor B is .30 (assume these misclassifications are independent).
   a. What is the probability of misclassification on factor A or factor B?
   b. What is the probability of correct classification—that is, no misclassification?
7. Suppose you have these frequencies for grades and majors in a statistics class:

Grade	Math	Major: Psychology	Pharmacy	Total
A	5	5	1	11
B	7	9	9	25
C	12	15	15	42
D	3	10	10	23
F	1	0	5	6
Total	28	39	40	107

   a. What is the probability that a student selected at random is a math major who got an A? A pharmacy major who got a D?
   b. If you don't know a student's major, what is the probability of that student getting an A?

c. If a student is a psychology major, what is the probability of that student getting an A?

d. Label each probability in parts a, b, and c as joint, marginal, or conditional.

8. For two tosses of a coin, the four combinations are given in the table. Also given are several different sets of numbers. Some could be true sets of probabilities if the coin is fair or biased. Some of them are not true. Which ones are not true sets of probabilities and why not?

	Set 1	Set 2	Set 3	Set 4	Set 5
HH	.25	.49	.70	.30	6
TH	.25	.21	.30	.20	17
HT	.25	.21	.20	.10	21
TT	.25	.09	.01	.10	9

9. Suppose a developmental psychologist interested in gender role development decides to study toy selection as a function of the gender of the child. The following frequencies of children are observed:

	M	F	Total
Truck	35	25	60
Doll	15	25	40
Total	50	50	100

a. What is the probability of any child selecting the truck?

b. What is the probability of a boy selecting the truck?

c. What is the probability of a girl selecting the truck?

d. Is toy selection independent of the gender of the child? Use formula 8.4 to support your answer.

e. What is the probability that a child will be in the cell for truck and male? Can you show how to get this answer by using the multiplication (And) rule?

10. Look back to Research Example 8 at the first line of Table 8.1 for the entire United States.

a. Copy down all of the percentages for men and then convert them to probabilities.

b. Now add all of the probabilities from "cigarette" through "pipe." Why is this probability larger than the probability for "at least one tobacco product"?

c. In the addition (Or) rule, you have to subtract the joint probability. What probabilities, if subtracted from the sum you obtained in part b, would make this sum equal to the probability for "at least one tobacco product"?

11. Willis and Briggs (1992) studied the initiation of hand touches by couples in public settings. The researchers watched male–female couples in restaurants, theaters, parks, and sporting events and recorded the gender of the person who intentionally touched the other person first. The observers then approached the couple, explained what they were studying, and asked the nature of the couple's relationship. Their results are given in the table.

Frequency of female initiated, male initiated, and no contact in three types of couples

Type of Couple	F Initiated	M Initiated	No Contact	Totals
Engaged/dating	51	70	106	227
Married/cohabiting less than one year	9	16	4	29
Married/cohabiting one year or more	41	32	171	244
Totals	101	118	281	500

Source: Willis and Briggs (1992).

a. What is the sample space?

b. Give an example of an elementary event.

c. Give an example of an event.

d. What is the probability of the elementary event you named in part b?

e. What is the probability of the event you named in part c?

f. Give a verbal example of a conditional probability.

g. What is the value of that conditional probability?

h. Is the probability of any male-initiated touch equal to the probability of male-initiated touch among engaged/dating couples? What principle of probability are you addressing in this question?

i. What rule would you use to find the probability of being a touch-initiating female and being married more than one year?

j. Compute the probability described in part i.

k. What rule would you use to find the probability of being engaged/dating or being a male who initiates touch?

l. Compute the probability described in part k.

m. What is the probability of no contact and female-initiated touch? What principle of probability are you addressing here?

Section 8.3

12. In each of the following situations, decide whether the sampling is done with or without replacement.
  a. When you roll a single fair die
  b. When you toss a single fair coin
  c. When the teacher chooses who out of a class of 23 children will serve on a three-person committee
  d. When children in a class of 23 elect persons for the offices of class president, vice president, and secretary

Section 8.4

13. If the final examination scores in a physics class are normally distributed with mean 50 and standard deviation of 10, what is the probability of any student selected at random scoring 75 or higher?

14. You are given two dice, each with six faces with the numbers 1 to 6. On any given roll of the two dice, you will come up with a number on each die and a total for the two dice.
  a. What is the probability of any given number, 1 to 6, turning up on one die?
  b. For the event of 1 on the first die and 1 on the second die for a total of 2, what rule would you use to find the probability of this event? Compute it.
  c. Write out the three ways you can get a total of 4 on one roll of the two dice.
  d. In part b, there was only one way of getting a total of 2. In part c, there were three ways of getting a total of 4. Each of these three ways (elementary events) has a probability associated with it (1/36). What rule would you use to find the probability of getting a 4 the first way or the second way or the third way? Compute it.
  e. Find the probability distribution for all possible outcomes (2, 3, 4, . . . , 12) on a roll of the two dice. Check your answer by adding all of the probabilities of the outcomes. They should total to one.

15. If you take a multiple-choice test with ten questions that have four responses each, what is the probability of getting two or fewer items correct if you guess on each item (see Table 8.6)?

16. (This question requires use of the material in Box 8.1.) Suppose there was a type of cell that could be detected in the blood of a healthy person with a probability of .1, and a laboratory could do a test to show the presence or absence of the cell in a single sample. The laboratory took four samples from a person and found the cell present in three of the four samples. What is the probability of three or more samples out of four showing the presence of the cell if the person is healthy? If "person is sick" would raise the probability of detecting the cell to .6 for a single sample, what is the probability of three or more samples out of four showing the presence of the cell?

9

Sampling Distributions

You are now ready to study the pivotal subject of statistics: the distributions of statistics. It is as important to statistics as a sure foundation is to a solid building. This topic is the linchpin of statistics: Without sampling distributions, you lack information required for estimation, and you cannot get probabilities of statistics, so you cannot make inferences. To say this area is important is an understatement; to say it is crucial is closer to the truth.

Research Example 9

9.1 Introduction and Review
Review
Sampling: More information

9.2 Three Different Types of Distributions

9.3 Population Distribution
Populations are usually large
Populations are usually unobtainable and hypothetical
Numerical characteristics of populations
Shape of the population distribution
Populations and inference

9.4 Sample Distribution
Numerical characteristics of the sample distribution
Shape of the sample distribution
Samples and inference

9.5 Sampling Distribution
Statistics have variability
Statistics have distributions
Sampling distributions defined
Shape of sampling distributions
Numerical characteristics of sampling distributions
An example of a sampling distribution of $\overline{X}$
Sampling distributions and inference
The need for sampling distributions

9.6 Sampling Distribution of $\overline{X}$ as an Example
Information about the sampling distribution of $\overline{X}$
Mean of the sampling distribution of $\overline{X}$ Is μ
Variance of the sampling distribution of $\overline{X}$ Is σ^2/N
Shape of the sampling distribution of $\overline{X}$
Defining $z_{\overline{X}}$
When to use $z_{\overline{X}}$

Is $z_{\overline{X}}$ practical?

Computing probabilities

As N increases, $\sigma_{\overline{X}}^2 = \sigma^2/N$ decreases

9.7   Sampling Distributions of Other Statistics

Sampling distribution of $\overset{*}{s}{}^2$

Sampling distribution of s^2

Sampling distribution of r

9.8   Estimation: Means of Sampling Distributions and Unbiased Estimates

Parameters and estimates

Unbiased

$\overline{X}$ is unbiased

Biased and unbiased sample variance

Biased standard deviations

9.9   Estimation: Confidence Interval for the Population Mean

Interval estimation versus point estimation

Confidence intervals

Another example

Language

9.10   Summary, Study Tips, and Computation

Chapter summary

Study tips

Computation

Exercises

Research Example 9

How well do deaf people perform on standardized tests, given that they use a different language, American Sign Language (ASL)? ASL has a different syntax (that is, sentence structure) than spoken English, to such an extent that it might be difficult for a deaf person to comprehend English. Because standardized tests, such as intelligence tests, are in English, the performance of deaf people on at least the verbal parts of the test might be lower than that of the hearing population. For example, the Wechsler Intelligence Scale for Children-Revised (WISC-R) has two subscales, giving a verbal score and a performance scale. These are combined for a total score, the common IQ score. Some researchers think that the Performance IQ (WISC-R PIQ) is an adequate measure for the intelligence of deaf people (see Phelps & Branyan, 1988).

In a study of deaf children, Hirshoren, Hurley, and Kavale (1979) used the total IQ score. They found that a sample of 59 deaf children had an average total IQ score on the WISC-R of 88.07. The population mean for hearing children on the total score for WISC-R is $\mu = 100$. The researchers wanted to provide standardization information on the revised WISC for future research with deaf children. One question from this research is: Is the population average IQ for deaf children equal to 100?

You can see that 88.07 is not equal to 100, but 88.07 is the value of a *sample* mean $\overline{X}$, and the question is about the *population* mean IQ for deaf children. Obviously the sample mean is not 100, but what about the population mean? Could the researchers have obtained a sample with $\overline{X} = 88.07$ from a population with a mean of 100? Yes, it is *possible* to get an $\bar{X}$ this low if $\mu = 100$, but what is the *probability* of getting such an $\bar{X}$? This is an important question, so it should be restated more precisely. What is the probability of getting 88.07 or lower as a sample mean ($\bar{X}$) if the population mean is $\mu = 100$? The answer to this question will give you information about how unusual this value of 88.07 is *if* $\mu = 100$. If 88.07 is an unusual value from a distribution with $\mu = 100$, then the probability is low and you doubt that $\mu = 100$ for the population of IQ scores for deaf children.

Another way of thinking about this problem is to ask: If I repeatedly sampled 59 deaf children and computed $\bar{X}$ on each sample, what would be the mean of the distribution of those $\bar{X}$ values? Would it be 100? It is impractical to sample repeatedly in this fashion, so these questions must be answered with the single $\bar{X} = 88.07$. You are led back to the earlier question: If $\mu = 100$, what is the probability of getting $\bar{X} = 88.07$ or lower? This question is going to require information about the distribution of $\bar{X}$. Knowing about the distribution of $\bar{X}$ is crucial to your decision making about μ.

To answer any question about the probability of $\bar{X}$, you have to learn about the distribution of $\bar{X}$, called the *sampling distribution* of $\bar{X}$. If you know the mean, variance, and shape of the sampling distribution of the statistic $\bar{X}$, you can find probabilities associated with $\bar{X}$. You can find the probability of $\bar{X}$ being less than or equal to 88.07 if $\mu = 100$, and ultimately you can make a decision about the parameter μ.

Just to satisfy your curiosity, we'll tell you that the probability of getting a sample that has $\bar{X} = 88.07$ or lower from a population with $\mu = 100$ is small. A small probability leads you to decide to reject the idea that $\mu = 100$ for the population of IQ scores for deaf children. This result lends credence to not using the verbal part of the IQ test for deaf children. This research is referred to several times in this and future chapters.

9.1 Introduction and Review

Chapter 1 began with a list of conclusions that researchers have drawn from studies on sudden infant death syndrome, white suicide rates, caffeine withdrawal, and so on. In Chapter 8 you read that researchers use probability to make decisions about their results. Does your occupation make a difference on your ability to catch a liar? Is a certain outcome, such as the number of liars detected by Secret Service personnel, a highly likely result or an unlikely result?

When research results are reported in the popular media, the conclusion sometimes is the only part of the study that is reported. But statistics is concerned with *how that conclusion was reached.* You know that a small probability will lead you to doubt some premise, such as "All people detect liars equally well." But many concepts are foundational to your ability to draw conclusions like this.

You first read about a sampling distribution in Chapter 1, where we listed the seven topics common to all inferential statistical methods. Periodically you should review these seven topics to maintain your perspective on statistics. You have also learned about descriptive statistics, one theoretical reference distribution (normal distribution), and probability. Now you are ready to cover three more topics in this chapter: estimation, variability of statistics, and distributions of statistics. Understanding these topics allows you to move on to Chapter 10 on hypothesis testing, where you'll see the

Table 9.1
Secret Service deception accuracy scores (percentage correct)

60	40	50	80
60	80	40	60
70	70	50	80
50	90	70	50
70	80	70	60
60	60	70	
70	80	60	$\overline{X} = 64$
70	90	60	$\overset{*}{s}{}^2 = 166.86$
60	50	70	
60	40	60	

connection between a small probability (just how small does it have to be?) and conclusions that researchers draw.

We use the Secret Service deception accuracy scores to review important concepts you have learned and to illustrate concepts in this chapter. The scores and the values of $\overline{X}$ and $\overset{*}{s}{}^2$ are given in Table 9.1.

Review

The process of drawing samples from populations is important to this chapter. Students sometimes have trouble fitting the material in this chapter into the big picture of statistics, so let's back up and get a broad view of what we are doing in statistics.

Recall the definitions of the following three concepts: population, sample, and random sampling. A *population* is the target group for your inferences, some large group of participants, or an entire set of participants, objects, measurements, or events that share some common characteristic. The population for the Secret Service group is any current or future Secret Service employees. A *sample* is some subgroup, subset, or part of the population actually used in the research. The sample here is the 35 Secret Service people who participated in the study. *Random sampling* is a procedure in which the selection of any one observation from a population is independent of the selection of any other observation from the same population. In the liar-catching study, random sampling was not used. Secret Service personnel were attending a workshop in Washington, DC, when they were tested by Ekman and O'Sullivan (1991).

Sampling: More Information

Sampling is the process of selecting the subgroup of the population called the *sample*. Random sampling is independent selection, which reduces the chances of systematic biases in the sample if the correct population is sampled. There could be bias in any one sample, but the average bias over many samples is zero.

It is still possible to draw a random sample and reach an incorrect conclusion. This can happen when the sample is randomly selected from the wrong population. An example is the random sample taken by *Literary Digest* in the 1936 presidential election. From the results of a preelection poll, Landon was predicted to defeat Roosevelt. The *Literary Digest* had accurately predicted the 1932 election using the same process as used in 1936, but in 1936 the prediction was wrong. What happened? You might be tempted to blame sampling variability or chance, but there was actually a severe bias in the population sampled. The sample was randomly selected from subscribers to *Literary Digest* who had telephones. What systematic biases were present? First, the subscribers may not have represented the voting population. Second, people who had telephones in their homes may not have represented the voting population. In 1936 only a small percentage of Americans had telephones because telephones were concentrated in urban areas and could be afforded only by the wealthy. In this case, random sampling did not guarantee freedom from bias because the wrong population was sampled. So the statistics used in the inferential process are no better than the sampling. If the sampling is inferior, then so are the statistics and the inferential process.

In most behavioral science research, the difficulty of actually accomplishing random sampling causes researchers to use volunteers or some other form of judgment sampling. The use of volunteers may introduce biases into the process, as might any judgment sampling procedure. The researcher must judge that the sample appears to be as though it were randomly selected from a given population, and this judgment and its quality determine the quality of the inferences. However they are taken, most samples are treated as if they are random. Because of this assumption and because of the mathematical simplicity that random sampling brings to statistical procedures, random sampling is assumed throughout the remainder of this text.

Let's continue to view the big picture of statistics by looking at different kinds of distributions.

Quick Quiz

Consider the country music airtime suicide rate study in Research Example 6. What is the population? What is the sample? Did random sampling take place?

Answers

The population is American metropolitan areas. The sample consists of 49 metropolitan areas. As for random sampling, Research Example 6 says nothing about how Stack and Gundlach (1992) selected the cities for the study. (Their journal article says they used metro areas for which data on music were available from the *Radio and Records Rating Report and Directory,* so sampling was not random.)

9.2 Three Different Types of Distributions

If you could look at the deception accuracy scores for the whole population of Secret Service personnel, you would see a distribution. In Chapter 3 you learned about frequency distributions; you could rearrange the sample data from Table 9.1 into one of those. The sample of $N = 35$ has a distribution with $\overline{X} = 64$ and $\overset{*}{s}{}^2 = 166.86$. But what if you studied 35 other Secret Service personnel? It's unlikely you would get the same 35 scores, the same $\overline{X}$, and the same $\overset{*}{s}{}^2$. What if you did a third study, with 35 different people? A fourth study? What if you could take all possible samples from the population of Secret Service personnel and compute $\overline{X}$ every time? Then you could arrange the $\overline{X}$ values into a distribution. Now, instead of a distribution of raw scores, you have a distribution of the statistic $\overline{X}$. This distribution of $\overline{X}$ is an example of a *sampling distribution,* illustrated in Figure 9.1. And $\overline{X} = 64$ is just one value of $\overline{X}$ in this distribution.

You never actually do this repeated sampling to obtain sampling distributions; rather, you get information about sampling distributions from mathematical statistics. This

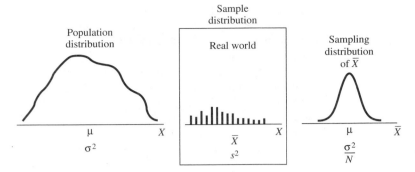

Figure 9.1
Three different types of distributions

information results from mathematical calculations or from computer simulations called Monte Carlo (from gambling simulations) studies. Still, it is helpful to think of sampling distributions as if they were formed by repeatedly drawing samples of a given size from a population, even though you don't get information in this way. As you see in Figure 9.1, the population is a distribution of X's and the sample is a distribution of X's, but the sampling distribution of $\overline{X}$ is a distribution of $\overline{X}$'s. In the coverage of populations, samples, and sampling distributions that follows, keep Figure 9.1 in mind and refer to it often, looking for differences and similarities in these three types of distributions.

Quick Quiz

How is a *sampling* distribution different from a *sample* distribution?

Answer

A sampling distribution is a distribution of a statistic, such as all possible $\overline{X}$ or s^2 values. A sample distribution is a distribution of the scores in a single study or sample. A single $\overline{X}$ can be calculated for the N scores in that sample.

9.3   Population Distribution

Sampling distributions have some similarities to population distributions and sample distributions, so let's review the characteristics of these distributions.

Populations Are Usually Large

Populations are usually characterized by being large, unobtainable, and hypothetical. Populations are usually large because behavioral science researchers want to generalize to some broadly defined group even though their sampling is restricted to some local, narrowly defined group. The target of the inferences defines the population. For example, scientists who studied sudden infant death syndrome (SIDS) in Avon County, England, were looking for factors involved in these unexplained deaths. They cared about the babies who had died, but that's not all: They wanted to prevent future SIDS cases. The sample consisted of 257 infants, and the researchers concluded that babies were less likely to die of SIDS when they were placed on their backs at bedtime. The researchers inferred to a population of all future babies in England when they concluded, "We therefore recommend the supine position as the safest for babies when sleeping and believe that a nationwide return to this traditional practice would save a significant number of babies' lives" (Wigfield, Fleming, Berry, Rudd, & Golding, 1992).

Although populations are usually large, most statistical procedures idealize this largeness to assume that the population is infinite. If there are infinitely many scores in the population, then infinitely many samples of size N could be selected.

Populations Are Usually Unobtainable and Hypothetical

By the very fact that populations are usually large, they are usually unobtainable. This does not mean that the population is unknown. The SIDS researchers had identified a population of babies who had died or might die of unknown causes. Researchers usually cannot identify all subjects in the population, assign them unique numbers to do random sampling, or measure them. Additionally, not all subjects can be given the conditions of an experiment, in which case the population is hypothetical. In the life-style/heart study, the researchers were interested in the population of all current and future heart disease patients, but they certainly couldn't find them all, randomly assign them to a change of life-style, and then pay for all of their medical tests.

These three characteristics (large, unobtainable, and hypothetical) emphasize an important point: The main thrust of statistics is generalization from the known to the unknown. You know your sample and your sample statistics, and you want to generalize to the typically unknown population parameters.

Numerical Characteristics of Populations

Populations can be described by their numerical characteristics, or parameters. Parameters are typically unknown, but they are given certain defined symbols, such as μ and σ^2.

Shape of the Population Distribution

Population distribution
Distribution of raw scores, X values, in the population

We usually draw the population distribution as an ambiguously shaped, continuous curve such as in Figure 9.1 so it won't give any false impression about the population. The **population distribution** is made up of raw scores or X values, but because it is unobtainable, its exact shape is usually unknown. A notable exception is when you are using a standardized test score like IQ, which is assumed to have a normal population distribution.

Populations and Inference

Any interest in the population distribution is in terms of the final generalization. The researcher wants to be able to make some decisions about the parameters of this distribution or about the distribution itself. For instance, Wechsler and Isaac (1992) from the Harvard School of Public Health analyzed surveys from 1669 first-year college students on their alcohol-drinking habits. They categorized 56.1% of the men and 34.5% of the women as binge drinkers because they had consumed five or more drinks in a row at least once in the two weeks before completing the survey. The researchers acknowledged some limitations to their study: "since this study was performed in Massachusetts, our findings may not be entirely generalizable outside of the New England region."

The first step in the decision process is to draw a random sample of size N from the population. That leads to a distribution of the sample, to be discussed next.

Quick Quiz

Researchers at the University of Texas–San Antonio (UTSA) looked into factors that affect how people respond to persons who have AIDS. One factor was fear of contagious diseases. Bishop, Alva, Cantu, and Rittiman (1991) measured the attitudes of 160 undergraduate psychology students at UTSA. Their report concluded that "there is evidence that AIDS is categorized by people as a contagious disease. . . . Convincing people that casual transmission of AIDS is not possible requires countering deeply held ideas about the nature of contagious disease." What was the population?

Answer

Although only undergraduate psychology majors participated in the study, the conclusions indicate that the researchers inferred to a population of adults.

9.4   Sample Distribution

Sample distribution
Distribution of raw scores, X values, in the sample

You now have a sample, N values of X. Use Figure 9.1 to compare the sample distribution with the population distribution. Like the population, the **sample distribution** is a distribution of X values. In other words, X is the random variable for the distribution.

Numerical Characteristics of the Sample Distribution

Samples can be described in terms of their numerical characteristics, or statistics. Because the sample is real and obtained, you have formulas to compute statistics. When you read about the numerical characteristics of sampling distributions, you will see why we make such obvious statements about the numerical characteristics of populations and samples. For the Secret Service deception accuracy scores, the sample contains 35 observations with $\overline{X} = 64$ and $\overset{*}{s}{}^2 = 166.86$.

Shape of the Sample Distribution

The sample distribution is discrete, and its exact shape can be shown pictorially, like the histogram in Figure 9.1. Note that the shape of the sample is rarely normal. The sample, unlike the population, is known, obtainable, and real. For these reasons, the distribution of the sample is in the region of Figure 9.1 labeled "Real World."

Samples and Inference

For the moment, the focus of your attention is on the statistics from a sample. You are interested in the value of $\overline{X}$ or $\overset{*}{s}{}^2$ or some other statistic computed from the N scores and your ability to infer from the statistic to its corresponding parameter. For the liar data, you are interested in using the value of $\overline{X} = 64$ to make decisions about the population mean μ. You will use the sampling distribution of $\overline{X}$ as the basis for inference from a statistic to a parameter.

Quick Quiz

Cronin (1991) surveyed mountain climbers and a control group using an instrument called the Sensation-Seeking Scale (SSS). The climbers had an average SSS score of 23.3, whereas the control group's $\overline{X}$ was 18.5. Cronin concluded that the personality characteristic of sensation seeking was found in those who participate in this sport. What parameters did Cronin infer to?

Answer

Cronin inferred to at least two parameters: (1) the average SSS score in the population of mountain climbers, and (2) the population average SSS score for the control group.

9.5   Sampling Distribution

Statistics Have Variability

Researchers compute statistics, such as $\overline{X}$ and $\overset{*}{s}^{2}$, for each sample. It is important to remember that statistics have variability. The researchers in the liar study computed only one $\overline{X}$ for the Secret Service personnel's deception accuracy scores. But if they drew another sample with $N = 35$ from the same population, the second $\overline{X}$ most likely would not equal the first $\overline{X}$. Another way to look at the statistic is like a random variable that can take on many potentially different values before the sample is actually drawn and the statistic is computed. Thus, $\overline{X} = 64$ is just one of many values that the researcher could have obtained. The sample that gave $\overline{X} = 64$ just happened to be selected.

Statistics Have Distributions

Thinking of any statistic as a random variable should help you to see that every statistic has a distribution. That is, any statistic that can be computed from sample data could take on many potentially different values that theoretically have a distribution. Many of you may think this idea is ridiculous. You may ask: You mean that my single value of $\overline{X} = 64$ has a distribution? Of course, when you have only a single value of a statistic, it is difficult to imagine the distribution from which the statistic has come. But the fact remains that theoretically there exists a distribution of the potential values of the statistic.

Before the sample is actually drawn and the statistic computed, any number of values for the statistic potentially exist. Hence, the actual value of $\overline{X}$ that is computed from the data is only one value from potentially many values of $\overline{X}$ that could have been obtained in this sampling procedure. Imagine the population of mountain climbers in the world and the scores they would have on the Sensation-Seeking Scale. Only a few of them actually made it into a study and had an $\overline{X}$ computed from their scores. But potentially, the population of mountain climbers could have been combined into a sample in countless ways, and therefore countless $\overline{X}$'s were possible. Those $\overline{X}$ values theoretically could be arranged into a sampling distribution.

Sampling Distributions Defined

Sampling distribution
Distribution of all possible
values of a statistic

Here is a more complete definition of a **sampling distribution:**

> **The sampling distribution of a statistic is a distribution that could be formed by drawing all possible samples of a given size N from some population, computing the statistic for each sample, and arranging these statistics in a distribution.**

This definition is packed with important points:

1. The size of each sample is N, which is the number of scores in the sample distribution. Do not confuse N with the number of statistics in the sampling distribution.
2. We consider that all possible values of the statistic have been computed, so the sampling distribution is made up of many statistics.
3. A sampling distribution could be formed by values of a statistic computed from samples of a common size N.
4. The sampling distribution of any statistic is theoretical and is never actually obtained by repeated sampling. This point is obvious because of the difficulty of drawing all possible samples.
5. Each different statistic computed from every different size sample has a distinct sampling distribution. There are sampling distributions for $\overline{X}$, $\overset{*}{s}^2$, s^2, r, among others, and these sampling distributions are different for every possible N.
6. The sampling distribution of any statistic is a probability distribution (a theoretical relative frequency distribution) from which you can compute probabilities and make decisions.

Quick Quiz

Cronin (1991) surveyed 20 mountain climbers and computed their average Sensation-Seeking Score of 23.3. Suppose you surveyed 25 mountain climbers from the same population and found $\overline{X} = 23.1$. Do your statistic and Cronin's statistic have the same sampling distribution?

Answer

Both statistics have a sampling distribution of $\underline{X}$, but they are not the same sampling distribution. There will be a sampling distribution of $\underline{X}$ for the sample of $N = 20$ and a different sampling distribution of $\underline{X}$ for $N = 25$.

Shape of Sampling Distributions

Examine Figure 9.1, where the sampling distribution of $\overline{X}$ is shown along with the population and sample distributions. Like the population distribution, the sampling distribution is theoretical and is drawn as a smooth continuous curve. Unlike the other two distributions, this sampling distribution is a distribution of statistics, $\overline{X}$ values, not raw scores. In other words, the sampling distribution has $\overline{X}$ as its random variable rather than X. A final distinction is that the sampling distribution of $\overline{X}$ has lower variability than that of the population, which we explain momentarily.

Numerical Characteristics of Sampling Distributions

As you know, the numerical characteristics of a population are parameters, and the numerical characteristics of a sample are statistics. The numerical characteristics of sampling distributions also are called parameters, but this term has a slightly different connotation in this context.

Let's look at one numerical characteristic, the mean. You calculate the sample mean $\overline{X}$ by using the N scores in the sample. You cannot calculate the population mean μ, mainly because populations are usually large and unobtainable. Similarly, you cannot compute the mean of a sampling distribution of $\overline{X}$. Theoretically, all possible $\overline{X}$ values are in a sampling distribution of $\overline{X}$, and "all possible" is an enormous number, so you cannot obtain the average $\overline{X}$. But the sampling distribution of $\overline{X}$ has a mean as one of its numerical characteristics, and it is a parameter. The symbol for this parameter is the same as the symbol for the population mean, μ. Mathematical theorems tell us that the mean of the sampling distribution of $\overline{X}$ is μ.

An Example of a Sampling Distribution of $\overline{X}$

Recall the sampling distribution of $\overline{X}$ that was built in Chapter 8. The population had only three scores (1, 2, and 3), each with a large equal frequency. All possible samples of size $N = 2$ were taken, and $\overline{X}$ was computed on each. Then the probabilities for the distribution of the $\overline{X}$ values were computed. This sampling distribution of $\overline{X}$ is reproduced in Figure 9.2. It is not typical of the sampling distribution of $\overline{X}$ for several reasons. First, the population has a very small number of possible values. Second, the sample size $N = 2$ is small. This combination gives a sampling distribution of $\overline{X}$ that is discrete and deceptively simple. But it does show several features of the sampling

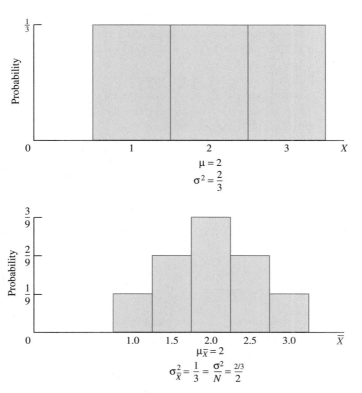

Figure 9.2
Population with three values and sampling distribution of $\overline{X}$, $N = 2$

distribution of $\overline{X}$ that would be much more difficult to demonstrate with a larger population or sample size:

1. The mean of the sampling distribution of $\overline{X}$ is the same as the mean of the population, $\mu = 2$.
2. The variance of the sampling distribution of $\overline{X}$ is $\sigma_{\overline{X}}^2 = 1/3$, which is the same as $\sigma^2/N = (2/3)/2$.
3. A normal distribution gives a reasonable approximation to the shape of the sampling distribution of $\overline{X}$.

Sampling Distributions and Inference

Thanks to mathematical statistics, you don't have to worry about repeated sampling and creating sampling distributions. You usually want to know the parameters that specify the sampling distribution and the shape of the theoretical distribution that the sampling distribution follows or approximates. Once you know these important characteristics, there is no need for repeated sampling because you can use a tabled theoretical distribution such as the normal distribution to make probability statements about the statistics.

Shape of the sampling distribution of $\overline{X}$
If X is distributed normally, then $\overline{X}$ is also distributed normally

For the sampling distribution of $\overline{X}$, if you have a random sample of N independent X's, and if X is distributed normally with mean μ and variance σ^2, then **$\overline{X}$ is distributed normally with mean μ and variance σ^2/N.**

Thus, if X is normally distributed, then $\overline{X}$ is also normally distributed with the same μ but with variance equal to the population variance divided by the sample size, σ^2/N. The sampling distribution of $\overline{X}$ is fit by the theoretical normal distribution. The mean, variance, and shape of the sampling distribution of $\overline{X}$ are discussed more thoroughly in a few pages.

Parameters of the sampling distribution of $\overline{X}$
Sampling distribution of $\overline{X}$ has a mean of μ and a variance of σ^2/N

For a summary of the three types of distributions, see Table 9.2. Cover up the answers in the body of the table and quiz yourself about this information. If you do not know three or more of the entries in the table, review the material in this section before proceeding to the next topic.

Table 9.2
Summary of population, sample, and sampling distributions

	Population Distribution	Sample Distribution	Sampling Distribution of $\overline{X}$
Random variable	X	X	$\overline{X}$
(what is in distribution)	(raw score)	(raw score)	(statistic)
Summary characteristics	μ σ^2	$\overline{X}$ s^{*2}	μ σ^2/N
Size of distribution	Usually large	Small	Large
Obtainable?	Not usually	Yes	No
Hypothetical or real?	Hypothetical	Real	Hypothetical
Continuous or discrete?	Continuous	Discrete	Continuous
Shape	Generally unknown	Can describe	Normal if population is normal

Quick Quiz

Assume you have drawn a random sample of 45 people and measured their IQs. From extensive work with IQ scores, researchers know more about the population than usual. IQ is normally distributed in the population with a mean of 100 and a variance of 225. You find $\overline{X} = 103$. (a) What is X? (b) What is μ? (*Hint*: Two answers are possible.) (c) What should be the mean and variance of the sampling distribution of $\overline{X}$?

Answers

(a) X represents the dependent variable of IQ scores. There are X's in the population and in the sample. (b) μ can be the population mean of 100 or the mean of the sampling distribution of $\overline{X}$. (c) The sampling distribution of $\overline{X}$ has a mean $\mu = 100$ and a variance of $\sigma^2/N = 225/45 = 5$.

The Need for Sampling Distributions

You need sampling distributions to obtain probabilities about statistics for decision making about parameters. In Chapter 1 you used probability to make a decision about the fairness of a coin. The use of *fair* in connection with a coin is equivalent to saying that the probability of getting a head on a coin toss is .5, or $p = .5$. You can consider p to be a parameter, and decision making about the fairness of the coin is decision making about p. You counted the number of heads to get some indication of the fairness of the coin. The number of heads is considered the statistic. We asked, What is the probability of getting ten heads on ten tosses of a coin if it is fair? It was decided that the answer $1/1024 = .0009766$ made the premise of the fair coin doubtful. You needed the probability of the obtained statistic (number of heads) to make a decision about the parameter ($p = .5$ or "coin is fair").

Reread the last sentence because this is the heart of the issue: *From sampling distributions of statistics you can find probabilities of obtained statistics and make decisions about parameters.*

Now shift your thinking to the sampling distribution of $\overline{X}$. In using $\overline{X}$ to make decisions about μ you need a probability from the sampling distribution of $\overline{X}$. Without the sampling distribution of $\overline{X}$, you cannot find probabilities associated with the obtained $\overline{X}$ and you cannot make decisions about the parameter μ. You need probabilities of statistics that you can get only from sampling distributions of statistics. The entire process of inferential statistics is dependent on sampling distributions.

Here are the reasons you need sampling distributions:

1. The population and its parameters are typically unknown, yet you want to make decisions about them.
2. The sample and its statistics are known, and the statistics are estimates of parameters. However, you cannot simply consider a statistic as equal to a parameter and make your decision directly because statistics have variability.
3. The sampling distribution of a statistic is used to quantify into probability the information about the variability of the statistic.

A decision is made indirectly from the sample statistic through the sampling distribution to the population parameter. For example, you calculate $\overline{X}$ from the sample, refer it to the sampling distribution of $\overline{X}$ for a probability statement, and then use the probability statement to make a decision about the population mean μ.

Sampling distributions are the bridge between the known and the unknown, the statistic and the parameter. The sampling distribution of the statistic is used to obtain a probability to make the inference from the obtained statistic to the obtainable parameter.

Quick Quiz

McCown and Johnson (1991) studied the relationship between chronic procrastination and various personality traits. They surveyed 114 students at two universities and found that extraversion "correlated positively with confidence in exam preparedness and negatively with self-reported hours studying." (a) What statistic did they most likely use to draw their conclusions? (b) To what parameter would they infer? (c) How would the researchers find the probability of their statistic?

Answers

(a) The researchers computed correlation coefficients r. (b) They would use r to infer to the population correlation ρ. (c) They would refer their obtained r to a sampling distribution of r to find the probability of their results.

9.6   Sampling Distribution of $\overline{X}$ as an Example

Any statistic that can be computed from a sample has a sampling distribution. Not only is there a sampling distribution of $\overline{X}$, but also there is a sampling distribution of $\overset{*}{s}{}^2$, a sampling distribution of X_{50}, a sampling distribution of r, and so on. Several other sampling distributions are covered later, but now let's use the sampling distribution of $\overline{X}$ as an example.

Information About the Sampling Distribution of $\overline{X}$

This section reviews what you know and adds to your knowledge about the sampling distribution of $\overline{X}$. Given that the definition of a sampling distribution includes the idea of all possible samples, here are three key facts about the sampling distribution of $\overline{X}$:

1. The mean of the sampling distribution of $\overline{X}$ is μ.
2. The variance of the sampling distribution of $\overline{X}$ is $\sigma_{\overline{X}}^2 = \sigma^2/N$.
3. The shape of the sampling distribution of $\overline{X}$ is normal if the population is normal in shape or if the sample size, N, is sufficiently large.

Mean of the Sampling Distribution of $\overline{X}$ Is μ

The mean of the sampling distribution of $\overline{X}$ is exactly equal to the mean of the population. Many of you might miss this point, so it bears repeating: $\mu_{\overline{X}} = \mu$. Let's use as an example the sampling distribution of the mean of IQ scores from Research Example 9. Tentatively entertain the idea that the mean of the population of IQ scores for deaf children is the same as that for the hearing population, $\mu = 100$. Remember that the μ for deaf children's IQ is unknown, even though the hearing population has $\mu = 100$. If the mean of the population is $\mu = 100$, then the mean of the sampling distribution of $\overline{X}$ is $\mu = 100$. Whatever the value of μ, even though it is usually unknown, the mean of the sampling distribution of $\overline{X}$ has exactly the same value. The sampling distribution of $\overline{X}$'s calculated from the IQ scores of all possible repeated samples of 59 deaf children has the same mean as the population of IQ scores for all deaf children, whatever its value.

Quick Quiz

Suppose you studied 25 children who had taken music lessons for about 5 years. You are interested in their self-esteem. Your subjects fill out a questionnaire, and you find that their average self-esteem score is 22. (a) What parameter are you estimating? (b) To what sampling distribution would you refer your statistic? Be specific. (c) What is the mean of that sampling distribution?

Answers

(a) μ, which is estimated by $\overline{X}$. (b) You would use the sampling distribution of $\overline{X}$ for $N = 25$. Every sample size has a different sampling distribution. (c) The $\mu_{\overline{X}}$ would be equal to the average population self-esteem score, which is unknown.

Variance of the Sampling Distribution of $\overline{X}$ Is σ^2/N

The variance of the sampling distribution of $\overline{X}$ is made up of two parts: the variance of the population, σ^2, and the size of the sample, N. As N increases, the variance of the sampling distribution of $\overline{X}$, σ^2/N, decreases and is less than σ^2. In the IQ example, if the variance of IQ is 225 and $N = 59$, then the variance of the sampling distribution of $\overline{X}$ is $\sigma^2/N = 225/59 = 3.81$.

The standard deviation of the sampling distribution of $\overline{X}$ is

$$\sigma_{\overline{X}} = \sqrt{\frac{\sigma^2}{N}} = \frac{\sigma}{\sqrt{N}}$$

Standard error of the mean
Standard deviation of $\overline{X}$ is $\sigma/\sqrt{N}$

It is given a special name, the **standard error of the mean.** The symbol $\sigma_{\overline{X}}$ indicates a standard deviation and is conceptually the same as other standard deviations. For the IQ scores in Research Example 9, the value of σ is $\sqrt{225}$, or 15. Because $N = 59$, the value of the standard error of the mean of these IQ scores is $\sigma_{\overline{X}} = 15/\sqrt{59} = 1.95$. The standard error of the mean is used frequently, every time you compute a z score on $\overline{X}$.

Shape of the Sampling Distribution of $\overline{X}$

In Chapter 1, you read that theoretical reference distributions are used to approximate sampling distributions of statistics. Certain mathematical theorems and the results of research give the shape of any given sampling distribution, which can often be closely approximated by a known theoretical distribution.

The shape of the sampling distribution of $\overline{X}$ is generally considered to be normal. From the assumption that the population is normally distributed, the sampling distribution of $\overline{X}$ is also normally distributed. However, most researchers do not know the actual shape of the population, or if they do know the shape, it is not normal. So most researchers are not able to assert that the population is normal. Earlier you were given a hint that a large sample size, N, solves a serious dilemma: that $\overline{X}$ is normally distributed only if X is normally distributed. You need to be able to compute probabilities for $\overline{X}$, but you have learned only how to use Table A.2 to get probabilities for normally distributed z's. Remember that you want to use $\overline{X}$ to make decisions about μ, and you need probabilities from the sampling distribution of $\overline{X}$ to make these decisions. This problem is solved by one of the most amazing theorems in all mathematics: the **Central Limit Theorem:**

Central Limit Theorem
The theorem that the sampling distribution of $\overline{X}$ approaches a normal shape as N approaches infinity

If you are sampling independently from a population that has mean μ and variance σ^2, then as the sample size N approaches infinity, the sampling distribution of the sample mean $\bar{X}$ approaches normality without regard to the shape of the sampled population.

The Central Limit Theorem says that as N approaches infinity, the distribution of $\bar{X}$ approaches a normal distribution with mean μ and variance σ^2/N. Another way to state this theorem is that the larger the sample size, the more closely the sampling distribution of $\bar{X}$ is approximated by the normal distribution. So the shape of the sampling distribution of $\bar{X}$ can be considered to be normal if the sample is large.

At this point, many students say, "The theorem sounds great, but we don't have infinitely many rats for our experiment. How does the theorem help for realistic sample sizes?" As long as the population is not unusual in shape, the approximation is quite good for even moderate sample sizes such as those used by most behavioral scientists. For samples sizes of even 25 or 30 from most populations, the sampling distribution of $\bar{X}$ approaches a normal shape. Figure 9.3 shows two populations and the sampling distribution of $\bar{X}$ for $N = 2$ and $N = 30$.

The sampling distribution of $\bar{X}$ approaches normality fairly rapidly as N increases. So for many applied situations, you can use a normal distribution to compute probabilities for the sampling distribution of $\bar{X}$, even though you cannot say that the population

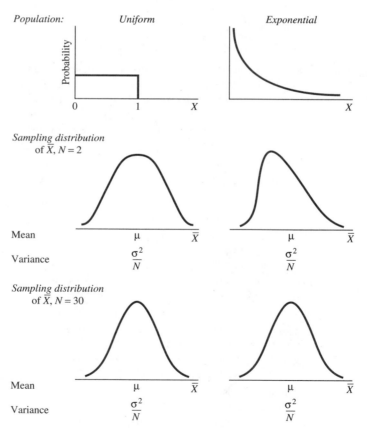

Figure 9.3
Central Limit Theorem effect for small samples: sampling distribution of $\bar{X}$

is normally distributed. The Central Limit Theorem applies only to $\bar{X}$. Other statistics have other theorems for the shape of their sampling distributions, but the Central Limit Theorem does not apply to them.

For the liar study, let's pretend we know things about the population that we really don't know. Suppose you found some theory that says the population average deception accuracy for Secret Service personnel is $\mu = 62.01$ and the population variance is $\sigma^2 = 40.46$. You obtained the sample in Table 9.1 of $N = 35$ deception accuracy scores with $\bar{X} = 64$. Assume that the deception accuracy scores are normally distributed in the population. Now list everything you know about the sampling distribution of $\bar{X}$ for this situation.

Here are the answers: The mean of the sampling distribution of $\bar{X}$ is $\mu = 62.01$; the variance of the sampling distribution of $\bar{X}$ is $\sigma^2/N = 40.46/35 = 1.156$; the shape of the sampling distribution of $\bar{X}$ is normal; and the standard error of the mean is $\sigma_{\bar{X}} = \sigma/\sqrt{N} = \sqrt{1.156} = 1.075$.

Defining $z_{\bar{X}}$

In Chapter 5 you learned about z scores, which show the relative position of a score in a distribution. We use a similar idea to find the relative position and probability of an $\bar{X}$ within the sampling distribution of $\bar{X}$. Do you recall the verbal definition of a z score? Something minus its mean divided by its standard deviation.

What if you convert your sample mean to a z score? You could use Table A.2 in Appendix A to look up probabilities if you change the sampling distribution of $\bar{X}$ from a normal distribution with mean μ and standard deviation $\sigma/\sqrt{N}$ to the standard normal distribution with mean zero and standard deviation one.

To compute probabilities in the sampling distribution of $\bar{X}$, you need to form a **z score for $\bar{X}$,** which is

z score for $\bar{X}$
$z_{\bar{X}}$ is formed by subtracting μ from $\bar{X}$ and dividing by the standard error of $\bar{X}$

$$z_{\bar{X}} = \frac{\bar{X} - \mu}{\sigma/\sqrt{N}} \tag{9.1}$$

Remember that z doesn't change the shape of the distribution, so, because $\bar{X}$ values have a normal distribution, $z_{\bar{X}}$ does, too. Formula 9.1 takes on the same form as z for raw scores given in formula 5.2: something minus its mean divided by its standard deviation. Note that we said "*its* mean." What is the mean of $\bar{X}$? You have to get it from the sampling distribution of $\bar{X}$, so the mean of $\bar{X}$ is μ. What is "*its* standard deviation"? The standard deviation of $\bar{X}$, $\sigma/\sqrt{N}$, also comes from the sampling distribution of $\bar{X}$. In order to get a z score for $\bar{X}$, you take $\bar{X}$, subtract its mean μ, and divide by its standard deviation $\sigma/\sqrt{N}$. Be sure to divide by the standard error of the mean, $\sigma/\sqrt{N}$, not the variance.

Even though this formula is slightly more complicated than that for a regular z score, the general form is the same. Using formula 9.1, you can convert $\bar{X}$ to $z_{\bar{X}}$ and then use Table A.2 to obtain the desired probability. In Research Example 9, you would tentatively entertain the idea that the population mean IQ for deaf children is the same as that for the hearing population, $\mu = 100$. Then use $\sigma = 15$ because the raw scores are IQ scores, $N = 59$, and $\bar{X} = 88.07$. The value of $z_{\bar{X}}$ is

$$z_{\bar{X}} = \frac{\bar{X} - \mu}{\sigma/\sqrt{N}} = \frac{88.07 - 100}{15/\sqrt{59}} = -6.11$$

From what you know about z scores, this value of -6.11 tells you that $\bar{X} = 88.07$ is more than six standard deviations of $\bar{X}$ (standard errors) below 100. This value of $\bar{X}$ would be highly unusual if the population of IQ scores of deaf children had a mean of 100.

When to Use $z_{\bar{X}}$

From the formula for $z_{\bar{X}}$, you can see that you need to have numerical values for μ and σ^2 before you can obtain a numerical value for $z_{\bar{X}}$. If you are dealing with a random variable that is a score on a standardized test, such as IQ or GRE scores, then you can use a formula for $z_{\bar{X}}$ if μ and σ^2 are both known. The values of μ and σ^2 are often given as norms for norming populations for standardized tests. Sometimes you want to test whether the population you sample is the same as that on which norms were calculated (the norming population). So you want to test whether your unknown μ is the same as the norm value.

Suppose you are testing a group of actors on various personality traits measured by Eysenck's Personality Profiler. You are particularly interested in aggressiveness, and you have norms of 26.44 for the mean and 6.88 for the standard deviation (Marchant-Haycox & Wilson, 1992). You want to see how your group compares to the norms, especially in terms of the average. Because the prior work has been done to provide the norm values of μ and σ^2 for a specific population, you can proceed to compute $z_{\bar{X}}$.

Quick Quiz

Suppose you have tested a group of 33 actors, and their average aggressiveness score is $\bar{X} = 21.94$. Given the norms for aggressiveness of $\mu = 26.44$ and $\sigma = 6.86$, find $z_{\bar{X}}$.

    Answer

                                              $z_{\bar{X}} = (21.94 - 26.44)/1.1942 = -3.77.$

The most common error is to divide by the variance instead of the standard deviation. For the sampling distribution of $\bar{X}$ when $N = 33$, $\mu = 26.44$, and $\sigma_{\bar{X}} = 6.86/\sqrt{33} = 1.1942$, we get

---

Is $z_{\bar{X}}$ Practical?

For most research in the behavioral sciences, the values of μ and σ^2 are unknown because the dependent variables are not standardized tests. The deception accuracy test used in the study by Ekman and O'Sullivan (1991) probably isn't used commonly by the Secret Service, so the population values are unknown. Because parameters are rarely known, the use of $z_{\bar{X}}$ is restricted to hypothetical examples used in statistics classes or with standardized tests with known norms. In spite of its restricted use, $z_{\bar{X}}$ and probabilities computed from $z_{\bar{X}}$ illustrate the principles of decision making.

Computing Probabilities

You cannot say the statistic you calculate is equal to the parameter, but you can find out how likely your statistic is, given certain parameter values. You can find the probability of one $\bar{X}$.

Suppose you have IQ scores ($\mu = 100$, $\sigma = 15$) for nine firefighters. If $\bar{X} = 105$ for the $N = 9$ firefighters, what is $p(\bar{X} \geq 105)$? Because

$$z_{\bar{X}} = \frac{\bar{X} - \mu}{\sigma/\sqrt{N}} = \frac{105 - 100}{15/\sqrt{9}} = \frac{5}{5} = 1.00$$

and

$$p(z_{\bar{X}} \geq 1.00) = .1587 \qquad \text{(from Table A.2)}$$

then

$$p(\bar{X} \geq 105) = .1587$$

Figure 9.4 shows the area in a normal distribution for $\bar{X}$'s larger than 105 (and for $z_{\bar{X}}$ larger than 1.00).

As N Increases, $\sigma_{\bar{X}}^2 = \sigma^2/N$ Decreases

Let's return to the fact that σ^2/N, the variance of the sampling distribution of $\bar{X}$, decreases as N increases. This can be illustrated by computing the variance of $\bar{X}$ for various sample sizes. Table 9.3 contains such computations for sample sizes of 3, 5, and 15 and compares the values of σ^2/N for these samples to the variance of the population.

As N increases from 3 to 15, σ^2/N decreases from 75 to 15, when the variance of the population is $\sigma^2 = 225$. As the sample size increases, the values of $\bar{X}$ tend to cluster more closely around μ, which gives less variability. Figure 9.5 shows the distributions for the population and the sampling distributions of $\bar{X}$ for $N = 3, 5,$ and 15. For most statistics, the variability of the statistic decreases as N increases, as you have seen here for $\bar{X}$.

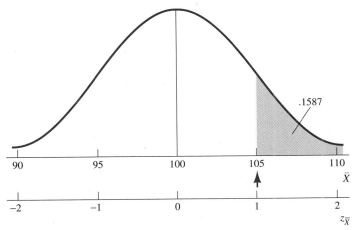

↑Indicates an $\bar{X}$ of 105, which has $z_{\bar{X}} = 1.00$; $p\,(\bar{X} \geq 105) = p\,(z_{\bar{X}} \geq 1.00) = .1587$

Figure 9.4
Sampling distribution of $\bar{X}$ and $z_{\bar{X}}$ ($\mu = 100,\ \sigma = 15$); $N = 9,\ \sigma/\sqrt{N} = 5,$
$\bar{X} = 105,\ z_{\bar{X}} = 1.00$

Table 9.3
Computation of $\sigma^2_{\bar{X}} = \sigma^2/N$ for various sized samples from a normal population with $\mu = 100$ and $\sigma^2 = 225$

	Variance
Single score	$\sigma^2 = 225$
$N = 3$	$\sigma^2/N = 225/3 = 75$
$N = 5$	$\sigma^2/N = 225/5 = 45$
$N = 15$	$\sigma^2/N = 225/15 = 15$

9.7   Sampling Distributions of Other Statistics

Let's briefly gather some facts about the sampling distributions of some other descriptive statistics covered so far in this text. We will discuss the mean and shape of the sampling distributions of $\overset{*}{s}{}^2$, s^2, and r. One benefit of this section is that you will see that the sampling distributions of most other statistics are not normal in shape. Another benefit is that the information here serves as the foundation for tests of hypotheses covered in Chapter 12.

Sampling Distribution of $\overset{*}{s}{}^2$

Sampling distribution of $\overset{*}{s}{}^2$
A distribution of $\overset{*}{s}{}^2$ that is positively skewed and has a mean of $[(N - 1)/N]\sigma^2$

Like all statistics, the sample variance $\overset{*}{s}{}^2$ has a sampling distribution. Conceptually, it can be formed from $\overset{*}{s}{}^2$ values computed on all possible samples of a given size N from some population. The facts that you need to know about the **sampling distribution of $\overset{*}{s}{}^2$** are its mean and shape.

The mean of the sampling distribution of $\overset{*}{s}{}^2$ is

$$\mu_{\overset{*}{s}{}^2} = \frac{(N - 1)}{N}\sigma^2 \tag{9.2}$$

which is always a fraction of σ^2. In the example of the IQs of deaf children, $\sigma^2 = 225$ and $N = 59$. So $\mu_{\overset{*}{s}{}^2} = [(N - 1)/N]\sigma^2 = (58/59)225 = 221.19$.

If the population sampled is normal in shape, then the shape of the sampling distribution of $\overset{*}{s}{}^2$ is a function of a theoretical distribution called *chi-square* (χ^2), which is

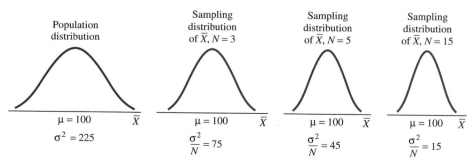

Figure 9.5
Distributions for X and $\bar{X}$

positively skewed. The extent of the skewness is related to the sample size, N, and lessens as N increases. Figure 9.6 summarizes these two key facts: the mean and shape of the sampling distribution of $\overset{*}{s}{}^2$. For $N = 3$, the sampling distribution of $\overset{*}{s}{}^2$ is extremely positively skewed. As the sample size increases, this skewness lessens, and the mean of the sampling distribution of $\overset{*}{s}{}^2$ gets closer to σ^2.

Sampling Distribution of s^2

Unbiased sample variance
s^2, a measure of variability in the sample that is formed by dividing the sum of squares by $N - 1$; the mean of the sampling distribution of s^2 is σ^2

In Chapter 4, we introduced the statistic s^2, the unbiased variance estimate, or **unbiased sample variance.** The definitional formula for s^2 is:

$$s^2 = \frac{\Sigma(X - \bar{X})^2}{N - 1} \tag{9.3}$$

One way that students sometimes remember which variance, s^2 or $\overset{*}{s}{}^2$, is unbiased is to look for the one that is "unstarred"; s^2 is unstarred and unbiased.

The following formula is for computational purposes:

$$s^2 = \frac{N\Sigma X^2 - (\Sigma X)^2}{N(N - 1)} \tag{9.4}$$

Sampling distribution of s^2
A distribution of s^2 that is positively skewed and has a mean of σ^2

The statistic s^2, too, has a sampling distribution. Conceptually, it is formed from s^2 values computed on all possible samples of a given size N from some population. Like $\overset{*}{s}{}^2$, the facts that you need to know about the **sampling distribution of s^2** are its mean and shape.

Calculation of the mean of the sampling distribution of s^2 is simpler than that of $\overset{*}{s}{}^2$ because it is

$$\mu_{s^2} = \sigma^2$$

If you are working with the IQs of deaf children with $\sigma^2 = 225$, then $\mu_{s^2} = 225$.

Like $\overset{*}{s}{}^2$, if the population sampled is normal in shape, then the shape of the sampling distribution of s^2 is a function of a theoretical distribution called χ^2, which is positively skewed. The degree of skewness lessens as N increases. Figure 9.7 summarizes these two key facts: the mean and shape of the sampling distribution of s^2. Similar to the sampling distribution of $\overset{*}{s}{}^2$, for $N = 3$, the sampling distribution of s^2 is extremely positively skewed, but this skewness lessens as the sample size increases. However, unlike the sampling distribution of $\overset{*}{s}{}^2$, the mean of the sampling distribution of s^2 is always equal to σ^2 regardless of the sample size.

Sampling Distribution of r

Sampling distribution of r
A distribution of r that is symmetric but not normal and has a mean of ρ if ρ is zero

In Chapter 6, you learned about the Pearson correlation coefficient r. The statistic r also has a sampling distribution. Conceptually, it is formed by computing r values on all possible samples of a given size N from some population. Like $\overset{*}{s}{}^2$ and s^2, the facts that you need to know about the **sampling distribution of r** are its mean and shape.

The mean of the sampling distribution of r has a condition placed on it that makes it different from s^2 and $\overset{*}{s}{}^2$. The mean of the sampling distribution of r is

$$\mu_r = \rho \quad \text{if } \rho = 0$$

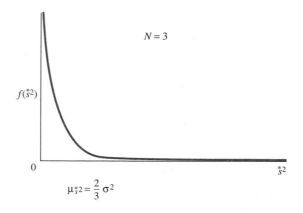

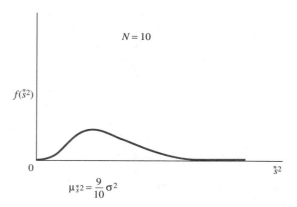

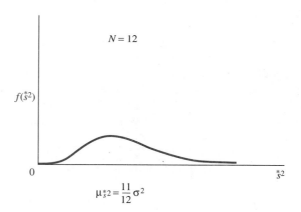

Figure 9.6
Sampling distribution of $\overset{*}{s}{}^2$ with $N = 3$, 10, and 12

If the population correlation ρ is zero, then the mean of the sampling distribution of r also is zero. Suppose you are working with the variables country music airtime and white suicide rate. If these two variables are independent and $\rho = 0$, then $\mu_r = 0$; there is no linear relationship between the variables.

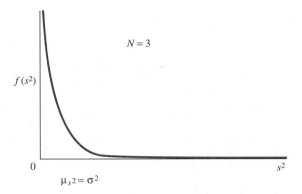

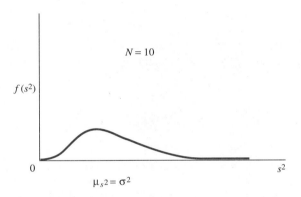

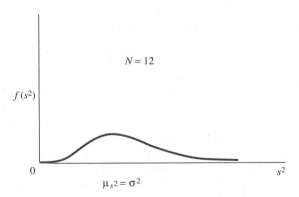

Figure 9.7
Sampling distribution of s^2 with $N = 3$, 10, and 12

If the populations for both variables are normal in shape, then the shape of the sampling distribution of r is a theoretical distribution called t, which is symmetric and unimodal, but not normal. You will learn more about this distribution in Chapter 12. Figure 9.8 summarizes these two key facts of mean and shape of the sampling distribution of r. Remember that the shape of the sampling distribution of r given in Figure

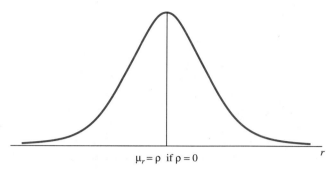

$$\mu_r = \rho \ \text{if } \rho = 0$$

r

Figure 9.8
Sampling distribution of r

9.8 is dependent upon the idea that the mean of the sampling distribution is zero. If ρ is some value other than zero, then the sampling distribution of r is skewed.

Quick Quiz
For a given population and sample data set, $\mu = 120$, $\sigma^2 = 66$, $s^2 = 48$, $\overline{X} = 118$, and $N = 30$. What is the mean of the sampling distribution of s^2?

Answer

The μ_{s^2} is $\sigma^2 = 66$. Remember: The sampling distribution of s^2 consists of all possible values of s^2 computed on samples of a certain size (here, $N = 30$). The average of those s^2 values is a variance. Don't confuse μ_{s^2} with the *variance of the sampling distribution* of $\underline{X}$.

9.8   Estimation: Means of Sampling Distributions and Unbiased Estimates

Estimation
Calculation of an approximate value of a parameter

Estimation is the calculation of an approximate value of a parameter. If you want some idea of the value of the population mean, you can calculate the sample mean as an estimate. When you use the sample mean as an estimate of the population mean, $\overline{X}$ is a **point estimate**—a single value, or point, of the statistic used to estimate the parameter. The sample mean is not equal to the population mean, but it is an available indicator of the approximate value of μ. When you do not know the value of a population parameter, you can estimate it with the corresponding sample statistic. For example, from Research Example 9, $\overline{X} = 88.07$ is the best estimate of μ for the IQs of deaf children.

Point estimation
Using a statistic as a single value (point) to estimate a parameter

Another type of estimation is called *interval estimation*. The goal of interval estimation is to obtain an interval of potential values for a parameter. Rather than giving just $\overline{X} = 88.07$ as your best estimate of μ for the IQs of deaf children, you could calculate an interval of potential values of μ. Interval estimation is covered further in Section 9.9.

Parameters and Estimates

Table 9.4 lists population parameters that may be estimated by statistics that you have covered so far in the text. You might be surprised by some of the combinations, such

Table 9.4

Parameters and statistics as point estimates

Parameter	*Statistic*	*Parameter*	*Statistic*
Population mode	Mode	Population range	Range
Population median	X_{50}	σ^2	$\overset{*}{s}{}^2$
μ	$\overline{X}$	σ	$\overset{*}{s}$
μ	X_{50}	$\sigma^2_{Y \cdot X}$	$s^2_{Y \cdot X}$
μ	Mode	$\sigma^2_{\overline{X}} = \sigma^2/N$	$\overset{*}{s}{}^2/N$
ρ	r	$\sigma_{\overline{X}} = \sigma/\sqrt{N}$	$\overset{*}{s}/\sqrt{N}$

as the sample median as an estimate of the population mean. Because any statistic can be used to estimate any population parameter, you need to know which statistics are good estimates. For example, is X_{50} a good estimate of μ?

In Table 9.4, pay attention to the parameters σ^2/N and $\sigma/\sqrt{N}$. These entries are the variance and standard error of $\overline{X}$, respectively, with their estimates given in the next column. Because N is a constant, only σ^2 or σ needs to be estimated by a corresponding statistic $\overset{*}{s}{}^2$ or $\overset{*}{s}$, and then combined with N or $\sqrt{N}$ to give the estimates. Any of the statistics that use $\overset{*}{s}{}^2$ or $\overset{*}{s}$ have a problem: They are not good estimates. You will see why shortly.

Unbiased

There are many definitions of *good* statistics as estimates. The way we define a *good estimate* is "one that is unbiased." A statistic is an unbiased estimate of a parameter if the mean of the sampling distribution of the statistic is equal to the parameter.

Although you can make no statement equating the parameter and the statistic itself, **unbiased** means that the parameter and the mean of the sampling distribution are equal. In other words, on the average the statistic equals the parameter. This does not say that the statistic equals the parameter; rather, the mean of the statistic's sampling distribution equals the parameter; that is,

$$\mu_{\text{statistic}} = \text{parameter}$$

$\overline{X}$ Is Unbiased

The sample mean $\overline{X}$ is an unbiased estimate of the population mean μ. Check this statement against the definition of *unbiased* given above: Is the mean of the sampling distribution of the statistic $\overline{X}$ equal to the parameter μ? That is, is $\mu_{\overline{X}} = \mu$? Yes, and this means that even though you cannot be guaranteed that your single sampled value of $\overline{X}$ equals μ, you know that $\overline{X}$ is a statistic whose average value equals μ. If you repeatedly drew samples of size N from the same population, some of the $\overline{X}$'s would be too high and others would be too low, but the average value of the $\overline{X}$'s would be right on target. Unbiased means that on the average, $\overline{X}$ is free from any systematic tendencies to be larger or smaller than μ. Additionally, $\overline{X}$ is an unbiased estimate of μ regardless of the shape of the population of raw scores. No restrictions are put on the unbiasedness of $\overline{X}$ as an estimate of μ.

In a study of sudden infant death syndrome (SIDS), you might calculate the average number of smokers who live in households where an infant has died from SIDS. The

Unbiased

A statistic is an unbiased estimate of a parameter if the mean of its sampling distribution is equal to the parameter sample is not equal to the population, but you will use the sample as representative of the population. The $\overline{X}$ for the number of smokers probably won't exactly equal the population average μ. It might be a little higher or a little lower; there's no way of knowing because you cannot obtain parameters. But if you could repeatedly sample from the population, the average $\overline{X}$ would equal μ, so $\overline{X}$ is unbiased.

Using the least-squares criterion and the property of unbiasedness helps you to choose $\overline{X}$ as the best estimate of μ. The sample median is unbiased as an estimate of μ only if the population is symmetric. If the population is not symmetric, then the mean of the sampling distribution of X_{50} is not equal to μ. If you had reason to believe that your population was not symmetric and you wanted your statistic to be an unbiased estimate of μ, you would choose $\overline{X}$ over X_{50}. This fits with a commonsense notion that the sample mean should be the best estimate of the population mean.

Biased and Unbiased Sample Variance

Unfortunately, common sense is not always correct. You have used the sample variance $\overset{*}{s}{}^2$ for descriptive purposes as a measure of the variability of the sample. But $\overset{*}{s}{}^2$ has a serious drawback as an estimate of σ^2: It is biased. Remember, for a statistic to be an unbiased estimate of σ^2, the statistic's sampling distribution must have a mean equal to σ^2. The mean of the sampling distribution of $\overset{*}{s}{}^2$ is

$$\mu_{\overset{*}{s}{}^2} = \frac{(N-1)}{N} \sigma^2$$

which is not equal to σ^2. On the average, $\overset{*}{s}{}^2$ is too small as an estimate of σ^2; $\overset{*}{s}{}^2$ underestimates the population variance on the average. Not every value of $\overset{*}{s}{}^2$ is smaller than σ^2, but the average of all possible values of $\overset{*}{s}{}^2$ is smaller than σ^2. For example, if $N = 10$, then the mean of the sampling distribution of $\overset{*}{s}{}^2$ is $(0.9)(\sigma^2)$, or nine-tenths of σ^2.

Reconsider the sampling experiment given in Section 9.5 and earlier in Chapter 8. The population had only three scores (1, 2, and 3), each with a large equal frequency.

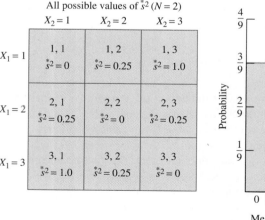
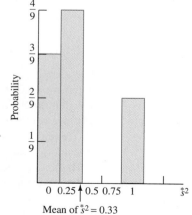

Figure 9.9
Sampling distribution of $\overset{*}{s}{}^2$ from population in Figure 9.2; $\sigma^2 = \frac{2}{3} = 0.67$

You took all possible samples of $N = 2$. Now you want to compute the sample variance $\overset{*}{s}{}^2$ for each sample and arrange the $\overset{*}{s}{}^2$ values in a distribution. Figure 9.9 contains the possible samples, the sample variances $\overset{*}{s}{}^2$, and the sampling distribution of $\overset{*}{s}{}^2$. The mean of the sampling distribution of $\overset{*}{s}{}^2$ for $N = 2$ from this small population is 1/3, which is $[(N-1)/N]\sigma^2 = [(1)/2](2/3)$. So $\overset{*}{s}{}^2$ is too small on the average. By the way, the sampling distribution of $\overset{*}{s}{}^2$ is positively skewed. See Box 9.1 for an explanation of why $\overset{*}{s}{}^2$ is too small on the average.

Box 9.1   The Bias in $\overset{*}{s}{}^2$

As an estimate of the population variance σ^2, the sample variance $\overset{*}{s}{}^2$ is too small on the average. Why? To see that the bias in $\overset{*}{s}{}^2$ is toward being too small, consider the "ideal" estimate of population variance:

$$\frac{\Sigma(X - \mu)^2}{N}$$

This estimate of σ^2 has no bias; that is, the average of the sampling distribution of $\Sigma(X - \mu)^2/N$ is σ^2. Unfortunately, you never know the value of μ, so you cannot compute $\Sigma(X - \mu)^2/N$. Using $\overline{X}$ as an estimate of μ gives $\overset{*}{s}{}^2 = \Sigma(X - \overline{X})^2/N$. Remember that $\overline{X}$ minimizes the sum of the squared deviations. That is, $\Sigma(X - \overline{X})^2$ is as small as it can be and thus smaller than $\Sigma(X - \mu)^2$. By this least-squares property of $\overline{X}$, when $\overline{X}$ is substituted for μ in $\Sigma(X - \mu)^2/N$, $\overset{*}{s}{}^2$ becomes too small. The exact amount by which $\overset{*}{s}{}^2$ is too small is shown when you consider the mean of the numerator of the ideal estimate. The mean of the sampling distribution of $\Sigma(X - \mu)^2$ can be shown to be:

Mean of sampling distribution of $\Sigma(X - \mu)^2 = N\sigma^2$

When you substitute $\overline{X}$ for μ, you get:

Mean of sampling distribution of $\Sigma(X - \overline{X})^2 = N\sigma^2 - \sigma^2$

That is, the numerator is too small by σ^2. Rewriting $N\sigma^2 - \sigma^2$ as $\sigma^2(N-1)$ gives the solution to the problem:

Mean of sampling distribution of $\Sigma(X - \overline{X})^2 = \sigma^2(N-1)$

Because $\Sigma(X - \overline{X})^2$ has an average value of $\sigma^2(N-1)$, all you have to do is divide this numerator by $N-1$ instead of N and you have an unbiased estimate of σ^2, or:

Mean of sampling distribution of $\dfrac{\Sigma(X - \overline{X})^2}{N - 1} = \sigma^2$

Also, $s^2 = \Sigma(X - \overline{X})^2/(N-1)$ is called the *unbiased sample variance.*
    Another way of looking at the problem is to correct the bias in $\overset{*}{s}{}^2$. All you need to do is multiply $\overset{*}{s}{}^2$ by $N/(N-1)$, giving

$$s^2 = (\overset{*}{s}{}^2)\,\frac{N}{N-1} = \frac{\Sigma(X - \overline{X})^2}{N}\,\frac{N}{N-1} = \frac{\Sigma(X - \overline{X})^2}{N-1}$$

The tendency to underestimate σ^2 is corrected by dividing $\Sigma(X - \bar{X})^2$ by $N - 1$ instead of by N, giving s^2. You now have s^2 as an unbiased estimate of σ^2; that is, $\mu_{s^2} = \sigma^2$. On the average, using s^2 as an estimate of σ^2 is correct. However, because s^2 is a statistic and has variability, it is not certain how close any one sample statistic s^2 is to σ^2, but you can be confident that the sampling distribution of s^2 has a mean that is exactly equal to σ^2. Figure 9.10 shows the sampling distribution of all possible values of s^2 for the sampling experiment from the population with scores of 1, 2, and 3. The mean of the sampling distribution of s^2 is exactly $\sigma^2 = 2/3$ because s^2 is unbiased.

The only difference between the computation of s^2 and $\overset{*}{s}{}^2$ is the denominator. Table 9.5 shows the computation of s^2 for the Secret Service deception accuracy data of Table 9.1. Formula 9.4 gives $s^2 = 171.76$ which corrects for $\overset{*}{s}{}^2 = 166.86$ being too small. The following is important: The biased sample variance $\overset{*}{s}{}^2$ is no longer used in this text. The unbiased sample variance s^2 is used whenever an estimate of σ^2 is needed.

To form an unbiased estimate of σ^2/N, substitute s^2 for σ^2 to get s^2/N. Whenever you need an estimate of σ^2/N (the variance of the sampling distribution of $\bar{X}$), you can use

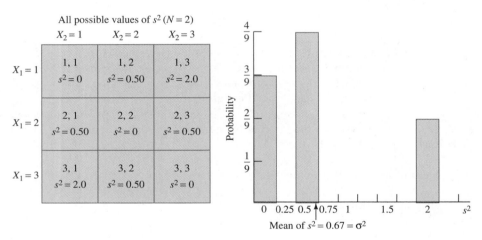

Figure 9.10
Sampling distribution of s^2 from population in Figure 9.2. $\sigma^2 = \frac{2}{3} = .67$

Table 9.5
Computation of s^2 for data of Table 9.1

$$s^2 = \frac{N\Sigma X^2 - (\Sigma X)^2}{N(N - 1)}$$

$$= \frac{(35)(149,200) - 2240^2}{(35)(35 - 1)} = \frac{204,400}{(35)(34)} = \frac{204,400}{1190}$$

$$= 171.7647 = 171.76$$

versus

$$\overset{*}{s}{}^2 = 166.86$$

s^2/N. The general principle in finding an unbiased estimate of a parameter is to find a statistic whose sampling distribution has its mean equal to the parameter. Table 9.6 shows some parameters and their unbiased estimates.

Biased Standard Deviations

Neither $\overset{*}{s}$ nor s is an unbiased estimate of σ. The reason is that the property of unbiasedness is not retained for a nonlinear transformation such as square root. So $s = \sqrt{s^2}$ is not an unbiased estimate of σ. Both $\overset{*}{s}$ and s are **biased standard deviations.** However, the bias in s is appreciable for only small samples, and as N increases, the bias decreases. For $N = 2$, the mean of the sampling distribution of s is 0.798σ, and for $N = 10$ it is 0.973σ (see Marascuilo & McSweeney, 1977, p. 81). For subsequent statistics that use s as an estimate of σ, the degree of bias is taken into account in the statistic and in its sampling distribution.

As you conclude this section on the property of unbiasedness, quiz yourself using Table 9.7. For each parameter–statistic pair, give the mean of the statistic's sampling distribution and tell whether the statistic is unbiased. If you do not answer them all correctly, review the information in this section.

This section has shown the importance of sampling distributions in connection with a part of inferential statistics, estimation. Sampling distributions play a crucial role in other aspects of inferential statistics, including hypothesis testing, which is covered in Chapter 10.

Biased standard deviations
The square root of s^2 gives the standard deviation s, which is biased, as is $\overset{*}{s}$

Table 9.6
Unbiased estimates of parameters

Parameter	Statistic	Parameter	Statistic
μ	$\overline{X}$	σ^2	s^2
ρ	r (if $\rho = 0$)	σ^2/N	s^2/N
$\sigma^2_{Y \cdot X}$	$s^2_{Y \cdot X}$		

Table 9.7
Quiz on unbiased estimates

Desired Parameter	Statistic	Mean of Statistic's Sampling Distribution	Unbiased?
μ	$\overline{X}$	μ	Yes
μ	s^2	σ^2	No
σ^2	$\overset{*}{s}^2$	$\dfrac{(N-1)}{N}\sigma^2$	No
σ^2	s^2	σ^2	Yes
σ	s ($N = 10$)	$0.973\sigma^2$	No

Quick Quiz

Imagine that your friend has extensive training in statistics. She tells you about a new statistic called L, which measures central tendency. Unlike the sample mean, L is not pulled in the direction of outliers. If you want to use L in the same places you had been using $\overline{X}$, what would you ask your friend about the sampling distribution of L?

Answer

If you are going to use L as an estimate of μ, you would want to ask about the mean of the sampling distribution of L. If $\mu_L = \mu$, then L is an unbiased estimate of μ.

9.9   Estimation: Confidence Interval for the Population Mean

Interval Estimation Versus Point Estimation

In the preceding section, estimating a parameter with a single value of a statistic was called *point estimation*. Now you will learn about interval estimation. Going beyond simply obtaining a single value of a statistic, **interval estimation** involves obtaining an interval of potential values for a parameter.

Interval estimation
Allows you to obtain an interval of potential values for a parameter

Confidence Intervals

In the Secret Service example in Table 9.1, $\overline{X} = 64$ is the point estimate of μ. You cannot say that the population mean deception accuracy score equals 64 because there is error in the estimate $\overline{X}$. If some measure of error could be incorporated into the estimation, it would improve your point estimate. A measure of the extent or degree of error in $\overline{X}$ as an estimate of μ is given by the standard error of the mean $\sigma/\sqrt{N}$. Suppose $\sigma^2 = 170$ and $N = 35$; then the standard error of the mean equals $\sigma/\sqrt{N} = \sqrt{170}/\sqrt{35} = 2.204$. Because there is error in the estimate of μ, you would like to place some bounds on $\overline{X}$ by using $\sigma/\sqrt{N}$, the measure of the error in $\overline{X}$. These bounds should be formed such that you are confident that they bracket or include the true value of μ a certain percentage of the times μ could be estimated. The confidence interval will be centered on $\overline{X}$, and the ends of the interval will depend on the standard error and the percentage of the time you wish to include the true value of μ. This percentage is usually expressed as a probability and is sometimes called the **confidence coefficient**, $1 - \alpha$.

Confidence coefficient
Percentage of the intervals that include the true value of the parameter, symbolized by $1 - \alpha$

To get a conceptual idea of confidence intervals, suppose you want to include the true value of μ in your interval about 95% of the time, so $1 - \alpha = .95$. You know that in a normal distribution, about 95% of the scores lie within about plus or minus two standard deviations of μ. So in the sampling distribution of $\overline{X}$, about 95% of the $\overline{X}$ values lie within plus or minus two standard errors of μ. So an approximate 95% confidence interval for μ is formed by taking the interval of $\overline{X}$'s from $\overline{X} - 2.00\sigma/\sqrt{N}$ to $\overline{X} + 2.00\sigma/\sqrt{N}$. The interval extends from minus two standard errors below $\overline{X}$ to plus two standard errors above $\overline{X}$. For the liar data in Table 9.1, where $\overline{X} = 64$, $\sigma^2 = 170$, and $N = 35$, you get $64 - (2.00)(2.204) = 59.59$ and $64 + (2.00)(2.204) = 68.41$. The approximate 95% confidence interval is from 59.59 to 68.41.

Now let's make this idea of a 95% confidence interval a bit more precise. With $1 - \alpha = .95$, the lower bound of the interval is

$$\overline{X} - 1.96 \, \frac{\sigma}{\sqrt{N}}$$

and the upper bound of the interval is

$$\overline{X} + 1.96 \, \frac{\sigma}{\sqrt{N}}$$

where -1.96 and $+1.96$ are the exact values of z in a standard normal distribution (see Table A.2) that include 95% of the $\overline{X}$ values in the sampling distribution of $\overline{X}$. For the data in Table 9.1, where $\overline{X} = 64$, $\sigma^2 = 170$, and $N = 35$, you should get $64 - (1.96)(2.204) = 59.68$ and $64 + (1.96)(2.204) = 68.32$. The exact 95% confidence interval for μ is from 59.68 to 68.32.

The confidence interval for μ has its basis in the sampling distribution of $\overline{X}$. You use the standard deviation of the sampling distribution of $\overline{X}$ (the standard error of $\overline{X}$) as the measure of error. Also, because $\overline{X}$ is an unbiased estimate of μ, you know that in the sampling distribution of $\overline{X}$, the mean of all the $\overline{X}$ values is the true value of μ. Because these $\overline{X}$'s are distributed around μ, if you compute intervals that are centered on the $\overline{X}$'s, then a certain percentage of the intervals will include μ, depending on the length of the intervals.

With a general $1 - \alpha$, the lower bound of the interval is

$$\overline{X} - z_{\text{crit}} \, \frac{\sigma}{\sqrt{N}}$$

and the upper bound of the interval is

$$\overline{X} + z_{\text{crit}} \, \frac{\sigma}{\sqrt{N}}$$

where $-z_{\text{crit}}$ and $+z_{\text{crit}}$ are the exact values that will include $100 \, (1 - \alpha)\%$ of the z values in the normal distribution. The "crit" stands for "critical" because these values of z are critical to computing the interval correctly. They give the desired boundaries on the z values and therefore on the $\overline{X}$.

Putting these two bounds together gives a general formula for the $100(1 - \alpha)\%$ **confidence interval for μ:**

Confidence interval for μ
Interval that includes μ for $100(1 - \alpha)\%$ of such intervals

$$\overline{X} - z_{\text{crit}} \, \frac{\sigma}{\sqrt{N}} \quad \text{to} \quad \overline{X} + z_{\text{crit}} \, \frac{\sigma}{\sqrt{N}} \tag{9.5}$$

If $1 - \alpha = .95$, then this is the formula for a 95% confidence interval for μ, and 95% of such intervals will include the true value of μ. Of course, in practice you compute only one interval, and either it includes the true value of μ or it does not. But you can say that you are 95% confident that your single computed interval includes the true value of μ.

The length of the confidence interval is important and it depends only on N, σ, and the degree of confidence, $1 - \alpha$. Increasing N results in a shorter or tighter confidence interval. To improve the interval estimation of μ, you need to take the largest sample you can afford. Anything that you can do to decrease the standard deviation, σ, also gives a shorter confidence interval. You can reduce the confidence needed, $1 - \alpha$, which also shortens the confidence interval. However, most researchers use 95% or 99% as the degree of confidence for their intervals. Note that $\overline{X}$ only centers the interval on the number line and does not influence its length.

Another Example

What if you want to estimate the population mean self-esteem of singers (see Marchant-Haycox & Wilson, 1992)? You give a self-esteem scale to $N = 38$ singers and get $\overline{X} = 28.28$; from Eysenck and Wilson (1991) you know that $\sigma = 8.13$. Thus, $\sigma/\sqrt{N} = 8.13/\sqrt{38} = 1.3189$. You obtain $z_{crit} = \pm 1.96$ from Table A.2 and compute the 95% confidence interval for the population mean of the self-esteem scores of singers:

$$\overline{X} - z_{crit}\frac{\sigma}{\sqrt{N}} \quad \text{to} \quad \overline{X} + z_{crit}\frac{\sigma}{\sqrt{N}}$$

$$28.28 - (1.96)(1.3189) \quad \text{to} \quad 28.28 + (1.96)(1.3189)$$

$$25.695 \quad \text{to} \quad 30.865$$

You can say that you are 95% confident that 25.695 to 30.865 includes the true value of μ. If you computed many such intervals from many different $\overline{X}$ values, then 95% of such intervals would include the true value of μ. Figure 9.11 illustrates that a high percentage of such intervals include or bracket the true value of μ, even though you do not know this value.

Some points about Figure 9.11 are worthy of your attention. First, the value of μ is a constant; second, the values of $1 - \alpha$ (and thus z_{crit}), σ, and N also are constant; and, third, the intervals vary in location because of different $\overline{X}$ values. Remember that in practice you compute only one such interval, and it will either include or not include μ, just like any single interval in Figure 9.11. Your interpretation of that single interval is based on principles of sampling and on the idea that a high percentage of potential intervals include μ.

Language

There is great potential for incorrect language to be used in connection with confidence intervals, so let's discuss both incorrect and correct statements. The first issue surrounds the idea of a random variable.

In the confidence interval problem, the interval can be different from sample to sample; that is, the interval is a random variable. Now examine the interval itself. In formula 9.5, what component is a random variable, changing from sample to sample? $\overline{X}$ is a sample statistic and thus a random variable. If you drew another sample of singers, you most likely would get another value of $\overline{X}$. This new $\overline{X}$ would more than likely not equal 28.28, even though you used the same sample size ($N = 38$). The other components of the formula are fixed. Figure 9.11 shows that the interval varies from sample to sample around a fixed μ. The value of μ is fixed because it is a parameter and not a function of the sample; so μ does not vary from sample to sample. Because μ is not a random variable, you cannot use the phrase "μ falls" in connection with

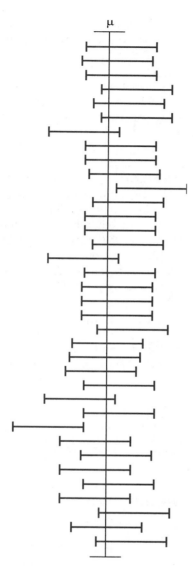

Figure 9.11

Confidence intervals for μ, each based on a different sample of size N. The vertical line represents the constant fixed value of μ; the horizontal lines represent different confidence intervals for μ. Most intervals bracket (include) μ; some do not. Note that the intervals vary, but μ does not. The location of each interval is a function of $\overline{X}$; the length of each interval is fixed for a given N, σ^2, and degree of confidence.

confidence intervals. You do *not* say, "We are 95% confident that μ falls between 25.695 and 30.865." Statements should be about the *interval* of doing something, either including or not including the true value of μ (which is fixed). A correct statement is, "We are 95% confident that 25.695 to 30.865 includes the true value of μ." Be sure you understand that the interval is the random variable, not μ. Consider the analogy of the game of horseshoes: The pin is fixed, and either the shoe includes the pin on any given throw or it does not. When you miss the pin on a given throw, you do not say, "Oh, the pin didn't get inside the shoe!" but rather, "Oh, the shoe didn't go over the pin!"

Another area with potential for language problems for confidence intervals is probability statements versus confidence statements. Probability statements can be made about the general case, before you compute the interval. In the specific case, after you compute the interval, you use the word *confident*. Probability statements should not be made about an obtained interval, such as, "The probability is .95 that the interval 25.695 to 30.865 includes μ." This statement is false because 25.695 to 30.865 either includes μ or it does not. That is, the probability is either one or zero that this particular interval includes the true value of μ. Probability statements can be made about intervals in general (such as "The probability is .95 that intervals such as those given by formula 9.5 include μ") but not about a particular interval after it is already computed. You can say that you are 95% *confident* that 25.695 to 30.865 includes μ because this statement is clearly understood to be different from a probability statement. The basis of this statement is the hypothetical sampling of many $\overline{X}$ values and computing many intervals, 95% of which include the true value of μ.

Quick Quiz

Let's say that you test 40 new Secret Service personnel, and they have an average deception accuracy score of $\overline{X} = 63.7$. If $\mu = 62.01$ and $\sigma^2 = 41.08$, find the 95% confidence interval for your result and decide whether it brackets μ.

Answer

The standard error of the mean $= \sigma/\sqrt{N} = \sqrt{41.08}/\sqrt{40} = 1.01341$. The 95% confidence interval is from $63.7 - (1.96)(1.01341) = 61.71372$ to $63.7 + (1.96)(1.01341) = 65.68628$, or from 61.71 to 65.69 (rounded). Yes, this 95% confidence interval brackets $\mu = 62.01$.

9.10   Summary, Study Tips, and Computation

Chapter Summary

The important concept of sampling distributions includes three general types of distributions. You randomly sample scores from a population distribution to get a sample distribution. The sampling distribution of any statistic is formed by repeatedly drawing samples of a given size, computing the statistic, and arranging the statistics in a distribution. Decision making about parameters involves using the probability of the statistic from the sampling distribution.

If the $\overline{X}$ values are independent and X is distributed normally with mean μ and variance σ^2, then $\overline{X}$ is distributed normally with mean μ and variance σ^2/N. The Central Limit Theorem and a sufficiently large N let you use a normal distribution to approximate the distribution of $\overline{X}$ even when the population shape is unknown. Probabilities for $\overline{X}$ are obtained from the standard normal distribution by transforming $\overline{X}$ to $z_{\overline{X}}$.

The mean and shape of the sampling distributions of $\hat{s}^2$, s^2, and r are $[(N - 1)/N]\sigma^2$, σ^2, and ρ if $\rho = 0$ and positively skewed, positively skewed, and unimodal/symmetric (but not normal), respectively.

An unbiased estimate has a sampling distribution with its mean equal to the parameter estimated. Examples of unbiased estimators are $\overline{X}$, s^2, and r if $\rho = 0$.

Interval estimation was introduced with the confidence interval for μ. To avoid incorrect language you must realize that the interval is the random variable and that you cannot make statements about μ falling in the interval.

The key terms introduced in this chapter are:

Population distribution	Unbiased
Sample distribution	Unbiased sample
Sampling distribution	variance, s^2
σ^2/N	Point estimate
Standard error of	Confidence interval
the mean	$1 - \alpha$, confidence
$z_{\bar{X}}$	coefficient
Central Limit Theorem	Interval estimation
Estimation	

Study Tips

Most students have some confusion over the three distributions summarized in Table 9.2. That is, they confuse the names (sample distribution with sampling distribution), or the variances (σ^2, $\overset{*}{s}{}^2$, and σ^2/N), or some other characteristic of the three distributions. Study Table 9.2 until you can reproduce the items in it for the population distribution, the sample distribution, and the sampling distribution of $\bar{X}$. Make sure you know the definition of *sampling distribution* and why you need such distributions (to compute probabilities of statistics so you can make inferences about parameters). Another common mistake is for students to think that *unbiased* means that the statistic equals the parameter. Of course, this is *not* true; it *is* true that $\mu_{\text{statistic}}$ = parameter, so focus on the mean of the sampling distribution of a statistic in order to answer questions about unbiasedness.

Use the characteristics listed on the left-hand side of Table 9.2 to organize information about the sampling distributions of $\overset{*}{s}{}^2$, s^2, and r.

Computation

Because much of this chapter is conceptually based, there is little computation, none of which is new. Computation of $z_{\bar{X}}$ and the confidence interval used the basic operations presented in Chapter 5. None of the exercises need to be done on the computer.

Exercises

Section 9.1

1. A university researcher randomly samples ten subjects from a list of 175 volunteers from an introductory psychology class. Is the population actually sampled "all students in introductory psychology this semester"? Why or why not?
2. How could judgment sampling justify the population described in Exercise 1? Could judgment sampling stretch the population to include all college students in the United States enrolled in a similar course? Why or why not?

Sections 9.2–9.5

3. Without referring to Figure 9.1 or Table 9.2, compare the population distribution, the sample distribution, and the sampling distribution of $\bar{X}$ on the following:
   a. Random variable in the distribution
   b. Shape of the distribution
   c. Mean of the distribution
   d. Variance of the distribution
   e. Reality of obtaining the distribution
4. Describe each of the following populations in terms of large (or small), unobtainable (or obtainable), and hypothetical (or real):
   a. Whooping cranes
   b. All college students taking any statistics course in the next 3 years
   c. All rats deprived of food for 24 hours
   d. All professional basketball players
5. If the population has only four values of X, (5, 6, 7, 8), each with equal probability, then $\mu = 6.5$ and $\sigma^2 = 1.25$.
   a. Form all possible values of $\bar{X}$ from samples of size $N = 2$. One easy way to do this is to draw a box with four rows and four columns. Label the columns with 5, 6, 7, and 8 on the top. Label the rows with 5, 6, 7, and 8 on the left side of the box. Then the samples are the values of the row and column labels—for example, 5, 5 for the left column in the top row, 5, 6 for the second column in the top row, and so on.

b. Compute $\bar{X}$ for each of the 16 samples in the box.

c. Arrange these $\bar{X}$ values in a distribution. For the horizontal axis use the values of $\bar{X}$ from the smallest $\bar{X}$ of 5 up to the largest $\bar{X}$ of 8. For the vertical axis, use the frequency of the values of $\bar{X}$.

d. From what you know about the sampling distribution of $\bar{X}$, what should be the value of the mean of this sampling distribution of $\bar{X}$? Does that appear to be correct?

e. From what you know about the sampling distribution of $\bar{X}$, what should be the value of the variance of this sampling distribution of $\bar{X}$?

f. From what you know about the sampling distribution of $\bar{X}$, what should be the shape of the sampling distribution of $\bar{X}$? Comment on the shape of this sampling distribution you obtained.

Section 9.6

6. Suppose you believed that women over age 25 were average in anxiety about going to the dentist, where average is 7.5 on the Dental Anxiety Scale (DAS). You know the population variance is 1.34. You obtain a sample of 31 women over age 25. If the DAS is thought to be normally distributed, list everything you know about the sampling distribution of $\bar{X}$ for this situation.

7. Suppose a researcher in Japan translated the California Personality Inventory (CPI) to Japanese and wants to test a group of Japanese to see whether the Japanese population mean on the Self-Acceptance (SA) scale differs from the English norm of 20. Prior research has shown that $\sigma^2 = 3.7$ and that the SA scale is normally distributed. For your sample of 84 Japanese people, list all that you know about the sampling distribution of $\bar{X}$.

8. Suppose you computed the average IQ of the students in your statistics class and found it to be $\bar{X} = 115$. IQ is normally distributed with mean 100 and variance 225, and there are 25 students in your class.

a. Give the mean of the sampling distribution of $\bar{X}$.

b. Give the variance of the sampling distribution of $\bar{X}$.

c. Compute $z_{\bar{X}}$ for $\bar{X} = 115$.

d. Use Table A.2 to find the probability of getting the $z_{\bar{X}}$ you computed in part c or larger. Is this the same as the probability of getting 115 or larger for the value of $\bar{X}$?

9. If $N = 100$, how does the probability in Exercise 8 change? For $N = 9$? If this population is not normal, how would the Central Limit Theorem influence your ability to find these probabilities?

10. Suppose you work in a car manufacturing plant where the average number of defects per car is 16 with a standard deviation of 3. If the quality control program samples four cars that have $\bar{X} = 18$ defects, what is the probability of getting an $\bar{X}$ greater than or equal to 18? State the assumptions you made in order to calculate this probability. Would you recommend changes in the assembly line?

11. If the sample in Exercise 10 used nine cars that had $\bar{X} = 18$ defects, what is the probability of getting an $\bar{X}$ greater than or equal to 18? Would you recommend changes in the assembly line? Explain the difference between your answers to this question and Exercise 10, given that $\bar{X} = 18$ in both cases.

12. A psychological clinic claims that its patients treated for anxiety are "normal" on this mood state after 4 weeks of therapy. The norms for a standard anxiety test are 25 for the mean and 5 for the standard deviation. If you randomly sample $N = 16$ patients and obtain an anxiety score for each, yielding $\bar{X} = 27.8$, what is the probability of getting an $\bar{X}$ at least this extreme?

Section 9.8

13. Is *unbiased* the only way to define a good estimate? Are all statistics biased? Do all statistics have a sampling distribution? Does the Central Limit Theorem apply to all statistics?

14. True or false? An unbiased statistic is equal to the parameter estimated. Defend your answer.

Section 9.9

15. Suppose you computed a confidence interval for μ using $\sigma^2 = 34$, $N = 14$, and $1 - \alpha = .95$. Which of the following changes will result in a shorter confidence interval?

a. $N = 44$

b. $\sigma^2 = 23$

c. $1 - \alpha = .99$

d. $N = 6$

e. $\sigma^2 = 45$

f. $1 - \alpha = .90$

16. If $\bar{X} = 112$, compute the confidence interval for μ with the values $\sigma^2 = 34$, $N = 14$, and $1 - \alpha = .95$. What is the meaning of your computed interval?

Write a statement of this meaning using correct language.

17. Hirshoren, Hurley, and Kavale (1979), in their study of 59 deaf children, found that their average IQ score on the Wechsler Intelligence Scale for Children–Revised (WISC-R) was 88.07 (see Research Example 9). The population mean for the hearing standardization group is 100, and the population standard deviation is 15.
    a. Compute $\sigma/\sqrt{N}$.
    b. For a 95% confidence interval, find z_{crit}.
    c. Compute the 95% confidence interval for μ.
    d. If $\mu = 100$ is the true mean of the IQs of deaf children, is this μ in the interval?
    e. Explain this interval as if you were talking to a friend who does not know statistics.

18. A psychologist is studying the effects of high blood pressure, hypertension, on memory and learning. He uses a task that requires each participant to study either two, four, or six digits shown on a screen and then later to indicate whether a single digit presented on the screen was part of the original set. He knows that the average time to answer for a large number of nonhypertensive adults on the six-digit task is 1.35 s with a standard deviation of 0.23 s. He believes that hypertensives will answer differently. A sample of hypertensives gave the following times for the six-digit task: 1.43, 1.67, 2.13, 3.12, 1.23, 1.29, 1.56, 1.43, 3.89, 2.34, 1.89, 1.78.
    a. Compute $\overline{X}$.
    b. Compute $\sigma/\sqrt{N}$.
    c. For a 95% confidence interval, find z_{crit}.
    d. Compute the 95% confidence interval for μ.
    e. If $\mu = 1.35$ is the true mean of the time to answer for hypertensives, is this μ in the interval?
    f. Write an explanation of this interval as if you were talking to a friend who does not know statistics.

19. A psychologist has been studying the effects of different instructions on the intensity of pain. She had college students hold their hand in a jar of freezing water for as long as possible. Most students could tolerate only about 2 min and reported high-intensity pain. Then they removed their hands from the water and over the next 2 min were asked periodically to rate the intensity of the pain. The standard instructions given before this task started were to suppress all awareness of the sensations in their hand—that is, to ignore the pain. For the standard condition, the researcher knew that the average pain intensity on a 1 (low, tolerable pain) to 5 (high, intolerable pain) scale was 4.06 with a standard deviation of 0.41 when pain intensity was measured 1.5 min after they removed their hand from the water. The latest experiment had 63 college students do the same task but with instructions to monitor the details of their hand sensations—that is, to concentrate or focus on the pain and its intensity. When pain intensity was measured at 1.5 min after they removed their hand from the water, $\overline{X} = 3.85$ for the 63 students with the new instructions.
    a. List all that you know about the sampling distribution of $\overline{X}$.
    b. Compute $z_{\overline{X}}$ for $\overline{X} = 3.85$.
    c. Use Table A.2 to find the probability of getting the $z_{\overline{X}}$ you computed in part b or more extreme. Is this the same as the probability of 3.85 or more extreme for the value of $\overline{X}$?
    d. For a 95% confidence interval, find z_{crit}.
    e. Compute the 95% confidence interval for μ.
    f. If $\mu = 4.06$ is the true mean of pain intensity after 1.5 min for the "focus on the pain" instructions, is this μ in the interval?
    g. Write an explanation of this interval as if you were talking to a friend who does not know statistics.

10

Introduction to Hypothesis Testing

Having built the solid foundation of sampling distributions, we now turn to testing hypotheses. How do you make decisions in statistics? In this chapter, you will learn most of the basic language and steps in hypothesis testing, using the familiar statistic $z_{\bar{X}}$.

Research Example 10
10.1   Introduction
10.2   Overview: Integration of Probability, Sampling Distributions, and Decision Making
10.3   Rat Shipment Example
10.4 $z_{\bar{X}}$: Example of a Test Statistic
    Identify problem
    Formulate hypotheses
    Design and run the study
    Test hypotheses
    Draw conclusions
    Another research example
    Assumptions
10.5   Null and Alternative Hypotheses
    Null hypothesis
    Alternative hypothesis
10.6   Significance Level
10.7   Directional and Nondirectional Hypotheses
    Directional hypotheses
    Nondirectional hypotheses
    Example
10.8   One- and Two-Tailed Tests, Critical Values, Rejection Values, and Decision Rules
    One- and two-tailed tests
    Critical values
    Rejection values
    Decision rules using critical values
    Decision rules using p-values
    Examples
10.9   Logic of Hypothesis Testing
    Null hypothesis probabilities
    p-values and significance

Cannot *Prove*
Strength of rejection, or why you put what you believe in H$_1$
Why you use *Retain*
10.10   Summary, Study Tips, and Computation
Chapter summary
Study tips
Computation
Exercises

Research Example 10

The developers of standardized tests usually provide means and standard deviations that can be considered standards, or values for normal people. These standards are called *norms*. Researchers who use the standardized test can compare their sample statistics to these norms. Norms typically are computed for some large representative sample of people for whom the test was designed. Sometimes norms are computed separately for different groups of people, such as males and females and various age groups.

For the broad-spectrum personality test called the Eysenck Personality Profiler (EPP), a personnel selection company in England has been developing norms in an interesting way (Eysenck & Wilson, 1991). They can provide means and standard deviations for samples that are balanced with respect to major demographic variables, such as age, ratio of number of males to number of females, and socioeconomic status. That is, you can get means and standard deviations of parts of the EPP for a control sample that is much like the sample in your research, with the only difference being whatever important variable you are investigating. The obvious advantage of this approach to obtaining norms is that many extraneous demographic variables can be controlled.

For example, Marchant-Haycox and Wilson (1992) examined personality variables in performing artists. They used the EPP and had a norming group of 800 participants balanced for all the variables listed above. The performing artist sample included actors, dancers, musicians, and singers. The sample had about the same average age, same male/female ratio, and so on as the norming group.

One hypothesis of interest might be to ask whether any of these artist groups differ from the norms on various parts of the EPP. For example, compared to the norms, are dancers different on happiness, anxiety, or introversion? Table 10.1

Table 10.1
EPP Scores for dancers

	Norms				
Scale	*Mean*	*(SD)*	$\overline{X}$	$z_{\overline{X}}$	*Probability*
Unhappy/happy	32.31	(8.17)	22.92	-5.86	$p(z \leq z_{\overline{X}}) < .00003$
Anxiety/calm	29.58	(8.24)	21.03	-5.29	$p(z \leq z_{\overline{X}}) < .00003$
Introversion	19.15	(4.32)	19.79	0.75	$p(z \geq z_{\overline{X}}) = .2266$

Source: Marchant-Haycox and Wilson (1992).

shows these three of the 24 scales/subscales reported by Marchant-Haycox and Wilson for the dancers, including the norms (mean and standard deviation, *SD*), the means for the $N = 26$ dancers, the $z_{\bar{X}}$ values, and the probability.

The notation $p(z \geq z_{\bar{X}})$ means the probability of obtaining a z at least as extreme as the $z_{\bar{X}}$ in the fifth column. The small probabilities for the scales unhappy/happy and anxiety/calm indicate that the dancers studied by Marchant-Haycox and Wilson (1992) on the average differed significantly from the norms. You would reject a hypothesis that the mean value of the population of dancers sampled by Marchant-Haycox and Wilson is equal to the value given by the norms (Eysenck & Wilson, 1991).

For the introversion scale, the $\bar{X} = 19.79$ is closer to the value of the mean for the norms, 19.15, the $z_{\bar{X}}$ is closer to zero, and the probability is closer to .50. In this case, you would retain the hypothesis of equality of the population and the Eysenck and Wilson norm.

In this chapter, you will learn how to test hypotheses like these, using the statistic $z_{\bar{X}}$ and probability.

10.1 Introduction

Quick Quiz

What are the two major areas of statistics?

Answer

Descriptive statistics and inferential statistics.

We start this chapter with a Quick Quiz because we want you to recall the ideas of descriptive and inferential statistics. This chapter marks a move into the second area of statistics, inference. As you read in Chapter 1, data analysis involves examing and exploring data, depicting them with graphs, looking for patterns in the results, and computing statistics that summarize the scores. These are some aspects of **exploratory data analysis (EDA).** EDA is concerned with finding structure in the data. Data analysis also involves making decisions about the results. **Confirmatory data analysis (CDA)** revolves around the idea of what caused the structure—that is, what processes are occurring in the population. If you find a pattern of results in one study, you might conduct more studies to confirm it, look for causes, and test theories about the causes. In a confirmatory study, you still compute descriptive statistics and depict the data with pictures, but there's more. Consider an example.

> **Exploratory data analysis (EDA)**
> Exploring data to find structure

> **Confirmatory data analysis (CDA)**
> Confirming the process that caused the structure in the population

Suppose a friend who works at a family crisis center tells you she is appalled by the number of pregnant women who are beaten by their mates, and she shows you some numbers on pregnant and nonpregnant battered women. You explore her data to see whether pregnant women are more likely to become victims of family violence. You might notice a pattern of younger women being more likely than older women to be beaten. You think: The younger women also are the ones who get pregnant, so is my friend actually observing an age difference? You examine the data with many kinds of graphs, such as the ones you learned in Chapter 3, and you compute descriptive statistics. So far you have conducted EDA. Now you want to look for evidence of whether pregnant and nonpregnant women in the population are at equal risk of being beaten by a family member. You are entering the area of CDA. You might collect data from your state government's human services department to confirm whether pregnant women are more vulnerable to physical abuse than nonpregnant women, and whether younger women are more likely than older women to be victims of violence at home. You look beyond the data you have collected and make inferences to the population from which they came.

Research on violence and pregnancy has been done. Gelles (1988) concluded, "Although pregnant women are not a specially vulnerable group, pregnancy also does not insulate them from the high rates of violence experienced by young women." Whatever the results of a study you conduct in your state, you will encounter more new questions, requiring more data to be explored and more possible explanations to be confirmed. Gelles reported several ideas that could still be studied. He said victims of violence during pregnancy may be so outraged that they are more likely to volunteer for a study on spouse abuse. Gelles also said abusive men might change the frequency or severity of the attacks during pregnancy. "Of particular value would be longitudinal studies that could determine whether some husbands increase or decrease their violence when their wives become pregnant and the conditions under which such changes occur," he reported in the *Journal of Marriage and the Family*. This is an example of how scientific research is cyclical; one study's results turn up new, more precise questions to be answered.

Hypothesis testing
Process of testing tentative guesses about relationships between variables in populations

Central to confirmatory data analysis is **hypothesis testing.** Remember that a *hypothesis* is a testable guess or a tentative statement about the relationship between variables. When you test a hypothesis, you decide whether your data support the tentative statement or contradict it. A hypothesis about violence against pregnant women could be: "The rate of violence against pregnant women is equal to the rate of violence against nonpregnant women." The data you collect in your confirmatory study will be used to decide whether to hang onto that idea or throw it out in favor of a better explanation.

10.2   Overview: Integration of Probability, Sampling Distributions, and Decision Making

Chapter 9 emphasized the importance of sampling distributions. Think about the core idea: *With sampling distributions of statistics you can find probabilities of obtained statistics and you can make decisions about parameters.*

That sentence says a lot, and you need to have its meaning locked into your working knowledge of statistics. If you can explain that statement to a classmate, hypothesis testing will make more sense to you. Before you learn the steps of hypothesis testing, go through the following logic underlying the need for sampling distributions:

1. You want to make decisions about a population and its parameters, but they are usually unknown.

2. You can obtain a sample from the population and you can compute statistics as estimates of parameters. But statistics have variability, so you cannot say your statistic equals the unobtainable parameter.

3. Sampling distributions take into account the variability of statistics. You find the probability of a statistic, such as $\overline{X}$, by referring it to its sampling distribution. You use its probability to make a decision about the parameter it estimates.

Here's an example. In the population, do people with high blood pressure, or hypertension, perform as well as people with normal blood pressure on tests of memory and learning? You could run a study like Blumenthal, Madden, Pierce, Siegel, and Appelbaum (1993) and compute the average time for hypertensives to process information on a computer screen. Perhaps you know the average time for people with normal blood pressure on this task, as if it were a norm. Let the following be your hypothesis, or the idea you will test: If hypertensives are similar to people with normal blood pressure when it comes to mental processing time, then the average time for hypertensives should be similar to the norm.

If the $\overline{X}$ for hypertensives is close to the norm for people with normal blood pressure, then it is probable that the hypertensives are similar to the average people on this task. If the hypertensives' $\overline{X}$ is not close to the norm, then it may be unlikely or have a low probability when compared with the norm. In that case, you might conclude that there is a difference between hypertensives and people with normal blood pressure. You know there is variability in the $\overline{X}$ for the hypertensive group. If you allow for some range of values around $\overline{X}$, does that range overlap the norm? If so, maybe there's no real difference between the mental processing speeds of hypertensives and others. Maybe it's a chance result, and the average for another group of hypertensives would be on the reverse side of the norm in another study.

You use a theoretical reference distribution to find a probability statement about your statistic. Look back at your hypothesis:

1. *If hypertensives are similar to people with normal blood pressure . . .* You might compare your hypertensive $\overline{X}$ with a value of μ, or the average time for the population with normal blood pressure.

2. *. . . the average time for hypertensives should be similar to the norm for people with normal blood pressure.* Is your $\overline{X}$ for hypertensives close to μ? What is the probability of your $\overline{X}$ in the sampling distribution of $\overline{X}$? If your $\overline{X}$ is a highly likely outcome and it has a high probability, you would decide that your results support the idea that hypertensives are like people with normal blood pressure. In this case, *you will retain your hypothesis.* However, if your $\overline{X}$ has a small probability, it is unlike the average for people with normal blood pressure, and your results do not support the idea that hypertensives and others are alike. In that case, *you will reject your hypothesis.* You will draw a conclusion about μ based on your statistic and its probability.

In this chapter, you will learn the steps of hypothesis testing by using a simple statistic from Chapter 9, $z_{\overline{X}}$. In practical research, this statistic is almost never used because the only research for which you would have μ and σ^2 involves standardized tests. But its simplicity makes $z_{\overline{X}}$ a perfect teaching tool. Once you have learned the process of hypothesis testing with this statistic, you can apply the same steps to more complex and realistic statistical procedures.

Quick Quiz

Ornish and colleagues (1990) studied the effects of life-style changes on heart disease (see Chapter 1). The experimental group followed a regimen of moderate exercise, stress reduction, and reduced fat intake, while the control group followed a normally recommended diet plan for controlling heart disease. The experimental group reduced its total cholesterol level by 55 mg/dL, and the control group had a reduction of 13 mg/dL. If the two ways of treating heart disease are the same, the probability of this outcome is .0192. Given that this is a small probability, what conclusion would you draw?

Answer

A large probability would be about .5, meaning the two groups aren't different. But .0192 is a small probability, leading you to doubt the idea that the two methods of treating heart disease are the same.

10.3   Rat Shipment Example

Read this story. We know it's unrealistic, but it is designed to illustrate what you will learn in this chapter.

> Dr. Why, an animal learning psychologist, uses in his research the Sprague-Dawley strain of the albino rat, usually purchased from Sci Supply Co. in Chicago. One day in January, Dr. Why's graduate assistant reported that the last shipment of 600 rats seemed to behave differently from those in previous shipments, and she asked her mentor to examine the rats. Dr. Why closely scrutinized the behavior of the rodents for several minutes and then declared that he, too, suspected something was wrong. He speculated that the rats had some illness, had been left in the cold too long on some loading dock in Illinois, or had been dropped in the process of shipping. Dr. Why began to think of how to persuade Sci Supply that the rats were defective and needed to be replaced with another shipment. Dr. Why had vast reserves of data on usual rats. For years he had been following standard procedures for running rats in straight-alley mazes after they had undergone standard food deprivation. Dr. Why knew that once the rats were acquainted with the maze and reward, they would run the 138 cm from the start gate to the photoelectric cell in the goal box in an average of 33 s with a standard deviation of 19 s. That is, $\mu = 33$ and $\sigma = 19$. If the shipment of rats did indeed have something wrong with them, then they would not run the same maze with a 33-s average. He could have decided to run all of the rats and get the average value of run time. However, Dr. Why had a considerable amount of money invested in the rats. If he trained all of them in the maze, they no longer could be used in experiments where they had to be naive about the maze. So he randomly selected a sample of $N = 25$ rats and instructed his graduate assistant to run the sample of rats and record their run times. All of the procedures they used were consistent with standards approved by a local board established to ensure fair treatment of animals and humans in research. After a few days of acquainting the rats with the food and the goal box, the graduate student completed the experiment and brought the result of $\overline{X} = 44.4$ to Dr. Why for further statistical work. Realizing that he would have to rely on his knowledge of the sampling distribution of $\overline{X}$ and the Central Limit Theorem to use the normal distribution, Dr. Why computed

$$z_{\overline{X}} = \frac{\overline{X} - \mu}{\sigma/\sqrt{N}} = \frac{44.4 - 33}{19/\sqrt{25}} = 3.00$$

Now, because $p(z_{\overline{X}} \geq 3.00) = .0013$ (from Table A.2) is a fairly low probability (see Figure 10.1), Dr. Why realized that the rats most likely did not come from

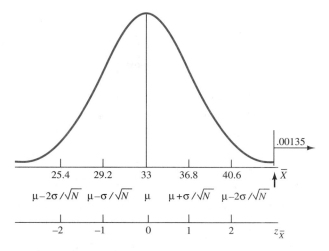

† Indicates an $\overline{X}$ of 44.4, which has $z_{\overline{X}} = 3.00$; $p\ (\overline{X} \geq 44.4) = p\ (z_{\overline{X}} \geq 3.00) = .00135$

Figure 10.1
Sampling distributions for $\overline{X}$ and $z_{\overline{X}}$ for rat shipment data ($\mu = 33$, $\sigma = 19$, $N = 25$, $\overline{X} = 44.4$, $\sigma/\sqrt{N} = 3.8$)

the population that he typically used (the population of healthy rats). It was more likely that they came from a population of rats that had something wrong with them. Armed with this information, he called the shipping company and Sci Supply and asked them to exchange the rats for another shipment at no charge. With the information that Dr. Why was able to present, the companies complied with his request.

In Chapters 1 and 8 we tossed a coin 10 times and got 10 heads. This had a probability of 1/1024 or .0009766 of occurring by chance alone if the coin was fair, and we decided to doubt the fairness of the coin because getting ten heads in a row was so unlikely. What we really did was perform a coin-tossing experiment to test the hypothesis that the coin was fair. We obtained a small probability of the result happening by chance alone if the coin were fair, so we doubted that the hypothesis was true.

How did Dr. Why reach the conclusion that the rats most likely did not come from the population of healthy rats? The probability obtained is the probability of the result occurring by chance alone *if* the rats are healthy, or if $\mu = 33$. A small probability may indicate that something other than chance alone is operating. In this example, the small probability indicates that the rats probably did not come from the healthy population, and sampling from some other population of rats (sick rats?) is more likely. You doubt the "if" part of the statement—"*if* the rats are healthy." The small probability did not cause you to doubt that $\mu = 33$ for the population of healthy rats but to doubt that $\mu = 33$ for the *sampled population*. Dr. Why hypothesized that the population was healthy, when he believed it to be otherwise, in order to test $\mu = 33$ and "the population is healthy rats."

Let's touch base with reality. Dr. Why really could not know the population parameters necessary to use $z_{\overline{X}}$. As you learned in Chaper 9 $z_{\overline{X}}$ is useful for standardized tests where μ and σ^2 can be given as norms.

At this point, you should have a good intuitive feel for how probability is used to make decisions. If you can complete the following two exercises, proceed to the next section; if not, go back to Chapter 1, review Section 1.6, return to the first part of this chapter, and reread this point:

1. Explain why you decide to doubt the "if" part of a statement when you get a small probability.
2. Explain why you decide not to doubt the "if" part of a statement when you get a large probability.

Quick Quiz

Suppose Dr. Why received the new shipment of rats and he wanted to check whether they were healthy. His graduate student sampled $N = 25$ from the 600 new rats, deprived them of food for the standard time, and measured their running speed through the same straight-alley maze. The student and Dr. Why computed $z_{\bar{X}} = 0.25$, which has a probability of .4013. (a) What hypothesis do they want to test? (b) Given that .4013 is a large probability, what conclusion can they draw about the new shipment?

Answers

(a) If the rats come from a population of healthy rats, then the average running speed in the population is $\mu = 33$. (b) Because the probability is large, they do not doubt the "if" part of the hypothesis. The results support the idea that the rats are healthy.

10.4 $z_{\bar{X}}$: Example of a Test Statistic

Let's go back through the rat shipment example and look at each step of using $z_{\bar{X}}$ as a statistical procedure. The steps of scientific methods given in Section 2.2 are used as a basic framework. Before you start, the term *test statistic,* which is in the title of this section, needs to be defined. Many statistics, such as $\bar{X}$ and s^2, can be used to describe data or to estimate a parameter. Other statistics are used only for testing hypotheses; these are **test statistics,** and $z_{\bar{X}}$ is an example. The statistic $z_{\bar{X}}$ isn't used to describe sample data or to estimate any parameter; it is used only to test hypotheses. The new statistics you learn in subsequent chapters are test statistics.

Test statistic
A statistic used only for the purposes of testing hypotheses

Identify Problem

The first step in the procedure is to decide what question is being asked by the scientist. That is, what is the general situation of the research question? This step allows you to decide on the hypothesis to be tested and to choose the appropriate statistical procedure. In the rat shipment example, the general question is whether the sampled population is the same as the healthy population of rats. The population mean is one characteristic of the population that is known to the researcher. The researcher has one sample and the sample mean, which point to a general situation typified by (1) a one-sample problem and (2) a hypothesis about the mean of a sampled population equaling a known population mean.

Formulate Hypotheses

Next, determine the general question of the research situation, sometimes called the *scientific hypothesis* or *research hypothesis.* The scientific hypothesis is a general verbal statement or question about the research problem. In the rat shipment example, Dr. Why's scientific hypothesis would be "I believe something is wrong with the rats." The hypothesis stated in terms of parameters to be tested is sometimes called the *statistical hypothesis*. In this case, the statistical hypothesis to be tested is $\mu = 33$, based on Dr. Why's knowledge. For the one-sample case to be realistic, this hypothesized value of μ should come from experience, previous research results, some theory associated with the experiment, or most likely norms of a standardized test. If the rats are from the population of healthy rats, then you would expect $\overline{X}$ from the sample to be fairly close to 33. If the rats are from some other population, then you would expect $\overline{X}$ to deviate considerably from 33.

Design and Run the Study

To run the research, Dr. Why chose the sample size $N = 25$ and randomly sampled 25 rats from the shipment. Note that $N = 25$ is large enough to invoke the Central Limit Theorem. The assistant took several days to acquaint the rats with the food and the goal box, deprived the rats of food for the standard time, ran each rat through the maze, and recorded each rat's time from start to goal. Recording the time for the rats was the data collection phase.

Test Hypotheses

The computation of $\overline{X}$ began the data analysis/hypothesis testing part of the research. The researchers knew from the outset of the study that they had one sample, they knew some parameters, and they were interested in comparing a sample mean to a population mean. The fact that the problem had one sample and dealt with the population mean told the researchers that they needed to compute $\overline{X}$. With σ^2 known, the test statistic was $z_{\overline{X}}$. The use of $z_{\overline{X}}$ requires the following:

1. One sample
2. Knowledge of μ and σ^2
3. Interest in testing a hypothesis about a single population mean

Computing $z_{\overline{X}} = 3.00$ and using the standard normal distribution (Table A.2) to get the probability associated with $z_{\overline{X}} \geq 3.00$ yielded a decision against the hypothesis of $\mu = 33$.

Draw Conclusions

A decision against $\mu = 33$ is the same as deciding that the population of healthy rats is not the population sampled. The conclusion was that there was something wrong with the rats and that appropriate action should be taken by the shipping company and the rat supplier.

Another Research Example

To make sure you know the basics of the $z_{\overline{X}}$ test, we present the following data on locus of control from Coggins (1984) for sixth-grade normally achieving boys. Locus of control is the extent to which people believe they control their own destiny, or the source of their reinforcement. If people see themselves as being in control of their lives, and reinforcement as the consequence of their own actions or characteristics, then they

Table 10.2

Locus of control scores for sixth-grade normally achieving boys

8	14	18	7	11	6	6	9	7	13
15	12	7	5	11	8	11	18	11	

Hypothesized population mean $\mu = 13.73$
Population standard deviation $\sigma = 5.16$
(from Nowicki & Strickland, 1973)

$N = 19 \qquad \Sigma X = 197$

$$\overline{X} = \frac{197}{19} = 10.37$$

$$z_{\overline{X}} = \frac{10.37 - 13.73}{5.16/\sqrt{19}} = -2.84$$

$\text{Prob}(z_{\overline{X}} \leq -2.84) = .0023 \quad \text{(from Table A.2)}$

Source: Coggins (1984).

are said to have an *internal* locus of control. If people see their lives as being controlled by chance, fate, or outside forces such as other people, then they are said to have an *external* locus of control (see Rotter, 1966). Internal and external loci of control are viewed as ends of a continuum, with individuals distributed along this continuum. Assume that locus of control scores are normally distributed.

We want to compare the performance of the sixth-grade boys to the norm provided by Nowicki and Strickland (1973). We test the hypothesis that the mean of the population sampled by Coggins is equal to the value of the norm (13.73) from Nowicki and Strickland. You should do the computations for this test and compare your answers with those in Table 10.2. Do you get $z_{\overline{X}} = -2.84$? Then use Table A.2 to find the probability of getting a value of $z_{\overline{X}}$ less than or equal to -2.84. This is the same as the probability of getting a value of $z_{\overline{X}}$ greater than or equal to 2.84. This probability is .0023. What is your decision? Would you reject the hypothesis that the population sampled by Coggins has a population mean of 13.73? Because .0023 is a very small probability, you should decide to reject this hypothesis. Figure 10.2 shows $\overline{X}$ and $z_{\overline{X}}$ and the associated probability.

The only snag that you should have hit is whether a probability of .0023 is considered small. This issue is dealt with in a later section, but for now it is sufficient for you to know that most behavioral scientists consider .0023 a small probability and would use it to decide against $\mu = 13.73$. You would conclude that the population mean of sixth-grade normally achieving boys sampled by Coggins is different from the specified $\mu = 13.73$ and that these boys may be considered significantly different in locus of control when compared to those measured in 1973 by Nowicki and Strickland.

Assumptions

Any statistical procedure used to test hypotheses is based on certain assumptions. **Assumptions** are:

Assumptions
Conditions placed on a test statistic necessary for its valid use in hypothesis testing

1. Statements about the population or the sampled data
2. Necessary for the validity of the statistical test (without the assumption you would

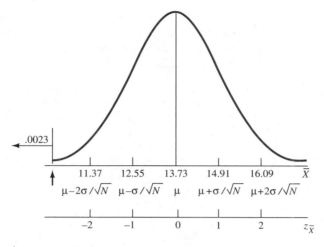

† Indicates an $\overline{X}$ of 10.37, which has $z_{\overline{X}} = -2.84$; $p\,(\overline{X} \leq 10.37) = p\,(z_{\overline{X}} \leq -2.84) = .0023$

Figure 10.2
Sampling distributions for $\overline{X}$ and $z_{\overline{X}}$ for locus of control scores ($\mu = 13.73$, $\sigma = 5.16$, $N = 19$, $\overline{X} = 10.37$, $\sigma/\sqrt{N} = 1.18$)

---

not be able to know the distribution of the statistic and therefore you could not compute the necessary probabilities)
3. Not associated with the hypotheses (for example, if the hypothesis is about μ, the assumptions won't be about μ)
4. Assumed true regardless of the outcome of the decision (for example, you assume normality of a population regardless of whether the statistical hypothesis is rejected).

To use $z_{\overline{X}}$, you assume that the population sampled is *normal* in shape and that the observations sampled are independent. *Independence* of observations is usually tied to random sampling, so essentially random sampling is assumed. These two assumptions make the test using $z_{\overline{X}}$ valid; without them, $z_{\overline{X}}$ is not normally distributed and you cannot compute probabilities. However, you know from previous discussions about random sampling that judgment sampling will suffice if you judge your sample to be as it would be if it were random. Also, you know from the discussion of the Central Limit Theorem that $\overline{X}$ is approximately normally distributed for large enough N (sample size) and population distributions that are not unusual, so $z_{\overline{X}}$ is also approximately normally distributed.

Students usually ask, If we can compute $z_{\overline{X}}$ and use the normal distribution to get probabilities even when one of the assumptions is not met, then why even make the assumptions? Two reasons may be given. First, the assumptions are needed for the strict validity of $z_{\overline{X}}$ so you know that $z_{\overline{X}}$ is normally distributed; second, for some tests you may not compute probabilities unless the normality assumption (or some other assumption) is exactly met. We give the assumptions for every test you learn and tell whether the assumption must be met. The assumption of independence of observations is usually met unless obvious dependency is present. For example, the independence assumption would be violated if you sampled one subject twice, if you sampled subjects who had worked together on the dependent variable so their scores were highly related, and so on. The assumption of normality of the population distribution is usually not met, but the Central Limit Theorem allows you to proceed as if $\overline{X}$ is normally distributed, which ensures that $z_{\overline{X}}$ is normally distributed.

Quick Quiz

Suppose you suspect that dancers have a different level of introversion than nondancers who are otherwise similar. You read about the Marchant-Haycox and Wilson (1992) article discussed in Research Example 10. You find that on an introversion scale, where a high score means greater introversion, the 26 dancers in the sample have an average introversion score of 19.79. The article gives norms of $\mu = 19.15$ and $\sigma^2 = 18.6624$. (a) What hypothesis will you test? (b) Why is $z_{\overline{X}}$ the appropriate statistic to compute? (c) Compute $z_{\overline{X}}$. (d) If the probability of your statistic is $p = .2266$, what does that mean about your statistic? About your hypothesis?

Answers

(a) The population average introversion score for dancers is 19.15. (b) You have one sample and you know μ and σ^2. (c) You should get approximately $z_{\overline{X}} = 0.75$. (Notice that you are given a variance, σ^2, so you have to take the square root and find σ. Then you have to divide σ by $\sqrt{26}$ to get the denominator of the statistic.) (d) The $p = .2266$ is the probability of finding a statistic this extreme or more extreme than $z_{\overline{X}} = 0.75$. It is a large probability, so the dancers' average introversion score is not significantly different from the normal introversion score.

10.5   Null and Alternative Hypotheses

In this chapter, the biggest hurdle to overcome is the language that surrounds hypothesis testing. New terms and operation must be learned, but they are based on using probability to make decisions, which should be part of your statistics vocabulary by now. If you are uncertain about the use of probability, review the examples in Chapter 8.

This section elborates on hypotheses, the logic of a statistical test, and other components of hypothesis testing. Statistical hypotheses may be about population parameters or about the population distribution itself. Hypotheses are never stated in terms of sample statistics because these sample characteristics are not hypothetical but will be known values after the research is conducted.

Null Hypothesis

Null hypothesis
Hypothesis that is tested, symbolized by H_0

Any statistical test involves a pair of hypotheses. One member of this pair is called the **null hypothesis,** which is the hypothesis that is tested. Therefore, it must be stated so that it can be tested. For example, you have to be able to measure the dependent variable mentioned or implied by the null hypothesis. The null hypothesis is symbolized by H_0 (which some people pronounce as "H-oh," while others say "H-naught") and is a statement about parameters that is usually the opposite of the belief of the researcher. Among many plausible competing hypotheses, H_0 is the one that contains the argument that the results occurred by chance through the fluctuations of sampling (Cook & Campbell, 1979). You tentatively hold H_0 to be true until the statistical test brings evidence that lets you decide against it or for it. (Remember the fair coin example? The null hypothesis was: The coin is fair. This idea was tested by flipping the coin several times to find the proportion of heads.)

Any actions or decisions that result from the statistical test are expressed in terms of H_0. If the decision is against H_0, you say that you *reject* H_0. In the rat shipment example, the decision was against H_0: $\mu = 33$, so you say that you *reject* H_0: $\mu = 33$. If the decision is in favor of H_0, you say that you *retain, accept, tentatively accept,* or *fail to reject* H_0. We use the first phrase, *retain,* to indicate a decision in favor of H_0. Some of the other phrases make too strong a statement about your belief in H_0. *Fail to reject* is a bit clumsy, but it does give an accurate presentation of what you do. Retaining H_0 implies that you don't have enough information to reject it. Traditionally H_0 derives its name from the two-sample situation in which a hypothesis of no (null) differences is usually tested.

Here's an analogy to show why you test the H_0. Pretend that you have lost your keys. In your search for them, you might adopt a strategy to look for them in places you don't expect to find them, just to eliminate those places from consideration. You don't think they are on the top of the dresser, but you look there anyway to eliminate the dresser as a place the keys might be. In a similar way, you test the null hypothesis to eliminate it as a possible explanation for the phenomenon observed in your data.

Alternative Hypothesis

Alternative hypothesis
Hypothesis that expresses the researcher's belief, symbolized by H_1

Statistical tests involve the comparison of two hypotheses, so every null hypothesis has its corresponding **alternative hypothesis,** symbolized by H_1. You do not test H_1. Because it is the complement of H_0, H_1 usually expresses your belief about the parameter. Within each pair of hypotheses, the set of potential values of the parameter to be tested is usually all possible numbers. Only one of these hypotheses could be true. For example, if the null hypothesis is given as H_0: $\mu = 33$, then the alternative is usually given as H_1: $\mu \neq 33$, so the pair of hypotheses is:

$$H_0: \mu = 33 \qquad H_1: \mu \neq 33 \tag{10.1}$$

The scientific hypothesis that accompanies formula 10.1 is that the rats have something wrong with them. The scientific hypothesis usually agrees with the statistical alternative hypothesis. The statistical hypotheses in formula 10.1 reflect the scientific hypothesis in terms of the average time for healthy rats to run a straight-alley maze, 33 s. This alternative is stated so that the test will detect deviant values of the sample mean in either direction from the population mean. After all, the example didn't say Dr. Why thought the rats looked sluggish or jumpy. Values of $\overline{X}$ that are much larger or much smaller than 33 will lead us to reject the null hypothesis.

Quick Quiz
Look back at the last Quick Quiz. (a) Determine H_0 and H_1 for that scenario. (b) Which hypothesis reflects what you believe? (c) What decision would you make about the null hypothesis?

Answers

(a) H_0: $\mu = 19.15$ and H_1: $\mu \neq 19.15$. (b) The alternative hypothesis reflects your belief that dancers have a different level of introversion. (c) The statistic computed earlier would lead you to *retain* the null hypothesis. The statistic does not support the idea that the average introversion score for dancers is different from the norm.

10.6   Significance Level

In this one-sample case for hypotheses about μ, you have seen that if $\bar{X}$ deviates extremely from the value hypothesized for μ in H_0, then you reject H_0. You ask whether $\bar{X}$ is an unusual value and examine the tail probability of $z_{\bar{X}}$ to see whether it is small. In the rat shipment example, $p(z_{\bar{X}} \geq 3.00) = .0013$, so you rejected H_0: $\mu = 33$. If $\bar{X}$ is close to the value hypothesized for μ in H_0, then the tail probability of $z_{\bar{X}}$ is not small and you retain H_0. The question you should ask now is: How do you define "small" regarding the probability used to reject or retain the null hypothesis? The answers require more new vocabulary.

Significance level

The small probability used in hypothesis testing to determine an unusual event that leads you to reject H_0, symbolized by α

1. The small probability value that determines an unusual event is called the **significance level** and is symbolized by α (pronounced "alpha").
2. The value of α may be determined arbitrarily by the researcher, but it is usually set at $\alpha = .05$ or $\alpha = .01$ in the behavioral sciences. If you choose $\alpha = .05$, then you are willing to risk making a wrong decision about 5 times out of 100. (More on errors is given in Chapter 11.)
3. The value of α is chosen before the experiment is performed.
4. If H_0 is rejected with $\alpha = .05$, you say, "H_0 is rejected at the 5% level of significance," or "The result is significant at the .05 level," or "$p < .05$." The terminology varies considerably, depending on the publishing source and the author's style of reporting results.

You might ask about point 2: Why is α usually set at .05 or .01? We would answer, along with Tevya from *Fiddler on the Roof,* Tradition! The tradition of publishing practices, which includes journal editoral practices, has led to these values for α. The value of α has been chosen to be low because true scientists don't want to fill the pages of journals with results that have occurred by chance alone. Because of publishing traditions, researchers actually have little control over the value of α. When a statistic has a probability smaller than α, you can say that the results are *significant,* or you reject H_0. In the case of $z_{\bar{X}}$, a significant result means that the sample mean deviates significantly from the hypothesized μ.

Quick Quiz

In an earlier Quick Quiz, you read that $z_{\bar{X}}$ for dancers' introversion was 0.75, which had a probability of $p = .2266$. Is $p = .2266$ the same as the significance level?

       Answer

No, $p = .2266$ is the probability of obtaining a statistic equal to or more extreme than $z_{\bar{X}} = 0.75$, given the μ hypothesized in H_0. The significance level is chosen before the research is done; for this study, it was $\alpha = .05$.

10.7   Directional and Nondirectional Hypotheses

Suppose Dr. Why thought the new rats seemed sluggish. He believed the rats would take more time to run the straight-alley maze than healthy rats. Because Dr. Why is an expert and knows a sluggish rat when he sees one, he wouldn't need to account for the possibility that the rats might be faster than healthy rats. The only question he would have to answer is whether the new rats are *significantly* slower than healthy rats.

In the original scenario, Dr. Why thought the rats were different from healthy rats, which is represented by this pair of hypotheses:

$$H_0: \mu = 33 \qquad H_1: \mu \neq 33$$

Now, if Dr. Why believes the rats are slower than normal and will have longer running times than healthy rats, the scientific hypothesis has changed and so must the statistical hypotheses. They are:

$$H_0: \mu \leq 33 \qquad H_1: \mu > 33 \tag{10.2}$$

Dr. Why puts what he believes in H_1, and the alternative is stated so that the test will detect deviant values of the sample mean only in the direction predicted by the scientific hypothesis. Everything else goes into the null hypothesis. You still use the value given in H_0 as the μ in the formula for $z_{\bar{x}}$.

As another example, think back to Research Example 9, where the researchers suspected that the differences between English and American Sign Language would mean that deaf children would have lower IQ scores than hearing children. The statistical hypotheses are:

$$H_0: \mu \geq 100 \qquad H_1: \mu < 100 \tag{10.3}$$

These statistical hypotheses reflect the scientific hypothesis in terms of the scale of the IQ test and its mean, 100. The alternative is stated so that the test will detect deviant values of the sample mean only in the direction predicted by the scientific hypothesis. Lower IQ scores are indicated by the alternative $<$, or "less than."

Directional Hypotheses

Directional hypotheses
Hypotheses that specify a particular direction for values of the parameter

The pairs of hypotheses in formulas 10.2 and 10.3 are examples of directional hypotheses. **Directional hypotheses** specify direction, greater than or less than, by the use of an inequality sign. The language of the scientific hypothesis indicates the type of statistical hypothesis to be used. Directional hypotheses are implied by words such as *less than, better than, smaller than, increased, decreased, declined.* Both H_0 and H_1 are directional hypotheses in formulas 10.2 and 10.3. The equal sign is always used in H_0, which gives you a specific value of the parameter to use in your test.

Nondirectional Hypotheses

Nondirectional hypothesis
Hypothesis that does not specify a particular direction for values of the parameter

The first hypotheses introduced in this chapter were nondirectional hypotheses. A **nondirectional hypothesis** does not specify a particular direction for the values of the parameter but allows for results in either direction, greater than or less than the parameter. This lack of a particular direction is specified in H_1 by the use of a negated equal sign. It is indicated by words such as *not equal to, different from,* or *not the same as* in the scientific hypothesis.

Example

We have used the rat shipment example to illustrate the directional and nondirectional hypotheses. In a real-life situation, researchers must choose between a directional and a nondirectional alternative hypothesis. Although initially it might appear to make no difference which type of H_1 is chosen, the selection is important. Because directional hypotheses specify direction, an incorrect choice of the direction could lead to an inability to reject H_0 even when a low probability is found. In the rat shipment example, the average running time for the rats in the sample was 44.4 s. If $H_1: \mu < 33$ was selected, you would not be able to reject $H_0: \mu \geq 33$ because the result of $\overline{X} = 44.4$ would be in favor of H_0. The directional sign in $H_1: \mu < 33$ points toward the lower tail to the left of $\mu = 33$, so in order to reject the null hypothesis, the results must be in the lower tail.

Behavioral scientists choose directional hypotheses only when they feel quite strongly that the results will be in a particular direction. The ability to predict direction is related to the amount and quality of knowledge in the research area. People who are just beginning to research a certain area are well advised to use nondirectional hypotheses unless the theories investigated give overwhelming indications of directionality.

Quick Quiz

Are musicians happier than nonmusicians? This is one of the questions that can be answered with data from the Marchant-Haycox and Wilson (1992) article in Research Example 10. Suppose you believe musicians are happier than nonmusicians. The norms on the happiness scale in the article are $\mu = 32.31$ and $\sigma = 8.17$, where a high score means greater happiness. The 65 musicians in the study had a mean of 27.14. (a) Reread this scenario and write your statistical hypotheses. (b) Compute $z_{\overline{X}}$. (c) *Without any further work such as finding probabilities,* you should be able to make your decision about H_0. What is it?

Answers

(a) $H_0: \mu \leq 32.31$ and $H_1: \mu > 32.31$. (b) $z_{\overline{X}} = -5.10$. (c) You must retain H_0 because you predicted greater happiness for musicians, but your statistic is in the opposite direction.

10.8   One- and Two-Tailed Tests, Critical Values, Rejection Values, and Decision Rules

One- and Two-Tailed Tests

Suppose you are conducting a locus of control study with sixth-grade boys, similar to the study by Nowicki and Strickland (1973) discussed in Section 10.4. You decide to use a significance level of $\alpha = .05$. You aren't sure whether those boys have internal or external locus of control, so you use a nondirectional hypothesis. Suppose the norm you are using is $\mu = 13.73$, so your hypotheses are:

$$H_0: \mu = 13.73 \qquad H_1: \mu \neq 13.73$$

If $\alpha = .05$, where in the sampling distribution of $z_{\overline{X}}$ will you put the probability of α?

In Chapter 9, you practiced drawing distributions and the mean and the observed value of your statistic, and you found the probability of your statistic. This time, you already know a probability: α, the significance level. Remember that α defines "small" and is the standard probability that will appear in any picture you draw of a sampling distribution. With a nondirectional hypothesis, you need to provide for outcomes in either tail of the distribution. So we split α into two parts (usually equal parts) and put one part in each tail. If $\alpha = .05$, each tail contains $\alpha/2 = .025$. If both tails of the distribution are used, this is a **two-tailed test.** If you put all of the α in one tail, as Dr. Why would have done when he was sure the rats were sluggish, it is a **one-tailed test.**

One- and two-tailed tests
Statistical tests that use only one tail or two tails, respectively, of the sampling distribution of the test statistic

It is easy to confuse this concept and the concept of directionality. Directionality is a characteristic or label of hypotheses, and "tailedness" is a property of the sampling distribution or of a statistical test. You can talk about a directional hypothesis or a one-tailed test, but *not* about a one-tailed hypothesis or a directional test. A directional hypothesis always leads to a one-tailed test, but a nondirectional hypothesis can yield a two-tailed test or a one-tailed test, depending on the theoretical distribution used. Review the example given in Table 10.2 and decide on the type of alternative hypothesis (directional or nondirectional) and the type of test (one- or two-tailed). The answers are given in the next section.

Critical Values

In the locus of control study, where the alternative hypothesis is nondirectional, we are concerned about deviant values of $\overline{X}$ that are either larger or smaller than the specified value of μ. You are interested in knowing whether a value of $\overline{X}$ smaller or larger than 13.73 is unusual in terms of probability. You place one-half of α in each tail of the distribution. If $\alpha = .05$, then you would place $\alpha/2 = .025$ in each tail of the sampling distribution of $z_{\overline{X}}$. You would do this before computing the statistic, thus allowing you to reject H_0 if $\overline{X}$ were significantly smaller or larger than the value of μ specified by H_0. In Figure 10.3 this nondirectional hypothesis results in a two-tailed test.

You want to know the value of $z_{\overline{X}}$ that will cut off $\alpha/2$ in each tail. Then you can run your study, calculate your statistic, and ask, Is my statistic out there in the tail? If so, you can reject H_0. For the standard normal distribution, Table A.2 gives the values that cut off .025 in each tail of the distribution as $z = -1.96$ and $z = 1.96$. The z values of -1.96 and 1.96 are called **critical values** of $z_{\overline{X}}$ because they are critical to the decision you make about H_0. If $\alpha = .01$, then you would put $\alpha/2 = .005$ in each tail and find $z = -2.58$ and $z = 2.58$ as the critical values.

Critical values
Values that cut off α or $\alpha/2$ in the tail(s) of the theoretical reference distribution; these values are critical to the decision to reject or retain H_0

If your hypotheses are like those in formula 10.2 or 10.3, where the alternative hypothesis is directional, then you are concerned about deviant values of $\overline{X}$ in only one direction. In the rat shipment example, if the alternative hypothesis were given as $H_1: \mu > 33$, then you would look for only deviant values of $\overline{X}$ that are larger than $\mu = 33$. You would be interested in knowing whether any larger value was unusual in terms of probability and would place all α in the upper tail of the distribution. If $\alpha = .05$, then you would put .05 in the upper tail of the sampling distribution of $z_{\overline{X}}$ and use Table A.2 to find $z = 1.645$ as the critical value. The directional sign in the *alternative* hypothesis points toward the tail in which you'll put α. Because you do this before the statistic is computed, you can reject H_0 only if $\overline{X}$ is significantly larger than the value of μ specified by H_0. This directional hypothesis gives you a one-tailed test (see Figure 10.3).

Similarly, for an alternative such as $H_1: \mu < 100$, you would look for only those values of $\overline{X}$ that are significantly smaller than $\mu = 100$. For $\alpha = .05$, you would put .05 in the lower tail of the sampling distribution of $z_{\overline{X}}$ and would reject H_0 only if $z_{\overline{X}}$ were less than some negative critical value (see the third distribution in Figure 10.3).

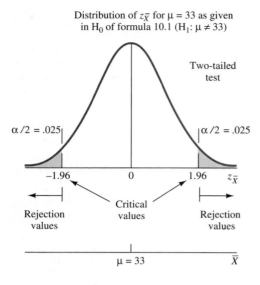

Distribution of $z_{\bar{X}}$ for $\mu = 33$ as given in H_0 of formula 10.1 (H_1: $\mu \neq 33$)

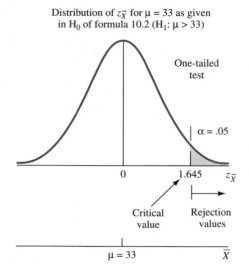

Distribution of $z_{\bar{X}}$ for $\mu = 33$ as given in H_0 of formula 10.2 (H_1: $\mu > 33$)

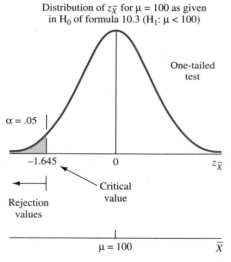

Distribution of $z_{\bar{X}}$ for $\mu = 100$ as given in H_0 of formula 10.3 (H_1: $\mu < 100$)

Figure 10.3
Critical values, rejection values, and probabilities

For the standard normal distribution, the upper-tail critical value of 1.645 cuts off $\alpha = .05$. For $\alpha = .01$, the upper-tail critical value is 2.33. For lower-tail tests, the signs change: The .05 critical value is -1.645 and the .01 critical value is -2.33.

Rejection Values

Many possible values of an observed statistic lead to rejecting H_0. If the critical $z_{\bar{X}}$ is -1.645, then -1.70, -2.12, or -1.645 are significant. In fact, any value of $z_{\bar{X}}$ that is equal to or more extreme than a critical value of -1.645 is significant and leads to

Rejection values
Values of the statistic, established by the critical values, that lead to rejection of H_0

rejection of H_0. The values of the statistic that are equal to or beyond the critical value are the **rejection values.** For two-tailed tests you have two sets of rejection values, but for one-tailed tests there is only one set of rejection values. Rejection values are values of the *statistic;* they are not expressed in terms of probability. For a two-tailed test using $z_{\overline{X}}$ with $\alpha = .05$, the rejection values are $z \leq -1.96$ and $z \geq 1.96$—that is, all z's less than or equal to -1.96 and all z's greater than or equal to 1.96. For a lower-tail test using $z_{\overline{X}}$ with $\alpha = .05$, the rejection values are $z \leq -1.645$. For an upper-tail test using $z_{\overline{X}}$ with $\alpha = .05$, the rejection values are $z \geq 1.645$. It is important not to confuse rejection values, which are values of $z_{\overline{X}}$, with α or $\alpha/2$, which are probabilities. Re-examine Figure 10.3, which shows the sampling distributions of $z_{\overline{X}}$ for the three different pairs of hypotheses given in formulas 10.1, 10.2, and 10.3, each using $\alpha = .05$. Find the critical values, rejection values, and α (or $\alpha/2$).

When you use directional hypotheses, make sure you locate the rejection values in agreement with the alternative hypothesis. Values of the statistic that coincide with rejection values are those statistics that favor the alternative hypothesis. So to find the rejection values for any statistical test, examine H_1 and locate the rejection values in the indicated tail or tails of the sampling distribution of $z_{\overline{X}}$.

Decision Rules Using Critical Values

Decision rules
Precise statements that tell you when to reject H_0

Now you have all the necessary language to understand the formal decision rules for testing hypotheses with $z_{\overline{X}}$. **Decision rules** are precise statements that tell you when a statistic will lead you to reject or retain H_0. They summarize what you have just learned. For a two-tailed test using $z_{\overline{X}}$, the decision rule is:

$$\text{If } z_{\overline{X}} \leq -z_{\text{crit}} \text{ or } z_{\overline{X}} \geq z_{\text{crit}}, \text{ reject } H_0; \text{ otherwise, retain } H_0 \qquad (10.4)$$

where z_{crit} is the critical value associated with $\alpha/2$ in the standard normal distribution. This decision is stated in terms of a general α value, so you can substitute any α you choose.

For a one-tailed test that uses the upper tail of the distribution of $z_{\overline{X}}$, the decision rule is:

$$\text{If } z_{\overline{X}} \geq z_{\text{crit}}, \text{ then reject } H_0; \text{ otherwise retain } H_0 \qquad (10.5)$$

where z_{crit} is the critical value associated with α from the standard normal distribution. The decision rule for a one-tailed test in the lower tail of the sampling distribution of $z_{\overline{X}}$ is:

$$\text{If } z_{\overline{X}} \leq -z_{\text{crit}}, \text{ then reject } H_0; \text{ otherwise, retain } H_0 \qquad (10.6)$$

where z_{crit} is the critical value associated with α from the standard normal distribution. You could summarize the decision rules for $z_{\overline{X}}$ this way: If the observed $z_{\overline{X}}$ is *more extreme* than the critical value, then reject H_0.

Decision Rules Using *p*-Values

p-value
Probability of the obtained statistic

Another way that researchers commonly test hypotheses is by using the **p-value,** the probability of the obtained statistic. Because the critical value for a *two-tailed test* cuts off $\alpha/2$ of each tail, you can compute the probability of the absolute value of the obtained statistic (sometimes called a *two-tailed p-value*) and compare that probability value, or *p*-value, to α. If the *p*-value is less than or equal to α, then you reject H_0; otherwise, you retain H_0. For a two-tailed test, the *p*-value decision rule is:

If $p \leq \alpha$, then reject H_0; otherwise, retain H_0 (10.7)

where $p = p(|z_{\bar{X}}| \geq |\text{obtained } z_{\bar{X}}| \mid H_0)$, a two-tailed *p*-value. The *p*-value is a conditional probability computed in the sampling distribution of the statistic as if H_0 were true. The absolute values in this probability statement are there to account for both tails of the sampling distribution in this two-tailed test. Remember, *probability* and *area* are synonymous. The obtained statistic is associated with a probability of an interval, the area cut off in the tail from the obtained statistic or more extreme. In the rat shipment example, the probability .0013 is the area for $z_{\bar{X}} = 3.00$ and more extreme, $p(z_{\bar{X}} \geq 3.00)$. So the two-tailed probability is twice .0013, or $p = .0026$.

Two different sources have influenced the increased use of *p*-value decision rules: computers and journals. Most common computer programs in statistical packages do not use critical values; instead, they calculate the probability of getting a value of the statistic as extreme or more extreme than the obtained value. Journal editoral practice that emphasizes terseness also has led to more use of the *p*-value. Because of these influences, when H_0 is rejected with $\alpha = .05$, journals report $p \leq .05$ or they give the actual *p*-value, such as $p = .043$. The critical value decision rules and *p*-value decision rules are equivalent in terms of the decision that is reached, so it does not matter which you use.

For a *one-tailed upper-tail test,* the decision rule in terms of a one-tailed *p*-value where $p = p(z_{\bar{X}} \geq \text{obtained } z_{\bar{X}} \mid H_0)$ is:

If $p \leq \alpha$, then reject H_0; otherwise, retain H_0 (10.8)

The same decision rule (formula 10.8) can be used for a *one-tailed lower-tail test,* where $p = p(z_{\bar{X}} \leq \text{obtained } z_{\bar{X}} \mid H_0)$.

In using *p*-value decision rules for one-tailed tests, you have to pay attention not only to the size of the one-tailed *p*-value but also to the tail where the observed $z_{\bar{X}}$ occurs. You reject H_0 only when the *p*-value is small enough *and* the $z_{\bar{X}}$ occurs in the tail of the sampling distribution predicted by H_1.

Before we present some examples where you can practice these decision rules, study the following steps, which you should use as you go through each example:

1. Draw a picture of the sampling distribution of the test statistic, $z_{\bar{X}}$, putting the mean at zero.
2. Write the hypotheses.
3. Decide whether the alternative hypothesis calls for a one-tailed or two-tailed test.
4. Draw the vertical line(s) for the critical value(s), shade and label the areas of α or $\alpha/2$, and look up the critical value(s).
5. Compute the statistic.
6. Draw an arrow pointing up the horizontal line for the obtained statistic.
7. Decide whether the obtained statistic is equal to or more extreme than the critical value.
8. Decide whether to reject or retain H_0.

Suppose a high school teacher has moved to a new school and is perplexed by the intelligence of the students in one of her classes. The topics that she introduces are usually met with silence. She can not decide whether the students are a bit lower than average in intelligence and therefore do not understand or are a bit higher than average in intelligence and therefore are bored. She gives them a quick-scoring form of an intelligence test to test whether they are of average IQ, which is 100 for this test. The test manual for the IQ test gives $\sigma^2 = 225$, and 25 students take the test. From the data in Table 10.3, help the teacher with this hypothesis-testing situation.

Why is $z_{\bar{X}}$ selected as the test statistic? Why is it a two-tailed test? What conclusion should the teacher draw about the intelligence of her students? Can she make a directional statement such as, They are higher than average in intelligence? This last question suggests a controversy about conclusions from nondirectional hypotheses (see Steger, 1971, chap. 4). Some people believe you can say only that the true μ is different from 100, whereas others believe you can state the directionality that appears in the data. Figure 10.4 illustrates this example using the eight steps outlined earlier.

In another fictitious situation, an army instructor in an artillery school wonders about the arithmetic literacy of his class. The students seem to have difficulty solving simple arithmetic problems that are part of the course material, so he thinks they have lower than average arithmetic skills. The instructor administers a test that the army has used often in the past. Then he seeks your help in this hypothesis-testing problem. The test booklet gives norms of $\mu = 70$ and $\sigma^2 = 81$ and tells you that scores other than whole numbers are typical because of a correction for guessing on some items. Nine students are in the class. The data and computations are shown in Table 10.4. Cover up the computations until you have finished your own work; then check.

Why is it a one-tailed test? Why is it a lower-tail test? Why is the alternative hypothesis $\mu < 70$? If you have problems with the negative numbers and the decision you reached, return to formula 10.6, review the decision rule there, and then look at the distribution drawn in Figure 10.5.

Table 10.3

IQ data and $z_{\bar{X}}$ test

104	112	114	116	109	107	111	114	106	104	105	113	114
117	111	112	109	108	104	116	117	103	104	115	105	

$\sigma^2 = 225 \qquad \sigma = 15 \qquad \alpha = .05$

$H_0: \mu = 100 \qquad H_1: \mu \neq 100$

Critical values: -1.96 and 1.96

$\Sigma X = 2750 \qquad N = 25$

$$\bar{X} = \frac{\Sigma X}{N} = \frac{2750}{25} = 110$$

$$z_{\bar{X}} = \frac{\bar{X} - \mu}{\sigma/\sqrt{N}} = \frac{110 - 100}{15/\sqrt{25}} = \frac{10}{15/\sqrt{5}} = \frac{10}{3} = 3.33$$

Because $z_{\bar{X}} = 3.33 > 1.96$, reject H_0 and conclude that there is a significant difference at $\alpha = .05$.

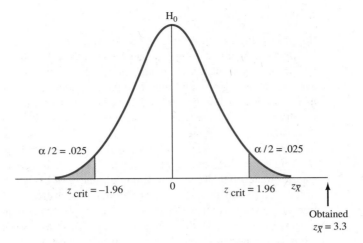

Figure 10.4
Sampling distribution of $z_{\bar{X}}$ and eight steps for the IQ data: (1) see picture; (2) H$_0$: $\mu = 100$, H$_1$: $\mu \neq 100$; (3) two-tailed test; (4) see picture; (5) $z_{\bar{X}} = 3.33$; (6) see picture; (7) more extreme; (8) reject H$_0$

Table 10.4
Arithmetic data and $z_{\bar{X}}$ test

60.1	64.2	70.4	66.0	65.1
68.3	67.1	67.5	63.5	

$\sigma^2 = 81 \qquad \sigma = 9 \qquad \alpha = .05$

$H_0: \mu \geq 70 \qquad H_1: \mu < 70$

Critical value: -1.645

$\Sigma X = 592.2 \qquad N = 9$

$\bar{X} = \dfrac{592.2}{9} = 65.8$

$z_{\bar{X}} = \dfrac{65.8 - 70}{9/\sqrt{9}} = \dfrac{-4.2}{9/3} = \dfrac{-4.2}{3} = -1.4$

Because $z_{\bar{X}} = -1.4 > -1.645$, retain H$_0$ and conclude that there is not a significant difference using $\alpha = .05$.

Quick Quiz
Let's say you believe actors have higher self-esteem than nonactors. You find norms of $\mu = 30.46$ and $\sigma = 8.13$ for a self-esteem scale, where higher scores mean higher self-esteem, and you set $\alpha = .05$. You give the self-esteem quiz to 33 actors and compute $\bar{X} = 26.18$. (a) Write the statistical hypotheses. (b) Draw a picture of the distribution of $z_{\bar{X}}$ and determine where to put α. (c) Find the critical value(s) that cut(s) off α. (d) Calculate $z_{\bar{X}}$. (e) From Table

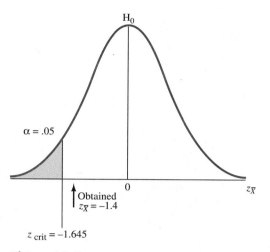

Figure 10.5
Sampling distribution of $z_{\bar{X}}$ and eight steps for the arithmetic data: (1) see picture;
(2) H_0: $\mu \geq 70$, H_1: $\mu < 70$; (3) one-tailed test, lower tail; (4) see picture; (5) $z_{\bar{X}} = -1.4$;
(6) see picture; (7) not more extreme; (8) retain H_0

A.2, look up the probability of your observed statistic. (f) State your decision in terms of the critical value decision rule. (g) State your decision in terms of the *p*-value decision rule.

Answers

(a) H_0: $\mu \leq 30.46$ and H_1: $\mu > 30.46$. (b) α will be set in the upper tail because the alternative hypothesis has a directional sign pointing toward the upper tail. (c) $z_{crit} = 1.645$. (d) $z_{\bar{X}} = -3.02$. (e) $p(z \geq z_{\bar{X}}) = .0013$. (f) Retain H_0 because $z_{\bar{X}} = -3.02$ is not more extreme than $z_{crit} = 1.645$. The result is in the lower tail, not the tail where you had predicted the outcome to be. (g) Even though the probability of the observed statistic is less than .05, you cannot reject the null hypothesis. Look back at the *p*-value decision rule. It says the probability must be smaller than α, *and the direction must be predicted correctly.*

10.9 Logic of Hypothesis Testing

This section is a collection of seemingly unrelated topics that all involve the logic of hypothesis testing. These are not all the problematic or controversial subjects in hypothesis testing, but they may answer questions you have had from earlier sections. You need to integrate these nuances into your knowledge of hypothesis testing.

Null Hypothesis Probabilities

If the test statistic is more extreme than a critical value, you say to reject H_0 in favor of H_1. You are really saying that the statistic has small likelihood given H_0 but greater likelihood given some value of μ in H_1. Examine Figure 10.6. If the obtained $z_{\bar{X}}$ is among the rejection values—say, just above the critical value—then it has low

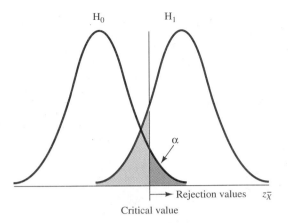

Figure 10.6
Probabilities in H_0 or H_1

probability, $p(z \geq z_{\bar{X}})$, in the distribution of H_0—say, less than .05. However, it has greater probability in the distribution for H_1—say, about .60.

Although you actually compute the probability of the statistic given H_0, you usually assume a greater probability given some value of μ in H_1 and do not make a practice of computing the probability of the obtained statistic for the alternative. One reason is that you don't know the true values of parameters. Still, you choose H_1 so that you have some value of the parameter that will give a higher likelihood of the statistic than that calculated given H_0. If you actually know enough about your area of science to specify a particular value for the parameter consistent with H_1, you can calculate probabilities for the statistic for both the null and alternative hypotheses. Then you can see whether the result is more likely given your specified H_1 or more likely given H_0.

Typically, behavioral scientists are content to calculate null hypothesis probabilities, reject H_0, and imply a greater likelihood for some unspecified value of the parameter consistent with H_1. Another approach is to decide in advance what kind of treatment effect in a certain area of research is important and noteworthy. This is the idea behind the "good-enough principle" (Serlin & Lapsley, 1985), which is a topic for advanced statistics courses. For the most part, behavioral scientists follow the steps of hypothesis testing outlined in this chapter.

p-Values and Significance

Another issue pertains to the significance level and the obtained *p*-value for the test statistic, two components of hypothesis testing. Before computing statistics, the researcher chooses the significance level. The *p*-value is the actual probability associated with the obtained statistic, calculated given the value of the parameter from H_0. Obviously, these two quantities are different because you compare them to reach a *p*-value decision. The confusion comes when researchers try to take the *p*-value as a measure of the "degree" of significance. The statistic is either significant or nonsignificant at the chosen α; the *p*-value is not a measure of the degree of significance.

Cannot *Prove*

You have learned to use the phrases *reject* H_0 and *retain* H_0 in connection with hypotheses. The words *prove* and *disprove* have not been used in any of the discussions of hypothesis testing. These words are used to indicate the establishment of some concept that is unalterably true. In mathematics and some of the physical sciences, *prove* may be used correctly in connection with various theorems. For example, there is a proof that the Central Limit Theorem is true. However, in the applied sciences where experimentation is used, the variability of observations precludes the final establishment of truth without any chance for error. You cannot prove or disprove hypotheses, but you can use probability to show a small likelihood of results given some hypothesis and thus reject the hypothesis. As long as there is a probability of making a mistake, you cannot say you've proved something.

Strength of Rejection; or Why You Put What You Believe in H_1

When you say that you reject H_0, you have made the strongest possible statement in hypothesis testing. Remember, you set up the hypotheses so that what you believe is in H_1 and what you do not believe is in H_0. Imagine a situation where you have results that favor H_1 and lead you to reject H_0. For example, in Research Example 9 for H_0: $\mu = 100$, you found $\overline{X} = 88.07$ (supporting H_1: $\mu \neq 100$) for the IQs of deaf children. Suppose that you set up the hypotheses in the opposite way: H_0: $\mu \neq 100$ and H_1: $\mu = 100$. Now $\overline{X} = 88.07$ supports H_0, so you cannot reject H_0. Under this reverse system, you are not able to reject any values as not being consistent with the results, and you have only a weak statement of retaining your belief. You have made the error of inductive reasoning—trying to argue from the specifics ($\overline{X} = 88.07$) to the general ($\mu \neq 100$). Switching back to the usual approach, you can say that the results favor your belief, stated in H_1, but you also can reject H_0, which is a statement of the complement of your belief. You have avoided the error inherent in induction.

If you want to show that all professional basketball players are over 6 ft tall, you could trot out dozens of players over 6 ft tall to support your argument. But it takes just one example of a player under 6 ft tall to show that your statement is false. The strength of rejection is like dealing with a theorem in mathematics; many examples that fit the theorem do not allow you to say it is true, but you need only one counterexample to prove it false.

Another analogy may help: a paternity suit. Blood types of the baby and the father are often used as evidence in a paternity suit. If the suspected father and baby do not match in blood type, then the hypothesis that he is the father can be rejected. The strongest statement that can be made on the basis of blood typing is that the suspected father is not the father of the baby. If the blood types of the baby and the suspected father do match, all that can be said is that it is *possible* that he is the father. It is too strong to say you *accept* the hypothesis that he is the father; instead, you *retain* this hypothesis. At this point, the trial has to move to other evidence, such as elaborate DNA testing. Just as there could be another man with the same blood type who is the father of the child, when you retain H_0 there could be other values of μ that are true and give the same results. Rejecting H_0 is a strong statement, but retaining H_0 is a relatively weak statement.

Doubting Santa's existence: Falsely rejecting the null?

Why You Use *Retain*

For many of the reasons given in the last paragraph, you do not say that you *accept* H_0. The statement of acceptance is stronger than what can be truthfully said because the evidence is not enough to reject H_0. The word *accept* means that you believe H_0 is exactly true, when in fact it rarely is. Often μ is so close to the μ stated in H_0 that you cannot detect the difference. Or H_0 could be true, or the research didn't give evidence that it wasn't true. For these reasons, you use the word *retain*. You accept your in-laws, but you retain a lawyer!

Quick Quiz

A friend is studying inhibition among singers compared to nonsingers, and she shows you the following hypotheses: H_0: $\mu \geq 22.55$ and H_1: $\mu < 22.55$. High scores mean more inhibition. (a) What does your friend believe about inhibition among singers? (b) In which tail should α be placed?

Answers

(a) By looking at the alternative hypothesis, you can see she believes the average inhibition score for singers will be lower than the mean for nonsingers, so she believes singers will be less inhibited. (b) Again, the alternative hypothesis gives the anwer: The directional sign is pointing toward the lower tail, so that's where α should be placed.

10.10   Summary, Study Tips, and Computation

Chapter Summary

The use of probability in the sampling distribution of the statistic is formalized by using $z_{\overline{x}}$ to test hypotheses about the population mean. You follow steps like those in the scientific method, and you pay close attention to the assumptions of your test statistic. You test the null hypothesis H_0 and put what you believe about the parameter into the alternative hypothesis H_1. H_1 can be directional or nondirectional. The significance level α is the small probability of finding a deviant result by chance alone when H_0 is true. The value of α is chosen before the research begins and is usually set at .05. If you put all of the α in one tail of the sampling distribution of the test statistic, you have a one-tailed test. If you put $\alpha/2$ in each tail of the sampling distribution of the test statistic, you have a two-tailed test. Values of the statistic that cut off α or $\alpha/2$ in the tail are called critical values. Rejection values are those statistics that equal or exceed the critical values. Decision rules are based on rejecting H_0 either when the statistic equals or exceeds the critical values, or when the obtained probability is less than or equal to α (for directional hypotheses, you must also predict direction correctly).

The following key terms are used in this chapter:

Exploratory data analysis	Significance level, α
Confirmatory data analysis	Directional hypotheses
	Nondirectional hypothesis
Hypothesis testing	One-tailed test
Test statistic	Two-tailed test
Assumptions	Critical value(s)
Null hypothesis	Rejection values
Alternative hypothesis	Decison rules
Reject H_0	*p*-value
Retain H_0	

Study Tips

Many new vocabulary terms for you to learn are in this chapter. Be careful and precise in memorizing each definition. Two important points are: (1) H_1 tells you where to put α (or $\alpha/2$) and the critical value(s); and (2) you can't reject a directional hypothesis unless the statistic is *both* extreme (*p*-value small) and in the direction predicted by H_1. Be sure to follow the eight steps for testing hypotheses given in Section 10.8, including drawing the sampling distribution and labeling the critical values, and others.

The most frequent mistakes made by students are: (1) missing the clues in the language of what the researcher believes (these lead to H_1), (2) not drawing a picture of the sampling distribution, and (3) confusing the critical value and *p*-value decision rules.

Computation

One serious problem with the use of the decision rules based on the *p*-value is the lack of distinction between one- and two-tailed tests in some computer programs. Check the manual for the statistics package you use and find out what probability is reported. If it is a one-tailed probability, you cannot do a two-tailed test by comparing *p* to α as in the one-tailed test. This is an incorrect application of the decision rule, and this misuse increases your chances for error. The solution for computer programs that compute a one-tailed *p*-value is to compare it to $\alpha/2$ when doing a two-tailed test. For one-tailed tests, you have to have a small *p*-value and the statistic has to be in the direction predicted by H_1.

As an example, consider the arithmetic data in Table 10.4. The result is in the correct direction (negative), but the *p*-value decision rule approach gives a *p*-value of .0808, and .0808 > .05, so you retain H_0. This is consistent with the decision reached by using the critical value approach. Also consider the IQ data in Table 10.3. There the one-tailed *p*-value is .0005, and it is compared to $\alpha/2 = .05/2 = .025$. You reject H_0, consistent with the critical value decision rule.

If the default for your computer program is a two-tailed *p*-value, then two-tailed tests of nondirectional hypotheses are very easy: Reject H_0 if $p \leq \alpha$. However, one-tailed tests of directional hypotheses are now more difficult. The solution for computer programs that compute a two-tailed *p*-value is to take one-half of the *p*-value, compare it to α, and then check to see whether the statistic is in the direction predicted by H_1.

Using the same examples as above, consider the arithmetic data in Table 10.4. The result is in the correct direction (negative), but a two-tailed *p*-value decision rule approach gives a *p*-value of .1616. To do this one-tailed test, take one-half of .1616, .0808, and compare it to α. Because .0808 > .05, you retain H_0. This is consistent with the decision reached by using the critical value approach. Also consider the IQ data in Table 10.3. There the two-tailed *p*-value is .0010. Because this is a two-tailed test of a nondirectional hypothesis, the *p*-value of .0010 is compared directly to $\alpha = .05$. You reject H_0, consistent with the critical value decision rule.

Because much of this chapter, like Chapter 9, is conceptually based, you learned no new computational procedures. You have computed $z_{\bar{X}}$ and used Table A.2, which do not require a computer.

Exercises

Section 10.1

1. Rodgers, Harris, and Vickers (1992) used a large national data set that included information from thousands of young Americans. Among hundreds of other questions, women were asked at age 25 to report the month and year they first had sexual intercourse. The researchers graphed the responses according to month to find out whether one month was reported more frequently than the rest. On a dot chart, which is similar to a histogram, the summer months had the highest frequencies. The researchers tentatively stated that the summer effect might be apparent only among women of high school age or younger. They graphed the data again, this time according to the age of the women. They graphed each month for each age from 13 to 23 years old. They discovered that the frequencies for the summer months were highest for those aged 18 and under, but those months didn't stand out after age 18.
   a. What phase of this research is exploratory data analysis?
   b. At what point were the researchers moving into the area of confirmatory data analysis?
   c. Reread Section 10.1 and identify the elements of CDA that are missing from this example.

Section 10.2

2. Suppose you are intrigued by the country music airtime/suicide rate relationship discussed in Research Example 6. Stack and Gundlach (1992) found that cities with more airtime devoted to country music also had higher suicide rates. Based on this study, you developed the idea that country songs make people more depressed and more likely to commit suicide. Imagine you have found a measure of depression that has a mean of 100 and a standard deviation of 10. You want participants in your study not to listen to any music except country music, which they must hear for 2 hours a day for 3 weeks. Then you will give them the questionnaire to determine their average depression level.
   a. Using a sentence similar to the hypothesis about

hypertensives in Section 10.2, write a hypothesis for your country music study.
   b. What part of your statement about country music will you doubt if the average depression score for your participants has a small probability?
   c. What will you conclude if your participants' mean on depression has a high probability?

Section 10.3

3. Your friend in the last Quick Quiz was interested in comparing the average inhibition score for singers to the average for nonsingers. According to Marchant-Haycox and Wilson (1992), nonsingers have a mean inhibition score of 22.55 and a standard deviation of 6.19. For 38 singers with an average inhibition score of 20.47, your friend computes $z_{\bar{X}} = -2.07$. The probability of this statistic is .0192.
   a. In a sentence, write out the pair of hypotheses your friend would use. (Look at the rat shipment example for a model.)
   b. Given that .0192 is a small probability, which of your friend's hypotheses would you doubt?
   c. What conclusion would your friend draw about inhibition among singers?

Section 10.4

4. Suppose you believe that women over age 25 have less anxiety about going to the dentist than the average of 7.5 on the Dental Anxiety Scale (DAS). You know the population variance is 1.34. For this problem, go through the five steps of scientific methods outlined in Section 10.4, and write out what you would need to know and do for each step.

Sections 10.5–10.8

5. For each of the following, give the correct H_0 and H_1, and then tell which tail(s) of the distribution of $z_{\bar{X}}$ would be used (in each case, assume that σ^2 or σ is known).
   a. You are given the situation in Exercise 4.
   b. A teacher believes that the average IQ of a class is higher than the population average of 100.

c. A teacher merely suspects that the average IQ of the class is different from 100.

d. A researcher in Japan translated the California Personality Inventory to Japanese and wants to test a group of Japanese to see whether the Japanese population mean on the self-acceptance scale differs from the English norm of 20.

6. For each of the following, give the correct H_0 and H_1, and then tell which tail(s) of the distribution of $z_{\bar{X}}$ would be used (in each case, assume that σ^2 or σ is known).

a. University U claims that the average GPA is 3.10. An official wonders if it is different for those who work part-time.

b. A machine in a plant manufactures a car part and is set to make the part 6.70 in. long. The shift supervisor has responsibility to make sure the setting on the machine has not shifted, and thereby altered this length, in either direction.

c. A large-scale yearly survey at University Y has established that full-time students study an average of 12.10 h per week. You think that engineering majors study more than that.

d. Salaries for female administrators and faculty at your college average $43,750. You suspect that the faculty are underpaid.

7. How much probability is in each tail of a two-tailed test if $\alpha = .05$? If $\alpha = .01$?

8. If you are using $z_{\bar{X}}$ as your test statistic, use each of the following α values to give the critical value(s). Draw a picture of each distribution, and answer any additional questions asked.

a. $\alpha = .05$; a one-tailed upper-tail test. Give the rejection values.

b. $\alpha = .01$; a one-tailed upper-tail test. Give the rejection values and tell how they differ from $\alpha = .01$.

c. $\alpha = .05$; a one-tailed lower-tail test. Why are the rejection values less than or equal to -1.645 instead of greater than or equal to -1.645?

d. $\alpha = .01$; a one-tailed lower-tail test. Give the rejection values.

e. $\alpha = .05$; a two-tailed test. Give the rejection values.

f. $\alpha = .01$; a two-tailed test. Give the rejection values.

9. Hirshoren, Hurley, and Kavale (1979), in their study of 59 deaf children, found that the average IQ score on the Wechsler Intelligence Scale for Children-Revised (WISC-R) was 88.07 (see Research Exam-

ple 9). If the population mean for the standardization group is 100 and the population standard deviation is 15, is the average performance by these deaf children significantly different from that for hearing children?

a. Give H_0 and H_1.

b. If $\alpha = .05$, give the critical value(s).

c. Compute $z_{\bar{X}}$.

d. Use $\alpha = .05$ and test H_0.

e. Now explain these results as if you were telling them to a friend who does not know statistics.

10. Suppose you ask whether the average performance of the deaf children in Exercise 9 is significantly lower than that for hearing children. What changes should be made in the hypotheses? Use $\alpha = .01$ and test H_0.

11. A psychologist has been studying the effects of different instructions on the intensity of pain. She had college students hold their hand in a jar of freezing water for as long as possible. Most students could tolerate only about 2 min and reported high-intensity pain. Then they removed their hands from the water and over the next 2 min were asked periodically to rate the intensity of the pain. The standard instructions given before this task started were to suppress all awareness of the sensations in their hand—that is, to ignore the pain. For the standard condition, the researcher knew that the average pain intensity on a 1 (low, tolerable pain) to 5 (high, intolerable pain) scale was 4.06 with a standard deviation of 0.41 when pain intensity was measured 1.5 min after they removed their hand from the water. The latest experiment had 63 college students do the same task but with instructions to monitor the details of their hand sensations—that is, to concentrate on the pain and its intensity. When pain intensity was measured 1.5 min after they removed their hand from the water, $\bar{X} = 3.85$ for the 63 students with the new instructions. Was the pain intensity lower than for the standard instructions?

a. Give H_0 and H_1.

b. $\alpha = .05$, give the critical value(s).

c. Compute $z_{\bar{X}}$.

d. Use $\alpha = .05$ and test H_0.

e. Now explain these results as if you were telling them to a friend who does not know statistics.

12. A psychologist has been studying the effect of deterioration of memory over time. He has been interested in how memory for particularly startling events, called *flashbulb memories,* might differ from memory for everyday events. He asked college students to try to remember all the circumstances of an ordinary event (such as meeting a friend) and then immediately after the event to fill out a survey about the details of the event. He knew from vast amounts of prior research that the average proportion of details accurately remembered 1 yr later is .85 with a standard deviation of .04. When the Persian Gulf War began in January 1991, he asked students to do the same task of filling out the survey about the details of the beginning of the bombing. He thought that the proportion of details remembered 1 yr later would be higher. The following are the proportions correct for 22 students:

| .81 | .65 | .93 | .78 | .79 | .87 | .86 | .83 | .87 | .85 | .77 |
| .86 | .80 | .81 | .82 | .83 | .87 | .85 | .85 | .84 | .83 | .90 |

  a. Give H_0 and H_1.
  b. If $\alpha = .05$, give the critcial value(s).
  c. Compute $z_{\bar{x}}$.
  d. Use $\alpha = .05$ and test H_0.

13. The use of estrogen replacement in postmenopausal women to lower the risk of heart attack brings with it the negative side effect of increased chances of a type of uterine cancer. To counter this, some doctors advise that estrogen be combined with progestin to block uterine cell production. A group of researchers studying 173 women whose doctors had them take both estrogen and progestin observed $\bar{X} = 41$ mg/dL HDL (high-density lipoproteins, the "good" fat molecules that help reduce cholesterol and thus help prevent heart disease). If the average level of HDL for this age women is $\mu = 34$ mg/dL with a standard deviation of $\sigma = 4.5$, has the combination of the two drugs increased the level of HDL?
  a. Give H_0 and H_1.
  b. If $\alpha = .05$, give the critical value(s).
  c. Compute $z_{\bar{x}}$.
  d. Use $\alpha = .05$ and test H_0.
  e. What serious flaw exists in this study that would make one hesitant to say that the two drugs together protect against heart disease?

14. Suppose Sunola Fruit Company cans peaches in a can labeled 48 oz that a machine actually fills with 50 oz (on the average) of peaches and juice. The standard deviation for the filling machine is 2.4 oz. You sample $N = 10$ cans that yield $\bar{X} = 48.6$. Now test the null hypothesis that the filling machines are still set on 50 oz or higher. Use $\alpha = .05$. What conclusion do you draw?

15. Suppose that in Exercise 14 you are concerned about detecting any deviation from 50 oz. Test H_0: $\mu = 50$ with the information in Exercise 14, using $\alpha = .05$. Discuss any differences between the results in these two exercises.

16. Give the *p*-value decision rules for Exercises 11–13.

17. If $\alpha = .01$ and the critical values are -2.57 and $+2.57$, what is the *p*-value decision rule?

18. A psychologist is studying the effects of high blood pressure, hypertension, on memory and learning. He uses a task that requires a person to study either two, four, or six digits shown on a screen and then later to indicate whether a single digit presented on the screen was part of the original set. He knows that the average time to answer for a large number of adults with normal blood pressure on the six-digit task is 1.35 s with a standard deviation of 0.23 s. He believes that hypertensives will answer more slowly than people without hypertension. A sample of hypertensives gave the following data for the six-digit task:

| 1.43 | 1.67 | 2.13 | 3.12 | 1.23 | 1.29 | 1.56 | 1.43 | 3.89 | 2.34 |
| 1.89 | 1.78 |

  a. Give H_0 and H_1.
  b. Compute $z_{\bar{x}}$ and find the appropriate *p*-value.
  c. Use $\alpha = .05$ and the *p*-value decision rule to test H_0.

19. Suppose a psychologist claims that her patients treated for anxiety will have an average score of 50 or less on the Flip-Flop Anxiety Scale (FFAS). The standard deviation on the FFAS is 2.7. You suspect that these patients will average higher than 50 on the FFAS, more like typical people. You sample $N = 16$ patients and find $\bar{X} = 51.3$. Test the psychologist's claims, using $\alpha = .05$.

Section 10.9

20. Your friend who found that singers have a significantly different level of inhibition than nonsingers obtained a statistic with a probability of .0192. Now your friend is reading a similar study in which the researchers' statistic has a probability of .0002, and your friend says those researchers "must have found a more significant result." What can you say about the probabilities and your friend's statement to console your friend?

11

Types of Error and Power

What errors can be made in testing hypotheses? What are the probabilities of those errors? What are the chances of detecting a true difference if it exists? These questions are the heart of this chapter on types of error and power. You will learn about the two types of errors and their probabilities, the variables that influence power, how to compute power for $z_{\bar{X}}$, and how to compute sample size to get a desired power.

Research Example 11
11.1 Overview: Types of Error, Power, and Variables That Influence Power
  Example
11.2 Two Potential Decisions and Associated Errors
  Introduction
  Four outcomes
  Definitions
  Thought problem
  Control of error
11.3 Power
  Power defined
  Relationships among power, β, and $1 - \beta$
11.4 Variables That Influence Power
  Sample size
  Control of σ^2
  Choice of α
  Hypotheses
  Importance of N
  Summary problem
11.5 Computing Power and Sample Size
  Notation
  Computing power
  Computing sample size
  Beyond these power calculations
11.6 Summary, Study Tips, and Computation
  Chapter summary
  Study tips
  Computation
Exercises

Research Example 11

Let's return to an example used in Chapter 1, the study of exam stress. To refresh your memory, DasGupta (1992) randomly assigned 30 students to one of two conditions that differed with respect to the students' perceived control over a test-taking situation. Control over the test is the independent variable. The perceived-control (PC) students submitted questions for an upcoming test in their introductory psychology class, believing the questions might be used on the test. The no-control (NC) students also submitted questions, but they were told only that this task would help them study for the test. The actual test contained questions that were similar to 82% of the questions from the PC group and 87% from the NC group. Dependent variables included the number of symptoms indicated on a form of the *Stress Self-Assessment Checklist* (SSAC) (Neidhardt, Weinstein & Conry, 1985), an average stress frequency rating, and test performance.

DasGupta (1992) was able to reject the null hypothesis of no difference between the two groups on the dependent variable of number of symptoms. But no significant differences were found on two other dependent variables, average stress frequency rating and performance on the exam. The groups were different enough on the number of symptoms to conclude that the perceived-control group had fewer reported symptoms. On this dependent variable, the researcher may have rejected H_0 falsely; that is, there is some risk of making the wrong decision about H_0. But the groups were not different enough on the other measures to reject H_0, so the researcher retained H_0. Again, the researcher runs the risk of making an error, but this is the error of retaining falsely.

You might ask what DasGupta could have done to increase the likelihood of finding significant differences on the other two dependent variables. More students could have been used in the research—say, 40 in each group. Increasing the sample size works to help find differences by reducing the variance of $\bar{X}$, σ^2/N. Perhaps there could have been better control of extraneous variability. Perceived control might affect students with high ability differently than it affects those with lower ability. The researcher could control that extraneous variable by dividing the students into ability groups before randomly assigning them to the treatments. A directional hypothesis leads to a smaller critical value, which makes it easier to reject the null hypothesis. DasGupta could have used a directional hypothesis, predicting that the perceived-control group would do better on the exam than the no-control group. A larger α could have been used—say, $\alpha = .10$—instead of the usual .05, although the results probably wouldn't have been published because of the strong tradition for $\alpha = .05$.

Researchers want to be able to show that something happened as a result of their manipulation of variables, and they want to reject null hypotheses. The probability of rejecting H_0 is called *power*. Any of the approaches mentioned earlier would give higher power for the dependent variables where DasGupta didn't find significant differences. The option most often used is to increase the sample size.

What about when research finds significant differences? If you have a small sample size and find a difference, then you are not concerned about ways to increase the power—that is, to increase the probability of rejecting H_0. For example, researchers have found a new way to treat anemias, such as sickle-cell anemia and beta thalassemia, both inherited blood disorders. These anemias are characterized by a faulty gene in adult hemoglobin, the protein in red blood cells that carries oxygen.

In people who have sickle-cell anemia, the faulty gene causes the cells to bend into a curved shape resembling a sickle. The sickle cells lodge in small blood vessels, which results in severe pain. Perrine and colleagues (1993) found that a food additive, a flavor enhancer called *butyrate,* caused patients to produce large amounts of fetal hemoglobin, ordinarily produced only in infants up to the age of 6 months. Fetal hemoglobin helps alleviate symptoms caused by lack of adult hemoglobin. The researchers treated three sickle-cell anemia patients and three beta thalassemia patients by giving them a daily butyrate solution intravenously for 2 to 3 weeks and boosted the production of fetal hemoglobin by up to 45%. They measured levels of fetal hemoglobin before and after the treatment, looking for a change. The differences they found were significant in the six patients, so they did not need to investigate ways to increase the probability of rejecting the null hypothesis. Because significant differences were found, they already rejected H_0. These researchers needed more individuals, but not to increase the power of the statistical tests. They needed to replicate the research because the small sample size limited their ability to generalize their conclusions.

Decisions about H_0 are important to a researcher. Types of errors and the factors that influence the ability to reject H_0 are discussed in this chapter.

11.1 Overview: Types of Error, Power, and Variables That Influence Power

Country music airtime and white suicide rates—two variables that you might have thought to be unrelated seem to be positively correlated. Stack and Gundlach (1992) concluded that there is a significant correlation between the two variables, $r = .54$. Let's reconsider this example, using the vocabulary you learned in Chapter 10 on hypothesis testing. Stack and Gundlach were testing a null hypothesis of no correlation. Did they reject H_0? Yes, they found that the relationship is significant at the .05 level. Like most researchers, Stack and Gundlach chose $\alpha = .05$. The error they could have made was to reject H_0 when they shouldn't. Because they did not retain H_0, they could not have made the error of retaining H_0 when they shouldn't.

Do you remember how many cities were studied by Stack and Gundlach? It was 49 metropolitan areas. Intuitively, that seems like a good number. Suppose they used only a dozen cities. Let's say you plotted their data for 12 cities and found that most of the data appeared uncorrelated, but that a few cities had extremely high suicide rates and country music airtime. Is the effect being driven by just a few cities? After all, the correlation coefficient r can be inflated or reduced by outliers. A small sample's results are more affected by a few outliers than are a large sample's statistics. So the number of cities being studied by Stack and Gundlach is important. If they didn't have enough, readers who know statistics might wonder whether outliers are affecting the correlation coefficient.

Could the opposite situation be a problem? Consider what could happen if Stack and Gundlach had studied every city that has a country music radio station. Where do you think country music is more popular, in big cities or in less heavily populated areas? In this case, the study could be affected by the inclusion of too many smaller cities and towns, where country music may be the only thing aired on the single radio station in town. The characteristics of the cities in the study are important, but the sheer number of cities, observations, or participants in a study can affect the statistics,

Power
Probability of rejecting H_0

too. The probability of rejecting the null hypothesis, or **power,** is influenced by many variables, but researchers have the most control over one of them: sample size.

Example

Let's apply some of these concepts to another example, the study of the polio vaccine reported in Chapter 2. The researchers had a lot of extraneous variables to control—site, general health of child, socioeconomic status of family, and exposure to polio, for instance. To control them, the researchers randomized children to either a vaccine group or a placebo control group. Without randomization, there would have been some question about what caused the significant differences between the two groups. (You should stop and think here. If that statement about randomization isn't clear, go back to Chapter 2 and review the purpose of randomizing subjects to groups.) Now consider the hypotheses. The null hypothesis would be that the vaccine was not effective, that the vaccine group would have the same results as the placebo control group. If the researchers rejected the null hypothesis falsely, they would market an ineffective vaccine. The cost of this error would be the lack of an effective vaccine and financial loss to the drug company that produced the vaccine. If the researchers retained the null hypothesis when the vaccine indeed was effective, then they would not put a lifesaving vaccine on the market. Both errors needed to be minimized, but in this study the probability of the second type of error needed to be very small. This dictated a large sample size.

Another reason for having a large sample size was that the rate (proportion) of polio was small, only about 70 per 100,000 in the actual research. This rate was only .07%, so the researchers needed to take a large N to be able to detect any differences in the rates for the two groups. If the vaccine was only 50% effective, the rate would drop to one-half of .07%. For example, using only $N = 1000$ children, the researchers would expect less than one case; for $N = 10,000$, about seven cases. Chance fluctuation could account for a reduction to three or four cases, so the researchers had to use a large N to be able to detect differences in such small proportions. They used more than 400,000 children in this part of the research, or more than 200,000 in each group. But there is a problem with having huge samples. Sometimes researchers can pick up trivial differences between large groups. Scientists need to look for important differences, not trivial ones. When you are planning research, you need to make many decisions, including how many people to have in your study. You want to have a good probability of rejecting the null hypothesis without increasing the risk of detecting a trivial difference as important.

Because researchers are looking for significant treatment effects but want to avoid being wrong, the relationship among power and the two types of error are important considerations in planning research.

Quick Quiz

In the exam stress study discussed in Research Example 11, what would have happened to the chance of rejecting H_0 for performance on the exam if DasGupta had increased the sample size?

Answer

The chance (probability) of rejecting H_0 would have increased, and significant differences might have been found in addition to that for the number of stress symptoms.

Table 11.1
Outcomes of hypothesis testing

		True State of the World	
		H_0 True	H_0 False
Decision	Reject H_0	False alarm = Type I error	Hit = correct decision
	Retain H_0	Hit = correct decision	Miss = Type II error

11.2   Two Potential Decisions and Associated Errors

Introduction

When hypothesis testing was introduced in Chapter 1, the concepts of two hypotheses, two potential decisions, and two potential errors were included. For each of the two potential decisions, there is a corresponding error. Here, error means *mistake,* not a deviation score as it was used previously. This section introduces these types of errors and the probability associated with each.

Four Outcomes

In the example of the IQs of high school students in Chapter 10, the decision was to reject H_0: $\mu = 100$. In the example of the arithmetic skills of the artillery students in Chapter 10, the decision was to retain H_0: $\mu \geq 70$. Each decision may have been right, or it might have been an error. Pairing each decision with H_0 being true and H_0 being false gives the four potential outcomes of any hypothesis test, as shown in Tables 11.1 and 11.2.

Table 11.1 lists all four of these outcomes in the language of errors (false alarm and miss) and correct decisions (hits). Compare Table 11.1 with Table 11.2. Table 11.2 lists all four of these outcomes in terms of their probabilities. Each probability is defined as

Table 11.2
Probabilities of outcomes in hypothesis testing

		True State of the World	
		H_0 True	H_0 False
Decision	Reject H_0	α = probability of Type I error	$1 - \beta$ = probability of correct decision
	Retain H_0	$1 - \alpha$ = probability of correct decision	β = probability of Type II error

a conditional probability; for example, $\alpha = p(\text{reject } H_0 | H_0 \text{ true})$ is conditional upon H_0 being true.

The importance of these tables and the information in them cannot be overemphasized. This is one of the rare occasions in this text where we recommend memorization. Memorize Table 11.2 and be able to reproduce it and discuss it; it will help you master the concepts of hypothesis testing.

Definitions

Let's define each cell of Table 11.2.

1. *Reject H_0 when H_0 is true.* This is an error, a "false alarm," when you reject H_0 and you shouldn't have. In the IQ example, this would be represented by finding $\overline{X} = 110$ and rejecting H_0: $\mu = 100$ when in fact $\mu = 100$. This false-alarm error is defined as:

Type I error
ejecting H_0 when H_0 is true

$$\textbf{Type I error} = \text{rejecting } H_0 \text{ when } H_0 \text{ is true} \qquad (11.1)$$

$$= \text{falsely rejecting } H_0$$

The probability of a Type I error is defined as

$$p(\text{Type I error}) = \alpha \qquad (11.2)$$

where α is the significance level set by the researcher. The probability of a Type I error, α, is controlled *directly* by the researcher.

2. *Retain H_0 when H_0 is false (H_1 is true).* This is an error, a "miss." In the arithmetic skills example, this would be represented by finding $\overline{X} = 65.8$ and retaining H_0: $\mu \geq 70$ when in fact μ was 66. If the alternative hypothesis is true (H_1: $\mu < 70$), then you want to reject H_0. If you retain H_0, you have "missed." So if the true value of μ is 66 (or any value of μ consistent with H_1), then you should have rejected H_0. This "miss" error is defined as:

Type II error
Retaining H_0 when H_0 is false (H_1 is true)

$$\textbf{Type II error} = \text{retaining } H_0 \text{ when } H_0 \text{ is false } (H_1 \text{ is true}) \qquad (11.3)$$

$$= \text{falsely retaining } H_0$$

The probability of a Type II error is defined as

$$p(\text{Type II error}) = \beta \qquad (11.4)$$

where β is beta (pronounced "bait-uh"). Researchers cannot directly control β, but they can control other variables that influence β. You'll learn more about this later. (Incidentally, the terms *Type I* and *Type II errors* are widely used in research; their meaning is not confined to this text.)

3. *Reject H_0 when H_0 is false.* This is a "hit," a correct decision. In the IQ example, this would be represented by finding $\overline{X} = 110$ and rejecting H_0: $\mu = 100$ when in fact μ was 115. If the alternative hypothesis is true (H_1: $\mu \neq 100$), then you want to reject H_0. If you reject H_0, you have a "hit." So if the true value of μ was 115 (or any value

of μ consistent with H_1), then you should have rejected H_0. This correct decision has probability $1 - \beta$, which is sometimes called the *power* of the test.

4. *Retain H_0 when H_0 is true.* This is a correct decision, a "hit." In the arithmetic skills example, this would be represented by finding $\overline{X} = 65.8$ and retaining H_0: $\mu \geq 70$ if in fact $\mu = 70$. This correct decision has probability $1 - \alpha$.

Thought Problem

To help you begin thinking in terms of these types of errors and their probabilities, consider this: Why do firefighters answer every call? If you take the null hypothesis to be "no fire," what is each cell of Table 11.1 and what is being risked? Table 11.3 shows Table 11.1 in terms of this problem to help you understand the issues.

First, what if H_0 is true and the firefighters reject H_0? If they reject H_0: *no fire* and answer the call when there is no fire, they have responded to a false alarm. If there is no fire and they answer the call, the cost is time, fuel, risk of vehicle accident, and risk of being gone when a real fire is called in.

Second, what if H_0 is false and they reject H_0? If the firefighters reject H_0: *no fire* and answer the call when there is a fire, they have a hit (no error).

Third, what if H_0 is true and they retain H_0? If the firefighters retain H_0: *no fire* and don't answer the call when there is no fire, they have a hit (no error).

Fourth, what if H_0 is false and they retain H_0? If the firefighters retain H_0: *no fire* and don't answer the call when there is a fire, they have a miss. That is, if there is a fire and they don't answer, the cost is in lives and property. This high cost of a Type II error is why firefighters answer every call.

Control of Error

Obviously, researchers don't want to make mistakes in their decisions, just as firefighters don't want to let property and lives be destroyed or taxpayers' money wasted. The difference in social science research is that you don't know whether you are right or wrong in rejecting H_0. It's important to control the probabilities of both kinds of errors. If you reject a null hypothesis about introversion among performing artists and conclude that dancers are more introverted than nondancers, you can't be sure you are right or wrong. You make α small to minimize the possibility of a Type I error (rejecting the

Table 11.3
Outcomes of decisions for firefighters

		True State of the World	
		H_0 *True: No Fire*	H_0 *False: Fire*
Decision	Reject H_0	Type I error: false alarm (time, fuel, etc.)	Correct decision: hit
	Retain H_0	Correct decision: hit	Type II error: miss (lives, property)

null when it is true), but you have no way of being sure that dancers' introversion scores in the population are different from nondancers' scores. The cost may be that other people will do research to expand on your findings, only to find conflicting results in replications of your study. If you retain the null hypothesis when it is false, you have made a Type II error. Using the same example, let's say you found no significant differences between dancers and nondancers on introversion. Such results usually aren't published. If you were wrong and there *is* a difference on introversion, someone in counseling psychology might have been able to benefit from the information in treating performing artists.

These errors in the social sciences may seem trivial next to the error of firefighters deciding not to respond to a house fire. But researchers must try to reduce the possibility of spreading false information about how the world works. Consider an example in medicine. What would a Type I error mean in testing a vaccine for AIDS? It could result in a useless product being marketed as a cure. What would a Type II error mean? It could rob people of a potentially life-changing medication.

Researchers have to consider how they can control the probability of these errors. They focus on the fact that they have direct control over α, the probability of a Type I error. They can set α at a small value.

Equally important is the probability of a Type II error, but researchers cannot directly control β. They can directly control several variables that influence both the power and β: If β is kept small, then power will be large. In Section 11.4, you will learn about four variables used to control β at a small value and keep power high.

Figure 11.1 illustrates all of the probabilities in Table 11.2 for an upper-tail one-tailed test. The distribution for H_0 shows the area for α shaded in a darker tone. The distribution for H_1 shows the area for β shaded in a lighter tone. The α and $1 - \alpha$ are evaluated in the distribution for H_0, whereas β and $1 - \beta$ are in the distribution for H_1. The tail area that contains α would get smaller as you move the line for the critical value to the right. (A bigger critical value is a more stringent test and has a smaller probability.) What happens to β, the Type II error rate? The area for β also is a tail area, but it is in the distribution under the alternative hypothesis. As the critical value

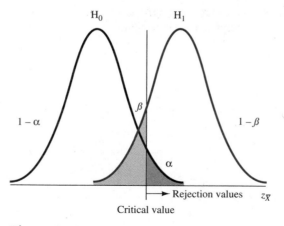

Figure 11.1
Probabilities of outcomes in hypothesis testing, upper-tail test

line is moved to the right, the β tail area would get bigger. As you can see, there is a trade-off between the probabilities of a Type I and a Type II error.

Quick Quiz

Reconsider the rat shipment example from Chapter 10. Dr. Why concluded that the new rats were significantly slower in running the straight-alley maze than are healthy rats. (a) What are the meaning and probability of a Type I error in this case? (b) What are the meaning and probability of a Type II error in this scenario?

Answers

(a) If Dr. Why made a Type I error, then he concluded that the rats were different when they actually were not. The probability is $\alpha = .05$. The cost would involve shipping new healthy rats and delaying research projects until they arrived. (b) If Dr. Why found a significant difference and rejected the null hypothesis, then he could not be making a Type II error, so the probability of a Type II error is $\beta = 0$ in this case. A Type II error is possible only when the null is retained. In this scenario, Dr. Why rejected H_0. (If he had retained the null hypothesis, a Type II error would mean he decided there was nothing wrong with the rats and he would run research using rats that actually had something wrong with them.)

Before getting into the discussion of power and the variables that affect it, you must have a strong understanding of hypothesis testing and the probabilities of Type I and Type II errors.

When Marchant-Haycox and Wilson (1992) studied the personalities of performing artists, they had a number of personality measures for each group of participants—singers, musicians, dancers, and actors (see Research Example 10). For each personality measure, they had norms for people who were similar but were not performers. For each group and personality measure you could set up a hypothesis comparing the performing artist group to the norming group. In some of the Quick Quizzes in Chapter 10 you did just that. For instance, one Quick Quiz concerned actors' self-esteem. You set up a null hypothesis of H_0: $\mu \leq 30.46$ and an alternative of H_1: $\mu > 30.46$, meaning you believed actors' average self-esteem would be higher than the norm of 30.46.

We will use actors' self-esteem to review all of the possible combinations of decisions and true states of the world associated with hypothesis testing (see Table 11.2). Before the research is done, you have two potential decisions and an error that could be committed when either decision is made. You could reject the null hypothesis, concluding that actors' self-esteem is higher than the norm. Of course, you might be wrong; if actors' self-esteem in the population actually is not higher than the norm, then you have made a Type I error. You could retain H_0, concluding that actors' self-esteem is lower than or equal to the norm. If actors' self-esteem is truly greater than the norm, then a decision to retain the null hypothesis was erroneous; when you retain falsely, you make a Type II error.

This is an illustration of what is possible in any hypothesis-testing situation: There are two hypotheses and two potential decisions. The two hypotheses, H_0 and H_1, cannot both be true for any one experiment because the expressed values for the parameters are nonoverlapping (mutually exclusive). For H_0: $\mu \leq 30.46$ and H_1: $\mu > 30.46$, if the true value of μ is 40, then H_1 is true; if the true value of μ is 23, then H_0 is true. For any hypothesis-testing situation, either H_0 is true or H_0 is false at any one time, but both cannot be the true state of the world simultaneously. In addition to the two possible states of the world, you could make two decisions: to reject H_0 or to retain H_0. In any given test of H_0, you can make only one of these two decisions. The decisions also are said to be mutually exclusive because both cannot occur at the same time. You cannot both reject H_0 and retain H_0 for the same statistical test. These two decisions combined with the two states of the world give four possible outcomes for the hypothesis test.

Before a research project is run, you must be concerned about both types of error. The research must be run with the idea of keeping both α and β low. However, once results have been obtained and a decision has been made, only one type of error could have been made. In the specific case of having results and a decision, only one of these probabilities will be important to you.

Now, **if H_0 is true and you reject H_0,** you have made a Type I error. If the actors' self-esteem really has an average of 30.46, the value specified in H_0, and you make the decision to reject the null, you have falsely rejected H_0. The probability of this error is α. If H_0 is true, the desired decision is to retain H_0.

If H_0 is true and you retain H_0, you have made a correct decision. If the actors' self-esteem really has an average of 30.46, and you make the decision to retain the null, you have correctly retained H_0. The probability of this combination is $1 - \alpha$.

If H_0 is false and you retain H_0, you have made a Type II error. If the actors' self-esteem really has an average greater than 30.46, and you make the decision to retain the null, you have falsely retained H_0. The probability of this error is β. If H_0 is false, the desired decision is to reject H_0.

If H_0 is false and you reject H_0, you have made a correct decision. If the actors' self-esteem really has an average greater than 30.46, and you make the decision to reject the null, you have correctly rejected H_0. The probability of this combination is $1 - \beta$, which is sometimes called the *power* of the test.

The following comments summarize the material in this section:

1. Be precise and correct in your language as you learn these concepts. For example, do not say *alpha error;* instead, say *Type I error;* and α and β are *probabilities,* not types of errors.

2. Know which distribution you are dealing with when you discuss any given probability. The first column of Table 11.2 represents the sampling distribution of the statistic when H_0 is true, so the probabilities in the first column (α and $1 - \alpha$) must be defined and represented in that distribution. If H_0 is false, then you are dealing with the second column and the sampling distribution of the statistic given H_1. Thus, β and $1 - \beta$ are represented in the H_1 distribution.

3. Realize which decision you are dealing with when you discuss any given probability. If you are discussing α or $1 - \beta$, the decision was to reject H_0. If you are discussing $1 - \alpha$ or β, the decision was to retain H_0. Once the decision is made, you know which row of Table 11.2 you are in and you can discuss the appropriate probabilities.

4. Once you have made your decision, you cannot make both errors at the same time. (Remember the firefighter example? The firefighters would be wrong to ignore a fire alarm when there really is a house ablaze, and they would be making a different error to check on a fire alarm when there is no fire. They can't simultaneously be ignoring the fire alarm and responding to it, so they can't make both errors at the same time.) If you have rejected H_0, you can make only a Type I error and you cannot make a Type II error, so practically $\beta = 0$. Similarly, if you have retained H_0, you can make only a Type II error and you cannot make a Type I error, practically $\alpha = 0$. This concept is discussed again later.

5. The sole purpose of this section on errors in hypothesis testing is to learn potential errors in making a decision about H_0. Both types of error and both probabilities can be defined and discussed before the actual testing of H_0. You can set α to be a small value, which controls the probability of a Type I error. And you can control the probability of a Type II error by controlling certain variables, which in turn keep β small. The probabilities of both types of error can be controlled at low values before you test H_0, so regardless of your decision, you feel confident of a small chance of a mistake. However, in each specific case, after the test is completed and a decision is reached, only one error could have been made, and the probability of the other type of error is zero.

6. Increasing α decreases β; similarly, decreasing α increases β. If you decrease α by using, say, an α of .01 or .001 instead of $\alpha = .05$, you increase β. You will see this relationship again in the discussion of power.

Now we expand the concept of a test's power, show the relationship between power and the probability of a Type II error, and discuss variables that influence power.

Quick Quiz

Imagine you have written a report about your study of performing artists and personality measures. You concluded that singers are significantly less adventuresome than the norm, with an average score of 18.22 on a measure of sensation seeking. A study partner says that you should discuss how your conclusion could be influenced by the probability of a Type II error. What do you have to say?

Answer

A Type II error can be made only when you retain H_0 falsely. If you have found a significant difference between singers and nonsingers, you have rejected the null hypothesis, so the only kind of error you need to be concerned about at this point is a Type I error, which you should have controlled before the study was run by setting α small.

11.3   Power

Power Defined

The power of a statistical test can be thought of as the strength of the test, or the ability of the test to reject H_0. Because power is a probability, power is also the proportion of repeated tests (for the same research situation) that reject H_0. A formal definition is:

$$\text{Power} = p(\text{rejecting } H_0) \tag{11.5}$$

This definition does not specify a particular hypothesis, so you can think of power in distributions either with H_0 true or with H_1 true. Usually you think of power in connection with rejecting H_0 when H_1 is true, or as $1 - \beta$. Power as $1 - \beta$ is the probability of rejecting H_0 *correctly*. In fact, in most cases, power and $1 - \beta$ are used interchangeably. However, occasionally power must be discussed as the probability of rejecting H_0 when H_0 is true; in this case, power is between zero and α.

Let's return to the exam stress study in Research Example 11. The researcher most likely considered the question of the power of the tests before the study started. Using the definition in formula 11.5, the researcher wants the probability of rejecting H_0 to be large if true differences exist between the perceived-control group and the no-control group. That is, the researcher wants good power to detect real differences if they exist.

Relationships among Power, β, and 1 − β

Whereas α, the probability of a Type I error, is easy to set and control (within some limits), you cannot easily set or control directly the probability of a Type II error, β. As mentioned earlier, you can control α directly by choosing α and critical values.

Direct control of β is not possible for three reasons. First, hypothesis testing is done in terms of the null hypothesis, and critical values are determined in the distribution for H_0, not H_1. Second, μ has many different potential values consistent with H_1 (each with a different distribution), but only one value of μ is tested in H_0. Finally, you usually don't have any idea which value of μ consistent with H_1 to choose in order to control β. So you set up tests that control β for all potential values of μ in H_1. Several indirect methods of controlling β are available: Sample size, variability in the experimental design, α, and kinds of hypotheses all affect β.

Don't think that you know the true value of μ when you test hypotheses. Nothing could be further from the truth. In practice, you never really know the value of μ. But you try to control the probabilities of both types of error at values low enough that you can be reasonably confident that your decision about μ will be correct. As mentioned earlier, you focus on power so that you can control β at a low value and have a low risk of a Type II error. The relationship between power and β is simple if you are dealing with a case where H_1 is true. Then power is $1 - \beta$, so the relationship is a complementary one. If power is high, β is low. If, for a specified μ, power $= .90$, then $\beta = .10$. Any variable that influences the power to be high will influence the probability of a Type II error to be low. So you generally try to maintain power at a high level to control β at a low level. Unlike α, which is controlled directly, β is controlled indirectly by the researcher. The researcher has control over certain variables that influence the power of a test; therefore, they influence β.

Quick Quiz

Your study buddy has another suggestion for you. Maybe you need more power in your study of singers and sensation seeking. Is this a good suggestion?

Answer

No, because you were already able to reject the null hypothesis. You don't need to increase the power of the test because you had enough power to detect a significant difference from the hypothesized μ.

11.4   Variables That Influence Power

Many variables influence power. Sample size is the most important and most easily controlled influence on power. Power is also affected by α; a higher significance level means higher power. And a one-tailed test is more powerful than a two-tailed test if you choose the correct tail. Let's look at these variables, plus the effects of σ^2 and the true differences that exist in the population.

Effect size

Size of the true difference between μ and the value tested in H_0

The size of the true difference, **effect size,** is the major influence on the value of the power. The actual difference between the "true" value of μ and that tested in H_0 has more impact on power than all other variables. Effect size is defined as some difference in population means divided by a standard deviation, so for $z_{\bar{X}}$, effect size is

$$\gamma = \frac{\mu - \mu_0}{\sigma} \tag{11.6}$$

We ignore the sign of γ (gamma). Here μ is the true value of the population mean and μ_0 is the value of the population mean specified in the null hypothesis.

For instance, the study on the IQs of deaf people in Research Example 9 tested a null hypothesis of $\mu = 100$. Keep in mind the definition of power: the probability of rejecting H_0. Are those researchers more likely to reject the null hypothesis if the true population mean is 95 or 82? It is easier to detect a bigger difference than a smaller one, isn't it? The *sample* mean was 88.07; sample statistics probably rarely equal the value of the parameter exactly. It makes sense that a whopping difference from 100 given by $\mu = 82$ in the population will find its way into the sample and be easier to detect than the milder difference given by $\mu = 95$.

An informal example may make the distinction between large and small effect sizes and the connection with sample size. Think about how advertisers might try to show the difference between Lincolns and Cadillacs. In the past there were car commercials about a study in which 100 Cadillac owners rode blindfolded in both types of cars over a specified course, and a large percentage chose the Lincoln as the smoother-riding car. Why 100 people? Because the difference between Cadillacs and Lincolns is small, the study needed a large N to detect this small difference. Now, consider this twist: The new Lincoln is compared to a 1971 Chevy that has 289,000 mi on it and was used as a cab in Chicago. Not only do you need few people to detect the difference, but also you may not even need to drive the specified course; when you slam the door and fire up the engine, they know there is a difference. Large differences are easy to detect and require smaller sample sizes.

What about the case where you have large differences from μ? Then good power is achieved by small sample sizes. In the anemia study in Research Example 11, the researchers used a very small sample size, $N = 6$, but still found significant gains in fetal hemoglobin levels. The impact of butyrate on the production of fetal hemoglobin was very large. In fact, the larger the difference, the smaller the N necessary to obtain a given high power.

In observational research, such as the country music airtime/suicide rate study in Research Example 6, researchers usually have no influence over the effect size. In true experiments, the researcher controls the independent variable and the number of groups in the study. For example, researchers might look at the effect of caffeine on laboratory animals. The designers of the study might decide to have six groups, with each group having just a slightly different level of caffeine. Other researchers might have a study with three groups, with large differences in the amounts of caffeine given to the groups. In Research Example 11, the researcher had control over the two levels of perceived control. If the researcher had made the perceived-control condition too similar to the no-control condition, the differences in the numbers of symptoms might not have been significant. However, in some research, the effect size is fixed. For example, the difference between the average IQs for hearing and deaf children is fixed, not manipulated by the researcher. In this case, whatever difference existed, the researchers were able to detect it. In any research, once the treatments are decided for each group, the researcher has to examine the remaining variables in order to influence power.

Sample Size

For any given effect size, by far the most potent influence on the power of a test is the sample size N. Generally, the larger the sample size, the larger the power. With all other variables held constant, increasing the sample size increases the power if μ is consistent with H_1. The last sentence was important, so reread it. Now, consider the case where μ is consistent with the null hypothesis. If no difference exists in the population, then increasing the sample size does nothing to the power of the test.

The increase in power for larger N, given that μ is in H_1, is because the variance of the sampling distribution of the statistic decreases as N increases. More of the distribution is beyond the critical value. For example, the sampling distribution of $\bar{X}$ has variance σ^2/N, so as N increases, this variance decreases and power increases. Remember that σ^2/N is the denominator of $z_{\bar{X}}$, and this statistic gets bigger as its denominator gets smaller. Figure 11.2 shows the sampling distributions for two different sample sizes with a fixed value of μ for H_1. There is clearly more power for the larger N. You should practice with the formula for $z_{\bar{X}}$. Decide what α and critical values you want to use. Then pick values for μ, $\bar{X}$, and σ^2, and compute the statistic for $N = 5$, then $N = 10, 15, 25$, and 50. What happens to the value of $z_{\bar{X}}$? With everything else held constant, the statistic gets bigger as N gets larger. Were your last few $z_{\bar{X}}$ values significant, but not the first few?

Caution: If N is very large, you will reject H_0 for even trivial differences from H_0, and you will be telling the scientific community that the difference is important when

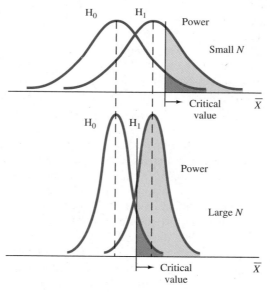

Figure 11.2
Sampling distributions of $\bar{X}$ showing the powers for different N's

it is not. Statistical significance is not the same as practical significance; statistically significant differences are not always meaningful. Very small differences from μ can be detected and the null hypothesis about μ can be rejected when N is large. In fact, it is possible to get arbitrarily high power for any difference just by using a large enough sample. However, some real but small effects need large sample sizes to be detected. Polio vaccine research is such an example.

The first author often tells his classes, "If you will give me 1 million people for my sample, I will let you choose both the dependent and independent variables (within reason) and will bet all I own on significant differences with $\alpha = .05$ and a two-tailed test." For example, use gender as the independent variable and IQ as the dependent variable. Do males and females differ with respect to intelligence? With $N = 1,000,000$, one can virtually guarantee some significant difference with $\alpha = .05$. Because you choose the independent and dependent variables, it just as easily could be the use of eyeglasses and whether bespectacled people differ from normal-vision people in the number of dental cavities. With an extremely large N, any tiny difference that exists will be declared significant.

What is the point of all this? You must be aware that N is a potent influence on power, and you must choose N carefully, avoiding extremes in size. For subsequent statistical procedures, you should use "moderate" sample sizes—large enough to give you power sufficient to detect large or moderate differences but small enough to avoid detecting trivial differences.

Control of σ^2

When running an experiment, researchers try to isolate the variable being manipulated. By randomly assigning subjects to groups, the researcher studying exam stress in Research Example 11 controlled extraneous variables, which allowed an interpretation of the effect of perceived control on exam stress. If extraneous variables aren't controlled, they could be influencing the dependent variable and the researcher might not be able to say what caused the difference in the number of stress symptoms. The probability of rejecting the null hypothesis, or power, is maximized when extraneous variability is kept to a minimum. Another factor that influences the variance is the sensitivity of the measuring instrument. The more sensitive the measurement of the dependent variable, the lower the variance. With all other variables fixed, decreasing variance increases power. Figure 11.3 shows sampling distributions with different variances and the resulting power values.

Once the researcher has chosen N, the experiment should be designed so as to control variability as much as possible. Within the constraints of careful experimentation, lowering the variability has minimal influence on the power compared to the choice of N.

Choice of α

Another influence on power is the choice of α. Like σ^2, α has a minimal effect on power compared to the influence of N. With all other factors held constant, increasing α increases power. More of the distribution is beyond the critical value. Figure 11.4 shows the gain in power from using $\alpha = .05$ instead of $\alpha = .01$. As mentioned earlier, the choice of α is limited by tradition and journal editorial practices, so researchers really have little ability to manipulate α.

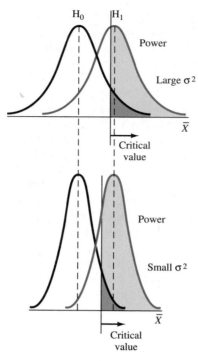

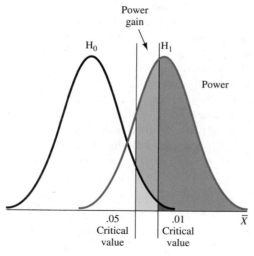

Figure 11.3
Sampling distributions of $\overline{X}$ showing the powers for different σ^2's

Figure 11.4
Influence of α on power

Hypotheses

Finally, the choice of hypotheses influences power. Directional hypotheses have greater power if you are correct in predicting the direction. If you incorrectly predict the direction, then you have virtually no power, and you don't even need to compute the statistic to retain H_0. The sampling distributions and power values given in Figure 11.5 show the influence of hypotheses.

One obvious advantage of the nondirectional hypothesis is that the researcher has good power to detect differences in either direction of the value specified in H_0. The disadvantage of nondirectional hypotheses is that the power is not quite as high in one direction as that of the appropriate directional hypothesis. The advantage is that the researcher does not run the risk of zero power, as is the case when a directional hypothesis is used and the prediction of direction is wrong.

Importance of *N*

Of the variables that affect power, *N* has the most potent influence and is most easily controlled by the researcher. That's why the focus has been on the choice of sample size. The next section addresses the calculation of power and the calculation of *N* for $z_{\bar{X}}$. In other statistics courses, you will learn methods for calculating *N* for desired differences in parameters for many of the practical statistical procedures covered in this text.

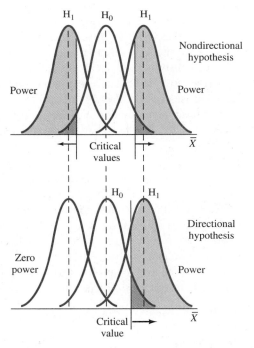

Figure 11.5
Influence of hypotheses on power

What happens when you have too much power in your study?

To emphasize the importance of power, sample size, and errors, here is another story, this one true. Try to pick out any mistakes in the arguments presented by the main characters. The names have been changed to protect the innocent and the guilty.

A professor, Dr. D, used white rats in her study of various learning theories. In one complex study with several groups of rats, she used a fairly small number of rats in each group. The results included statistics that rejected H_0. She wrote an article on the research and submitted it to a reputable scientific journal. After waiting several months for the review, the editor of the journal, Dr. E, wrote back with several suggestions for improving the research and the article. Most of the suggestions were minor, except for one that said, "We are concerned about the small sample size that you used for each group and think you might not have had enough power. We suggest you run that part of the study over with more rats per group." After consulting her local statistician, Dr. D wrote back to Dr. E that according to the most elementary principles of statistics, she did indeed have enough power because she had already rejected H_0. In fact, she argued that by the definition of power given by her statistician, the power for her study was 1.00. She agreed to make all minor changes but insisted that she did not need to run any more rats.

What do you think? Could Dr. D have made a Type II error? Was the power low, as claimed by Dr. E, or was it perfectly high, 1.00, as claimed by Dr. D? By the way, the first author of this text was the statistical consultant, and the definition of power used was that given in formula 11.5. You must realize that Dr. D designed the research to control the probabilities of both types of error. Then, after she ran the study and rejected H_0, she could have made only a Type I error.

In general, you want to control the probabilities for both errors at low values, but in each specific hypothesis-testing case, you can make only one decision and risk only one type of error.

Summary Problem

Instead of ending this section with a Quick Quiz, here are several questions for you to answer. *Do these computations;* then check your work.

Suppose you have H_0: $\mu = 100$, H_1: $\mu \neq 100$, $N = 16$, $\sigma = 8$, $\alpha = .05$, and $\overline{X} = 103$.

1. Would you reject H_0?
2. If $\sigma = 6$, would you reject H_0? What would this change do to the power?
3. For the original values except $N = 36$, would you reject H_0? What would this change do to the power?
4. For the original values except the hypotheses H_0: $\mu \leq 100$ and H_1: $\mu > 100$, would you reject H_0? What would this change do to the power?
5. For the original values except $\alpha = .20$, would you reject H_0? What would this change do to the power? Would most journal editors allow you to use $\alpha = .20$?

Now for the answers:

1. No, because $z_{crit} = \pm 1.96$

$$z_{\bar{X}} = \frac{\bar{X} - \mu}{\sigma/\sqrt{N}} = \frac{103 - 100}{8/\sqrt{16}} = \frac{3}{2} = 1.5 \quad \text{and} \quad z_{\bar{X}} = 1.5 < 1.96$$

2. Yes, because

$$z_{\bar{X}} = \frac{103 - 100}{6/\sqrt{N}} = \frac{3}{1.5} = 2.00 \quad \text{and} \quad z_{\bar{X}} = 2.00 > 1.96$$

The smaller value of σ increased the power and you rejected H_0.
3. Yes, because

$$z_{\bar{X}} = \frac{\bar{X} - \mu}{\sigma/\sqrt{N}} = \frac{103 - 100}{8/\sqrt{36}} = \frac{3}{1.33} = 2.25 \quad \text{and} \quad z_{\bar{X}} = 2.25 > 1.96$$

The larger value of N increased the power, so you rejected H_0.
4. No, because $z_{\bar{X}} = 1.5 < 1.65 = z_{crit}$. The change to a one-tailed test for the directional hypothesis increased the power, but not enough for us to reject H_0.
5. Yes, because $z_{\bar{X}} = 1.5 > 1.29 = z_{crit}$. Because of the substantial change in α, there was a large gain in power, which allowed for the rejection of H_0. No, the editorial policy of most journals would not allow the use of $\alpha = .20$.

11.5 Computing Power and Sample Size

Let's return to the study of actors' self-esteem as an example. The norm for self-esteem was $\mu = 30.46$ and, in Chapter 10, the standard deviation was given as 8.13. Suppose you have $N = 49$ and the alternative hypothesis of H_1: $\mu > 30.46$. Our goal is to learn how to compute power. We will answer this question, How can you compute the power of $z_{\bar{X}}$ for some μ different from 30.46?

Notation

In computing power and sample size, you'll be interested in two distributions: the H_0 distribution and the H_1 distribution. Both are centered on some value of μ. You've seen two values of μ before in the section on effect size. The mean under the null distribution was labeled as μ_0, and the symbol μ with no subscript referred to the "true" value of μ. For a given σ, the effect size increased as the difference $|\mu - \mu_0|$ grew. For the next computations, you will sometimes be using μ_0. When you are supposed to use some other value associated with the alternative distribution, you'll see the symbol μ_1. What follows now is fairly computationally oriented, and you might tend to lose sight of the forest for the trees. Remember, you want to know the power.

Computing Power

The first step in computing power is to find the critical value of $z_{\bar{X}}$. In our present example, we have H_1: $\mu_0 > 30.46$, so you need an upper-tailed critical value at $\alpha = .05$. The upper-tailed .05 critical value is $z_{\bar{X}} = 1.645$.

Second, you need to find the $\bar{X}$ that will give 1.645 in the $z_{\bar{X}}$ formula. That is, you are going to use the formula for $z_{\bar{X}}$ to find a critical value of $\bar{X}$. As you recall, the formula for $z_{\bar{X}}$ is:

$$z_{\bar{X}} = \frac{\bar{X} - \mu_0}{\sigma/\sqrt{N}}$$

Multiply both sides of the formula by $\sigma/\sqrt{N}$ and add μ_0 to both sides to isolate $\bar{X}_{crit}$, or the $\bar{X}$ that will result in the $z_{\bar{X}}$ critical value:

$$z_{\bar{X}}\frac{\sigma}{\sqrt{N}} = \bar{X} - \mu_0$$

$$\mu_0 + z_{\bar{X}}\frac{\sigma}{\sqrt{N}} = \bar{X}_{crit}$$

or

$$\bar{X}_{crit} = \mu_0 + z_{\bar{X}}\frac{\sigma}{\sqrt{N}} \tag{11.7}$$

You know that $\mu_0 = 30.46$, $\sigma = 8.13$, and $N = 49$. So plug in these known values, including 1.645 for the $z_{\bar{X}}$:

$$\bar{X}_{crit} = \mu_0 + z_{\bar{X}}\frac{\sigma}{\sqrt{N}} = 30.46 + 1.645\frac{8.13}{\sqrt{49}} = 32.37055 = 32.37$$

Because 5% of the z values are to the right of 1.645, 5% of the $\bar{X}$ values are to the right of the critical value of $\bar{X} = 32.37$ in the sampling distribution of $\bar{X}$ if $\mu_0 = 30.46$ (if H_0 is true).

But what do you want to find? You want to know how much area in the alternative distribution is to the right of this value. This area corresponds to power. If you chose the correct direction in H_1, how likely are you to reject H_0? The answer depends on how far apart the two distributions are. Effect size is a standardized difference between μ_0 and the "true" value of μ. If you could know the "true" value of μ, you wouldn't need statistics. Because you can't know the true μ, you have to choose some value of

μ_1. The value of μ_1 might represent some interesting difference from the value specified in H_0. For this example, we'll choose $\mu_1 = 34$.

The third step is to compute the $z_{\overline{X}}$ for the critical value of $\overline{X} = 32.37$ when $\mu_1 = 34$:

$$z_{\overline{X}} = \frac{\overline{X}_{crit} - \mu_1}{\sigma/\sqrt{N}} \tag{11.8}$$

If we know where the critical value cutoff point is in the alternative distribution, we can find power. Compute

$$z_{\overline{X}} = \frac{\overline{X}_{crit} - \mu_1}{\sigma/\sqrt{N}} = \frac{32.37 - 34}{8.13/\sqrt{49}} = -1.40$$

Fourth, find the probability of getting $\overline{X} = 32.37$ or larger when $\mu_1 = 34$, which will equal the probability of getting $z_{\overline{X}} = -1.40$ or larger. Table A.2 in Appendix A shows that the area between -1.40 and 0 is .4192. To get all of the area to the right of -1.40, add .5 for the right half of the distribution. You should get .9192 as the probability of getting $z_{\overline{X}} = -1.40$ or larger. (Draw a picture of a normal distribution, make a line for -1.40, and shade the area to the right to help you visualize this probability.) So the power is .9192 because this is the area to the right of the critical $\overline{X} = 32.37$ when $\mu_1 = 34$. Examine Figure 11.6 to see this area and all the relevant values of $\overline{X}$ and $z_{\overline{X}}$. The line associated with 1.645 in the null distribution also represents $z_{\overline{X}} = -1.40$ in the alternative distribution.

To give another example of computing power and to show what happens when you increase N, let's increase the sample size to $N = 90$. Keep the other values the same: $\mu_1 = 34$, $H_1: \mu_0 > 30.46$, $\sigma = 8.13$, and the critical value of $z_{\overline{X}} = 1.645$.

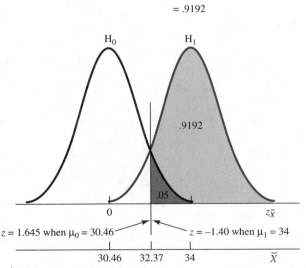

Figure 11.6
Power of $z_{\overline{X}}$ if $\mu_1 = 34$, $N = 49$, $H_1: \mu > 30.46$, $\sigma = 8.13$, and $\alpha = .05$

First you need to find the value of $\overline{X}$ that corresponds to the critical value of $z_{\overline{X}} = 1.645$. This critical value of $\overline{X}$ is given by

$$\overline{X}_{\text{crit}} = \mu_0 + z_{\overline{X}}\frac{\sigma}{\sqrt{N}} = 30.46 + 1.645\frac{8.13}{\sqrt{90}} = 31.87$$

So 5% of the $\overline{X}$ values are to the right of the critical value of $\overline{X} = 31.87$ in the sampling distribution of $\overline{X}$ if $\mu_0 = 30.46$ (if H_0 is true). Now you want the probability of $\overline{X}$'s to the right of 31.87 in the sampling distribution of $\overline{X}$ if $\mu_1 = 34$.

The next step is to compute the $z_{\overline{X}}$ for the critical value of $\overline{X} = 31.87$ when $\mu_1 = 34$:

$$z_{\overline{X}} = \frac{\overline{X}_{\text{crit}} - \mu_1}{\sigma/\sqrt{N}} = \frac{31.87 - 34}{8.13/\sqrt{90}} = -2.49$$

Third, find the probability of getting $\overline{X} = 31.87$ or larger when $\mu_1 = 34$, which will equal the probability of getting $z_{\overline{X}} = -2.49$ or larger. Table A.2 shows that the area between -2.49 and 0 is .4936; add .5 for the top half of the distribution, and you should get .9936 as the probability of getting $z_{\overline{X}} = -2.49$ or larger. So the power is .9936 because this is the area to the right of $\overline{X} = 31.87$ when $\mu_1 = 34$. Examine Figure 11.7 to see this area and all the relevant values of $\overline{X}$ and $z_{\overline{X}}$.

The distance between $\mu_0 = 30.46$ and $\mu_1 = 34$ is constant (3.54), but the variance of the sampling distribution shrinks as N increases. As N increased from 49 to 90, power increased from .9192 to .9936.

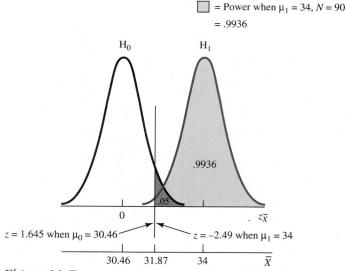

Figure 11.7
Power of $z_{\overline{X}}$ if $\mu_1 = 34$, $N = 90$, H_1: $\mu > 30.46$, $\sigma = 8.13$, and $\alpha = .05$

Computing Sample Size

Now let's approach the sample size/power issue from another direction. Let's compute sample size, N, for a given power. Again, as you go through the following computations, don't lose sight of the goal: to find the sample size.

You need to select the power—say, .90—and the value of μ_1 for which you want this power—say, $\mu_1 = 34$. You need to know σ (we'll use 8.13 again) and the critical value $z_{\bar{x}} = 1.645$. Use H_0: $\mu_0 \leq 30.46$.

The first step is to find the $z_{\bar{x}}$ that gives the selected power in the distribution centered on the selected value of μ_1. Use Table A.2 to find the $z_{\bar{x}}$ in the left tail that cuts off the power of .90 to the right. This value is $z_{\bar{x}} = -1.28$. Examine Figure 11.8 to see that this is the correct value of $z_{\bar{x}}$ in the distribution centered on 34. If you look up -1.28 in Table A.2, you'll find that the area between -1.28 and 0 is .40; add .5 for the upper part of the distribution, and you get .90.

To compute sample size, use the notation z_0 to signify the critical value for $z_{\bar{x}}$ under the null distribution and z_1 for the critical value that is associated with the alternative distribution. Here is the formula for N:

$$N = \frac{\sigma^2(-z_0 + z_1)^2}{(\mu_0 - \mu_1)^2} \tag{11.9}$$

If we let $1.645 = z_0$, $-1.28 = z_1$, $30.46 = \mu_0$, and $34 = \mu_1$, then all of the appropriate values can be inserted in the formula. It is important to maintain the correct signs on the values of z.

$$N = \frac{\sigma^2(-z_0 + z_1)^2}{(\mu_0 - \mu_1)^2} = \frac{(8.13)^2(-1.645 + (-1.28))^2}{(30.46 - 34)^2} = 45.13 = 45$$

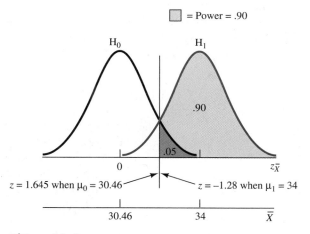

Figure 11.8
Computing N so $z_{\bar{x}}$ has power $= .90$ when $\mu_1 = 34$, H_1: $\mu > 30.46$, $\sigma = 8.13$, and $\alpha = .05$

We use the whole number nearest to the result given by the formula. So $N = 45$ is the sample size necessary to give the power of .90 for $z_{\bar{x}}$ to detect $\mu_1 = 34$ if H_1: $\mu_0 > 30.46$, $\sigma = 8.13$, and $\alpha = .05$. This is logical because $N = 49$ gave a power of .9192 for this same situation. It would take a slightly smaller sample size to give slightly less power. Similar computations for power and sample size can be done if the test is lower tail or two tailed.

Quick Quiz

If you knew that the norms for introversion among dancers were $\mu = 19.15$ and $\sigma = 4.32$ (see Research Example 10), and you wanted a power of .85 to detect a μ of 22, what sample size would you need? Use $\alpha = .05$ and H_1: $\mu > 19.15$.

Answer

First, find $z_1 = -1.04$, $z_0 = 1.645$, $\mu_0 = 19.15$, $\mu_1 = 22$, and $\sigma = 4.32$. Entering these into the formula for N gives 17 as the sample size.

Beyond These Power Calculations

Although you've seen sample size and power computation for only one statistic, $z_{\bar{x}}$, it is possible to compute power for any statistic (Cohen, 1977). Some major decisions have to be made in the process. You may have to state whether you are interested in a small, medium, or large effect size, for instance. For most behavioral scientists, this may not be easy. If you are just starting to do research in a certain area, such as depression among teenage alcoholics, you may not know what would constitute a large effect versus a small effect on the depression scale you're using. You also may not know what value of power you need—.70, .80, .90. What you should take from this chapter is an appreciation of the effect that your sample size can have on your statistical analysis. The number of observations in a data set may be directly responsible for the significance or nonsignificance of the results. Be aware that too many subjects can lead to statements of significance about trivial differences, and that too few subjects can mean important differences weren't detected because of lack of power.

11.6   Summary, Study Tips, and Computation

Chapter Summary

Errors in hypothesis testing include the Type I error (rejecting H_0 when H_0 is true) and the Type II error (retaining H_0 when H_0 is false). The probability of a Type I error is α and is set directly by the researcher. The probability of a Type II error is β and is controlled indirectly by variables that influence the power of the test. The power of the test is the probability of rejecting H_0 and is influenced by N, control of variability in the experimental design, α, and choice of hypotheses. The larger the N, the larger the power if μ is specified by H_1. Too large a sample size can result in excessive power for small differences from H_0. Smaller variability yields larger power. The larger the α, the greater the power. Directional hypotheses give more power than nondirectional hypotheses if the prediction of the direction is correct, but essentially zero power if the prediction of the direction is wrong. Nondirectional hypotheses give good power in either direction. The choice of N is the most potent and easily controlled variable that influences power. You can compute power for any given N, value of μ in H_0, value of μ you desire to detect, σ, and α. You can compute N for a desired power, value of μ you desire to detect, σ, and α.

The key terms and symbols used in this chapter are:

Type I error	$1 - \alpha$
Type II error	$1 - \beta$
α	Power
β	Effect size

Variables that influence power:

N	α
Variability	Hypotheses

Study Tips

Have you memorized the 2×2 table of errors and correct decisions? If not, do so now. Make sure you know the four variables that influence power and how each influences power.

Computation

Much of this chapter, like Chapters 9 and 10, is conceptually based. The computational procedures for finding sample size and power involve only $z_{\bar{x}}$, a little-used statistic that is a good teaching tool. Computer programs are available for computing the power for many statistics, but these computations are beyond the scope of this text.

Exercises

Section 11.1

1. Duncan and Klein (1992) were interested in a nation-wide study in Germany of smoking and respiratory health. Measures of lung capacity and smoking behavior were taken from 15,028 people at banks, shopping areas, and exhibitions. The researchers found that nonsmokers had a significantly lower average lung capacity than smokers. They happened to notice that nonsmokers were an average of 2 cm shorter than smokers. Their data analysis indicated that this difference was significant at the .01 level. The researchers concluded that smokers had a larger average lung capacity because they were taller, not because they smoked.
   a. Someone could use this study to bolster the argument, "Smoking doesn't stunt growth; it causes growth." Thinking back to Chapter 6 on correlation, why would this argument be erroneous?
   b. Does a 2 cm (slightly more than 3/4 in.) difference in height seem to be a big or little difference to you?
   c. What characteristics of the study would affect power?

Section 11.2

2. Consider the liar study (Ekman & O'Sullivan, 1991), in which people from various occupations tried to guess whether someone on a videotape was lying.
   a. For a participant in the study, what would be a Type I error? A Type II error?
   b. If you have decided that an acquaintance has lied to you, what kind of error could you be making? What kind of error can you *not* make if you've already rejected the hypothesis of truth telling? What would be the cost of your error?
   c. Ekman and O'Sullivan found that only Secret Service personnel were significantly better than chance at detecting a liar. What kind of error is possible here?

3. A large-scale yearly survey at University Y has established that full-time students study an average of 12.10 h per week. You think that engineering majors study more than that.
   a. Could you both reject and retain H_0: $\mu \leq 12.10$ in the same study?
   b. Explain your answer in part a.

4. In Exercise 1, what kind of error might the researchers have made in the two tests of hypotheses? (*Hint:* In the description, the two tests are associated with the word *significant.*) What is the probability of the error in the second decision?

5. The use of estrogen replacement in postmenopausal women to lower the risk of heart attack brings with it

the negative side effect of increased chances of a type of uterine cancer. To counter this side effect, some doctors advise that estrogen be combined with progestin to block uterine cell production. A group of researchers studying 173 women whose doctors had given them both estrogen and progestin observed $\overline{X} = 41$ mg/dL HDL (high-density lipoproteins, the "good" fat molecules that help reduce cholesterol levels and thus help prevent heart disease). If the average HDL level for this age women is $\mu = 34$ mg/dL with a standard deviation of $\sigma = 4.5$, has the combination of the two drugs increased the level of HDL?

a. For H_0: $\mu \leq 34$ and H_1: $\mu > 34$, can both H_0 and H_1 be true for this research situation?

b. Explain your answer in part a.

c. If you did not test the H_0 when this example was used in the Chapter 10 exercises, do it now. Compute $z_{\overline{X}}$ and use $\alpha = .05$.

d. What have you done if you rejected H_0 when it is true? When it is false?

e. How did you control the probability of a Type I error?

f. If you rejected H_0, could you have made a Type II error?

6. A psychologist has been studying the effect of deterioration of memory over time. He has been interested in how memory for particularly startling events, called *flashbulb memories,* might differ from memory for everyday events. He asked college students to try to remember all the circumstances of an ordinary event (such as meeting a friend) and then immediately after the event to fill out a survey about the details of the event. He knew from vast amounts of prior research that the average proportion of details accurately remembered 1 yr later is .85, with a standard deviation of .04. When the Persian Gulf War began in January 1991, he asked students to do the same task of filling out the survey about the details of the beginning of the bombing. He thought that the proportion of details remembered 1 yr later would be higher. The following are the proportions correct for 22 students:

| .81 | .65 | .93 | .78 | .79 | .87 | .86 | .83 | .87 | .85 | .77 |
| .86 | .80 | .81 | .82 | .83 | .87 | .85 | .85 | .84 | .83 | .90 |

a. For H_0: $\mu \leq .85$ and H_1: $\mu > .85$, can both H_0 and H_1 be true for this research situation?

b. Explain your answer in part a.

c. If you did not test H_0 when this example was used in the Chapter 10 exercises, do it now. Compute $z_{\overline{X}}$ and use $\alpha = .05$.

d. What have you done if you retained H_0 when it is true? When it is false?

e. How did the researcher control the probability of a Type II error?

f. If you retained H_0, could you have made a Type I error?

7. A computer program is designed to be used by a bank to take background information from business loan applicants. The program then accesses information from other computer information sources (such as those kept by credit bureaus) to verify the information. Finally, the program gives a decision to approve or deny the application.

a. If the null hypothesis is that the bank should make the loan, what is a Type I error? A Type II error?

b. What is the cost of each type of error?

8. A machine in a plant manufactures a car part and is set to make the part 6.70 in. long. The shift supervisor has the responsibility to make sure the setting on the machine has not shifted, and thereby altered this length, in either direction.

a. If the null hypothesis is that the setting is correct, what is a Type I error? A Type II error?

b. What is the cost of each type of error?

Section 11.3

9. Define power in terms of some research on the intelligence of deaf children that tests H_0: $\mu = 100$.

10. Suppose power $= .90$ for some effect size. If you have that effect size in your research and you ran the same study 200 times, how many tests would you expect to reject H_0?

Section 11.4

11. For a nondirectional H_1, what is the minimum power? The maximum power?

12. For a directional H_1, what is the minimum power? The maximum power?

13. For a nondirectional H_1: $\mu \neq 100$, suppose that power for $\mu = 105$ is .80. If you put $\alpha/2 = .025$ area into each tail of the distribution for H_0: $\mu = 100$, what is the power for $\mu = 95$?

14. For a directional H_1: $\mu < 100$, suppose that the power for $\mu = 95$ is .80. If you put $\alpha = .05$ area into only the lower tail of the distribution for H_0: $\mu \geq 100$, what is the power for $\mu = 105$?

15. McNeil, LeBlanc, and Joyner (1991) looked into the effect of exercise on moderately depressed residents of a retirement home. Thirty people qualified for the study; participants had to show no cognitive impairment and were not being treated for emotional problems. The participants were randomly assigned to one of three conditions: walking in the company of an experimenter, social contact that didn't involve exercise, or a waiting list. Their depression levels, aerobic fitness, and somatic symptoms (poor appetite, increased fatigue, sleep disturbances, and so on) were measured by the researchers before and after the treatment program. The researchers found:

   i. Only the subjects who engaged in researcher-accompanied exercise showed aerobic improvement.

   ii. Both social conditions resulted in lower depression scores.

   iii. The researcher-accompanied exercise group was the only one to show a reduction in somatic symptoms.

   a. Which conclusions might have been affected if more subjects were included in the study?

   b. Which conclusions probably would *not* change as a result of increased sample size?

   c. The researchers acknowledged that their exercise program wasn't rigorous or standardized and that their measure of aerobic fitness could have been better. How would these factors affect power?

16. A psychologist is studying the effects of high blood pressure, hypertension, on memory and learning. He uses a task that requires a person to study either two, four, or six digits shown on a screen and then later to indicate whether a single digit presented on the screen was part of the original set. The psychologist knows that the average time to answer for a large number of normal adults on the six-digit task is 1.35 s with a standard deviation of .23 s. He believes that hypertensives will answer more slowly than people with normal blood pressure. Compute $z_{\bar{X}}$ and find the p-value for the test of H_0: $\mu \le 1.35$ and H_1: $\mu > 1.35$ for each of the following:

   a. A sample of $N = 12$ hypertensives gave $\bar{X} = 1.44$ s for the six-digit task.

   b. A sample of $N = 18$ hypertensives gave $\bar{X} = 1.44$ s for the six-digit task.

   c. A sample of $N = 78$ hypertensives gave $\bar{X} = 1.44$ s for the six-digit task.

   d. Comment on how the p-values you computed show that increasing N increases the power for the difference of 0.09 s.

17. Suppose someone is studying the average IQ score for deaf children on the Wechsler Intelligence Scale for Children-Revised (WISC-R). If the population mean for the standardization group is 100 and the population variance is 225, the researcher wants to know whether the average performance by these deaf children is significantly different from that for hearing children. For H_0: $\mu = 100$, H_1: $\mu \ne 100$, $\alpha = .05$, $N = 15$, $\sigma^2 = 225$, and power .80 for some value of μ, which of the following changes will increase power?

   a. Use $N = 20$.

   b. Use $N = 10$.

   c. Use H_0: $\mu \le 100$ and H_1: $\mu > 100$ (if μ is less than 100).

   d. Use H_0: $\mu \le 100$ and H_1: $\mu > 100$ (if μ is larger than 100).

   e. Use $\alpha = .01$.

   f. New research shows that $\sigma^2 = 150$.

18. A psychologist has been studying the effects of different instructions on the intensity of pain. She had college students hold their hand in a jar of freezing water for as long as possible. Most students could tolerate only about 2 min and reported high-intensity pain. Then they removed their hands from the water and over the next 2 min were asked periodically to rate the intensity of the pain. The standard instructions given before this task were to suppress all awareness of the sensations in their hand—that is, to ignore the pain. For the standard condition, the researcher knew that the average pain intensity on a 1 (low, tolerable pain) to 5 (high, intolerable pain) scale was 4.06 with a standard deviation of 0.41 when pain intensity was measured at 1.5 min after they removed their hand from the water. The latest experiment had 63 college students do the same task but with instructions to monitor the details of their hand sensations—that is, to concentrate on the pain and its intensity. When pain intensity was measured 1.5 min after they removed their hand from the water, $\bar{X} = 3.85$ for the 63 students with the new instructions. Use H_0: $\mu \ge 4.06$ and H_1: $\mu < 4.06$.

   a. Compute $z_{\bar{X}}$ and find the p-value.

   b. If $N = 10$, compute $z_{\bar{X}}$, find the p-value, and comment on the impact of N on the power of the test.

   c. If the result were $\bar{X} = 4.27$, compute $z_{\bar{X}}$, find the *p*-value, and comment on the impact of hypotheses on the power of the test.

19. How could the researcher studying exam stress in Research Example 11 have increased the power of the test? Suppose the sample size was increased considerably so that the test detected as significant the difference on test performance between the perceived-control and no-control groups, when that difference was—say—0.1 on a 100-point test. Could you find fault with increasing the sample size to this extent? Explain.

20. You have studied the personalities of performing artists. One of the personality measures you used is a Manipulation/Empathy Scale, where a high score means high empathy for others. Marchant-Haycox and Wilson (1992) gave the empathy norms for non-performers as $\mu = 22.59$ and $\sigma = 6.79$. Here are your summary statistics (actually from Marchant-Haycox and Wilson):

Actors: $N = 33$, $\overline{X} = 22.33$
Dancers: $N = 26$, $\overline{X} = 25.26$
Musicians: $N = 65$, $\overline{X} = 25.44$
Singers: $N = 38$, $\overline{X} = 24.34$

a. What kind of study is this: observational research or a true experiment?
b. What kind of variable is empathy?
c. What kind of variable is occupation?
d. If you believe performers will have greater empathy than nonperformers, what are the null and alternative hypotheses?
e. Find the critical value(s) to test your hypothesis at the .05 significance level.
f. For each group of performers, calculate $z_{\overline{X}}$.
g. For each group of performers, test your hypothesis.
h. For which of the hypothesis tests might you have made a Type I error? A Type II error?
i. For which of the hypothesis tests did you probably have the most power? Why?
j. For which of the tests might you need to increase power? What are two ways that you could increase power when comparing this study to the next one you might do in this area?

21. Consider again the study of the personalities of performers. Suppose you also measured the performers' sociability/unsociability, where a high score means more avoidance of others (less sociability).

You believe that actors and dancers are more sociable (will have lower scores) than nonperformers; you think that musicians are less sociable (will have higher scores) than nonperformers; and you think singers will be different from nonperformers, but you aren't sure whether they will be more sociable or less sociable. (Statistics are from Marchant-Haycox and Wilson, 1992.) Nonperformers have norms of an average unsociability score of 13.16 with a standard deviation of 8.31. You find:

Actors: $N = 33$, $\overline{X} = 15.27$
Dancers: $N = 26$, $\overline{X} = 17.50$
Musicians: $N = 65$, $\overline{X} = 18.28$
Singers: $N = 38$, $\overline{X} = 16.86$

a. Write the null and alternative hypotheses for each group.
b. Find the critical values for each hypothesis test, using $\alpha = .05$.
c. Before calculating your test statistic, which hypothesis test appears to be most likely to reject the null hypothesis? (Which appears to have the most power?) Why?
d. Calculate $z_{\overline{X}}$ for each group.
e. Test the hypotheses.
f. Which test(s) turned out to have zero power? Why?
g. Why do researchers have to specify their hypotheses before they see their data?

22. Newcomb, Rabow, Monto, and Hernandez (1991) investigated factors that influence people to intervene and stop friends from driving drunk. They gave a questionnaire to 388 students in sociology classes at UCLA and found that 303 students had been faced with this situation. The researchers found several factors that significantly correlated with whether a student would intervene and try to stop a drunk friend from driving: (1) whether the driver needed help, (2) how well the student knew the driver, (3) whether other people encouraged the student to intervene, and (4) whether the student was able to intervene.

a. What kind of study is this: observational research or true experiment?
b. For each of the following variables, identify its type as it is used in this study: intervention, how well the person knew the driver, and the person's ability to intervene.

c. What affected the power of the hypothesis tests that led to the conclusion that certain factors are important to intervention?

d. Does this study have too much power? Give one argument to justify the sample size.

Section 11.5

23. You are studying the depression levels of teenage alcoholic girls. You have found a questionnaire that measures depression. The designers of the questionnaire say that American adults who are being treated for depression score an average of 17.9 out of 30 points, where a high number indicates more depression. The variance for the norming group is $\sigma^2 = 82.4$. You are working with 42 depressed girls, and you believe teenage alcoholic girls are more depressed than the average depressed adult because of the stress of the adolescent years. You think a girl from your population will have an average depression score of 22.

a. What are H_0, H_1, μ_0, and μ_1?

b. If you want a power of .85 for your μ_1, what $z_{\bar{X}}$ will have a proportion of .85 to the right of it?

c. Find the N needed to obtain a power of .85.

d. Do you already have enough girls for a power of .85?

e. Suppose you want to use all 42 girls available to you and you want to know how much power you would have.

   i. What is the critical value of $z_{\bar{X}}$ for H_0? What is the critical $\bar{X}$?

   ii. Find the $z_{\bar{X}}$ that is associated with the critical $\bar{X}$ and μ_1.

   iii. Find the probability of $z \geq z_{\bar{X}}$. This probability is the power when $N = 42$. Is this answer consistent with the sample size you calculated for a power of .85? Explain.

Part Two

Inferential Statistical Methods

By this point in the text you have learned basic tools for using statistics to test hypotheses. Now you need to expand your collection of inferential statistics. All the concepts and principles learned in the past eleven chapters apply to each of these new inferential methods. For each statistical procedure, the following will be given: the *situation* where the statistic should be used (including the *hypothesis* tested), the *test statistic,* the *theoretical reference distribution* and *decision rules,* and the *assumptions.* An example will be used for each method.

12

Statistics for Evaluating One-Sample Experiments

Using $z_{\bar{x}}$ as an example, you have learned the steps of hypothesis testing. However, $z_{\bar{x}}$ is an unrealistic statistic because you rarely know the population standard deviation when testing a hypothesis about a population mean. In this chapter you'll learn more one-sample statistics: a statistic to test a hypothesis about a population mean when you don't know the population standard deviation, confidence intervals for the population mean, statistics for testing hypotheses about a population correlation, and a statistic for testing a hypothesis about a population proportion.

Research Example 12
12.1   Overview: Available Statistical Procedures
12.2   One-Sample *t*-Test: A More Practical One-Sample Test
    Introduction
    Example
    Situation/hypotheses
    Need for *t*
    t-statistic
    t distributions
    Degrees of freedom
    Use of the *t* table
    Decision rules
    Assumptions
    Another example
12.3   Confidence Interval for the Population Mean
    Introduction
    Example
    Confidence interval with *s* as an estimate of σ
    Another example
    Language
    Relationship to hypothesis testing
12.4   Test of a Hypothesis about a Population Correlation
    Introduction
    Example
    Situation/hypotheses
    Test statistic and distribution
    Decision rules
    Assumptions
    Another example
12.5   Large-Sample Test of a Hypothesis about a Population Proportion
    Introduction
    Example

Situation/hypotheses
Test statistic and distribution
Decision rules
Assumptions
Another example
12.6 Summary, Study Tips, and Computation
Chapter summary
Study tips
Computation
Exercises

Research Example 12

Consider this title of a journal article: "Predictions of dental pain: The fear of any expected evil is worse than the evil itself" (Arntz, van Eck & Heijmans, 1990). Your reaction might be like that of the second author of this text, "Oh, yeah? *My* dental pain is *always* worse than I predicted!" Arntz and colleagues investigated 40 dental patients' expectations and actual experiences of dental pain and anxiety. The researchers had several hypotheses about how memory of pain might be related to predictions of pain and actual experienced pain.

The patients were all volunteers, 20 men and 20 women, had an average age of 33.9 (age ranged from 17 to 71), and were all treated twice. They received treatment from several dentists in the same city. The average time between treatments was 10.4 days, ranging from 1 to 37 days. The treatments, though varying among the patients, all involved typical dental work and had the potential for being painful in both sessions. Patients completed a questionnaire before and after each treatment. Predicted pain was measured before treatment on a scale using a 10-cm line ranging from 0 = "not at all painful" to 100 = "the worst pain imaginable." Immediately after each treatment, patients were asked to rate the actual experienced pain on the same scale. Five months after the second treatment, the researchers were able to contact 31 of the 40 patients and ask them about their memories of pain on the same scale. Other measures were taken each time, such as measures of anxiety and fear, but the predicted, actual, and remembered pain are the focus of our attention now.

The results showed that memories of pain are influenced by both predicted and actual experienced pain. Here is an extensive quote from the article by Arntz and colleagues about the results of this part of the research. It includes several statistics that you will learn later in this text.

Memories of pain experienced during the second treatment were assessed 5 months after this treatment. Remembered pain was generally higher than experienced pain [$t (30) = 2.73, P = 0.01$], but lower than pain predicted at treatment 1 [$t (30) = -2.43, P = 0.02$]. Although the anxious S's remembered significantly more pain than they actually experienced, and low-anxiety S's remembered their pain quite accurately, the between effect was NS with respect to inaccuracy. However, a direct comparison between the memories of pain was significant ($P = 0.05$). It can be concluded that memories of pain were influenced both by experienced pain [$r = 0.39, P = 0.03$] and by original predictions of pain [$r = 0.66, P = 0.001$].

The notation "$P =$" shows the probability associated with each statistic; we use a lowercase "$p =$" to mean the same thing. "NS" means "nonsignificant"; that is, they did not reject H_0. In this chapter you will learn about the statistic r as a test statistic, and in later chapters you'll learn the other statistics from the article quotation.

Do these results about dental pain reflect your experiences? Or do you think your predictions of pain turn out to be pretty close to your actual experienced pain? Of course, you are having to remember the pain, and the results show that such memories are influenced more by predictions than by actual experienced pain.

12.1 Overview: Available Statistical Procedures

Having learned the basic concepts of hypothesis testing using $z_{\overline{X}}$ as a one-sample test of hypotheses about a population mean, you now need to expand your repertoire of statistical procedures. This chapter on one-sample methods introduces the one-sample t-test for hypotheses about a population mean, confidence intervals for the population mean, the use of r to test for hypotheses about a population correlation, and the large-sample test for hypotheses about a population proportion. For each new statistical procedure introduced you'll learn:

1. Situation/hypotheses (when to use the statistic)
2. Test statistic
3. Theoretical reference distribution used to obtain critical values, and decision rules
4. Assumptions associated with the statistic

You can use these four topics as an outline for comparing the various statistics. All of the statistics you'll learn in this chapter will help you practice the steps of hypothesis testing.

Quick Quiz

Explain how each of the four topics applies to the statistic $z_{\overline{X}}$.

Answer

(1) This is a one-sample test statistic that is used when σ^2 is known and you are interested in a hypothesis about a single population mean (H_0: $\mu = 100$, for example). (2) The test statistic is $z_{\overline{X}}$; the formula has been given. (3) When N is large enough, you can use the standard normal distribution as the theoretical reference distribution. If your statistic exceeds the critical value(s), reject H_0. (4) The population is normal and the observations are independent.

12.2 One-Sample t-Test: A More Practical One-Sample Test

Introduction

You should be comfortable with a z score as a measure of an individual X value's relative position in a distribution. From there you went on to $z_{\overline{X}}$, your first test statistic, which measures $\overline{X}$'s position relative to μ. This is the same idea behind other test statistics.

The statistic $z_{\bar{X}}$ is an impractical but simple one-sample test for hypotheses about the population mean.

The statistic we introduce now is a more realistic and practical test for this one-sample situation. The new test is the **one-sample *t*-test.** (This lowercase *t* should not be confused with *T*-scores, introduced in Chapter 5.) Even though it is also used to test hypotheses about the population mean, the one-sample *t*-test is more practical and realistic than $z_{\bar{X}}$ because it is used when you do not know the population variance σ^2 or the standard deviation σ. This important distinction needs to be emphasized: When you have one sample and are testing a hypothesis about a single population mean, use $z_{\bar{X}}$ if σ^2 is known and use the one-sample *t*-test if σ^2 is unknown. The language, principles, and logic of hypothesis testing that you learned for $z_{\bar{X}}$ apply to this new test statistic as well as to every other statistical procedure covered in this text. (By the way, use the full name "one-sample *t*" because there are several other kinds of *t*-statistics. You will learn some of them in the next chapter.)

One-sample *t*-test
A one-sample test of a hypothesis about a single population mean when the population variance is unknown

Example

In a study of 59 deaf children, Hirshoren, Hurley, and Kavale (1979) found that their average IQ score on the Wechsler Intelligence Scale for Children-Revised (WISC-R) was 88.07 (also used in Research Example 9 and Exercises 9 and 10, Chapter 10). They wanted to provide standardization information on the WISC-R for future research with deaf children. You could test a null hypothesis that these deaf children have the same average performance as that for the hearing standardization group ($\mu = 100$). In this case, the variance (or standard deviation) of the deaf children's score on the WISC-R was unknown. How would you test H_0: $\mu = 100$?

Situation/Hypotheses

The one-sample *t*-test is used to test exactly the same hypotheses that are tested by $z_{\bar{X}}$, so the pairs of hypotheses for the IQs of deaf children could be

$$H_0: \mu = 100 \qquad H_1: \mu \neq 100 \tag{12.1}$$

$$H_0: \mu \leq 100 \qquad H_1: \mu > 100 \tag{12.2}$$

$$H_0: \mu \geq 100 \qquad H_1: \mu < 100 \tag{12.3}$$

Just as you did with the $z_{\bar{X}}$, pay attention to the language used in the scientific hypothesis to see whether directionality is implied. For example, in the rat shipment example in Chapter 10, if the rats had appeared sluggish, this would imply slowness and a mean running time higher than the standard, 33 s. If direction is predicted, use hypotheses like those in formula 12.2 or 12.3, substituting the hypothesized value of μ. Because the researchers said deaf children would have the same average IQ, direction was not predicted and you should use the hypotheses in formula 12.1.

Need for *t*

In order to use

$$z_{\bar{X}} = \frac{\bar{X} - \mu}{\sigma/\sqrt{N}}$$

to test a hypothesis about the population mean, you need to hypothesize a value for μ and know the population variance or standard deviation (σ^2 or σ). If published test norms do not give a value for σ^2 or if previous research does not give this information, then the researcher must estimate σ^2 with

$$s^2 = \frac{\sum(X - \bar{X})^2}{N - 1} = \frac{N\sum X^2 - (\sum X)^2}{N(N - 1)}$$

and use the one-sample t instead of $z_{\bar{X}}$.

To summarize: You use the one-sample t-statistic instead of $z_{\bar{X}}$ when the population variance is unknown. Sample size and knowledge of other variables are irrelevant. If you know σ^2 or σ, use $z_{\bar{X}}$; if you do not know σ^2 or σ, estimate σ^2 with s^2 (or σ with s) and use the one-sample t. In the problem of the IQs of deaf children, the σ^2 for the IQ of deaf children is not known and s is available, so the one-sample t is appropriate.

t-Statistic

Although the hypotheses for the one-sample t-test are the same as those for $z_{\bar{X}}$, the test statistic is different. Because you do not know the population standard deviation, you estimate it with the sample standard deviation to obtain the test statistic called the *t*-statistic:

t-statistic
Something minus its mean divided by its *estimated* standard deviation

$$t = \frac{\bar{X} - \mu}{s/\sqrt{N}} \tag{12.4}$$

The only difference between this formula for the one-sample t and that for $z_{\bar{X}}$ is that s replaces σ. A general verbal formula for any t is: something minus its mean divided by its *estimated* standard deviation.

For the IQs of deaf children, $\bar{X} = 88.07$, $\mu = 100$ (from H_0), $N = 59$, and $s = 17.84$. The one-sample t-statistic is:

$$t = \frac{\bar{X} - \mu}{s/\sqrt{N}} = \frac{88.07 - 100}{17.84/\sqrt{59}} = \frac{-11.93}{2.32} = -5.14$$

t Distributions

Once you compute a sample value for a test statistic, you compare it to critical values from a theoretical reference distribution. When you used $z_{\bar{X}}$, you compared it to z_{crit}. But now you are using the one-sample t, so you need critical values of t. The change in the test statistic leads to a change in the theoretical reference distribution used to obtain critical values. The theoretical reference distribution for the one-sample t-test is called a **t distribution.** A t distribution is symmetric and unimodal, has mean equal to zero, and looks much like the standard normal distribution, as you can see from Figure 12.1. A t distribution has more variability than the standard normal distribution because of the substitution of s for σ: Not only will $\bar{X}$ vary from sample to sample, but also s will vary.

t distribution
Theoretical distribution that is symmetric, smooth, and unimodal with mean equal to zero, but with more variability than the standard normal distribution

Another difference between normal distributions and t distributions is the number of parameters. Normal distributions have two parameters, μ and σ^2. But t distributions have only one parameter, **degrees of freedom (df).** For the one-sample t,

Degrees of freedom
The parameter of t distributions; formula of $N - 1$ for the one-sample t; symbolized by *df*

$$df = N - 1 \tag{12.5}$$

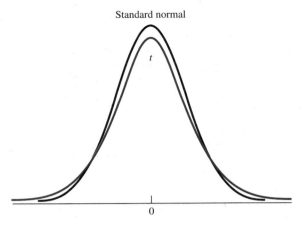

Figure 12.1
The *t* distribution with *df* = 4 and the standard normal distribution

What we have called the *t* distribution is really a family of different distributions, one for each value of the parameter *df*. Figure 12.1 shows a *t* distribution with *df* = 4 with the standard normal distribution superimposed.

Degrees of Freedom

The best definition of *degrees of freedom* is a parameter of a theoretical distribution, such as *t*. Even though this is accurate, it does not give any insight into why *df* has different formulas for different hypothesis-testing situations. Why is *df* equal to $N - 1$ for this one-sample *t*? To find the value of *df* for a statistical test, you need another definition of *df*, something like a computational formula. The following **working definition of degrees of freedom** fits most situations where *df* is used:

Working definition of degrees of freedom
In an estimate of variability, the number of independent components minus the number of parameters estimated

In an estimate of variability,   (12.6)

df = number of independent components

   − number of parameters estimated

To apply formula 12.6, you have to look at the test statistic for an estimate of variability. This estimate of variability can be a sample variance or a sample standard deviation. Once you find an estimate of variability, you need to write its definitional formula. Then you go inside the formula and search for the number of independent components and the number of parameters estimated. Here *independent* means "not related to."

Let's use the *df* for the one-sample *t*-statistic as an example. What is the difference between *t* and $z_{\bar{X}}$? Well, $z_{\bar{X}}$ has σ in its denominator, and *t* has *s* in its denominator. Did $z_{\bar{X}}$ have any concept of *df* associated with it? No, *df* as a concept was not associated with $z_{\bar{X}}$ or normal distributions, but it has been introduced as a parameter of the *t* distribution. So the concept of *df* must be a function of *s* as it is used in *t*. To apply formula 12.6, you need to find an estimate of variability in the test statistic; *s* in the formula for t qualifies. To see how to use formula 12.6 to verify that the one-sample t has $df = N - 1$, you need to examine the definitional formula for s:

$$s = \sqrt{s^2} = \sqrt{\frac{SS}{df}} = \sqrt{\frac{\Sigma(X - \overline{X})^2}{N - 1}}$$

In this formula for s, pay attention to the numerator, which contains X and $\overline{X}$. How many values of X are there in your sample? You should answer N. These N values of X are independent because of random sampling, so you have N as the number of independent components. Now, let's find how many parameters are being estimated. In other words, how many statistics are in the variability formula? Because there is only one statistic, $\overline{X}$, for this sample and $\overline{X}$ is an estimate of a parameter, 1 is the number of parameters estimated. You have N independent components, the N values of X, and you have one $\overline{X}$, a statistic, that estimates one parameter, μ. Therefore, N independent components minus one parameter estimated gives $N - 1$. So s has $N - 1$ degrees of freedom, and because s is the variability estimate in t, you know that t has $df = N - 1$. (See Box 12.1 for more explanations about degrees of freedom.)

If a variance estimate is unbiased, then the df of the variance estimate appears in its formula, in the denominator. In s^2, $N - 1$ is the denominator of the definitional formula given above. Degrees of freedom are associated with many test statistics, so the df formula is different for other statistics. In situations other than the one-sample t-test, the actual value of df is different. But you can still use formula 12.6 to see why the df takes on its particular value. It is helpful to know the df formulas for the various test statistics reported in scientific journals. There are many t-statistics, but articles sometimes don't specify which t was calculated. If you know the number of subjects and the df, you can usually figure out which statistic was used. As a consumer of scientific research, you'll find that degrees of freedom will help you understand what you read.

In the problem on the IQs of deaf children, $N = 59$, so $df = N - 1 = 59 - 1 = 58$.

Use of the *t* Table

Every t distribution (one for each value of df) has its own set of probabilities and its own critical values for different levels of significance α. Table A.4 in Appendix A gives the probabilities for many t distributions. Values of df ranging from 1 to ∞ (infinity) form the rows, and various levels of significance (α) form the columns. The tabled entries are the critical values of t for a given df and α. The t distribution is symmetric, so Table A.4 contains only the upper-tail critical values (the lower-tail critical values may be obtained by using the negative of the upper-tail values). The critical values for $df = \infty$ are the same as those from the standard normal distribution in Table A.2. This shows that as df increases, the t distributions approach the standard normal distribution. In any column, the critical values decrease toward a critical value of the standard normal distribution. As df increases, the variance of the t distribution approaches one, which is the variance of the standard normal distribution.

To use Table A.4, you need to know the df for your problem, the α that you have selected, and whether the test is one or two tailed. (You might notice that total α is used in this table; the headings for one- and two-tailed tests divide α accordingly.) For example, suppose you have $N = 16$ subjects, you have selected $\alpha = .01$, and you have a two-tailed test. Your $df = N - 1 = 15$. Table A.4 gives the critical values -2.947 and 2.947.

Box 12.1   An Informal Look at the Concept of Degrees of Freedom

Let's set aside the formal definition of degrees of freedom for a moment and see what it means to have values that are free to vary.

Suppose you want to see how many different sets of five numbers can have a mean of 10. We are fixing $\overline{X}$ and we are choosing five numbers to average out to 10. Here is one set of X values that averages to 10: 6, 8, 10, 12, and 14:

$$\overline{X} = \frac{\sum X}{N} = \frac{50}{5} = 10$$

Let's make a statement and see if the numbers will back it up: You can choose *any four numbers* to go into the calculation of $\overline{X} = 10$, but once you have chosen those four numbers, the fifth one is not free to vary. Suppose you choose these four numbers: 1, 2, 5, and 21. There is only one number that can be the fifth value and still have $\overline{X} = 10$. The sum of the four numbers you chose is 29, and the sum of the five numbers must be 50 to give the sample mean of 10. We know that (29 + the fifth number) = 50. To find the fifth number, we calculate:

$$29 + X = 50$$
$$X = 50 - 29$$
$$X = 21$$

So the fifth number is 21. (Calculate the mean of 1, 2, 5, 21, and 21 to see if we are correct.) Now choose four wild numbers: 680, 4, 119, and 221. There is only one number that can be the fifth member of the set and still have $\overline{X} = 10$. Try the calculation above with these four numbers. Did you get $X = -974$?

This is the idea behind degrees of freedom. Only a certain number of values are free to vary. You lose one degree of freedom in the calculation of the sample mean, which is an estimate of a parameter. Now look back at the working definition of degrees of freedom and see if it makes more sense to you.

If the value that you calculate for *df* is not given in the table, choose the critical value for the next *smaller* value of *df*. This practice leads to a slightly smaller probability of a Type I error (slightly conservative tests). In other words, you are choosing a slightly bigger critical value than you need. It's farther out in the tail, so it is cutting off slightly less probability than α. If the test is significant at the more conservative *df*, then it would also have been significant at the exact *df*. In using Table A.4 for the problem on the IQs of deaf children, you can see that there is no row that represents *df* = 58, so you use *df* = 55. With $\alpha = .05$ for a two-tailed test, the tabled value for *df* = 55 is 2.004, so the critical values are ±2.004. The critical value for *df* = 58 is actually somewhere between the critical values for *df* of 55 (2.004) and 60 (2.000), but the use of 2.004 will give an acceptable, approximate (conservative) test.

Decision Rules

All the decision rules for the statistics in this chapter are similar. A general critical value decision rule is to reject H_0 if the statistic is equal to or more extreme than the critical value. The one-sample *t*-test uses critical values from a *t* distribution.

For a two-tailed test with the one-sample *t*-test, the decision rule is:

$$\text{If } t \le -t_{\text{crit}} \text{ or } t \ge t_{\text{crit}}, \text{ reject } H_0; \text{ otherwise, retain } H_0 \tag{12.7}$$

where t_{crit} is the $\alpha/2\%$ critical value from the *t* distribution with $df = N - 1$. In the example of deaf children's IQs, for $df = 58$, you used $df = 55$ and the $\alpha = .05$ critical values -2.004 and 2.004. An obtained one-sample *t*-statistic that is more extreme than one of these values will lead you to reject H_0. The observed value is $t = -5.14$, so you reject H_0 because $t = -5.14$ is more extreme than -2.004. A *t* distribution for $df = 55$ is given in Figure 12.2, showing the critical values, rejection values, and areas, with $\alpha/2 = .05/2 = .025$ in each tail.

For a one-tailed test that uses the upper tail of the *t* distribution, the decision rule is:

$$\text{If } t \ge t_{\text{crit}}, \text{ then reject } H_0; \text{ otherwise, retain } H_0 \tag{12.8}$$

where t_{crit} is the critical value from the *t* distribution with the chosen α and $df = N - 1$.

The decision rule for a one-tailed test in the lower tail of the *t* distribution is:

$$\text{If } t \le -t_{\text{crit}}, \text{ then reject } H_0; \text{ otherwise, retain } H_0 \tag{12.9}$$

where t_{crit} is the critical value from the *t* distribution with the chosen α and $df = N - 1$. For a one-tailed test, all of α is in the tail that the directional sign in the alternative hypothesis is pointing toward because the prediction is that the statistic will be found in that tail.

For a two-tailed test of a nondirectional hypothesis, if the two-tailed *p*-value is less than or equal to α, reject H_0; otherwise, retain H_0. For one-tailed tests of directional hypotheses, you have to pay attention to not only the size of the one-tailed *p*-value but also the tail where the observed statistic occurs. You reject H_0 only when the *p*-value is small enough *and* the statistic occurs in the tail of the sampling distribution predicted by H_1.

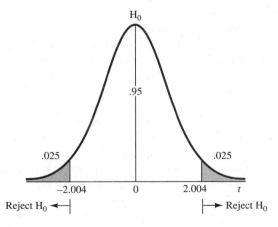

Figure 12.2
The *t* distribution with $df = 55$, showing critical values, rejection values, and areas

Assumptions

The assumptions for the one-sample *t*-test are the same as those for $z_{\overline{X}}$: normality of the population and independence of observations. When H_0 is true, the sampling distribution of the one-sample *t*-statistic is exactly fit by the *t* distribution with parameter $df = N - 1$ if the original scores are independent and normally distributed in the population. As was the case for $z_{\overline{X}}$, the assumption of independent observations is usually met unless there is obvious dependency. The IQs of deaf children are approximately normally distributed, so this problem probably meets this assumption. Typically, however, the population distribution is not normal, but the use of a large sample size and the Central Limit Theorem (see Section 9.6) allow you to assume that the sampling distribution of $\overline{X}$ is normal in shape. You can also assume that the sampling distribution of the one-sample *t*-statistic is well fit by the theoretical *t* distribution.

Quick Quiz

Find the critical value(s) for the given information: $\alpha = .01$, H_0: $\mu \leq 500$, $N = 48$.

Answer

The test is one tailed and the alternative hypothesis is the opposite of H_0, so H_1: $\mu > 500$. The $\alpha = .01$ is in the upper tail. The formula for degrees of freedom for the one-sample *t* is $N - 1$, so $df = 47$. The table doesn't give an entry for $df = 47$, so use the next smaller df, which is 45, and $t_{crit} = 2.412$.

Another Example

Have you heard about the research showing that as married couples age, they become similar in physical appearance (see Zajonc, Adelmann, Murphy & Niedenthal, 1987)? Suppose you have $N = 37$ people rate photographs of men and women for resemblance. You have photographs of six couples who have been married 25 yr or more, but you do not tell the raters which man is married to which woman. Instead, you scramble the pictures and ask the raters to just score how much each man looks like each woman. The photos are presented to the 37 raters on a display board that has six plastic pockets in a row with one plastic pocket above the six. The 12 photos are displayed in these seven plastic pockets in the following way.

First, the six women's photos are shown in the row and each man is presented one at a time as the "target" in the one pocket above the row. The raters are asked to put a 1 under the photo of the woman who most closely resembles the man in the target photo, down to a 6 under the one who least resembles the target. So each rater has given each man's actual wife a score from 1 to 6. If the rater thinks she resembles him, the score for the wife will be low, close to 1. Second, the six men's photos are treated the same way, with each woman presented as the target. So each woman's actual husband has a score from 1 to 6. If the rater thinks the husband resembles the woman, the score for the husband will be low, close to 1.

Now, we want to focus on the 37 raters and the scores they gave to the actual couples. The actual husband was rated when his wife's photo was the target, and vice versa. So each rater has 12 of these scores. The average of these 12 scores is used as a measure of the rater's ability, and we call this average the rater's resemblance score. It ranges from 1 to 6.

Table 12.1
Resemblance scores for $N = 37$ raters (scoring 25 yr married couples)

2.50	3.75	2.75	2.42	2.92	3.33
3.42	3.00	3.42	3.33	2.08	3.25
3.92	2.83	3.08	2.67	3.50	2.83
2.42	3.17	3.67	3.17	4.00	2.67
4.08	4.33	3.08	3.33	1.58	2.42
3.50	3.67	2.67	2.67	3.17	3.33
3.17					

If there is no resemblance and raters assign the ranks from 1 to 6 randomly, then the average resemblance score should be 3.5, the average of the scores 1 through 6. So a hypothesis of no resemblance for couples is H_0: $\mu = 3.5$. Table 12.1 lists simulated scores for this problem.

For the resemblance of older couples, the mean ranking is $\bar{X} = 3.11$, $\mu = 3.5$ (from H_0), $N = 37$, $df = 36$, and $s = 0.5762$. The one-sample t-statistic is

$$t = \frac{\bar{X} - \mu}{s/\sqrt{N}} = \frac{3.11 - 3.5}{0.5762/\sqrt{37}} = \frac{-0.39}{0.0947} = -4.12$$

Because the observed $t = -4.12$ is less than the t_{crit} of -2.03 (the two-tailed critical value for $df = 35$), you reject H_0 and conclude that resemblance of older married couples is greater than expected by chance alone. In the original research (Zajonc et al., 1987), the researchers also had another set of 37 raters examine the photos of the same couples taken at the time they were just married. The resemblance of these "young" couples was not different from expected from chance alone (mean of 3.43 was not different from 3.5, $t = 0.68$).

Quick Quiz
You've heard about contests for the pet owner who looks most like his or her animal. Imagine you have run a study somewhat similar to the husband–wife study above. Thirty raters gave scores on a scale of 1 (most resembles) to 10 (least resembles) for ten pet owners. Each pet was shown individually in the "target" position, and the owners' resemblances to the target pet were rated. If the ratings were given randomly, you would expect the average resemblance rating to be 5.5, the average of 1 through 10. Your raters have $\bar{X} = 6.4$ and $s^2 = 4.1$. Do you reject H_0: $\mu \geq 5.5$? Use $\alpha = .05$.

Answer

For $\alpha = .05$ and a one-tailed test with $df = 29$, $t_{crit} = -1.699$. You should calculate $t = 2.43$, so you retain the null hypothesis and conclude that your raters scored the similarity of pets and pet owners as not significantly greater than chance.

12.3 Confidence Interval for the Population Mean

Introduction

In Chapter 9 you learned that point estimation involves the estimation of a single parameter with a single statistic, such as using $\bar{X}$ to estimate μ. Interval estimation provides an interval of potential values for a parameter. However, the confidence interval you learned in Chapter 9 involved the use of σ, which is rarely known. Now we introduce a confidence interval for μ that does not require you to know σ.

Example

Let's return to the research showing that as married couples age, they become similar in physical appearance (see Zajonc et al., 1987, and the one-sample t-test earlier). You have $N = 37$ raters judge photographs of men and women for resemblance, where the photographs are of six couples who have been married 25 yr or longer. Each rater generates a resemblance score that is the average of the 12 scores he or she gave the 12 people in the six couples; these scores range from 1 to 6.

If there is no resemblance and subjects rate from 1 to 6 randomly, then the population average score should be 3.5, the average of the scores 1 through 6. For the resemblance of older couples, the obtained mean ranking is $\overline{X} = 3.11$, $N = 37$, and $s = 0.5762$.

Confidence Interval with *s* as an Estimate of σ

You cannot say that the population mean equals your value of $\overline{X}$ because there is some error in the estimate $\overline{X}$. Is the true population mean for the resemblance of older couples 3.11? Probably not, but it should be close to this value of $\overline{X}$, which is only a point estimate. You can improve on your point estimate by including some measure of error. A measure of the extent or degree of error in $\overline{X}$ as an estimate of μ is given by the standard error of the mean, $\sigma/\sqrt{N}$.

You rarely know the value of the population variance, σ^2, or the standard deviation, σ, so you use s in place of σ and $s/\sqrt{N}$ for $\sigma/\sqrt{N}$. This allows you to place bounds on $\overline{X}$ such that you are confident that they bracket, or include, the true value of μ a certain percentage $[100(1 - \alpha)\%]$ of the times μ could be estimated. The confidence interval is centered on $\overline{X}$, and the ends of the interval depend on the estimated standard error, $s/\sqrt{N}$, and a critical value that reflects the percentage of the time you wish to include the true value of μ. The value of α is used to find the critical value.

To estimate the true population mean of the resemblance of older couples, you can get a confidence interval for μ that improves on the point estimate, $\overline{X} = 3.11$. With a general $1 - \alpha$, the lower bound of the interval is

$$\overline{X} - t_{\text{crit}} \frac{s}{\sqrt{N}} \tag{12.10}$$

and the upper bound of the interval is

$$\overline{X} + t_{\text{crit}} \frac{s}{\sqrt{N}} \tag{12.11}$$

where $-t_{\text{crit}}$ and $+t_{\text{crit}}$ are the critical values for t with $df = N - 1$ that will cut off $\alpha/2\%$ in the tail—that is, the two-tailed critical values for α. Putting these two together gives the $100 (1 - \alpha)\%$ confidence interval for μ when σ^2 is unknown:

$$\bar{X} - t_{\text{crit}} \frac{s}{\sqrt{N}} \quad \text{to} \quad \bar{X} + t_{\text{crit}} \frac{s}{\sqrt{N}} \tag{12.12}$$

If $\alpha = .05$ and $1 - \alpha = .95$, then this is the formula for a 95% confidence interval for μ, and 95% of such intervals will include the true value of μ. Of course, in practice you compute only one interval, and either it includes the true value of μ or it does not. But you can say that you are 95% confident that your one computed interval includes the true value of μ. For resemblance in older couples, the interval is:

$$\bar{X} - t_{\text{crit}} \frac{s}{\sqrt{N}} \quad \text{to} \quad \bar{X} + t_{\text{crit}} \frac{s}{\sqrt{N}}$$

$$3.11 - 2.03\frac{0.5762}{\sqrt{37}} \quad \text{to} \quad 3.11 + 2.03\frac{0.5762}{\sqrt{37}}$$

$$2.92 \quad \text{to} \quad 3.30$$

If the computed value of *df* is not in the table, then t_{crit} is chosen for the next smaller *df* (30 instead of 35) to be conservative. You are 95% confident that the interval 2.92 to 3.30 contains the true value of μ for the resemblance of older couples.

The width of the confidence interval depends on N, s, and the degree of confidence, $1 - \alpha$. Increasing N, decreasing s, or reducing the confidence needed, $1 - \alpha$, will shorten the confidence interval. Examine Figure 12.3 to refresh your memory about how intervals vary. Intervals differ not only in position, but also in length because of the computation of s for every sample.

Once the confidence interval is constructed, the probability that it contains the parameter is either zero (not contained) or one (contained). Your interpretation of your single interval is based on principles of sampling and on the idea that a high percentage of potential intervals include μ.

Quick Quiz

For the confidence interval for μ for the resemblance of older couples, which of the following changes would result in a shorter confidence interval: $N = 45$, $s = 0.75$, $1 - \alpha = .80$, $\bar{X} = 2.89$?

Answer

Using a larger sample of size $N = 45$, a smaller confidence coefficient of $1 - \alpha = .80$, or both would give a shorter interval, but a bigger standard deviation, $s = 0.75$, would make the interval wider. The value of $\bar{X}$ does not influence the width of the confidence interval, but it does give the center of the interval.

Another Example

Suppose you are interested in the behavioral characteristics of people who belong to Mensa (IQ > 130 is the sole criterion for membership). You want to estimate the population mean on a scale for narcissism (vanity, exaggerated self-importance), and you have scores on this scale for $N = 36$ Mensans. You have computed $\bar{X} = 21.1$ and $s = 6.7$, and you know that the norm for college students is 20.9. Obtaining a two-

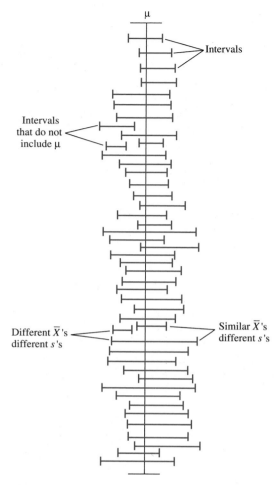

Figure 12.3
Confidence intervals for μ, each based on a different sample of size N. The vertical line represents the constant, fixed value of μ; the horizontal lines represent different confidence intervals for μ. Most intervals bracket (include) μ; some do not. Note that the intervals vary, but the constant μ does not. The location of each interval is a function of $\overline{X}$; the length of each interval depends on s.

tailed critical value for t with $\alpha = .05$ and $df = 35$ from Table A.4, $t_{\text{crit}} = 2.03$, you can compute the 95% confidence interval for the population mean of the Mensans on the narcissism scale as:

$$\overline{X} - t_{\text{crit}}\frac{s}{\sqrt{N}} \quad \text{to} \quad \overline{X} + t_{\text{crit}}\frac{s}{\sqrt{N}}$$

$$21.1 - 2.03\frac{6.7}{\sqrt{36}} \quad \text{to} \quad 21.1 + 2.03\frac{6.7}{\sqrt{36}}$$

$$18.83 \quad \text{to} \quad 23.37$$

You can say you are 95% confident that the interval 18.83 to 23.37 includes the true value of μ. If you computed many such intervals from many different $\overline{X}$ values, then 95% of such intervals would include the true value of μ.

Language

Reviewing the correct language will bolster your understanding of confidence intervals.

1. The random variables $\overline{X}$ and s are in the formula for the interval, so the interval is a random variable. Thus, you can say, "I am 95% confident that my interval includes the true value of μ." Be careful not to use the phrase "μ falls," as in "I am 95% confident μ falls between 18.33 and 23.37."

2. Probability statements can be made about intervals in general (such as, "the probability is .95 that intervals such as those given by formula 12.12 will include μ") but not about a particular interval after it is already computed. You can say that you are 95% *confident* that 18.83 to 23.37 includes μ because this statement is clearly understood to be different from a probability statement.

Relationship to Hypothesis Testing

Confidence intervals are related to hypothesis testing in a simple way: Any hypothesized value of μ that is not included in a particular computed confidence interval may be rejected as if you had used a two-tailed test. For the Mensa example, H_0: $\mu = 24$ would be rejected because 24 is not included in the interval 18.83 to 23.37. However, the hypothesis suggested by the norm for college students, H_0: $\mu = 20.9$, would not be rejected. This confidence interval gives the equivalent of a two-tailed test, which would not reject $\mu = 20.9$. You would conclude that the Mensans' average narcissism score was not significantly different from the norm for college students.

Quick Quiz
Given the confidence interval for μ for the resemblance of older couples, 2.92 to 3.30, would you reject the hypothesis H_0: $\mu = 3.50$? Explain.

Answer

Yes, because 3.50 is not included in the confidence interval. This test using the 95% confidence interval is the equivalent of using a one-sample t with $\alpha = .05$ and a two-tailed test.

12.4 Test of a Hypothesis about a Population Correlation

Introduction

Testing a hypothesis about a population correlation leads us to another one-sample test. In Chapter 6 we introduced the Pearson correlation coefficient r as a sample measure of the degree of linear relationship between two variables. The corresponding population correlation is usually symbolized as ρ. Up to this point, sample correlations have been considered as only descriptive statistics about the degree of linear relationship between two variables. But you may have wondered, How strong does r have to be to indicate a *real* linear relationship? Could your observed correlation coefficient occur by chance, or does the obtained r reflect a nonzero degree of linear relationship in the population? You can test a hypothesis of zero population correlation and make decisions regarding the chance occurrence of sample correlations.

For example, the dental pain/anxiety study in Research Example 12 had two tests of hypotheses about correlations. In one of these, the relationship between predicted pain and remembered pain was tested to see whether it was nonzero. The principles of hypothesis testing that you have learned and used to test hypotheses about population means also apply to hypotheses about population correlations.

Example

Research Example 12 gave information about the relationship between predicted dental pain and remembered pain. These results were for all 40 men and women lumped together. Might the results be different if you examined each gender separately? For women, is the linear relationship between predicted dental pain and remembered pain significantly greater than zero? The word *relationship* is a clue that you can use the test of a hypothesis about a correlation. The data in Table 12.2 can be used to compute r and test a hypothesis about the relationship between predicted dental pain and remembered dental pain for women. Even though there were 20 women in the first part of the study, only 15 were available at the time of the follow-up, when the memories of pain were assessed. Do the women who predicted high dental pain also remember high pain? Do those who predicted low dental pain actually remember low pain? Compute r for the data in Table 12.2 and check your work.

Table 12.2
Dental pain, women

Woman	X = Predicted Pain	Y = Remembered Pain	X^2	Y^2	XY
1	80	6	6400	36	480
2	11	4	121	16	44
3	7	1	49	1	7
4	24	15	576	225	360
5	1	3	1	9	3
6	20	25	400	625	500
7	98	49	9604	2401	4802
8	99	82	9801	6724	8118
9	7	22	49	484	154
10	45	22	2025	484	990
11	49	20	2401	400	980
12	3	24	9	576	72
13	30	30	900	900	900
14	10	6	100	36	60
15	6	11	36	121	66
	$\Sigma X = 490$	$\Sigma Y = 320$	$\Sigma X^2 = 32,472$	$\Sigma Y^2 = 13,038$	$\Sigma XY = 17,536$

$$r = \frac{N\Sigma XY - (\Sigma X)(\Sigma Y)}{\sqrt{[N\Sigma X^2 - (\Sigma X)^2][N\Sigma Y^2 - (\Sigma Y)^2]}} = \frac{15(17,536) - (490)(320)}{\sqrt{[15(32,472) - (490)^2][15(13,038) - (320)^2]}}$$

$$= \frac{263,040 - 156,800}{\sqrt{(487,080 - 240,100)(195,570 - 102,400)}} = \frac{106,240}{\sqrt{(246,980)(93,170)}} = \frac{106,240}{151,694.1878} = .70$$

Situation/Hypotheses

When you tested hypotheses using $z_{\bar{X}}$ and the one-sample t, the hypotheses contained μ. In this example, you aren't interested in the central tendency of the data. Instead, you're asking about the linear relationship between two variables. For a pair of hypotheses, you put what you believe into H_1 and test H_0. You also must decide whether your hypotheses will be directional or nondirectional. Like hypotheses about means, the directional hypotheses can lead to upper-tail or lower-tail tests. You can have:

$$H_0: \rho = 0 \qquad H_1: \rho \neq 0 \tag{12.13}$$

$$H_0: \rho \leq 0 \qquad H_1: \rho > 0 \tag{12.14}$$

$$H_0: \rho \geq 0 \qquad H_1: \rho < 0 \tag{12.15}$$

How do these hypotheses compare to the ones you've seen before? The only difference is the parameter because now we care about the degree of linear relationship between two variables, not about the mean of one variable. In the problem of women's predicted dental pain/remembered pain, the initial question asked whether the relationship between these two variables is significantly greater than zero. Thus, you want the hypotheses in 12.14 because the alternative says that the relationship will be positive, greater than zero. In this text, we test null hypotheses about zero correlation.

Test Statistic and Distribution

The simplest test statistic for testing hypotheses about ρ is the Pearson correlation coefficient r. For $\rho = 0$ and with certain assumptions (discussed later), the sampling distribution of r is given in Table A.5 in Appendix A. You need three pieces of information to use this table: α, one- or two-tailed test, and the degrees of freedom. The formula for **degrees of freedom for r** is

Degrees of freedom for r
When r is used as a test statistic, $df = N - 2$

$$df = N - 2 \tag{12.16}$$

or the number of pairs of scores minus 2.

Why are degrees of freedom $df = N - 2$? Consider the standard error of measurement, $s_{Y \cdot X}$, as the measure of variability:

$$s_{Y \cdot X} = \sqrt{\frac{\Sigma(Y - Y')^2}{N - 2}}$$

Remember formula 12.6: df is the number of independent components minus the number of parameters estimated. What are the "independent components"? Any woman patient is independent of another, so the N values of Y are independent. The N independent Y values are the number of independent components. What are the "parameters estimated," or statistics? Because r is the *linear* correlation coefficient, you have to estimate two parameters: the slope and the Y intercept of the linear regression line. The two statistics are b and a. So $df = N - 2$.

The researcher can compare r directly to critical values obtained from Table A.5. As was the case for the t table, if your value of df is not in the table, choose the next smaller df to give a conservative test. For the problem with women's predicted dental pain/remembered pain, $r = .70$ and $df = N - 2 = 15 - 2 = 13$. From Table A.5, the one-tailed, upper-tail critical value with $\alpha = .05$ and $df = 13$ is .441. (You'll learn the decision rule shortly.)

Another test statistic is

$$t = \frac{r - \rho}{\sqrt{(1 - r^2)/(N - 2)}} \tag{12.17}$$

which, for $\rho = 0$, becomes

$$t = \frac{r\sqrt{N - 2}}{\sqrt{1 - r^2}} \tag{12.18}$$

This is distributed as a t distribution with $df = N - 2$. Because of the simplicity of using Table A.5 and r, the only advantage in using t to test hypotheses about zero correlation is the wider range of values of α given in the t table as compared to Table A.5, which has only .05 and .01.

For the problem with women's predicted dental pain/remembered pain, $r = .70$, so

$$t = \frac{r\sqrt{N - 2}}{\sqrt{1 - r^2}} = \frac{.70\sqrt{15 - 2}}{\sqrt{1 - .70}} = \frac{2.5239}{.5477} = 4.61$$

Because $df = N - 2 = 15 - 2 = 13$, the one-tailed, upper-tail t critical value with $\alpha = .05$ and $df = 13$ from Table A.4 is 1.771.

Quick Quiz

For the 31 patients with complete data in Research Example 12, what would be the df for the r values reported there?

Answer

For the r values for predicted pain, experienced pain, and remembered pain, $N = 31$ and $df = N - 2$, so $df = 29$.

Decision Rules

The decision rules for the statistical tests covered so far should seem similar. The decision rules for the test of a population correlation are stated in terms of Table A.5 with r as the test statistic. (If you use the t transformation in formula 12.18, look up critical values in Table A.4.) For a two-tailed test with r, the decision rule is:

If $r \leq -r_{\text{crit}}$ or $r \geq r_{\text{crit}}$, reject H_0; otherwise, retain H_0 (12.19)

where r_{crit} is the $\alpha/2\%$ critical value from Table A.5 with $df = N - 2$. For example, for $df = 10$ and $\alpha = .05$ with a two-tailed test, the tabled value is .576. The critical values are $-.576$ and .576. Any obtained value of r computed on $N = 12$ pairs of scores that exceeds one of these critical values will lead you to reject H_0. Figure 12.4 shows

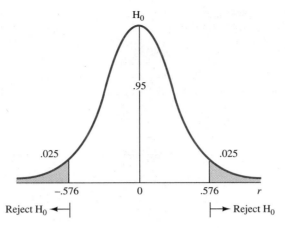

Figure 12.4
Distribution of r if $\rho = 0$ for $df = 10$, $\alpha = .05$, showing critical values, rejection values, and areas

the distribution of r for $df = 10$ and includes the critical values, rejection values, and areas.

For the directional hypotheses in formula 12.14, the one-tailed test uses the upper tail of the sampling distribution of r. The decision rule for the test is:

$$\text{If } r \geq r_{\text{crit}}, \text{ reject } H_0; \text{ otherwise, retain } H_0 \qquad (12.20)$$

where r_{crit} is the $\alpha\%$ critical value from Table A.5 with $df = N - 2$. Here, only positive values of r that exceed the critical value will allow rejection of H_0.

For the problem on women's predicted dental pain/remembered pain, $r = .70$ and the critical value is .441, so you reject the null hypothesis and conclude that there is a significant positive linear relationship between predicted and remembered pain. The women who predicted low pain remembered low pain, and the women who predicted high pain remembered high pain. (Another way of thinking about this relationship is to calculate r^2, the proportion of variability in the criterion variable that is explained by the predictor variable. Here, $r^2 = .49$, so 49% of the variability in remembered pain is accounted for by the prediction of pain.)

A research project that focuses on a theory that predicts a negative linear relationship between variables will use the directional hypotheses in formula 12.15. One example is the study on the relationship between locus of control and achievement test scores (Nowicki & Strickland, 1973). Locus of control is the extent to which people believe they control their own destinies. Low scores mean that they are relatively internal in their locus of control, that they are in control of their lives and that reinforcement comes as the consequence of their own actions or characteristics. Because high achievers may realize their own abilities and know that their hard work results in higher performance, the researchers might predict a negative correlation. The resulting one-tailed test uses the lower tail of the sampling distribution of r and gives the decision rule:

$$\text{If } r \leq -r_{\text{crit}}, \text{ reject } H_0; \text{ otherwise, retain } H_0 \qquad (12.21)$$

where r_{crit} is the $\alpha\%$ critical value from Table A.5 with $df = N - 2$.

The *p*-value decision rules for *r* are like the other *p*-value decision rules you've seen. For a two-tailed test of a nondirectional hypothesis, if the two-tailed *p*-value is less than or equal to α, reject H_0; otherwise, retain H_0. For one-tailed tests of directional hypotheses, you have to pay attention not only to the size of the one-tailed *p*-value but also to the tail where the observed statistic occurs. You reject H_0 only when the *p*-value is small enough *and* the statistic occurs in the tail of the sampling distribution predicted by H_1.

Quick Quiz

Nowicki and Strickland found that for the relationship between locus of control and achievement for fifth-grade boys, $r = -.398$ for $N = 42$. (a) With $df = N - 2 = 42 - 2 = 40$, what is the critical value for $\alpha = .05$? (b) What decision would you reach? (c) What does your decision mean?

Answers

(a) You should get $r_{crit} = -.257$ because the researchers predicted a negative correlation. (b) Because $r = -.398 < -.257$, you would reject H_0. (c) There is a significant linear relationship between locus of control and achievement for this sample of fifth-grade boys.

Assumptions

Bivariate normality
The assumption that the joint distribution of *X* and *Y* is jointly normal as well as normal in form for each variable

For the use of *r* with Table A.5 to be valid and the *t*-statistic in formula 12.18 to be distributed as *t* with $df = N - 2$, we assume that *X* and *Y* have a joint distribution that is bivariate normal. The assumption of **bivariate normality** means that not only are *X* and *Y* each normally distributed, but also *X* and *Y* are jointly normally distributed. When you consider *X* and *Y* as pairs, the joint distribution takes on a smooth, symmetric, moundlike shape. (Think about the drawings you've seen in this book of normal distributions and consider what they would look like in a three-dimensional rendering.) The assumption of bivariate normality is rarely met, but the consequences of violating this assumption are not serious if the skewness of the distribution of *X* or *Y* is not severe. If the distribution of *X* or *Y* is severely skewed, then the test of the hypothesis is only approximate. The statistics still can be computed and compared to critical values, but the results should be interpreted with some caution. For the data on women's predicted pain/remembered pain, you likely do not know much about the joint distribution of these variables. It is unlikely that it is bivariate normal.

The other assumption for the test using *r* is that the pairs of scores are independent or that the subjects are independent. Random sampling of subjects is the usual way of ensuring independence, but sound judgment sampling will suffice. Little is known about the effects of violating the assumption of independence of pairs of scores on the test of the correlation. But if the pattern holds from other statistical tests, the effects are severe. If you have serious doubts about meeting this independence assumption because of obvious dependence of the subjects or pairs of scores, you should not run this test. Nothing indicates that the assumption of independence is violated in the example of women's predicted pain/remembered pain, so the test is probably valid.

One final note. The test using Table A.5 is only for $\rho = 0$ as the point in H_0 to be tested. This does not mean than $\rho = 0$ is an assumption; it is a condition necessary for us to even consider using this test, much like having to know the value of μ when using $z_{\bar{X}}$ to test hypotheses about the population mean.

Another Example

Do students who procrastinate have personality variables that relate to study behavior? This question was addressed by McCown and Johnson (1991) as they studied college students who had delayed a required research involvement until the last possible day. They further screened the students by giving them a procrastination scale and using only those who scored in the top quartile. These 162 students were administered the Eysenck Personality Questionnaire, Revised, Scales E (extraversion), P (psychoticism), and N (neuroticism) (Eysenck, Eysenck & Barrett, 1985). Then the students received packets of various scales about anxiety, study behavior, and confidence in exam pre-paredness. They were asked to return the packets by mail postmarked on the day of their first final exam. $N = 114$ complied with the request.

Scale E measures the continuum of introversion to extraversion. Low scores mean the person is introverted and shy, likes to be alone, and is self-centered. High scores mean the person is extraverted, outgoing, and bold and likes being with other people. Among these 114 procrastinators, the E scores correlated with the number of hours spent during finals week in planned social activities, $r = .30$, impulsive activities, $r = .22$, and studying, $r = -.29$. Are these values of r significantly different from zero? For $N = 114$ and $df = 112$, the critical values of r for $df = 100$ are $\pm.195$ for a two-tailed test with $\alpha = .05$. All three of the r values reported here are significantly different from zero. It seems that extraverted procrastinators have a tendency not only to spend more time in planned social activities, but also to be impulsive with respect to their use of time during finals week, resulting in less study time.

Quick Quiz

A study by Arcuri and Lester (1990) asked 28 police officers how many hours a week they moonlight at a second job. The officers also completed questionnaires that measured their stress levels. The researchers believed more moonlighting would be associated with higher stress. (a) Write H_0 and H_1. (b) Use Table A.5 to find the critical value(s) with $\alpha = .05$. (c) Arcuri and Lester found $r = .45$ for moonlighting and stress. Is this significant?

Answers

(a) $H_0: \rho \leq 0$ and $H_1: \rho > 0$. (b) $r_{crit} = .317$. (c) Yes, because $r_{observed}$ is more extreme than r_{crit}.

12.5 Large-Sample Test of a Hypothesis about a Population Proportion

Introduction

You and a friend are having a rather heated discussion about whether men or women are more expressive in a dating relationship. Your friend says neither men nor women have cornered the market on showing affection publicly. You contend that times have changed and men are unafraid of showing gentleness and are more likely to initiate physical touch with a female significant other. What proportion of men in a dating relationship will make the first touch in a public setting? We'll return to this question after you learn the concepts and computations needed to test a hypothesis about a proportion.

Because a proportion is simply a frequency of events (that have some characteristic in common) divided by the total number of events, proportions are often used with qualitative data or data that have a nominal scale of measurement. With such qualitative data, the researcher can work with frequencies, percentages, or proportions. An example is the number of pieces of food eaten by Animal 1 in a pair of animals in a study of dominance in that species. What proportion of the food is eaten by one animal? The number of pieces of food could be transformed to a percentage or proportion.

Sometimes you might have data that are quantitative but you want to categorize them. For instance, an important factor in a study on attitudes toward taxation might be annual salary, which many people are unwilling to reveal, except when given intervals. You might need to determine whether the proportion of local residents who earn $70,000 to $80,000 a year is the same as the proportion in the population at large. If a bigger fraction of your sample contains people in that range compared with the population at large, you might have to keep that in mind as you draw conclusions about their attitudes toward taxation. Occasionally researchers need to compare a sample proportion to a population proportion and ask whether the difference is significant.

Example

An example of a proportion for quantitative data is the proportion of vehicles that exceed the 55-mph speed limit at a given site. Each car can be given a precise number that is its speed, but the researcher is interested in the proportion of vehicles that have values of that number (speed) greater than an arbitrary value (55 mph). Perhaps the researcher wants to test the hypothesis that the proportion of drivers who exceed the 55-mph speed limit is .50. Under the alternative hypothesis, the researcher believes that the results will show a significantly larger proportion. Suppose the researcher chose a section of level rural interstate, clocked 203 cars, and found that 132 (about 65%) of the 203 drivers exceeded 55 mph. The sample proportion is .65. Is this significantly larger than .50?

Situation/Hypotheses

The hypotheses that are formed for population proportions are similar to all of the other hypotheses you've seen; just the parameter is different. You can have directional or nondirectional hypotheses, and the directional hypotheses can lead to upper-tail or lower-tail tests. Consider the animal dominance experiment, where it is believed that one animal will dominate the other and eat more food, but you don't know which animal will dominate. The hypothesis to be tested is that each animal will eat half the food, or that $p = .50$ with a nondirectional alternative. For tests of hypotheses about the **population proportion p,** you can have:

Population proportion
Symbolized by p

$$H_0: p = .50 \qquad H_1: p \neq .50 \tag{12.22}$$

$$H_0: p \leq .50 \qquad H_1: p > .50 \tag{12.23}$$

$$H_0: p \geq .50 \qquad H_1: p < .50 \tag{12.24}$$

The speeding example would use the hypotheses in 12.23 because the researcher believed the proportion would be greater than .50. In other examples, you might hypothesize a population parameter different from .50. Your theory might lead you to test a hypothesis about $p = .75$.

This is the first time you've seen a population parameter that is not a Greek character. In fact, you previously saw p being used to symbolize a probability. Be aware that the context here is different and we're talking about proportions; the population proportion is p and the sample proportion (statistic) is P.

Test Statistic and Distribution

Sample proportion
The frequency divided by N, symbolized by P

To find the best sample estimate of p, you obtain the **sample proportion:**

$$P = \frac{f}{N} \tag{12.25}$$

where f is the frequency or number of subjects that possess the characteristic in question and N is the total number of subjects in the sample. (In Chapter 8 on probability, we used X to symbolize the number of successes; f is the same as X.) The mean of the

Sampling distribution of P
The exact distribution is the binomial, which can be approximated by the normal distribution with mean p and variance pq/N if p is close to .5 or N is large

sampling distribution of P (sample proportion) is the population proportion p, so P is an unbiased estimate of p. The variance of the sampling distribution of P is pq/N, where $q = 1 - p$. So if you know N and have a hypothesized value for p, you can obtain both the mean and the variance of the sampling distribution of P. You can form the test statistic

$$z_P = \frac{P - p}{\sqrt{pq/N}} \tag{12.26}$$

z score for the sample proportion
Test statistic for P that allows use of the standard normal distribution, symbolized by z_P

as a z **score for the sample proportion.** Again, the verbal definition of a z score holds true: something, P, minus its mean, p, divided by its standard deviation, $\sqrt{pq/N}$.

For the speeding example, the researcher found that of 203 cars clocked on a stretch of level rural interstate highway, $f = 132$, so $65\% = 132/203$ ($P = .65$) of the speeds exceeded 55 mph. Suppose some theory said that you should expect about 50% ($p = .50$) of the cars to speed. The test statistic would be

$$z_P = \frac{P - p}{\sqrt{pq/N}} = \frac{.65 - .50}{\sqrt{(.5)(.5)/203}} = \frac{.15}{.0351} = 4.27$$

Table 12.3
Requirements for adequacy of the normal approximation in formula 12.27 (using the moderate rule from Samuels & Lu, 1992)

p	Minimum Required f
.05	48
.10	40
.15	33
.20	25
.25	19
.30	14
.35	8
.40	5
.45	5
.50	5

The exact distribution of P is the binomial distribution (see Chapter 8). Even though the binomial is a discrete distribution that is skewed if p is not .50, often you can fairly closely approximate the distribution of P with a normal distribution. So the distribution of z_P in formula 12.26 can be approximated with the standard normal distribution. If p is close to .50 or N is large or both, then:

z_P is approximately normally distributed with $\mu = 0$ and $\sigma^2 = 1$ (12.27)

Samuels and Lu (1992) give improved rules for sample size requirements for this standard normal approximation. A shortened version of their requirements is presented in Table 12.3. If p is larger than .50, then use $q = 1 - p$ to enter the table.

You can use the standard normal distribution and Table A.2 to obtain critical values or p-values for z_P if conditions given in Table 12.3 are met. If conditions given in Table 12.3 are not met, your only recourse is to compute probabilities for the f in your P and more extreme values using Table A.3 or the binomial probabilities in Section 8.4. You can use the sum of these probabilities as a p-value to compare to α, and reject H_0 if the p-value is less than or equal to α.

For the speed limit example, $p = .5$ (and $q = 1 - p = .5$), $N = 203$, and $f = 132$. Because $f = 132$ is larger than 5, the normal distribution is a good fit to the sampling distribution of z_P. Because this statistic is approximately normally distributed, you are not using a t distribution, so you do not need the concept of degrees of freedom for this test.

Quick Quiz

Suppose you have a sample where $N = 50$ and $P = .38$. Can you use the z_P and the normal approximation to test a hypothesis of $p = .40$?

Answer

The value for f can be computed as $(N)(P) = (50)(.38) = 19$. From Table 12.3 with $p = .40$, you find that you must have f of 5 or larger, so you can use the z_P and the normal approximation.

Decision Rules

You might be able to predict the rules by which you decide whether to reject or retain the null hypotheses about a population proportion stated in formulas 12.22 through 12.24. You've seen similar rules for other one-sample tests, especially for $z_{\bar{X}}$. For a two-tailed test using z_P, the decision rule is:

$$\text{If } z_P \leq -z_{\text{crit}} \text{ or } z_P \geq z_{\text{crit}}, \text{ reject H}_0; \text{ otherwise, retain H}_0 \tag{12.28}$$

where z_{crit} is the $\alpha/2\%$ critical value from the standard normal distribution in Table A.2. The critical values from the standard normal distribution of ± 1.96 give $\alpha = .05$. Any statistic that is more extreme than one of these values will lead you to reject H$_0$. Figure 12.5 shows a discrete sampling distribution of P with $p = .5$ and $N = 20$, with the scale

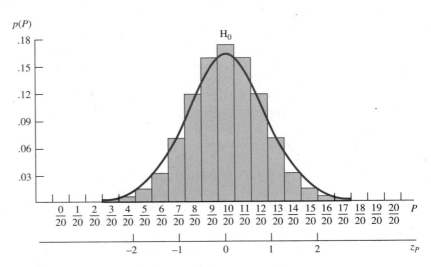

Figure 12.5
Binomial with $p = .5$ and $N = 20$: sampling distribution of the sample proportion P with the standard normal

for z_P also given. The standard normal distribution is superimposed on the sampling distribution to give you an idea how well it fits.

For a one-tailed test that uses the upper tail of the sampling distribution of z_P, the decision rule is:

$$\text{If } z_P \geq z_{crit}, \text{ reject } H_0; \text{ otherwise, retain } H_0 \qquad (12.29)$$

where z_{crit} is the $\alpha\%$ critical value from the standard normal distribution. For the speeding example, $z_P = 4.27$, and if $\alpha = .05$, then, from Table A.2, $z_{crit} = 1.645$. You would reject H_0 because $4.27 > 1.645$.

The decision rule for a one-tailed test in the lower tail of the sampling distribution of z_P is:

$$\text{If } z_P \leq -z_{crit}, \text{ reject } H_0; \text{ otherwise, retain } H_0 \qquad (12.30)$$

where z_{crit} is the $\alpha\%$ critical value from the standard normal distribution.

If you get a probability for your observed P, you can use the decision rules based on probability. For a two-tailed test of a nondirectional hypothesis, if the two-tailed p-value is less than or equal to α, reject H_0; otherwise, retain H_0. For one-tailed tests of directional hypotheses, you have to pay attention not only to the size of the one-tailed p-value but also to the tail where the observed statistic occurs. You reject H_0 only when the p-value is small enough *and* the statistic occurs in the tail of the sampling distribution predicted by H_1.

Let's look back at the question posed at the beginning of this section: What proportion of men in a dating relationship will make the first touch in a public setting? Suppose you find a research article on this topic (Willis & Briggs, 1992). Experimenters observed many couples in public settings, recorded whether the man or the woman made the first hand touch, and then approached the couple to find out their status—dating/engaged, married/cohabiting less than a year, or married/cohabiting more than a year. Out of the 121 dating/engaged couples who made physical contact, 70 of the men made the first touch. So P is 70/121, or .5785. To test H_0: $p \leq .50$ (because you believe the proportion of men initiating touch will be greater than .50), calculate z_P. You should find $z_P = 1.73$. Use this information for the following Quick Quiz.

Quick Quiz

(a) Can you use the normal approximation? (b) What critical value(s) should you use to test the hypothesis about public affection? (c) With $z_P = 1.73$, what decision should you make? (d) What does that mean about public affection between men and women in a dating relationship?

Answers

(a) Because $f = 70$ is larger than 5 (Table 12.3), you can use the normal approximation. (b) The critical value of $z = 1.645$, an upper-tail critical value because you believe the proportion of men initiating touch will be greater than .50. (c) Reject H_0. (d) The data indicate that in a dating relationship, significantly more men than women show public affection first. [Is that true for married couples? Willis and Briggs (1992) say no.]

Assumptions

The assumptions necessary for the sampling distribution of P to be exactly fit by a binomial distribution are that the outcomes are independently sampled and that they are sampled from a distribution that has only two possible outcomes. One of these outcomes has probability equal to p, and the other has probability equal to $q = 1 - p$. Additionally, there is the condition of a large sample size (see Table 12.3). For the speeding example, this large sample size condition was met. Even though this condition is not exactly an assumption, it is important for the use of z_P as a test statistic and the standard normal distribution as a reference distribution.

If you violate the assumption of independence, the consequences are severe, as for all tests. Without independent observations, you cannot be assured that the test statistic is even approximately normally distributed. However, the assumption of independence is usually met, and it is obvious if it has not been met. For example, if you set up your clocking position to check speed only a mile from where some state trooper parked for lunch, then the observations would most likely be dependent because the drivers have seen the trooper's car.

The assumption of two possible outcomes is met any time you use this test by the very nature of the experimental situation. You choose z_P to test hypotheses about proportions only when there are only two possible outcomes.

Finally, if you use z_P as a test statistic when the requirements of Table 12.3 are not met, you probably will have either a skewed sampling distribution or a discrete sampling distribution, neither of which is well fit by the symmetric, continuous, standard normal distribution. You need to meet the two assumptions and the large sample size "Table 12.3 conditions" given for the use of z_P and the standard normal distribution.

Another Example

In a study of everyday forgetting, Terry (1988) investigated 50 people for types of forgetting. Using a diary method, the participants "were instructed to record each instance of a forgetting that they realized had occurred." They also gave background information about each instance. The researchers categorized the recorded instances in a memory inventory, with categories such as "failure to comply with request after a brief delay" or "forgetting things." For the category "forgetting to bring something today that will be needed and you had intended to bring," there were entries for 66% of the 50 participants, $f = 33$. You might wonder if this is significantly different from 50%.

Converting the percentages to proportions gives $P = .66$ for the sample proportion and $p = .50$ for the population proportion. Table 12.4 gives the hypotheses, the statistics, and all the computations for this test. Given that p is .50, Table 12.3 shows that f must be 5 or larger. So the use of z_P and the standard normal distribution is valid for this test.

Table 12.4

Testing a hypothesis about the proportion of "bring something" forgettings

$\alpha = .05$ $N = 50$

$H_0: p = .50$ $H_1: p \neq .50$

Because $p = .50$, $q = 1 - p = .50$

Critical values: -1.96 and 1.96

$P = .66$

$$z_P = \frac{P - p}{\sqrt{pq/N}} = \frac{.66 - .50}{\sqrt{(.50)(.50)/50}} = \frac{.16}{\sqrt{.005}} = \frac{.16}{.07071} = 2.26$$

Because $z_P = 2.26 > 1.96$, we reject H_0. Significantly more than 50% of the participants recorded in their diaries: "forgetting to bring something today that will be needed and you had intended to bring."

12.6   Summary, Study Tips, and Computation

Chapter Summary

New one-sample statistical procedures were introduced. When you do not know σ^2, you may test a hypothesis about the population mean by using the one-sample t-test, which is distributed as the t distribution with $df = N - 1$. Degrees of freedom are found in any situation by computing the number of independent components minus the number of parameters estimated when you examine the definitional formula for a variability estimate in the test statistic. The assumptions for the one-sample t-test are independence of observations and normality of the population sampled. Random sampling ensures independence, and the Central Limit Theorem allows most violations of normality to have little effect on the t-test.

You learned how to get the confidence interval for μ when you do not know σ^2 or σ. For this interval, you use s to estimate σ, and you use a critical value from a t distribution with $df = N - 1$ rather than from the standard normal distribution. Correct use of language includes realizing that the interval is the random variable and that you cannot make statements about μ "falling in the interval." The interval is related to hypothesis testing because any hypothesized μ may be rejected if that μ is not included in the computed sample interval.

A hypothesis about a population correlation may be tested by using a formula for t, or r may be used directly with Table A.5. Degrees of freedom for this t or r are $df = N - 2$. Assumptions of the test for correlation are independence of subjects, usually met by random sampling, and bivariate normality. Violation of bivariate normality does not have a severe effect on the test as long as the individual distributions of X and Y are not severely skewed.

Finally, a large-sample test of a hypothesis about a population proportion is available in z_P, which is approximately distributed as the standard normal distribution. Assumptions include independence, usually met by random sampling, and a two-outcome situation. Sample size criteria were given for adequacy of the standard normal approximation.

Key terms used in this chapter are:

One-sample t-test	Population correlation ρ
Degrees of freedom	$df = N - 2$
$df = N - 1$	Bivariate normality
t distribution	assumption
Normality assumption	Sample proportion P
Independence assumption	Requirements for z_P to be
Confidence interval	approximately normally
for μ with s as an	distributed
estimate of σ	

The statistical tests mentioned in this chapter are summarized in Table 12.5. Shown for each procedure are the situation where the statistic is used (including the hypothesis), the name of the statistic, and the theoretical reference distribution. For decision rules, assumptions, and any restrictions on the use of each procedure, refer to the section where the procedure is introduced.

Table 12.5

Situation	Statistic	Distribution
One sample H_0: $\mu = $ _____ (some value from theory goes into H_0) σ^2 known	$z_{\bar{X}}$	Standard normal
One sample H_0: $\mu = $ _____ (some value from theory goes into H_0) σ^2 unknown	One-sample t-test	t with $df = N - 1$
One sample H_0: $\rho = 0$	Pearson correlation coefficient r	Table A.5 with $df = N - 2$ (a function of t)
One sample H_0: $p = $ _____ (some value from theory, such as .50, goes into H_0)	z_P	Standard normal

Study Tips

Start a one-page chart that includes four topics: situation/hypotheses, test statistic, distribution/decision rules, and assumptions with the different statistics covered here. On a notebook page turned sideways, put the four topics as the rows on the shorter dimension (left side) and the statistics as the columns across the top. Be terse in your description of each cell in your chart. If the statistic's formula is too long, don't include it. Keep your chart and add to it in following chapters. This is a handy reference and will get you used to deciding which statistic is appropriate for a given research project. Choosing the right statistic is the topic of Chapter 20.

Computation

Even though the statistical procedures in this chapter are fairly simple to compute, there are computer programs to lighten the computing load even further.

SAS Examples

The SAS package contains PROC UNIVARIATE that computes t and the probability for t for one sample. The following example uses the data from Table 12.1.

```
(SAS system's lines)
DATA TEACH;
INPUT RESEM@@;
D=RESEM-3.5;    (here you need to form a new variable, D = resemblance score − hypothesized population mean of 3.5 because PROC
                UNIVARIATE will test for only a zero value of the population mean)

CARDS;
2.50 3.75 2.75 2.42 2.92 3.33
3.42 3.00 3.42 3.33 2.08 3.25
3.92 2.83 3.08 2.67 3.50 2.83
2.42 3.17 3.67 3.17 4.00 2.67
4.08 4.33 3.08 3.33 1.58 2.42
3.50 3.67 2.67 2.67 3.17 3.33
3.17
PROC PRINT;
PROC UNIVARIATE; VAR D;    (computes a t-statistic and its probability for the variable D)
TITLE 'ONE-SAMPLE T EXAMPLE';
(system's line)
```

① The SAS System

OBS	RESEM	D
1	2.50	−1.00
2	3.75	0.25
3	2.75	−0.75
4	2.42	−1.08
5	2.92	−0.58
6	3.33	−0.17
7	3.42	−0.08

Figure 12.6
SAS output from PROC UNIVARIATE (one-sample t)

(continued)

8	3.00	−0.50
9	3.42	−0.08
10	3.33	−0.17
11	2.08	−1.42
12	3.25	−0.25
13	3.92	0.42
14	2.83	−0.67
15	3.08	−0.42
16	2.67	−0.83
17	3.50	0.00
18	2.83	−0.67
19	2.42	−1.08
20	3.17	−0.33
21	3.67	0.17
22	3.17	−0.33
23	4.00	0.50
24	2.67	−0.83
25	4.08	0.58
26	4.33	0.83
27	3.08	−0.42
28	3.33	−0.17
29	3.33	−0.17
30	1.58	−1.92
31	2.42	−1.08
32	3.50	0.00
33	3.67	0.17
34	2.67	−0.83
35	2.67	−0.83
36	3.17	−0.33
37	3.17	−0.33

ONE-SAMPLE T EXAMPLE

Univariate Procedure

Variable=D

	Moments			Quantiles(Def=5)				Extremes		
N	37	Sum Wgts	37	100% Max	0.83	99%	0.83	Lowest	OBs	Highest
Mean	−0.38919	Sum	−14.4	75% Q3	−0.08	95%	0.58	−1.92(	30)	0.25(
Std Dev	0.576177	Variance	0.33198	50% Med	−0.33	90%	0.42	−1.42(	11)	0.42(
Skewness	−0.23837	Kurtosis	0.367846	25% Q1	−0.83	10%	−1.08	−1.08(	31)	0.5(
USS	17.5556	CSS	11.95128	0% Min	−1.92	5%	−1.42	−1.08(	19)	0.58(
CV	−148.045	Std Mean	0.094723			1%	−1.92	−1.08(	4)	0.83(
② T:Mean = 0	−4.10871	Pr>|T|	0.0002 ③	Range	2.75					
Num = 0	35	Num > D	7	Q3-Q1	0.75					
M (Sign)	−10.5	Pr > = |M|	0.0005	Mode	−0.83					
Sgn Rank	−220	Pr > = |S|	0.0001							

Figure 12.6 (continued)

For PROC UNIVARIATE, the SAS output in Figure 12.6 gives the following:

1. The results of PROC PRINT, which prints the values of OBS (tells which observation), the values of the variable RESEM, and the values of the variable D formed as D = RESEM − 3.5.

2. PROC UNIVARIATE gives a *t*-test for D. This actually tests the hypothesis that the population mean for D is zero. Thus, it tests the hypothesis that the population mean for RESEM is 3.5 (the value you subtracted to form D).

3. Note that the probability (PR > |T|) is a two-tailed probability used for nondirectional hypotheses. To do a one-tailed test of a directional hypothesis, you must correctly predict the sign (+ or −) of *t* and reject H$_0$ if one-half the given probability is less than or equal to the chosen α (significance level).

The SAS package also contains the procedure CORR, which computes correlations and gives a probability for each computed *r*. The program is designed to obtain all the correlations between many variables, but you use it to get *r* for only two variables. The following example illustrates the use of CORR with the speed and miles per gallon (MPG) data from Exercise 15 in the exercises for this chapter.

(SAS system's lines)
```
DATA PEARSON;
INPUT SPEED MPG;
CARDS;
54.8 14.28
60.6 14.15
63.8 13.58
64.9 13.67
65.0 13.29
57.6 13.65
57.6 13.74
58.2 13.93
58.8 14.15
58.8 14.26
PROC PRINT;
PROC CORR;
TITLE CORRELATION EXAMPLE;
```
(system's line)

VARIABLE	N	MEAN	STD DEV	SUM	MINIMUM	MAXIMUM
SPEED ①	10	60.0100	3.4719	600.1000	54.8000	65.0000
MPG	10	13.8700	0.3343	138.7000	13.2900	14.2800

Figure 12.7
SAS output from PROC CORR, test on correlation

(continued)

```
CORRELATION COEFFICIENTS / PROB > |R| UNDER HO:RHO=0 / N = 10
```

	SPEED	MPG
SPEED	1.00000	−0.67164 ②
	0.0000	0.0334 ③
XPG	−0.67164	1.00000
	0.0334	0.0000

Figure 12.7 (continued)

For PROC CORR, the SAS output in Figure 12.7 gives the following:

1. Various descriptive statistics for the variables SPEED and MPG.
2. The Pearson correlation coefficient r for SPEED and MPG.
3. The probability (PROB > |R|) is a two-tailed probability used to test H_0: $\rho = 0$. To do a one-tailed test of a directional hypothesis, you must correctly predict the sign (+ or −) of r and reject H_0 if one-half the given probability is less than or equal to the chosen α (significance level).

SPSS Example

SPSS has the command CORRELATION that computes the Pearson r and gives a probability so that you can test hypotheses using r. The following example also was used in Chapter 6:

(SPSS system's lines)
```
SET WIDTH 80
DATA LIST FREE/BABY ADULT
BEGIN DATA
18.0 70.0 18.0 69.0 20.0 69.0 21.0 67.0 20.0 67.5 19.5 64.0
22.0 67.5 21.0 71.0 20.5 70.0 19.0 69.0 19.0 64.0 20.0 63.0
20.0 66.0 20.5 63.5 21.0 71.0 21.0 65.5 20.0 70.0 21.5 65.0
20.5 73.0 23.0 67.0 21.0 62.0 19.0 64.0 17.0 62.0 19.0 60.5
19.0 66.0 20.0 68.5 21.0 72.0 23.5 69.0 19.5 69.5 20.0 62.5
22.0 67.0 20.5 65.0 21.0 68.0 20.5 67.0 20.5 67.0 19.0 60.0
20.0 63.5 20.5 67.0 21.5 58.0
END DATA
CORRELATION VARIABLES=BABY ADULT/PRINT TWOTAIL SIG
```
(computes r for the variables listed, BABY and ADULT, and asks for two-tailed probabilities used in hypothesis testing)

```
FINISH
```
(system's line)

```
                   - -  Correlation Coefficients   - -

              BABY          ADULT

BABY        1.0000        .1781 ①
           (  39)        (   39) ②
           P= .           P= .278


ADULT       .1781         1.0000
           (  39)        (   39)
           P= .278        P= .


(Coefficient / (Cases) / 2-tailed sig) ③
''.'' is printed if a coefficient cannot be computed
```

Figure 12.8
SPSS output for CORRELATION

For the CORRELATION command, the SPSS output in Figure 12.8 shows the following:

1. The value of r for BABY and ADULT.
2. The value of N for each pair of variables.
3. The labeling key showing that the correlations (r) have N (in parentheses, called Cases) below the r's and probability values below the N's. The probabilities are two-tailed probabilities used to test H_0: $\rho = 0$ (see note 3 for the SAS output in Figure 12.7).

Exercises

Section 12.2

1. Use these questions to familiarize yourself with computing df for the one-sample t and obtaining critical values from the t distribution.
   a. For the one-sample t, if $N = 18$, what is the value of df?
   b. For the one-sample t, if $N = 61$, what is the value of df?
   c. If $df = 17$, what is the t that cuts off 5% in the lower tail?
   d. If $df = 40$, what are the t values that cut off a total of 5% in the tails?
   e. If $N = 13$, what are the critical values for t for a two-tailed test using $\alpha = .01$?
   f. If $N = 21$, what is the critical value for t for an upper-tail test using $\alpha = .05$?

   g. If $N = 14$, H_0: $\mu \geq 79$, H_1: $\mu < 79$, and $\alpha = .05$ for a one-sample t, what is the critical value?
2. Use these scores for college men on the self-acceptance (SA) scale: 21, 19, 23, 24, 22, 20. (Note that 19 is the norm for men.)
   a. What is N?
   b. What is the value of df?
   c. If the hypotheses are H_0: $\mu = 19$ and H_1: $\mu \neq 19$, give the critical value(s) for $\alpha = .05$.
   d. Compute $\overline{X}$, s, and then the one-sample t.
   e. Test the H_0.
   f. What does your decision on H_0 mean in terms of self-acceptance?
3. A psychologist has been studying the effect of deterioration of memory over time. He has been interested in how memory for particularly startling

events, called *flashbulb memories,* might differ from memory for everyday events. He asked college students to try to remember all of the circumstances of an ordinary event (such as meeting a friend) and then immediately after the event to fill out a survey about the details of the event. He knew from vast amounts of prior research that the average proportion of details accurately remembered 1 yr later was .85. When the Persian Gulf War began in January 1991, he asked students to do the same task of filling out the survey about the details of the beginning of the bombing. He thought that the average proportion of details remembered 1 yr later would be higher than the average. The following are the proportions correct for 22 students:

.81 .65 .93 .78 .79 .87 .86 .83 .87 .85 .77
.86 .80 .81 .82 .83 .87 .85 .85 .84 .83 .90

a. Give H_0 and H_1.
b. Compute *df.*
c. If $\alpha = .05$, give the critical value(s).
d. Compute $\bar{X}$, *s,* and then the one-sample *t.*
e. Test H_0.
f. What does your decision mean in terms of the problem?

4. A psychologist is studying the effects of high blood pressure, hypertension, on memory and learning. He uses a task that requires adults to study either two, four, or six digits shown on a screen, and then later to indicate whether a single digit presented on the screen was part of the original set. He knows that the average time to answer for a large number of typical adults on the six-digit task is 1.35 s. He believes that adults with hypertension will answer more slowly than those with average blood pressure. A sample of hypertensive adults gave the following data (in seconds) for the six-digit task:

1.43   1.67   2.13   3.12   1.23   1.29
1.56   1.43   3.89   2.34   1.89   1.78

a. Give H_0 and H_1.
b. Compute *df.*
c. If $\alpha = .05$, give the critical value(s).
d. Compute $\bar{X}$, *s,* and then the one-sample *t.*
e. Test H_0.
f. What does your decision mean in terms of the problem?

5. Suppose Sunola Fruit Company cans peaches in cans labeled 48 oz that they actually fill with 50 oz (on the average) of peaches and juice. You sample $N = 10$ cans and get $\bar{X} = 48.3$ oz and $s = 1.3$.
a. Test the null hypothesis that the filling machines are still set on 50 oz or higher. Use $\alpha = .01$.
b. What assumptions are you making to do this test?

6. Suppose a psychologist claims that her patients treated for anxiety will have an average score of 50 or less on the Flip-Flop Anxiety Scale (FFAS). You suspect that these patients will average higher than 50 on the FFAS. You sample $N = 16$ of her patients and find $\bar{X} = 51.3$ and $s = 3.7$.
a. Test the psychologist's claim using $\alpha = .05$.
b. Suppose you had sampled $N = 100$ of her patients and found $\bar{X} = 51.3$ and $s = 3.7$. Again test the psychologist's claim using $\alpha = .05$.
c. Does a difference of 1.3 seem small or large to you? What do the results of the tests in parts a and b tell you about the impact of a large sample size?

Section 12.3

7. A machine in a plant manufactures a car part and is set to make the part 6.70 in. long. The shift supervisor has responsibility to make sure the setting on the machine has not shifted, and thereby altered this length, in either direction. One day a sample of $N = 35$ of these parts was randomly taken from the assembly line and measured for length. The supervisor found $\bar{X} = 6.83$ in. and $s^2 = 0.1024$.
a. Compute the 95% confidence interval for μ.
b. Write a statement about μ that correctly interprets the computed confidence interval.
c. Should the supervisor change the setting on the machine? Explain.

8. Use the data in Exercise 2.
a. Form a 95% confidence interval for the population mean of self-acceptance scores for college men.
b. Write a statement about μ that correctly interprets the computed confidence interval.
c. Would a 99% confidence interval be wider or narrower than the one you computed? Explain.
d. Write a statement about how increasing the degree of confidence affects confidence intervals.

9. Suppose a smoking reduction clinic reports that it recently helped a group of smokers cut back from an average of 2.7 packs per day to an average of $\bar{X} = 1.9$ packs per day.

a. If there are 17 people in the group and the sample variance is 4.0, form a 95% confidence interval for μ.

b. Would you reject H_0: $\mu = 2.7$ using the confidence interval in part a? Is 1.9 significantly different from 2.7 in number of packs smoked per day?

c. If the sample variance had been 2.4, form the 95% confidence interval for μ, and answer the questions in part b.

d. Write a statement that tells how reducing variance affects confidence intervals.

10. From the example on the IQs of deaf children in Section 12.2, you know that $\bar{X} = 88.07$, $N = 59$, and $s = 17.84$.

a. Compute a 95% confidence interval for μ of the IQs of deaf children.

b. Would you reject H_0: $\mu = 100$?

c. What does your decision in part b mean in terms of the problem?

Section 12.4

11. Use these questions to familiarize yourself with computing df for the Pearson r and obtaining critical values from Table A.5.

a. For the Pearson r, if $N = 18$, what is the value of df?

b. For the Pearson r, if $N = 62$, what is the value of df?

c. If $df = 17$, what is the r that cuts off 5% in the lower tail?

d. If $df = 40$, what are the r values that cut off a total of 5% in the tails?

e. If $N = 13$, what are the critical values for r for a two-tailed test using $\alpha = .01$?

f. If $N = 21$, what is the critical value for r for an upper-tail test using $\alpha = .05$?

g. If $N = 14$, H_0: $\rho \geq 0$, H_1: $\rho < 0$, and $\alpha = .05$ for a Pearson r, what is the critical value?

12. You have 15 people with measures of both self-acceptance and locus of control, and you want to test H_0: $\rho \leq 0$ and H_1: $\rho > 0$.

a. What is the critical value for the test? Use $\alpha = .05$.

b. If $r = .41$, what is your decision?

c. What does your decision mean in terms of the variables in this problem?

13. An argument can be made that intelligence is largely inherited. If that is the case, then there should be a large positive correlation between parent and child IQ scores. Use the father and son IQ scores in the table to examine this relationship with $\alpha = .05$.

Father's IQ	Son's IQ
102	126
112	116
102	101
102	128
118	159
85	110
104	107
133	135

a. Compute r.

b. Compute df for r.

c. Using $\alpha = .05$ and the hypotheses H_0: $\rho \leq 0$ and H_1: $\rho > 0$, find the critical value.

d. For these data, test H_0 and write your conclusion.

14. Researchers may have found a link between cancer and the body's ability to repair itself. They have found that individuals differ not only in susceptibility to factors that cause skin cancer, but also in their ability to fix damaged DNA genes. After the researchers extract white blood cells from a person, they inject into these cells a small piece of genetic material that contains a mutant bacterial gene that is "broken." This gene, when fixed, causes the white cells to produce an enzyme that occurs only in combination with the fixed gene. If the gene is not fixed, then the enzyme will not be produced. Thus, the level of the enzyme produced after 40 h is a measure of the body's ability to repair itself. One issue in this research is the impact of age on this repair ability. The table lists the enzyme scores and ages for some healthy participants in the research.

Age	Enzyme Score
23	73
31	65
55	42
70	21
47	51
19	79
20	82
27	75
34	61
61	37
42	55

a. Compute r.

b. Compute df for r.

c. Using $\alpha = .05$ and the hypotheses H_0: $\rho \geq 0$ and H_1: $\rho < 0$, find the critical value.

d. For these data, test H_0 and write your conclusion.

15. Test to see whether there is any significant relationship between average speed of cars and average miles per gallon, using the data given here with $\alpha = .05$. For further analysis, draw a rough scatterplot of the data, and speculate on the degree of the relationship between speed and miles per gallon for the first five pairs and the last five pairs, separately.

Speed	Miles per Gallon
54.8	14.28
60.6	14.15
63.8	13.58
64.9	13.67
65.0	13.29
57.6	13.65
57.6	13.74
58.2	13.93
58.8	14.15
58.8	14.26

Section 12.5

16. Researchers examined a large number of men admitted to a hospital to see whether there was any connection between baldness and the incidence of heart attack. After classifying the men with respect to type of baldness, they found that for $N = 140$ men with top-of-the-head baldness, 91 of them had recently had a heart attack. Out of all the men, only $p = .25$ had recently had a heart attack.

a. Is $f = 91$ large enough so you can use z_P? If so, continue.

b. Compute P and z_P.

c. Using $\alpha = .05$, would you reject H_0: $p \leq .25$?

d. Is this an example of a true experiment or observational research?

17. According to a recent large-scale survey (with subsequent interviews), 10.9% of urban adult populations in the United States are affected by phobias. You have an interest in studying phobias in college populations, and you have found 32 phobias out of the 312 students in your survey/interview process.

a. What is p?

b. Is $f = 32$ large enough so you can use z_P? If so, continue.

c. If you cannot use z_P, what other way do you have to compute the p-value to compare to α?

d. For this situation, the number of computations is excessive (one probability computation for 0, one for 1, and so on through 32). Do several of them just for practice.

18. A university plans to adopt a new health care plan only if the majority of its faculty and staff favor it. They sample $N = 200$ employees and find that 110 favor the plan. Would they reject H_0: $p \leq .50$ (use $\alpha = .05$)? What if 112 favored the plan?

19. If 27 out of 40 students help to pick up surveys dropped by an interviewer, is the proportion of students who help significantly greater than .50 (use $\alpha = .05$)?

20. In a study of the effect of handgun control laws on suicide rates, Lester (1988) investigated the change in proportions for states that strengthened their handgun laws during 1964–1977. In question is the impact these changes had on the proportion of suicides by guns. Part of this study showed that Utah made a change in 1973 and that the proportion of suicides by guns for the 3 years after the change was .613. The U.S. rate for suicides by guns was .552. Is the proportion for the 3 years after the change significantly different from the U.S. proportion? Use $N = 527$ and $f = 323$.

21. Decide which statistical procedure from this chapter is appropriate to test each of these questions.

a. Is the average self-acceptance score in Great Britain the same as in the United States, when measured on the self-acceptance scale of the California Personality Inventory?

b. Is the annual income of adult men related to their height?

c. Is locus of control in children related to their self-acceptance?

d. Can you predict self-acceptance in children from their grade point averages?

e. Is the average locus of control score for sixth-grade students today the same as the 1973 norm?

f. Has the percentage of high school students who smoke marijuana changed since a large survey done in 1979?

g. Is the proportion of women who graduate with bachelor's degrees in psychology different from .50?

h. Is the rejection rate for the journal *Obscuria* still 90%?

i. Can you place some bounds on the average grade point averages of students admitted to a doctoral program, such that the bounds will include 95% of the students admitted in the last 5 yr?

22. Use SAS or SPSS to do a test of the hypotheses $H_0: \rho \leq 0$ and $H_1: \rho > 0$ for predicted and remembered pain with the data in Table 12.2. Compare the decision based on the p-value obtained with the computer program to the decision based on the critical value in the text.

13

Statistics for Evaluating Two-Sample Experiments

The one-sample statistics you learned in Chapter 12 are more realistic than $z_{\overline{X}}$. The statistics in this chapter are more widely used in even more realistic situations. Researchers often want to compare two independent groups, such as a treatment group and a control group, or two related groups, such as husband–wife pairs or pretest–posttest measures on one group of study participants. You'll learn new t-statistics for these purposes. You'll also learn a special statistic to use when you have unequal n values in two independent groups, confidence intervals for two independent groups, and a test of two independent proportions.

Research Example 13
13.1 Overview: Two-Sample Experiments and Tests for Means
    Comparison with one-sample experiments
    Examples
    Two independent samples or two dependent samples
    How dependent samples are formed
    Randomization and research design
    Difference in means and mean difference
13.2 Two Independent Samples: Means
    Example
    Hypotheses
    Test statistic
    Distribution
    Decision rules
    Sampling distribution of $\overline{X}_1 - \overline{X}_2$ for independent samples
    Assumptions
    Robustness
    The AWS test
    Strength of association
    Confidence intervals for $\mu_1 - \mu_2$
13.3 Two Dependent Samples: Means
    Example
    Hypotheses
    Test statistic
    Distribution
    Decision rules
    Sampling distribution of $\overline{X}_1 - \overline{X}_2$ for dependent samples
    Assumptions and robustness
13.4 Comparison of Independent and Dependent Sample Cases
    Sampling distributions
    Power
    Assumptions and robustness

13.5 **Two Independent Samples: Proportions**
        Example
        Hypotheses
        Test statistic and distribution
        Decision rules
        Assumptions
13.6 **Summary, Study Tips, and Computation**
        Chapter summary
        Study tips
        Computation
      Exercises

Research Example 13

Is your memory of an event affected by the words someone uses to ask you about the event? Research indicates that the wording of a questionnaire can influence your recollection of details. In a study on the interaction of language and memory, Loftus and Palmer (1974) manipulated language to see how memories for the details of a traffic accident are changed by the language used to elicit details about the accident. Students who participated in the experiment saw a film of a multiple-car accident and then completed a questionnaire. The film was less than 1 min long, and the accident took about 4 s. The questionnaire asked students to describe the accident in their own words and then to answer questions about the collision. The researcher wanted to know whether changing the wording of questions would cause students to have different answers. The independent variable was therefore the language used in the questions. One dependent variable of interest was the students' response to a question on the speed of the vehicles. Another was the response to a question about the presence of broken glass (no broken glass was shown in the film).

Fifty students were asked, "About how fast were the cars going when they smashed into each other?" Another 50 were asked, "About how fast were the cars going when they hit into each other?" Notice that the only difference in the questions is the verb, *smashed* versus *hit*. Because *smashed* is more suggestive of high speed, the question with *smashed* could be considered similar to the legal concept of a leading question. The research question is: On the average, would *smashed* and *hit* give different estimates of speed?

The results of this study showed that the mean estimate of speed for students who heard *smashed* was 10.46 mph. Those students asked the question with the verb *hit* estimated the speed to be 8.00 mph on the average. The difference in estimates of speed was $10.46 - 8.00 = 2.46$ mph. The researchers wanted to know whether the 2.46-mph difference in means was significantly different from zero. Zero would be the hypothesized value of the difference in population means if *smashed* and *hit* had the same effect on speed estimates. A difference in means of 2.46 mph may not seem large. One reason is that the speed was low. This also is a difference in means, not observed scores. This difference in means was significant at the .05 level ($t_{98} = 2.00, p < .05$).

For the responses to the question about broken glass, 16 of the 50 students, or $P = .32$, in the *smashed* group responded yes, broken glass was present. In the *hit* group, 7 of 50, or $P = .14$, said yes. If *smashed* and *hit* had the same effect on students, then the hypothesized difference in population proportions would be zero. The difference in sample proportions of $.32 - .14 = .18$ was significant at the .05 level ($z_{P_1-P_2} = 2.14$, $p = .0324$).

Differences in the mean estimates of speed were analyzed with the two independent-sample t-test, and differences in the sample proportions were analyzed by using $z_{P_1-P_2}$. These methods are covered in this chapter. A variety of other questions, hypotheses, and inferential statistical procedures were used by Loftus and Palmer, which is typical of most research reports.

13.1 Overview: Two-Sample Experiments and Tests for Means

Comparison with One-Sample Experiments

Imagine you are a counseling psychologist. You receive a phone call from the director of a retirement center, who says the residents seem to go through a period of depression at this time of the year. The director asks you to conduct group counseling to help the retired residents combat their apparent depression. Because you aren't used to working exclusively with older people, you are unsure that group therapy is the answer. You agree to try out the counseling technique on a sample of 15 residents; you tell 15 other residents they are on a waiting list. In truth, you want to conduct several sessions with your therapy group and then compare them to similar people who didn't go through the therapy. Will the treatment make a difference? Will the average depression level of the treatment group be different from that of the control group?

Think about the test statistics you have learned so far—$z_{\bar{X}}$, one-sample t, test of correlation, and others. Can you use any of these statistics to compare a treatment group and a control group?

Many of the one-sample statistics from Chapter 12 require you to know one or more population parameters. The statistic $z_{\bar{X}}$ requires that you know both the population mean and the population variance. The one-sample t-test uses the sample variance, but you still have to know the value of the population mean. Most behavioral research does not fit the one-sample situation simply because neither the population mean nor the population variance is known. In the retirement center example, you are unlikely to know anything about the population average depression level of residents of retirement centers, so those statistics won't work.

When hypotheses about population means are tested, most research projects use two or more groups and focus on comparing the sample means. In the retirement center example, you're asking: Is the average depression level for group therapy participants equal to the average depression level of persons in a control group? Two-sample situations like this do not require knowledge of population parameters (they can have any values), which makes them much more realistic than the one-sample situations.

Examples

You have seen several two-sample situations in earlier chapters. The study on exam stress, introduced in Chapter 1 and covered again in Research Example 11, had two groups of students: perceived control and no control. The perceived-control students on the average had fewer symptoms of stress, but the groups were not significantly different on exam performance or on a measure of severity of stress.

Research Example 13 is another example of a two-sample situation. The two groups were 50 students whose question on speed contained the verb *smashed* and 50 whose question used *hit*. The research question asked whether, on the average, *smashed* and *hit* would result in different estimates of speed. This study focused on the differences in the mean estimates of speed (and proportions of students who saw broken glass) for the *smashed* and *hit* groups. No parameters had to be known.

Consider the common aspects of these studies. In each study, the researcher:

1. Used two groups, usually with equal sample sizes
2. Was interested in the difference in the means (or proportions) from the two groups
3. Focused on a comparison of the two groups and their means (or proportions) rather than a comparison with some known standard value of a parameter

These three characteristics can be found in any two-sample experiment that tests a hypothesis about means (or proportions).

Two Independent Samples or Two Dependent Samples

Two-independent-sample *t*-test
Test of a hypothesis about equality of means from two independent samples

Test for two independent proportions
Test of a hypothesis about equality of proportions from two independent samples

Two-dependent-sample *t*-test
Test of a hypothesis about equality of means from two related samples

Once you have determined that you have a two-sample problem, you need to decide whether you have independent or dependent samples. If the observations in the two groups are independent and the sample sizes are equal, then you use the **two-independent-sample *t*-test** for means or a **test for two independent proportions.** These two tests are reserved for research where the observations are unrelated between groups.

However, sometimes an experimental design results in related observations, and then the tests for independent samples are not appropriate. If the observations are related between groups, then you use the **two-dependent-sample *t*-test,** also known as the *two-correlated-sample t-test* or the *matched-pairs t-test.*

How Dependent Samples Are Formed

Use the two-dependent-sample *t*-test if you have scores from:

1. Researcher-produced pairs
2. Naturally occurring pairs
3. Repeated measures

Researcher-produced pairs occur where study participants are matched or paired on some extraneous variable. Examples are professional and amateur golfers paired on their handicap, children in a learning study matched on intelligence, and children in a developmental study matched on age. The pairs do not occur naturally but are formed artificially by the researcher. The matching is taken into consideration in the two-dependent-sample *t*-test.

Some examples of naturally occurring pairs are husband–wife pairs, sibling pairs, parent–child pairs, roommates, and officemates. Here *naturally* means that the subjects are not paired by the researcher. The pair existed prior to the start of the research. A correlation probably exists between the attitudes of husbands and wives, so the two-dependent-sample *t*-statistic must take this connection into account.

Repeated measures, or two measures taken on the same subject, include pretests and posttests, scores on two succeeding trials, and a judge's ratings on two different objects.

There would be a correlation between your scores if you took a pretest and a posttest, or if someone tested your memory on two occasions. For each person who is measured repeatedly, the first and second measurements are correlated because the same person is involved. Again, the two-dependent-sample *t*-test must account for the connection between the person's two measurements.

Randomization and Research Design

From the discussion on randomization in Chapter 2 you know something about how participants are assigned to groups. But the way they are assigned to groups in the two-independent-sample case is different from how they are randomized in the two-dependent-sample case. The two-independent-sample *t*-test is used as the test statistic for the completely randomized design with two groups. "Completely randomized" means the participants are simply randomly assigned to two groups. This design is simple and controls extraneous variables only by randomization. Look back at Figure 2.3 in Chapter 2 for a review of proper randomization of *n* participants to each group for the independent-samples case.

Randomization is different when there are two related samples. It depends on how the pairs were created. Consider the three main ways of getting pairs of scores:

1. If two individuals have been matched or paired on some extraneous variable, then you randomly assign one of the two in each pair to one group, and the other is assigned to the remaining group. For example, you could match two retirement center residents of the same age, and then randomly assign one to the therapy group, leaving the other one on the waiting list. The extraneous variable of age is controlled by the matching, and the other extraneous variables are controlled by randomization.

2. The use of naturally occurring pairs could lead to the randomization of subjects within pairs to the two conditions if the conditions are not a function of the pairs themselves. For example, the pairs could be roommates at the retirement center, and the roommates could be randomly assigned to either therapy or the waiting list. However, if the pairs are married couples and you are examining attitudes of men and women toward some issue, then there is no randomization possible; it is already determined who goes into the male group or the female group.

3. If the pairs come from two measures taken on the same individuals, then for each participant you randomly assign the order of measurement under the two conditions, if such random assignment is possible. Suppose you were studying whether stress levels are affected by the brightness of a room where participants perform some difficult task in front of a small audience. Each participant will perform the task once in a dim room where the audience can't be seen well, and another time in a bright room where everyone is clearly visible. You can randomly assign the order in which the participants perform the task; you can flip a coin to see which condition comes first. In the retirement center example, you could measure everyone twice—before a month of group therapy begins and after the month is completed, but in this case you couldn't randomly assign the order of the measurement. Repeated measures on the same participants control all subject variables (IQs, personality traits, and so on).

Another important point about research design and the two-sample *t*-tests is that two-sample *t*-statistics can be computed in a true experiment or in observational research. A true experiment can lead to statements that imply causation, whereas observational research can imply only predictive relationships. Too often researchers and students slip into making statements about causation based on observational research using a *t*-statistic, when in fact the statistic has nothing to do with the type of statement that can be made. Causation can be implied only when there has been proper randomization of subjects and manipulation of an independent variable. If you compute a *t*-statistic that tests for equality of intelligence test scores between men and women, you cannot state that gender causes any differences that you might find. There was no random assignment or manipulation. Computation of the *t*-statistic does not change observational research into a true experiment.

Difference in Means and Mean Difference

Consider two groups of children who have the following spelling scores (ten possible):

Group 1:   5, 2, 8, 9, 10

Group 2:   6, 7, 5, 8, 9

The average for Group 1 is 6.8, and the mean for Group 2 is 7.0. Subscripts on the sample means in this chapter indicate which group's mean is given—here, $\overline{X}_1 = 6.8$ and $\overline{X}_2 = 7.0$. In both the independent and dependent cases, we compute the difference in means, $\overline{X}_1 - \overline{X}_2$. In this example, $6.8 - 7.0 = -0.2$.

Now, what if you find the difference between pairs of scores? The first score in Group 1 minus the first score in Group 2 is -1, the next difference is -5, the next is 3, then 1, and finally 1. These five differences add up to -1. If you average the five differences, you get -0.2—*the same answer as* $\overline{X}_1 - \overline{X}_2$. So the difference in means is the same value as the average of the differences, called the *mean difference*. This last term is used only when the groups are dependent and those differences are computed.

The language, principles, and logic of hypothesis testing for the two-sample *t*-statistics are the same as those for previous statistical methods. The hypotheses, formulas for the statistics, distributions of the test statistics, decision rules, and assumptions are different.

Quick Quiz

You are in the third week of your study at the retirement center. You discover that three pairs of women in your treatment group are roommates, and two other group members say their husbands are on the waiting list. You had planned to compare the groups' average depression scores using the two-independent-sample *t*-test. Instead, should you use the two-dependent-sample *t*-test?

Answer

No, the two-dependent-sample *t*-test is used when you plan the research such that every score in the first group is paired somehow with a score in the second group. The dependence in your study seriously threatens your ability to draw any conclusions about the treatment, and you probably should use the experience to learn more about running research. Use graphs to describe your results and plan your next study more carefully.

13.2   Two Independent Samples: Means

Here's another quiz question: When is the two-independent-sample *t*-test used? Answer: When there are two groups, the scores are all independent of one another, you have equal sample sizes, you want to test a hypothesis of equality of means, and the assumptions are met. This information is used to decide whether a given research problem can be analyzed with the two-independent-sample *t*-test. With the exception of textbook examples, all research problems require quite a bit of thought to determine the appropriate statistical analysis. In each case, you have to examine the characteristics of the research problem and choose the statistical method that most closely fits the problem characteristics.

Example

Let's use the exam stress study as an example (see Chapter 1 and Research Example 11). To briefly review, DasGupta (1992) randomly assigned 30 students to one of two conditions that were different with respect to their perceived control over a test-taking situation. The perceived-control (PC) students submitted written questions for a test in their introductory psychology class, believing the questions might be used on the test. The no-control (NC) students also submitted questions, but they were told this task was just a study aid. The actual test contained questions that were similar to 82% of the questions from the PC group and 87% from the NC group. Dependent variables included the number of symptoms indicated on a form of the *Stress Self-Assessment Checklist* (SSAC) (Neidhardt, Weinstein & Conry, 1985), an average stress frequency rating, and performance on the in-class test. Would perception of control make any difference in exam stress? The data for the 30 students in each group are given in Table 13.1.

The research question focused on the difference between the two groups in terms of the average number of stress symptoms, which can best be tested by using a hypothesis about the difference in population means. Because the researcher randomly assigned students to the two groups and there is no obvious pattern of relationship among students between groups, the groups are independent. There are two groups, the groups are independent, the sample sizes are equal, and the hypothesis concerns the difference in group means, so you can use the two-independent-sample *t*-test.

Hypotheses

One characteristic of the two-independent-sample case is a hypothesis of zero difference in the population means. As in other hypothesis-testing situations, you'll put what you believe in the alternative hypothesis and test the null hypothesis. If you believe there will be a difference between the means, you use the nondirectional case, where the hypotheses are:

$$H_0: \mu_1 - \mu_2 = 0 \qquad H_1: \mu_1 - \mu_2 \neq 0,$$

or equivalently,

$$H_0: \mu_1 = \mu_2 \qquad H_1: \mu_1 \neq \mu_2 \tag{13.1}$$

where H_0 states that the difference in population means is zero (or the means are equal). The alternative hypothesis indicates you are interested in any difference in the two population means, regardless of direction. For example, in Research Example 13, H_0 states that the population mean of speed estimates for *smashed* is equal to that for *hit*.

Table 13.1

Number of symptoms for perceived-control and no-control groups

Perceived Control	No Control
12	9
12	12
8	9
5	11
12	11
5	15
11	14
12	7
7	11
15	11
11	9
6	17
12	14
11	17
8	11
11	13
12	19
11	14
13	11
11	13
13	12
12	14
7	7
13	11
9	16
7	15
5	13
15	13
7	10
7	16

This difference of zero (equality of means) does not depend on the value of a population mean.

When you predict that one particular population mean will be larger than the other, one of these pairs of hypotheses should be used:

$$H_0: \mu_1 - \mu_2 \leq 0 \qquad H_1: \mu_1 - \mu_2 > 0$$

or equivalently,

$$H_0: \mu_1 \leq \mu_2 \qquad H_1: \mu_1 > \mu_2 \tag{13.2}$$

and

$$H_0: \mu_1 - \mu_2 \geq 0 \qquad H_1: \mu_1 - \mu_2 < 0$$

or equivalently,

$$H_0: \mu_1 \geq \mu_2 \qquad H_1: \mu_1 < \mu_2 \tag{13.3}$$

In these directional alternatives, a larger μ_1 indicates the use of formula 13.2, whereas a larger μ_2 leads to the use of formula 13.3. (Look at the alternative hypotheses for what you believe to be true.) Use directional hypotheses only when you are sure you can correctly predict direction.

In the exam stress example, you should choose the nondirectional alternative in the hypotheses in 13.1 because the earlier discussion indicated that the perceived-control and no-control groups would be different in terms of stress scores. That is, the mean number of stress symptoms of the perceived-control group (μ_1) would be different from that of the no-control group (μ_2). If the researcher had felt strongly that the perceived-control group would have the smaller mean ($\mu_1 < \mu_2$), then a directional alternative hypothesis would have been selected.

Test Statistic

Let's think about why we need a new statistic. Could you use one of the statistics you've already learned? For the exam stress study, you want to know about the average number of stress symptoms, so why can't we use the one-sample t? You should have this formula memorized by now, so write it down and answer these questions:

1. What are you going to use as $\overline{X}$ when you have two groups?
2. What are you going to do when you don't know μ?

Look back at your hypotheses. The null hypothesis for the exam stress study is $H_0: \mu_1 - \mu_2$. The main thing you are interested in is a difference in means. To estimate the population mean difference, $\mu_1 - \mu_2$, you use the difference in the sample means, $\overline{X}_1 - \overline{X}_2$. Now, look back at the one-sample t-test formula and think about its verbal definition: *something minus its mean divided by its estimated standard deviation.* You can apply this same verbal definition to the two-independent-sample t-test. You just need to identify the "something" and find its mean and estimated standard deviation. In the one-sample t-test, you found the mean and the estimated standard deviation for

$\bar{X}$, and you used the sampling distribution of $\bar{X}$ to do this. We'll do the same thing here. The "something" is the mean difference, $\bar{X}_1 - \bar{X}_2$, so think of this difference as a statistic. It has a sampling distribution with an average and a standard deviation. The statistic $\bar{X}_1 - \bar{X}_2$ is an unbiased estimate of the difference in the population means, $\mu_1 - \mu_2$, so the mean of its sampling distribution is $\mu_1 - \mu_2$. The estimated standard deviation of the mean difference is denoted by $s_{\bar{X}_1 - \bar{X}_2}$ (also called the *estimated standard error* of $\bar{X}_1 - \bar{X}_2$). So the definitional formula for the two-independent-sample *t*-test is

$$t = \frac{(\bar{X}_1 - \bar{X}_2) - (\mu_1 - \mu_2)}{s_{\bar{X}_1 - \bar{X}_2}} \tag{13.4}$$

We'll explain the denominator of the two-independent-sample *t*-test more later.

Now let's look at some computational formulas. The two-independent-sample *t*-statistic can be written this way:

$$t = \frac{(\bar{X}_1 - \bar{X}_2) - (\mu_1 - \mu_2)}{\sqrt{\left[\dfrac{(n_1 - 1)s_1^2 + (n_2 - 1)s_2^2}{n_1 + n_2 - 2}\right]\left(\dfrac{1}{n_1} + \dfrac{1}{n_2}\right)}} \tag{13.5}$$

This formula uses an appropriate estimate of the standard error of the difference in the means by assuming that the population variances are equal ($\sigma_1^2 = \sigma_2^2$) and by pooling the sample variances, s_1^2 and s_2^2, into a single estimate of a common variance σ^2. Another form of the formula for the two-independent-sample *t*-statistic is

$$t = \frac{(\bar{X}_1 - \bar{X}_2) - (\mu_1 - \mu_2)}{\sqrt{\left[\dfrac{\Sigma X_1^2 - (\Sigma X_1)^2/n_1 + \Sigma X_2^2 - (\Sigma X_2)^2/n_2}{n_1 + n_2 - 2}\right]\left(\dfrac{1}{n_1} + \dfrac{1}{n_2}\right)}} \tag{13.6}$$

Because $\mu_1 - \mu_2$ is usually hypothesized to be zero, the formula for the *t*-statistic is usually written as

$$t = \frac{\bar{X}_1 - \bar{X}_2}{\sqrt{\left[\dfrac{\Sigma X_1^2 - (\Sigma X_1)^2/n_1 + \Sigma X_2^2 - (\Sigma X_2)^2/n_2}{n_1 + n_2 - 2}\right]\left(\dfrac{1}{n_1} + \dfrac{1}{n_2}\right)}} \tag{13.7}$$

The specific hypotheses, statistic, distribution of the statistic, and decision rules are illustrated in Table 13.2 by the computation of the two-independent-sample *t*-test for the simulated data on the number of exam stress symptoms in Table 13.1.

The value of $\bar{X}_1$ from the perceived-control group is smaller than the $\bar{X}_2$ from the no-control group. The *t*-statistic shows that $\bar{X}_1$ is significantly different from $\bar{X}_2$, so you can reject H_0 of a zero value of $\mu_1 - \mu_2$. The data support the hypothesis that $\mu_1 - \mu_2$ is not zero, or that students with perceived control over an exam situation have fewer symptoms of stress than students with no control.

The formulas for the two-independent-sample *t* have $\bar{X}_1 - \bar{X}_2$ in the numerator. For a nondirectional hypothesis, you have a two-tailed test and provide for outcomes in either direction. It wouldn't matter if you switched the subtraction to $\bar{X}_2 - \bar{X}_1$.

Table 13.2
Computation of the two-independent-sample *t*-test for the exam stress study

$\alpha = .05$
$df = n_1 + n_2 - 2 = 30 + 30 - 2 = 58$
$H_0: \mu_1 - \mu_2 = 0 \qquad H_1: \mu_1 - \mu_2 \neq 0$
Critical values $= \pm 2.021$

Group 1: Perceived Control	Group 2: No Control
$\Sigma X_1 = 300$	$\Sigma X_2 = 375$
$\Sigma X_1^2 = 3256$	$\Sigma X_2^2 = 4937$
$\overline{X}_1 = 10.00$	$\overline{X}_2 = 12.50$
$s_1^2 = 8.8276$	$s_2^2 = 8.6034$

$$t = \frac{\overline{X}_1 - \overline{X}_2}{\sqrt{\left[\dfrac{\Sigma X_1^2 - (\Sigma X_1)^2/n_1 + \Sigma X_2^2 - (\Sigma X_2)^2/n_2}{n_1 + n_2 - 2}\right]\left(\dfrac{1}{n_1} + \dfrac{1}{n_2}\right)}}$$

$$= \frac{10.00 - 12.50}{\sqrt{\left(\dfrac{3256 - 300^2/30 + 4937 - 375^2/30}{30 + 30 - 2}\right)\left(\dfrac{1}{30} + \dfrac{1}{30}\right)}}$$

$$= \frac{-2.5}{\sqrt{(505.5/58)(2/30)}}$$

$$= \frac{-2.5}{\sqrt{0.5810}} = \frac{-2.5}{0.7623}$$

$$= -3.2797 = -3.28$$

Because $t = -3.28 < -2.004$, we reject H_0.

What about a directional hypothesis? You need the subtraction in the sample means to correspond to your alternative hypothesis. For instance, suppose you are doing the retirement home study of depression, where Group 1 undergoes therapy and Group 2 is on a waiting list. You measure the depression levels of all participants on a 50-point scale, where high scores indicate greater depression. You think there is no way the participants in therapy could have greater depression than the control group, so you predict $H_1: \mu_1 < \mu_2$ or $\mu_1 - \mu_2 < 0$. Let's say you obtain $\overline{X}_1 = 40$ and $\overline{X}_2 = 25$. How should you do the subtraction? The same way as in your alternative hypothesis: $\overline{X}_1 - \overline{X}_2$, or $40 - 25 = 15$. The alternative hypothesis is pointing toward the lower tail, which is where you'll put α. Your result, however, is in the positive tail; you predicted incorrectly. If you had not been careful about which sample mean came first in the computation, you would have made an incorrect decision about H_0. You must be sure that you set up your computations in the same order as the population means appear in the alternative hypothesis.

Distribution

If all assumptions are met, the two-independent-sample *t*-statistic in formula 13.7 has a sampling distribution that is exactly the *t* distribution with degrees of freedom

$$df = n_1 + n_2 - 2 \tag{13.?}$$

Degrees of freedom for the two-independent-sample *t*-statistic
$df = n_1 + n_2 - 2$

This value of the **degrees of freedom for the *t* distribution of the two-independent-sample *t*-statistic** is the sum of the degrees of freedom from each of the two sample variances, or $(n_1 - 1) + (n_2 - 1) = n_1 + n_2 - 2$. This also fits the general working definition given in Chapter 12: the number of independent components minus the number of parameters estimated. When you examine the sample variances, s_1^2 and s_2^2, in the denominator of *t*, the number of independent components is the total number of observations $n_1 + n_2$, and the number of parameters estimated is 2 because sample means $\overline{X}_1$ and $\overline{X}_2$ are used to estimate two population means. The exam stress example had $n_1 = n_2 = 30$, so $df = 30 + 30 - 2 = 58$.

What would be the degrees of freedom for Research Example 13? There were $n_1 = n_2 = 50$ observations in each group. You should get $df = 50 + 50 - 2 = 98$.

Because *t* in formula 13.7 is distributed as *t* with $df = n_1 + n_2 - 2$ if all assumptions are met, you can use the *t* table to obtain the critical values—the same *t* table you used with the one-sample *t*. Enter Table A.4 in Appendix A using the computed value of *df* and the chosen α value for the one- or two-tailed test. In the exam stress example, $df = 58$ and $\alpha = .05$ for a two-tailed test. Here you encounter a problem that occurs frequently with real-life data: There are no entries in Table A.4 for $df = 58$. Using the convention introduced in Chapter 12, you use the next smaller value of *df* in the table. In this example, you would use $df = 55$ and obtain critical values of ± 2.004. Sometimes this convention is slightly conservative; that is, the *t*-test rejects H_0 slightly less often than it should. Obviously, if the obtained value of *t* is extreme, as in the exam stress example, then you reject H_0 even with this conservative convention.

What are the critical values for $\alpha = .05$ for a two-tailed test for the study in Research Example 13? Because $df = 98$ and there is no entry for this value, you should use $df = 90$ and get critical values of ± 1.987. See Figure 13.1 for an illustration of critical values in the *t* distribution.

Decision Rules

The decision rules for the two-independent-sample *t*-test are similar to those given in previous chapters, but we use the two-independent-sample *t*-statistic given in formula

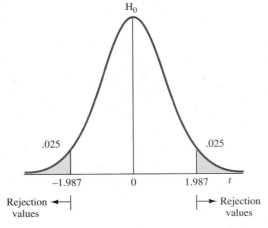

Figure 13.1
Sampling distribution of *t* with $df = 90$, $\alpha = .05$, two-tailed test, showing critical values, rejection values, and areas

"*df*? D. F. who?"

13.7 and the degrees of freedom in formula 13.8. As you read through the rules that follow, find which one was used for the exam stress example in Table 13.2.

For the two-tailed test of the hypothesis given in formula 13.1, the decision rule is:

$$\text{If } t \leq -t_{\text{crit}} \text{ or } t \geq t_{\text{crit}}, \text{ reject } H_0; \text{ otherwise, retain } H_0 \qquad (13.9)$$

where t_{crit} is the $\alpha/2\%$ critical value from the t distribution with df given in formula 13.8 as $df = n_1 + n_2 - 2$.

For a one-tailed test of the H_0 given in formula 13.2, use the upper tail of the t distribution. The decision rule is:

$$\text{If } t \geq t_{\text{crit}}, \text{ reject } H_0; \text{ otherwise, retain } H_0 \qquad (13.10)$$

where t_{crit} is the critical value from the t distribution with appropriate df and α.

The decision rule for a one-tailed test of the H_0 given in formula 13.3 uses the lower tail of the t distribution and the statement:

$$\text{If } t \leq -t_{\text{crit}}, \text{ reject } H_0; \text{ otherwise, retain } H_0 \qquad (13.11)$$

where t_{crit} is the critical value from the t distribution with appropriate df and α. You should have concluded that the decision rule given in formula 13.9 for a two-tailed test was used in the exam stress example in Table 13.2.

For a two-tailed test of a nondirectional hypothesis, if the two-tailed p-value is less than or equal to α, reject H_0; otherwise, retain H_0. For one-tailed tests of directional hypotheses, you have to pay attention not only to the size of the one-tailed p-value but also to the tail where the observed statistic occurs. Reject H_0 only when the p-value is small enough *and* the statistic occurs in the tail of the sampling distribution predicted by H_1.

Quick Quiz

In the retirement center study, 15 people are in group therapy and 15 are on a waiting list. You don't know how the therapy will affect the retirees. (a) What is the numerical value of df? (b) What are your hypotheses?

Answers

(a) $df = 28$. (b) H_0: $\mu_1 = \mu_2$ and H_1: $\mu_1 \neq \mu_2$.

Sampling Distribution of $\overline{X}_1 - \overline{X}_2$ for Independent Samples

Because $\overline{X}_1 - \overline{X}_2$ is unbiased, the mean of its sampling distribution is $\mu_1 - \mu_2$. What about the shape and variance of the sampling distribution of $\overline{X}_1 - \overline{X}_2$?

Normal Distribution of $\overline{X}_1 - \overline{X}_2$

The sampling distribution of $\overline{X}_1 - \overline{X}_2$ is normally distributed. The Central Limit Theorem says that the sampling distributions of $\overline{X}_1$ and $\overline{X}_2$ are normally distributed, and other statistical theorems prove that the differences between normally distributed quantities are also normally distributed. Therefore, you know that the sampling distribution of $\overline{X}_1 - \overline{X}_2$ is normally distributed. Figure 13.2 shows the distributions of the populations and the samples and the sampling distribution of $\overline{X}_1 - \overline{X}_2$.

Variance of $\overline{X}_1 - \overline{X}_2$

For independent groups, the variance of the sampling distribution of $\overline{X}_1 - \overline{X}_2$ is the sum of the variances for each $\overline{X}$. That is,

$$\sigma^2_{\overline{X}_1 - \overline{X}_2} = \frac{\sigma_1^2}{n_1} + \frac{\sigma_2^2}{n_2} \tag{13.12}$$

where σ_1^2 is the variance for Population 1, σ_2^2 is the variance for Population 2, n_1 is the sample size for Group 1, and n_2 is the sample size for Group 2. See Box 13.1 for an explanation of how this formula for the variance of the sampling distribution of

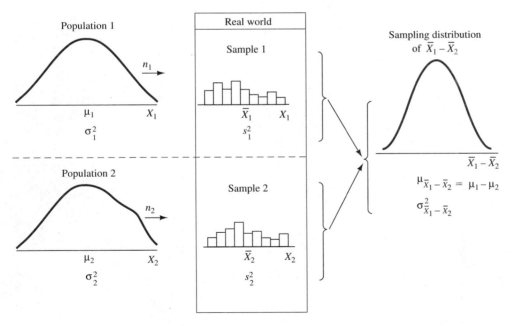

Figure 13.2
Populations, samples, and sampling distribution of $\overline{X}_1 - \overline{X}_2$

Box 13.1   The Estimated Standard Deviation of the Sampling Distribution of $\bar{X}_1 - \bar{X}_2$

The variance of the sampling distribution of $\bar{X}_1 - \bar{X}_2$ is:

$$\sigma^2_{\bar{X}_1 - \bar{X}_2} = \frac{\sigma^2_1}{n_1} + \frac{\sigma^2_2}{n_2}$$

but how does this formula relate to the computational formulas used to calculate the two-independent-sample t-test? If you assume that $\sigma^2_1 = \sigma^2_2$, then you can use one symbol, σ^2 in this formula, and from algebra you find:

$$\sigma^2_{\bar{X}_1 - \bar{X}_2} = \frac{\sigma^2}{n_1} + \frac{\sigma^2}{n_2} = \sigma^2 \left(\frac{1}{n_1} + \frac{1}{n_2} \right)$$

Now, you need an estimate of σ^2 using the two sample variances. In other words, you need to find a pooled sum of squares divided by a pooled df, or SS/df. For the two-independent-sample t, $df = n_1 + n_2 - 2$. If you use the sum of the sample variances, they have the problem of containing df; they are each in the form SS/df:

$$s^2_1 + s^2_2 = \frac{SS_1}{df_1} + \frac{SS_2}{df_2}$$

So you need to multiply each sample variance by its df and isolate the sample SS. To isolate SS and obtain SS_{pooled}, you have:

$$SS_{\text{pooled}} = (s^2_1)(n_1 - 1) + (s^2_2)(n_2 - 1)$$

$$= \left(\frac{SS_1}{n_1 - 1} \right)(n_1 - 1) + \left(\frac{SS_2}{n_2 - 1} \right)(n_2 - 1)$$

$$= SS_1 + SS_2$$

It is also helpful to note that

$$SS_{\text{pooled}} = SS_1 + SS_2 = \left[\sum X^2_1 - \frac{(\sum X_1)^2}{n_1} \right] + \left[\sum X^2_2 - \frac{(\sum X_2)^2}{n_2} \right]$$

This SS_{pooled} needs to be divided by the pooled df, $n_1 + n_2 - 2$, and you get your estimate of σ^2, which you plug back into the second formula in this box:

$$\sigma^2_{\bar{X}_1 - \bar{X}_2} = \sigma^2 \left(\frac{1}{n_1} + \frac{1}{n_2} \right) = \left[\frac{\sum X^2_1 - \frac{(\sum X_1)^2}{n_1} + \sum X^2_2 - \frac{(\sum X_2)^2}{n_2}}{n_1 + n_2 - 2} \right] \left(\frac{1}{n_1} + \frac{1}{n_2} \right)$$

Put a square root symbol over this formula and you have the computational formula for an estimate of the standard deviation of the sampling distribution of $\bar{X}_1 - \bar{X}_2$.

$\overline{X}_1 - \overline{X}_2$ is related to the denominator of the computational formula for the two-independent-sample t.

Assumptions

The sampling distribution of the two-independent-sample t-statistic in formula 13.7 is exactly fit by the t distribution with parameter $df = n_1 + n_2 - 2$ if H_0 is true and the assumptions are met. You assume that the original scores in both populations:

1. Are normally distributed
2. Are independent
3. Have equal variances

The two-independent-sample t-test has the same assumptions as the one-sample t-test plus the assumption of equal population variances. This assumption was made necessary in the derivation of the test statistic where the pooled estimate of the common population variance was formed and it was assumed that $\sigma_1^2 = \sigma_2^2$.

If these three assumptions are met and if H_0 is true, then the t distribution exactly fits the sampling distribution of the two-independent-sample t-statistic, and you can use critical values or computed p-values from this distribution to make decisions about H_0. One implication of this exact fit is that α will be exactly the value you set. Along with the characteristic of high power, an exact α is an important aspect of a good statistical test. If all assumptions are met, the two-independent-sample t-test is a good statistical test. However, if the assumptions are *not* met, then you might question the quality of the t-test. If an assumption is not met, you are said to have *violated* it. In that case, is your statistic any good? The quality of a statistical test when an assumption of the test is violated is called the *robustness* of the test.

Robustness

Robust means "strong" or "resistant to," so a statistic is robust to violation of an assumption if that statistic is strong or resistant to the violation. This is an introduction to the topic of what happens to the performance of the statistical test if the assumptions are not met—that is, if the assumptions are violated.

A statistic is said to be **robust** to violation of a particular assumption if, when that assumption is violated, the α for the statistic is approximately equal to the set value, or

Robust
Strength of a statistic against violation of an assumption; the true α is approximately equal to the set α

$$\alpha_{\text{true}} \approx \alpha_{\text{set}}$$

Note that α_{true} is the α in the sampling distribution of the statistic, whereas α_{set} is the α in the theoretical reference distribution. Examine Figure 13.3 for distributions that show robustness and nonrobustness.

When you want to find the critical values of a test statistic, where do you go? You find them in a table in the back of the book, right? The tabled values in Appendix A are from theoretical reference distributions. When we test H_0, we are asking, If the null hypothesis is true, how likely is our statistic? Reread that question and think, How likely . . . compared to what? Most of the statistics you've learned so far have involved *something minus its mean divided by its (estimated) standard deviation*. Did *something*'s mean and (estimated) standard deviation come from the theoretical reference distribution? No, they came from the sampling distribution. To find the likelihood of

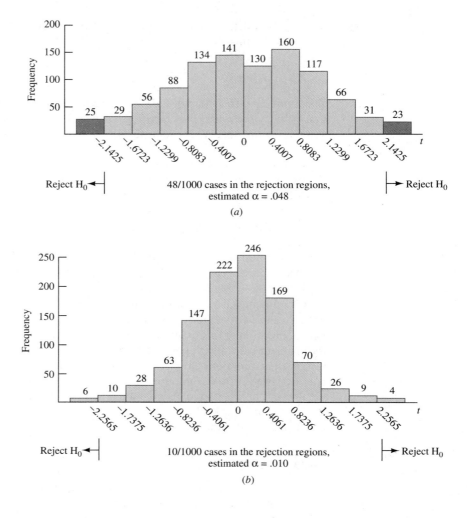

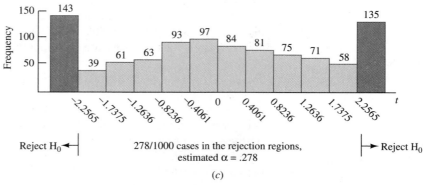

Figure 13.3

t distributions for $\alpha = .05$ showing robustness with α for the histogram of t values estimated at .048 (*a*) and nonrobustness with α for the histogram of t values estimated at .010 (*b*) and with α for the histogram of t values estimated at .278 (*c*).

your statistic, you have to think about its probability within its sampling distributions; instead, we use something available, something mathematical and similar. The sampling distribution can be closely matched by the theoretical reference distribution *if the assumptions of the statistic are met.* In Figure 13.3, you can see that if you have robustness, then the sampling distribution of the statistic (the histogram) closely agrees with the theoretical distribution (the smooth curve), especially in the tail areas of the distribution.

A broader definition of robustness would include adequate power in the case of violation of the assumption, but in this text we restrict our attention to α robustness. Here are a couple of questions to ask about each statistic you learn: If you set α at .05, is α exactly equal to .05? How far off from .05 is the true, or exact, value of α? If the answer is, No, α is not exactly .05 but it's close, then the statistic is robust. If the answer is No, α is not .05 and is very much larger than (or smaller than) .05, then the statistic is not robust.

How do you know the true values of α? Researchers in statistics use calculus and computer simulations to compute or estimate the true α, so we know what happens to α under certain conditions. This research has led to the following guidelines about the robustness of the two-independent-sample *t*-test:

1. The *t* is generally robust to nonnormality, with a notable exception of any population distribution that has 5% to 10% of the scores in one tail as extreme scores.
2. The *t* is not robust to dependence of observations, but independence is usually obtainable if the research is done carefully, including correct randomization of subjects to groups.
3. For near-normal distributions, the *t*-test is generally robust to unequal variances if $n_1 = n_2$ is larger than or equal to 15 (with α set at .05, for α true to be between .04 and .06; see Ramsey, 1980).

You should use equal sample sizes of 15 or larger and watch for obvious causes of dependence in the observations. The real world gives data that are usually nonnormal but independent with unequal variances. You can use the two-independent-sample *t* in most circumstances because it is robust to nonnormality, you can meet the independence assumption, and you can make certain that your samples are of equal size and have at least 15 observations per group (for $\alpha = .05$) to have robustness to unequal variances. If the normality assumption is not met, one alternative is to use nonparametric statistical procedures, which don't assume normality. A nonparametric procedure for two independent samples is introduced in Chapter 19.

Could the researcher in the exam stress study assume the statistic was robust? The study used $n_1 = n_2 = 30$ participants and randomly assigned them to one of the two groups. In this example, you can rely on robustness to nonnormality, you can assume independence, and you can rely on robustness to unequal variances because the sample sizes are equal and large.

To summarize these assumptions and the two-independent-sample *t*-test's robustness, here's an analogy we use in our classes. If you get a cold, you're probably robust enough to live with it. It probably doesn't derail you from life. That's how the two-independent-sample *t*-test usually reacts when the normality assumption is violated. It's still a good statistic. What happens when there are reports of measles in your area? This is far more serious than a cold, but if you get a measles shot, you are robust and would make it through the measles outbreak. Violating the equality of variances assumption is the measles to the two-independent-sample *t*-test. If you inoculate your statistic by making sure you have equal n's with at least 15 subjects per group, the two-independent-sample t-test can weather the violation of the equal variances assumption. Now, imagine that you are living near a nuclear plant, and there is a meltdown. No one can live through such an event. No one is robust to it. Similarly, the two-independent-sample t cannot withstand the violation of the independence assumption. If you have dependence in the observations, dig a grave for your paperwork because your statistic is worthless. Make sure you know the difference between planned dependence, such as the three situations that lead to the two-dependent-sample t, and dependence that ruins the two-independent-sample t.

One final note on robustness concerns preliminary testing for whether the data meet the assumptions. Some sources recommend testing to see whether the assumptions are met for a given set of data. We do not recommend preliminary testing procedures because many are not robust themselves.

The AWS Test

What if you have independent samples with unequal sample sizes or small equal sample sizes? Sometimes you can plan research carefully and still unavoidably have unequal sample sizes. The exam stress study could have ended up with unequal values of n if one student had dropped out of the class before the study was completed. Research shows that the two-independent-sample t is not robust to unequal population variances when you have unequal n's and should not be used. The AWS (Aspin-Welch-Satterthwaite) test is an approximate test for this situation.

Testing a hypothesis of equality of means when population variances are unknown and potentially unequal is called the *Behrens-Fisher problem*. Many attempts have been made to solve this problem, but no exact distribution is known for any of the approximate statistics that have been developed. The AWS test is one of the best approximate solutions to this problem because it has good control of α and good power. Compared to the two-independent-sample t-test, the AWS gives a different statistic and a different distribution (because of a different df).

The test statistic is given as

$$t' = \frac{\overline{X}_1 - \overline{X}_2}{\sqrt{\dfrac{s_1^2}{n_1} + \dfrac{s_2^2}{n_2}}} \tag{13.13}$$

which has a sampling distribution that is approximately the t distribution with degrees of freedom:

$$df' = \frac{(s_1^2/n_1 + s_2^2/n_2)^2}{\dfrac{(s_1^2/n_1)^2}{n_1 - 1} + \dfrac{(s_2^2/n_2)^2}{n_2 - 1}} \tag{13.14}$$

The AWS test statistic t' is simpler than that for the two-independent-sample t, but the df' formula is much more complex than $df = n_1 + n_2 - 2$. For the AWS, the decision rules are the same as for the two-independent-sample t, and the assumptions are normally distributed populations and independent observations. The AWS makes no assumption of equal variances. If the sample sizes are equal and 15 or greater, use the two-independent-sample t because it is more powerful than the AWS. If you have fewer than 15 subjects per group, or the sample sizes are not equal, or both, use the AWS because in that case the two-independent-sample t is not robust to unequal population variances. Research in statistics has shown that *any* inequality of n's is grounds for using the AWS instead of the two-independent-sample t.

As an example, consider research on the variable locus of control (LOC) in obese females (Mills, 1991). Because LOC measures the tendency to attribute the control of factors in your life to internal sources (self-control, low LOC scores) or external sources (outside factors control their lives, high LOC scores), obese people might tend to be external in LOC. Do adults and adolescents differ in LOC scores? The study used $n_1 = 46$ adult females and $n_2 = 19$ adolescent females who were medically diagnosed as obese using clinical standards for obesity and who were at least 50 lb over their ideal weight. LOC scores were collected before they started weight loss treatment. The means (and variances) were: for adults 6.45 (8.3521) and for adolescents 10.89 (6.1504). The AWS test is the method of choice.

The t' and df' are:

$$t' = \frac{\overline{X}_1 - \overline{X}_2}{\sqrt{\dfrac{s_1^2}{n_1} + \dfrac{s_2^2}{n_2}}}$$

$$= \frac{6.45 - 10.89}{\sqrt{\dfrac{8.3521}{46} + \dfrac{6.1504}{19}}}$$

$$= \frac{-4.44}{\sqrt{0.5053}} = \frac{-4.44}{0.7108}$$

$$= -6.25$$

$$df' = \frac{(s_1^2/n_1 + s_2^2/n_2)^2}{\dfrac{(s_1^2/n_1)^2}{n_1 - 1} + \dfrac{(s_2^2/n_2)^2}{n_2 - 1}}$$

$$= \frac{(8.3521/46 + 6.1504/19)^2}{\dfrac{(8.3521/46)^2}{45} + \dfrac{(6.1504/19)^2}{18}}$$

$$= \frac{0.255300}{0.006554}$$

$$= 38.95$$

As this example shows, df' is usually not a whole number. When critical value decision rules are used, the convention is to round df' to the nearest whole number. Here it is $df' = 39$. Then, from Table A.4, $t_{crit} = \pm 2.030$ for $df = 35$, the closest conservative value because $df = 39$ isn't in the table. Because $t' = -6.25$ is less than -2.042, you should reject H_0 of equal population means for the adults and adolescents.

The adults' average for LOC was lower than the adolescents' average, and the difference is significant. Lower LOC scores mean the participants attribute control of their lives to internal sources, which characterizes the adults in the sample. The higher LOC scores for adolescents might indicate that at their age, they feel less control over their lives. A therapist who works with overweight women may be able to use this information.

Quick Quiz

In Research Example 13, Loftus and Palmer (1974) asked 50 students about the speed of the cars that *hit* each other and 50 students about the speed of the cars that *smashed* into each other. Suppose you run a similar experiment with 30 participants in each group. If you suspect unequal population variances, should you use the AWS statistic instead of the two-independent-sample *t*?

Answer

No, you don't have to use the AWS because the unequal variances would be a problem only if your samples were small or unequal in size or both. They are equal and greater than 15, so you can rely on the robustness of the two-independent-sample *t*.

Strength of Association

What if you have run a study and obtained a significant result, only to realize later that you may have had too much power? Did the high power lead you to find a trivial difference to be significant? This question can be answered with a statistic that uses an idea you learned in Chapter 6 on correlation.

The concept of the proportion of variance of *Y* that is accounted for by *X* was introduced in the form of r^2. You used r^2 as a measure of the strength of the linear prediction of *Y* from *X*. For the two-independent-sample *t*-test, you want a similar index to examine the strength of the relationship between the independent variable and the dependent variable. The **strength of association** is the proportion of variability in the dependent variable that is accounted for by the independent variable. For the exam stress study, you can ask, How much of the variability in the number of stress symptoms is explained by the students' perceived control over the test? If the sample sizes are large enough, almost any study can produce a significant *t*-test, even with small $\mu_1 - \mu_2$ and small strength of association. Let's examine two estimates of the strength of association.

Strength of association
Proportion of variability in the dependent variable that is accounted for by the independent variable

The first measure is η^2 (eta squared). A direct estimate of the strength of association is given by

η^2 and ω^2
Two sample measures of the strength of association

$$\eta^2 = \frac{t^2}{t^2 + df} \tag{13.15}$$

where t^2 is the square of the observed value of the two-independent-sample *t*-statistic and $df = n_1 + n_2 - 2$. The problem with η^2 is that it sometimes overestimates the true strength of association.

The second measure of the strength of association is ω^2 (omega squared). Like η^2, it is an estimate of the strength of association, but it has the property of being somewhat conservative (underestimation). The formula for ω^2 is:

$$\omega^2 = \frac{t^2 - 1}{t^2 + df + 1} \tag{13.16}$$

which is set equal to zero if t^2 is less than one.

Let's compute both these measures for the exam stress data in Table 13.2:

$$\eta^2 = \frac{-3.2797^2}{-3.2797^2 + 58} = \frac{10.7564}{68.7564} = .16$$

$$\omega^2 = \frac{-3.2797^2 - 1}{-3.2797^2 + 58 + 1} = \frac{9.7564}{69.7564} = .14$$

Both measures show that a relatively low proportion (as percentages, 16% or 14%) of the variability in the number of stress symptoms can be accounted for by differences in perceived control. So although the perceived-control group had significantly fewer stress symptoms than the other group, factors other than perceived control over the test account for most of the variability in the number of stress symptoms.

Confidence Intervals for $\mu_1 - \mu_2$

Confidence interval for the difference between two independent population means
Interval that will include $\mu_1 - \mu_2$ for $100(1 - \alpha)\%$ of such intervals

You obtained a confidence interval of potential values for a single population mean in Chapters 9 and 12. In a similar way, you can obtain a **confidence interval for the difference between two independent population means.** The $100(1 - \alpha)\%$ confidence interval for $\mu_1 - \mu_2$ is given by

$$(\overline{X}_1 - \overline{X}_2) - (t_{\text{crit}})(s_{\overline{X}_1 - \overline{X}_2}) \quad \text{to} \quad (\overline{X}_1 - \overline{X}_2) + (t_{\text{crit}})(s_{\overline{X}_1 - \overline{X}_2}) \tag{13.17}$$

where t_{crit} is the two-tailed ($\alpha/2\%$) critical value for t with $df = n_1 + n_2 - 2$. The formula for $s_{\overline{X}_1 - \overline{X}_2}$ is given by the denominator of the two-independent-sample t-statistic in formula 13.5:

$$s_{\overline{X}_1 - \overline{X}_2} = \sqrt{\left[\frac{(n_1 - 1)s_1^2 + (n_2 - 1)s_2^2}{n_1 + n_2 - 2}\right]\left(\frac{1}{n_1} + \frac{1}{n_2}\right)}$$

For example, in the exam stress study, $\overline{X}_1 = 10.00$ stress symptoms for the perceived-control group and $\overline{X}_2 = 12.50$ symptoms for the no-control group. The difference in the means was $10.00 - 12.50 = -2.50$. The estimated standard error of $\overline{X}_1 - \overline{X}_2$ (the denominator of the t-statistic) was 0.7623. For a 95% confidence interval, you would use the t critical value for $df = 55$ because $df = 58$ is not in Table A.4, and $t_{\text{crit}} = 2.004$. The 95% confidence interval for $\mu_1 - \mu_2$ is

$$-2.50 - (2.004)(0.7623) \quad \text{to} \quad -2.50 + (2.004)(0.7623)$$

or

$$-4.0276 \quad \text{to} \quad -0.9724$$

We are 95% confident that the interval of -4.0276 to -0.9724 includes the true value of $\mu_1 - \mu_2$. The same warnings about using correct language apply to this confidence interval as to the confidence interval for a single population mean. Also you can use the confidence interval to test H_0: $\mu_1 - \mu_2 = 0$ by seeing whether zero is included in the interval. If zero is not included in the interval, you reject H_0.

Quick Quiz

For the exam stress study, you are 95% confident that the true value of the difference in population means is bracketed by -4.0276 and -0.9724. The null hypothesis is $\mu_1 - \mu_2 = 0$. Will you reject the null? What does that mean about perceived control and number of symptoms?

Answer

Yes, you will reject H_0 because the confidence interval does not include zero. You can conclude that the perceived-control group had significantly fewer stress symptoms than the no-control group because the difference in the two groups' average numbers of symptoms is significantly different from zero. This is the same conclusion you reached with the two-independent-sample t.

13.3   Two Dependent Samples: Means

The two-dependent-sample *t*-test is reserved for situations with specific types of between-groups relationships. You use the two-dependent-sample *t*-test if the observations in the two groups are paired in one of these ways:

1. Naturally occurring pairs
2. Repeated measures (two measures taken on the same subject)
3. Researcher-produced pairs

The primary reason for using two dependent samples is to control extraneous variability. To the extent that the scores within each pair are related, the two-dependent-sample *t*-test removes the variability due to the extraneous variables that cause the relationship. For example, in a naturally occurring pair such as a husband and wife, any variability due to similar attitudes, experiences, socioeconomic variables, and so on, is accounted for. You are controlling for those extraneous variables because you have two similar people. With those variables controlled, you can look at the difference between the man and woman on a dependent variable, such as attitude toward the level of male commitment in male–female relationships.

In any study that uses two measures taken on the same subject, any variability due to individual differences in personality, physical, social, or intellectual variables is accounted for by the fact that each subject possesses those characteristics in both measures.

Finally, any study that matches or pairs the subjects on some extraneous variable introduces the relationship between the scores in a pair through the extraneous variable. You will see later that the two-dependent-sample *t*-test accounts for the relationship between the two scores in the pair and the extraneous variability by using the correlation between the scores within the pairs.

Example

Als, Tronick, Lester, and Brazelton (1979) provided normative data on the Brazelton Neonatal Behavior Assessment Scale (BNBAS). They collected data for most of the first 10 days of the lives of 54 healthy full-term white newborn babies. These babies were selected according to strictly defined criteria, which included medical normalcy of the baby and uncomplicated obstetric history and delivery for the mothers. They found "definite improvement in behavioral performance" in the babies over the first ten days of their lives. This improvement was statistically significant for 14 of the 26 items in the BNBAS. Attention items such as orientation to face and voice showed significant improvement as well as items on physiological adjustment, such as number of times startled.

Suppose you are interested in replicating this study with another type of infant— say, full-term but small babies. You collect data on $N = 15$ babies on only days 1 and 10, and you want to know whether there is significant improvement. Table 13.3 gives simulated data for the orientation to face and voice. The two rightmost columns contain values that you will need in the eventual calculation of the *t*-test. To test the hypothesis of significant change in orientation to face and voice, the appropriate statistic is the two-dependent-sample *t*-statistic because you have two groups of scores, and the scores are repeated measures on the same subjects.

Table 13.3

Orientation to face and voice for 15 full-term but small babies

Baby	Day 1	Day 10	$d = X_1 - X_2$	d^2
1	6	7	1	1
2	5	7	2	4
3	3	6	3	9
4	8	8	0	0
5	6	8	2	4
6	6	8	2	4
7	6	8	2	4
8	7	8	1	1
9	8	6	-2	4
10	5	7	2	4
11	6	7	1	1
12	7	7	0	0
13	5	7	2	4
14	6	8	2	4
15	4	6	2	4
ΣX	88	108	$\Sigma d = 20$	$\Sigma d^2 = 48$

Hypotheses

The hypotheses that can be tested by using the two-dependent-sample *t*-test have exactly the same form as those tested for the two-independent-sample *t*-test, except that the means are from dependent populations. The null hypothesis in each pair of hypotheses in formulas 13.1, 13.2, and 13.3 can be tested by using the two-dependent-sample *t*-test. Rejecting H_0 in the two-dependent-sample case leads to slightly different conclusions than you draw in the two-independent-sample case. For example, in the retirement center example, suppose you matched the participants on age and then randomly assigned them within each pair to therapy or the waiting list. You would use the two-dependent-sample *t*. Let's say the therapy group's average depression level is significantly lower than the waiting-list group's average depression level. You would conclude that the therapy group had significantly lower depression, with the extraneous variable of age controlled by the pairing of subjects. Your interpretation of the results should include some statement about how the pairs were created.

One way to show the two-dependent-sample statistic's distinction from the two-independent-sample case is to call the difference in dependent population means the **mean difference:**

Mean difference

Difference in correlated population means

$\mu_d = \mu_1 - \mu_2$

$$\mu_d = \mu_1 - \mu_2 \tag{13.18}$$

For the two-dependent-sample case, you write the nondirectional null hypothesis as

$$H_0: \mu_1 - \mu_2 = 0$$

or

$$H_0: \mu_d = 0$$

Many extraneous variables are controlled for when repeated measures are used. In the study of full-term but small babies measured on day 1 and day 10 (see Table 13.3), the hypotheses would be about the average difference between the scores for days

1 and 10. The individual babies act as their own controls, and this includes any variables associated with their mothers or their births.

Test Statistic

We use the same definitional formula for the two-dependent-sample t-statistic as we used for the other t-tests: something minus its mean divided by its estimated standard deviation. What are you interested in? You are hypothesizing about the mean difference, $\mu_d = \mu_1 - \mu_2$, the difference between two dependent means. What statistic will you use to estimate μ_d? There are two ways of writing the two-dependent-sample t-test. First, let's look at the conceptually easier one.

Suppose you measured five people's depression levels on a 20-point scale and then measured them again a week later. You can look at the change in their depression scores over time by forming a **difference score,** the difference between the scores taken on two occasions. We use the symbol d for difference score. Notice that we are always going in the same direction when we subtract one score from another. Here, $d = X_1 - X_2$.

The mean of the scores at Time 1 is 14.8, and the mean of the Time 2 scores is 14.4. If you are interested in the difference in means, you find $\overline{X}_1 - \overline{X}_2 = 0.4$. Now, compute the average of the d values. You should get 0.4. The mean of the differences equals the difference of the means. Here, $\mu_d = \mu_1 - \mu_2$. These difference scores are something new, but you can use your existing knowledge to compute a test statistic. Once you have computed the d's, you have simplified your data to one set of scores. From this point on, the two-dependent-sample t-test like a one-sample t-test on the difference scores. This is the basis for the computational formula for the two-dependent-sample t.

The computational formula relies entirely on the first step of computing $d = X_1 - X_2$. These differences, d values, contain not only variability due to X_1 and X_2 but also variability due to the correlation between X_1 and X_2, which are dependent. You can work directly with the differences and no longer use information on the original X values.

The next step is to obtain the **mean of the differences,** $\overline{d}$:

$$\overline{d} = \frac{\Sigma d}{N} \tag{13.19}$$

and the **variance of the differences,** s_d^2:

$$s_d^2 = \frac{\Sigma(d - \overline{d})^2}{N - 1} = \frac{N\Sigma d^2 - (\Sigma d)^2}{N(N - 1)} \tag{13.20}$$

where the first formula is the definitional formula for s_d^2 and the second is the computational formula. You are doing the same computation you did when finding the unbiased variance estimate s^2 on a group of X values. Now you have "something" (the $\overline{d}$) minus its mean (hypothesized to be zero) divided by its estimated standard deviation. The computational formula for the two-dependent-sample t-statistic is

$$t = \frac{\overline{d} - \mu_d}{\sqrt{s_d^2/N}} = \frac{\overline{d} - \mu_d}{s_d/\sqrt{N}} \tag{13.21}$$

The specific hypotheses and statistic are illustrated in Table 13.4 by the computation of the two-dependent-sample t-test for the data in Table 13.3.

Difference score
$d = X_1 - X_2$

Time 1: X_1	Time 2: X_2	d
15	16	−1
17	19	−2
18	15	3
14	12	2
10	10	0

Mean of the differences
$\overline{d} = \overline{X}_1 - \overline{X}_2$ is the sample mean of the differences
$d = X_1 - X_2$

Variance of the differences
s_d^2 is the unbiased sample variance of the differences
$d = X_1 - X_2$

Table 13.4
Computation of the two-dependent-sample t-test for the simulated Brazelton data

$\alpha = .05$

$df = N - 1 = 15 - 1 = 14$

$H_0: \mu_d = 0$ $H_1: \mu_d \neq 0$

$t_{crit} = \pm 2.145$

Day 1: X_1	Day 10: X_2
$\Sigma X = 88$	$\Sigma X = 108$
$\overline{X} = 5.87$	$\overline{X} = 7.20$

$d = $ day 10 score $-$ day 1 score

$\Sigma d = 20$ $\Sigma d^2 = 48$

$\overline{d} = 20/15 = 1.33 = \overline{X}_2 - \overline{X}_1 = 7.20 - 5.87$

$$s_d^2 = \frac{15(48) - (20)^2}{(15)(14)} = 1.5238$$

$$t = \frac{\overline{d} - \mu_d}{\sqrt{s_d^2/N}}$$

$$= \frac{1.33}{\sqrt{1.5238/15}} = \frac{1.33}{\sqrt{0.1016}}$$

$$= 4.18$$

Because $t = 4.18 > 2.145$, you reject H_0.

Because the mean score for orientation to face and voice for day 10 is larger than that for day 1, the average of the differences, $\overline{d}$, is positive and is equal to 1.33. In other words, each d is formed by taking $X_2 - X_1$. The question to be answered by the t-test is whether 1.33 is likely to have happened by chance if $\mu_1 = \mu_2$ (if $\mu_d = \mu_2 - \mu_1 = 0$). The t-statistic shows that 1.33 is significantly larger than zero, so you can reject the H_0 of zero difference in the population means. This means that the data support the hypothesis that μ_d is not zero, or that definite improvement occurs from day 1 to day 10 in orientation to face and voice for full-term but small babies. A nondirectional alternative was used because the researcher wanted to remain open to the possibility of a drop in behavior because of the small size of the babies.

Distribution

If all the assumptions are met, the two-dependent-sample t-statistic in formula 13.21 has a sampling distribution that is exactly the t distribution with

$$df = N - 1 \qquad (13.22)$$

Degrees of freedom for the two-dependent-sample t-statistic
$df = N - 1$, the number of pairs minus 1

So $N - 1$ is the formula for the **degrees of freedom for the two-dependent-sample t-statistic,** where N is the number of pairs of scores.

Because you can use the two-dependent-sample t-test in different situations, the degrees of freedom are defined as the *number of pairs of scores minus 1.* Some students get confused when the symbol N is used for anything besides the total number of participants in a study. In the two-dependent-sample t-test's df formula, N represents number of pairs of scores. In the Brazelton scale example, there were 15 pairs of scores, so the degrees of freedom were 14.

N can be defined according to the three main ways of obtaining pairs of scores:

1. Naturally occurring pairs of participants provide N pairs of scores. How many individual participants do you have? You have $2N$.
2. When participants are matched on a variable, you again have $2N$ individuals but N pairs of scores.
3. When you have repeated measures (pretest, posttest) on the same participants, you have N individuals and N pairs of scores.

For the two-dependent-sample case, where do you get the "independent components" for the working definition of degrees of freedom? (Remember: $df =$ number of independent components minus the number of parameters estimated.) The dependence in the observations is only within each pair of scores; the pairs are independent of each other, which makes sense no matter how you got the pairs. The first baby measured on day 1 and day 10 is independent of the second baby measured the same way. The first husband–wife pair in a study of political attitudes is independent of the next husband–wife pair. You focus on the independence of the pairs; in reality, you use the d values as the independent components. In the variance estimate in the denominator of the t-statistic, s_d^2, there are indeed N independent values of d. There is one statistic, $\bar{d}$, that estimates the population difference in the means, μ_d. So the working definition of degrees of freedom gives $df = N - 1$.

As in the two-independent-sample case, you use Table A.4 to obtain the critical value of t. You have to know df, α, and whether the test is one or two tailed. In the Brazelton scale example, $df = 14$, $\alpha = .05$, and the test was two tailed. The critical values for this case were ± 2.145. Examine Figure 13.4 for the critical values and rejection values for the Brazelton study.

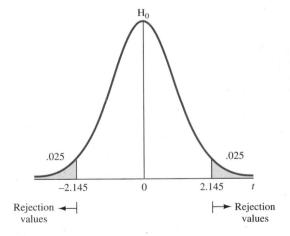

Figure 13.4
Sampling distribution of t with $df = 14$, $\alpha = .05$, two-tailed test, showing critical values, rejection values, and areas

Decision Rules

As you read through these decision rules, note which was used in Table 13.4. For a two-tailed test, the decision rule is:

$$\text{If } t \leq -t_{\text{crit}} \text{ or } t \geq t_{\text{crit}}, \text{ reject } H_0; \text{ otherwise, retain } H_0 \tag{13.23}$$

where t_{crit} is the $\alpha/2\%$ critical value from the t distribution with $df = N - 1$.

For a one-tailed test that uses the upper tail of the t distribution, the decision rule is:

$$\text{If } t \geq t_{\text{crit}}, \text{ reject } H_0; \text{ otherwise, retain } H_0 \tag{13.24}$$

where t_{crit} is the $\alpha\%$ critical value from the t distribution with $df = N - 1$.

The decision rule for a one-tailed test that uses the lower tail of the t distribution is:

$$\text{If } t \leq -t_{\text{crit}}, \text{ reject } H_0; \text{ otherwise, retain } H_0 \tag{13.25}$$

where t_{crit} is the $\alpha\%$ critical value from the t distribution with $df = N - 1$.

The Brazelton scale example had a nondirectional alternative hypothesis H_1: $\mu_d \neq 0$. You used the decision rule in formula 13.23 along with degrees of freedom for the two-dependent-sample t-test of $df = N - 1 = 14$ to obtain the critical values of ± 2.145. Computing the t-statistic gave $t = 4.18$, which is larger than the critical value of 2.145; consequently, you rejected H_0, consistent with the decision rule.

For a two-tailed test of a nondirectional hypothesis, if the two-tailed p-value is less than or equal to α, reject H_0; otherwise, retain H_0. For one-tailed tests of directional hypotheses, you have to pay attention not only to the size of the one-tailed p-value but also to the tail where the observed statistic occurs. You reject H_0 only when the p-value is small enough *and* the statistic occurs in the tail of the sampling distribution predicted by H_1.

Quick Quiz

In the retirement center example, suppose you believe that group therapy will result in lower depression scores for the therapy group compared to the 15 age-matched control group subjects. You compute $t = -1.61$. (a) What hypothesis are you testing? (b) What are the df? (c) Find the critical values with $\alpha = .05$. (d) What decision do you make about H_0? (e) What can you conclude about the therapy?

Answers

(a) H_0: $\mu_1 \geq \mu_2$, where 1 stands for the therapy group. Always make sure you are using the p values in the same direction as your hypothesis. Here, you compute $d = X_1 - X_2$. If you expect the X_1's to be smaller than the X_2's, then the d's should be negative, which corresponds to the tail in which you placed α. (b) $N_{\text{pairs}} - 1 = 15 - 1 = 14$. (c) -1.761. (d) Retain H_0 because the observed statistic doesn't exceed the critical value. (e) With the extraneous variable of age controlled, the therapy didn't make a significant difference in average depression levels.

Sampling Distribution of $\overline{X}_1 - \overline{X}_2$ for Dependent Samples

Another way of conceptualizing the two-dependent-sample t-test is more difficult, but you'll be able to see its connection to the two-independent-sample t.

Let's look at the difference in the dependent means and the inferential statistic that can be used to test hypotheses. In the two-dependent-sample case, the main descriptive statistic is $\overline{X}_1 - \overline{X}_2$, which is equal to the average of the d values. For now, let's focus on the difference in group means. This statistic is an unbiased estimate of the difference between two dependent population means, symbolized again as $\mu_1 - \mu_2$, although keep in mind that these are dependent population means. Because $\overline{X}_1 - \overline{X}_2$ is an unbiased statistic, the mean of its sampling distribution is $\mu_1 - \mu_2$. The shape of the sampling distribution of the dependent $\overline{X}_1 - \overline{X}_2$ is normal, like the shape of the sampling distribution $\overline{X}_1 - \overline{X}_2$ for independent samples.

But what about the variance of the sampling distribution of $\overline{X}_1 - \overline{X}_2$ when the samples are dependent? Here is the formula:

$$\sigma^2_{\overline{X}_1-\overline{X}_2} = \frac{\sigma^2_1}{N} + \frac{\sigma^2_2}{N} - 2\rho\frac{\sigma_1}{\sqrt{N}}\frac{\sigma_2}{\sqrt{N}} \tag{13.26}$$

Part of this equation is identical to the variance formula for the independent-means case. But what is the last component? It is a function of the correlation between the two samples. If the samples are independent, then there is no correlation ($\rho = 0$), and this component is zero. So the variance of $\overline{X}_1 - \overline{X}_2$ for independent samples is a special case of this formula where the correlation is zero.

Formula 13.26 is in the form of parameters. You need an estimate of $\sigma^2_{\overline{X}_1-\overline{X}_2}$ so you can take the square root of it and place it in the denominator of a definitional formula for t. You can find the estimate of $\sigma^2_{\overline{X}_1-\overline{X}_2}$ by using separate estimates for each of its pieces. The best estimates for σ^2_1 and σ^2_2 are the sample variances s^2_1 and s^2_2, respectively. The best estimate for the correlation ρ is the sample correlation r, the sample correlation coefficient between X_1 and X_2. When you plug these estimates into the formula, you obtain an estimate of $\sigma^2_{\overline{X}_1-\overline{X}_2}$:

$$s^2_{\overline{X}_1-\overline{X}_2} = \frac{s^2_1}{N} + \frac{s^2_2}{N} - 2r\frac{s_1}{\sqrt{N}}\frac{s_2}{\sqrt{N}} \tag{13.27}$$

The square root of formula 13.27 is used in the definitional formula for the two-dependent-sample t-test:

$$t = \frac{(\overline{X}_1 - \overline{X}_2) - \mu_d}{\sqrt{\frac{s^2_1}{N} + \frac{s^2_2}{N} - 2r\frac{s_1}{\sqrt{N}}\frac{s_2}{\sqrt{N}}}} \tag{13.28}$$

but this is not recommended for computing t. This t fits the general verbal definition of any t: something minus its mean divided by its estimated standard deviation.

What happens to the denominator of the definitional formula for the two-dependent-sample t when the correlation between the samples increases? A bigger chunk is subtracted from the denominator, which makes it smaller. As the denominator shrinks, the overall value of t becomes larger and the power of the two-dependent-sample t-test increases. Large positive values of r occur when the scores within a pair are related in some way, such as by matching or control of an extraneous variable. So to the extent that the pairing is effective, the two-dependent-sample t-test can give higher power than the two-independent-sample t-test.

You may be wondering about the connection between the definitional and computational formulas for the two-dependent-sample t. It is not obvious that

$$s^2_d = \frac{s^2_1}{N} + \frac{s^2_2}{N} - 2r\frac{s_1}{\sqrt{N}}\frac{s_2}{\sqrt{N}}$$

Perhaps the most convincing argument is that both the definitional and the computational formulas give exactly the same numerical answer. Exercise 10 at the end of this chapter asks you to verify that both formulas give the same answer for the Brazelton scale data in Table 13.3.

Assumptions and Robustness

Because the two-dependent-sample t is computed on the values of d, the assumptions for this statistic revolve around the difference scores. If (1) the d's in the population are normally distributed and (2) the d's are independent, then the two-dependent-sample t-statistic in formula 13.21 is distributed exactly as the t distribution with $df = N - 1$. These assumptions are the same as those for the one-sample t-test, except that here they are on the d values. There is no assumption of equality of variance for the two-dependent-sample t-test because there is only one set of d's.

If the d's are not normally distributed, then the sampling distribution of the two-dependent-sample t-statistic usually fits the t distribution fairly well with $df = N - 1$. The two-dependent-sample t-test is fairly robust to violation of the normality assumption, with the robustness related to N as well as the severity of skewness and kurtosis in the population of the d's. As in the two-independent-sample case, this relative robustness to nonnormality of the d's is fortunate because you have little or no control over the shape of the population distribution of the d's. For most situations, you rely on the robustness of the two-dependent-sample t-test to nonnormality. If the normality assumption has been violated, one alternative is the appropriate nonparametric method. Chapter 19 introduces such a method for two dependent samples.

Similar to the two-independent-sample t-test, the two-dependent-sample t-test is not robust to violation of the assumption of independence of the d values. Fortunately, the assumption of independence is usually met; the pairs of scores (the d's) are usually independent because of random sampling. If sampling is not random, then avoiding obvious dependency between the pairs of scores most likely will suffice to meet the assumption of independence of the d's. If this assumption is not met, the true α can be drastically different from the value of α you set.

13.4 Comparison of Independent and Dependent Sample Cases

This overview of the t-statistics for two samples should help you remember some important concepts and clarify when to use each t-test.

Sampling Distributions

For the two-independent-sample case, if all the assumptions are met, then the t-statistic has a sampling distribution that is the t distribution with $df = n_1 + n_2 - 2$. For the two-dependent-sample case, the t-statistic and the t distribution are different. If both assumptions are met, then the t-statistic for the two-dependent-sample case has a sampling distribution that is the t distribution with $df = N - 1$.

Comparison of the sampling distributions uncovers several interesting points. First, although the numerators of both statistics have the same form, $\bar{X}_1 - \bar{X}_2$ or the equivalent $\bar{d}$, the means can be either independent or dependent. Second, the degrees of freedom for the t-distributions are different. Suppose you can choose between the two-independent-sample t or the two-dependent-sample t. You have 20 study participants who you can match on some extraneous variable. Then $df = 18$ for the two-independent-sample t, but $df = 9$ for the two-dependent-sample t because there are only 10 pairs from the 20 participants. If you want to do repeated measures on the 20 subjects, then the two-dependent-sample t degrees of freedom are $df = 19$. Finally, the two-independent-sample t-test works with the original raw scores, whereas the two-dependent-sample t-test uses the difference scores.

Power

As the correlation between two means increases, the denominator of the two-dependent-sample t-statistic gets smaller and the t-statistic increases. Remember that a function of the correlation was subtracted from the variance of the mean difference? The power of the two-dependent-sample t-test increases as the positive value of r increases. What makes r go up? The correlation is strong if the matching or other control of an extraneous variable is effective.

When the power of the two-dependent-sample t-test is compared to that of the two-independent-sample t-test, the degrees of freedom also play an important role. If you have effective control of the extraneous variable, then you get a high positive value of r. This makes the denominator of the two-dependent-sample t-statistic smaller than that of the two-independent-sample t-statistic, so the actual value of t is larger. However, a larger obtained t does not guarantee that the power is higher because the power also depends on the critical value, which depends on the degrees of freedom. Earlier we demonstrated that the degrees of freedom for the two-dependent-sample t would be one-half those for the two-independent-sample t if the research setting allowed choice between the two basic designs. This reduction in degrees of freedom results in an increase in the critical value and a subsequent *loss* in power. For the two-independent-sample t-test with $df = 18$, the critical value for $\alpha = .05$ for a one-tailed test is 1.734, whereas the critical value for the two-dependent-sample t-test with $df = 9$ and $\alpha = .05$ for a one-tailed test is 1.833.

Basically, then, the question of which test has the higher power becomes a question of whether the gain in power from the effective control of extraneous variability—and the resulting positive value of r—is larger than the loss of power from fewer degrees of freedom and a larger critical value. In other words, you must ask whether the loss in power from the lower degrees of freedom and larger critical value for the two-dependent-sample t-test is offset by the increase in power resulting from the larger value of the t-statistic. If the answer is yes, then the two-dependent-sample t-test will be more powerful than the two-independent-sample t-test. Of course, the question you are trying to answer with your research usually dictates which statistic you use. As the first step in designing an experiment, you should decide which questions you want to answer and then determine which statistic will help you find the answers.

Assumptions and Robustness

Let's compare the two t-tests from this chapter on the basis of their assumptions and robustness. The two-independent-sample t-test has the assumptions of independence, normality, and equality of variances, whereas the two-dependent-sample t-test has only the assumptions of independence and normality. Not only is there a difference in the number and type of assumptions, but also there is a difference in the random variable that is the subject of those assumptions. For the two-independent-sample t-test, you assume that the original raw scores, X values, are independent and normally distributed with equal variances in the populations for both groups. For the two-dependent-sample *t*-test, however, you assume that the difference scores, values of *d,* are independent and normally distributed in the population. The original raw scores are actually dependent for the two-dependent-sample case, to the extent that the Pearson *r* is nonzero. Although there is dependence within each pair of scores, the pairs themselves are independent. When you form the difference $d = X_1 - X_2$, the *d*'s are assumed independent.

Robustness to violation of assumptions does not differ for the two assumptions that the statistics hold in common, normality and independence. Most carefully run experimental studies meet the independence assumption, and the statistics are generally robust to violation of the normality assumption. The two-independent-sample *t*-test works with two sets of *X* values and assumes equal population variances for the two groups. Using equal sample sizes, each larger than or equal to 15, makes the two-independent-sample *t*-test robust to violation of the equal variance assumption for near-normal distributions. If the sample sizes are not equal or are less than 15 each, you should use the AWS test for independent samples.

Quick Quiz

Suppose you are interested in whether an alcohol awareness program will reduce the reported incidence of drinking (number of drinks consumed in the immediate prior week). You randomly sample 20 students from an introductory psychology class and ask them about their recent alcohol consumption. You measure the number of drinks consumed. All 20 students go to three speeches in which the effects of alcohol are discussed. A week later, they again complete the survey about their recent drinking. (a) What is the appropriate statistic? (b) Compute *df.*

Answers

(a) For repeated measures on the same subjects, the appropriate statistic is the two-dependent-sample *t*. (b) $df = N - 1 = 19$.

13.5   Two Independent Samples: Proportions

You learned in Chapter 12 how to test a hypothesis about a single population proportion. Occasionally a research project gives the number or proportion of participants who simply possess some characteristic rather than giving a numerical score on the characteristic. When this occurs, you need a special statistic for the proportions from two samples.

You often use proportions in connection with qualitative data or data that have a nominal scale of measurement. With such qualitative data for each participant, the researcher can work with frequencies, percentages, or proportions. For example, researchers found that 70 men in 227 couples who were engaged or dating initiated a public display of affection. Each man either had the characteristic of initiating a public display of affection or not. The 70 could be transformed to a percentage or a proportion. Alternatively, a researcher may have data that are quantitative but that have been categorized with respect to some theoretical or arbitrary value. An example is the proportion of people who report annual salaries of $70,000 to $80,000. If you have proportions when comparing two independent samples, the data don't lend themselves to tests of hypotheses about equality of means. In this situation, you can use the test of *two independent proportions.*

Example

Did patterns of alcohol abuse among college students change from 1977 to 1989? In view of decreasing drug use during that time period, this was one of the prime questions in research done by Wechsler and Isaac (1992). Part of a study on the drinking behavior of college students included the number of men who reported getting drunk one to three times per month. In 1977, the number who got drunk one to three times per month was 194 of the 777 men surveyed. In 1989, 212 of the 519 men surveyed fell into this category. Is there a significant difference between the proportion for 1977, $P_1 = 194/777 = .2497$, and the proportion for 1989, $P_2 = 212/519 = .4085$?

Hypotheses

To use the test of two independent proportions, you have two independent samples in a comparative study and you know the proportion of individuals in each sample who have some characteristic. As in the binomial distribution discussed in Chapter 8, it helps to label the characteristic of interest a "success." In the case of the one-sample proportion from Chapter 12, N was the number of events and f was the number of successes, or events of interest. With the two sample sizes expressed as n_1 and n_2, the number of successes in each sample will be f_1 and f_2. The sample proportions of successes will be $P_1 = f_1/n_1$ and $P_2 = f_2/n_2$, and the population proportions will be p_1 and p_2. The hypotheses can be expressed as one of the following pairs:

$$\text{H}_0: p_1 - p_2 = 0 \qquad \text{H}_1: p_1 - p_2 \neq 0$$

or equivalently,

$$\text{H}_0: p_1 = p_2 \qquad \text{H}_1: p_1 \neq p_2 \tag{13.29}$$

Here H_0 states that the difference in population proportions is zero (or the proportions are equal). This difference of zero (equality of proportions) does not depend on the value of p, a population proportion. This is similar to the two-sample t-tests, where you don't have to know μ and instead your focus is on $\mu_1 - \mu_2$. The alternative hypothesis indicates interest in any difference in the two population proportions regardless of direction. In the drinking example, H_0 states that the population proportion of men who reported getting drunk one to three times per month in 1977 is equal to that for men in 1989.

You might predict that one particular population proportion will be larger than the other, which would change your hypotheses:

$$\text{H}_0: p_1 - p_2 \leq 0 \qquad \text{H}_1: p_1 - p_2 > 0$$

or equivalently,

$$\text{H}_0: p_1 \leq p_2 \qquad \text{H}_1: p_1 > p_2 \tag{13.30}$$

If your prediction is in the opposite direction, the hypotheses are

$$\text{H}_0: p_1 - p_2 \geq 0 \qquad \text{H}_1: p_1 - p_2 < 0$$

or equivalently,

$$H_0: p_1 \geq p_2 \qquad H_1: p_1 < p_2 \tag{13.31}$$

In these directional alternatives, a larger p_1 signals the use of formula 13.30, whereas a larger p_2 leads to the use of formula 13.31. Of course, you should heed the earlier warning to use directional hypotheses only when you are sure about the predicted direction.

Test Statistic and Distribution

The test statistic is

$$z_{P_1-P_2} = \frac{P_1 - P_2}{\sqrt{P(1-P)\left(\dfrac{1}{n_1} + \dfrac{1}{n_2}\right)}} \tag{13.32}$$

where

$$P = \frac{f_1 + f_2}{n_1 + n_2}$$

Pooled estimate of a common population proportion
P is an estimate of the proportion of successes in both populations pooled together

The P without any subscript is a **pooled estimate of a common population proportion** because it combines, or pools, information from both samples. If H_0 is true, then P is the best estimate of the proportion of successes in the common populations. For the drinking example, it's $(194 + 212)/(777 + 519) = 406/1296 = .3133$. Note that the general form of $z_{P_1-P_2}$ is that of any z: something minus its mean divided by its standard deviation.

For the drinking example,

$$z_{P_1-P_2} = \frac{P_1 - P_2}{\sqrt{P(1-P)\left(\dfrac{1}{n_1} + \dfrac{1}{n_2}\right)}}$$

$$= \frac{.2497 - .4085}{\sqrt{(.3133)(.6867)\left(\dfrac{1}{777} + \dfrac{1}{519}\right)}}$$

$$= \frac{-.1588}{\sqrt{.0006914}} = \frac{-.1588}{.02629} = -6.04$$

where

$$P = \frac{f_1 + f_2}{n_1 + n_2} = \frac{194 + 212}{777 + 519} = \frac{406}{1296} = .3133$$

You can test H_0 with this test statistic by using the standard normal distribution. If H_0 is true, then

$$z_{P_1-P_2} \text{ is approximately distributed as the standard normal} \tag{13.33}$$

and you can use Table A.2 to get critical values.

Table 13.5
Requirements for adequacy
of the normal approximation
(using the moderate rule
from Samuels & Lu, 1992)

p	Required f
.05	48
.10	40
.15	33
.20	25
.25	19
.30	14
.35	8
.40	5
.45	5
.50	5

In Chapter 12, you learned improved rules for sample size requirements for the approximation of a z for a test on a one-sample proportion (Samuels & Lu, 1992). For the two-sample case, follow the guidelines in Table 13.5, using $f = f_1 + f_2$ and the common P for p.

You can use the standard normal distribution and Table A.2 to obtain critical values or p-values for $z_{P_1-P_2}$ if the conditions given in Table 13.5 are met for the common P computed in the test statistic. (If P is larger than .50, use $Q = 1 - P$ to enter the table.) Ideally, you should have the hypothesized value of the common population p, but most often this value is unknown. So you can estimate the common p with the common sample P.

For the drinking example,

$$P = \frac{f_1 + f_2}{n_1 + n_2} = \frac{194 + 212}{777 + 519} = \frac{406}{1296} = .3133$$

total $N = 1296$, and total $f = 406$. Enter the table with $p = .30$, the closest entry to the value of P. Because $f = 406$ is larger than 14 (from Table 13.5 for $p = .30$), the normal distribution is a good fit to the sampling distribution of $z_{P_1-P_2}$.

Quick Quiz

Suppose you are doing a study on pet ownership among high school students. You survey 25 girls and 25 boys about what kind of pets they own. You discover that 6 of the boys and 16 of the girls own cats. What statistical test should you use to see whether this boy–girl difference in cat ownership is significant?

Answer

Because you have a characteristic that each student either has or does not, cat ownership, the information on each student is qualitative and you must work with proportions. The appropriate test statistic is the test of equality of independent proportions, $z_{P_1-P_2}$.

Decision Rules

The rules by which you decide whether to reject or retain the null hypotheses about equality of population proportions stated in formulas 13.29 through 13.31 are similar to those given for other two-sample tests. For a two-tailed test using $z_{P_1-P_2}$, the decision rule is:

$$\text{If } z_{P_1-P_2} \leq -z_{\text{crit}} \text{ or } z_{P_1-P_2} \geq z_{\text{crit}}, \text{ reject } H_0; \text{ otherwise, retain } H_0 \qquad (13.34)$$

where z_{crit} is the $\alpha/2\%$ critical value from the standard normal distribution in Table A.2. From the standard normal distribution, $\alpha = .05$ gives the critical values of ± 1.96. Any statistic that is more extreme than ± 1.96 leads you to reject H_0. For the drinking example, you can reject H_0 because $-6.04 < -1.96$.

For a one-tailed test that uses the upper tail of the sampling distribution of $z_{P_1-P_2}$, the decision rule is:

$$\text{If } z_{P_1-P_2} \geq z_{\text{crit}}, \text{ reject } H_0; \text{ otherwise, retain } H_0 \qquad (13.35)$$

where z_{crit} is the $\alpha\%$ critical value from the standard normal distribution.

The decision rule for a one-tailed test in the lower tail of the sampling distribution of $z_{P_1-P_2}$ is:

$$\text{If } z_{P_1-P_2} \leq -z_{\text{crit}}, \text{ reject } H_0; \text{ otherwise, retain } H_0 \qquad (13.36)$$

where z_{crit} is the $\alpha\%$ critical value from the standard normal distribution.

The p-value decision rules are similar to those you used for other two-sample tests. For a two-tailed test of a nondirectional hypothesis, if the two-tailed p-value is less than or equal to α, reject H_0; otherwise, retain H_0. For one-tailed tests of directional hypotheses, you have to pay attention not only to the size of the one-tailed p-value but also to the tail where the observed statistic occurs. You reject H_0 only when the p-value is small enough *and* the statistic occurs in the tail of the sampling distribution predicted by H_1.

Assumptions

Like the one-sample test using a proportion, the assumptions necessary for this two-sample test of independent proportions are that the outcomes are independently sampled and that they are sampled from distributions that have only two possible outcomes. If you violate the assumption of independence, the consequences are severe, as for all tests. Without independent observations, you cannot be assured that the test statistic is even approximately normally distributed. However, independence is usually met; when it's not, the violation usually is obvious. Under certain restrictive settings, a test for dependent proportions is available but is not given in this text (see McNemar, 1969).

The assumption of two possible outcomes is met any time you use this test by the very nature of the experimental situation. You choose $z_{P_1-P_2}$ to test hypotheses about equality of two independent proportions only when there are only two possible outcomes.

In addition, you have the condition given in Table 13.5 to ensure the adequacy of the normal approximation. For the drinking example, this condition was met. Even though this condition is not exactly an assumption, it is important for the use of $z_{P_1-P_2}$ as a test statistic and the standard normal distribution as a reference distribution. If you use $z_{P_1-P_2}$ as a test statistic when the requirements of Table 13.5 are not met, you most likely will have either a skewed sampling distribution or a discrete sampling distribution, neither of which is well fit by the symmetric, continuous, standard normal distribution.

13.6 Summary, Study Tips, and Computation

Chapter Summary

You have studied statistical procedures for realistic two-sample cases. With two independent samples, you can use the two-independent-sample t-test of a hypothesis of equality of population means by referring the statistic to a critical value from the t distribution with $df = n_1 + n_2 - 2$. If you use $n_1 = n_2 \geq 15$, the statistic is generally robust to, or not affected by, violation of the assumptions of normality and equal variances, and careful experimentation usually will enable you to meet the independence assumption. If you don't have equal large sample sizes, you should use the AWS test.

Two dependent samples result when there are N pairs of scores from naturally occurring pairs, two measures taken on the same participant, or researcher-produced

Table 13.6

Situation	Statistic	Distribution
Two independent samples $n_1 = n_2 \geq 15$ $H_0: \mu_1 = \mu_2$	Two-independent-sample t-test	t with $df = n_1 + n_2 - 2$
Two independent samples $n_1 \neq n_2$ or < 15 $H_0: \mu_1 = \mu_2$	AWS test, t'	Approximately t with df'
Two dependent samples $H_0: \mu_1 = \mu_2$ or $H_0: \mu_d = 0$	Two-dependent-sample t-test	t with $df = N - 1$ (N = number of pairs)
Two independent samples $H_0: p_1 = p_2$	Test of two independent proportions, $z_{P_1 - P_2}$	Standard normal

pairs. In these cases, you should use the two-dependent-sample t-test. You can test a hypothesis of equality of dependent population means by referring the statistic to a critical value from the t distribution with $df = N - 1$. The statistic is generally robust to violation of the assumption of normality of the d's, and careful experimentation usually will enable you to meet the assumption of independence of the d's.

If you have proportions for each of two independent samples, then $z_{P_1 - P_2}$ can be used to test hypotheses about equality of population proportions.

The following key terms are used in this chapter:

Two-independent-sample t-test	ω^2
Randomization	AWS test
$df = n_1 + n_2 - 2$	Behrens-Fisher problem
Normality	t'
Independence	df'
Equal variances	Two-dependent-sample t-test
Robustness	Pairs of scores (three ways)
$n_1 = n_2 \geq 15$	$df = N - 1$
η^2	

$\bar{d}$	Sample proportions,
s_d^2	P_1 and P_2
Test of two independent proportions	

The statistical tests introduced in this chapter are summarized in Table 13.6. The situation where the statistic is used, the name of the statistic, and the theoretical reference distribution are given for each procedure. For decision rules, assumptions, and any restrictions on the use of these procedures, refer to the sections where they were introduced.

Study Tips

Continue the chart you started in Chapter 12, adding a column for each of the statistics covered in this chapter. Memorize the formulas for df. Learn each of the three ways to get pairs of scores for the two-dependent-sample case and be able to think of an example of each. One of the most frequent mistakes is for students to miss clues given in the language describing some research that point to use of the two-dependent-sample t.

Computation

Almost every statistical package of computer programs offers programs or procedures to compute two-independent-sample and two-dependent-sample t-tests. Although the computational labor is not excessive for these procedures, it is greater than for the simpler one-sample tests. The use of computer programs lightens the computing load while giving accurate answers when there is accurate input. Most of these programs give a probability value associated with the absolute value of the statistic rather than compare the statistic to some critical value. As mentioned in Chapters 8 and 10, this is a two-tailed probability. We give examples of SAS and SPSS programs for computing t-tests for two groups.

SAS Examples

By using SAS, the procedure TTEST computes both the two-independent-sample *t*-test (and its probability) and the AWS *t'* (and its probability). The procedure UNIVARIATE can be used to compute the two-dependent-sample *t*-test and its probability. Examples of these are given here for the data in Tables 13.1 and 13.3.

(SAS system's lines)
```
DATA T;
INPUT CONT$ N;    (input the independent variable, CONT for control, and the sample size for each group)
DO I=1 TO N;    (this statement is like the subscript on a summation sign, changing i from 1 to the sample size for each group to do
                 everything between here and the end of the program N times)
INPUT X @@;    (input the score for each subject, and the @@ lets you put them on a line one following the other)
OUTPUT;    (puts all the scores in the data set so you can compute t-tests on them)
END;    (ends the DO statement)
CARDS;
PC 30
12 12 8 5 12 5 11 12 7 15 11 6 12 11 8 11 12 11 13 11
13 12 7 13 9 7 5 15 7 7
NC 30
9 12 9 11 11 15 14 7 11 11 9 17 14 17 11 13 19 14 11 13
12 14 7 11 16 15 13 13 10 16
PROC PRINT;
PROC TTEST;    (asks for both t-tests)
CLASS CONT;    (tells the program that the independent variable is control)
VAR X;    (tells the program that the dependent variable is X)
```
(system's line)

The SAS System
TTEST PROCEDURE

Variable: Y

Group	N ①	Mean	Std Dev	Std Error	Minimum	Maximum
NC	30	12.50000000	2.93316353	0.53551994	7.00000000	19.00000000
PC	30	10.00000000	2.97112541	0.54245080	5.00000000	15.00000000

For HO: Variances are equal, F' = 1.03   DF = (29,29)   Prob>F' = 0.9453

Variances	T	DF	Prob>|T| ④
② Unequal	3.2797	58.0	0.0018
③ Equal	3.2797	58.0	0.0018

Figure 13.5
SAS output from PROC TTEST

For PROC TTEST, the SAS output in Figure 13.5 gives the following:

1. n, $\bar{X}$, s, $s/\sqrt{N}$, and the minimum and maximum for the dependent variable X for each group (NC and PC).

2. The AWS t' statistic (T) for use when $n_1 \neq n_2$ or for small equal samples because it is not sensitive to unequal variances. Note that here $n_1 = n_2$, and only the degrees of freedom potentially differ from the values given in item 3. For this example, df rounds to 58.

3. The two-independent-sample t-statistic (T) given in this text for use when $n_1 = n_2 \geq 15$. The value of $df = n_1 + n_2 - 2$.

4. The probabilities are two-tailed for use with a nondirectional hypothesis. To do a one-tailed test of a directional hypothesis, you must correctly predict the sign of t and reject H_0 if one-half the given probability is less than or equal to your chosen α (significance level).

```
(SAS system's lines)
DATA TC;
INPUT ONE TEN @@;
DIFF=TEN-ONE;
CARDS;
6 7 5 7 3 6 8 8 6 8 6 8 6 8 7 8 8 6 5 7 6 7 7 7 5 7 6 8 4 6
PROC PRINT;
PROC UNIVARIATE;
VAR DIFF;
TITLE 'BRAZELTON SCALE DATA, TWO DEPENDENT SAMPLE T-TEST';
(system's line)
```

BRAZELTON SCALE DATA, TWO DEPENDENT SAMPLE T-TEST

Univariate Procedure

Variable=DIFF ①

Moments				Quantiles(Def=5)				Extremes			
N	15	Sum Wgts	15	100% Max	3	99%	3	Lowest	Obs	Highest	Obs
Mean	1.333333	Sum	20	75% Q3	2	95%	3	-2(	9)	2(	10)
Std Dev	1.234427	Variance	1.52381	50% Med	2	90%	2	0(	12)	2(	13)
Skewness	-1.52866	Kurtosis	2.814303	25% Q1	1	10%	0	0(	4)	2(	14)
USS	48	CSS	21.33333	0% Min	-2	5%	-2	1(	11)	2(	15)
CV	92.58201	Std Mean	0.318728			1%	-2	1(	6)	3(	3)
② T:Mean=0	4.1833	Pr>|T|	0.0009③	Range	5						
Num −, =0	13	Num > 0	12	Q3-Q1	1						
M(Sign)	5.5	Pr>=|M|	0.0034	Mode	2						
Sgn Rank	37.5	Pr>=|S|	0.0042								

Figure 13.6
SAS output from PROC UNIVARIATE, two-dependent-sample t-test

For PROC UNIVARIATE, the SAS output in Figure 13.6 for a two-dependent-sample *t*-test (because you formed DIFF=TEN−ONE in the program) gives the following:

1. Results for the variable DIFF
2. The *t*-statistic
3. The two-tailed probability for *t* (see item 4 in the SAS output for Figure 13.5)

SPSS Examples

In SPSS, the command T-TEST computes both the two-independent-sample *t*-test (and its probability) and the AWS *t'* (and its probability). The command T-TEST also can be used to compute the two-dependent-sample *t*-test and its probability. Examples of these follow for the data in Tables 13.1 and 13.3.

(SPSS system's lines)
```
SET WIDTH 80
DATA LIST FREE/CONT X     (the variables CONT, the independent variable control, and X, the dependent variable of number of
                           symptoms, are input in free format)
BEGIN DATA
1 12 1 12 1 0 1 5 1 12 1 5 1 11 1 12 1 7 1 15 1 11 1 6 1 12
1 11 1 0 1 11 1 12 1 11 1 13 1 11 1 13 1 12 1 7 1 13 1 9
1 7 1 5 1 15 1 7 1 7
2 9 2 12 2 9 2 11 2 11 2 15 2 14 2 7 2 11 2 11 2 9 2 17 2 14
2 17 2 11 2 13 2 19 2 14 2 11 2 13 2 12 2 14 2 7 2 11 2 16
2 15 2 13 2 13 2 10 2 16
END DATA
T-TEST GROUPS=CONT/VARIABLES=X    (the command T-TEST uses GROUPS= to identify the grouping or independent
                                   variable, here CONT for control, and VARIABLES= to identify the dependent
                                   variable, here X)

FINISH
```
(system's line)

```
t-tests for independent samples of  CONT

GROUP 1 - CONT  EQ     1.00
GROUP 2 - CONT  EQ     2.00

Variable        Number ①              Standard    Standard
                of Cases    Mean   Deviation      Error
-----------------------------------------------------------
X
      GROUP 1     30    10.0000     2.971        .542
      GROUP 2     30    12.5000     2.933        .536
```

Figure 13.7
SPSS output for T-TEST, independent groups

(continued)

		I	Pooled Variance Estimate			I	Separate Variance Estimate		
F Value	2-tail Prob.	I	t Value	Degrees of Freedom	2-tail Prob.	I	t Value	Degrees of Freedom	2-tail Prob.
1.13	.945	I	−3.28	58	.002	I	−3.28	57.99	.002
			②		④		③		④

Figure 13.7 (continued)

For the command T-TEST, the SPSS output in Figure 13.7 gives the following:

1. n, $\overline{X}$, s, and $s/\sqrt{N}$ for the dependent variable X for each group.
2. The two-independent-sample t-statistic given in this text for use when $n_1 = n_2 \geq 15$. The value of $df = n_1 + n_2 - 2$.
3. The AWS t' statistic for use when $n_1 \neq n_2$ or for small equal samples because it is not sensitive to unequal variances. Note that here $n_1 = n_2$, and only the degrees of freedom differ from the values given in item 2.
4. The two-tailed probability for t (see item 4 in the SAS output for Figure 13.5).

(SPSS system's lines)
```
SET WIDTH 80
DATA LIST FREE/ONE TEN    (input the two scores for each pair, ONE and TEN)
BEGIN DATA
6 7 5 7 3 6 8 8 6 8 6 8 6 8 7 8 8 6 5 7 6 7 7 7 5 7 6 8 4 6
END DATA
T-TEST PAIRS=ONE TEN    (this is the way you use the command T-TEST to show you want the two-dependent-sample t-test, simply
                         put PAIRS= followed by the names you use for the two scores, here ONE and TEN)

FINISH
```
(system's line)

- - - t-tests for paired samples - - -

Variable ①	Number of Cases	Mean	Standard Deviation	Standard Error
ONE				
	15	5.8667	1.356	.350
	15	7.2000	.775	.200

Figure 13.8
SPSS output for T-TEST, two-dependent-sample t

(continued)

TEN

(Difference) Mean	Standard Deviation	Standard Error	I I	2-tail Corr. Prob.	I I	t Value	Degrees of Freedom	2-tail Prob.
−1.3333 ②	1.234	.319	I	.435 .105	I	−4.18 ③	14	.001 ④

Figure 13.8 (continued)

For the command T-TEST, the SPSS output in Figure 13.8 for a two-dependent-sample *t*-test gives the following:

1. Information for each of the groups of data, ONE and TEN, including N, $\overline{X}$, s, and $s/\sqrt{N}$ for the dependent variable X
2. For the differences, d, the mean, standard deviation, and standard error
3. The *t*-statistic and *df*
4. The two-tailed probability for *t* (see item 4 in the SAS output for Figure 13.5)

Exercises

Section 13.1
1. List the differences between the one-sample case and the two-sample case.

Section 13.2
2. Suppose a teaching methods study was designed to test a hypothesis of equal means on the final examination scores for an experimental teaching method and the traditional lecture method. Subjects were randomly assigned to one of the two methods, classes were taught, and final examination scores were recorded. Use the two-independent-sample *t*-test with the following statistics to test H_0: $\mu_1 - \mu_2 = 0$ using $\alpha = .05$.

Experimental: $N = 16$ $\overline{X} = 87.5$ $s^2 = 38.13$

Traditional: $N = 16$ $\overline{X} = 82.0$ $s^2 = 42.53$

3. Suppose a researcher did a study comparing the worries of boys and girls aged 11. Given a numerical scale ranging from 1 (never) to 5 (always), the children were asked to respond to questions about worries (for example, "failing a test," "talking too much," "my mother getting sick"). Worry scores were averaged for several general categories in order to test a hypothesis of no gender differences in the averages for each category.

Boys: $N = 61$ $\overline{X} = 2.94$ $s^2 = 1.21$

Girls: $N = 61$ $\overline{X} = 3.37$ $s^2 = 1.64$

a. Use the two-independent-sample *t*-test with the statistics given here on family worries to test H_0: $\mu_1 - \mu_2 = 0$ using $\alpha = .05$.
b. Obtain η^2 and ω^2 for these data. Approximately what percentage of the variability in worry scores can be explained by gender?

4. Brumback, Jackoway, and Weinberg (1980) studied the relationship between depression and intelligence test scores. Children who had school problems and were subsequently referred for educational assessment were diagnosed as depressed or not depressed according to previously established criteria (primarily commonly agreed-on symptoms). The scores on the full-scale IQ measurements for depressed and nondepressed children are given here. (Simulated data are based on Brumback, Jackoway & Weinberg, 1980.)

Depressed	100	118	91	127	96
	103	108	86	90	118
Nondepressed	81	105	118	119	118
	111	106	85	115	106

a. Would you use the two-independent-sample t-test or the AWS test? Explain.

b. With $\alpha = .05$, use these data to test the hypothesis that average IQ scores are equal for depressed and nondepressed children. Can you make cause-and-effect statements about depression and intelligence from this study? Explain.

5. Assume the study in Exercise 3 reported only $N = 45$ girls and all the other numbers were the same.

a. Would you use the two-independent-sample t-test or the AWS test? Explain.

b. With $\alpha = .05$, use the numbers given in Exercise 3 except $N = 45$ girls to test the hypothesis H_0: $\mu_1 - \mu_2 = 0$.

6. Based on Research Example 13, the data given here are speed estimates from two groups asked how fast cars were going when they *smashed* or *hit* into each other.

Smashed	12	10	10	7	8
	16	16	9	9	8
Hit	14	5	7	11	7
	4	6	8	11	7

a. If you really believed that the mean for *smashed* would be larger than that for *hit*, what H_0 would you test? Would you reject this H_0 using $\alpha = .05$?

b. Was the study in Research Example 13 a true experiment?

c. Obtain both η^2 and ω^2 for these data. Approximately what percentage of the variability in speed estimates is explained by the verb condition?

7. Form a 95% confidence interval for $\mu_1 - \mu_2$ from the data in Exercise 2.

8. a. Form a 99% confidence interval for $\mu_1 - \mu_2$ from the data in Exercise 3.

b. How can you test H_0: $\mu_1 - \mu_2 = 0$ using the confidence interval in part a?

c. Do you come to the same conclusion here as you did in Exercise 3?

Section 13.3

9. Now suppose the research in Exercise 3 used 61 brother–sister pairs to control for family variables (socioeconomic status, single-parent families, and

so on). Use the two-dependent-sample t-test with the following statistics on family worries to test H_0: $\mu_1 - \mu_2 = 0$ using $\alpha = .05$. The statistics for differences between brother–sister pairs are: $N = 61$, $\bar{d} = 0.43$, and $s_d^2 = 1.03$.

10. Verify that the definitional and computational formulas for the two-dependent-sample t-test (13.28 and 13.21, respectively) give the same answer for the data in Table 13.3. You have to use the definitional formula and compare the results to those for the computational formula in Table 13.3. You should get the same value for t.

11. In a study on attraction, suppose people were asked to rate pictures of females taken before orthodontic treatment (braces). The participants rated the females in the pictures on a number of variables. Two weeks later the participants returned to the study to rate another set of pictures, the same females after orthodontic treatment. Both pictures showed females with mouths closed and teeth not visible. Ratings of intelligence are given in the table. Test the hypothesis that there is no change in intelligence ratings before and after braces (use $\alpha = .05$).

Female	Prerating	Postrating
1	113	115
2	105	117
3	120	125
4	119	117
5	104	107
6	100	105
7	111	110
8	130	125
9	119	121
10	127	130
11	111	110
12	115	117
13	107	113
14	102	105

Section 13.4

12. Describe the situation in which you would use a two-independent-sample t-test. Include in your description the answers to these questions:

a. What hypothesis is tested?

b. How many groups of subjects are there?

c. What characterizes the group(s)?

d. What assumptions or conditions must be met?

13. Describe the situation in which you would use an

AWS *t*-test. Include in your description the answers to the questions in Exercise 12.

14. Describe the situation in which you would use a two-dependent-sample *t*-test. Include in your description the answers to the questions in Exercise 12.

15. In comparing the *t*-tests in Exercises 3 and 9, what is the potential gain in using a two-dependent-sample situation (if possible)? Are the two critical values identical? What is the potential loss in using a two-dependent-sample situation?

16. In the dental anxiety study (Arntz, van Eck, & Heijmans, 1990) there were 19 high-anxiety and 21 low-anxiety participants. The report states that immediately after a certain treatment, "there seems to be a temporary decrease in pain predictions in the HA group, which is NS, however [$t(18) = 1.55$, $P = .070$, 1 tailed]."
   a. What two groups of scores are being compared?
   b. Given that $t(18)$ indicates $df = 18$ for that *t*-test, what statistic was used?
   c. What does P stand for, and how is it connected to the abbreviation NS?

17. Use the following data for women alcoholics and nonalcoholics on the Tactual Performance Test (see Exercise 22 in Chapter 1).

Alcoholics					Nonalcoholics				
34	28	26	28	19	15	13	27	12	15
26	14	10	1	10	2	9	28	18	15
18	33	21	30	20	23	23	12	18	31
26	43	33	25	14	7	8	4	14	15
9	50	24	27	7	18	16	28	6	15

Simulated data based on Silberstein and Parsons (1981).

   a. What test statistic is appropriate? Explain.
   b. Use your choice in part a to test H_0: $\mu_1 - \mu_2 = 0$ with $\alpha = .05$.

18. Reconsider the data from Exercise 17 with the last column of data for nonalcoholics missing.
   a. What test statistic is appropriate? Explain.
   b. Use your choice in part a to test H_0: $\mu_1 - \mu_2 = 0$ with $\alpha = .05$.

19. A fertilizer must be tested for its percentage of nitrogen. Tests are done by the producing company and a state laboratory. Samples of the fertilizer are taken from the most recent batch. Each sample is ground into a powder and divided into two equal parts. The parts are randomly assigned to the two laboratories. The results are listed in the table.

Sample	Company	State
1	10.10	10.02
2	9.92	9.90
3	10.83	10.59
4	9.34	9.71
5	10.04	9.92
6	10.29	10.11
7	10.07	10.06

   a. What test statistic is appropriate? Explain.
   b. Use your choice in part a to test a hypothesis that the laboratories have the same average results. Use $\alpha = .05$.

20. A manufacturing process uses a raw material that is periodically changed to try to increase the weight of the final product. A sample of 15 items of the final product gave $\bar{X} = 2.72$ lb with $s^2 = 0.33$. The raw material was changed, and another sample of 15 items of the final product gave $\bar{X} = 2.81$ lb with $s^2 = 0.23$.
   a. What test statistic is appropriate? Explain.
   b. Use your choice in part a to answer this question: Can you conclude that the new raw material increased the weight of the final product? Use $\alpha = .05$.

21. Suppose a smoking reduction clinic allowed clients to select which type of treatment they wanted to take. Here are the data for 20 clients divided into each of two treatments. (Scores are the number of cigarettes per week reduced since the program started.)

Treatment A	10	17	13	20	21
	14	19	19	21	29
Treatment B	11	13	12	9	17
	28	15	17	13	14

   a. What test statistic is appropriate? Explain.
   b. Use your choice in part a to test H_0: $\mu_1 - \mu_2 = 0$ with $\alpha = .05$.
   c. Can you conclude that the treatments are different in their effectiveness in reducing smoking?
   d. Is this a true experiment? What are some possible extraneous variables? Have they been controlled? Could confounding exist?

22. Participants in a weight loss experiment first are paired by gender, age, weight, and body type, and then within each pair, they are randomly assigned to one of two treatments. Here are the data for ten pairs of participants. (Data are the pounds lost since the start of the program.)

Pair	1	2	3	4	5	6	7	8	9	10
Treatment A	5	7	20	13	11	9	8	19	16	15
Treatment B	4	6	18	14	12	10	7	16	13	10

a. What is the correct test statistic? Explain.
b. Use your choice in part a to test H_0: $\mu_1 - \mu_2 = 0$ with $\alpha = .05$.
c. Can you conclude that the treatments are different in their effectiveness of weight reduction?
d. Is this a true experiment? What are some possible extraneous variables? Have they been controlled? Could confounding exist?

23. From Research Example 11, suppose you have the data in the table for the three sickle-cell anemia patients. They were measured before the butyrate treatment started and after 3 weeks of daily intravenous doses of a butyrate solution. The research laboratory examination of a slide of blood gives a measurement that is a count of the number of sickle cells in 50 fields of 50 cells.

Subject	1	2	3
Before treatment	776	547	932
After treatment	43	21	49

a. What is the correct test statistic? Explain.
b. Use your choice in part a to test H_0: $\mu_d = 0$ with $\alpha = .05$.
c. Can you conclude that the butyrate treatment is effective? What concern does the small sample size give you?

Section 13.5

24. Following up on the research on pets of high school students given earlier in a Quick Quiz, you might want to know whether the proportion of students who own cats is different for males and females. The relevant numbers are $n_1 = n_2 = 25$, $f_1 = 6$, and $f_2 = 16$. The proportion of males with the characteristic of cat ownership is $P_1 = 6/25 = .24$. For females it is $P_2 = 16/25 = .64$.
a. Compute the value of the common P.
b. Compute the value of $z_{P_1 - P_2}$.
c. Test the hypothesis of equal population proportions using $\alpha = .05$.

25. Wechsler and Isaac (1992) reported that the number of women abstainers from alcohol in 1977 was 45 out of the sample of 1038. In 1989, there were 162 women abstainers out of 1090. Test the hypothesis of equal population proportions using $\alpha = .05$.

26. Using a definition of binge drinking as consuming five or more drinks in a row in the previous two weeks, Wechsler and Isaac (1992) also found that binge drinkers had problems in other areas of their lives. For example, of the 302 men binge drinkers, 141 reported that their drinking caused them to damage property, whereas only 30 of the 187 nonbinge drinkers had this problem. With $\alpha = .05$, is this difference significant?

27. Violence against women by their husbands has been a controversial topic (see Council Reports, 1992). When the wife is pregnant, the crime seems even more heinous. One researcher (Gelles, 1988) hypothesized that age was a confounding variable that needed to be controlled when comparing violence rates against pregnant and nonpregnant women. For women under age 25 who reported husband-to-wife violence, there were 63 from the sample of 208 nonpregnant women and 9 from the 30 pregnant women. Test the hypothesis of equal population proportions using $\alpha = .05$.

28. Access and ownership of handguns among youth of school age are a growing concern. In one study (Callahan & Rivara, 1992), ownership of a handgun was reported by 51 of 446 males and 7 of 462 females. Reported ownership of a handgun also was given by social class: 6 of 195 class I (highest social class), 17 of 208 class II, 11 of 163 class III, 5 of 97 class IV, and 4 of 20 class V (lowest social class). Among deviant behaviors considered, reported selling of drugs was given by 83, 27 of whom owned handguns, as compared to 854 who never sold drugs, 34 of whom owned handguns. Use $\alpha = .05$ for all tests.
a. Do males differ from females in the proportion of reported handgun ownership?
b. Which social classes differ significantly from class I in terms of the proportion of reported ownership of a handgun?
c. Is there a significant difference in the proportion of reported handgun ownership between those who sell and don't sell drugs?

14

One-Way Analysis of Variance

Chapter 13 described some realistic and widely used statistics for two-sample situations. This chapter introduces a statistic that is among the most commonly used inferential procedures, the analysis of variance (ANOVA). The ANOVA F statistic is used to test hypotheses about equality of group means when you have two or more independent groups.

Research Example 14
14.1 Introduction
    Comparison of more than two means
    Notation
    Example
    Problems with using multiple t-tests
14.2 Logic of ANOVA
    Two ways to estimate variance
    F ratio
    Group differences versus group equality
14.3 ANOVA: Partitioning of Variability
    Notation and terminology
    Variability
    Sums of squares
    Degrees of freedom
    Mean squares
14.4 ANOVA F Test
    Hypotheses
    F ratio
    F distribution
    Decision rules
    Assumptions
    Example
    Relationship of t to F
    Strength of association
    Beyond the one-way ANOVA
14.5 Summary, Study Tips, and Computation
    Chapter summary
    Study tips
    Computation
Exercises

Research Example 14

You've heard about cigarette smoking being bad for your health, but what about its detrimental effects on your thinking? Does smoking have any effect on cognitive functioning, either immediately after smoking or in the long run? Are the effects, if any, positive or negative? Spilich, June, and Renner (1992) did five studies on the effects of smoking on cognitive functioning. The studies examined tasks with increasing processing complexity. On the low end, the tasks were repetitive, used mostly short-term memory (STM), and used little resources of long-term memory (LTM). On the high end, the tasks required extensive use of LTM or were simulations of real-world activities.

All studies used the same procedure: three groups of adults with the same number in each group. Nonsmokers (NS) were participants who had never smoked regularly and did not smoke at the time of the research. The smokers in the study reported to have smoked at least one pack of cigarettes per day during the last year; cigar and pipe smokers were excluded. Smokers were assigned to one of two groups: those who had just actively smoked (AS) and those who were deprived of smoking for 3 h (DS). In the 6-min interval before the study started, the AS smokers were provided with a cigarette with 1.2 mg of nicotine and were "requested to inhale normally every 25 s and hold that puff for 5 s, for a total of 12 puffs." All subjects sat in a waiting room for 6 min before the study. The NS and DS participants "sham-smoked" an imaginary cigarette, so their experience was as similar as possible to the AS group's experience.

Consider their simplest task (Task 1): looking for a target letter in a 96-letter array. All letters were capitals. In an array of K, T, V, and W's, the target was either an X or an O. If it was an X, the target was considered similar to letters in the array; an O was a dissimilar target. Fifty percent of the trials were done with these letters. The other trials were done with an array of Q, U, C, and D's, with the O being the similar target and the X being the dissimilar target. The researchers measured the time to locate the target. Each group had 15 participants.

There were no differences between the groups, even when combining data from all target/array conditions ($F < 1$). Smoking had no effect on this task, which was repetitive and low in use of LTM.

Now consider a more realistic task. Task 4 was comprehension of a text. Participants were asked to read an interesting story aloud and were told that they would later be asked to recall the story accurately and completely, trying to capture the meaning of sentences, phrases, and words. Each participant's oral free recall was taped for later analysis into idea units called propositions. Independent raters judged the number of propositions recalled. There were 21 participants in each group for Task 4.

There were significant differences in the percentage of propositions in free recall of textual material, $F(2, 60) = 22.4$, $p < .01$. Multiple comparison analysis (see Chapter 15) showed that the NS group recalled significantly more than either DS or AS, and that the DS group recalled significantly more than AS. Further analysis on the type of recalled material showed that the NS group recalled more central material and the other two groups recalled relatively unimportant facts.

Finally, in a driving simulation (Task 5), the AS group had significantly more rear-end collisions than either NS or DS. Spilich, June, and Renner (1992) concluded "that subprocesses such as working memory or attentional capacity which are involved in dealing with complex tasks are disrupted by an agent or agents in cigarettes." Parents in the future may warn their kids that smoking can impair their growth, health, thinking, and driving!

In this chapter, you will learn how to compute the value used in this example.

14.1 Introduction

In the last few chapters you've been learning statistics for testing hypotheses about means, correlations, or proportions. The examples have become increasingly realistic. This trend continues; in fact, the statistic introduced in this chapter is one of the most widely used statistics in behavioral science research. The statistics you've learned so far are used for evaluating one- and two-sample experiments ($z_{\overline{X}}$, t, r, z_P, two-independent- and two-dependent-sample t-tests, the AWS test, and $z_{P_1 - P_2}$). The statistic in this chapter is for evaluating experiments with two or more independent samples. This procedure, called the *one-way analysis of variance* (*ANOVA*), uses a general methodology and gives a test statistic for testing a hypothesis of equality of two or more means from independent groups. The ANOVA is a general extension of the t-test.

Comparison of More Than Two Means

The two-independent-sample t-test is used to test hypotheses about equality of means from two independent groups. For instance, the exam stress study looked at the difference in the number of stress symptoms for two groups: students who perceived they had some control over exam questions and students who believed they had no control over the test content. The numerator of the t-statistic contains the difference in means, $\overline{X}_1 - \overline{X}_2$.

What if you added a third group, perhaps an "actual control" group in which student-written questions were guaranteed to appear on the exam? (Any volunteers?) Let's say you found the average number of stress symptoms for the students in the perceived-control group to be $\overline{X}_1 = 8$. The mean number of symptoms for the no-control group was $\overline{X}_2 = 10$, and the actual-control subjects had an average of $\overline{X}_3 = 6$. How are you going to calculate the difference in means so you can test a hypothesis that the groups are the same? If you compute some arbitrary arrangement, like $\overline{X}_1 - \overline{X}_2 - \overline{X}_3$, you get $8 - 10 - 6 = -8$, which is an arbitrary answer. If you get all possible differences of pairs, $\overline{X}_1 - \overline{X}_2$, $\overline{X}_1 - \overline{X}_3$, and $\overline{X}_2 - \overline{X}_3$, you get more than one test statistic. Do you see the problems? Now, think back to the introduction of sample variance. You computed the dispersion of scores by comparing each score to the mean. Couldn't you do something like that here? You could compute a variance to see whether these means are spread out or bunched together. If you compute the variance of 8, 10, and 6, then the order of arrangement doesn't matter because you compare each of these three numbers to their overall mean. You'll also have just one test statistic.

Suppose these means aren't significantly different from one another. Each mean, then, can be thought of as representing one of three overlapped groups. Each sample mean has a value that is just like any score in the groups. So the variance based on sample means shouldn't be much different from the variance of all of the scores within the groups. That's conceptually what you do when you perform an analysis of variance. You look at the variance between groups and see how it compares to the within-groups variance. If the between-groups variance is much bigger than the within-groups variance, then the means are spread out and the groups are different. This outcome would lead us to reject a hypothesis that the group means are the same.

Let's tie this idea back to the two-independent-sample *t*-statistic. What does the numerator of *t* tell you? *It tells you about the difference between groups.* What does the denominator of *t* tell you? *It tells you about the variance within groups.* The analysis of variance has conceptual and computational ties to the two-independent-sample *t*.

You may be wondering why this new statistic is called a *one-way* analysis of variance. *One-way* refers to the number of independent variables being manipulated. You could say the two-independent-sample *t* is a one-way statistic because the only variable being manipulated is the one that sets off Group 1 from Group 2. You can have a one-way ANOVA with three groups or five groups or seven groups; it's still a one-way when you are manipulating only one variable.

Now you have enough background to understand the following definition: A **one-way analysis of variance** is a procedure that tests the effect of one independent variable (several independent groups) on the means of one dependent variable. The ANOVA *F* statistic is a ratio, with the between-groups variance estimate in the numerator and the within-groups variance estimate in the denominator.

One-way analysis of variance
Statistical test of a hypothesis of equality of two or more means from independent groups that are formed from one independent variable

Notation

It is necessary to explain some notation for the one-way ANOVA. A subscript on an *X*, such as X_3, has indicated the subject's number. For the first time now, there will be two subscripts on *X*, with one subscript representing the subject and the other representing the group to which the score belongs. X_{ij} stands for a score for the *i*th subject in the *j*th group. So X_{11} is the score for the first subject in the first group, and X_{43} is the score for the fourth subject in the third group. In this text the symbol *J* stands for the number of groups, and *n* is the number of subjects in each group. The general notation for all subjects is:

$$X_{ij} = \text{score for the } i\text{th subject in the } j\text{th group, where } i = 1 \text{ to } n \text{ and } j = 1 \text{ to } J$$

The capital *N* is not equal to lowercase *n*; the total number of subjects *N* is the sum of the *n* values. If the *n*'s are equal, then *N* is equal to *nJ*, or *n* observations in each of *J* groups. Box 14.1 gives information on summation notation that you can use as a review.

X_{ij}
Score for the *i*th subject in the *j*th group

Box 14.1   Summation Notation

One Subscript

If you have one sample with *N* = 10 observations and let *X* be the symbol for one of these observations, then you need a subscript for *X* to tell you which of the ten *X* values you are discussing. The notation

$X_i \qquad i = 1, \ldots, 10$

is used to indicate all the values, and X_4 indicates the fourth value of X. More generally, because the sample size is given as N, you use the notation

$$X_i \quad i = 1, \ldots, N$$

to stand for the N data points in the sample.

The sum of the ten scores in the sample is symbolized by

$$X_1 + X_2 + \cdots + X_{10}$$

where the "$+ \cdots +$" in the middle of the expression means "plus and so on plus." In summation notation,

$$\sum_{i=1}^{10} X_i = X_1 + X_2 + \cdots + X_{10}$$

Here i is the subscript that tells us which X is the starting point of the summation (that is, with 1) and 10 is the ending point of the summation. The notation is read "the sum of X sub i, i equals 1 to 10." The general expression for N values of X is:

$$\sum_{i=1}^{N} X_i = X_1 + X_2 + \cdots + X_N$$

This can be used without the "$i = 1$" and "N" to mean exactly the same thing, with the starting point and ending point assumed to be 1 and N. So

$$\sum X_i = X_1 + X_2 + \cdots + X_N$$

Two Subscripts

When you have two subscripts i and j to stand for subjects and groups, respectively, you can use two summation signs. Three different sums are available. First, there is the sum using the subscript i. This adds the subjects' scores for a given group:

$$\sum_i X_{ij} = X_{1j} + X_{2j} + \cdots + X_{nj}$$

or the sum of all the scores in the jth group. Second, there is the sum of all the scores in all the groups:

$$\sum_j \sum_i X_{ij} = \sum_j (X_{1j} + X_{2j} + \cdots + X_{nj})$$

which uses both the subscript i for subjects and the subscript j for groups. Here you add the scores in each group ($\sum_i X_{ij}$) and then add these sums for all groups using $\sum_j$. Third, sometimes you combine the summation signs with the operation of squaring and then summing as in:

$$\sum_j (\sum_i X_{ij})^2 = \sum_j (X_{1j} + X_{2j} + \cdots + X_{nj})^2$$

Here you get the sum of the scores in each group using $\sum_i$, then square those sums, and finally add together these squared sums using $\sum_j$.

Table 14.1

Numbers of correct responses

	Images	*Rehearse*	*Control*	
	$X_{11} = 17$	$X_{12} = 8$	$X_{13} = 4$	n = number of observations
	$X_{21} = 16$	$X_{22} = 4$	$X_{23} = 7$	per group = 4
	$X_{31} = 13$	$X_{32} = 3$	$X_{33} = 0$	J = number of groups = 3
	$X_{41} = 12$	$X_{42} = 1$	$X_{43} = 2$	
	$\sum_i X_{i1} = 58$	$\sum_i X_{i2} = 16$	$\sum_i X_{i3} = 13$	$\sum_j \sum_i X_{ij} = 87$
Group means	$\overline{X}_1 = 58/4$	$\overline{X}_2 = 16/4$	$\overline{X}_3 = 13/4$	Grand mean $\overline{X} = 87/12 = 7.25$
	= 14.50	= 4.00	= 3.25	
Group variances	$s_1^2 = 5.67$	$s_2^2 = 8.67$	$s_3^2 = 8.92$	

Example

Suppose you want to know whether people can improve their memory for pairs of words by using certain memory aids. You randomly assign four people to each of three groups. All participants are told they will be asked to recall pairs of words later. The first group is instructed to form zany mental images or pictures that connect the two words in each word pair. The second group is told to rehearse each pair of words as fast as possible immediately after they are presented. A third group is given no suggestions on how to remember the word pairs. The simulated data in Table 14.1 are the numbers of correct responses out of 20 pairs of words. The table also lists the sample group means (means of the n observations in each group), $\overline{X}_1$, $\overline{X}_2$, and $\overline{X}_3$; the sample group variances (unbiased variances of the n observations in each group), s_1^2, s_2^2, and s_3^2; and the sample grand mean, $\overline{X}$ (mean of all observations in the study).

Problems with Using Multiple *t*-Tests

You might think that you could use the two-independent-sample t-test to test the hypothesis of equality of the three means, but such an approach has at least four problems. First, there would be three different t-tests; you would have Groups 1 and 2, Groups 1 and 3, and Groups 2 and 3. The number of t-tests increases as J, the number of groups, increases. For $J = 3$, you would have three t-tests, but for $J = 6$, you would have 15 t-tests. Obviously, the computational labor increases as the number of t-tests increases. The use of computers helps to minimize this problem, but not the other three problems.

The second problem is that the many t-tests are not independent. If you do the t-tests that compare Groups 1 and 2 and Groups 1 and 3, there is obviously some overlap because both tests have Group 1 in common. The t-test for Groups 2 and 3 gives additional overlap.

The third problem in doing all possible t-tests on J means is that the probability of at least one Type I error increases as a function of the number of t-tests. If you let C equal the number of independent t-tests you do, then

$$p(\text{at least one Type I error}) = 1 - (1 - \alpha)^C \le C\alpha \tag{14.1}$$

This gives the probability of making one or more Type I errors in the whole family of t-tests when using α for each test. We'll return to this concept in Chapter 15 when multiple comparisons are discussed. Because the C t-tests are not independent, this formula gives only the maximum probability. The actual probability is larger than α and less than $C\alpha$ but closer to $C\alpha$. If $\alpha = .05$, for example, then the probability of at least one Type I error for $C = 3$ tests is larger than .05 but less than $3(.05) = .15$. For $J = 6$ means and $C = 15$, this probability is somewhere between .05 and .75. This problem is serious because the probability of at least one Type I error almost certainly would be larger than .05.

The last problem with doing all possible t-tests is that you would have C tests for one hypothesis. For all of the tests up to this point, you have had one test for one hypothesis. Using C t-tests for one hypothesis of equality of J population means gives you the problem of deciding when to reject H_0—when any one of the t-tests is significant, or any two, or all of them. Because t-tests present so many problems, you need another test.

Of the four remaining sections of this chapter, two give a conceptual overview of the one-way ANOVA. The latter sections focus on practical matters of computational formulas and use of the ANOVA in real-world settings.

Quick Quiz

For $J = 4$, $C = 6$ t-tests could be done. If you set $\alpha = .05$ for each test, what is the maximum value for the probability of at least one Type I error?

Answer

The maximum value for the probability of at least one Type I is $C\alpha = 6(.05) = .30$.

14.2   Logic of ANOVA

Students are often bothered that they test a hypothesis about equality of *means* with a procedure called the analysis of *variance*. The disparity between the hypothesis and the name gives a great opportunity to call attention to the logic of the ANOVA. Once you understand the logic of the ANOVA, you can explain the discrepancy.

The following logic of the ANOVA is the outline for the rest of this section:

1. You obtain two estimates of σ^2, one based on the variance of sample means and the other the variance of observations within groups.
2. Both estimate the population variance σ^2 if the null hypothesis of equal population means is true, but they estimate different quantities if H_0 is false.
3. With these two estimates of σ^2, you form the F ratio. You expect the F ratio to be approximately one if H_0 is true but larger than one if H_0 is false.
4. You reject H_0 if F is larger than or equal to a critical value.

Information from each of the J samples (groups) is combined into the one statistic, F Figure 14.1 shows the distributions of the populations, the samples, and the sampling distribution of F This figure is similar to Figure 9.1, which you saw when you learned about sampling distributions. Now you are sampling from several populations of X's. The sampled observations go into your J samples in the "real world," where you can compute statistics such as $\overline{X}$ and s^2. If you sampled the same number of participants in the same number of groups repeatedly and computed a statistic each time, you could arrange those statistics in a sampling distribution. But before we talk about the statistic

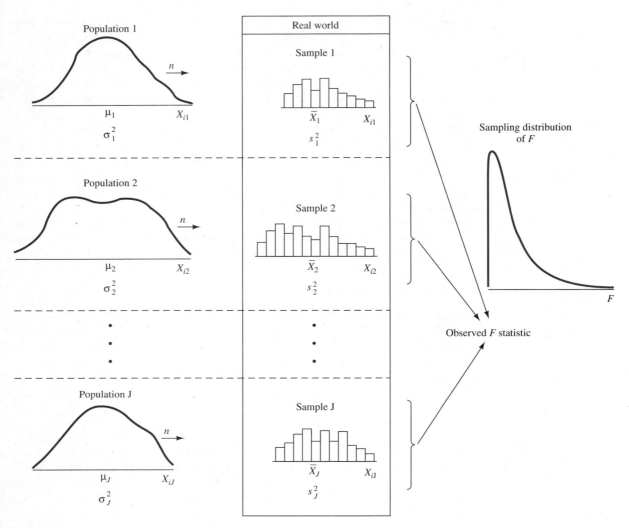

Figure 14.1
Populations, samples, and sampling distribution of F

for use in the J-independent-sample case, let's examine each point in the logic of the ANOVA without introducing too many more technical terms. To do so will require you to "think through" some already familiar statistics without seeing formulas for them.

Two Ways to Estimate Variance

The first part of the logic of the ANOVA is to obtain two estimates of σ^2. If you think of all the ways you know to estimate the population variance σ^2 from the three groups of data in Table 14.1, you surely would mention the sample variances of observations in each group. You also might have the idea of pooling these variances, perhaps in a way similar to the denominator of the two-independent-sample *t*-test. However, without the prompt of the preceding paragraph, most of you would not think of computing the variance of the sample means—that is, treat each $\overline{X}$ as if it were a score and then compute an unbiased sample variance on these $\overline{X}$ values.

Take the formula for the variance of $\overline{X}$ from Chapter 9:

$$\sigma_{\overline{X}}^2 = \frac{\sigma^2}{n}$$

Solve for σ^2 to get:

$$\sigma^2 = n\sigma_{\overline{X}}^2$$

If you multiply an estimate of $\sigma_{\overline{X}}^2$ by the number of observations per group, you have another estimate of σ^2. The variance of the sample means provides us with an estimate of $\sigma_{\overline{X}}^2$. Because $\sigma_{\overline{X}}^2$ is the population variance of the $\overline{X}$'s, the logical estimate of it would be $s_{\overline{X}}^2$, which is the unbiased sample variance of the $\overline{X}$'s. The idea is to compute an unbiased sample variance on the numbers that are the group $\overline{X}$'s. For example, compute the unbiased sample variance of 14.50, 4.00, and 3.25, the group means from Table 14.1. You should get $s_{\overline{X}}^2 = 39.5625$. Later in the chapter we give a computational formula, but for now just remember that $s_{\overline{X}}^2$ is simply the unbiased sample variance of the group $\overline{X}$'s. Substituting $s_{\overline{X}}^2$ for $\sigma_{\overline{X}}^2$ in $\sigma^2 = n\sigma_{\overline{X}}^2$ gives n times the unbiased sample variance of the group means:

Estimate of σ^2 from the group means
$ns_{\overline{X}}^2$ is n (number of observations per group) times the unbiased sample variance of the $\overline{X}$ values (group means)

$ns_{\overline{X}}^2 = $ **estimate of σ^2 from the group means**

This is one of your two estimates of σ^2 for the ANOVA F ratio. For the memory aid data in Table 14.1, $ns_{\overline{X}}^2 = (4)(39.5625) = 158.25$.

If H_0: equal population group means is true, then the only variability in the sample group $\overline{X}$'s is due to chance or sampling variability. If H_0 is true, then $ns_{\overline{X}}^2$ is an unbiased estimate of σ^2. If H_0 is false, then the population group means are not equal, and you would not expect the sample group means to be equal either. So if H_0 is false, $ns_{\overline{X}}^2$ contains variability due to true differences in the population group means in addition to chance or sampling variability. This last statement is so important that it needs to be restated: If H_0 is false, $ns_{\overline{X}}^2$ is not an unbiased estimate of σ^2 because it also contains variability due to true differences in the population group means. Sometimes the σ^2 plus true differences is called variance due to *error plus treatment effect.*

Variance of observations within groups
s_{pooled}^2 is the estimate of σ^2 based on pooling the values of s_j^2; for equal sample sizes per group, s_{pooled}^2 is the average of the s_j^2 values

The second estimate of σ^2 is the **variance of observations within groups** mentioned in the statement of the logic of ANOVA. First, calculate the unbiased sample variances s_j^2 for the observations within each group. Next, pool these s_j^2's into a single variance called s_{pooled}^2. This s_{pooled}^2 is similar to the first part of the denominator of the two-independent-sample *t*-statistic where you pooled two sample variances,

$$\sqrt{\left[\frac{(n_1 - 1)s_1^2 + (n_2 - 1)s_2^2}{n_1 + n_2 - 2}\right]\left(\frac{1}{n_1} + \frac{1}{n_2}\right)}.$$

If the sample sizes are equal, then s_{pooled}^2 is simply an average of the s^2 values: Add them and divide by the number of groups, *J*. For example, for the memory aid data in Table 14.1, s_{pooled}^2 is 7.75, the average of $s_1^2 = 5.67$, $s_2^2 = 8.67$, and $s_3^2 = 8.92$. We give a computational formula later in the chapter. It is crucial for you to realize that s_{pooled}^2

always estimates σ^2, regardless of whether H_0 is true or false. Unlike $ns_{\overline{X}}^2$, s_{pooled}^2 is always an unbiased estimate of σ^2. It is sometimes called variance due to *error*. Both $ns_{\overline{X}}^2$ and s_{pooled}^2 estimate σ^2 if H_0 is true, but they estimate different quantities if H_0 is false. You now have the two sample variances necessary to form the F ratio.

F Ratio

F ratio

Test statistic for the one-way ANOVA, the ratio of two estimates of σ^2, one from the group means and the other from the variance of observations within groups

The logic of the ANOVA indicates that the two sample variances $ns_{\overline{X}}^2$ and s_{pooled}^2 are to be put into a ratio called F. As Figure 14.1 shows, the sample statistics $\overline{X}_j$'s and the s_j^2's are brought together into one statistic, F. The **F ratio** for the one-way ANOVA is defined as

$$F = \frac{ns_{\overline{X}}^2}{s_{pooled}^2} \tag{14.2}$$

Every F ratio fits the general verbal definition: a ratio of two variance estimates. If H_0: equal population group means is true, then both $ns_{\overline{X}}^2$ and s_{pooled}^2 estimate σ^2 and you would expect F to be approximately one. That is, the ratio of (*error + treatment effect*)/*error* will be close to one if the groups are similar and there is no treatment effect. Of course, statistics always have variability, so any given F ratio could differ from one by chance, even with H_0 true.

If H_0 is false, then $ns_{\overline{X}}^2$ estimates σ^2 plus a treatment effect (based on true differences in the population group means), so $ns_{\overline{X}}^2$ should be larger than s_{pooled}^2 and F should be larger than one. Table 14.2 summarizes the two sample variances and the F ratio by showing what the variances estimate and what you expect F to be for H_0 true and H_0 false.

Even though you usually don't compute statistics with the definitional formulas, let's use the data from Table 14.1 to compute the F ratio. The sample group means and variances are already given as well as the grand mean, so all you need to compute F are $ns_{\overline{X}}^2$ and s_{pooled}^2. The details are given in Table 14.3. Because n times the variance of the sample group means $ns_{\overline{X}}^2$ is large relative to the variance of the observations s_{pooled}^2, the F is considerably larger than one. However, chance variability can cause F to be larger than one, so you need to compare F to a critical value.

If H_0 is true and certain assumptions are met, the F ratio is distributed as the F distribution. Table A.6 in Appendix A contains critical values of F for $\alpha = .05$ and $\alpha = .01$. Consistent with tradition, use $\alpha = .05$ so that 5% of the F ratios for situations like this would be larger than the critical value if H_0 were true.

Table 14.2

	H_0 *True*	H_0 *False*
$ns_{\overline{X}}^2$	Estimates σ^2	Estimates σ^2 plus treatment effect
s_{pooled}^2	Estimates σ^2	Estimates σ^2
F ratio	Expect	Expect
	$F \approx \dfrac{\sigma^2}{\sigma^2} = 1$	$F \approx \dfrac{\sigma^2 + \text{treatment effect}}{\sigma^2} > 1$

Table 14.3
Computation of $ns_{\overline{X}}^2$ and s_{pooled}^2

To find the numerator of F, you need to use the three group means as observations and find their variance. You could use a definitional formula for an unbiased variance:

$$s^2 = \frac{\Sigma(X - \overline{X})}{N - 1}$$

Using the sample means as the X values and the grand mean (mean of all the scores in the study), you get:

$$s_{\overline{X}}^2 = \frac{(14.5 - 7.25)^2 + (4 - 7.25)^2 + (3.25 - 7.25)^2}{2} = \frac{79.125}{2}$$

$$= 39.5625$$

$$ns_{\overline{X}}^2 = 4(39.5625) = 158.25$$

Getting the average of the s^2 values, we find:

$$s_{pooled}^2 = \frac{5.6667 + 8.6667 + 8.9167}{3} = \frac{23.25}{3}$$

$$= 7.75$$

$$F = \frac{ns_{\overline{X}}^2}{s_{pooled}^2} = \frac{158.25}{7.75} = 20.4194$$

$$= 20.42$$

The F distribution has two parameters that are used to find critical values. To use Table A.6, you need to have α and the two parameters, called df_B and df_W, to enter the table. The value of df_B gives the correct column of Table A.6 and is found by

$$df_B = J - 1 \tag{14.3}$$

Degrees of freedom between
$df_B = J - 1$, the number of groups minus 1

The abbreviation df_B stands for **degrees of freedom between** means or between groups and is associated with $ns_{\overline{X}}^2$, the numerator of F. For $F = 20.42$ from the data of Table 14.1, $df_B = J - 1 = 3 - 1 = 2$.

The value of df_W gives the correct row of Table A.6 and is found by

$$df_W = N - J \tag{14.4}$$

Degrees of freedom within
$df_W = N - J$, the total number of observations minus the number of groups

where $N = nJ$ is the total number of subjects. The abbreviation df_W stands for **degrees of freedom within** groups and is associated with s_{pooled}^2, the denominator of F.

The degrees of freedom for the ANOVA F are explained more fully in the next section, but they need to be defined here so you can get a critical value for F. For $J = 3$ and $n = 4$, $df_W = N - J = 12 - 3 = 9$. With $\alpha = .05$, $df_B = 2$, and $df_W = 9$, the critical value is $F_{crit} = 4.26$. Because $F = 20.42$ is larger than $F_{crit} = 4.26$, you reject H_0. You expect the F ratio to be large when H_0 is false. Plus, because you are dealing with variances, F is always positive and always uses a one-tailed test. So you use only the upper tail of the F distribution to find the rejection values (see Figure 14.2).

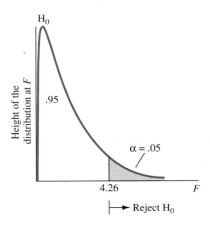

Figure 14.2
F distribution, $df_B = 2$, $df_W = 9$, showing critical value, rejection values, and area

---

Quick Quiz
For the study on Task 4 in Research Example 14, there were three groups with 21 participants in each. The researchers reported "$F(2, 60)$," where the 2 is the numerator *df* or df_B and the 60 is the denominator *df* or df_W. Are the *df* values reported for the F on the number of recalled propositions correct?

Answer

Because there are three groups of subjects, NS, DS, and AS, $J = 3$ and $df_B = J - 1 = 3 - 1 = 2$. There are $n = 21$ subjects per group with three groups, for a total of $N = 63$ subjects. Within-groups degrees of freedom are given by $df_W = N - J = 63 - 3 = 60$. The *df* values are correct.

Group Differences versus Group Equality

This final topic concludes the coverage of the logic of the ANOVA. The example data in Table 14.1 yielded sample group means that were considerably different from one another and a significant F ratio. It is likely that group differences in the populations were reflected in the samples. Your conclusion would be that there were differences in the effectiveness of the memory aids. However, sometimes the data and group means are not so clear-cut. What if you had obtained the data in Table 14.4?

Even though the sample group means are different and in the expected order, the differences are not significantly larger than those expected by chance, so you retain H_0. It is important to realize that differences in sample group means in the ANOVA are always discussed in terms of $ns_{\bar{X}}^2$ relative to the variance of the observations within the groups (s_{pooled}^2). You cannot tell whether the differences in the sample means themselves are large, nor can you tell whether $ns_{\bar{X}}^2 = 11.58$ is large, but you can tell whether $F = 1.49$ is large. You always have to compute F and compare it to an F critical value to make a decision about H_0.

14.3   ANOVA: Partitioning of Variability

To use the ANOVA as a general methodology, you have to learn some new notation and new terminology. What you learn for the single-independent-variable (one-way) situa-

Table 14.4

Number of correct responses (group equality)

	Images	Rehearse	Control	
	9	8	4	$n = 4$
	8	4	7	$J = 3$
	5	3	0	$df_B = J - 1 = 3 - 1 = 2$
	4	1	2	$df_W = N - J = 12 - 3 = 9$
	$\Sigma_i X_{i1} = 26$	$\Sigma_i X_{i2} = 16$	$\Sigma_i X_{i3} = 13$	$\Sigma_j \Sigma_i X_{ij} = 55$
Group means	$\overline{X}_1 = 26/4$	$\overline{X}_2 = 16/4$	$\overline{X}_3 = 13/4$	Grand mean
	$= 6.50$	$= 4.00$	$= 3.25$	$\overline{X} = 55/12 = 4.58$
Group variances	$s_1^2 = 5.67$	$s_2^2 = 8.67$	$s_3^2 = 8.92$	

$$s_{\overline{X}}^2 = \frac{(6.5 - 4.58)^2 + (4 - 4.58)^2 + (3.25 - 4.58)^2}{2} = \frac{5.7917}{2}$$

$$= 2.8958$$

$$ns_{\overline{X}}^2 = 4(2.8958) = 11.58$$

$$s_{pooled}^2 = \frac{5.6667 + 8.6667 + 8.9167}{3} = \frac{23.25}{3}$$

$$= 7.75$$

$$F = \frac{ns_{\overline{X}}^2}{s_{pooled}^2} = \frac{11.58}{7.75} = 1.4946$$

$F = 1.49$, which is less than $F_{crit} = 4.26$, so retain H_0.

tion will help you in Chapter 16, where we cover the two-independent-variable situation (two-way ANOVA).

Notation and Terminology

The notation X_{ij} represents the score of the ith subject in the jth group. Similarly, $\overline{X}_j$ stands for the sample mean of the jth group:

$$\overline{X}_j = \frac{\Sigma_i X_{ij}}{n} \tag{14.5}$$

so $\overline{X}_1$ is the sample mean of the first group. For example, in Table 14.4, $\overline{X}_1 = 26/4 = 6.50$. For each sample group mean $\overline{X}_j$, there is a population mean of the jth group, μ_j. We let $\overline{X}$ stand for the sample grand mean of all the observations:

$$\overline{X} = \frac{\Sigma_j \Sigma_i X_{ij}}{N} \tag{14.6}$$

In Table 14.4, $\overline{X} = 55/12 = 4.58$. For the sample grand mean $\overline{X}$, there is a population grand mean, μ.

Levels
Conditions that group
the participants in a study;
these conditions indicate
some aspect of the
independent variable

You also need some new terminology. **Levels** are the conditions that group the participants in a study, such as the levels of the independent variable (see Chapter 2). Sometimes you can think of levels as being equal to doses. For instance, if you were testing a cold remedy's tendency to make people sleepy, you might have four groups taking different doses of the remedy—0 mg, 5 mg, 10 mg, and 15 mg. Here, the single independent variable is amount of cold remedy, which has four levels. The independent variable in the memory aid study in Table 14.1 has three levels. Note that J = number of groups = number of levels.

Quick Quiz

Consider Task 1 in Research Example 14. (a) What was the independent variable? (b) How many levels does smoking behavior have in this experiment? (c) What type of variable is "time to locate the target"?

Answers

(a) You may answer "smoking behavior," or indicate the three groups of NS, DS, and AS. (b) Three levels. (c) The dependent variable.

One-way
The part of the ANOVA
terminology that indicates
the number of independent
variables in the design

The term **one-way** refers to one independent variable being manipulated. All of the ANOVAs in this chapter are one-way ANOVAs, regardless of the number of levels they have. A one-way ANOVA is classified by the number of levels, such as a one-way ANOVA with three levels, as was the case for the studies in Research Example 14 and Table 14.1. Students often confuse the number of levels and the number of independent variables. An ANOVA with two independent variables is called a *two-way ANOVA* and is classified by the number of levels of each variable, such as a 2×2 ANOVA. You also can have a 3×4 ANOVA, which has three levels of the first independent variable and four levels of the second independent variable. (You'll learn about two-way ANOVAs in Chapter 16.) Now that you have some of the necessary notation and terminology, you can learn about partitioning the variability in the one-way ANOVA.

Quick Quiz

Examine Figure 14.3. Label the ANOVAs given there in diagram form.

Answers

(a) One-way ANOVA with four levels, (b) 2×3 two-way ANOVA, and (c) one-way ANOVA with two levels.

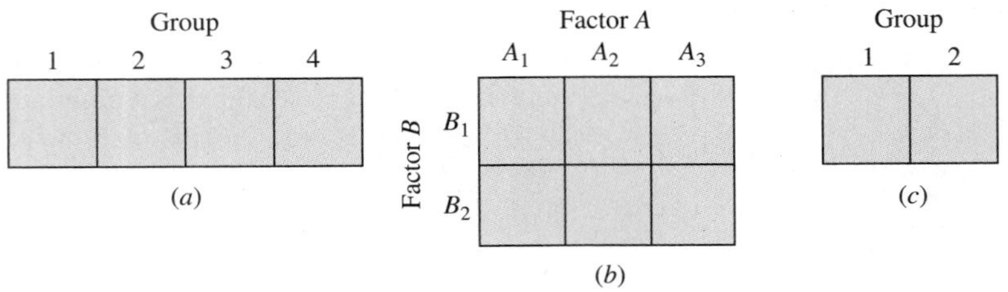

Figure 14.3
Some diagrams of ANOVAs

Variability

The total variability in the population for a one-way ANOVA can be represented by any one score as $X_{ij} - \mu$, the difference between that score and the population grand mean. That total can be **partitioned** into a part that represents between-groups variability, $\mu_j - \mu$, and a part that represents within-groups variability, $X_{ij} - \mu_j$. This partitioning is shown for H_0 false in Figure 14.4(a) as a score in Group 3 broken into the two parts. When H_0 is true, all values of μ_j are equal to μ and there is no between-groups variability in the population, only within-groups variability [see Figure 14.4(b)].

Now you have the two nonoverlapping parts (between and within groups), mentioned earlier, for any one score in terms of population means, but you need to do this for all scores and use sample means. You need to estimate each population mean with its corresponding sample mean. You also need to square these differences and add them for all scores. Then you will have partitioned the variability in the sample into the desired parts.

Table 14.5 lists the steps to partition the total variability into the two parts for the one-way ANOVA. When the degrees of freedom and their formulas are explained, you will be asked to return to Step 2 in the table. Step 3 is considerably more complex

Partition

To break the total variability of the observations into parts that represent between-groups variability and within-groups variability

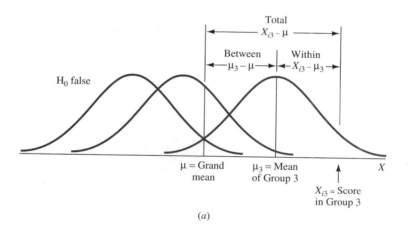

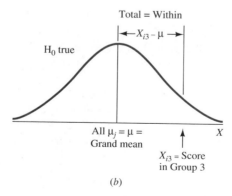

Figure 14.4
Variability of a score in Group 3

Table 14.5
Partitioning of total variability

	Total	=	Between	+	Within
Step 1: Write out differences in terms of scores and means.	$X_{ij} - \mu$	=	$\mu_j - \mu$	+	$X_{ij} - \mu_j$
Step 2: Replace population means with sample means.	$X_{ij} - \overline{X}$	=	$\overline{X}_j - \overline{X}$	+	$X_{ij} - \overline{X}_j$
Step 3: Square and sum all differences.	$\sum_j\sum_i(X_{ij} - \overline{X})^2$	=	$\sum_j\sum_i(\overline{X}_j - \overline{X})^2$	+	$\sum_j\sum_i(X_{ij} - \overline{X}_j)^2$
Sums of squares	SS_T	=	SS_B	+	SS_W

than indicated in Table 14.5 and may be oversimplified for those of you with strong mathematics backgrounds. For those who have math anxiety, the subscripts are explained more thoroughly in Section 14.4, after we've defined the components of the *F* ratio. Try for conceptual understanding at this point.

Sums of Squares

Sum of squares
A sum of squared deviations; a numerator of a sample variance

The last quantities in Table 14.5 are called the sums of squares (*SS*). A **sum of squares** (introduced in Chapter 4) is the numerator of the sample variance used in the *F* ratio. Actually, any unbiased sample variance is composed of a sum of squares divided by degrees of freedom. For example, the unbiased sample variance from Chapter 4 is:

$$s^2 = \frac{\sum(X - \overline{X})^2}{N - 1} = \frac{SS}{df}$$

SS_B is the sum of squares between groups, which is equal to the numerator of the variance estimate from the means, $ns_{\overline{X}}^2$. SS_W is the sum of squares within groups, and it equals the numerator of the variance estimate from the observations, s_{pooled}^2. The value of SS_T, total sum of squares, is not used to form a variance estimate but is usually used as a computational check. The formulas for sums of squares in Table 14.5 are definitional formulas; computational formulas are given later.

Degrees of Freedom

Having defined the sums of squares for total, between, and within, you now can learn more about the degrees of freedom. Degrees of freedom are parameters necessary to use the *F* table and obtain a correct critical value. From the working definition of degrees of freedom as the number of independent components minus the number of parameters estimated, you can get Table 14.6.

In SS_T, there are *N* observations, X_{ij} (independent components), and only one parameter, μ, estimated by $\overline{X}$, so the total degrees of freedom are $N - 1$. In SS_B, the *J* values of $\overline{X}_j$ are the independent components, and you again estimate one μ with $\overline{X}$, so $df_B = J - 1$. In SS_W, there are *N* independent observations (components) but *J* parameters (the μ_j) estimated by the $\overline{X}_j$, so $df_W = N - J$. For equal *n* per group, an alternative formula for df_W is $df_W = J(n-1)$. For example, in Research Example 14 there were three groups of 15 observations per group in Task 1. So $df_B = J - 1 = 3 - 1 = 2$ and $df_W = N - J = 45 - 3 = 42$. Because the degrees of freedom are the

Table 14.6
Sums of squares and degrees of freedom

SS_T	$=$	SS_B	$+$	SS_W
$\Sigma\Sigma(X_{ij} - \overline{X})^2$	$=$	$\Sigma\Sigma(\overline{X}_j - \overline{X})^2$	$+$	$\Sigma\Sigma(X_{ij} - \overline{X}_j)^2$
df_T	$=$	df_B	$+$	df_W
$N - 1$	$=$	$J - 1$	$+$	$N - J$

denominators for the sample variances used in the ANOVA, you are now ready to define these sample variances.

Quick Quiz

If you read in a journal article, "The result was significant, $F(3, 58) = 7.64$, $p < .05$," what can you say about the sample sizes?

Answer

$df_B = J - 1 = 3$, so $J = 4$, and $df_W = N - J = N - 4 = 58$, so $N = 62$. Because 62 isn't evenly divisible by 4, the sample sizes must have been unequal.

Mean Squares

Mean square

A sum of squares divided by its degrees of freedom; a sample variance

In ANOVA terminology, all of the sample variances are renamed mean squares, abbreviated *MS*. **Mean squares** are sums of squares divided by degrees of freedom, so they are *average sums of squares*. The estimate of σ^2 from the $\overline{X}_j$ values is defined as "mean square between groups" and is equal to SS_B/df_B:

$$MS_B = \frac{SS_B}{J - 1} \tag{14.7}$$

which is also $ns_{\overline{X}}^2$. Mean square between, MS_B, is the estimate of σ^2 formed from the variability between or among the group means. In some sense, MS_B is the variance between the groups. Because MS_B is equal to $ns_{\overline{X}}^2$, they both estimate the same thing. That is, MS_B estimates σ^2 if H_0 is true but estimates σ^2 plus a positive quantity based on the true differences in the μ_j if H_0 is false (see Table 14.2).

The estimate of σ^2 from the observations is defined as "mean square within groups" and is equal to SS_W/df_W:

$$MS_W = \frac{SS_W}{N - J} \tag{14.8}$$

which is also s_{pooled}^2. Mean square within, MS_W, is the estimate of σ^2 formed from the variability within the groups. It is the estimate of σ^2 based on observations within the groups. You get the variance for each group and pool the within-groups variability into this one measure. Because MS_W is equal to s_{pooled}^2, they both estimate the same thing. That is, MS_W estimates σ^2 whether H_0 is true or false.

MS_B and MS_W are the only two mean squares obtained because you don't form a sample variance from the total sum of squares. After we give computational formulas for the sums of squares in Section 14.4, you will be able to use formulas 14.7 and 14.8 to compute MS_B and MS_W, the mean squares necessary to form the F ratio.

14.4   ANOVA F Test

You have learned the logic of the ANOVA and how the ANOVA partitions the variability of the data. Now we can review the testing of hypotheses using the ANOVA notation and terminology. Methods in this section give exactly the same answers as the conceptual approach in Section 14.2, but here you use the ANOVA notation and terminology. The memory aid data from Table 14.1 are used to show that the approaches are equivalent.

Hypotheses

The null hypothesis in the one-way ANOVA comes from the concept of equality of the population means. The one-way ANOVA you'll learn is technically called a *one-way fixed-effects ANOVA* because the groups are defined in such a way that someone else could replicate your study. The actual levels of the treatment are not randomly selected but are chosen arbitrarily by the researcher. Equality of treatment effects is another way to state the general idea of population equality, which leads to the null hypothesis

$$H_0: \mu_1 = \mu_2 = \cdots = \mu_J = \mu \tag{14.9}$$

Equal values of μ_j also mean that they are all equal to the grand mean μ.

The alternative hypothesis for the one-way ANOVA simply states that there is some difference in the means without stipulating which means are different. Because of the many possibilities for differences, alternative hypotheses for the ANOVA are always nondirectional. Any specific differences that are directional can be tested by using the methods in Chapter 15. The overall H_0 can be tested by using the F ratio.

F Ratio

F ratio
MS_B divided by MS_W, the test statistic for the one-way ANOVA

The test statistic used by the ANOVA to test H_0 is the **F ratio,** given as

$$F = \frac{MS_B}{MS_W} \tag{14.10}$$

where

$$MS_B = \frac{SS_B}{df_B} = \frac{SS_B}{J - 1}$$

$$MS_W = \frac{SS_W}{df_W} = \frac{SS_W}{N - J}$$

as in formulas 14.7 and 14.8. Formula 14.10 for F is just a restatement of formula 14.2 for F, here in terms of MS_B and MS_W.

The computational formula for SS_B is:

$$SS_B = \sum_j \frac{(\sum_i X_{ij})^2}{n_j} - \frac{(\sum_j \sum_i X_{ij})^2}{N} \tag{14.11}$$

The computational formula for SS_W is:

$$SS_W = \sum_j \sum_i X_{ij}^2 - \sum_j \frac{(\sum_i X_{ij})^2}{n_j} \tag{14.12}$$

Formulas 14.11 and 14.12 both allow for unequal sample sizes per group by using the notation n_j to stand for the number of observations in the *j*th group. With equal *n*'s, simply use *n* in place of n_j. Examine Table 14.7 to find the basic pieces of SS_B and SS_W for the data of Table 14.1. The two crucial questions for each piece are: What is being squared? How many items are being squared?

The first step is to obtain the group sums (58, 16, and 13) and the grand sum (87). The group sums are found by using the summation sign with subscript *i* for each group, $\sum_i X_{ij}$, and the grand sum is obtained by using both summation signs with subscripts *i* and *j*, $\sum_j \sum_i X_{ij}$. When the first piece of SS_B asks for $\sum_i X_{ij}$, you know to use 58, 16, and 13. Then you square these group sums (because of the square after the parenthesis), divide each by 4, and add them, which $\sum_j$ tells you to do.

Table 14.7
Number of correct responses (data from Table 14.1)

Images	Rehearse	Control	
$X_{11} = 17$	$X_{12} = 8$	$X_{13} = 4$	$n = 4$
$X_{21} = 16$	$X_{22} = 4$	$X_{23} = 7$	$J = 3$
$X_{31} = 13$	$X_{32} = 3$	$X_{33} = 0$	
$X_{41} = 12$	$X_{42} = 1$	$X_{43} = 2$	
$\sum_i X_{i1} = 58$	$\sum_i X_{i2} = 16$	$\sum_i X_{i3} = 13$	$\sum_j \sum_i X_{ij} = 87$

$$SS_B = \sum_j \frac{(\sum_i X_{ij})^2}{n_j} - \frac{(\sum_j \sum_i X_{ij})^2}{N} = \frac{58^2}{4} + \frac{16^2}{4} + \frac{13^2}{4} - \frac{87^2}{12}$$

$$= 947.25 - 630.75 = 316.5$$

$$MS_B = \frac{SS_B}{J-1} = \frac{316.5}{2} = 158.25$$

$$SS_W = \sum_j \sum_i X_{ij}^2 - \sum_j \frac{(\sum_i X_{ij})^2}{n_j} = 17^2 + 16^2 + \cdots + 0^2 + 2^2 - \left(\frac{58^2}{4} + \frac{16^2}{4} + \frac{13^2}{4} \right)$$

$$= 1017 - 947.25 = 69.75$$

$$MS_W = \frac{SS_W}{N-J} = \frac{69.75}{9} = 7.75$$

$$F = \frac{MS_B}{MS_W} = \frac{158.25}{7.75} = 20.42$$

Table 14.8
ANOVA summary table with formulas

Source	SS	df	MS	F
Between	Formula 14.11	$df_B = J - 1$	$MS_B = SS_B/df_B$	MS_B/MS_W
Within	Formula 14.12	$df_W = N - J$	$MS_W = SS_W/df_W$	
Total	Between + within	$N - 1$ or $df_B + df_W$		

When the second piece of SS_B asks for $\sum_j\sum_i X_{ij}$, you use the grand sum, 87, and square it. Then you divide by N, which is 12. The square operation in conjunction with the parentheses tells you what is to be squared—either the three group sums, in the first piece, or the one grand sum, in the second piece.

SS_W also has two pieces, and the second piece is exactly the same as the first piece of SS_B. The first piece of SS_W is simply the sum of the squares of all the scores. You square each individual score X_{ij} and then sum these squared scores over both summation signs; that is, you add all the squared scores. Here, the score X_{ij} is what is being squared, and there are N scores.

Computation of MS_B and MS_W proceeds by division of the respective sums of squares, SS_B and SS_W, by degrees of freedom, df_B and df_W.

Here MS_B equals 158.25, which is equal to $ns_{\bar{X}}^2$ from the conceptual approach, and MS_W equals 7.75, which is equal to s_{pooled}^2 from the conceptual approach. Of course, $F = 20.42$ is the same for both approaches.

ANOVA summary table
Table that summarizes the results of the ANOVA; organized in terms of the source of variability, sums of squares, degrees of freedom, mean squares, and F ratio

The results of the ANOVA are sometimes presented in what is called an **ANOVA summary table.** Table 14.8 is an ANOVA summary table with formulas, and Table 14.9 gives the values for the memory aid data.

Limited space in journals has led to a more terse reporting style, such as $F(2, 9) = 20.42$, $p = .0005$, or $F = 20.42$, $df_B = 2$, $df_W = 9$, $p = .0005$.

F Distribution

Once you have computed the observed F ratio, you can test H_0 by comparing F to a critical value from the F distribution. If H_0 is true and if certain assumptions (discussed in the next section) are met, then the F statistic is distributed as the

$$F \text{ distribution with parameters } df_B = J - 1 \text{ and } df_W = N - J \qquad (14.13)$$

Table 14.9
ANOVA summary table with values for the memory aid data

Source	SS	df	MS	F
Between	316.50	2	158.25	20.42
Within	69.75	9	7.75	
Total	386.25	11		

F distribution
A family of distributions
that has two parameters,
df_B and df_W; the
theoretical distribution
for the *F* statistic

Like the family of normal distributions and the family of *t* distributions, there is actually a family of **F distributions.** Rather than a single *F* distribution, there are many, one for each combination of df_B and df_W. These two parameters uniquely determine each *F* distribution. Any *F* distribution is positively skewed, ranging from zero to infinity.

Once you have $df_B = J - 1$ and $df_W = N - J$ and you have selected α, you can look up the critical value from Table A.6. The value of $df_B = 2$ as the degrees of freedom for the numerator gives the column of the table, and $df_W = 9$ as the degrees of freedom for the denominator gives the row. Be sure not to reverse these values of *df* because you will get different critical values. With $\alpha = .05$, you choose the top value at the intersection of column 2 and row 9, $F_{crit} = 4.26$ (for $\alpha = .01$, use the lower value).

Decision Rules

The decision rules for the ANOVA are based on the use of a chosen α and the corresponding critical value. The critical value decision rule is:

Reject H_0 if $F \geq F_{crit}$; otherwise, retain H_0. (14.14)

Because $F = 20.42 > 4.26$, you reject H_0: $\mu_1 = \mu_2 = \mu_3 = \mu$ in favor of an alternative hypothesis of some difference in the population means. You decide that the memory aids made a difference in the number of correct responses. However, you don't know what specific means are significantly different from each other without further testing (see Chapter 15). Computer programs for the one-way ANOVA typically give *p*-values for the observed *F* ratio; you most likely would use a critical value decision rule if you did the analysis with a calculator or by hand.

To use the *p*-value decision rule, which is usually the preferred decision rule when you do the work on a computer, you choose α in advance and then compare the probability of your observed *F* to your chosen α. The computer will give you the probability of a result equal to or more extreme than your obtained *F*. If this probability is equal to or smaller than α, then reject H_0. You don't have to worry about two-tailed *p*-values because the *F* test is always one-tailed.

Assumptions

If H_0 is true, then the sampling distribution of the one-way ANOVA *F* ratio in formula 14.10 exactly fits the *F* distribution with parameters $df_B = J - 1$ and $df_W = N - J$ if the original scores in the *J* populations are normally distributed and independent and if the populations have equal variances. These assumptions are the same as those for the two-independent-sample *t*-test: normality, independence, and equal variances. Again, the equal variance assumption was made necessary when you pooled the *J* sample variances to form $s^2_{pooled} = MS_W$ because the pooling process assumes that each s^2_j estimates a common σ^2.

Unfortunately, the robustness of the ANOVA *F* test to violation of these assumptions is not as good as that of the two-independent-sample *t*-test. You might need to review Section 13.2 to refresh your memory about assumptions and robustness. The *F* ratio is generally robust to nonnormality, is not robust to dependence of observations, and is robust to only small inequalities in variances if the sample sizes are equal. Even with large equal sample sizes, the ANOVA *F* is not robust to large differences in population variances when $J > 2$. For example, with $J = 4$ and $n = 50$, if the population variances are in the ratio 16:1:1:1, then the true α is .088 when the set α is .05 (see Wilcox, Charlin & Thompson, 1986). With unequal n's, the ANOVA F is even more nonrobust.

The one-way ANOVA has been presented as usable with unequal sample sizes n_j, but it should be used only with equal n's because of its lack of robustness to unequal variances for unequal n. Because real-world data usually are independent but nonnormal with unequal variances, you are usually able to use the ANOVA if you have only slightly unequal variances. The combination of relying on robustness to nonnormality, meeting the assumption of independence, and using equal n's to have robustness to slightly unequal variances allows the researcher to compare an observed F ratio to an F_{crit}. As we said in the discussion of assumptions for t-statistics, we don't recommend tests to see whether any given assumption is met (such as tests for equal variances) because many of these preliminary tests lack robustness themselves. Because many researchers want to test specific differences in the means using methods described in Chapter 15, the lack of robustness of the ANOVA F to large ratios of unequal variances is not of grave concern. However, you still should use equal sample sizes. If you have unequal sample sizes, you need to use one of the alternatives to the ANOVA F given in Wilcox (1987).

Example

To consider a realistic data set for the one-way ANOVA, let's return to the data on detecting liars from Chapter 2. This was the example about which occupations teach people to be able to recognize lies. You would like to find out whether there are any differences among judges, psychiatrists, and Secret Service personnel in detecting a liar. People in each career group were shown 1-min videotape segments of ten individuals telling how they felt about a film. Participants were then asked to indicate whether the person in the videotape was telling the truth. The score for each subject is the deception accuracy score, which is the percentage of correct responses given that exactly five of the ten were lying. Simulated data for this study are given in Table 14.10 along with computations for the one-way ANOVA F test.

Quick Quiz

If you have four groups, $df_W = 44$, $SS_B = 10.50$, and $SS_W = 96.44$, find: (a) df_B, (b) MS_B, (c) MS_W, (d) the observed F, and (e) the critical F for $\alpha = .05$. What decision do you make about H_0?

Answers

(a) $df_B = J - 1 = 4 - 1 = 3$ (b) $MS_B = SS_B/df_B = 10.50/3 = 3.5$ (c) $MS_W = SS_W/df_W = 96.44/44 = 2.191818$ (d) $F = MS_B/MS_W = 3.5/2.191818 = 1.60$ (e) $F(3, 44) = 2.82$. Retain H_0 because the observed F does not exceed the critical F.

Relationship of t to F

When ANOVA was introduced at the beginning of this chapter, you saw that it can be used to test for equality of two or more means. Because the ANOVA is appropriate for independent groups, both the ANOVA and the two-independent-sample t-test can be used if you have $J = 2$ independent groups. Not only can both t and F be used if $J = 2$

and not only do both have the same assumptions, but also there is a mathematical relationship between these two tests.

For two independent groups,

$$t_{df}^2 = F_{1, df} \quad \text{where } df = n_1 + n_2 - 2 = 2(n - 1) \text{ for equal } n \tag{14.15}$$

This relationship holds for only $J = 2$, and that is why $df_B = 1$ for the F. If $n_1 = n_2$, then $df_W = N - J = N - 2$, which is the same as $n_1 + n_2 - 2$, the df for t.

Table 14.10
Liar data: Influence of occupation on deception accuracy scores (percent correct)

Secret Service	Judges	Psychiatrists	
60	50	60	
60	60	90	$n_1 = n_2 = n_3 = 35$
70	50	60	
50	60	70	$J = 3$
70	70	60	
60	50	50	$df_B = J - 1$
70	60	50	$\quad = 3 - 1 = 2$
70	50	50	$df_W = N - J$
60	40	60	$\quad = 105 - 3 = 102$
60	70	70	
40	50	60	$F_{crit} = 3.09$ for
80	70	60	$df_B = 2$ and $df_W = 100$
70	40	60	and $\alpha = .05$
90	90	50	
80	50	70	
60	60	30	
80	40	60	
90	60	50	
50	60	60	
40	40	60	
50	50	40	
40	50	60	
50	40	70	
70	70	40	
70	70	50	
70	50	50	
60	50	60	
60	70	60	
70	60	60	
60	50	50	
80	80	40	
60	70	80	
80	70	60	
50	50	40	
60	30	80	

				Total
$\Sigma_i X_{ij}$	2,240	1,980	2,020	6,240
$\Sigma_i X_{ij}^2$	149,200	117,800	121,800	388,800
$\overline{X}_j$	64.00	56.57	57.71	

(continued)

Table 14.10 (continued)

$$SS_B = \sum_j \frac{(\sum_i X_{ij})^2}{n_j} - \frac{(\sum_j \sum_i X_{ij})^2}{N} = \frac{2240^2}{35} + \frac{1980^2}{35} + \frac{2020^2}{35} - \frac{6240^2}{105}$$

$$= 371{,}954.2857 - 370{,}834.2857 = 1120$$

$$MS_B = \frac{SS_B}{J-1} = \frac{1120}{2} = 560$$

$$SS_W = \sum_j \sum_i X_{ij}^2 - \sum_j \frac{(\sum_i X_{ij})^2}{n_j} = 60^2 + 60^2 + \cdots + 40^2 + 80^2 - \left(\frac{2240^2}{35} + \frac{1980^2}{35} + \frac{2020^2}{35}\right)$$

$$= 388{,}800 - 371{,}954.2857 = 16{,}845.7143$$

$$MS_W = \frac{SS_W}{N-J} = \frac{16{,}845.7143}{102} = 165.1541$$

$$F = \frac{MS_B}{MS_W} = \frac{560}{165.1541} = 3.39$$

Because $F = 3.39 > 3.09$, you can reject H_0 and conclude that occupation significantly affects one's ability to detect a liar.

Not only does $t^2 = F$ for the observed statistics in a two-independent-group situation, but also the same relationship holds for critical values. Examine Table A.4 for t and Table A.6 for F using $df = 60$ for t and $df_B = 1$ and $df_W = 60$ for F. If you use $\alpha = .05$, you should find $t_{crit} = 2.00$ for a two-tailed test and $F_{crit} = 4.00$. Examine Figure 14.5 to see that the negative values of t that make up 2.5% in the left tail of the distribution become positive F's when squared. The 2.5% from the left tail of t combines with the 2.5% from the right tail of t to form the 5% in the upper (right) tail of F.

Because you can use either the two-independent-sample t-test or the one-way ANOVA F test to test a hypothesis of equality of two independent means, you might wonder whether there are any guidelines by which to choose a test. Beyond personal preference or availability of computer programs, there is little to guide you. Some researchers prefer t because of the ease of doing one-tailed tests of directional hypotheses, whereas others prefer F because of its generality. We present both tests in this text because they are used by publishing researchers and because t-tests have applications in testing for specific differences associated with the ANOVA.

Strength of Association

The concept of strength of association as introduced for the two-independent-sample t-test also can be useful for the ANOVA. To review, strength of association is the proportion of variability in the dependent variable that is accounted for by the independent variable. It gives some idea about the importance of an independent variable. The higher the proportion of variability in the dependent variable that is explained by the independent variable, generally the more important the result. As we did in the two-independent-sample case, let's examine two estimates of the strength of association.

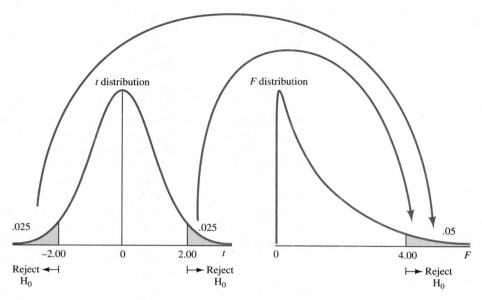

Figure 14.5
$t^2 = F$, shown for critical values for $df = 60$

First, consider the measure η^2 (eta squared). For the one-way ANOVA, η^2 is given by

$$\eta^2 = \frac{SS_B}{SS_T} \tag{14.16}$$

which is the ratio of the between-groups sum of squares to the total sum of squares.

The second measure of the strength of association is ω^2 (omega squared). For the one-way ANOVA, ω^2 is given by

$$\omega^2 = \frac{SS_B - (J-1)MS_W}{SS_T + MS_W} \tag{14.17}$$

which is set equal to zero if the observed F ratio is less than one. As was true earlier, η^2 sometimes overestimates but ω^2 sometimes underestimates the strength of association.

Let's compute both measures for the liar example, using values from Table 14.10:

$$\eta^2 = \frac{SS_B}{SS_T} = \frac{1120}{17{,}965.7143} = .062$$

$$\omega^2 = \frac{SS_B - (J-1)MS_W}{SS_T + MS_W} = \frac{1120 - (2)(165.1541)}{17{,}965.7143 + 165.1541} = .044$$

Even though the observed F ratio of 3.39 was significant, the values for these estimates are low. Here η^2 gives 6.2% and ω^2 gives 4.4% as estimates of the percentage of variability of deception accuracy scores accounted for by occupation.

Beyond the One-Way ANOVA

Most likely you've noticed references to Chapters 15 (multiple comparisons) and 16 (two-way ANOVA). That's because the one-way ANOVA discussed in this chapter is limited. The hypothesis states that the group means are equal. If you find a significant F, the only conclusion you can draw is that the groups are different. You cannot say which group is different from the rest. Imagine how limited you would be if you had just conducted a study of three forms of therapy for alcoholics. An alcoholic comes to you for advice on kinds of therapy. If you stop at your significant F from a one-way ANOVA, your only recommendation would be, "Well, these three forms of therapy are different from each other." The alcoholic would say, "But which one is *best*?" The one-way ANOVA does not give you the answer, and you can't simply look at the means to tell which treatment is best. After all, we never told you to just look at the two means in the two-independent-sample case and decide whether they were significantly different. You had to compute a test statistic. The same is true in the multiple-group situation, and the answer is found using multiple comparison procedures. Perhaps the three forms of therapy depend on whether your client is a man or a woman. You would have to run a two-way ANOVA, with gender and form of therapy as your two variables. Suppose a woman client asks, "Which one is best for me?" After Chapters 15 and 16, you'll know how to find the answer.

14.5   Summary, Study Tips, and Computation

Chapter Summary

The logic of the ANOVA is to obtain two sample variances, one based on the variance of J sample means and the other the variance of n observations within each of the J groups. Both sample variances estimate σ^2 if H_0: $\mu_1 = \mu_2 = \cdots = \mu_J = \mu$ is true. If H_0 is false, MS_B estimates the variability due to true differences in the μ_J values in addition to chance or sampling variability (σ^2), whereas MS_W estimates only σ^2. You form $F = MS_B/MS_W$, which you expect to be approximately one if H_0 is true but larger than one if H_0 is false. You reject H_0 if F is larger than a critical value from an F distribution with $df_B = J - 1$ and $df_W = N - J$.

The one-way fixed-effects ANOVA F test has assumptions of normally distributed independent observations from populations with equal variances. F is not robust to unequal variances with unequal n's and is robust to only slightly unequal variances if the n's are equal. Concern about the lack of robustness to unequal variances is lessened by the fact that most researchers want

to do additional tests of specific differences in group means (see Chapter 15).

These key terms are introduced in this chapter:

p (at least one Type I error)	Levels
	One-way
$ns_{\bar{X}}^2$	SS_B
s_{pooled}^2	SS_W
F	MS_B
df_B	MS_W
df_W	$t^2 = F$
Partitioning of variability	η^2
Grand mean	ω^2

The statistical test introduced in this chapter is summarized in Table 14.11. There you will find the situation where the statistic is used, the name of the statistic, and the theoretical reference distribution. For decision rules, assumptions, and any restrictions on the use of the procedure, refer to the appropriate section of the text.

Table 14.11

Situation	Statistic	Distribution
One factor J independent samples $H_0: \mu_1 = \mu_2 = \cdots = \mu_J = \mu$	One-way ANOVA F	F with $df_B = J - 1$ and $df_W = N - J$

Study Tips

Do you read a chapter before or after your instructor discusses the chapter's topic? If you read after a lecture, you probably pay closer attention to the points emphasized by your teacher. Here's a way to coordinate your readings with your class notes: Make a list of important topics covered during the last couple of weeks. Then take some removable adhesive note tabs and write the same key words on two tabs. For instance, one important topic is the null hypothesis for the one-way ANOVA. Write those words on two tabs. Put one tab on the edge of the page in your notes from the day your instructor talked about it, and put the other tab on the corresponding page in the textbook. After you've done this for each topic on your list, look through your notes for other topics your teacher may consider important and make reference tabs. This process will help you organize what is important to study, and you can find the book's explanation of difficult material. If you write your own Quick Quiz, your tabs can help you find the answers. This process may seem elaborate, but it will help your memory.

You should memorize the logic of the ANOVA. This important topic will help you to think your way through other problems in the ANOVA and will help you with the two-way ANOVA in Chapter 16. Finally, add the one-way ANOVA F to your chart of statistics.

Computation

Most packages of statistical programs have very good ANOVA programs. SAS and SPSS are no exceptions. SAS has PROC ANOVA, which has great flexibility. SPSS uses the command ONEWAY. Because the ANOVA as a statistical method has high generality (one-way, two-way, and so on), it is no surprise to find that ANOVA programs also have high generality. With slight modifications, the same SAS programs can be used for the two-way as well as for the one-way. You will get to use these again in Chapter 16.

SAS Example

(SAS system's lines)

```
DATA TT;
INPUT LIAR$;      (inputs the level of the independent variable, which is groups of people being tested for their ability to detect liars)
DO I = 1 TO 35;   (These next four lines input the 35 observations in each group without having to input the level of liar-group for
                   each score. When used with the preceding statement, they get all the data for each group. Of course, all the data
                   for each level of the independent variable, liar-group, must be grouped together. X is the dependent variable.)
INPUT X @@;
OUTPUT;
END;
CARDS;
SECRSER
60 60 70 50 70 60 70 70 60 60 40 80 70 90 80 60 80 90
50 40 50 40 50 70 70 70 60 60 70 60 80 60 80 50 60
JUDGES
```

50 60 50 60 70 50 60 50 40 70 50 70 40 90 50 60 40 60
60 40 50 50 40 70 70 50 50 70 60 50 80 70 70 50 30
PSYCHIAT
60 90 60 70 60 50 50 50 60 70 60 60 60 50 70 30 60 50
60 60 40 60
70 40 50 50 60 60 60 50 40 80 60 40 80
PROC PRINT;
PROC SORT; BY LIAR;   (SAS allows multiple statements per line if you put the semicolon after each statement.)
PROC MEANS; BY LIAR; VAR X;
PROC ANOVA;
CLASS LIAR;   (Identify the classification variable, also called the independent variable or the variable that classifies observations into groups; here it is LIAR.)
MODEL X=LIAR;   (Tells the ANOVA program what type of ANOVA to use. For a one-way, specify dependent variable = independent variable.)

(system's line)

```
                        The SAS System     12:11 Saturday, December 4, 1994
                     Analysis of Variance Procedure
① 
Dependent Variable: Y
Source                  DF      Sum of Squares      Mean Square    F Value     Pr > F
Model                    2 ③   1120.00000000       560.00000000       3.39     0.0375
Error                  102     16845.71428571      165.15406162
Corrected Total        104     17965.71428571
                   R-Square              C.V.           Root MSE               Y Mean
                   0.062341          21.62466       12.85122802           59.42857143
② Source                DF          Anova SS ④      Mean Square  ⑤ F Value ⑥ Pr > F
  LIAR                   2       1120.00000000       560.00000000       3.39     0.0375
```

Figure 14.6
SAS output from PROC ANOVA

For PROC ANOVA, the SAS output in Figure 14.6 gives the following:

1. For the dependent variable *X*, indicated in the MODEL statement by "*X* =", *df* and *SS* are given for the source's model (total of whatever is to the right of "=" in the MODEL statement, here only LIAR), error (within), and corrected total (total). Then the *MS* are given for model and error and the *F* and probability for model.

2. A list of the sources in the MODEL statement is given. Because only LIAR is in the model, for a one-way ANOVA this list is identical to the results for the model in item 1. However, this list and the *F* test(s) given here are the results of interest to you.

3. The *df* here is $df_B = J - 1 = 2$; df_W is given as *df* for error.

4. This is SS_B.

5. Here is $F = MS_B/MS_W$.

6. This is the probability of *F* being larger than or equal to the observed *F*.

SPSS Example

(SPSS system's lines)

```
SET WIDTH 80
DATA LIST FREE/LIAR X      (Here we tell the computer that we will input the variables LIAR and X. The values of LIAR will be
                            1 for Secret Service, 2 for judges, and 3 for psychiatrists.)
BEGIN DATA
1 60 1 60 1 70 1 50 1 70 1 60 1 70 1 70 1 60 1 60 1 40 1 80
1 70 1 90 1 80 1 60 1 80 1 90 1 50 1 40 1 50 1 40 1 50 1 70
1 70 1 70 1 60 1 60 1 70 1 60 1 80 1 60 1 80 1 50 1 60
2 50 2 60 2 50 2 60 2 70 2 50 2 60 2 50 2 40 2 70 2 50 2 70
2 40 2 70 2 50 2 60 2 40 2 60 2 60 2 40 2 50 2 50 2 40 2 70
2 70 2 50 2 50 2 70 2 60 2 50 2 80 2 70 2 70 2 50 2 30
3 60 3 90 3 60 3 70 3 60 3 50 3 50 3 50 3 60 3 70 3 60 3 60
3 60 3 50 3 70 3 30 3 60 3 50 3 60 3 60 3 40 3 60 3 70 3 40
3 50 3 50 3 60 3 60 3 60 3 50 3 40 3 80 3 60 3 40 3 80
END DATA
ONEWAY X BY LIAR (1,3)      (asks for a one-way ANOVA using X as the dependent variable and LIAR as the independent variable,
                            where 1 and 3 are the minimum and maximum values of LIAR)
```

(system's line)

- O N E W A Y -

        Variable   X   ①
      By Variable LIAR

ANALYSIS OF VARIANCE

② SOURCE	③ D.F.	SUM OF④ SQUARES	MEAN ⑤ SQUARES	F ⑥ RATIO	F ⑦ PROB.
BETWEEN GROUPS	2	1120.0000	560.0000	3.3908	.0375
WITHIN GROUPS	102	16845.7143	165.1541		
TOTAL	104	17965.7143			

Figure 14.7
SPSS output for ONEWAY

For the command ONEWAY, the SPSS output in Figure 14.7 gives the following:

1. For the dependent variable *X*, the one-way ANOVA is given for the independent variable LIAR.
2. A list of the sources includes between, within, and total.

3. The column of df gives $df_B = J - 1 = 2$ and $df_W = N - J = 102$.
4. The column of SS gives SS_B and SS_W.
5. Here are MS_B and MS_W.
6. This is $F = MS_B/MS_W$.
7. This is the probability of F being larger than or equal to the observed F.

Exercises

Section 14.1

1. You have a one-way ANOVA with three groups and 14 observations per group.
   a. What is N?
   b. What is n_3?
   c. What is J?
   d. What is meant by $X_{13,2}$?
2. You have a one-way ANOVA with five groups and nine observations per group.
   a. What is N?
   b. What is n_5?
   c. What is J?
   d. What is meant by $X_{8,4}$?

Section 14.2

3. In each of the following, give df_B and df_W.
   a. $J = 3$ and $n = 21$
   b. $J = 2$ and $n = 4$
   c. $J = 4$ and $n = 5$
   d. $J = 3$ and $n_1 = 10$, $n_2 = 12$, $n_3 = 5$
4. If $df_B = 3$ and $df_W = 16$, what are the values of J and n?
5. For each of the following, find F_{crit} with $\alpha = .05$.
   a. $df_B = 2$ and $df_W = 60$
   b. $df_B = 1$ and $df_W = 6$
   c. $df_B = 3$ and $df_W = 16$
   d. $df_B = 4$ and $df_W = 30$
6. For each of the following, find F_{crit} with $\alpha = .01$.
   a. $df_B = 3$ and $df_W = 60$
   b. $df_B = 2$ and $df_W = 30$
   c. $df_B = 1$ and $df_W = 16$
   d. $df_B = 4$ and $df_W = 50$
7. What critical value would you use if $\alpha = .05$, $df_B = 4$, and $df_W = 83$? Explain your answer.
8. Explain the logic of the one-way ANOVA. That is, what two variances does the one-way ANOVA "analyze"?
9. For each of the following, think through your answer. Each question is meant to deal with the logic of the ANOVA rather than the mechanics of testing

hypotheses with it.
   a. If $df_B = 2$, $df_W = 30$, and $\alpha = .05$ and if $ns_{\bar{X}}^2 = 14{,}543.72$, should you reject H_0? Explain your answer.
   b. If $df_B = 2$, $df_W = 30$, and $\alpha = .05$ and if $ns_{\bar{X}}^2 = 14{,}543.72$ and $s_{pooled}^2 = 13{,}000$, should you reject H_0? Explain your answer.
   c. If $df_B = 2$, $df_W = 30$, and $\alpha = .05$ and if $ns_{\bar{X}}^2 = 14{,}543.72$ and $s_{pooled}^2 = 2000$, should you reject H_0? Explain your answer.
10. Suppose a one-way ANOVA with $J = 4$ groups has the following group means: $\bar{X}_1 = 14$, $\bar{X}_2 = 15$, $\bar{X}_3 = 17$, $\bar{X}_4 = 22$.
    a. If there are $n = 5$ observations in each group and if $s_{pooled}^2 = 26$, would you reject H_0: $\mu_1 = \mu_2 = \mu_3 = \mu_4$?
    b. If there are $n = 10$ observations in each group and if $s_{pooled}^2 = 26$, would you reject H_0: $\mu_1 = \mu_2 = \mu_3 = \mu_4$?
    c. If there are $n = 5$ observations in each group and if $s_{pooled}^2 = 13$, would you reject H_0: $\mu_1 = \mu_2 = \mu_3 = \mu_4$?
    d. If there are $n = 10$ observations in each group and if $s_{pooled}^2 = 13$, would you reject H_0: $\mu_1 = \mu_2 = \mu_3 = \mu_4$?
    e. Comment on the influence of n and the variance on the power of the F test. Is this the same influence as noted in Chapter 11?

Sections 14.3 and 14.4

11. Complete the following ANOVA summary tables.

a.

Source	SS	df	MS	F
Between	———	2	10	———
Within	54	———	———	
Total	———	29		

b.

Source	SS	df	MS	F
Between	____	3	8	2
Within	____	40	____	
Total	____	____		

12. Suppose a group of nonexercisers who wanted to lose weight and volunteered for an exercise program were all put through a general conditioning program for 6 months. Then they were randomly assigned to one of three groups: continue with the general exercise program, increase the amount of exercise, or stop exercising ("not enough instructors, wait for others to finish"). At the end of 6 weeks, a mood state inventory found the scores given in the table for vigor.

No Exercise	General Exercise	Increased Exercise
10	20	21
11	19	23
12	24	27
9	17	30

   a. Calculate sample means, the grand mean, and the grand median to get a feel for your data.

   b. Compute the one-way ANOVA F test using the definitional formulas for $ns_{\bar{X}}^2$ and s_{pooled}^2.

   c. Compute the one-way ANOVA F test using the computational formulas for sums of squares (SS) and mean squares (MS). Compare your answers here to those obtained in part b.

   d. Using the names of the variables in this study, explain the logic of the ANOVA, including a description of between-groups variability and within-groups variability.

13. A study was concerned with the effects of instructions to young children and their subsequent attempts to help another child (apparently) in distress (based on Staub, 1970). So 42 first-grade students were randomly assigned to one of three groups. The first group was indirect responsibility (IR), where students were informed that another child was alone in an adjoining room and had been warned not to climb up on a chair. The second group was direct responsibility (DR1), where students were told the same story as in IR but also that they (the students) were being left in charge and to take care of anything

that happened. The students were given a simple task, and the researcher left the room. The students then heard a loud crash from the adjoining room followed by a minute of crying and sobbing. Students in the third group (DR2) had the same instructions as the DR1 group, but the sounds of distress also included calls for help. Ratings from 1 (no help) to 5 (went to adjoining room) were given to each student from behind a one-way mirror. The results are given in the table.

IR	DR1	DR2
3	5	4
4	4	4
2	5	3
1	3	4
1	4	5
2	5	4
1	5	5
2	5	5
3	5	3
3	4	2
2	3	3
1	1	2
1	4	4
2	3	1

   a. Draw a frequency distribution for each group's data. What do these graphs tell about your data?

   b. Test the hypothesis of equal population means of the three conditions.

14. Reproduced here are the data from Table 13.1, the numbers of stress symptoms reported for two groups. One group perceived they had some control over an exam's content, whereas the other group was told to write exam questions as a study technique.

Perceived Control	No Control
12	9
12	12
8	9
5	11
12	11
5	15
11	14
12	7
7	11
15	11
11	9
6	17
12	14
11	17
8	11

(continued)

Data for Exercise 14 *(continued)*

Perceived Control	No Control
11	13
12	19
11	14
13	11
11	13
13	12
12	14
7	7
13	11
9	16
7	15
5	13
15	13
7	10
7	16

a. Compute the one-way ANOVA *F* test.

b. Now go to Table 13.2 and square the observed *t* statistic found there. Is t^2 equal to the *F* you found in part a? Should it be?

15. Compute η^2 and ω^2 for the data in Exercise 12.

16. Compute η^2 and ω^2 for the data in Exercise 13.

17. Researchers investigating how children learn the past tense of verbs developed two computer models to simulate such learning. One rule children use is to add "-ed" to the present tense of a verb, such as "learn, learned." One computer model was based on a "stage theory" that says that children go through three distinct stages: First, learn important common verbs and learn the general rule of adding "-ed." Second, use the rule without exception. Third, learn the exceptions. The second computer model used a neural network that mimics patterns of learning when making the same mistakes children make. The network "learns" by changing the strength of the connections between elements in the network as it responds to input. To test how good the computer models learned, the researchers compared them to children who were in the process of learning the past tenses of verbs. Such computer models use random numbers in their learning processes, and the numbers given to the models at the start of their "learning" determine how well they "learn." Each computer model was given a starting number 15 different times and then tested at the end of the learning phase. A group of 15 children were also tested. The test was the same for both computer models and the children and consisted of 20 present-tense verbs for which the past tense was to be given.

The number of correct responses are given in the table for all groups.

Stages Model	Network Model	Children
8	12	14
10	16	12
5	11	17
9	13	14
13	13	17
11	17	11
12	9	10
10	11	9
7	15	11
13	8	11
12	12	10
11	13	15
9	14	13
14	10	16
10	13	11

a. For each group, compute descriptive statistics and do graphical displays to get some feel for the data.

b. Compute a one-way ANOVA on the data, including the strength of association measures.

c. Write a few short paragraphs about your results that would serve as the results section of a journal article.

18. The area of interpersonal attraction uses a research strategy called the bogus stranger paradigm to manipulate the percentage of attitude similarity between a hypothetical stranger and the participant in the research. The research proceeds in a sequence of orderly steps. First, give an attitude survey to a group of potential participants. Second, select the participants for the research; for each participant, construct a unique listing of attitudes that agree (disagree) with his or her own attitudes for a certain percentage of the items on the survey. Differing levels of agreement (percentage of similarity) are one of the major manipulations in this type of research. Subjects are randomly assigned to a level of similarity. Also, other manipulations are done in the research by giving additional information with the bogus stranger's attitude survey. Participants are then randomly assigned to combinations of any independent variables. Third, schedule the participant in the experiment, give the bogus stranger's attitude survey, and ask the participant to rate the stranger on how he or she would like to work with the stranger on some project. The rating scale is called the Interpersonal Judgment Scale (IJS) and is a measure of attraction toward the stranger.

One independent variable is the percentage of attitude similarity. Other independent variables can be introduced to the paradigm by descriptions of the bogus stranger. The dependent variable is the score on the IJS. These studies are usually true experiments.

Wrather and Padd (1971) wanted to explore the impact of competence and similarity on attraction. They hypothesized that each of these two variables would influence attraction as measured by the IJS. They randomly assigned 72 participants to six groups defined by two levels of attitude similarity (80% similar and 80% dissimilar) and three levels of competence of the stranger (college professor, graduate assistant, and first-year student). After reading the attitude survey and the description of the stranger, each subject rated the hypothetical stranger on the IJS. The ratings are listed in the table.

A one-way ANOVA can be done on the attraction data for the effect of competence by itself, but the correct two-way ANOVA is delayed until Chapter 16.

Attraction data (IJS scores)

	Low Competence (First-Year Student)	Medium Competence (Graduate Assistant)	High Competence (Professor)
	8	9	10
	6	9	10
	10	8	10
	12	12	12
	9	12	13
	8	12	9
High Similarity	13	11	10
(80% similarity)	7	12	10
	12	12	11
	10	11	10
	12	10	12
	12	12	10
	8	5	10
	5	10	8
	6	6	8
	8	10	9
	7	5	6
	5	8	12
Low Similarity	8	7	12
(20% similarity)	8	8	7
	4	5	8
	6	6	7
	4	10	4
	6	5	11

a. For each level of competence, compute descriptive statistics and do graphical displays to get some feel for the data.

b. Compute a one-way ANOVA using competence as the independent variable, including strength of association measures.

c. Write about your results in a few short paragraphs that would serve as the results section of a journal article.

19. Researchers think that moderate exercise may help relieve depression, especially among the elderly (see McNeil, LeBlanc & Joyner, 1991). Because of social contact while exercising, the researchers want to include a group that has social contact but no exercise. They establish a waiting-list control group. They recruit 30 elderly depressed people who are capable of moderate exercise and randomly assign ten each to three groups: exercise, social contact, and wait list. Those in the exercise group walked outside (or in a mall during bad weather) with a researcher two times a week and alone once a week for 20 min each time (increasing to 40 min) for 6 weeks. The social contact group met with a researcher for two 20–40-min sessions each week for 6 weeks for casual conversation like that in the exercise condition. The data in the table are scores on the 14-item psychological portion of the Beck Depression Inventory (BDI; Beck & Beamesderfer, 1974). Participants were similar on this scale prior to treatment (means of 8.9, 9.1, and 8.4 for the three groups, respectively).

Exercise	Social Contact	Wait List
1	2	6
5	11	10
6	11	11
7	10	8
3	8	7
8	6	5
7	2	7
5	1	7
9	3	8
7	5	11

a. For each level of treatment, compute descriptive statistics and do graphical displays to get some feel for the data.

b. Compute a one-way ANOVA using treatment as the independent variable, including strength of association measures.

c. Write up all your results in a few short paragraphs that would serve as the results section of a journal article.

Section 14.5

20. Use SAS PROC ANOVA or the SPSS command ONEWAY to do as much of Exercise 19 as you can.

Do you get the same results? Do you reach the same conclusion using the p-value decision rule with the computer program as you did with the critical value decision rule? How would you incorporate the p-value into your write-up?

15

Multiple Comparison Procedures

ANOVA (analysis of variance) is one of the most widely used statistical procedures in the behavioral sciences, but it has a limitation. ANOVA tests a hypothesis of equality of multiple means, but it doesn't tell *which* groups are equal or unequal. A significant ANOVA *F* test tells only that there is a difference someplace among the means. If you have four groups and only one of them is significantly different from the rest, you need to be able to say that. Statistics introduced in this chapter will allow you to find out where the significant differences lie among *J* independent groups. Be sure you are comfortable with the concept of power and how α affects it before starting this chapter.

Research Example 15
15.1 Introduction
　　Example
15.2 Error Rates and Statistics
　　Pairwise comparisons
　　Error rates
　　Statistics
15.3 Tukey, Fisher-Hayter, and Ryan MCPs
　　Tukey MCP
　　Fisher-Hayter MCP
　　Ryan MCP
　　Example
15.4 Unequal Sample Sizes
　　Games-Howell method
　　Example
15.5 Orthogonal Comparisons
　　Comparisons and weights
　　Orthogonal comparisons
　　Beyond these MCPs
15.6 Summary, Study Tips, and Computation
　　Chapter summary
　　Study tips
　　Computation
Exercises

Research Example 15

Frank (1984) conducted an experiment that combined two variables: the effect of a note-taking study technique and cognitive styles. The cognitive styles were field independence and field dependence. Researchers in education are interested in cognitive styles because field-dependent people need structure provided for them to organize knowledge. In contrast, a field-independent person can provide the cognitive structure for the task, such as outlining a lecture. Field independence was defined as those 52 students who scored high (≥ 14) on the Hidden Figures Test (French, Ekstrom & Price, 1963). Field dependence was defined as those 52 students who scored low (≤ 9) on that test. The note-taking study technique was manipulated. Students in each cognitive style group listened to a taped lecture under one of the following study techniques:

1. Students took no notes.
2. Students took their own notes.
3. Students received an outline framework of major headings and subheadings and took additional notes using this outline.
4. Students were provided with a complete outline with key terms, brief definitions, and important ideas given in addition to the major headings and subheadings. They took notes of their own, too.

The dependent variable was performance on a 20-item multiple-choice test on the lecture material. Within each of the cognitive styles, students had been randomly assigned to one of the four study techniques. This design allowed the researchers to look at how people with different cognitive styles perform using the various note-taking study techniques.

Even though this study had two variables, study technique and cognitive style, let's combine the cognitive style groups assigned to each study technique and consider only the effect of study technique. That is, there are $n = 26$ subjects in each of the four levels of study technique. A significant F won't answer some of the most interesting questions from this study. Which group of subjects has the highest average score on the test about the lecture material? That is, which note-taking study method is best? The group means for numbers of items correct were 13.04 (the no-notes group), 16.58 (students who took their own notes), 17.04 (students who took notes on an outline framework), and 17.46 (those who took notes on a complete outline). Which differences in study techniques are significant? These questions can be answered with procedures presented in this chapter called *multiple comparison procedures (MCPs)*.

The original research used the Tukey MCP to compare the four means for the main effect of study technique. They found that, on the average, students in the no-notes group responded with significantly fewer correct items compared with students in the other three groups. There were no other significant differences. However, you should note that you might not get these same results at each level of cognitive styles. That is, maybe the significant difference would hold for field-independent students, but more differences would be found for field-dependent students. More will be given on this study in Chapter 16, when you learn about ANOVAs with two independent variables.

15.1   Introduction

The one-way ANOVA, one of the most widely used statistics, has a severe limitation: A significant ANOVA F test allows researchers to say only that some difference exists among the J group means. ANOVA doesn't tell which groups are different from each other.

You might have five groups of people who have dental anxiety. Each group goes through a different situational-stress treatment program to try to overcome the dental anxiety. Afterward, you measure each group on the Dental Anxiety Scale. What if only one of the anxiety-fighting treatments works? You can get a significant *F*, but it does not tell you whether one treatment worked or three treatments were effective. All the ANOVA says is: There's a difference here someplace. To seek out which groups are significantly different from the others requires you to ask: Is Group 1 different from Group 2? From Group 3? From Group 4? From Group 5? How about Group 2 versus each of the other groups? You can see how the comparisons become numerous. These are **multiple comparisons,** and the statistics used to test for the significance of the mean differences are **multiple comparison procedures** (MCPs). The specific type of multiple comparisons illustrated here are **pairwise comparisons** (differences in pairs of means).

In Chapter 13 you learned how to compare two groups' means with *t*-tests. You'll build on that idea in this chapter, but remember what you read in Chapter 14: Each time you do a *t*-test, you have a probability of a Type I error. Those probabilities add up. You don't want to do a bunch of *t*-tests and guarantee that you've made at least one Type I error! You have to control the error rate, and that's one of the main ideas in this chapter.

Because of the complexities associated with multiple comparison procedures (MCPs), we depart from the approach of covering the situation/hypotheses, test statistic, theoretical distribution/decision rules, and assumptions. The situation is similar for all of the MCPs covered in this chapter: *J* independent samples and you want to test hypotheses about the equality of all pairs of means. Most of the MCPs have the same three assumptions as the two-independent-sample *t*: normality of observations in the populations, equal population variances, and independent observations. They largely follow the same patterns of robustness as the two-independent-sample *t*. The test statistic and theoretical distribution/decision rules are given separately for each MCP.

Multiple comparisons
The many mean differences that exist in comparing *J* means

Multiple comparison procedures
MCPs, statistics used to test for significance of two or more mean differences

Pairwise comparisons
Differences in means taken two at a time

Example

Returning to the liar data set, you would like to find out which judges, psychiatrists, and Secret Service personnel are best at catching a liar. People in each career group were shown 1-min videotape segments of ten individuals telling how they felt about a film. The participants then indicated whether the person in the videotape was telling the truth. The score for each participant is the deception accuracy score, which is the percentage of correct responses, given that exactly five of the ten were lying.

Group means are given in Table 15.1 along with values of *n*, MS_W, and df_W from the

Table 15.1
Liar data: Means, *n*'s, MS_W, and df_W

	Secret Service	*Judges*	*Psychiatrists*	
$\overline{X}$	64.00	56.57	57.71	
n	35	35	35	Total *N* = 105

$MS_W = 165.1541$

$df_W = N - J$

$\quad = 105 - 3 = 102$

one-way ANOVA done in Chapter 14. This information will be used to illustrate three MCPs for equal sample sizes. You'll also learn an MCP to use with unequal sample sizes and the concept of orthogonal comparisons.

Quick Quiz

Refer to Table 15.1. (a) Which occupation group has the highest average deception accuracy score? (b) Which group is best at detecting a liar?

Answers

(a) Secret Service. (b) You cannot answer this question without doing a test called a multiple comparison procedure. The Secret Service group may not be different from psychiatrists, the group with the next highest mean, so one group may not be the best.

15.2   Error Rates and Statistics

At the beginning of Chapter 14 you read about problems associated with doing many *t*-tests to find differences among *J* means. One problem is that the probability of at least one Type I error increases as a function of the number of *t*-tests. Naturally, you want to reduce the likelihood of being wrong, so you want to control this error rate. There are different ways to control α; that is, there are different error rates.

Here's something else that complicates the situation: Different statistics are available for the same situation. So which multiple comparison statistic do you use when several procedures can be applied to the same situation? You want a statistic that controls the error rate and still gives you a good chance of finding a significant difference. Recall what you learned about *power,* the probability of rejecting the null hypothesis. The different error rates and multiple comparison procedures combine to give different values for power. We'll show you how to find a statistic that controls α and gives good power.

Pairwise Comparisons

Before you read about the control of error, you need to learn two things about pairwise comparisons: a simple formula for figuring out how many pairwise comparisons are possible on *J* means, and the hypotheses for pairwise comparisons. You easily can figure out the number of pairs of means when you have *J* = 3, but what about when *J* = 7? Here's the formula:

$$C = \frac{J(J-1)}{2} \tag{15.1}$$

where *C* is the number of comparisons. If *J* = 3, then *C* = 3(3 − 1)/2 = 6/2 = 3. If *J* = 7, then 7(7 − 1)/2 = 42/2 = 21. So for *J* = 7 groups, there would be 21 pairwise comparisons. For a picture of the three pairwise comparisons on three means, see Figure 15.1.

You might wonder why we specify *pairwise* comparisons. It's to distinguish them from other kinds of comparisons, such as the average of the means of the first two groups versus the mean of the third group.

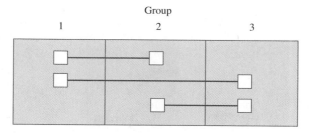

Figure 15.1
Pairwise comparisons on three means (☐——☐ indicates a comparison)

The hypotheses for pairwise comparisons are:

$$H_0: \mu_j = \mu_{j'} \qquad H_1: \mu_j \neq \mu_{j'} \tag{15.2}$$

where j and j' simply stand for any two different groups, such as 1 and 2. Directional hypotheses can be tested with pairwise comparisons, but this is rarely done in actual research.

Error Rates

When you have only one comparison, say the comparison between the means of the first and second groups, $\bar{X}_1 - \bar{X}_2$, there is only one test and one hypothesis. When you move to *multiple* comparisons, by adding the two pairwise comparisons $\bar{X}_1 - \bar{X}_3$ and $\bar{X}_2 - \bar{X}_3$, there are multiple (three) tests and hypotheses. With each of these tests comes the probability of a Type I error.

Every time you do a comparison, you're testing a hypothesis and setting some α level, the probability of the Type I error. If you assume that the tests on these comparisons are independent (nonoverlapping) t-tests and you use the same value of α for each comparison, then the maximum probability of at least one Type I error is given by:

$$p(\text{at least one Type I error}) = 1 - (1 - \alpha)^C \leq C\alpha \tag{15.3}$$

Actually, the C tests on pairwise comparisons are not independent (there is some overlapping when you compare Secret Service and psychiatrists and also Secret Service and judges). So this formula gives only the maximum probability for C pairwise comparisons. The actual probability is unknown, but it is larger than α and less than $1 - (1 - \alpha)^C$, which is less than or equal to $C\alpha$. If $\alpha = .05$, for example, then the probability of at least one Type I error for $C = 3$ tests is larger than .05 but less than .142625, which is less than $(3)(.05) = .15$. So you can see how the probability of at least one Type I error can increase rapidly beyond your chosen α.

There are two basic ways to control error rate—that is, to control Type I error probability: for each comparison or for some group of comparisons. **Error rate per comparison** controls the Type I error probability at α for each comparison. This approach does not control p(at least one Type I error) at some small value but lets it increase as the number of comparisons, C, increases, as in formula 15.3. Doing all

Error rate per comparison
Controls Type I error probability at α for each comparison

MCPs: Not for zombies

possible *t*-tests with α at .05 for each controls the α per comparison. In other words, you're risking $\alpha = .05$ for every *t*-test, but more than that for the collection of tests.

For the three *t*-tests needed to compare the means in the liar data, you could control error rate by using $\alpha = .05$ for each test. Recall the factors that affect power. Power is high when α is high, so controlling the error rate per comparison gives high power. But your probability of rejecting H_0 when you shouldn't also is high, so the high power comes at the expense of increased Type I error probability. (Do you need to review the factors that influence power? Draw two partly overlapping distributions with a vertical line for the critical value and identify the areas associated with the probability of Type I error and power.)

Error rate familywise
Controls *p*(at least one Type I error) at a maximum of α for a group of *C* comparisons

The second way is to control the error rate for some group of comparisons. **Error rate familywise** controls *p*(at least one Type I error) at a maximum of α for a group of *C* comparisons. The probability of wrongly rejecting the null hypothesis is controlled at the chosen α, such as .05, for the group of comparisons you're interested in. Obviously, any MCP that has this type of error rate control has to break up α somehow among the *C* comparisons. Each comparison has a small probability of Type I error—and lower power. But you might be willing to give up some statistical power in exchange for controlling the Type I error.

To see what happens when the error rate is controlled familywise, we need to distinguish between the probability of a Type I error for a single comparison and the probability of a Type I error for the family of comparisons. Let α' be the probability of a Type I error for each comparison and α be the probability of at least one Type I error for the family. The error rate familywise sets $\alpha \leq 1 - (1 - \alpha')^C$ for all of the tests. When you computed *p*(at least one Type I error) in the example of error rate per comparison, you plugged $\alpha = .05$ into the formula, so for the error rate per comparison, $\alpha' = .05$.

Now let's look at controlling the error rate familywise for the liar data. With $J = 3$ means, there are three pairwise comparisons. If you set $\alpha \leq 1 - (1 - \alpha')^C$ for all three tests, then you would have to solve for α'. For $\alpha = .05$:

$$\alpha' \leq 1 - \sqrt[C]{.95} \tag{15.4}$$

If you plug in $C = 3$, then $\alpha' = .016952427$ for each test. You can see that each comparison has a small probability of a Type I error (and the power is lower). So for all three comparisons put together, you've controlled *p*(at least one Type I error). All of the MCPs in Section 15.3 control α familywise. When you study each of these MCPs, you will learn how they accomplish this control of α.

Quick Quiz

See Research Example 15. (a) How many means were there for study technique? (b) How many pairwise comparisons could be done? (c) If we do each of these at $\alpha' = .05$, what is p(at least one Type I error)? (d) If you set $\alpha \leq 1 - (1 - \alpha')^C$ at .05 for all of the tests, then what value will you have for α'?

Answers

(a) $J = 4$ means. (b) $C = J(J-1)/2 = 4(4-1)/2 = 12/2 = 6$. (c) For $C = 6$ and $\alpha = .05$, p(at least one Type I error) $= 1 - (1 - .05)^C = 1 - (1 - .05)^6 = 1 - (.95)^6 = 1 - .7351 = .2649$. (d) Setting $\alpha \leq 1 - (1 - \alpha')^C$ at .05 for $C = 6$ gives $\alpha' = 1 - \sqrt[6]{.95} = .0085124451$ for each test.

Statistics

As if the confusion from multiple comparisons and different error rates were not enough, now you must confront different statistics. But the problem of "different statistics" is more apparent than real.

The first statistic is a *t*-statistic. For pairwise comparisons, the formula is

$$t = \frac{\bar{X}_j - \bar{X}_{j'}}{\sqrt{\frac{MS_W}{n}(2)}} \tag{15.5}$$

for the difference between any two of the *J* means, $\bar{X}_j$ and $\bar{X}_{j'}$; the mean square within groups, MS_W, from the one-way ANOVA; and the number of observations per group, *n*. The use of *n* shows you that equal group sizes are required in order to use this statistic. This *t* fits the general verbal definition of every *t*: something minus its mean divided by its estimated standard deviation. Here the "something" is the difference between the two sample means, which has a mean of zero if H_0 is true. The *t* is used for all of the MCPs in this chapter. When you get a critical value for any of the MCPs, the statistic in formula 15.5 is what you compute to get the observed value to compare to the critical value.

The second statistic is *q*. It is often given instead of *t*, and there is a simple relationship between them. For pairwise comparisons, *q* is given by

$$q = \frac{\bar{X}_j - \bar{X}_{j'}}{\sqrt{\frac{MS_W}{n}}} \tag{15.6}$$

One name given to *q* is "Studentized range." Every *q* has the general verbal definition: a range (difference) of two variables divided by the estimated standard deviation of one of the two variables. Here the variables are means, so the denominator is the estimated standard deviation of a sample mean. The *q* is related to *t* by

$$t = \frac{\bar{X}_j - \bar{X}_{j'}}{\sqrt{\frac{MS_W}{n}(2)}} = \frac{q}{\sqrt{2}} = \frac{\bar{X}_j - \bar{X}_{j'}}{\sqrt{\frac{MS_W}{n}}} \frac{1}{\sqrt{2}} \tag{15.7}$$

That is, simply divide *q* by $\sqrt{2}$ to obtain $t = q/\sqrt{2}$.

Why do we give you both q and t? Because both t and q are used in scientific research articles; your computer's statistics package may report either one, and you'll use tables of q critical values in this book. It would be nice if the whole world used the same statistic, but that's not reality.

If you have two multiple comparison procedures to compare, and one is based on a t and the other is based on a q, how do you find out which statistic would have better power? First, you need to remember the relationship between critical values and power. For the statistics you have learned, a smaller critical value means greater power; it's easier to reject the null hypothesis with a small critical value. Second, can you directly compare a t to a q when you're deciding between two multiple comparison procedures? No, you need to have a common basis of comparison. So you find the critical values for each one and convert the q to t by dividing q by $\sqrt{2}$. Then you have a level playing field and you can compare the critical values to see which one is smaller, giving a more powerful MCP.

Even though there are more statistics for multiple comparisons, these two are sufficient for our needs. If you are interested in more information about MCPs, see Toothaker (1991) or Toothaker (1993).

Quick Quiz

(a) If $q = 3.79$, what is the equivalent t? (b) If you are told that a t critical value for a certain MCP is 2.80, what is an equivalent q?

Answers

(a) $t = q/\sqrt{2}$, so $t = 3.79/\sqrt{2} = 2.68$ (rounded). (b) $t = q/\sqrt{2}$, so $q = (t)(\sqrt{2}) = (2.80)(\sqrt{2}) = 3.96$ (rounded).

15.3   Tukey, Fisher-Hayter, and Ryan MCPs

You might ask how to characterize the comparisons that are frequently used by researchers in the behavioral sciences. The most frequent combination probably is:

- All of the pairwise comparisons after a significant F.
- These comparisons happen to overlap and be chosen after the experiment is run.
- These comparisons are done with a method that controls α familywise.

You have overlapping comparisons when you compare means 1 with 2, 1 with 3, and 2 with 3. We use the notation 1–2, 1–3, and 2–3 to indicate these comparisons.

There are many procedures for doing multiple comparisons on J independent means. You want one that controls α at a given level (usually .05) for all the pairwise comparisons for the experiment. Some MCPs do not control α at the level claimed, such as the Newman-Keuls test, the protected t-test or least significant difference (LSD) test, the Duncan test, and the Duncan-Waller test. These methods all have a high probability of committing at least one Type I error. *The above-named procedures are not recommended.* Be suspicious when you read a scientific article in which the researchers have used those procedures. Two other procedures that *are* good methods but that we won't cover in this chapter are the MCPs of Dunn (see Chapter 17) and Scheffé. These procedures are conservative in most uses; that is, you can be sure that you've got a tight rein on your error rate, but you give up power compared to one of the methods covered in this chapter.

You are going to learn the Tukey, Fisher-Hayter, and Ryan methods. After all three MCPs are presented, we provide an example for which all three MCPs are computed. These three MCPs give different critical values and different powers for the set of all pairwise comparisons. You can use the statistic in formula 15.5 to compute the observed *t* for any of these MCPs.

Tukey MCP

Tukey's HSD
Tukey's *honestly significant difference* test for pairwise comparisons, controls α familywise

The most popular method that controls α familywise at .05 for all the pairwise comparisons for an experiment is the **Tukey HSD** (honestly significant difference) test. It is interesting that the Tukey method does not need the overall *F* test to be significant in order to maintain control of α familywise. However, most researchers use the overall *F* test to give a general indication of whether Tukey's method probably will find any significant differences.

The Tukey method is done in the following four steps:

1. Obtain all possible differences between pairs of group means.
2. Compute the *t*-statistics for all possible differences.
3. Compare the absolute values of the *t*-statistics to the critical value

$$\frac{q_{J, df_W}}{\sqrt{2}} \tag{15.8}$$

Studentized range distribution
Theoretical reference distribution for the Tukey HSD, has parameters *J* and df_W

where *q* is the α% critical value from the **Studentized range distribution** with parameters *J* and df_W given in Table A.7 in Appendix A. The parameter *J* is often called the *number-of-means parameter*. You use *J* to get the correct column of Table A.7 and df_W to get the correct row. The values in the body of the table are values of *q*.

4. Reject a null hypothesis of equal population means for any absolute value of *t* that equals or exceeds the critical value.

Fisher-Hayter MCP

Fisher-Hayter MCP
Hayter's modification of Fisher's test for pairwise comparisons, controls α familywise but requires that the overall *F* be significant

Whereas the Tukey HSD is well known, the **Fisher-Hayter MCP** is relatively new (Hayter, 1986). Like the Tukey MCP, it controls α familywise at .05 for all the pairwise comparisons in an experiment. Unlike the Tukey, the Fisher-Hayter method needs the overall *F* test to be significant in order to maintain control of α familywise. Because most researchers use the overall *F* test before doing MCPs, it is easy to use the Fisher-Hayter. The advantage of Fisher-Hayter over Tukey is that it gives a slight gain in power.

The Fisher-Hayter method is done in the following steps:

1. If the overall *F* test is significant, do steps 2–5; if not, retain all null hypotheses of no differences between all possible pairs of population means.
2. Obtain all possible differences between pairs of group means.
3. Compute the *t*-statistics for all possible differences.

4. Compare the absolute values of the t-statistics to the critical value

$$\frac{q_{J-1,\, df_W}}{\sqrt{2}} \tag{15.9}$$

where q is the $\alpha\%$ critical value from the Studentized range distribution with parameters $J - 1$ and df_W given in Table A.7 in Appendix A. Note that this differs from the Tukey MCP (which uses J) by using $J - 1$ as the number-of-means parameter to get the correct column of Table A.7.

5. Reject a null hypothesis of equal population means for any absolute value of t that equals or exceeds the critical value.

Ryan MCP

Ryan MCP

Ryan's stepwise test for pairwise comparisons, controls α familywise and should be computed with a computer package

The Tukey and Fisher-Hayter MCPs are simple and easy to compute, but the Fisher-Hayter is not yet in many computer packages. The **Ryan MCP** is a more powerful test than Tukey and is available in some computer packages of statistical methods, like SAS. The Ryan gains its power over Tukey at the cost of complexity. It is a stepwise method, requiring a statistic at any given step to be significant before the next step is taken.

To use the Ryan method, start by arranging the J means in order according to their numerical values. Next, do a test on the largest difference. If that is significant, then you can test the next largest difference in means, and so on. Before learning the exact steps to take, you need some new terminology associated with this stepwise procedure.

Stretch size

The number of ordered means between and including the two means in the comparison, symbolized by p

Once the J means are in order, the concept of *stretch size* can be introduced. For any given comparison, **stretch size** is the number of ordered means between and including the two means in the comparison. The symbol that is commonly used for stretch size is p, not to be confused with probability. (You'll have to face the reality that statisticians sometimes reuse the same symbol for different concepts!) For example, with four means in order, the stretch size for the comparison on the largest versus the smallest mean is four, $p = 4$ (see Figure 15.2). For the largest mean versus the second smallest mean, the stretch size is three, $p = 3$. What is the value of p for the comparison

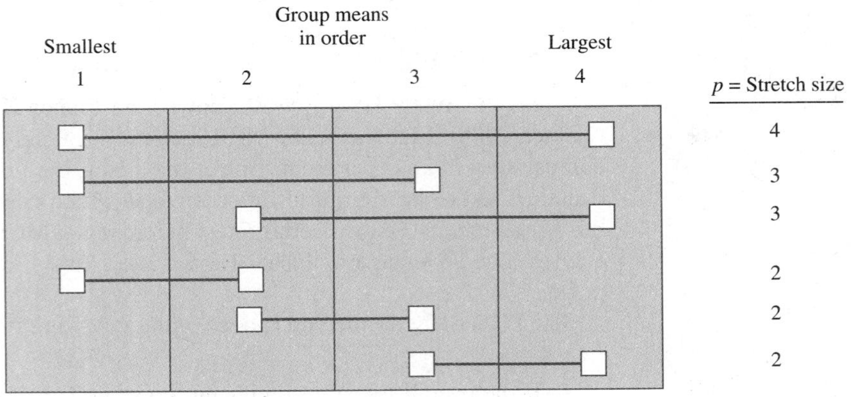

Figure 15.2
Stretch size for pairwise comparisons on four means (☐——☐ indicates a comparison)

Table 15.2

q critical values

	Tukey		Ryan	
p	$q/\sqrt{2}$	α_p		$q/\sqrt{2}$
4	2.80	.05		2.80
3	2.80	.05		2.53
2	2.80	.0253		2.41

on the largest mean versus the next largest mean? It is $p = 2$. Stretch size ranges from *J* down to 2.

For every stretch size, the Ryan MCP uses a different $q/\sqrt{2}$ critical value and a different α. The different critical values and α make this procedure complex, especially if you don't have a computer package that does Ryan's procedure. The value of α for each stretch size is called α_p and is given as

$$\alpha_p = \alpha \qquad\qquad \text{for } p = J \text{ and } J - 1$$
$$\alpha_p = 1 - (1 - \alpha)^{p/J} \qquad \text{for } p \leq J - 2 \tag{15.10}$$

So if $J = 4$ and $\alpha = .05$, these are the values of α_p for the different values of *p*:

$$p = 4: \qquad \alpha_p = .05$$

$$p = 3: \qquad \alpha_p = .05$$

$$p = 2: \qquad \alpha_p = 1 - (1 - .05)^{2/4} = 1 - .9747 = .0253$$

Then the critical values for Ryan are

$$\frac{q_{p,\,df_W}^{\alpha_p}}{\sqrt{2}} \tag{15.11}$$

Here the stretch size *p* is the number-of-means parameter, and it can take on different values for different comparisons.

See Table 15.2 for an example of the Ryan critical values for $J = 4$, $df_W = 20$, and $\alpha = .05$ as compared to those for Tukey. Note that you cannot get *q* critical values for $p \leq J - 2$ directly from Table A.7 because they have values of α_p that are neither .05 nor .01. You can either get approximations of the critical values by interpolation on the natural logarithms of the α's or use a canned package of computer programs that computes the Ryan MCP. Examine the critical values in Table 15.2. For the two smaller stretch sizes, Ryan's procedure gives a smaller critical value than Tukey's procedure. So Ryan is more powerful for those tests.

With these basics about the Ryan MCP, you are now ready to learn the stepwise logic it uses. We assume the means are in order.

Nonsignificant by implication

When a MCP test retains H_0 because the comparison is contained within the range of a comparison already declared nonsignificant

1. For $p = J$, the largest difference in means, do the test using the *t*-statistic and the critical value given in formula 15.11. If the test of the $p = J$ (the largest) comparison is not significant, then retain all H_0 for all pairwise comparisons. That is, if the test for the largest stretch is nonsignificant, then the tests for the smaller stretches contained within it are **nonsignificant by implication.** If the test for the largest stretch is significant, then reject H_0: $\mu_1 = \mu_J$ and go on to the two comparisons for stretch size $p = J - 1$ (step 2). Those comparisons are μ_1 versus μ_{J-1} and μ_2 versus μ_J.

2. For $p = J - 1$, do the two tests on the comparisons using the *t*-statistics and the critical values given in formula 15.11. If either of the comparisons is significant, then go on to the next smaller stretch size it contains. If a comparison is not significant, then retain all H_0 for comparisons that are contained in that comparison. By "contained," we mean any pair of means that are completely under the "umbrella" of the larger

Table 15.3
Hypothetical example for Ryan's MCP

Mean	1	2	3	4	t	p	Critical Value	S = significant, N = nonsignificant, NI = N by implication
	17.0	18.2	25.7	26.0				
	————————————————				2.90	4	2.80	S
	————————				2.80	3	2.53	S
		————————			2.52	3	2.53	N
	————				0.39	2	2.41	N
		————			2.42	2	2.41	NI
			————		0.10	2	2.41	NI

nonsignificant stretch. If you have $J = 5$ and the 1–4 comparison is nonsignificant, then all of the comparisons completely contained by 1 and 4 are declared nonsignificant by implication. This includes 1–2, 2–3, 3–4, 1–3, and 2–4. You can still do the 4–5 comparison, however, because it is outside of the 1–4 "umbrella."

3. Each remaining comparison down to $p = 2$ is tested in a similar way only if the H_0 its tests has not been previously retained (retained by implication).

Examine Table 15.3 to see a hypothetical example with $J = 4$, $df_W = 20$, and $\alpha = .05$, which shows you how the stepwise logic of Ryan works. First, you compare the t statistic for the largest comparison, with $p = J = 4$, to the critical value. Because $t = 2.90$ is larger than 2.80, you reject H_0 for that comparison and go on to the two $p = J - 1 = 3$ comparisons.

Second, you compare the t-statistic for the next largest comparisons, with $p = J - 1 = 3$, to the critical value. For the 1–3 comparison, $t = 2.80$ is larger than 2.53, so you reject H_0 for that comparison. For the 2–4 comparison, $t = 2.52$ is not larger than 2.53, so you retain H_0 for that comparison and, by implication, all of the comparisons it contains: 2–3 and 3–4.

Third, for any comparisons not retained in a prior step, you compare the t-statistic to the critical value. Only the 1–2 comparison is available, and $t = 0.39$ is not larger than 2.41, so you retain H_0 for that comparison, and you are finished. It is interesting to note that for the 2–3 comparison, $t = 2.42$ is larger than the 2.41 critical value, but the comparison is still not significant because it was contained in the nonsignificant 2–4 comparison at the prior step.

For the Ryan procedure, a comparison is significant only if: (1) the comparison is not contained in a comparison retained in a prior step and (2) the t equals or exceeds the critical value.

Example

For the liar data in Table 14.1, the means are $\bar{X}_1 = 64.00$ for the Secret Service group, $\bar{X}_2 = 56.57$ for judges, and $\bar{X}_3 = 57.71$ for psychiatrists. The significant overall ANOVA F test merely indicated that there was some significant difference in these sample means. If you want to find out which of the groups is best at detecting lies, you need to do more analysis with some MCP.

First, let's do the Tukey method. Because $J = 3$ and $df_W = 102$, go to Table A.7, use $J = 3$ for the column and $df_W = 60$ for the row, and find their intersection. (You'll

Table 15.4
Tukey tests for liar data

Differences in $\bar{X}$:

	Judges $\bar{X}_1 = 56.57$	Psychiatrists $\bar{X}_2 = 57.71$	Secret Service $\bar{X}_3 = 64.00$
Judges $\bar{X}_1 = 56.57$		1.14	7.43
Psychiatrists $\bar{X}_2 = 57.71$			6.29

How to compute t-statistics:

$$t = \frac{\bar{X}_j - \bar{X}_{j'}}{\sqrt{\frac{MS_W}{n}(2)}} = \frac{\bar{X}_j - \bar{X}_{j'}}{\sqrt{\frac{165.1541}{35}(2)}} = \frac{\bar{X}_j - \bar{X}_{j'}}{\sqrt{9.4374}} = \frac{\bar{X}_j - \bar{X}_{j'}}{3.0720}$$

t-statistics:

	Judges	Psychiatrists	Secret Service
Judges		0.3711	2.4186
Psychiatrists			2.0475

Critical value:
$t = q/\sqrt{2} = 3.40/\sqrt{2} = 2.4042$

Decisions:

H_0	Absolute Value of t	Decision
$\mu_1 - \mu_3 = 0$	$2.4186 \geq 2.4042$	Reject H_0
$\mu_1 - \mu_2 = 0$	$0.3711 \leq 2.4042$	Retain H_0
$\mu_2 - \mu_3 = 0$	$2.0475 \leq 2.4042$	Retain H_0

have to use $df_W = 60$ because the table doesn't go up to 102.) You should find $q = 3.40$ for the critical value of the Studentized range, using $\alpha = .05$. The t critical value is then $3.40/\sqrt{2} = 2.4042$. Table 15.4 contains all the steps for the liar data. The means are arranged in order, which will help you later with the Ryan method. The sign of the differences in the means doesn't matter because H_1 is nondirectional; also, we later use only the absolute value of the t-statistic. The conclusion would be that Secret Service personnel are significantly better than judges but not significantly better than psychiatrists at detecting liars and that psychiatrists are not significantly better than judges.

Second, use the Fisher-Hayter method on the liar data. The overall F is significant, so you can proceed with the pairwise comparisons. Because $J - 1 = 2$ and $df_W = 102$, go to Table A.7, use $J - 1 = 2$ for the column and $df_W = 60$ for the row, and find their intersection. There, $q = 2.83$ for the critical value of the Studentized range, using $\alpha = .05$. So the t critical value is $2.83/\sqrt{2} = 2.0011$. Table 15.5 contains all of the steps for the liar data. Because only the critical value and decisions are potentially different, the values for the differences in $\bar{X}$'s and t are taken from Table 15.4. The conclusion would be that Secret Service personnel are significantly better than either judges or psychiatrists at detecting liars and that psychiatrists are not significantly better than judges. The additional power of the Fisher-Hayter MCP allowed you to detect the Secret Service/psychiatrist difference as significant, when the Tukey method did not.

Finally, the Ryan method. Because $J = 3$ and $df_W = 102$, go to Table A.7, use $J = 3$ for the column and $df_W = 60$ for the row, and find their intersection. There, $q = 3.40$ for the critical value of the Studentized range, using $\alpha = .05$ (critical $t = 2.4042$). You

Table 15.5
Fisher-Hayter tests for liar data

Critical value:
$t = q/\sqrt{2} = 2.83/\sqrt{2} = 2.0011$

Decisions:

H_0	Absolute Value of t	Decision
$\mu_1 - \mu_3 = 0$	$2.4186 \geq 2.0011$	Reject H_0
$\mu_1 - \mu_2 = 0$	$0.3711 \leq 2.0011$	Retain H_0
$\mu_2 - \mu_3 = 0$	$2.0475 \geq 2.0011$	Reject H_0

also will use the critical value for $J - 1 = 2$ and $df_W = 60$, $q = 2.83$ for the critical value of the Studentized range, and $\alpha = .05$ (critical $t = 2.0011$). Table 15.6 contains all of the steps for the liar data. Because only the critical value and decisions are potentially different, the values for the differences in $\overline{X}$'s and t are taken from Table 15.4. The conclusion would be that Secret Service personnel are significantly better than either judges or psychiatrists at detecting liars and that psychiatrists are not significantly better than judges. The additional power of the Ryan MCP allowed you to detect the Secret Service/psychiatrist difference as significant, when the Tukey method did not. For these data, the Fisher-Hayter and Ryan MCPs gave the same results.

Examine the critical values used in the liar example for the Tukey, Fisher-Hayter, and Ryan MCPs in Table 15.7. Compare the Fisher-Hayter and Ryan MCPs to the Tukey. For the Fisher-Hayter, if the overall F is significant, then the smaller critical value for all comparisons gives higher power than the Tukey. However, the picture is somewhat clouded by the fact that the F must be significant for you to proceed with the Fisher-Hayter. The Tukey has no such requirement. Generally, however, the Fisher-Hayter should have better power than the Tukey. For the Ryan, if the largest comparison is significant, then it has a smaller critical value for the $p = 2$ comparisons and thus higher power than Tukey. Neither Tukey nor Ryan requires the overall F to be significant. It is difficult to determine whether Fisher-Hayter or Ryan would be the most powerful of the three MCPs, but both give better power than the Tukey.

So how do you choose which MCP to use? For any situation, you can compare the critical values of the MCPs by converting them all to t's. The MCP with the smallest

Table 15.6
Ryan tests for liar data

Critical values:
Stretch size $= p = 3$, $t = q/\sqrt{2} = 3.40/\sqrt{2} = 2.4042$
Stretch size $= p = 2$, $t = q/\sqrt{2} = 2.83/\sqrt{2} = 2.0011$

Decisions:

Mean	1 56.57	2 57.71	3 64.00	t	p	Critical Value	S = significant, N = nonsignificant, NI = N by implication
	————————————————			2.4186	3	2.4042	S
	———————			0.3711	2	2.0011	N
		———————		2.0475	2	2.0011	S

Table 15.7

Comparison of critical values

p	Tukey $q/\sqrt{2}$	Fisher-Hayter[a] $q/\sqrt{2}$	Ryan $q/\sqrt{2}$
3	2.4042	2.0011	2.4042
2	2.4042	2.0011	2.0011

[a] Requires that the overall F is significant.

critical value is the most powerful. Usually you would compare MCPs in this manner only if they control α in the same way—say, familywise. It is obvious that smaller critical values and higher power can be gained by controlling α per comparison. So power is an important consideration in the choice of an MCP. A second issue is simplicity, including ease of computation. If you have to do MCPs by hand, the Tukey is the easiest. The Fisher-Hayter is a close second, but it does require a significant overall F, and F isn't easy to calculate by hand. The Ryan requires a computer program except for $J = 3$. If you have all three tests on a computer program, do the most powerful. If you are doing them by hand, the Fisher-Hayter gives a nice balance of simplicity and high power.

Chapter 14 on ANOVA began by stating that conducting t-tests on all possible pairs of means would not be appropriate. Now you know about multiple comparisons, which test all possible pairwise differences in the means. Of course, the t-tests were not appropriate for a test of the overall ANOVA hypothesis, and they did not control α familywise. The multiple t-tests discussed in Section 14.1 allowed α to increase as a function of the number of comparisons and thus did not control α familywise. The MCPs in this chapter use critical values that account for the number of pairwise comparisons and control α familywise. So whenever you use one of these MCPs, α is controlled for all possible pairwise comparisons regardless of the number of groups.

Quick Quiz

You have $J = 5$ ordered means and are doing the Ryan MCP. The 1–3 comparison is declared nonsignificant. (a) What comparisons are nonsignificant by implication? (b) What comparisons *must* have been significant in previous steps? (c) Can you discuss the significance or nonsignificance of any other comparisons?

Answers

(a) The 1–2 and 2–3 comparisons. (b) The 1–3 comparison would not have been tested if it had been contained in a previously declared nonsignificant stretch. So the 1–5 and 1–4 comparisons must have been significant. (c) You don't have enough information to discuss the status of the 2–5, 2–4, 3–5, 3–4, and 4–5 comparisons.

15.4 Unequal Sample Sizes

The Tukey, Fisher-Hayter, and Ryan methods given in Section 15.3 are used only with equal sample sizes in each group to provide robustness to unequal population variances. When you have unequal n's within the groups, a special method is recommended, called the *Games-Howell method*.

Games-Howell Method

Remember the problem of lack of robustness of the two-independent-sample t-test to unequal variances when $n_1 \neq n_2$? Most MCPs have the same problem: α is inflated if the variances are not equal when $n_1 \neq n_2$. To control α when sample sizes are unequal and variances are unequal, you need to use a different MCP. In contrast to the Tukey method, the **Games-Howell MCP** modifies three things to make it robust. Games-Howell has a slightly different t-statistic, different df, and a slightly different critical value.

Let's first discuss the different t-statistic. For comparing any two groups designated by j and k, the statistic for Games-Howell is

$$t_{jk} = \frac{\bar{X}_j - \bar{X}_k}{\sqrt{\dfrac{s_j^2}{n_j} + \dfrac{s_k^2}{n_k}}} \tag{15.12}$$

The Games-Howell statistic, t_{jk}, is different from the t for other MCPs because it does not use a pooled estimate of σ^2. Rather than use the MS_W from all observations, t_{jk} uses only the local variance estimates, s_j^2 and s_k^2 from the jth and kth groups.

The second way the Games-Howell MCP is different from the Tukey MCP is the degrees of freedom for t_{jk}. The formula for df for this statistic is:

$$df_{jk} = \frac{(s_j^2/n_j + s_k^2/n_k)^2}{\dfrac{(s_j^2/n_j)^2}{n_j - 1} + \dfrac{(s_k^2/n_k)^2}{n_k - 1}} \tag{15.13}$$

The df_{jk} formula is much more complicated than $df_W = N - J$ from the one-way ANOVA because it is a function of the sample variances and sample sizes from the two samples in the comparison. It can be shown that the range for df_{jk} is

$$\text{Minimum}\{n_j - 1, n_k - 1\} \leq df_{jk} \leq n_j + n_k - 2$$

That is, df_{jk} is less than or equal to $n_j + n_k - 2$, and it is greater than or equal to the smaller of these two values: $n_j - 1$ or $n_k - 1$.

Because the formula for df for the Games-Howell is different than that for Tukey, the critical value for the Games-Howell MCP also is different. This third way the Games-Howell MCP differs from Tukey gives the critical value of

$$\frac{q_{J,\,df_{jk}}^{\alpha}}{\sqrt{2}} \tag{15.14}$$

You use an α-level critical value from the Studentized range in Table A.7 with J as the number-of-means parameter and df_{jk} as given in formula 15.13. When you do the Games-Howell by hand, you should round df_{jk} to the nearest whole number to get the q critical value from Table A.7.

You decide to reject H_0 if the absolute value of t_{jk} is greater than or equal to the critical value and otherwise retain H_0. So even though you compute a different df_{jk} for each pair of means, the q critical values all use J to find the correct column of Table A.7. The Games-Howell method is much like the AWS t in that it does not assume equal population variances. It does assume normality of observations in the populations and independence of observations.

Example

For the liar data, the original research had unequal sample sizes because of the different numbers of available participants in the groups. The data that you have used up to this point were simulated to have equal sample sizes to provide a useful teaching example. Simulated data from the original sample sizes for Secret Service personnel, judges, and psychiatrists are listed in Table 15.8. The computation of the Games-Howell MCP is given for all possible pairwise comparisons in Table 15.9.

The results of the Games-Howell MCP show that the Secret Service personnel are significantly better at detecting liars than are the judges, but there are no other significant differences.

Quick Quiz

Name the two-sample statistic from Chapter 13 that is similar to the Games-Howell MCP.

Answer

The AWS statistic. It is used in the two-independent-sample situation when sample sizes are unequal and, like the Games-Howell procedure, requires complex computation of df.

Table 15.8
Liar data with unequal n's

Secret Service ($n = 34$)		Judges ($n = 110$)					Psychiatrists ($n = 67$)		
60	50	50	30	50	40	40	70	80	50
50	80	90	80	80	60	50	90	30	70
80	70	30	70	60	50	50	60	40	40
50	70	60	50	40	70	40	70	40	50
70	60	70	50	50	50	60	60	80	40
60	60	50	70	70	60	60	60	80	30
60	70	60	60	80	60	60	50	60	30
70	60	50	50	90	50	70	60	50	50
60	80	50	80	50	50	20	80	40	70
60	60	70	70	50	70	50	70	80	50
30	80	50	70	40	80	20	60	60	50
90	60	30	50	60	30	70	60	40	60
60		40	30	50	50	30	60	80	70
90		90	80	70	60	40	50	40	50
80		50	40	60	60	30	70	60	40
60		60	70	70	70	50	90	70	70
80		40	50	60	70	50	60	60	80
90		60	50	50	80	50	50	50	50
50		60	50	50	70	60	60	60	60
40		40	50	60	70	70	60	50	50
50		50	60	70	60	60	40	70	40
40		50	60	70	80	70	60	50	50
							50		
$\overline{X}_j$ 64.12				56.73				57.61	
s_j^2 218.89				218.55				206.33	

Table 15.9
Computation of Games-Howell MCP for liar data with unequal n's ($1 =$ Secret Service, $2 =$ judges, $3 =$ psychiatrists)

1 versus 2:

$$t_{12} = \frac{\overline{X}_1 - \overline{X}_2}{\sqrt{\dfrac{s_1^2}{n_1} + \dfrac{s_2^2}{n_2}}} = \frac{64.12 - 56.73}{\sqrt{\dfrac{218.89}{34} + \dfrac{218.55}{110}}} = \frac{7.39}{\sqrt{8.4249}} = \frac{7.39}{2.9026} = 2.55$$

$$df_{12} = \frac{(s_1^2/n_1 + s_2^2/n_2)^2}{\dfrac{(s_1^2/n_1)^2}{n_1 - 1} + \dfrac{(s_2^2/n_2)^2}{n_2 - 1}} = \frac{(218.89/34 + 218.55/110)^2}{\dfrac{(218.89/34)^2}{34 - 1} + \dfrac{(218.55/110)^2}{110 - 1}}$$

$$= \frac{70.9766}{1.2560 + 0.0362} = \frac{70.9766}{1.2922} = 54.9275 \approx 55$$

Critical value: Use $J = 3$, $df = 40$, and $q = 3.44$. Then $t = 3.44/\sqrt{2} = 2.43$. Because the observed $t = 2.55$ is larger than 2.43, reject H_0.

1 versus 3:

$$t_{13} = \frac{\overline{X}_1 - \overline{X}_3}{\sqrt{\dfrac{s_1^2}{n_1} + \dfrac{s_3^2}{n_3}}} = \frac{64.12 - 57.61}{\sqrt{\dfrac{218.89}{34} + \dfrac{206.33}{67}}} = \frac{6.51}{\sqrt{9.5175}} = \frac{6.51}{3.0850} = 2.11$$

$$df_{13} = \frac{(s_1^2/n_1 + s_3^2/n_3)^2}{\dfrac{(s_1^2/n_1)^2}{n_1 - 1} + \dfrac{(s_3^2/n_3)^2}{n_3 - 1}} = \frac{(218.89/34 + 206.33/67)^2}{\dfrac{(218.89/34)^2}{34 - 1} + \dfrac{(206.33/67)^2}{67 - 1}}$$

$$= \frac{90.5827}{1.2560 + 0.1437} = \frac{90.5827}{1.3997} = 64.7175 \approx 65$$

Critical value: Use $J = 3$, $df = 60$, and $q = 3.40$. Then $t = 3.40/\sqrt{2} = 2.40$. Because the observed $t = 2.11$ is less than 2.40, retain H_0.

2 versus 3:

$$t_{23} = \frac{\overline{X}_2 - \overline{X}_3}{\sqrt{\dfrac{s_2^2}{n_2} + \dfrac{s_3^2}{n_3}}} = \frac{56.73 - 57.61}{\sqrt{\dfrac{218.55}{110} + \dfrac{206.33}{67}}} = \frac{-0.88}{\sqrt{5.0664}} = \frac{-0.88}{2.2509} = -0.39$$

$$df_{23} = \frac{(s_2^2/n_2 + s_3^2/n_3)^2}{\dfrac{(s_2^2/n_2)^2}{n_2 - 1} + \dfrac{(s_3^2/n_3)^2}{n_3 - 1}} = \frac{(218.55/110 + 206.33/67)^2}{\dfrac{(218.55/110)^2}{110 - 1} + \dfrac{(206.33/67)^2}{67 - 1}}$$

$$= \frac{25.6681}{0.0362 + 0.1437} = \frac{25.6681}{0.1799} = 142.6745 \approx 143$$

Critical value: Use $J = 3$, $df = 120$, and $q = 3.36$. Then $t = 3.36/\sqrt{2} = 2.38$. Because the absolute value of the observed $t = 0.39$ is less than 2.38, retain H_0.

15.5   Orthogonal Comparisons

The concept of orthogonal comparisons pertains to relationships between the actual comparisons. *Orthogonal* can be loosely defined as "unrelated." Sometimes you'll see other terms in place of *orthogonal,* such as *independent* or *nonoverlapping*; you've seen these terms in this chapter. But *orthogonal* has a precise meaning and is used frequently in the area of MCPs. Before you learn the proper definition of *orthogonal,* you have to learn about *weights* placed on means in a comparison.

Comparisons and Weights

A pairwise comparison is simply a difference between two means. However, a comparison can be either pairwise or a more complex combination of the group means. A general definition of a comparison of sample means is a sum of weighted means as given by:

$$\hat{\psi} = c_1\overline{X}_1 + c_2\overline{X}_2 + \cdots + c_J\overline{X}_J = \Sigma_j c_j\overline{X}_j \tag{15.15}$$

Weights
The values multiplied by the sample group means to average them into the comparison, symbolized by c_j, must sum to zero for a given comparison

where the sum of the **weights,** the c_j, equals zero, but not all of the c_j values are zero. (The symbol in formula 15.15 is called "psi-hat"; *psi* is pronounced "sigh.") For example, if you had three groups and the only comparison you wanted to make was the pairwise comparison $\overline{X}_1$ versus $\overline{X}_3$, then weight $c_1 = 1$, weight $c_3 = -1$, and weight $c_2 = 0$, and $\hat{\Psi} = c_1\overline{X}_1 + c_2\overline{X}_2 + c_3\overline{X}_3 = (1)\overline{X}_1 + (0)(\overline{X}_2) + (-1)(\overline{X}_3) = \overline{X}_1 - \overline{X}_3$.

For $J = 4$ means, suppose you want the following comparisons: $\overline{X}_3$ compared to $\overline{X}_4$, $\overline{X}_2$ compared to $\overline{X}_3$, and $\overline{X}_1$ compared to the average of $\overline{X}_3$ and $\overline{X}_4$. The first two are pairwise comparisons, but the third comparison is a more complex combination of the group means. The comparisons can be specified using their weights as:

$$\hat{\psi}_1 = \overline{X}_3 - \overline{X}_4 = (0)\overline{X}_1 + (0)\overline{X}_2 + (1)\overline{X}_3 + (-1)\overline{X}_4 \tag{15.16}$$

$$\hat{\psi}_2 = \overline{X}_2 - \overline{X}_3 = (0)\overline{X}_1 + (1)\overline{X}_2 + (-1)\overline{X}_3 + (0)\overline{X}_4$$

$$\hat{\psi}_3 = \overline{X}_1 - \frac{\overline{X}_3 + \overline{X}_4}{2} = (1)\overline{X}_1 + (0)\overline{X}_2 + (-\tfrac{1}{2})\overline{X}_3 + (-\tfrac{1}{2})\overline{X}_4$$

Examine the weights in the first comparison: $c_1 = 0$, $c_2 = 0$, $c_3 = 1$, and $c_4 = -1$. Here, as in any comparison, the sum of the c's is zero, or $0 + 0 + 1 + (-1) = 0$. This is an example of the weights for a pairwise comparison. The third comparison is a more complex comparison that averages some of the means before taking the difference.

Quick Quiz
For $J = 4$, what would be the weights for a comparison that examines the average of the first two means versus the average of the last two means?

Answer
$c_1 = \tfrac{1}{2}, c_2 = \tfrac{1}{2}, c_3 = -\tfrac{1}{2},$ and $c_4 = -\tfrac{1}{2}$

Orthogonal Comparisons

Before we define orthogonality, we need to emphasize that the comparisons you make should be determined by your research questions. If your questions are about differences in the J means or which treatment is best, then you want all possible pairwise comparisons. As you will see, all possible pairwise comparisons are not all orthogonal to each other. Sometimes research questions dictate comparisons that are orthogonal, and you need to be able to select the weights for the means so that the comparisons are orthogonal. Sometimes you need to be able to tell whether the comparisons you have selected are orthogonal or not. But above all, do the comparisons that will answer the questions of interest in your research, regardless of whether they are orthogonal.

Orthogonality of multiple comparisons is determined for *pairs of comparisons,* two at a time. For three pairwise comparisons, you would have:

Comparison 1: $\bar{X}_1$ versus $\bar{X}_2$
Comparison 2: $\bar{X}_1$ versus $\bar{X}_3$
Comparison 3: $\bar{X}_2$ versus $\bar{X}_3$

Orthogonal
A property of comparisons taken two at a time such that the comparisons don't contain any overlapping information, $\Sigma c_{1j} c_{2j} / n_j = 0$

Orthogonality is determined for comparisons 1 and 2, again for comparisons 1 and 3, and yet again for comparisons 2 and 3. Any two comparisons are **orthogonal** to each other if

$$\Sigma_j \frac{c_{1j} c_{2j}}{n_j} = 0 \tag{15.17}$$

Here c_{1j} and c_{2j} are the weights for comparisons 1 and 2 on the *j*th mean and n_j is the sample size for the *j*th group. With equal sample sizes, formula 15.17 simplifies to

$$\Sigma_j c_{1j} c_{2j} = 0 \tag{15.18}$$

If the sum in formula 15.17 or 15.18 is not zero, then the comparisons are non-orthogonal. Formula 15.18 says that for the first group, take the c_1 for comparison 1 and multiply it by the c_1 for comparison 2; then get both comparisons' weights for the second group and multiply the weights; and so on. Then, after taking all of those products, add them up. If the sum is zero, then the two comparisons are orthogonal to each other.

Return to the three comparisons given in formula 15.16 and determine whether they are orthogonal to each other. Remember that you have to consider whether each comparison is orthogonal to every other comparison, so you have to work with all possible pairs of comparisons. If you have trouble getting started, examine the first line of the work below for 1 versus 2, and then try to do the remaining work on your own.

1 versus 2: $\Sigma_j c_{1j} c_{2j} = (0)(0) + (0)(1) + (1)(-1) + (-1)(0) = -1$

1 versus 3: $\Sigma_j c_{1j} c_{3j} = (0)(1) + (0)(0) + (1)\left(-\frac{1}{2}\right) + (-1)\left(-\frac{1}{2}\right) = 0 \tag{15.19}$

2 versus 3: $\Sigma_j c_{2j} c_{3j} = (0)(1) + (1)(0) + (-1)\left(-\frac{1}{2}\right) + (0)\left(-\frac{1}{2}\right) = \frac{1}{2}$

Which comparisons are orthogonal? When you examine 1 versus 2, you get a sum of products of weights of -1, which is not zero. So comparisons 1 and 2 are not orthogonal. The sum of products of weights for 1 versus 3 is zero, so comparisons 1 and 3 are orthogonal. Finally, 2 versus 3 gives $\frac{1}{2}$, so comparisons 2 and 3 are

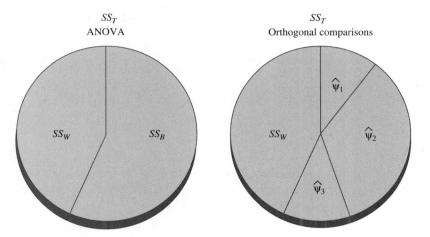

Figure 15.3
Number of orthogonal comparisons equals $J - 1$, the df_B ($J = 4$)

not orthogonal. Only comparisons 1 and 3 contain "nonoverlapping information"; the other pairs contain redundant information in some way.

If your research questions lead you to need a set of orthogonal comparisons on J means, you are now able to find such a set. One limitation you should be aware of is that the maximum number of comparisons in a set of orthogonal comparisons is $J - 1$. You can see a connection to the ANOVA: $df_B = J - 1$, so the number of orthogonal comparisons is the same as the degrees of freedom between groups. In fact, this connection mirrors the fact that the variability accounted for by the $J - 1$ orthogonal comparisons is the same as SS_B. Figure 15.3 illustrates this connection for $J = 4$.

For $J = 4$, let's find a set of comparisons that are all orthogonal to each other. Suppose you start with two pairwise comparisons: 1 versus 2 for the first comparison and 3 versus 4 for the second. This gives these comparisons and weights:

$$\hat{\psi}_1 = \bar{X}_1 - \bar{X}_2 = (1)\bar{X}_1 + (-1)\bar{X}_2 + (0)\bar{X}_3 + (0)\bar{X}_4$$
$$\hat{\psi}_2 = \bar{X}_3 - \bar{X}_4 = (0)\bar{X}_1 + (0)\bar{X}_2 + (1)\bar{X}_3 + (-1)\bar{X}_4$$

for which you can see that:

1 versus 2: $\sum_j c_{1j} c_{2j} = (1)(0) + (-1)(0) + (0)(1) + (0)(-1) = 0$

so these two comparisons are orthogonal. Now, you need another comparison that is orthogonal to both of these first two. The comparison that will do this is to average together means 1 and 2 and subtract the average of means 3 and 4 (see the previous Quick Quiz):

$$\hat{\psi}_3 = \frac{\bar{X}_1 + \bar{X}_2}{2} - \frac{\bar{X}_3 + \bar{X}_4}{2} = \left(\frac{1}{2}\right)\bar{X}_1 + \left(\frac{1}{2}\right)\bar{X}_2 + \left(-\frac{1}{2}\right)\bar{X}_3 + \left(-\frac{1}{2}\right)\bar{X}_4$$

Now, check to see whether this third comparison is orthogonal to the first two:

$$1 \text{ versus } 3: \quad \sum_j c_{1j}c_{3j} = (1)\left(\frac{1}{2}\right) + (-1)\left(\frac{1}{2}\right) + (0)\left(-\frac{1}{2}\right) + (0)\left(-\frac{1}{2}\right) = 0$$

$$2 \text{ versus } 3: \quad \sum_j c_{2j}c_{3j} = (0)\left(\frac{1}{2}\right) + (0)\left(\frac{1}{2}\right) + (1)\left(-\frac{1}{2}\right) + (-1)\left(-\frac{1}{2}\right) = 0$$

Because both sums of products of weights are zero, comparison 3 is orthogonal to comparisons 1 and 2. Note that $J - 1 = 4 - 1 = 3$ is the maximum number of comparisons you could find in this one set that are all orthogonal to each other. Do you realize that there are several such sets of orthogonal comparisons? Try this Quick Quiz.

Quick Quiz

Find another set of three comparisons on $J = 4$ means that are all orthogonal to each other.

Answer

There are several correct answers; we give one here:

$$\hat\psi_1 = (1)\bar{X}_1 + \left(-\frac{1}{3}\right)\bar{X}_2 + \left(-\frac{1}{3}\right)\bar{X}_3 + \left(-\frac{1}{3}\right)\bar{X}_4$$

$$\hat\psi_2 = (0)\bar{X}_1 + (1)\bar{X}_2 + \left(-\frac{1}{2}\right)\bar{X}_3 + \left(-\frac{1}{2}\right)\bar{X}_4$$

$$\hat\psi_3 = (0)\bar{X}_1 + (0)\bar{X}_2 + (1)\bar{X}_3 + (-1)\bar{X}_4$$

$$1 \text{ versus } 2: \quad \sum_j c_{1j}c_{2j} = (1)(0) + \left(-\frac{1}{3}\right)(1) + \left(-\frac{1}{3}\right)\left(-\frac{1}{2}\right) + \left(-\frac{1}{3}\right)\left(-\frac{1}{2}\right) = 0$$

$$1 \text{ versus } 3: \quad \sum_j c_{1j}c_{3j} = (1)(0) + \left(-\frac{1}{3}\right)(0) + \left(-\frac{1}{3}\right)(1) + \left(-\frac{1}{3}\right)(-1) = 0$$

$$2 \text{ versus } 3: \quad \sum_j c_{2j}c_{3j} = (0)(0) + (1)(0) + \left(-\frac{1}{2}\right)(1) + \left(-\frac{1}{2}\right)(-1) = 0$$

Some researchers use planned orthogonal comparisons (sometimes called *planned orthogonal contrasts*) extensively in their research. They use sets of comparisons like those in the last Quick Quiz or those in our earlier set to look for specific differences in the means. Another use of orthogonal comparisons is in testing for trends, where researchers look for linear, quadratic, cubic, and higher trends in the means for quantitative independent variables. The topic of orthogonal comparisons serves as the foundation for such analyses.

Beyond These MCPs

Most statistics textbooks at this level give little coverage to MCPs. If you take more statistics classes, you may come across multiple comparisons classified in several ways:

1. Whether they are all of the comparisons or some subset
2. Whether they are orthogonal or nonorthogonal

3. Whether they are pairwise comparisons or more complex combinations, such as comparing the average of two experimental conditions to a control condition

4. Whether they were planned before the research was done (a priori) or post hoc, which means they were selected after the overall F test was done (a posteriori)

5. Whether they can be done if the F is significant (usually associated with post hoc research) or regardless of the significance of the F (usually associated with planned research)

6. Whether they control α using different error rates, including controlling α for each comparison or for the whole experiment (familywise)

The comparisons might be called *post hoc tests, individual comparisons,* or *planned contrasts* in other sources.

The statistics associated with these comparisons also are classified in various ways:

1. They can be performed in several steps, each depending in some way on the step before it (stepwise MCPs like Ryan's procedure and Fisher-Hayter), or so that they stand alone (nonstepwise or simultaneous MCPs like Tukey's).

2. They can differ with respect to the statistic or the critical value they use, such as t and q.

We tend to classify procedures as "good" or "bad," depending on whether they control the error rate familywise. The issue of power should be used to decide among good procedures, those that control α. If you have two good procedures and one of them has a slightly smaller critical value, that's the MCP you should use because you will have a slightly better chance of rejecting the null hypothesis. At the risk of acquainting you with bad procedures, we've given the names of a few procedures that allow the Type I error rate to rise above acceptable levels. The three procedures you've learned in this chapter are good because they control α familywise. Whatever statistic you use, you should know how it handles α and whether it gives you the answers you need for your research.

15.6   Summary, Study Tips, and Computation

Chapter Summary

Interest in specific differences in means, or in detecting which treatment is best, leads you to use multiple comparisons. Tests that use multiple comparisons are called MCPs. The number of pairwise comparisons is $J(J - 1)/2$, and the hypotheses involve the equality of two means at a time. Control of α is control of the probability of a Type I error using error rate per comparison and error rate familywise. Control of the per comparison error rate gives high power at the cost of more Type I errors for a group of comparisons, whereas control of the familywise error rate gives fewer Type I errors at the cost of lower power. Statistics given were t and q as well as

the relationship $t = q/\sqrt{2}$ for pairwise comparisons. All work in this text is done using t. Steps were given for the Tukey, Fisher-Hayter, and Ryan MCPs. Comparison of the three MCPs on a common example showed the simplicity of the Tukey and Fisher-Hayter, the higher power of the Fisher-Hayter and Ryan, and the need to do Ryan using a computer program, like SAS. The Games-Howell procedure was given for use with unequal sample sizes. The conceptual approach of using weights to define a comparison paved the way for the topic of orthogonal comparisons. Examples included how to find sets of $J - 1$ orthogonal comparisons on J means. Dimensions of classification were given.

Table 15.10

Situation	Statistic	Distribution
All pairwise comparisons equal n's $H_0: \mu_j = \mu_{j'}$	Tukey MCP, t in formula 15.5	$q/\sqrt{2}$ with J, df_W, and α
All pairwise comparisons equal n's $H_0: \mu_j = \mu_{j'}$	Fisher-Hayter, t in formula 15.5	$q/\sqrt{2}$ with $J - 1$, df_W, and α
All pairwise comparisons equal n's $H_0: \mu_j = \mu_{j'}$	Ryan, t in formula 15.5	$q/\sqrt{2}$ with p, df_W, and α_p
All pairwise comparisons unequal n's $H_0: \mu_j = \mu_{j'}$	Games-Howell, t_{jk} in formula 15.12	$q/\sqrt{2}$ with J, df_{jk}, and α

These key terms are used in this chapter:

Multiple comparisons
MCPs
Pairwise comparisons
Error rate per comparison
Error rate familywise
Tukey's HSD
Number-of-means parameter
Studentized range distribution
Fisher-Hayter MCP
Ryan MCP
Stretch size
Nonsignificant by implication
Games-Howell MCP
Weights
Orthogonal

The statistical tests introduced in this chapter are summarized in Table 15.10. The situation where the statistic would be used, the name of the statistic, and the theoretical reference distribution are given for each procedure. For decision rules, assumptions, and any restrictions on the use of these procedures, refer to the sections where they were presented.

Study Tips

You should know by now to add each new statistical procedure to your chart of available methods, so you should have a column for each of the MCPs in this chapter: Tukey, Fisher-Hayter, Ryan, and Games-Howell. Students often get confused over the number-of-means parameter on q: With Tukey it is J, with Fisher-Hayter it is $J - 1$, with Ryan it is p (stretch size), which ranges from J to 2, and with Games-Howell it is J. Put the critical value for each of these in your chart under decision rules, and you may avoid this confusion.

Computation

Like most practical statistical procedures, MCPs are most easily done on the computer. What follows are SAS procedures and SPSS commands necessary to run some of the MCPs in this chapter.

SAS Example

SAS will compute all possible pairwise comparisons for several different MCPs. Of those covered in this chapter, the SAS list includes the Ryan, called *REGWQ,* and the Tukey, called *TUKEY.* MCPs are accessed through ANOVA or GLM using the MEANS statement as an option. The example here uses the liar detection data and the program from Chapter 14. Chapter 14 explained the ANOVA part of this program, so only the MCP part is covered here.

(SAS system's lines)

```
DATA TT;
INPUT LIAR$;
DO I = 1 TO 35;
INPUT Y @@;
OUTPUT;
END;
CARDS;
SECRSER
60 60 70 50 70 60 70 70 60 60 40 80 70 90 80 60 80 90
50 40 50 40 50 70 70 70 60 60 70 60 80 60 80 50 60
JUDGES
50 60 50 60 70 50 60 50 40 70 50 70 40 90 50 60 40 60
60 40 50 50 40 70 70 50 50 70 60 50 80 70 70 50 30
PSYCHIAT
60 90 60 70 60 50 50 50 60 70 60 60 60 50 70 30 60 50
60 60 40 60 70 40 50 50 60 60 60 50 40 80 60 40 80
PROC PRINT;
PROC SORT; BY LIAR;
PROC MEANS; BY LIAR; VAR Y;
PROC ANOVA;
CLASS LIAR;
MODEL Y=LIAR;
MEANS LIAR/REGWQ TUKEY;
```
(asks for all possible pairwise multiple comparisons to be done on the means for the classification variable LIAR using the Ryan, here called REGWQ, and the Tukey MCPs)

(system's line)

The SAS System

Analysis of Variance Procedure

① Ryan-Einot-Gabriel-Welsch Multiple Range Test for variable: Y

NOTE: This test controls the type I experimentwise error rate.

② Alpha= 0.05 df= 102 MSE= 165.1541

③ Number of Means   2   3
   Critical Range   6.0933598   7.306615

Figure 15.4
SAS output from MEANS LIAR/REGWQ TUKEY

(continued)

④Means with the same letter are not significantly different.

REGWQ Grouping		Mean	N	Group
⑤	A	64.000	35	SECRSER
	B	57.714	35	PSYCHIAT
	B			
	B	56.571	35	JUDGES

The SAS System

Analysis of Variance Procedure

Tukey's Studentized Range (HSD) Test for variable: Y

NOTE: This test controls the type I experimentwise error rate, but generally has a
⑥   higher type II error rate than REGWQ.

Alpha= 0.05   df= 102   MSE= 165.1541
Critical Value of Studentized Range= 3.364
Minimum Significant Difference= 7.3066

Means with the same letter are not significantly different.

Tukey Grouping		Mean	N	GROUP
	A	64.000	35	SECRSER
	A			
⑦B	A	57.714	35	PSYCHIAT
B				
B		56.571	35	JUDGES

Figure 15.4 (continued)

For the Ryan and Tukey MCPs, the SAS output in Figure 15.4 gives the following:

1. The REGWQ output tells the source for each of the letters in its output and thus acknowledges the people who contributed to the procedure that we now call "Ryan's MCP": Ryan, Einot, and Gabriel; and Welsch. The "Q" tells you they computed the q statistic. The dependent variable is Y.

2. This line gives α and information from the ANOVA.

3. "Number of Means" is the same as stretch size, and the numerical values given for the critical range are the minimum differences between group means to have significance. These critical ranges incorporate MS_W, n, and exact critical values of q for the df and stretch size given. Thus, SAS will do Ryan's MCP more accurately than you can do it by hand because of limitations in your table of q.

4. This message is crucial to understanding the SAS output: The means are grouped

by letters. If means have the same letter, they are *not* significantly different. If means have different letters, they are significantly different. The output shows this by using letters to draw a vertical line beside those $\overline{X}$'s that are not significantly different.

5. For Ryan's MCP, the Secret Service mean has an A by it and the other means have B's by them. This means that the Secret Service mean is significantly different from the other two means, but they are not significantly different from each other.

6. For Tukey's MCP on the means, you got some information in the output for Ryan's MCP. You also get a critical value for q and the minimum significant difference (the same as the critical range given for Ryan for stretch size 3).

7. For Tukey, the A's indicate that Secret Service and psychiatrist means do not differ significantly, and the B's show that psychiatrist and judge means do not differ significantly. Because Secret Service and judge do not have the same letter, there is a significant difference in those two $\overline{X}$'s.

SPSS Example

Of the MCPs covered in this chapter, only the Tukey is available in SPSS. It is accessed through the ONEWAY command by adding an optional subcommand called RANGES. The example here uses the liar detection data and the program from Chapter 14. Chapter 14 explained the ANOVA part of this program, so only the MCP part is covered here.

(SPSS system's lines)

```
SET WIDTH 80
DATA LIST FREE/LIAR X
BEGIN DATA
1 60 1 60 1 70 1 50 1 70 1 60 1 70 1 70 1 60 1 60 1 40 1 80
1 70 1 90 1 80 1 60 1 80 1 90 1 50 1 40 1 50 1 40 1 50 1 70
1 70 1 70 1 60 1 60 1 70 1 60 1 80 1 60 1 80 1 50 1 60
2 50 2 60 2 50 2 60 2 70 2 50 2 60 2 50 2 40 2 70 2 50 2 70
2 40 2 70 2 50 2 60 2 40 2 60 2 60 2 40 2 50 2 50 2 40 2 70
2 70 2 50 2 50 2 70 2 60 2 50 2 80 2 70 2 70 2 50 2 30
3 60 3 90 3 60 3 70 3 60 3 50 3 50 3 50 3 60 3 70 3 60 3 60
3 60 3 50 3 70 3 30 3 60 3 50 3 60 3 60 3 40 3 60 3 70 3 40
3 50 3 50 3 60 3 60 3 60 3 50 3 40 3 80 3 60 3 40 3 80
END DATA
ONEWAY X BY LIAR (1, 3)/RANGES=TUKEY
```
(the subcommand RANGES asks for an MCP to be computed following the one-way ANOVA, here specifying the Tukey MCP)

(system's line)

- O N E W A Y -

     Variable X   ①
  By Variable LIAR

MULTIPLE RANGE TEST

Figure 15.5
SPSS output for Tukey

(continued)

```
TUKEY-HSD PROCEDURE
RANGES FOR THE 0.050 LEVEL -

        3.37    3.37        ②

THE RANGES ABOVE ARE TABLE RANGES.
THE VALUE ACTUALLY COMPARED WITH MEAN(J) - MEAN(I) IS..

        9.0872 * RANGE * DSQRT(1/N(I) + 1/N(J))

   (*) DENOTES PAIRS OF GROUPS SIGNIFICANTLY DIFFERENT AT THE 0.050 LEVEL

                                G G G
                                r r r
                                p p p

      Mean        Group        2 3 1
                                     ③

     56.5714      Grp 2
     57.7143      Grp 3
     64.0000      Grp 1        *

   HOMOGENEOUS SUBSETS    (SUBSETS OF GROUPS, WHOSE HIGHEST AND LOWEST MEANS DO NOT
                          DIFFER BY MORE THAN THE SHORTEST SIGNIFICANT RANGE FOR A
                          SUBSET OF THAT SIZE)

SUBSET 1
                                   ④
GROUP          Grp 2              Grp 3
MEAN           56.5714            57.7143
- - - - - - - - - - - - - - - - - - - -
SUBSET 2

GROUP          Grp 3              Grp 1
MEAN           57.7143            64.0000
- - - - - - - - - - - - - - - - - - - -
```

Figure 15.5 (continued)

For the subcommand RANGES, the SPSS output in Figure 15.5 gives the following:

1. For the dependent variable X, the Tukey test is given for the independent variable LIAR.

2. All tests use the same q critical value, 3.37.

3. SPSS uses two ways to show significant differences. One is to put an asterisk in the row and column of this small table to show those pairs of groups that are significantly different at $\alpha = .05$. Note that group 1 is Secret Service, 2 is judges, and 3 is psychiatrists.

4. The second way SPSS shows significant differences is to show homogeneous subsets, or groups of means that are *not* significantly different, much like SAS does with its common letters. Note that if there is ever a discrepancy between the two ways of showing significant differences, the answer given in 4 is correct. Here there is agreement that the only significant difference is between Secret Service and judges.

Exercises

Note: A number in parentheses after the exercise number is the corresponding Chapter 14 exercise.

Section 15.1

1. Find what is wrong with each of the following statements and correct it to make it true.

a. Planned comparisons are also called a posteriori comparisons.

b. Controlling α familywise gives the highest power.

c. The overall ANOVA F tells which differences in group means are significant.

Section 15.2

2. For each of the following, compute p(at least one Type I error) using both formula 15.3 and the approximate $C\alpha$. Assume the C comparisons are orthogonal.

a. $C = 4$ comparisons with $\alpha = .05$ for each.

b. $C = 6$ comparisons with $\alpha = .01$ for each.

c. $C = 15$ comparisons with $\alpha = .05$ for each.

d. The approach in this item is using α control **per comparison** or **familywise**. Choose one of these two and explain your choice.

3. For each of the following, compute the number of pairwise comparisons you could do on J means.

a. $J = 5$

b. $J = 3$

c. $J = 6$

4. For each of the following, compute α' when the set value of α is given by $1 - (1 - \alpha')^C$. Assume the C comparisons are orthogonal.

a. $C = 4$ comparisons with $\alpha = .05$.

b. $C = 6$ comparisons with $\alpha = .01$.

c. $C = 15$ comparisons with $\alpha = .05$.

d. The approach in this item is using α control **per comparison** or **familywise**. Choose one of these two and explain your choice.

5. For each of the following, compute the t-statistic for pairwise MCPs.

a. $\overline{X}_1 = 13.1$, $\overline{X}_2 = 14.7$, $MS_W = 2.45$, $n = 10$

b. $\overline{X}_3 = 15.6$, $\overline{X}_2 = 14.7$, $MS_W = 2.45$, $n = 10$

c. $\overline{X}_3 = 56.6$, $\overline{X}_4 = 53.4$, $MS_W = 9.37$, $n = 23$

d. $\overline{X}_1 = 33.2$, $\overline{X}_4 = 36.5$, $MS_W = 8.54$, $n = 19$

6. Use the information given in Exercise 5, part a.

a. Compute the q statistic

b. Now transform it to t. Your answer should be the same as you computed in Exercise 5, part a.

Section 15.3

7. (10) Suppose a one-way ANOVA with $J = 4$ groups has the following group means: $\overline{X}_1 = 14$, $\overline{X}_2 = 15$, $\overline{X}_3 = 17$, $\overline{X}_4 = 22$. Using $\alpha = .05$, do the Fisher-Hayter MCP.

a. There are $n = 5$ observations in each group and $MS_W = 26$. Which means are significantly different, if any?

b. There are $n = 10$ observations in each group and $MS_W = 26$. Which means are significantly different, if any?

c. There are $n = 5$ observations in each group and $MS_W = 13$. Which means are significantly different, if any?

d. There are $n = 10$ observations in each group and $MS_W = 13$. Which means are significantly different, if any?

e. Comment on the influence of n and variance on the power of MCPs. Is this the same influence as noted in Chapter 11?

8. (12) The data in the table are vigor scores for three exercise groups.

No Exercise	General Exercise	Increased Exercise
10	20	21
11	19	23
12	24	27
9	17	30

a. On the average, which exercise program led to the highest report of vigor? Use the Tukey MCP to determine whether the differences in group means are significant.

b. Does the Fisher-Hayter give the same results as the Tukey?

9. (13) Three groups of children were given instructions of indirect responsibility (IR), or direct responsibility (DR1 and DR2). DR2 included calls for help. Ratings from 1 (no help) to 5 (went to adjoining room) were given to each child. In which group did the subjects give the highest degree of help? Is that degree of help significantly different from that for the other groups?

IR	DR1	DR2
3	5	4
4	4	4
2	5	3
1	3	4
1	4	5
2	5	4
1	5	5
2	5	5
3	5	3
3	4	2
2	3	3
1	1	2
1	4	4
2	3	1

10. (17) Researchers investigating how children learn the past tense of verbs developed two computer models to simulate such learning. The two models were compared to a group of children. The numbers of correct responses are given in the table for all groups.

Stages Model	Network Model	Children
8	12	14
10	16	12
5	11	17
9	13	14
13	13	17
11	17	11
12	9	10
10	11	9
7	15	11
13	8	11
12	12	10
11	13	15
9	14	13
14	10	16
10	13	11

a. Which differences between the $\bar{X}$'s for groups are significant? Use one of the MCPs in this chapter.

b. Write a brief paragraph summarizing your findings.

c. If you did Exercise 17 in Chapter 14, compare what you wrote there with your write-up in part b. Do you realize now that you need MCPs to be able to discuss significant differences between two groups at a time? What does the ANOVA tell you if you get a significant F?

11. (18) The results of Exercise 18 in Chapter 14 give the following group means for high, medium, and low competence, respectively: $\bar{X}_1 = 9.5417$, $\bar{X}_2 = 8.9583$, and $\bar{X}_3 = 8.0833$. Also $MS_W = 6.1848$, $df_W = 69$, and $n = 24$. Compute the Tukey MCP with $\alpha = .05$ for all pairwise comparisons on these means. How do these results compare to those for the overall ANOVA?

Section 15.4

12. For the data from Exercise 9, delete the last five observations of the third group and compute the Games-Howell MCP. Write up your results, noting any difference from what you found in Exercise 9.

13. For the data from Exercise 10, delete the last five observations of the third group and compute the Games-Howell MCP. Write up your results, noting any difference from what you found in Exercise 10.

Section 15.5

14. Give the weights, c_j, for the comparisons verbally described in each of the following for $J = 5$ means.

a. Find the difference between groups 1 and 4.

b. Average groups 1 and 2 and compare this to group 4.

c. Average groups 2 and 3 and compare this to the average of groups 4 and 5.

d. Average the first four groups and compare this to group 5.

15. Which of the four comparisons in Exercise 14 are orthogonal to each other?

16. Find a set of four comparisons that are orthogonal to each other for $J = 5$ means.

17. Use SAS or SPSS to compute the Tukey for the data in Exercise 8. Compare your results from Exercise 8 with those given by SAS for Tukey.

18. Use SAS to compute the Ryan for the data in Exercise 10. Compare the results for the MCP you chose in Exercise 10 with those given by SAS for Ryan.

16

Two-Way Analysis of Variance

The one-way ANOVA is suited for testing hypotheses about means for $J \geq 2$ groups, where the participants in the study are grouped on one independent variable. What do you do when participants are grouped on two independent variables in the same study? The two-way ANOVA is designed to test hypotheses about means in this situation.

Research Example 16
16.1 Introduction
    Review
    Example
    Logic
    Main effects
    Interaction
    Three F tests
    Advantages
16.2 ANOVA: Partitioning of Variability
    Notation and terminology
    Variability
    Sums of squares
    Degrees of freedom
    Mean squares
16.3 ANOVA F Tests
    Hypotheses
    F ratios
    F distributions
    Decision rules
    Assumptions
16.4 ANOVA Computation
    Computational formulas for sums of squares
    Example
    Interpretation
    Strength of association
    Beyond the two-way ANOVA
16.5 Summary, Study Tips, and Computation
    Chapter summary
    Study tips
    Computation
Exercises

Research Example 16

Does the degree to which you are in a hurry or the content of your thinking at that time determine how likely you are to help someone in distress? Darley and Batson (1973) conducted an experiment based on the parable of the Good Samaritan to test hypotheses about the variables "hurry" and "content of thinking" and their effect on helping behavior. The participants in the study were seminary students who were asked to prepare and record a short message. To influence the content of their thinking, participants read a passage that asked them to think about the effectiveness and enjoyment of jobs that seminary students might take when graduating. The passage ended with some statements or questions on ministering to others. Participants in the task-relevant condition received only this passage (thinking only about the topic in the passage). Participants in the helping-relevant condition received an additional paragraph quoting the parable of the Good Samaritan from the Revised Standard Version of the Bible (Luke 10:29–37). Then all participants were given more instructions and left alone for a few minutes to prepare their to-be-recorded message, for which they could use no notes. The researcher returned and directed them to the recording studio in the building next door and gave the "hurry" manipulation. "High-hurry" participants were told they were late, "medium-hurry" participants were told that it was time for them to go right over, and "low-hurry" participants were told that they had a few minutes but that they might as well head over because they wouldn't have to wait very long.

Between the two buildings, the students passed a person sitting slumped in a doorway, head down, eyes closed, not moving, coughing and groaning. If a student offered help, the victim had a standard statement (given while coughing) about pills, a medical condition, and resting. The dependent variable was a rating by the victim of helping behavior, ranging from 0 (failed to notice) to 5 (after stopping, refused to

Table 16.1

Helping Behavior Means:

| Message | | Hurry | | | |
		Low	Medium	High	Message Means
Message	Helping Relevant	3.800	2.000	1.000	2.263
	Task Relevant	1.667	1.667	0.500	1.333
	Hurry Means	3.000	1.818	0.700	

ANOVA Summary Table:

Source	SS	df	MS	F
Message (A)	7.766	1	7.766	2.65
Hurry (B)	20.884	2	10.442	3.56*
A × B	5.237	2	2.619	0.89
Within	99.633	34	2.930	

Note: $N = 40$.
*$p < .05$
Source: Darley and Batson (1973).

leave victim or offered to take him to infirmary, and so on). The results are given in Table 16.1.

The results showed that only the hurry variable was significant. The results for the message variable are in the direction of more helping behavior for the helping-relevant condition, but they were not significant. Darley and Batson noted that in the high-hurry/helping-relevant condition, several of the students literally stepped over the victim while hurrying to give a talk on the Good Samaritan. If not in a hurry, the students in the helping-relevant condition were more likely to stop and help.

In this chapter you will learn about the ANOVA appropriate for two variables and the associated *df, SS, MS,* and *F* ratios.

16.1   Introduction

Are you emotionally expressive? You might answer, It depends. You might be more expressive with a small group of people, or maybe it's easier for you to show your emotions in a large group, where you find safety in numbers. It might depend on the emotion itself. Consider these four emotions: anger, sadness, happiness, and fear. If you conducted a study of the relationship between willingness to express emotions and the number of people present, you would need to take into account the different emotions. People's willingness to verbalize their emotions might depend on the number of people present *and* the emotion in question. In fact, some researchers have found that people feel more free to verbally express happiness, fear, and sadness when they are in small groups, but when anger is involved, people say they have a greater need to control what they say in small groups (Babad & Wallbott, 1986). Perhaps they are protecting individual relationships in the small groups—maximizing the emotions that bring people closer, minimizing the potentially damaging anger.

This example is meant to give you an idea of why we need statistics that consider two variables at once. Your willingness to express emotion probably wouldn't be reflected by the statement, "Yes, I am emotionally expressive." It even might not be accurate to say, "I am emotionally expressive in small groups but not in large groups." The world is more complicated than that, and your willingness to be expressive most likely depends on the emotion, how many people are present, how well you know them, how involved you feel about the situation, and other variables. If you want to understand why people behave in certain ways, you sometimes want to consider more than one variable at a time. In this chapter you'll learn a statistical method to use when you want to know something about two variables and the combined effect of the two variables.

Review

In Chapter 14 you learned about the analysis of variance (ANOVA), a statistical procedure to test a hypothesis of equality of two or more means from independent groups. The *one-way* ANOVA is appropriate for research with one independent variable and two or more groups. In ANOVA, the conditions that define the groups are called *levels*. The one independent variable is what makes the ANOVA "one-way," while the levels (groups) give the two or more means to be tested. This chapter will show you how to use a statistical method when two independent (or extraneous) variables are studied simultaneously. This method is called the *two-way analysis of variance.*

Example

Research Example 15 introduced a study on note-taking strategies. Frank (1984) combined two variables: note-taking study techniques and cognitive styles. The cognitive styles were field independence and field dependence. Field independence was defined as those 52 students who scored high (≥ 14) on the Hidden Figures Test (French, Ekstrom & Price, 1963). Field dependence was defined as those 52 students who scored low (≤ 9) on that test. Simply put, field-independent people are fairly self-sufficient and provide their own structure in a situation. Field-dependent people need structure provided for them from the outside. The note-taking study technique was manipulated by having students in each cognitive style group listen to a taped lecture under one of the following conditions:

1. Students took no notes.
2. Students took their own notes.
3. Students received an outline framework with major headings and subheadings, and they took additional notes using this outline.
4. Students were provided with a complete outline with key terms, brief definitions, and important ideas given in addition to the major headings and subheadings. They took notes of their own, too.

The dependent variable was performance on a 20-item multiple-choice test on the lecture material. Within each of the cognitive styles, students had been randomly assigned to one of the four study techniques. The results are displayed in Table 16.2.

This experiment combined the effects of study technique (the four note-taking groups) and cognitive style (field independence and field dependence). The eight groups that resulted from combining the independent variable study technique and the extraneous variable cognitive style give what is called a two-way ANOVA.

In the two-way ANOVA, the independent variables (and the extraneous variables or both) are **factors.** The levels of the two factors combine to give **cells** (groups). In this example, no notes with field independence defines one cell. The average of the observations in a cell is the **cell mean.** Figure 16.1 illustrates the cell means for the eight cells that make up the two-way ANOVA in the example: field independence with no notes, $\overline{X} = 13.15$; field independence with student notes, $\overline{X} = 17.92$; and so on.

The topic of this chapter is the most obvious extension of the one-way ANOVA—the **two-way ANOVA** for two independent (or extraneous) variables (factors). We say "extraneous" because you may want to study a variable like gender, and people cannot be randomly assigned to the two levels of gender. If both of the factors are independent variables, they give what is called a *factorial design,* or a *factorial treatment arrangement.* Each of the two factors in a two-way ANOVA has two or more levels, and you label a two-way ANOVA by the number of levels of the two factors, such as 2×4. A 2×4 two-way ANOVA has two levels of the first factor and four levels of the second factor.

The two-way ANOVA is similar to the one-way ANOVA in logic and language, but it is more complex. You have not only a separate test for each of the two factors but also a test for their combined effect, which is called the *interaction.* The ability to detect

Factors
Variables that combine to form the groups in a two-way ANOVA, often independent variables

Cells and cell means
Groups formed by combining the levels of the factors, and the means of these groups

Two-way ANOVA
Statistical procedure for analyzing the data from the combination of two factors, used to test hypotheses about factor means and interaction

Table 16.2

Data and means for study technique and cognitive style
(FI = field independence, FD = field dependence)

	B_1 = no notes	B_2 = student notes	B_3 = outline framework	B_4 = complete outline	
			B = Study Technique		
A_1 = FI	13	15	19	15	
	13	19	18	19	
	10	19	17	16	
	16	17	19	17	
	14	19	17	19	
	11	17	19	15	
	13	20	17	20	
	13	17	19	16	
	11	18	17	19	
	16	17	15	16	
	15	18	18	19	
	16	18	17	19	
	10	19	15	18	
	Sum = 171	Sum = 233	Sum = 227	Sum = 228	Sum = 859
	$\bar{X}_{11}$ = 13.15	$\bar{X}_{12}$ = 17.92	$\bar{X}_{13}$ = 17.46	$\bar{X}_{14}$ = 17.54	$\bar{X}_{j=1}$ = 16.52
A_2 = FD	11	12	18	18	
	14	16	15	19	
	11	16	15	15	
	10	17	14	16	
	15	16	15	19	
	10	16	18	18	
	16	16	19	19	
	16	14	18	19	
	17	14	18	18	
	11	16	16	17	
	16	15	16	16	
	11	15	18	17	
	10	15	16	15	
	Sum = 168	Sum = 198	Sum = 216	Sum = 226	Sum = 808
	$\bar{X}_{21}$ = 12.92	$\bar{X}_{22}$ = 15.23	$\bar{X}_{23}$ = 16.62	$\bar{X}_{24}$ = 17.38	$\bar{X}_{j=2}$ = 15.54
Sums	Sum = 339	Sum = 431	Sum = 443	Sum = 454	Sum = 1667
Means	$\bar{X}_{k=1}$ = 13.04	$\bar{X}_{k=2}$ = 16.58	$\bar{X}_{k=3}$ = 17.04	$\bar{X}_{k=4}$ = 17.46	$\bar{X}$ = 16.03

A = Cognitive Styles labels the rows A_1 = FI and A_2 = FD.

interaction is perhaps the most important aspect of the two-way ANOVA. For now, think of interaction as a "unique combination."

Logic

First, let's use the example of cognitive styles and study techniques to illustrate the two-way ANOVA. You are interested in cognitive style, study technique, and their interaction. You can think of each of these three things as having a potential effect on the dependent variable, the scores on the 20-item test. The two factors and their inter-action, plus the within-groups variability, are *sources of variability*. Participants' scores might vary because: (1) students had different cognitive styles, (2) they were assigned

Cell means (standard deviations), row means, and column means

	Nonotes	Stunotes	Outframe	Compout	
FI	13.15 (2.19)	17.92 (1.32)	17.46 (1.39)	17.54 (1.76)	16.52
FD	12.92 (2.75)	15.23 (1.30)	16.62 (1.61)	17.38 (1.50)	15.54
	13.04	16.58	17.04	17.46	

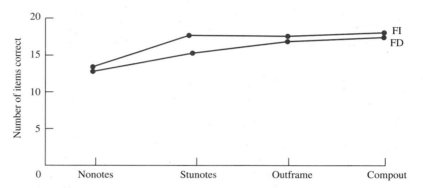

Figure 16.1

Cell means and a plot of the cell means for effect of cognitive style and study technique on number of items correct

to different study techniques, (3) the combination of cognitive style with a certain study technique had a unique effect on their test scores, or (4) other factors such as individual differences influenced the test scores (within-groups or error variability). The scores deviate from their cell mean to create the within-groups variability. You want to find out whether either factor or their interaction or both have a significant effect on test scores. For each of these three sources, you form an F ratio, with the variability of the factor or interaction in the numerator and the within-groups variability in the denominator. In the case of the one-way ANOVA, you had one F ratio for testing the effect of the one factor. You can see why there are three F ratios in the two-way ANOVA—one for each factor and a third for their unique combination (interaction).

The logic of the two-way ANOVA is to obtain estimates of variance for four sources. The sources are the two factors, the interaction, and the variance of observations within cells. Separate sample variances are obtained for each of these four sources. There are three sets of hypotheses: one H_0 and one H_1 for each of the two factors and the interaction.

For the H_0 for each effect (factors and interaction):

1. You test H_0 by comparing the sample variance for the effect to the sample variance of observations within cells.
2. Both of the sample variances estimate the population variance if H_0 is true, but they estimate different quantities if H_1 is true.
3. You put these two sample variances into a ratio called the F ratio, which you expect to be approximately one if H_0 is true but larger than one if H_1 is true.
4. You reject H_0 if F is larger than a critical value.

Table 16.3
Summary of sources and hypotheses

		H_0 *True*	H_0 *False*
MS_W = denominator of each F		Estimates σ^2	Estimates σ^2
Source and F	H_0		
A	H_0: no A effect (μ_j's equal)	Estimates σ^2	Estimates σ^2 plus A treatment effect
F_A		$F \approx \dfrac{\sigma^2}{\sigma^2} = 1$	$F \approx \dfrac{\sigma^2 + A \text{ treatment effect}}{\sigma^2} > 1$
B	H_0: no B effect (μ_k's equal)	Estimates σ^2	Estimates σ^2 plus B treatment effect
F_B		$F \approx \dfrac{\sigma^2}{\sigma^2} = 1$	$F \approx \dfrac{\sigma^2 + B \text{ treatment effect}}{\sigma^2} > 1$
AB	H_0: no interaction effect	Estimates σ^2	Estimates σ^2 plus AB interaction effect
F_{AB}		$F \approx \dfrac{\sigma^2}{\sigma^2} = 1$	$F \approx \dfrac{\sigma^2 + AB \text{ interaction effect}}{\sigma^2} > 1$

Table 16.3 summarizes each source, each H_0, and what you expect to happen when each H_0 is true or false. Each H_0 being true or false has bearing on only the source tested in that H_0. For any test, the H_0 True and H_0 False columns give information on the logic behind how to decide whether the H_0 is true or false. In Table 16.3, MS_W is the sample variance of observations within groups (cells). The notations A and B stand for the two factors.

Main Effects

The two-way ANOVA is complex because you want to examine the simultaneous effect of two variables (factors) and their combined effect, or interaction, on the dependent variable. In our example, the factors are cognitive style and study technique, and the dependent variable is number of items correct on a 20-item test. The one-way ANOVA had only one independent variable (study technique) with different levels (no notes, and others) that defined the groups. The total variability was partitioned into between-groups and within-groups pieces. For the two-way ANOVA, the total variability can be thought of as partitioned into between- and within-groups pieces and then the between-groups variability further partitioned. The between-groups variability is partitioned into the three sources of variability: the two factors and their interaction.

Main effects
Effects due to the factors in a two-way ANOVA

Effects are differences in population means. The effects due to the factors themselves are the **main effects.** Similar to a treatment effect for the one-way ANOVA, a main effect is the difference between a population mean for a level of a factor and the overall (grand) population mean. In the example, the main effects are cognitive style and study technique. Because there are two or more levels of each factor, the main effect for one factor is thought of as collapsed or averaged over the levels of the other factor. That is, the main effect for no notes is defined by collapsing across or averaging the no notes/field independence and the no notes/field dependence cells.

Quick Quiz
Refer to Research Example 16. (a) What are the main effects? (b) What are the levels of the main effects? (c) Why is this example called a 2 × 3 two-way ANOVA?

Answers

(a) Message and hurry instructions. (b) The levels of message are task relevant and helping relevant. The levels of hurry are low, medium, and high. (c) This is a two-way ANOVA because of the two main effects; it is 2 × 3 because of the two levels of message and three levels of hurry.

Interaction

Interaction
Combined effect of two factors over and above the main effects

We described interaction as a "unique combination." Now let's expand on that idea. **Interaction** is the combined, or joint, effect of the two factors over and above the main effects. Interaction is more than the simple addition of the effects from the two factors. It is the variability in the group means left over after you account for the two factors. Interaction is the variability in the group means that is not explained by (is separate from) the factors themselves. When interaction is present, the results across levels of one factor are not the same for all levels of the other factor. Interaction gives different results for one main effect when it is considered at various levels of the other main effect. When measuring interaction in an ANOVA, you always have random variation in the estimate of interaction, as you will see.

In the opening example about expressing emotion and the number of people present, you can see an interaction. If you compare willingness to express emotions in small groups or large groups, the results depend on which emotion you are talking about. In the study technique/cognitive style example, the effect of different study techniques is to give a difference for field dependence that does not exist for field independence—that is, student notes versus complete outline. When the cell means are plotted, interaction shows up as lines that are not parallel (see Figure 16.2). The ability to detect interaction is one of the advantages of a two-way ANOVA, and it is important because of the complexity of some phenomena that scientists study.

Three *F* Tests

A two-way ANOVA results in three *F* ratios to test three different null hypotheses. In the example, in terms of the effect on number of items correct, you have the null hypothesis of no effect of cognitive style, the null hypothesis of no effect of study technique, and the null hypothesis of no interaction effect of cognitive style and study technique. So you have an *F* test for cognitive style, an *F* test for study technique, and an *F* test for the interaction. Even though all three *F* ratios have the same denominator, the numerators are independent if the sample sizes in each cell are equal. Because of the independence of the numerators of the *F* ratios, you can get any pattern of significance or nonsignificance for the three *F* ratios.

For a 2 × 2 design, Figure 16.2 shows plots of cell means with all possible combinations of significance and nonsignificance for the *F* tests, labeled F_A for one main effect, F_B for the other main effect, and F_{AB} for the interaction. Assume that the denominator (the sample variance of observations within groups) is small enough that obvious differences are significant.

How do you graph a two-way ANOVA? You plot the cell means on a graph that has the dependent variable on the vertical axis. The horizontal axis is formed by levels of one of the factors (you decide which). Then you plot the cell means and draw lines that

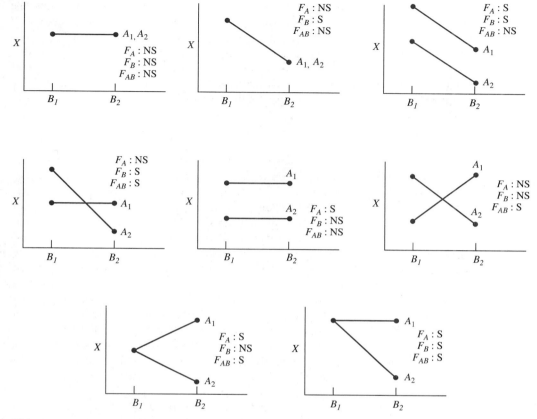

Figure 16.2
Cell mean plots of all possible combinations of significance and nonsignificance on F_A, F_B, and F_{AB} (assume small within-cells variability; S = significant, NS = nonsignificant)

represent the levels of the other factor. For example, consider the top right plot in Figure 16.2. Because the levels of *B* are on the horizontal axis, the lines are for the two levels of *A*. The cell mean for A_1B_1 might be, say, 60 and is plotted above B_1. The cell mean for A_1B_2 is 50 and is plotted above B_2. Now you connect these two points with a line that represents A_1. Similar steps lead to the line for A_2, 50 for the cell mean for A_2B_1 and 40 for the cell mean for A_2B_2.

To interpret plots of cell means where levels of *B* form the horizontal axis and levels of *A* are plotted as different lines, note the following features:

1. If the lines are not parallel, then interaction is indicated (may or may not be significant, depending on chance variability).
2. If the midpoints of the lines are not equal, then an *A* effect is indicated.
3. If the visual average (middle) of the points (cell means) above each level of *B* are not equal, then a *B* effect is indicated.

Be sure that you understand each pattern and why each *F* ratio is significant. Some of these patterns of significance are a challenge when you try to interpret the significant *F* ratios. The issue of interpretation is discussed later. Many different graphs could have been plotted for each pattern of F ratio results. These were selected merely to illustrate patterns of significance. The plots would be more complex for a two-way ANOVA with factors that have more than two levels. Finally, you won't make real research decisions about hypotheses just by looking at graphs. As in the one-way ANOVA, you need to compute each F ratio and compare it to a critical value to detect significance. This means that there is always random variability in the cell means and, for example, that nonparallel lines may not be accompanied by a significant interaction.

Advantages

In discussing the advantages of the two-way ANOVA over two one-way ANOVAs, it is helpful to consider two distinct cases. The first case is when the research is already finished and was done as a two-way ANOVA. What is lost if you do two one-way ANOVAs on the same data? When you do a one-way ANOVA for, say, factor A, you disregard the levels of factor B by summing across them. This would happen if you did a one-way ANOVA on field independence versus field dependence in the study technique example. You say you have summed or collapsed over factor B, study technique. This collapsing over factor B brings all the variability due to B and all the variability due to the AB interaction into the within-groups variability of the one-way ANOVA on factor A. That is, the MS_W of the one-way ANOVA on factor A will be inflated over what it should be. MS_W will no longer be an unbiased estimate of σ^2 unless there is no B or AB interaction. Consequently, the F ratio for factor A will be too conservative because the denominator is too large. Some real effects due to factor A might not be detected. You also could say that the power of F_A is reduced. Variability is sometimes referred to as *noise,* and you may no longer be able to "hear" the A effect (the signal) because of all the "noise" caused by B and AB. Similar conservatism for F_B is due to collapsing over the levels of factor A and bringing the variability due to A and AB into the MS_W for the one-way ANOVA on factor B. In our example, this would be a one-way ANOVA on study technique, collapsing over cognitive style. In Chapter 14, the one-way ANOVA with study technique was done for the data collapsed over cognitive styles. Finally, these two one-way ANOVAs give you no ability to detect interaction between factors A and B.

The second case occurs when the researcher, who has not yet run the study, can choose between a single two-way ANOVA and two one-way ANOVAs. That is, the researcher can run one design with both variables included or two designs, one for each factor. In this case, the two-way ANOVA has three distinct advantages over two separate one-way ANOVAs. First, in using a two-way ANOVA, the savings in study participants are large. It takes exactly one-half the number of participants to do one two-way ANOVA as to do two one-way ANOVAs with the same number of participants per level of each factor. For example, with $n = 10$ participants per cell in a 2×2 ANOVA, you have 20 participants per level of each factor, or total $N = 40$. To get 20 participants per level of each factor for the two one-way ANOVAs, it takes 40 participants for each factor, or a total of 80. Figure 16.3 shows diagrams for each design, along with sample sizes.

The second advantage of a two-way ANOVA is that it has greater generalizability. When you do a two-way ANOVA, you know the effects of one factor for two or more levels of the other factor, which are not available with two one-way ANOVAs. You know how study technique influences the number of items correct for both field-independent and field-dependent participants as well as how field independence/field dependence influences the number of items correct for the four levels of study technique. The one-way ANOVAs give information on only one level of the other factor.

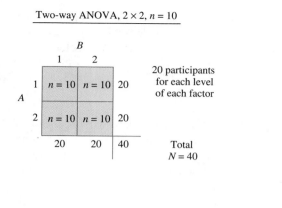

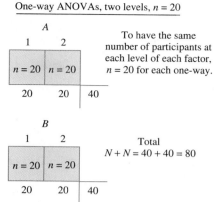

Figure 16.3
One two-way ANOVA versus two one-way ANOVAs, savings in subjects

Finally, the third advantage is that you can detect interaction only with a two-way or higher ANOVA. It is impossible to detect interaction with two one-way ANOVAs. You cannot predict the interaction from the main effects of factor *A* and factor *B*. Now, to be perfectly honest, some researchers do not view the increased interpretation problems caused by significant interaction as an advantage. However, because our world is complex and variables sometimes interact, it is good to have a statistical method that can detect such interactions.

Quick Quiz

You are studying the early upbringing of dogs trained to assist people who are visually impaired. These dogs spend the first months of life with an ordinary family before going to a training center. You want to know whether households with children or without children produce more trainable dogs. You want to use black Labradors, golden retrievers, and German shepherds in your study in case there are differences due to breed. Your dependent variable is a rating of trainability given by an expert trainer on the dog's first day at the training center. (a) Your design is a ____ × ____ ____-way ANOVA. (b) Name the main effects and interaction. (c) What one-way ANOVAs could be run? (d) What is the main disadvantage of the one-way ANOVAs?

Answers

(a) 2×3 two-way ANOVA. (b) Main effect of household, main effect of breed, and interaction of household and breed. (c) A one-way ANOVA on household and another one-way ANOVA on breed. (d) Certain breeds of dog might do better in households with children, whereas others might be better suited for households without children. The one-way ANOVAs don't provide a way to detect this interaction.

16.2   ANOVA: Partitioning of Variability

In the one-way ANOVA, you partitioned the total variability into two nonoverlapping parts so you could obtain the two independent variance estimates necessary to form the *F* ratio. You partitioned the total sum of squares into the between-groups sum of squares and the within-groups sum of squares. These sums of squares were divided by their degrees of freedom to form the variance estimates, called mean squares. The same general idea applies to the two-way ANOVA, except that you have four non-overlapping parts (sums of squares) and four independent variance estimates (mean squares).

Notation and Terminology

In this text, we consider only the two-way ANOVA with equal numbers of observations in each cell. This is important because these computational formulas are not accurate unless the n per cell is a constant. Unequal n's in a two-way ANOVA lead to some fairly difficult computation and interpretation. One problem is in overlap: If, say, A is significant, then it might overlap with B or with the interaction, so you don't know whether the significant results are clearly due to A. Note that the study in Research Example 16 had unequal cell sizes.

In the two-way ANOVA, you need three subscripts on X. The first subscript represents the subject; the second subscript represents the first factor, factor A; and the third subscript represents the second factor, factor B. So X_{ijk} stands for a score for the ith subject in the jth level of A and the kth level of B. And X_{111} is the score for the first subject in the first level of A and the first level of B. What is X_{312}? It is the score for the third subject in the first level of A and the second level of B. Because there are n subjects in each cell, or combination of the two factors, you can say:

$$X_{ijk} = \text{score for } i\text{th subject in } j\text{th level of } A \text{ and } k\text{th level of } B, \, i = 1 \text{ to } n,$$
$$j = 1 \text{ to } J, \, k = 1 \text{ to } K$$

which includes the notation for all $nJK = N$ scores.

In any two-way ANOVA, it is helpful to be able to talk about various means. In the study technique/cognitive style example, you might want to be able to compare, say, student notes to no notes averaged over cognitive style. The main effect means for study technique give you a way to do this comparison. For the following computations of means, refer to Table 16.2 and do each computation to see whether you understand the subscripts and can get the same results.

The first type of mean in the two-way ANOVA to be defined is the cell mean

$$\overline{X}_{jk} = \frac{\sum_i X_{ijk}}{n} \tag{16.1}$$

where n = number of observations per cell (a constant for all cells). So for a given cell jk, you add up the scores for the i subjects. Look at Table 16.2; what are j and k for the field-dependent students who used no notes? The field-dependent group is the second level of A, so $j = 2$. Those students who used no notes are at the first level of study technique, so $k = 1$. The X's in that cell are labeled X_{i21}, with i being the subscript for the subject. So $\overline{X}_{21} = 168/13 = 12.92$.

Now let's look at the row means. A mean for the jth level of factor A is

$$\overline{X}_j = \frac{\sum_k \sum_i X_{ijk}}{nK} \tag{16.2}$$

where nK = number of observations in the jth level of A. Look at Table 16.2 again. If you want to find the row mean for each level of j, you have to add all of the X's in A_j

and divide by nK ($13 \times 4 = 52$). To find $\overline{X}_{j=1}$, add all of the X's across subjects and all k levels of the other factor in row 1. So the mean of $A_1 = 859/52 = 16.52$.

Go through a similar computation for the column means, except now you fix k and add up the X's in each column k. A mean for the kth level of factor B is

$$\overline{X}_k = \frac{\sum_j \sum_i X_{ijk}}{nJ} \tag{16.3}$$

where nJ = number of observations in the kth level of B. Now the subscripts tell you to add across all subjects and all j levels of the other factor for each of the K columns. For the second column in Table 16.2, $nJ = 13(2) = 26$, and the sum of the X's is 431, giving $\overline{X}_{k=2} = 16.58$.

The grand (overall) mean is

$$\overline{X} = \frac{\sum_k \sum_j \sum_i X_{ijk}}{nJK} \tag{16.4}$$

where $nJK = N$ = total number of observations. Now you just add up all of the X's and divide by N.

We've gradually shifted from using the word *group* in the two-way ANOVA in favor of *cell* for the combination of the factors and *level* for one of the conditions of a factor. For example, no notes is a level of study techniques, and no notes/field dependence is one cell in the design.

Variability

The total variability in the population for a two-way ANOVA can be represented by any one score as $X_{ijk} - \mu$, the difference between that score and the population grand mean. That total can be partitioned into parts due to the first factor, A, the second factor, B, the interaction, AB, and the within-cells variability. As with the one-way ANOVA, you can partition the total variability for all of the subjects, square these differences, and add them for all scores. This partitioning gives you the sums of squares for the four different sources. Table 16.4 shows the steps to partition the total variability into the four parts for the two-way ANOVA.

Step 2 is used again when you examine the degrees of freedom to understand their formulas. Although the main effects due to A and B are similar to the "between" in the one-way ANOVA, the interaction is not at all familiar. Earlier, interaction was defined as that effect of cell means that remains after you account for the main effects. That is, the interaction is the variability in the cell means that is not explained by the

Table 16.4
Partitioning of total variability

	Total	=	A	+	B	+	AB	+	Within
Step 1. Write out differences in terms of scores and means.	$X_{ijk} - \mu$	$= (\mu_j - \mu)$		$+ (\mu_k - \mu)$		$+ (\mu_{jk} - \mu_j - \mu_k + \mu)$		$+ (X_{ijk} - \mu_{jk})$	
Step 2. Estimate population means with sample means.	$X_{ijk} - \overline{X}$	$= (\overline{X}_j - \overline{X})$		$+ (\overline{X}_k - \overline{X})$		$+ (\overline{X}_{jk} - \overline{X}_j - \overline{X}_k + \overline{X})$		$+ (X_{ijk} - \overline{X})$	
Step 3. Square and sum all differences.	$\sum\sum\sum(X_{ijk} - \overline{X})^2$	$= \sum\sum\sum(\overline{X}_j - \overline{X})^2$		$+ \sum\sum\sum(\overline{X}_k - \overline{X})^2$		$+ \sum\sum\sum(\overline{X}_{jk} - \overline{X}_j - \overline{X}_k + \overline{X})^2$		$+ \sum\sum\sum(X_{ijk} - \overline{X}_{jk})^2$	

factors themselves. If you start with $\mu_{jk} - \mu$ as symbolizing the variability in the cell means and subtract the A and B main effects $\mu_j - \mu$ and $\mu_k - \mu$, then you get:

Interaction effect
Variability in cell means minus the A and B main effects

Interaction effect = (variability in cell means)   (16.5)
                          $- (A$ main effect$) - (B$ main effect$)$

$$= (\mu_{jk} - \mu) - (\mu_j - \mu) - (\mu_k - \mu)$$

$$= \mu_{jk} - \mu - \mu_j + \mu - \mu_k + \mu$$

$$= \mu_{jk} - \mu_j - \mu_k + \mu$$

Can you see how the first and second lines of formula 16.5 fit the verbal definition? The last two lines come from removing the parentheses and collecting terms. The last line was used in Table 16.4.

Sums of Squares

The last quantities in Table 16.4 are called the *sums of squares*. Sums of squares are the numerators of the sample variances used in forming the F ratios. As you learned in Chapter 14, sample variances, also called mean squares, are composed of a sum of squares divided by degrees of freedom. *SS* stands for sum of squares, with the subscript of *SS* indicating which sum of squares. All the formulas for sums of squares in Table 16.4 are definitional formulas; computational formulas are given later.

Degrees of Freedom

To form mean squares, you need both sums of squares and degrees of freedom. The sums of squares for the two-way ANOVA have been defined, so now you need the degrees of freedom. Remember that degrees of freedom are parameters necessary to use the F table and obtain a correct critical value. Using the same working definition of degrees of freedom given earlier as the number of independent components minus the number of parameters estimated, you obtain Table 16.5. The last line of the table shows alternative ways of writing the degrees of freedom for interaction and within.

The interaction degrees of freedom in the last line of Table 16.5 illustrates a general principle: Degrees of freedom for any interaction are simply the product of the degrees of freedom for the components in the interaction. Here, $df_{AB} = (df_A)(df_B) = (J - 1)(K - 1)$.

Quick Quiz
Calculate df_A, df_B, and df_{AB} for Research Example 16.

Answer

The degrees of freedom for factor A, message, are $df_A = J - 1 = 2 - 1 = 1$. For factor B, the hurry instructions, $df_B = K - 1 = 3 - 1 = 2$. The AB interaction gives $df_{AB} = (J - 1)(K - 1) = 2$.

Degrees of freedom
For the two-way ANOVA,
$df_A = J - 1$, $df_B = K - 1$,
$df_{AB} = (J - 1)(K - 1)$, and
$df_W = JK(n - 1)$

Now, let's examine how the **degrees of freedom** are obtained. (Remember, df = number of independent components minus number of parameters estimated.) In SS_{total}, there are nJK observations X_{ijk} and only one parameter μ estimated by $\bar{X}$, so the total degrees of freedom are $nJK - 1$.

Table 16.5
Sums of squares and degrees of freedom

SS_{total}	$=$	SS_A	$+$	SS_B	$+$	SS_{AB}	$+$	SS_{Within}
$\sum\sum\sum(X_{ijk} - \overline{X})^2$	$= \sum\sum\sum(\overline{X}_j - \overline{X})^2$		$+ \sum\sum\sum(\overline{X}_k - \overline{X})^2$		$+ \sum\sum\sum(\overline{X}_{jk} - \overline{X}_j - \overline{X}_k + \overline{X})^2$		$+ \sum\sum\sum(X_{ijk} - \overline{X}_{jk})^2$	
df_{total}	$= df_A$		$+ df_B$		$+ df_{AB}$		$+ df_{\text{Within}}$	
$nJK - 1$	$= J - 1$		$+ K - 1$		$+ JK - J - K + 1$		$+ nJK - JK$	
$nJK - 1$	$= J - 1$		$+ K - 1$		$+ (J - 1)(K - 1)$		$+ JK(n - 1)$	

In SS_A and SS_B, the J values of $\overline{X}_j$ and the K values of $\overline{X}k$ behave like observations, and you again estimate one μ with $\overline{X}$, so $df_A = J - 1$ and $df_B = K - 1$.

The degrees of freedom for interaction are a bit more difficult to understand. The JK values of the cell means are like observations, and you subtract J because you estimate the J values of μ_j with $\overline{X}_j$ and K because you estimate the K values of μ_k with $\overline{X}_k$. In the formula $JK - J - K + 1$, the $+1$ always bothers students: How did you get $+1$? When you subtract J for estimating the J values of μ_j with $\overline{X}_j$, you have also subtracted 1 for estimating the grand mean, simply because knowing the J values of $\overline{X}_j$ allows you to know $\overline{X}$. So the $-J$ contains -1 for estimating μ. Similarly, the $-K$ contains -1 for estimating μ. Because you have subtracted the 1 for the grand mean twice, you need to add it back once; thus you need $+1$ for the interaction degrees of freedom to be correct. And $JK - J - K$ is 1 too small, so $JK - J - K + 1$ is correct.

For df_W, you have nJK observations and JK values of $\overline{X}_{jk}$, so $df_W = nJK - JK$.

Mean Squares

Mean squares are simply sums of squares divided by their degrees of freedom. For factor A, SS_A/df_A gives

$$MS_A = \frac{SS_A}{J - 1} \tag{16.6}$$

So MS_A estimates σ^2 if H_0 for the A main effect is true, but it estimates σ^2 plus a positive quantity based on the true differences in the A population means if H_0 for the A main effect is false.

For factor B, SS_B/df_B gives

$$MS_B = \frac{SS_B}{K - 1} \tag{16.7}$$

So MS_B estimates σ^2 if H_0 for the B main effect is true, but it estimates σ^2 plus a positive quantity based on the true differences in the B population means if H_0 for the B main effect is false.

For the interaction effect AB, SS_{AB}/df_{AB} gives

$$MS_{AB} = \frac{SS_{AB}}{(J - 1)(K - 1)} \tag{16.8}$$

MS_{AB} estimates σ^2 if H_0 for the interaction effect is true. But if H_0 for the interaction effect is false, then MS_{AB} estimates σ^2 plus a positive quantity based on the true interaction effects in the population.

For the variability within cells, SS_{within}/df_{within} gives

$$MS_{within} = \frac{SS_{within}}{JK(n-1)} \qquad (16.9)$$

MS_{within} estimates σ^2 regardless of whether any of the H_0 are true or false. As was the case for the one-way ANOVA in Chapter 14, MS_{within} is always an unbiased estimate of σ^2. You now have all you need to form the three F ratios in the two-way ANOVA.

Quick Quiz

Suppose you want to do research on exam stress and cognitive style. You have 30 field-independent students and 30 field-dependent students. You randomly assign students to either perceived control over test material (they are told to write test questions, which might be used on the exam) or no control over the exam (they are told to study for the test by writing questions). (a) Why is a two-way ANOVA appropriate? (b) Calculate all the degrees of freedom for a two-way ANOVA.

Answers

(a) A two-way ANOVA is appropriate because you have two factors (cognitive style and perceived control over exam). There are two levels of each variable, so this is a 2×2 design.
(b) For factor A, cognitive style, $df = J - 1 = 2 - 1 = 1$. For factor B, control, $df = K - 1 = 2 - 1 = 1$. For the within, $df = JK(n-1) = (4)(15-1) = (4)(14) = 56$. *(Hint:* Always check your work by adding the df values for A, B, AB, and within. The total should equal $N - 1$, the total df.)

16.3   ANOVA *F* Tests

Hypotheses

Null hypotheses for the main effects in a two-way ANOVA can be stated in terms of equality of means. For the A main effect, the null hypothesis is

$$H_0: \mu_1 = \mu_2 = \cdots = \mu_J = \mu \qquad (16.10)$$

For the study technique/cognitive style example, H_0 for cognitive style (field independence, field dependence) is that the mean for the field-independent participants is equal to the mean for the field-dependent students. Both would be equal to the grand mean. The alternative hypothesis for factor A is that some population means μ_j are not equal. This is similar to the alternative hypothesis in the one-way ANOVA, where H_1 states that there is a difference somewhere among the means.

For the B main effect, the null hypothesis is

$$H_0: \mu_1 = \mu_2 = \cdots = \mu_K = \mu \qquad (16.11)$$

For example, H_0 for study technique is that the mean for the no-notes condition equals the mean for the student notes condition equals the mean of the outline frame condition equals the mean of the complete outline condition. The alternative hypothesis for factor B is that some of the μ_k are not equal.

For the interaction, the null hypothesis is

H_0: no interaction effect (16.12)

For our example, H_0 is "no cognitive style/study technique interaction." The alternative hypothesis for the interaction is that some interaction effects (see formula 16.5) are not zero. There is no easy way to state the null hypothesis for the interaction in terms of means.

F Ratios

For each of the null hypotheses for the two-way ANOVA, there is a corresponding test, an ***F* ratio.** For the *A* main effect, the statistic is

F ratio

F_A, F_B, and F_{AB} are all formed by dividing the respective mean square in the numerator by MS_W

$$F_A = \frac{MS_A}{MS_W}$$ (16.13)

For the *B* main effect, the statistic is

$$F_B = \frac{MS_B}{MS_W}$$ (16.14)

For the interaction, the statistic is

$$F_{AB} = \frac{MS_{AB}}{MS_W}$$ (16.15)

As you saw in the one-way ANOVA, MS_W is an abbreviation for the mean square within cells.

For each of these *F* ratios, if the respective H_0 is true, then the mean squares of the numerator and denominator estimate σ^2. If the respective H_0 is not true, then the numerator *MS* estimates σ^2 plus a positive quantity due to true differences in population means or interaction effects, while MS_W still estimates σ^2. So you expect each *F* ratio to be large if its H_0 is false and approximately one if its H_0 is true.

Computational formulas for the sums of squares are given in Section 16.4. Once you have values for the *F* ratios, you can compare them to critical values from the appropriate *F* distributions.

F Distributions

A test is available for each of the three hypotheses in the two-way ANOVA by comparing the associated *F* ratio to a critical value from an *F* distribution. If a given H_0 is true and if certain assumptions are met, then the *F* statistic is distributed as *F* with degrees of freedom of the numerator and denominator. For the *A* main effect:

F_A is distributed as an *F* distribution with parameters $J - 1$ and $JK(n - 1)$ (16.16)

For the *B* main effect:

> F_B is distributed as an *F* distribution with   (16.17)
> parameters $K - 1$ and $JK(n - 1)$

For the interaction effect:

> F_{AB} is distributed as an *F* distribution with   (16.18)
> parameters $(J - 1)(K - 1)$ and $JK(n - 1)$

In some designs, three different *F* distributions are used to find three different critical values. For example, in a 3 × 4 design, $df_A = J - 1 = 3 - 1 = 2$, $df_B = K - 1 = 4 - 1 = 3$, and $df_{AB} = (J - 1)(K - 1) = (2)(3) = 6$, so the degrees of freedom of the numerator are different for each of the three *F* ratios. Thus, you would find three different critical values from Table A.6. For a 2 × 2 design, $df_A = J - 1 = 2 - 1 = 1$, $df_B = K - 1 = 2 - 1 = 1$, and $df_{AB} = (J - 1)(K - 1) = 1$, so you use the same critical value for each of the three *F* tests.

Decision Rules

Decision rules for the two-way ANOVA are exactly like those for the one-way ANOVA. The critical value decision rules are based on using a chosen α and the corresponding critical value to give:

> Reject H_0 if $F \geq F_{crit}$; otherwise, retain H_0 (16.19)

where *F* is F_A, F_B, or F_{AB} and F_{crit} is the $\alpha\%$ critical *F* value with numerator *df* of $J - 1$, $K - 1$, or $(J - 1)(K - 1)$, respectively, and $df_W = JK(n - 1)$ for the denominator.

You use the decision rule three times, once for each *F* ratio and its corresponding H_0. Because computer programs for two-way ANOVA typically give *p*-values for the observed *F* ratios, you most likely would use a critical value decision rule if you did the analysis by hand. To use the *p*-value decision rule, which is usually preferred when you do the work on a computer, you choose α in advance and then compare the probability of your observed *F* to your chosen α. The computer will give you the probability of a result equal to or more extreme than your obtained *F*. If this probability is equal to or smaller than α, then reject H_0. The rule is the same for all three *F* tests in the two-way ANOVA. You don't have to worry about two-tailed *p*-values because the *F* test is always one tailed.

Assumptions

Each of the three *F* ratios is exactly distributed as its *F* distribution as given in formulas 16.16 to 16.18 if the appropriate H_0 is true and the assumptions are met. These assumptions are that the observations are normally and independently distributed with equal variances for each cell. Because the use of the two-way ANOVA is restricted to the case of equal cell sizes *n*, the two-way ANOVA generally has the same robustness or lack of robustness as the one-way ANOVA (see Section 14.4).

Quick Quiz

Suppose you are doing the study of guide dogs for people who are visually impaired, and you have two levels of household and three breeds of dog. You have a trainability score for each of the 11 dogs in each cell. (a) Calculate all of the *df* values. (b) Find all of the *F* critical values you would need to test your hypotheses. Use $\alpha = .05$. (c) If you find a main effect of breed and no other significant effects, what does that mean?

Answers

(a) $df_A = J - 1 = 2 - 1 = 1$, $df_B = K - 1 = 3 - 1 = 2$, $df_{AB} = 2$, $df_{within} = JK(n - 1) =$ (2)(3)(11 − 1) = 60. (*Check:* $N - 1 = 66 - 1 = 99 - 1 = 65$, and $1 + 2 + 2 + 60 = 65$.) (b) For household, $F_{crit} = 4.00$; for breed, $F_{crit} = 3.15$; for household × breed interaction, $F_{crit} = 3.15$. (c) A significant *F* for breed means the breeds have different average trainability scores, the kind of household doesn't make a difference, and the average trainability for each breed doesn't depend on whether or not the dog is in a household with children.

16.4   ANOVA Computation

Computational Formulas for Sums of Squares

You've already seen the definitional formulas for the *SS*, and now you need the computational formulas so you can compute the *F* ratios. Copy the data from Table 16.2 onto a sheet of paper and calculate each of the following *SS*. We'll give you the answers so you can check your work.

The computational formula for SS_A is

$$SS_A = \frac{\sum_j (\sum_k \sum_i X_{ijk})^2}{nK} - \frac{(\sum_k \sum_j \sum_i X_{ijk})^2}{nJK} \tag{16.20}$$

The computational formula for SS_B is

$$SS_B = \frac{\sum_k (\sum_j \sum_i X_{ijk})^2}{nJ} - \frac{(\sum_k \sum_j \sum_i X_{ijk})^2}{nJK} \tag{16.21}$$

The computational formula for SS_{AB} is

$$SS_{AB} = \frac{\sum_k \sum_j (\sum_i X_{ijk})^2}{n} - \frac{\sum_j (\sum_k \sum_i X_{ijk})^2}{nK} - \frac{\sum_k (\sum_j \sum_i X_{ijk})^2}{nJ} + \frac{(\sum_k \sum_j \sum_i X_{ijk})^2}{nJK} \tag{16.22}$$

The computational formula for SS_W is

$$SS_W = \sum_k \sum_j \sum_i X_{ijk}^2 - \frac{\sum_k \sum_j (\sum_i X_{ijk})^2}{n} \tag{16.23}$$

The computational formula for SS_T is

$$SS_T = \sum_k \sum_j \sum_i X_{ijk}^2 - \frac{(\sum_k \sum_j \sum_i X_{ijk})^2}{nJK} \tag{16.24}$$

Example

Let's go through the computation of SS_A from the data in Table 16.2 so that you can practice using all of those subscripts. The computation of the other SS will be summarized verbally, and you can refer to Table 16.6 to check your work.

The first part of SS_A has $\sum_k\sum_i X_{ijk}$ in parentheses. Outside the parentheses is $\sum_j$. That means for a given value of j, you need to add up the $\sum_i X_{ijk}$ for all of the values of k. Once you have this sum, you square it. You obtain these squared sums for $j = 1$ and $j = 2$ and then add them together and divide by nK, which is 52, the number in each row. So for $j = 1$, the field-independent group, add up the scores for all of the levels of study technique. The total for row 1 is 859. Now you need to square 859. Next, do the same thing for $j = 2$. Your sum is 808 for the field-dependent group. Square that sum and add it to the first squared sum to get 1,390,745. Now divide by 52 to obtain 26,745.096. That's the first piece of SS_A. The second piece has $\sum_k\sum_j\sum_i X_{ijk}$ in parentheses. If you sum over k, j, and i, what do you have? The sum of all the scores in the sample, 1667. Now you square that sum and divide by nJK, the total number of subjects, to get 26,720.087. Subtract the first piece from the second piece, and you should get 25.009.

Here's a verbal summary of how to compute each SS:

- SS_A: *First part*—Find the row sums, square them, add them up, and divide by the number in a row (nK). *Second part*—Take the sum of all scores in the sample, square it, and divide by the total number of X's. *Finally*—Subtract the second part from the first part.
- SS_B: *First part*—Find the column sums, square them, add them up, and divide by the number in a column (nJ). *Second part*—Same as the second part of SS_A. *Finally*—Subtract the second part from the first part.
- SS_{AB}: *First part*—Find the cell sums, square them, add them up, and divide by the number in a cell (n). *Second part*—Same as the first part of SS_A. *Third part*—Same as the first part of SS_B. *Fourth part*—Same as the second part of SS_A and SS_B. *Finally*—Start with the first part, subtract the second and third parts, and add the fourth part.
- SS_W: *First part*—Square each X and then add them up. *Second part*—Same as the first part of SS_{AB}. *Finally*—Subtract the second part from the first part.

There are only five unique pieces in the four SS formulas: an A piece (first part of SS_A), a B piece (first part of SS_B), an AB piece (first part of SS_{AB}), a piece that contains the grand sum (last part of SS_A), and a piece that is the sum of the squared scores (first part of SS_W). Use the preceding summary to compute all of the SS from the data in Table 16.2. Then find the mean squares by dividing each SS by its *df*, and check your work by referring to Table 16.6.

Now all you have left to do is form the F ratios by dividing the appropriate MS by MS_W. Calculate each F, and then check your work with the ANOVA summary table in Table 16.7. We have rounded the results, but we calculated the F ratios *before* we rounded the SS and MS. Do not round off anything until you have obtained the final statistic. The *p*-values were obtained from a computer.

As you read in the chapter on the one-way ANOVA, many journals request a more terse reporting style, such as $F(1, 96) = 7.78$, $p = .0064$ or $F(1, 96) = 7.78$, $p < .05$.

How would you test hypotheses with these data? Remember, you have three null hypotheses, each regarding an effect on the number of items correct: no effect of

Table 16.6

SS and *MS* on study technique and cognitive style (FI = field independence, FD = field dependence)

Row, column, cell, and total sums:

	B_1 = no notes	B_2 = student notes	B_3 = outline framework	B_4 = complete outline	
					B = Study Technique
A_1 = FI	171	233	227	228	Row 1 sum 859
A = Cognitive Styles					
A_2 = FD	168	198	216	226	Row 2 sum 808
Column sums	339	431	443	454	Grand sum 1667

Degrees of freedom:

$df_A = J - 1 = 2 - 1 = 1$

$df_B = K - 1 = 4 - 1 = 3$

$df_{AB} = (J - 1)(K - 1) = (1)(3) = 3$

$df_W = JK(n - 1) = (2)(4)(13 - 1) = (8)(12) = 96$

SS and *MS* values:

$$SS_A = \frac{\Sigma_j(\Sigma_k\Sigma_i X_{ijk})^2}{nK} - \frac{(\Sigma_k\Sigma_j\Sigma_i X_{ijk})^2}{nJK} = \frac{859^2 + 808^2}{13(4)} - \frac{1667^2}{13(2)(4)}$$

$$= 26{,}745.096 - 26{,}720.087 = 25.009$$

$$MS_A = \frac{SS_A}{df_A} = \frac{25.009}{1} = 25.009$$

$$SS_B = \frac{\Sigma_k(\Sigma_j\Sigma_i X_{ijk})^2}{nJ} - \frac{(\Sigma_k\Sigma_j\Sigma_i X_{ijk})^2}{nJK} = \frac{339^2 + 431^2 + 443^2 + 454^2}{13(2)} - \frac{1667^2}{104}$$

$$= 27{,}040.269 - 26{,}720.087 = 320.182$$

$$MS_B = \frac{SS_B}{df_B} = \frac{320.182}{3} = 106.72733$$

$$SS_{AB} = \frac{\Sigma_k\Sigma_j(\Sigma_i X_{ijk})^2}{n} - \frac{\Sigma_j(\Sigma_k\Sigma_i X_{ijk})^2}{nK} - \frac{\Sigma_k(\Sigma_j\Sigma_i X_{ijk})^2}{nJ} + \frac{(\Sigma_k\Sigma_j\Sigma_i X_{ijk})^2}{nJK}$$

$$= \frac{171^2 + 233^2 + 227^2 + 228^2 + 168^2 + 198^2 + 216^2 + 226^2}{13} - 26{,}745.096 - 27{,}040.269 + 26{,}720.087$$

$$= 27{,}092.538 - 26{,}745.096 - 27{,}040.269 + 26{,}720.087 = 27.26$$

$$MS_{AB} = \frac{SS_{AB}}{df_{AB}} = \frac{27.26}{3} = 9.0867$$

$$SS_W = \Sigma_k\Sigma_j\Sigma_i X_{ijk}^2 - \frac{\Sigma_k\Sigma_j(\Sigma_i X_{ijk})^2}{n} = 27{,}401 - 27{,}092.538 = 308.462$$

$$MS_W = \frac{SS_W}{df_W} = \frac{308.462}{96} = 3.2131458$$

$$SS_T = \Sigma_k\Sigma_j\Sigma_i X_{ijk}^2 - \frac{(\Sigma_k\Sigma_j\Sigma_i X_{ijk})^2}{nJK} = 27{,}401 - 26{,}720.087 = 680.913$$

Table 16.7
ANOVA summary table

Source	SS	df	MS	F	p
A = cognitive style	25.009	1	25.009	7.78	.0064
B = study technique	320.182	3	106.727	33.22	.0001
AB = interaction	27.26	3	9.086	2.83	.0426
Within	308.462	96	3.21315		
Total	680.913	103			

cognitive style, no effect of study technique, and no interaction effect of cognitive style and study technique. To test the hypothesis about an A effect, cognitive style, look at F_A, which is 7.78. The degrees of freedom for this F are 1 and 96. What F_{crit} should you use from Table A.6 in Appendix A? There is no entry for 96 df for the denominator, so use the more conservative entry of 80. You should find $F_{crit} = 3.96$ for $\alpha = .05$. Because $F_A = 7.78$ exceeds the critical value, you reject the null hypothesis. What about F_B? The df for F_B are 3 and 96; looking to the next more conservative value in the table, you'll find $F_{crit} = 2.72$. You reject H_0 of no effect of study technique because F_B exceeds the critical value. The critical value for testing the null hypothesis of no interaction effect is the same as for F_B because in this case they happen to have the same df, 3 and 96. Because F_{AB} exceeds 2.72, you reject the null hypothesis of no interaction effect.

Interpretation

Because of the three F tests, the two-way ANOVA is more complicated to interpret than the one-way ANOVA. The first thing you should do is look for an interaction effect. If the interaction is significant, then the results across the levels of one factor are not the same for all the levels of the other factor. A significant F_{AB} makes it difficult to generalize about the main effects, whether they are significant or not. For instance, the F_{AB} in the study technique example indicates that the effect of study technique on test scores depends on whether you are looking at field-dependent or field-independent participants.

Figure 16.4 shows two different plots of the cell means for this example. The second plot is probably better for these data because it shows a separate line for field dependence and field independence and emphasizes the differences in study technique. You cannot say which study technique is best for everyone because it depends on the person's cognitive style. What if a teacher wanted to use the results of this study to improve his or her teaching? It would be difficult to draw conclusions when the interaction is significant in the two-way ANOVA. The conclusion from these data is that for field-independent students, any note taking is better than no notes. But for field-dependent students, only the outline frame and complete outline are better than no notes; the student notes are not significantly better than no notes at all.

If the interaction is not significant, then you proceed with interpreting the main effects. Look back at Research Example 16, where F_{AB} was not significant. The

Cell means (standard deviations), row means, and column means

	Nonotes	Stunotes	Outframe	Compout	
FI	13.15 (2.19)	17.92 (1.32)	17.46 (1.39)	17.54 (1.76)	16.52
FD	12.92 (2.75)	15.23 (1.30)	16.62 (1.61)	17.38 (1.50)	15.54
	13.04	16.58	17.04	17.46	

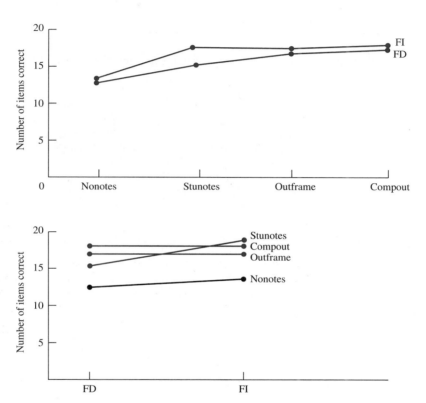

Figure 16.4
Cell means and two different ways to plot cell means for the effect of cognitive style and study technique on number of items correct

A effect, which had to do with the kind of message, was not significant, but the *B* effect, which influenced whether the person was in a hurry, was significant. So you can conclude that in this study, the person's helping behavior was not influenced by whether he or she read the passage about the Good Samaritan. What about the significant effect of the hurry condition? You can conclude that helping behavior is affected by people being in a hurry. You *cannot* say how rushed someone has to be in order for helping behavior to decline. This is the same situation you found in the one-way ANOVA. The significant *F* says only: There is a difference in these means. It doesn't say which group or groups have significantly lower helping behavior. Again, you have to turn to multiple comparisons to find significant differences between pairs of means. MCPs for main effect means are simple extensions of the methods in Chapter 15. However, MCPs for cell means are complex. See Toothaker (1993) for help on MCPs in the two-way ANOVA.

Your main challenge in interpreting a two-way ANOVA involves a significant interaction. Think of a significant F_{AB} as a red flag indicating that the main effect results may not be uniform across levels of the other main effect.

Quick Quiz

Look at the ANOVA summary table in Research Example 16. Test the hypotheses about the A, B, and AB effects. (*Hint:* You need to look up critical values.)

Answer

(upside-down answer text)

For $\alpha = .05$, $F_{crit}(1, 34) = 4.13$ (for F_A) and $F_{crit}(2, 34) = 3.28$ (for F_B and F_{AB}). First, do the test of interaction. Remember, it can complicate the interpretation of the main effects if it is significant. Because F_{AB} does not exceed 3.28, the interaction is nonsignificant. Now proceed to interpret the main effects. The effect of message is also nonsignificant because $F_A = 2.65$, which is less than 4.13. The effect of hurry instructions is significant because $F_B = 3.56$, which is greater than 3.28. You would conclude that helping behavior is affected by hurry instructions but not by the message that the participants rehearsed.

Strength of Association

In a two-way ANOVA, strength of association is measured separately for each of the main effects and the interaction. You are estimating the proportion of variability in the dependent variable that can be accounted for by A, B, and AB. Formulas for η^2 are:

$$\eta_A^2 = \frac{SS_A}{SS_T} \tag{16.25}$$

$$\eta_B^2 = \frac{SS_B}{SS_T} \tag{16.26}$$

$$\eta_{AB}^2 = \frac{SS_{AB}}{SS_T} \tag{16.27}$$

Formulas for ω^2 are:

$$\omega_A^2 = \frac{SS_A - (J-1)MS_W}{SS_T + MS_W} \tag{16.28}$$

$$\omega_B^2 = \frac{SS_B - (K-1)MS_W}{SS_T + MS_W} \tag{16.29}$$

$$\omega_{AB}^2 = \frac{SS_{AB} - (J-1)(K-1)MS_W}{SS_T + MS_W} \tag{16.30}$$

with ω^2 set equal to zero if the respective F is less than 1.00.

From the data in Table 16.2, you can compute η^2 and ω^2 for the A, B, and AB effects in the study technique example:

$$\eta_A^2 = \frac{25.009}{680.913} = .037$$

$$\eta_B^2 = \frac{320.182}{680.913} = .47$$

$$\eta_{AB}^2 = \frac{27.26}{680.913} = .04$$

$$\omega_A^2 = \frac{25.009 - (1)(3.2131458)}{680.913 + 3.2131458} = .03$$

$$\omega_B^2 = \frac{320.182 - (3)(3.2131458)}{684.12614} = .45$$

$$\omega_{AB}^2 = \frac{27.26 - (1)(3)(3.2131458)}{684.12614} = .03$$

The proportion of variability in test scores associated with study technique is estimated at .45 to .47. This represents a fairly large part of the total variability and a fairly strong relationship between study technique and test scores. Cognitive style and the interaction explain only small proportions of variability, even though both were significant.

Beyond the Two-Way ANOVA

The ability of the two-way ANOVA to detect interaction is a double-edged sword. You probably have a good intuition about variables interacting in the real world, and you'd like to be able draw conclusions that are relevant to the world. At the same time, it's difficult to interpret main effects when the interaction is significant. Some researchers go beyond the two-way ANOVA and incorporate three or more variables into their studies. If you believed cognitive styles were different for men and women, you could do this study with participants grouped by gender. In that case, you would have a three-way ANOVA, with the three variables cognitive style, study technique, and gender. The design would be $2 \times 4 \times 2$, with 16 cells. The logic of higher-order ANOVAs is the same and the computation of the *df* is similar, but now you would have to interpret multiple two-way interactions, one or more *three-way* interactions, and maybe even higher interactions. The complexity of the design is a more realistic model of the world, but the interpretation of the results is cumbersome.

Another issue is whether the levels of the factors themselves have been randomly sampled. If the levels have been randomly sampled, the factor is said to be random; if not, it is fixed. For example, you might want to be able to use a range of dose levels in a test of a cold remedy's tendency to cause drowsiness. In that case, you might randomly sample five doses between 0 and 50 mg; these would be the levels of the independent variable "dose." Designs that have both random and fixed factors are called mixed designs. Our coverage of ANOVAs examined only fixed factors. Some aspects of mixed designs are covered in Chapter 17 on repeated measures design. The fixed/random issue often brings complexity to the design that is beyond this text.

Another twist on the ANOVA involves measuring the same subjects repeatedly, which is what interests people who do research on learning and memory. Repeated measures ANOVAs are discussed in Chapter 17.

16.5   Summary, Study Tips, and Computation

Chapter Summary

The two-way ANOVA is a procedure to test null hypotheses of no treatment effects and no interaction effects for two factors. There are two or more levels of each of the two main effects, and you classify each two-way ANOVA by these levels, such as 2×3. Interaction is the unique combined, or joint, effect of the two factors. There are three F tests in the two-way ANOVA, and you can get any pattern of significance or nonsignificance for these three tests. One two-way ANOVA has the advantages of fewer participants (one-half), greater generalizability, and ability to detect interaction.

You want to use equal n's per cell in the two-way ANOVA. Total variability is partitioned into four sums of squares: SS_A, SS_B, SS_{AB}, and SS_W. Degrees of freedom for the A effect are $J - 1$, for the B effect $K - 1$, for the AB interaction $(J - 1)(K - 1)$, and for the within $JK(n - 1)$. Means squares (MS) are formed by dividing SS by df. F ratios are $F_A = MS_A/MS_W$, $F_B = MS_B/MS_W$, and $F_{AB} = MS_{AB}/MS_W$. Each depends on the numerator MS estimating σ^2 if the respective H_0 is true and estimating σ^2 plus some positive quantity (a function of treatment effects or interaction effects) if H_0 is false. MS_W always estimates σ^2.

Each F ratio is distributed as F if the associated H_0 is true and if assumptions of normality, equal variance, and independence are met. You reject each H_0 if its F ratio exceeds an $\alpha\%$ critical value of F. Interpretation of main effects is modified depending on the F test for interaction.

Key terms introduced in this chapter are:

Two-way ANOVA	Interaction
Factors	SS_A, SS_B, SS_{AB}, SS_W
Cells	df_A, df_B, df_{AB}, df_W
Cell means	MS_A, MS_B, MS_{AB}, MS_W
Factorial design	F_A, F_B, F_{AB}
Main effects	Strength of association

The statistical tests introduced in this chapter are summarized in Table 16.8. There you'll find the situation where the statistic is used, the name of the statistic, and the theoretical reference distribution. For decision rules, assumptions, and any restrictions on the use of each procedure, refer to the appropriate section of the chapter.

Study Tips

The two-way ANOVA is easier to learn if you have memorized the logic of the one-way ANOVA. If you haven't done that yet, do so. Then see if you can write out the logic of the two-way ANOVA without referring to the book or your class notes.

Next, you need to be able to compute all of the degrees of freedom and form the mean squares and F ratios correctly. Exercises 8 and 9 below have blanks in an ANOVA summary table. Make up similar tables and change the number of levels of each factor; then see if you can fill in the blanks. You need only a few terms to be able to reconstruct the whole table.

Finally, a good way to study the two-way ANOVA is to draw some plots of cell means similar to the ones in Figure 16.2. Then see if you can figure out which F's would be significant. Drawing cell means can help you understand interaction and main effects, even though you should keep in mind that you can't tell whether groups are significantly different just by looking at plots.

Table 16.8

Situation	Statistic	Distribution
Two factors		
Equal cell sizes n		
H_0: $\mu_1 = \mu_2 \cdots = \mu_J = \mu$	F_A	F with $df_A = J - 1$ and $df_W = JK(n - 1)$
H_0: $\mu_1 = \mu_2 \cdots = \mu_K = \mu$	F_B	F with $df_B = K - 1$ and $df_W = JK(n - 1)$
H_0: no interaction effect	F_{AB}	F with $df_{AB} = (J - 1)(K - 1)$ and $df_W = JK(n - 1)$

Computation

As mentioned in Chapter 14, SAS has very good ANOVA programs. SPSS also has a general ANOVA command, which you will learn here. Much of what is presented here is a simple extension of what you learned about the one-way ANOVA.

SAS Example

(SAS system's lines)

```
DATA TWO;
INPUT DRIVE$ DIF$;    (inputs the levels of DRIVE and DIF, the two factors)
DO I = 1 TO 10;
INPUT X @@;    (inputs each X in the cell)
OUTPUT;
END;
CARDS;
LOW EASY
16 16 15 18 15 20 14 18 14 15
HIGH EASY
14 20 17 19 16 17 20 17 15 17
LOW HARD
12 16 13 15 15 17 14 19 16 15
HIGH HARD
 9 13 11 14 12 10 12 13 8 13
PROC PRINT;
PROC SORT; BY DRIVE;    (sorts the data by DRIVE so you can get the DRIVE means)
PROC MEANS; BY DRIVE; VAR X;
PROC SORT; BY DIF;    (sorts the data by DIF so you can get the DIF means)
PROC MEANS; BY DIF; VAR X;
PROC SORT; BY DRIVE DIF;    (sorts the data by DRIVE and DIF so you can get the cell means)
PROC MEANS; BY DRIVE DIF; VAR X;
PROC ANOVA;
CLASS DRIVE DIF;
MODEL X=DRIVE DIF DRIVE*DIF;    (specifies the model of the dependent variable X in terms of two main effects, DRIVE and
                                 DIF, and the interaction DRIVE* DIF)
TITLE 'TWOWAY';
```

(system's line)

TWOWAY

ANALYSIS OF VARIANCE PROCEDURE

DEPENDENT VARIABLE: X ①

SOURCE	DF	SUM OF SQUARES	MEAN SQUARE	F VALUE	PR > F
MODEL	3	183.40000000	61.13333333	15.65	0.0001
ERROR	36	140.60000000	3.90555556		
CORRECTED TOTAL	39	324.00000000			

Figure 16.5
SAS output from PROC ANOVA, a two-way ANOVA

(continued)

SOURCE②	DF③	ANOVA SS④	F VALUE⑤	PR > F⑥
DRIVE	1	16.90000000	4.33	0.0447
DIF	1	108.90000000	27.88	0.0001
DRIVE*DIF	1	57.60000000	14.75	0.0005

Figure 16.5 (continued)

For PROC ANOVA, the SAS output in Figure 16.5 gives the following:

1. For the dependent variable X, indicated in the MODEL statement by "$X =$", the *df* and *SS* are given for the source's model (the total of all that is to the right of the "$=$" in the model statement, here DRIVE, DIF, and DRIVE*DIF—the two main effects and the interaction), error (within), and corrected total (total). Then the *MS* values are given for model and error and the F and probability for model.

2. A list for the sources in the MODEL statement is given. A source is given for each main effect, DRIVE and DIF, and the interaction, DRIVE*DIF. Each of these sources use the MS_W (*MS* for error) for the denominator. Notice that the sources are in the order in which they were entered in the MODEL statement.

3. The degrees of freedom are $df_A = J - 1$, $df_B = K - 1$, and $df_{AB} = (J - 1)(K - 1)$.

4. *SS* values for each of the sources are given.

5. These are the F tests of interest in a two-way ANOVA.

6. These are probabilities of each F being larger than or equal to the observed F.

SPSS Example

(SPSS system's lines)
```
SET WIDTH 80
DATA LIST FREE/DRIVE DIF X     (inputs the factors and the data, with drive indicated by 1 for low and 2 for high, and with
                                difficulty indicated by 1 for easy and 2 for hard)
BEGIN DATA
1 1 16 1 1 16 1 1 15 1 1 18 1 1 15 1 1 20 1 1 14 1 1 18 1 1 14 1 1 15
2 1 14 2 1 20 2 1 17 2 1 19 2 1 16 2 1 17 2 1 20 2 1 17 2 1 15 2 1 17
1 2 12 1 2 16 1 2 13 1 2 15 1 2 15 1 2 17 1 2 14 1 2 19 1 2 16 1 2 15
2 2  9 2 2 13 2 2 11 2 2 14 2 2 12 2 2 10 2 2 12 2 2 13 2 2  8 2 2 13
END DATA
ANOVA VARIABLES= X BY DRIVE (1, 2) DIF (1, 2)/STATISTICS=MEAN
```
(The ANOVA command gives the two-way using X as the dependent variable, and DRIVE (minimum value of 1, maximum value of 2) and DIF (minimum value of 1, maximum value of 2) as the factors. The subcommand STATISTICS asks for all the means to be printed.)

```
FINISH
```
(system's line)

```
* * *   C E L L   M E A N S * * *
```

```
            X
     BY  DRIVE①
         DIF
```

TOTAL POPULATION

```
     15.00②
  (    40)
```

DRIVE

```
        1             2
```

```
     15.65       14.35
  (    20)  (     20)③
```

DIF

```
        1             2
```

```
     16.65       13.35
  (    20)  (     20)④
```

```
        DIF
                 1            2
DRIVE
     1    16.10       15.20
        (    10)  (    10)⑤
```

```
     2    17.20       11.50
        (    10)  (    10)
```

```
* * *   A N A L Y S I S   O F   V A R I A N C E   * * *
```

```
            X
     by   DRIVE①
          DIF
```

Source of Variation	Sum of Squares ⑥	DF ⑦	Mean Square ⑧	F ⑨	Sig of F ⑩
Main Effects	125.800	2	62.900	16.105	.000
DRIVE	16.900	1	16.900	4.327	.045
DIF	108.900	1	108.900	27.883	.000

Figure 16.6
SPSS output for the two-way ANOVA

(continued)

2-Way Interactions	57.600	1	57.600	14.748	.000
DRIVE DIF	57.600	1	57.600	14.748	.000
Explained	183.400	3	61.133	15.653	.000
Residual	140.600	36	3.906		
Total	324.000	39	8.308		

40 cases were processed.
1 cases (.0 pct) were missing.

Figure 16.6 (continued)

For the command ANOVA, the SPSS output in Figure 16.6 gives the following:

1. The dependent variable and the two factors
2. The sample grand mean
3. The sample means for drive
4. The sample means for difficulty
5. The sample cell means
6. Sum of squares; be careful to use only those you want, those for DRIVE, DIF, the DRIVE by DIF interaction, and the within (here called Residual)
7. *df* (see note 6)
8. *MS* (see note 6)
9. *F* ratios; be careful to use only those you want, those for DRIVE, DIF, the DRIVE by DIF interaction
10. The *p*-values used to test hypotheses (see note 9)

Exercises

Sections 16.1–16.2

1. Consider the study technique/cognitive style experiment discussed at the beginning of the chapter.
   a. What are the factors? How many levels of each are there?
   b. What are the levels of each factor?
   c. Describe what is meant by interaction in terms of this study.

2. If the denominator of each *F* ratio is small (small within-cells variability), which *F* ratio(s) would be significant for the plots of cell means in Figure 16.7?

3. If the following cell means are observed with very small within-cells variability, which *F* ratio(s) would be significant?

a.

	B_1	B_2	B_3
A_1	10	10	10
A_2	15	5	10

b.

	B_1	B_2
A_1	30	15
A_2	20	15

c.

	B_1	B_2
A_1	30	10
A_2	30	10

4. Insert the missing cell means to make all the cell means consistent with the conditions given.
   a. F_A significant, F_B and F_{AB} both equal to zero

	B_1	B_2	B_3
A_1	10		
A_2	5		

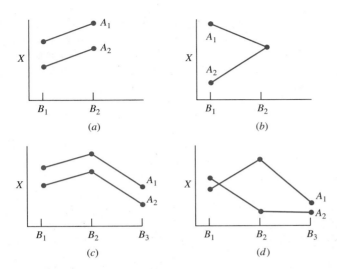

Figure 16.7
Plots of cell means

Source	SS	df	MS	F
A	120	3	___	___
B	400	2	___	___
AB	60	___	___	___
Within	2400	120	___	
Total	___	___		

b. Which *F* tests are significant? How do you interpret these results if factor *A* is grades 1 to 4 and factor *B* is methods of teaching reading?

9. In the partial ANOVA summary table, fill in the missing pieces.

Source	SS	df	MS	F
A	___	2	___	5
B	___	___	___	2
AB	___	___	___	10
Within	___	36	20	
Total	___	44		

b. F_A and F_B significant, F_{AB} equal to zero

	B_1	B_2	B_3
A_1	10	15	20
A_2	5		

c. F_{AB} and F_A significant, F_B equal to zero

	B_1	B_2	B_3
A_1	10	15	5
A_2	20		

5. What are the three advantages of using one two-way ANOVA over two one-way ANOVAs? Describe these advantages in terms of the study given in Research Example 16.

6. What is meant by X_{121}, X_{321}, X_{ijk}, $\overline{X}_k$, and $\overline{X}_{jk}$?

7. If $n = 10$ and the design is as shown in Exercise 3, part a, what are the values of df_A, df_{AB}, and df_W?

Sections 16.3–16.4

8. Use the following partial ANOVA summary table.
   a. Fill in the missing pieces.

10. Suppose you suspected that the method of teaching reading has a different effect for boys and for girls. You ran a small study using two methods for only first-grade students and found the following cell means for gender and teaching methods (dependent variable is the number of test items correct):

	Method	
	1	2
Girls	50	50
Boys	50	35

If F_{AB}, F_A, and F_B are all significant, what conclusions should you draw?

11. Calculate ω^2 and η^2 for each of the *F* tests in Exercise 8.

12. Gilliland and Andress (1981) studied caffeine consumption (coffee, tea, soft drinks, hot cocoa, and candy bars) by college students and its relationship to various variables, including anxiety, depression, and academic performance. Students were selected from abstainers, low-caffeine consumers [less than 1 coffee-cup-equivalent (CCE) per day], moderate-caffeine consumers (from 1 to less than 5 CCE/day), and high-caffeine consumers (5 or more CCE/day). Twenty men and twenty women were selected from the introductory psychology course from each caffeine consumption level.

a. What are the factors (main effects) in the study? How many levels of each are there? Draw a schematic of the design, and label the levels of each factor.

b. If A = caffeine level and B = gender, what are the values of df_A, df_B, df_{AB}, and df_W?

c. The following means on the trait anxiety score were observed for the caffeine level groups: none, 32.35; low, 34.82; moderate, 38.65; high, 35.95. If $MS_A = 272$ and $MS_W = 76.8$, are these means significantly different? (Use $\alpha = .05$.)

d. Is this a true experiment? What conclusions can you draw about caffeine consumption and trait anxiety?

e. The following means for grades in the psychology course were observed by caffeine consumption levels: none, 2.78; low, 2.79; moderate, 2.38; high, 2.06. If $F_A = 4.23$, can you conclude that you will get better grades if you reduce your caffeine consumption? Explain your answer.

Sections 16.4 and 16.5

13. Return to the attraction research of Wrather and Padd (1971) (see Exercise 18 in Chapter 14). They wished to assess the effect of both similarity and competence on attraction. In the experiment, they used two levels of attitude similarity: 80% similar and 80% dissimilar. They also used three levels of competence: high (college professor), medium (graduate student), and low (first-year student). Participants were randomly assigned to one of the six combinations of these two variables (2 × 3) and received the manipulation by the description of the hypothetical stranger and the attitudes of the stranger, which were either 80% similar or 80% dissimilar to their own attitudes. The results for the six cells are given in the table.

Wrather–Padd data (IJS scores)

	Low Competence (First-Year Student)	Medium Competence (Graduate Assistant)	High Competence (Professor)
	8	9	10
	6	9	10
	10	8	10
	12	12	12
	9	12	13
	8	12	9
High Similarity (80% similarity)	13	11	10
	7	12	10
	12	12	11
	10	11	10
	12	10	12
	12	12	10
	8	5	10
	5	10	8
	6	6	8
	8	10	9
	7	5	6
	5	8	12
Low Similarity (20% similarity)	8	7	12
	8	8	7
	4	5	8
	6	6	7
	4	10	4
	6	5	11

a. Do separate one-way analyses of the factors "competence" and "similarity" (collapse over the other factor and do one-way ANOVAs). You can use SAS or SPSS if you desire. Do you recognize that you could do a two-independent-sample t-test on similarity and get equivalent results ($t^2 = F$) for the similarity test?

b. Compute the two-way ANOVA with "competence" and "similarity" as the factors, using SAS or SPSS if you desire. Compute the strength of association measures.

c. Write a summary of your results in part b in a few short paragraphs that would serve as the results section of a journal article.

d. Now compare the results from part a with those from part b. Explain any differences. Why are the results (even those that are similar) not exactly the same?

14. A researcher wanted to see whether the type of motor activity used in training children on words results in different spelling abilities. Each child was shown a word on a 3 × 5 card, the researcher named the word and asked the child to repeat it, and then the child was asked to reproduce the word by one of three activities. The three motor activities were handwriting, typing the word on a computer keyboard, or using letter tiles (plastic tiles with two sets of the alphabet). Training was over four days, and 20 short words were used in each of the three training activities. The researcher was concerned about gender differences in the task, so she randomly assigned 30 first-grade boys, 10 each to the three motor activities. Similarly, she randomly assigned 30 first-grade girls, 10 each to the three motor activities. A spelling test was given on the fifth day. The numbers of correct words recorded for each child are listed in the table.

	Writing	Computer	Tiles
Boys	13	12	11
	15	13	12
	13	11	12
	12	11	11
	11	11	11
	16	13	12
	12	12	11
	13	12	13
	12	11	10
	14	13	11
Girls	15	11	13
	17	12	10
	15	10	14
	14	10	9
	13	10	13
	18	12	10
	14	11	9
	15	11	15
	14	10	8
	16	12	13

a. Compute all the means for the main effects and cells and draw a plot of the cell means.

b. Compute the two-way ANOVA with "motor activity" and "gender" as the factors, using SAS or SPSS if you desire. Compute the strength of association measures.

c. Write a summary of your results in a few short paragraphs that would serve as the results section of a journal article.

15. Suppose a group of nonexercisers who wanted to lose weight and volunteered for an exercise program were all put through a general conditioning program for 6 months. Then, within gender, they were randomly assigned to one of three groups: continue with the general exercise program, increase the amount of exercise, or stop exercising ("not enough instructors, wait for others to finish"). At the end of 6 weeks, a mood state inventory found scores for vigor, as shown in the table:

	No Exercise	*General Exercise*	*Increased Exercise*
Men	10	20	21
	11	19	23
	12	24	27
	9	17	30
Women	13	24	26
	14	23	28
	15	28	32
	12	21	35

a. Compute all the means for the main effects and cells and draw a plot of the cell means.

b. Compute the two-way ANOVA with "exercise" and "gender" as the factors, using SAS or SPSS if you desire. Compute the strength of association measures.

c. Write a summary of your results in a few short paragraphs that would serve as the results section of a journal article.

d. Using the names of the variables in this study, explain the logic of the two-way ANOVA.

16. A study was concerned with the effects of instructions to young children and their subsequent attempts to help another child (apparently) in distress (based on Staub, 1970). Wanting to check for gender differences, the researcher randomly assigned 42 first-grade students within gender to one of three groups. The first group was indirect responsibility (IR), where students were informed that another child was alone in an adjoining room and had been warned not to climb up on a chair. The second group was direct responsibility (DR1), where students were told the same story as in IR but also that they (the participants) were being left in charge and to take care of anything that happened. All students were given a simple task, and the researcher left the room. Students then heard a loud crash from the adjoining room followed by a minute of crying and sobbing. Those in the third group (DR2) had the same instructions as the DR1 group, but the sounds of distress also included calls for help. Ratings from 1 (no help) to 5 (went to adjoining room) were given to each student from behind a one-way mirror. The results are given in the table.

	IR	DR1	DR2
	3	5	4
	4	4	4
	2	5	3
Boys	1	3	4
	1	4	5
	2	5	4
	1	5	5
	2	5	5
	3	5	3
	3	4	2
Girls	2	3	3
	1	1	2
	1	4	4
	2	3	1

a. Compute all the means for the main effects and cells and draw a plot of the cell means.

b. Compute the two-way ANOVA with "instructions" and "gender" as the factors, using SAS or SPSS if you desire. Compute the strength of association measures.

c. Write a summary of your results in a few short paragraphs that would serve as the results section of a journal article.

17. Researchers think that moderate exercise may help relieve depression, especially among elderly people (see McNeil, LeBlanc & Joyner, 1991). Because of social contact while exercising, the researchers want to include a group that has social contact but no exercise. They establish a waiting-list control group. They recruit 30 elderly depressed people who are capable of moderate exercise and, because of potential age differences, randomly assign from within two age categories five people each to three groups: exercise, social contact, and wait list. Those in the exercise group walked outside (or in a mall during bad weather) with a researcher two times a week and alone once a week for 20 min each time (increasing to 40 min) for 6 weeks. The social contact group met with a researcher for two 20–40-min sessions each week for 6 weeks for casual conversation like that in the exercise condition. The data in the table came from the 14-item psychological portion of the Beck Depression Inventory (BDI; Beck & Beamesderfer, 1974).

	Exercise	Social Contact	Wait List
	1	2	6
	5	11	10
Age 70 or Younger	6	11	11
	7	10	8
	3	8	7
	8	6	5
	7	2	7
Older than 70	5	1	7
	9	3	8
	7	5	11

a. Compute all the means for the main effects and cells and draw a plot of the cell means.

b. Compute the two-way ANOVA with "treatment" and "age" as the factors, using SAS or SPSS if you desire. Compute the strength of association measures.

c. Write a summary of your results in a few short paragraphs that would serve as the results section of a journal article.

17

Repeated Measures ANOVA

When you studied statistics appropriate for testing hypotheses from two groups, you learned about both independent and dependent groups. Then you learned about one- and two-way ANOVAs, which are appropriate for two or more independent groups. You may have wondered what to do if you have data from more than two *dependent* groups. This chapter fills in that void by giving two of the most popular designs appropriate for dependent data.

Research Example 17
17.1 **Introduction**
17.2 **Characteristics of Repeated Measures Designs**
  Between- and within-subjects variability
  No estimate of error variance and different denominators
  Correlated data
  Subjects' variability controlled
17.3 **Simple Repeated Measures Design**
  Example
  Computation of the *F* test
  F distribution and decision rules
17.4 **Groups by Trials Repeated Measures Design**
  Example
  Computation of the *F* tests
  F distributions and decision rules
17.5 **Assumptions**
  Robustness
  Beyond these repeated measures designs
17.6 **Summary, Study Tips, and Computation**
  Chapter summary
  Study tips
  Computation
Exercises

Research Example 17

Have you ever tried to perform some task, like typing, while someone watched? Did you feel anxious, intimidated, or pressured to excel? This is the area of social facilitation and is an example of the "mere-presence" effect. The mere-presence effect as hypothesized by Zajonc (1965) is that the mere presence of another person affects performance. Worringham and Messick (1983) were concerned about the bias of the researcher's presence in earlier studies, including the fact that most participants were aware of being in an experiment. The researchers designed a simple study to test the mere-presence effect in a situation where the participants were not aware of being in an experiment.

The study involved runners on a footpath that went past one side of a dirt bank and then turned and went past the other side. The bank kept runners on one side from seeing the other side. Thirty-six runners—18 men and 18 women—were filmed and they did not know they were being observed. Each runner was measured twice, once for each 45-yd segment. The researchers counted the number of frames of film taken. The dependent variable was the number of frames taken for each of two adjacent 45-yd segments separated by the bank. On the first segment, all runners thought they were alone because they couldn't see over the dirt bank. For the second

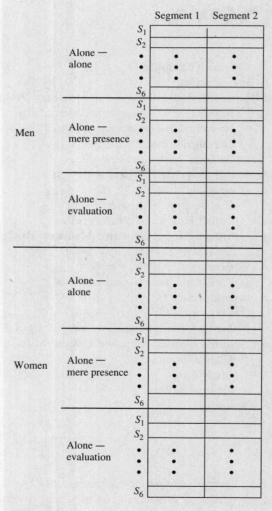

Figure 17.1
Schematic of Worringham and Messick (1983) repeated measures design

segment, the runners were able to see someone sitting near the footpath. The researchers manipulated whether the runners saw someone and whether the person was facing the runner. So runners were randomly assigned within gender to one of three conditions: alone–alone (for both segments of the path), alone–mere presence, and alone–evaluation. For the last two conditions, a woman reading a book was seated on the grass near the path on the second segment. The alone–mere presence condition had the woman with her back turned to the runners. The alone–evaluation condition had the woman facing the runners.

If you were a runner, would you speed up if you thought someone was watching you run? These researchers wanted to see whether the runners changed their speed on the second segment, depending on the condition to which they had been assigned. There were 12 runners in each of the three conditions. Figure 17.1 shows a schematic of the experimental design.

Although the emphasis here is on design, the results are interesting. Segments of path (before and after manipulation) interacted with condition, $F_{2,30} = 5.48$, $p < .01$. When they further analyzed the data, Worringham and Messick found that the increase in speed was dependent on condition. Increase in speed means fewer frames. For example, for the alone–evaluation condition, they found a mean of 294.1 frames for segment 1 but 281.3 for segment 2, a difference of 12.75. This difference for the alone–evaluation condition was significantly larger than that for either of the other two conditions (average difference of 2.95 for alone–alone and average difference of 3.65 for alone–mere presence).

You've seen the term *repeated measures* associated with the two-dependent-sample t-test. You can't use the two-independent-sample t-test on the correlated data. Similarly, you can't use the usual analysis of variance here because there is dependence between a runner's performance on the two segments. In this chapter you'll learn how to analyze data from two basic repeated measures designs by using special F tests.

17.1   Introduction

Does the progression from the one-way ANOVA to the two-way ANOVA indicate that you could have a three-way ANOVA? Indeed, three-way and even higher-order ANOVAs do exist and are used frequently in behavioral science research. These analyses are sometimes simple extensions of the two-way ANOVA as presented in Chapter 16, and as such they offer no new challenges except increased complexity. However, multifactor ANOVAs are also used to measure an individual two or more times on the same dependent variable, with these measurements arranged as the levels of a factor. These are **repeated measures designs,** extensions of one of the settings for the two-dependent-sample t. Repeated measures designs often are used in studies of learning and memory because you have to measure someone initially in order to see later how much he or she has learned or remembered. Here we use K as the number of measurements. In repeated measures designs, you have $K \geq 2$ measurements; this means the **repeated factor** has $K \geq 2$ levels. The repeated factor can be time, trials, or some treatment condition.

Many repeated measures designs result from the many ways of combining repeated factors and other factors. We will examine only two popular repeated measures designs. Because this chapter is an introduction, the emphasis is on examples and characteristics

Repeated measures designs
Any design in which individuals are measured two or more times on the same dependent variable

Repeated factor
Any factor that has levels defined by the repeated measures on the same dependent variable, also called a within-subjects factor

of these designs. Minimal explanation is given for the sums of squares, degrees of freedom, and mean squares, but computational examples are given. The computations can be overwhelming, but computer packages are available. Many research questions can be answered only by using a repeated measures design. Don't let computational difficulty deter you from using repeated measures designs if you need them to answer your research questions.

Quick Quiz

How would you compare the effects of two different weight loss programs on men's and women's weights?

Answer

Changes in weight can be studied only by making repeated measures. You could design a study with equal numbers of men and women in each of the two weight loss programs, and then measure all participants over time in the programs.

17.2   Characteristics of Repeated Measures Designs

Between- and Within-Subjects Variability

In the one-way ANOVA, the total variability is partitioned into between-groups and within-groups variability. In repeated measures designs, the total variability is divided into **between-subjects variability** and **within-subjects variability.** This partitioning of variability is sometimes written:

Total variability = between-subjects variability + within-subjects variability

We emphasize "subjects" here because in repeated measures designs, subjects are treated as a separate factor. Each subject is measured two or more times, so there is variability within subjects as well as variability between subjects. If you were in an experiment to improve your memory, your performance would vary from one time to another, even if the treatment didn't work.

The within-subjects variability includes the repeated factor with levels that are the $K \geq 2$ measurements, plus any interaction between the repeated factor and other factors, such as gender. Another name for a repeated factor is a *within-subjects factor.* In the mere-presence example, the measurements on the two segments of the path are the levels of the repeated factor—that is, the within-subjects factor. In this example, you could call the repeated factor "time" or "segment."

Two other terms you need to learn are *crossed* and *nested.* Both apply to factors considered two at a time. Two factors are **crossed** in a design if every level of one factor is combined with every level of the other factor. For example, the factor "subject" is crossed with any repeated factor because every subject is measured at every level of a repeated factor. In the mere-presence example, "subject" is crossed with "segment" because all subjects were measured on both segments, both levels of the repeated factor. Two factors are said to be **nested** if not every level of one factor is combined with every level of the other factor; that is, nested means "not crossed." For example, in the mere-presence study, 12 runners were in each of the conditions. A runner in the alone–alone condition was not in the other two conditions, so runner was nested in condition. Any factor in which subjects are nested cannot be a repeated factor.

Between-subjects variability and within-subjects variability
Between-subjects variability is that due to different subjects; within-subjects variability is that due to repeated measures on the same subjects

Crossed
Two factors with levels that are together in every possible combination

Nested
Two factors with levels that are not together in every possible combination, "not crossed"

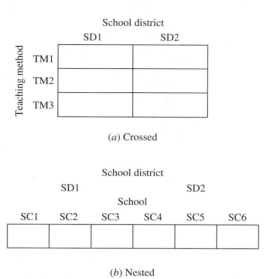

(a) Crossed

(b) Nested

Figure 17.2
Crossed versus nested factors

Look at Figure 17.2 and consider these examples to help you understand *nested* and *crossed*. Suppose you want to do research on three different teaching methods (TM1, TM2, and TM3) in each of two school districts (SD1 and SD2). Then every teaching method (TM1–TM3) will appear in every school district, so teaching method and district are crossed as in Figure 17.2(a). Suppose in another study you want to see whether there are differences on some variable between three different schools (SC1–SC6) in each of the two districts. Then only three of the six schools are in each district, so school and district are nested as in Figure 17.2(b).

Some repeated measures designs have sources of variability other than subjects that are between-subjects sources; in the mere-presence example, the between-subjects sources are "condition" and "gender." Such between-subjects factors must have subjects nested within them. Other repeated measures designs do not have any between-subjects sources of variability in addition to subjects. These latter designs have only within-subjects main effects, such as each subject completing all tasks. For example, in a study of car interior design, you could have drivers perform under all the conditions of type of control, twist knob versus toggle switch, combined with two distances from hand position on the steering wheel, 18 in. versus 24 in. Suppose your dependent variable is reaction time to turn the control to "on," you have each driver perform ten trials in each condition, and you average the times over trials. Then you would have two levels of each of the two repeated factors, "control" and "distance." See Figure 17.3 for a schematic of this experimental design.

Repeated measures designs can be classified by their number of between- and within-subjects factors, such as "zero between, two within" (the all within-subjects study of control and distance) or "two between, one within" (the mere-presence study). If possible, the order of presentation of the levels of the repeated factors is randomized for each subject. Such random assignment of order helps control for potential confounding variables such as fatigue, practice, and carryover effects. If the repeated

	Twist knob		Toggle switch	
	18 in.	24 in.	18 in.	24 in.
S_1				
S_2				
S_3				
•				
•				
•				
S_n				

Figure 17.3
Two repeated factors

factor is treatment, then randomization of order is possible. If participants are taste-testing new fruit drinks, you could randomly assign the order in which they receive the beverages. Without randomly assigning the order of beverages, you might not know whether participants truly prefer the first drink—say, cherry—or whether they just were more enthusiastic at the beginning of the experiment. Randomization of order is impossible if the repeated factor is time or trials, simply because the order of all the times or trials is already defined. For participants in a weight control program, time can't be randomly assigned; they are all weighed at the same time intervals.

No Estimate of Error Variance and Different Denominators

Another characteristic of repeated measures designs is that there is no true estimate of error variance. This happens because the total subjects' variability is broken into between- and within-subjects sources. Because subject is a factor and each subject is a level of that factor, each combination of subject and level of the repeated factor has only one observation. That is, each subject is measured once under each level of the repeated factor, so there is only one observation per cell. Reexamine Figure 17.1 and see that each condition-gender-subject-segment combination has only one measurement. You are unable to get within-cells variability with only one observation per cell.

For the one-way and two-way ANOVAs, the within-groups variance estimate is the denominator of the F ratios. But if there is no within-cells variability with $n = 1$, you have to find something else to use as the denominator. Repeated measures designs use different possible denominators, depending on the experimental design. For the two designs you'll learn in this chapter, the denominators won't always be the same as denominators for other designs.

Correlated Data

As you've read, repeated measures designs are analogous to the two-dependent-sample *t*-test because each subject is measured repeatedly. They both deal with dependent (correlated) data. Repeated measures designs have two or more levels of the repeated factor, however, whereas the two-dependent-sample *t*-test is restricted to two levels.

Subjects' Variability Controlled

When you deal with repeated measures designs, you'll sometimes hear, "Each subject acts as its own control." (In fact, you might remember such terminology from the two-dependent-sample *t* example of the Brazelton data on newborn babies measured on days 1 and 10 of life.) To understand this idea, think about a treatment group and a control group in the two-independent-sample case. You want the two groups to be as similar as possible except for the treatment. Then any difference between the groups can be attributed to the treatment. For a given subject, who is the perfect control subject? The same person. In a repeated measures design, each subject is measured two or more times, so a subject's performances can be compared in two or more conditions of the repeated factor. This was the same advantage as in the repeated measures application of the two-dependent-sample case, where the denominator of the two-dependent-sample *t* became smaller (see Section 13.3 for a review). Because subject variability is controlled, the tests of within-subjects factors and their interactions are more efficient than between-subjects tests. This gain in efficiency for the within-subjects tests is one of the advantages of repeated measures designs.

Quick Quiz

Consider again the question about the effects of two different weight loss programs on men's and women's weights. (a) Name the between-subjects and within-subjects factors. (b) Which factors are crossed? Nested?

Answers

(a) The within-subjects factor, which is the same as the repeated factor, is the weighing time, with the possibility of many levels or weigh-ins. The between-subjects factors are gender and treatment programs; neither of these factors is repeated. (b) Subjects are always a separate factor in repeated measures designs, and they are nested within gender and program. There are men and women in both weight loss programs, so gender is crossed with program. Weighing time is crossed with the other factors (subjects, gender, program) because all levels of time are found at all levels of the other factors.

17.3   Simple Repeated Measures Design

Simple repeated measures design
In addition to subjects, this design has one factor and it is repeated; factors other than subjects are zero between, one within

Let's consider the most basic repeated measures design. The **simple repeated measures design** has only one factor in addition to subjects, and it is repeated (zero between, one within). There are K levels of the repeated factor, and n subjects are measured in all K levels, as shown in Figure 17.4. This design is the basic building block for all repeated measures designs. We'll focus on the sums of squares, degrees of freedom, mean squares, and formation of the F ratio. Assumptions for all repeated measures designs are given in Section 17.5.

Example

Suppose you want to do a study similar to the mere-presence example and measure how people will perform on difficult math problems—long division of a three-digit

	T_1	T_2	T_3	$\cdots$	T_K
S_1					
S_2					
S_3					
$\cdot$					
$\cdot$					
$\cdot$					
S_n					

Figure 17.4
Simple repeated measures design: T = repeated factor with K levels, S = subjects with n subjects

Table 17.1
Simple repeated measures design

Subject	Alone	Present	Watching	Sums
1	15	14	11	40
2	14	11	6	31
3	15	17	13	45
4	12	11	8	31
5	9	10	6	25
6	15	12	8	35
7	17	19	15	51
8	20	17	9	46
9	19	15	10	44
10	13	10	9	32
Sums	149	136	95	380
Means	14.9	13.6	9.5	3.80

number divided into a six-digit number. Does performance while working alone on the problems differ from that while working with someone present but not watching, compared with performance when someone is present and watching? You could decide to use each subject as his or her own control and use the experimental factor as a repeated factor. All subjects would get three conditions: alone, present, and watching. The order of conditions would be randomly assigned to each of ten subjects. Suppose you obtain the data given in Table 17.1 on the numbers of math problems correctly solved.

Computation of the *F* Test

In any repeated measures design, the total *SS* is broken into between- and within-subjects variability:

$$SS_{\text{total}} = SS_{\text{between-subjects}} + SS_{\text{within-subjects}} \tag{17.1}$$

with further division of the within-subjects *SS* and, depending on the design, possible further division of the between-subject *SS*. In a simple repeated measures design, the total *SS* is broken into three pieces, with the latter two coming from $SS_{\text{within-subjects}}$:

$$SS_{\text{total}} = SS_S + SS_T + SS_{TS} \qquad (17.2)$$

The *T* subscript stands for treatment or trial, which is the repeated factor, *S* stands for subject, and *TS* stands for the interaction of trial and subject. SS_{TS} can be obtained by subtracting $SS_S + SS_T$ from SS_{total}. In the mere-presence/math problems example in Table 17.1, the effect of condition may depend on the subject. SS_S is all of the between-subjects variability, but the within-subjects variability is broken into the two pieces SS_T and SS_{TS}. Computational formulas for *SS* are given later.

The degrees of freedom for this design also can be broken into three parts:

$$df_{\text{total}} = df_S + df_T + df_{TS}$$
$$N - 1 = n - 1 + K - 1 + (K - 1)(n - 1) \qquad (17.3)$$

N stands for the total number of observations, even though the observations are correlated. For the mere-presence/math problems example, the ten subjects are measured three times each, so $N = 30$.

Mean squares are always formed by dividing the appropriate *SS* by its *df*: $MS = SS/df$. The mean squares for *T* and *TS* are used here, so we have

$$MS_T = \frac{SS_T}{df_T} = \frac{SS_T}{K - 1}$$

$$MS_{TS} = \frac{SS_{TS}}{df_{TS}} = \frac{SS_{TS}}{(K - 1)(n - 1)} \qquad (17.4)$$

The mean square for the interaction, MS_{TS}, is sometimes called the *residual mean square* because the SS_{TS} is what is left over after you account for the main effects of *T* and *S*. You've seen the term *residual* used as a synonym for *error*. The MS_{TS} is the error term, the denominator of the *F* test in the simple repeated measures design.

The hypothesis to be tested is given as

$$H_0: \mu_1 = \mu_2 = \cdots = \mu_K \qquad (17.5)$$

which is equality of the *K* population means for *T*. Like the related means in the two-dependent-sample case, these population means are correlated because they are the means for the *K* levels of the repeated factor. In the mere-presence/math problems example, you hypothesize no differences in the average numbers of correct solutions among the three conditions.

Now you are ready to form the *F* ratio for *T* using the *MS* in formula 17.4:

$$F_T = \frac{MS_T}{MS_{TS}} \qquad (17.6)$$

The *F* ratio is formed by putting MS_T in the numerator and MS_{TS} in the denominator. There is no MS_W, and there is no *F* test for *S*. (Would you even be interested in an *F* test

Repeated measures design: Science or religion?

for *S*? Naturally, people differ from each other. Such an *F* test typically wouldn't answer a research question.)

F Distribution and Decision Rules

The F_T computed in formula 17.6 can be used to test the hypothesis in 17.5 by comparing F_T to a critical value from an *F* distribution. If the H_0 is true and if certain assumptions are met (discussed in Section 17.5), then

> F_T is distributed as an *F* distribution   (17.7)
> with parameters $K - 1$ and $(K - 1)(n - 1)$

That is, F_T has degrees of freedom $df_T = K - 1$ for the numerator and $df_{TS} = (K - 1)(n - 1)$ for the denominator. You find the critical value, F_{crit}, by using Table A.6 in Appendix A with df_T for the column and df_{TS} for the row.

The critical value decision rule is based on using the chosen α and the corresponding critical value to give:

> Reject H_0 if $F_T \geq F_{crit}$; otherwise, retain H_0 (17.8)

Because computer programs give a *p*-value for the observed *F* ratio, you most likely would use a critical value decision rule if you did the analysis by hand.

The *p*-value decision rule for an ANOVA *F* test is fairly simple if the computer package gives the probability that $F \geq F_{observed}$ for H_0 true. The rule is:

> Reject H_0 if $p \leq \alpha$; otherwise, retain H_0 (17.9)

where $p = p(F \geq F_{observed} \mid H_0 \text{ true})$.

Table 17.2 contains the computations from the data in Table 17.1, including the *F* test and the decision. What does your significant *F* mean in the context of the participants who did math problems in solitude, in the presence of another, and in the presence of someone watching? The significant result means that there is a difference among the three conditions. Performance differs depending on the condition.

Do people perform significantly better alone compared to the other two conditions? What about comparisons among the other conditions? You should recognize that this is another multiple comparisons problem and that the probability of at least one Type I error needs to be controlled for all of these tests. The simplest approach is to do two-

Table 17.2
Computations for simple repeated measures design

$n = 10$ $K = 3$
S = subjects, T = trials, $TS = T \times S$ interaction
$df_S = n - 1 = 10 - 1 = 9$
$df_T = K - 1 = 3 - 1 = 2$
$df_{TS} = (df_T)(df_S) = (2)(9) = 18$
$F_{2, 18} = F_{crit} = 3.55$

$$SS_S = \frac{\sum_i(\sum_k X_{ik})^2}{K} - \frac{(\sum_k \sum_i X_{ik})^2}{nK} = \frac{40^2 + 31^2 + \cdots + 44^2 + 32^2}{3} - \frac{380^2}{10(3)}$$

$$= 5024.67 - 4813.33 = 211.33$$

$$SS_T = \frac{\sum_k(\sum_i X_{ik})^2}{n} - \frac{(\sum_k \sum_i X_{ik})^2}{nK} = \frac{149^2 + 136^2 + 95^2}{10} - \frac{380^2}{10(3)}$$

$$= 4972.2 - 4813.33 = 158.87$$

$$MS_T = \frac{SS_T}{K - 1} = \frac{158.87}{2} = 79.43$$

$$SS_{TS} = \sum_k \sum_i X_{ik}^2 - \frac{\sum_i(\sum_k X_{ik})^2}{K} - \frac{\sum_k(\sum_i X_{ij})^2}{n} + \frac{(\sum_k \sum_i X_{ik})^2}{nK}$$

$$= 15^2 + 14^2 + \cdots + 10^2 + 9^2 - 5024.67 - 4972.2 + 4813.33$$

$$= 5238 - 5024.67 - 4972.2 + 4813.33 = 54.47$$

$$MS_{TS} = \frac{SS_{TS}}{df_{TS}} = \frac{54.47}{18} = 3.0259$$

$$F_T = \frac{MS_T}{MS_{TS}} = \frac{79.43}{3.0259} = 26.25$$

Source	SS	df	MS	F	p
T	158.87	2	79.43	26.25	.0001
S	211.33	9			
TS	54.47	18	3.0259		

$F_{crit} = 3.55$, so F_T is significant and you reject H$_0$.

Multiple comparisons:
First, get d's (differences) for all pairs of conditions, and then get the sum, the sum of squares of the d's, and the mean of the d's, called $\bar{d}$.

Alone vs. Present	*Alone vs. Watching*	*Present vs. Watching*
1	4	3
3	8	5
−2	2	4
1	4	3
−1	3	4
3	7	4
−2	2	4
3	11	8
4	9	5
3	4	1
$\sum d$ 13	54	41
$\sum d^2$ 63	380	197
$\bar{d}$ 1.3	5.4	4.1

(*continued*)

Table 17.2 (continued)

Now, compute the two-dependent-sample *t*-tests.

$$t = \frac{\bar{d}}{\sqrt{\dfrac{n(\Sigma d^2) - (\Sigma d)^2}{n(n-1)/n}}}$$

$$t_{\text{alone-present}} = \frac{1.3}{\sqrt{\dfrac{10(63) - (13)^2}{10(9)/10}}} = \frac{1.3}{0.715697018} = 1.82$$

$$t_{\text{alone-watching}} = \frac{5.4}{\sqrt{\dfrac{10(380) - (54)^2}{10(9)/10}}} = \frac{5.4}{0.991071249} = 5.45$$

$$t_{\text{present-watching}} = \frac{4.1}{\sqrt{\dfrac{10(197) - (41)^2}{10(9)/10}}} = \frac{4.1}{0.566666667} = 7.24$$

Because the critical value for $\alpha = .05$ from Table A.8 with $df = 9$ and $C = 3$ is 2.933, $t_{\text{alone-watching}}$ and $t_{\text{present-watching}}$ are significant.

---

dependent-sample *t*-tests for all possible pairs of levels of the repeated factor. Each test uses an adjusted $\alpha' = \alpha/C$, where *C* is the number of tests, and $df = n - 1$. You don't have to make this adjustment to α; it is done for you in Table A.8. All you have to do is enter the table with the number of tests you are doing (*C*) and the degrees of freedom for the denominator of your tests (here $df = n - 1$). The entries in Table A.8 are the critical values for $\alpha = .05$ and $\alpha = .01$. This procedure is referred to as Dunn's or Bonferroni's procedure (Dunn, 1961) and is recommended for multiple comparisons in simple repeated measures designs (see Maxwell, 1980, or Toothaker, 1991).

Your conclusion from the computations in Table 17.2 would be that having someone watch you lowers your performance compared to being alone or having someone present. But simply having someone present compared to being alone doesn't make a difference in the number of math problems solved.

Quick Quiz

You are studying whether one's memory for lists of words is better when using rote recitation, elaboration, or a memory device or mnemonic called the *method of loci*. Elaboration in your study means each participant mentally writes one sentence for each object on the list. The mnemonic, method of loci, is for the participants to imagine placing each object in their homes; then, when the participants want to recall the words, they mentally walk through their home collecting the objects. You use 20 participants and randomly assign the order of condition (rote, elaboration, mnemonic). Each memory session is separated by a 30-min break, and participants are told to use only the memory tip as instructed during the session. (a) How would you partition SS_{total}? (b) Find df_S, df_T, and df_{TS}.

Answers

(a) $SS_{\text{total}} = SS_S + SS_T + SS_{TS}$. (b) $df_S = n - 1 = 19$, $df_T = K - 1 = 2$, and $df_{TS} = (n - 1)(K - 1) = 38$. (Check: $df_{\text{total}} = N - 1 = 60 - 1 = 59$, and $df_{\text{total}} = df_S + df_T + df_{TS} = 19 + 2 + 38 = 59$.)

17.4 Groups by Trials Repeated Measures Design

Groups by trials repeated measures design
In addition to subjects, this design has one repeated factor and one nonrepeated factor; factors other than subjects are one between, one within

The second repeated measures design we consider is one step up from the simple repeated measures design. The **groups by trials repeated measures design** has two factors in addition to subjects, with one repeated factor and one nonrepeated factor (one between, one within). This design also is called a *mixed design* or *mixed factorial* because you are combining a factor that has independent groups with another factor whose levels are dependent. There are J groups for the nonrepeated factor, K levels of the repeated factor (trials), and n subjects within each of the J groups. All subjects are measured in all K levels of trials but are nested in groups. See Figure 17.5 for a schematic of the groups by trials design. Each level of J is like its own simple repeated measures design. This design contains J basic building blocks, the simple repeated measures design. Again, let's focus on the sums of squares, degrees of freedom, mean squares, and formation of the F ratio.

Example

Rider and Daly (1991) researched the effects of flexibility training on spinal mobility in older women. They used 20 women volunteers with an average age of 71.8, who were in moderately good health including free from orthopedic problems. All women had medical clearance from their doctors to participate in the research. Ten women were randomly assigned to the control group and ten to the experimental group. Prior to the start of treatment, all women were measured for spinal flexion, which is bending forward, and spinal extension, which means bending backward. We consider only spinal extension here. Spinal extension was measured as the number of centimeters from the chin to the top of a table on which each woman was lying face down with her hands clasped behind her back. The experimental condition was a 10-week program,

		T_1	T_2	T_3	$\bullet\ \bullet\ \bullet$	T_K
G_1	S_1 $\bullet$ $\bullet$ $\bullet$ S_n					
G_2	S_1 $\bullet$ $\bullet$ $\bullet$ S_n					
G_3	S_1 $\bullet$ $\bullet$ $\bullet$ S_n					
$\bullet$ $\bullet$ $\bullet$	$\bullet$ $\bullet$ $\bullet$					
G_J	S_1 $\bullet$ $\bullet$ $\bullet$ S_n					

Figure 17.5
Groups by trials repeated measures design: T = repeated factor with K levels, S = subjects with n subjects per group, G = group with J levels

Table 17.3
Groups by trials repeated measures design

	Pretest	*Posttest*	*Sums*
	13	26	39
	19	27	46
	21	28	49
	15	26	41
	12	17	29
Experimental	26	30	56
	25	29	54
	11	15	26
	16	25	41
	21	27	48
	179	250	429
	15	19	34
	18	20	38
	26	26	52
	23	23	46
	24	26	50
Control	19	19	38
	14	16	30
	20	20	40
	11	9	20
	20	25	45
	190	203	393
Totals	369	453	822

3 days per week of spinal mobility and flexibility exercises. The control condition was a regular exercise program without flexibility training. At the end of the 10 weeks, all the women were measured for spinal extension and flexion. Simulated data for spinal extension scores are given in Table 17.3. The experimental group significantly improved their spinal extension scores compared to the control group.

Computation of the *F* Tests

In a groups by trials repeated measures design, the total *SS* is broken into five pieces:

$$SS_{total} = SS_G + SS_{S(G)} + SS_T + SS_{TG} + SS_{TS(G)} \qquad (17.10)$$

Here *G* stands for group, *S* stands for subject, and *T* stands for trial, the repeated factor. This is the first time you've seen the notation *S(G)*, which you can call "subjects within groups." The abbreviation *S(G)* indicates that, for the spinal study, the women are nested within the experimental and control groups. *TG* indicates the interaction of trial and group, and *TS(G)* symbolizes the interaction of trial and subjects, who are nested within groups. Computational formulas for these *SS* are given in Table 17.4.

For this design, the degrees of freedom also can be broken into five parts:

$$
\begin{aligned}
df_{total} &= df_G + df_{S(G)} + df_T + df_{TG} + df_{TS(G)} \\
N - 1 &= J - 1 + J(n - 1) + K - 1 + (K - 1)(J - 1) + (K - 1)J(n - 1)
\end{aligned} \qquad (17.11)
$$

The mean squares for all five of these parts are used here, so we have

$$MS_G = \frac{SS_G}{df_G} = \frac{SS_G}{J-1}$$

$$MS_{S(G)} = \frac{SS_{S(G)}}{df_{S(G)}} = \frac{SS_{S(G)}}{J(n-1)}$$

$$MS_T = \frac{SS_T}{df_T} = \frac{SS_T}{K-1}$$

(17.12)

$$MS_{TG} = \frac{SS_{TG}}{df_{TG}} = \frac{SS_{TG}}{(K-1)(J-1)}$$

$$MS_{TS(G)} = \frac{SS_{TS(G)}}{df_{TS(G)}} = \frac{SS_{TS(G)}}{(K-1)J(n-1)}$$

Three hypotheses are tested in the groups by trials repeated measures design, one each for groups, trials, and the groups by trials interaction. For groups, the null hypothesis is

$$H_0: \mu_1 = \mu_2 = \cdots = \mu_J$$

(17.13)

For trials, the null hypothesis is

$$H_0: \mu_1 = \mu_2 = \cdots = \mu_K$$

(17.14)

For the interaction, the null hypothesis is

$$H_0: \text{no interaction effect}$$

(17.15)

Now you are ready to form the F ratios, using the MS values in 17.12:

$$F_G = \frac{MS_G}{MS_{S(G)}}$$

(17.16)

$$F_T = \frac{MS_T}{MS_{TS(G)}}$$

(17.17)

$$F_{TG} = \frac{MS_{TG}}{MS_{TS(G)}}$$

(17.18)

The F ratios don't all use the same denominator. The F_G has $MS_{S(G)}$ for its denominator. The other F's, F_T and F_{TG}, use $MS_{TS(G)}$ for the denominators. There is no MS_W, and there are no F tests for $S(G)$ and $TS(G)$. [Again, you typically wouldn't be interested in those F tests if they existed. A test of $S(G)$ would look at whether subjects differed from each other within a group, and a test of $TS(G)$ would check whether subjects interacted with time.]

F Distributions and Decision Rules

The *F*'s computed in formulas 17.16–17.18 can be used to test the hypotheses in 17.13–17.15, respectively, by comparing the *F*'s to appropriate critical values from *F* distributions. If the H_0's are true and if certain assumptions are met (discussed in Section 17.5), then:

F_G is distributed as an *F* distribution   (17.19)
with parameters $J - 1$ and $J(n - 1)$

F_T is distributed as an *F* distribution   (17.20)
with parameters $K - 1$ and $(K - 1)J(n - 1)$

F_{TG} distributed as an *F* distribution   (17.21)
with parameters $(K - 1)(J - 1)$ and $(K - 1)J(n - 1)$

You find the critical values by using Table A.6 in Appendix A with appropriate numerator and denominator *df*'s.

The decision rules are the same as those for the simple repeated measures design. The critical value decision rule is based on the use of your chosen α and the corresponding critical value to give:

Reject H_0 if $F \geq F_{\text{crit}}$; otherwise, retain H_0 (17.22)

Because computer programs give a *p*-value for the observed *F* ratio, you probably would use a critical value decision rule if you did the analysis by hand.

The *p*-value decision rule for an ANOVA *F* test is fairly simple if the computer package gives the probability that $F \geq F_{\text{observed}}$ for H_0 true. The rule is:

Reject H_0 if $p \leq \alpha$; otherwise, retain H_0 (17.23)

where $p = p(F \geq F_{\text{observed}} \mid H_0 \text{ true})$.

Table 17.4 contains all of the computations for a groups by trials repeated measures design, including decisions based on the *F*-tests. The data are from Table 17.3.

Table 17.4
Computation for groups by trials repeated measures design

$n = 10 \quad J = 2 \quad K = 2$
$df_G = J - 1 = 2 - 1 = 1$
$df_{S(G)} = J(n - 1) = 2(10 - 1) = 18$
$df_T = K - 1 = 2 - 1 = 1$
$df_{TG} = (K - 1)(J - 1) = (2 - 1)(2 - 1) = 1$
$df_{TS(G)} = (K - 1)J(n - 1) = (2 - 1)2(10 - 1) = 18$
$F_{1, 18} = F_{\text{crit}} = 4.41$

$$SS_G = \frac{\sum_j (\sum_k \sum_i X_{ijk})^2}{nK} - \frac{(\sum_k \sum_j \sum_i X_{ijk})^2}{nJK} = \frac{429^2 + 393^2}{10(2)} - \frac{822^2}{40}$$

$$= 16{,}924.5 - 16{,}892.1 = 32.4$$

(continued)

Table 17.4 (continued)

$$SS_{S(G)} = \frac{\sum_j \sum_i (\sum_k X_{ijk})^2}{K} - \frac{\sum_j (\sum_k \sum_i X_{ik})^2}{nK} = \frac{39^2 + 46^2 + \cdots + 20^2 + 45^2}{2} - \frac{429^2 + 393^2}{20}$$

$$= 17{,}781 - 16{,}924.5 = 856.5$$

$$SS_T = \frac{\sum_k (\sum_j \sum_i X_{ijk})^2}{nJ} - \frac{(\sum_k \sum_j \sum_i X_{ik})^2}{nJK} = \frac{369^2 + 453^2}{10(2)} - \frac{822^2}{40}$$

$$= 17{,}068.5 - 16{,}892.1 = 176.4$$

$$SS_{TG} = \frac{\sum_k \sum_j (\sum_i X_{ijk})^2}{n} - \frac{\sum_j (\sum_k \sum_i X_{ijk})^2}{nK} - \frac{\sum_k (\sum_j \sum_i X_{ijk})^2}{nJ} + \frac{(\sum_k \sum_j \sum_i X_{ijk})^2}{nJK}$$

$$= \frac{179^2 + 250^2 + 190^2 + 203^2}{10} - \frac{429^2 + 393^2}{10(2)} - \frac{369^2 + 453^2}{10(2)} + \frac{822^2}{40}$$

$$= 17{,}185 - 16{,}924.5 - 17{,}068.5 + 16{,}892.1 = 84.1$$

$$SS_{TS(G)} = \sum_k \sum_j \sum_i X_{ijk}^2 - \frac{\sum_k \sum_j (\sum_i X_{ijk})^2}{n} - \frac{\sum_j \sum_i (\sum_k X_{ijk})^2}{K} + \frac{\sum_j (\sum_k \sum_i X_{ijk})^2}{nK}$$

$$= 13^2 + 19^2 + \cdots + 9^2 + 25^2 - \frac{179^2 + 250^2 + 190^2 + 203^2}{10} - \frac{39^2 + 46^2 + \cdots + 20^2 + 45^2}{2} + \frac{429^2 + 393^2}{10(2)}$$

$$= 18{,}106 - 17{,}185 - 17{,}781 + 16{,}924.5 = 64.5$$

$$MS_G = \frac{SS_G}{df_G} = \frac{32.4}{1} = 32.4$$

$$MS_{S(G)} = \frac{SS_{S(G)}}{df_{S(G)}} = \frac{856.5}{18} = 47.5833$$

$$MS_T = \frac{SS_T}{df_T} = \frac{176.4}{1} = 176.4$$

$$MS_{TG} = \frac{SS_{TG}}{df_{TG}} = \frac{84.1}{1} = 84.1$$

$$MS_{TS(G)} = \frac{SS_{TS(G)}}{df_{TS(G)}} = \frac{64.5}{18} = 3.5833$$

$$F_G = \frac{MS_G}{MS_{S(G)}} = \frac{32.4}{47.5833} = 0.68$$

$$F_T = \frac{MS_T}{MS_{TS(G)}} = \frac{176.4}{3.5833} = 49.23$$

$$F_{TG} = \frac{MS_{TG}}{MS_{TS(G)}} = \frac{84.1}{3.5833} = 23.47$$

Source	SS	df	MS	F	p
G	32.4	1	32.4	0.68	.4201
S(G)	856.5	18	47.5833		
T	176.4	1	176.4	49.23	.0001
TG	84.1	1	84.1	23.47	.0001
TS(G)	64.5	18	3.5833		

$F_{\text{crit}} = 4.41$, so F_T and F_{TG} are significant.

What do these results mean for this scenario? As with the two-way ANOVA, your interpretation begins by looking at the results of the interaction test. If it is significant, you cannot generalize about the main effects tests because the results depend on the level of the main effect. Here, there is a significant interaction. You can conclude that change in spinal extension between the pretest and the posttest depends on whether the women are in the experimental group or the control group. Multiple comparisons on cell means in a groups by trials design are beyond the scope of this text (see Toothaker, 1991). Without multiple comparisons, you cannot say which cell of the design contains significantly better spinal extension than the other cells. It appears that the experimental group had more improvement than did the control group; which group is significantly different would depend on the results of a multiple comparison test.

Quick Quiz

You are an elementary school counselor. You believe students will improve their performance in math classes if they learn more about basic logic. You recruit a specialist in this area to give a short course in logic to 20 boys and 20 girls in the fourth grade, and you want to find out whether the training affects boys and girls differently. The student's math ability is measured before and after the training. (a) How many between- and within-subjects factors do you have? (b) Compute the *df*. (c) How many *F* tests do you have? (d) If it were significant, which *F* test would hamper your interpretation of the results? (*Hint:* Think about the two-way ANOVA.)

Answers

boys or girls.

treatment that occurred between pretest and posttest depended on whether you were looking at

for *TG* would make it difficult to generalize your results because it would mean the effect of the

versus posttest); and a third for *TG*, the interaction of time and gender. (d) The significant *F* test

have three *F* tests: one for *G*, or the effect of gender; another for *T*, or the effect of time (pretest

$= N - 1 = 80 - 1 = 79$, and $df_{total} =$ sum of the other $df = 1 + 38 + 1 + 38 = 79$.) (c) You

$= K - 1 = 2 - 1 = 1$, $df_{TG} = (K - 1)(f - 1) = (df_T)(df_G) = 1$, $df_{TS(G)} = (df_S(G))(df_T) = 38$. (Check: df_{total}

pretest and posttest). (b) $df_G = f = 1$, $df_{S(G)} = f(n - 1) = 2(20 - 1) = 38$, df_T

(a) You have one between-subjects factor (gender) and one within-subjects factor (time—

17.5   Assumptions

Sphericity assumption
Equal variances of differences of observations for all possible pairs of levels of a repeated factor

Similar to other ANOVAs, the validity of *F* ratios for repeated measures designs depends on assumptions. Although these assumptions are not identical to the assumptions for the one- and two-way ANOVAs as presented in Chapters 14 and 16, the *F*'s in repeated measures designs have the assumptions of normality, independence, and equal variances. Additionally, repeated measures designs have a **sphericity assumption,** which is defined as equality of variances of differences of observations for all possible pairs of levels of a repeated factor. Stated in terms of a formula, sphericity is:

$$\sigma^2_{Y_k - Y_{k'}} = \text{constant} \qquad \text{for all } k \neq k' \tag{17.24}$$

Note that it is the variances that are constant, not the differences. The differences simply are a subscript to the assumed constant variances. It might help you to think about the difference formed in computing the two-dependent-sample *t* and the variance of those differences (called *d*'s in Chapter 13). In repeated measures designs, it is possible to have more than two levels of the repeated factor, so you can get multiple *d*'s, a set of *d*'s for each pair of levels of a repeated factor. The variances of these multiple sets of *d*'s are assumed to be equal.

Sphericity is assumed for all the *F*'s for within-subjects factors and their interactions. So the F_T in the simple repeated measures design and the F_T and F_{TG} in the groups by trials design require this assumption.

Robustness

If you have only two levels of the repeated factor, you have met the assumption of sphericity in a trivial way. In the mere-presence study in Research Example 17, the path had only two segments so there could be only one difference and one variance of a difference. That one variance of a difference is a constant; thus, the sphericity assumption is met for this example. For more than two levels of the repeated factor, the sphericity assumption typically is not met. The effect of violating the sphericity assumption is that the true α is increased by about .05. Because of this, we say that the *F*'s that have this assumption in repeated measures designs (within-subjects tests) are not robust to violation of sphericity. One approach to this problem involves reducing the degrees of freedom similar to the approach taken in the AWS statistic (Chapter 13) and the Games-Howell MCP (Chapter 15). A second way to deal with violation of the sphericity assumption is to use a multivariate procedure that doesn't assume sphericity. Both of these alternatives to the usual repeated measures ANOVA are beyond the level of this text; see Kirk (1995), Winer, Brown, and Michels (1991), and Girden (1992).

Beyond These Repeated Measures Designs

You can design many experiments that involve repeated measures and have more complicated designs than the two you learned in this chapter. For instance, you could have a zero between, two within design. The participants wouldn't be divided into groups, and they would be measured under two repeated factors. Using the example from a Quick Quiz, you could have three ways of memorizing lists of words and three levels of vocabulary. Each participant could be tested for memory ability on each of the three memory devices for easy words, medium-difficulty words and hard words. As the experimenter, you would have to randomly assign the combinations of difficulty and memory instructions so that the results wouldn't be attributed to order or practice effects. Another example of a zero between, two within design was the car interior design problem given earlier.

This chapter gives you an idea of how valuable repeated measures designs are for certain research situations. You also should remember the problem of the sphericity assumption. If you do research with more than two levels of the repeated factor, you might study the ways of protecting yourself from Type I errors by using multivariate approaches or reducing the degrees of freedom.

17.6   Summary, Study Tips, and Computation

Chapter Summary

Repeated measures designs have each subject with multiple measures on the same dependent variable with these measurements arranged as levels of a factor. These designs are characterized by the number of between-subjects factors and the number of repeated factors (within-subjects factors). Repeated measures designs have no true estimate of error variance, one observation per cell, potentially different denominators for the *F*'s, correlated data, and good control of subjects' variability for within-subjects tests. Only two designs were given. First, the simple repeated measures design has no between-subjects factors in addition to subjects and one repeated factor. This design has only one F ratio, F_T. The second design, the groups by trials design, has one between-subjects factor, groups, and one repeated factor, trials. This design has three F ratios; F_G, F_T, and F_{TG}. In addition to normality, independence, and equal variances assumed by other ANOVAs, repeated measures designs have the sphericity assumption for within-subjects tests. Sphericity means constant variances of differences of observations for all possible pairs of levels of the repeated factor.

The following terms are introduced in this chapter:

Repeated factor	Simple repeated
Within-subjects factor	measures design
Crossed	Groups by trials repeated
Nested	measures design
Between-subjects factor	Sphericity

The statistical tests introduced in this chapter are summarized in Table 17.5. There you'll find the situation where the statistic would be used, the name of the statistic, and the theoretical reference distribution. For decision rules, assumptions, and any restrictions on the use of each procedure, refer to the section where it was presented.

Study Tips

Exceptionally good students are attuned to their own learning process. They tend to know whether they understand material better when it is explained aloud, or whether they need to see a picture of the concept, or whether they learn best by reading on their own. Have you ever thought about which of these descriptions applies to you? If you know you learn best by *hearing* an explanation, make an appointment to see your instructor after class and ask him or her to back up and re-explain a concept. If you know your understanding is enhanced by seeing a picture, ask your teacher to draw a schematic of the concept.

Another part of your learning process to be aware of is the point where you become confused. If you become lost during a lecture or while reading a chapter, look for a point where you *did* understand. Then move ahead slowly until you recognize where you got lost. Ask your teacher to explain that part. Writing question marks in the margins of your class notes will help you find the confusing places.

Table 17.5

Situation	Statistic	Distribution
Simple repeated measures design: $H_0: \mu_1 = \mu_2 \cdots = \mu_K = \mu$	F_T	F with $df_T = K - 1$ and $df_{TS} = (K - 1)(n - 1)$
Groups by trials repeated measures design: For groups $H_0: \mu_1 = \mu_2 \cdots = \mu_J = \mu$	F_G	F with $df_G = J - 1$ and $df_{S(G)} = J(n - 1)$
For trials $H_0: \mu_1 = \mu_2 \cdots = \mu_K = \mu$	F_T	F with $df_T = K - 1$ and $df_{TS(G)} = (K - 1)J(n - 1)$
For interaction H_0: no interaction effect	F_{TG}	F with $df_{TG} = (K - 1)(J - 1)$ and $df_{TS(G)} = (K - 1)J(n - 1)$

Computation

Most statistical packages have adequate ANOVA programs for repeated measures designs. However, sometimes they are more involved than those for the other ANOVAs. The additional complexity of these programs is because the designs themselves and the F ratios are more complex. Some of the additional complexity comes from alternatives available when the sphericity assumption is violated. Because the SPSS commands to run repeated measures ANOVA are so complicated, we present only SAS procedures.

SAS Examples
SAS has two ways to compute the statistics in repeated measures designs: one is to use PROC ANOVA and the other is to use PROC GLM with the "repeated" option.

Although the latter gives desirable statistical approaches (see the discussion of robustness in Section 17.5), it is a bit more complex than what we want to cover in this text. We give the traditional ANOVA approach for both designs covered in this chapter.

For the simple repeated measures design, use the following SAS statements:

(SAS system's lines)

```
DATA SRMD;
INPUT S$@;     (inputs a value for the subject; with the entire data step acting as a loop, you can input all the information for all subjects)
DO T = 1 TO 3;     (This is a "gimmick" to get the levels of the repeated factor into the computer without using an INPUT statement.
                    Here the value in the DO statement is T, and it has levels 1, 2, and 3.)
INPUT Y @;     (inputs each Y for the subject)
OUTPUT;
END;
CARDS;
S01 15 14 11     (data are for alone, present, and watching from the mere-presence/math problems example)
S02 14 11  6
S03 15 17 13
S04 12 11  8
S05  9 10  6
S06 15 12  8
S07 17 19 15
S08 20 17  9
S09 19 15 10
S10 13 10  9
PROC PRINT;
PROC ANOVA;
CLASS T S;     (Note that subject is considered a main effect.)
MODEL Y=T S T*S;     (specifies the model of the dependent variable Y in terms of two main effects T and S and the interaction)
TEST H=T E=T*S;     (This TEST statement specifies how to do the F test; because there is only one observation per cell, with the
                     T*S specified in the model, SAS won't automatically form the F; H= stands for "hypothesis" and specifies
                     the variable or variables to be tested; E= specifies the error term, denominator, for the test or tests)
```

(system's line)

The SAS System

Analysis of Variance Procedure

Dependent Variable: Y

Source	Df	Sum of Squares	Mean Square	F Value	Pr > F
Model	①29	424.66666667	14.64367816	.	.
Error	0	.	.		
Corrected Total	29	424.66666667			

Figure 17.6
SAS output for simple repeated measures design

(continued)

	R-Square	C.V.	Root MSE	Y Mean
	1.000000	0	0	12.66666667

Source	DF	Anova SS	Mean Square	F Value	PR > F
T	2	158.86665667	79.43333333	② .	.
S	9	211.33333333	23.48148148		.
T*S	18	54.46666667	3.2592593	.	.

Tests of Hypotheses using the Anova MS for T*S as an error term

Source	DF	Anova SS	Mean Square	F Value	Pr > F
T	2	158.86666667	79.43333333	③26.25	0.0000

Figure 17.6 (continued)

Examine Figure 17.6 for the output from this SAS program, noting the following:

1. All of the $N - 1$ degrees of freedom are specified in the model, leaving 0 for *df* for error, because you specified T*S in the model.
2. No F is formed here because there is no mean square for error.
3. The F_T is formed here.

For the groups by trials repeated measures design, use the following SAS statements:

(SAS system's lines)

```
DATA GXT;
INPUT G$ S$@;    (inputs a value for the between-subjects factor and the subject; with the entire data step acting as a loop, you can
                  input all the information for all subjects)
DO T = 1 TO 2;   (This is the same "gimmick" used in the simple repeated measures program to get the levels of the repeated
                  factor into the computer without using an INPUT statement. Here the value in the DO statement is T, and it has
                  levels 1 and 2.)
INPUT Y @;   (inputs each Y for the subject)
OUTPUT;
END;
CARDS;
EXP S01 13 26    (data are for pretest and posttest from the spinal flexibility example)
EXP S02 19 27
EXP S03 21 28
EXP S04 15 26
EXP S05 12 27
EXP S06 26 30
EXP S07 25 29
EXP S08 11 15
EXP S09 16 25
EXP S10 21 27
CONT S11 15 19
CONT S12 18 20
CONT S13 26 26
```

```
CONT  S14  23  23
CONT  S15  24  26
CONT  S16  19  19
CONT  S17  14  16
CONT  S18  20  20
CONT  S19  11   9
CONT  S20  20  25
PROC PRINT;
PROC ANOVA;
CLASS G T S;      (Note that subject is considered a main effect.)
MODEL Y=G S(G) T T*G T*S(G);      (specifies the model of the dependent variable Y in terms of main effects G, T, and S, and
                                   the interactions T*G and T*S(G); note that subjects are nested in groups, so SAS uses a
                                   parentheses notation to indicate this, with S outside the parentheses and G, the variable S
                                   is nested in, inside the parentheses)
TEST H=G E=S(G);      (This TEST statement specifies how to do the F test for G; H= stands for "hypothesis" and specifies the
                       variable or variables to be tested; E= specifies the error term, denominator, for the test or tests.)
TEST H=T T*G E=T*S(G);      (This TEST statement specifies how to do the F tests for T and the T*G interaction.)
TITLE GROUPS BY TRIALS REPEATED MEASURES DESIGN;
(system's line)
```

The SAS System

Analysis of Variance Procedure

Dependent Variable: Y

Source	DF	Sum of Squares	Mean Square	F Value	Pr > F
Model	① 39	1213.90000000	31.12564103	.	.
Error	0	.	.		
Corrected Total	39	1213.90000000			

	R-Square	C.V.	Root MSE	Y Mean
	1.000000	0	0	20.55000006

Source	DF	Anova SS	Mean Square	F Value	PR > F
G	1	32.40000000	32.40000000	.	.
S(G)	1	56.50000000	47.58333333	.	.
T	1	176.40000000	176.40000000	.②	.
G*T	1	84.10000000	84.10000000	.	.
T*S(G)	16	64.50000000	3.58333333	.	.

Figure 17.7
SAS output for the groups by trials repeated measures design

(continued)

The SAS System

Analysis of Variance Procedure

Level of G	N	--------------Y-------------- Mean	SD
CONT	20	19.6500000	4.86961579
EXP	20	21.4500000	6.20250374

Level of T	N	--------------Y-------------- Mean	SD
1	20	18.4500000	4.91480042
2	20	22.6500000	5.51815186

Level of G	Level of T	N	--------------Y-------------- Mean	SD
CONT	1	10	19.0000000	4.69041576
CONT	2	10	20.3000000	5.20789998
EXP	1	10	17.9000000	5.32186266
EXP	2	10	25.0000000	4.98887652

The SAS System

Analysis of Variance Procedure

Dependent Variable: Y

Tests of Hypotheses using the Anova MS for S(G) as an error term

Source	DF	Anova SS	Mean Square	F Value	Pr > F
G	1	32.40000000	32.40000000	③ 0.68	0.4201

Tests of Hypotheses using the Anova MS for T*S(G) as an error term

Source	DF	Anova SS	Mean Square	F Value	Pr > F
T	1	176.40000000	176.40000000	49.23	0.0001
G*T	1	84.10000000	84.10000000	23.47	0.0001

Figure 17.7 (continued)

Examine Figure 17.7 for the output from this SAS program, noting the following:

1. All of the $N - 1$ degrees of freedom are specified in the model, leaving 0 for *df* for error, because you specified T*S(G) in the model.

2. No *F*'s are formed here because there is no mean square for error.
3. The *F*'s are formed here according to the specifications in the test statements.

Exercises

Section 17.1

1. You run an air traffic control school. A training program for increasing air traffic controllers' efficiency and work speed has been set up. The program is being incorporated into the regular training of new air traffic controllers and supposedly makes them more efficient on the job, compared with previous new graduates of the school. Someone has suggested, however, that experienced air traffic controllers also could become faster and more efficient by going through the 2-week special program. You disagree, saying experience is the only way to increase efficiency while maintaining quality work, but you allow ten experienced and ten new air traffic controllers to participate in a study.
   a. How many groups of participants do you have?
   b. How many times would you have to measure the participants?
   c. If you are right about experienced air traffic controllers, what results would you expect?
   d. If you were to measure each controller only once, when would you do it? What would be the disadvantage of this approach in terms of the research question being addressed?

Section 17.2

2. You are a developmental psychologist studying infants' ability to recognize faces. You are comparing 15 babies who were carried full term and 15 babies who were born prematurely.
   a. If you measure all babies one time during the fourth month of life, why is the two-independent-sample *t* the appropriate statistic? You know about variability and that the babies would have slightly different scores if they were measured again, so doesn't that introduce within-subjects variability?
   b. Let's say you measure both groups of babies each month for 6 months. Every time you have a session with a baby, you take measurements once with a parent present and again without a parent in the room.
      i. Which factors are crossed? Which ones are nested?
      ii. How many observations will you have (*N*)?

iii. How many between-subjects factors will you have? How many within-subjects factors?
   c. You have completed the study and now you want to study premature babies' development without comparing them to full-term babies. You decide to measure a new group of premature babies at ages 1 month and 3 months. What is the appropriate statistic?

3. Suppose a consumer group wanted to do a better comparison of preference for cars than that done by the Chrysler Corporation (see Box 1.2 in Chapter 1). They took 25 owners of 1988–1991 *Civics, Corollas, Cavaliers,* and *Escorts* and had them drive, in random order, a new *Dodge Shadow,* a new car of the same brand as their current car, and a 1988–1991 *Dodge Shadow.* After each test drive, the owners filled out a preference scale comparing their current car to the car they had test-driven.
   a. Compare this study to the one described in Chapter 1, including the criticism raised in that article.
   b. Classify the study in terms of number of between- and within-subject factors.

Section 17.3

4. As a college professor, you want to reduce your students' exam stress as much as possible. You want to find out whether students have different numbers of stress symptoms, depending on how much control they feel they have over the testing situation. You decide to run a study in which 34 students will write test questions. For each of the four exams you give during the term, you will give students one of four sets of instructions for writing the test questions. For one exam, a student will be told to write test questions for practice; for another exam, the student will be instructed to write questions that could appear on the exam; for another test, the student is told that 80% of the class-generated questions will be used; and the fourth set of instructions says the student's questions *will* be on the test. The week before each test, you give sealed instructions to the students, and the order of the sets of instructions is randomly assigned for all students.

a. How many between-subjects factors do you have? How many within-subjects factors? Which factors are crossed? Nested?

b. What is K?

c. Compute all of the *df* values.

d. How do you form MS_T, MS_{TS}, and F?

e. Imagine that someone else ran a similar study, except the order of instructions was not randomly assigned. Why might this be a problem?

5. Suppose a researcher wanted to test the effect of music on heart rate in a dart-throwing task. Following 20 practice throws to familiarize them with the dart-throwing game, the 30 participants completed the first set of ten throws (trial 1). Then each participant sat directly in front of a tape player and was instructed to concentrate on a fast popular vocal song that played for 90 s. Each participant then completed the second set of ten throws (trial 2). Heart rate was monitored before trial 1, after trial 1, after the music, and after trial 2.

a. Classify the study in terms of the number of between- and within-subjects factors.

b. For the dependent variable heart rate, how many measurements were there for each subject? Give the *df* values for *S, T,* and *TS.* Which two of these are the correct *df* for F_T?

c. If you added another group of 30 participants who had the same regimen as the first group except that they listened to classical music, how does the design change? Now answer part a for this design. List all the sources of variability and compute a numerical value for the *df* for each.

6. In a study on attraction, suppose people were asked to rate pictures of females taken before orthodontic treatment (braces). The participants rated the females in the pictures on a number of variables. Two weeks later the participants returned to rate another set of pictures, the same females after orthodontic treatment. In both sets of pictures, the females' mouths were closed and teeth not showing. Ratings of intelligence are given in the table.

Pair	Prerating	Postrating
1	113	115
2	105	117
3	120	125
4	119	117
5	104	107
6	100	105
7	111	110
8	130	125
9	119	121
10	127	130
11	111	110
12	115	117
13	107	113
14	102	105

a. Use the appropriate repeated measures design to test the hypothesis that there is no change in perceived intelligence ($\alpha = .05$).

b. These same data were used in Chapter 13 for the two-dependent-sample *t*-test. Compute the *t* and then see whether there is any relationship between it and the *F* computed in part a.

c. Interpret the meaning of your results. What can you conclude about these variables?

7. A researcher wanted to see whether different types of motor activity used in training children on words result in different spelling abilities. Each child was shown a word printed on a 3 × 5 card, the researcher named the word and asked the child to repeat it, and then the child was asked to reproduce the word by one of three activities: handwriting, typing the word on a computer keyboard, or using letter tiles (plastic tiles with two sets of the alphabet). Training was over four days, and ten short words were used in each of the three training activities (a total of 30 words), with random order of training. Each child received all three training activities. There were 12 first-grade students. A spelling test was given on the fifth day, and the number of correct words was recorded for each of the training activities. The data are listed in the table.

Student	Writing	Computer	Tiles
1	3	2	1
2	5	3	2
3	3	1	2
4	2	1	1
5	1	1	1
6	6	3	2
7	2	2	1
8	3	2	3
9	2	1	0
10	4	3	1
11	4	2	1
12	3	1	3

a. Use the appropriate repeated measures design to test the hypothesis that the different motor activities give the same performance in spelling ($\alpha = .05$). Use SAS if you desire.

b. What do your results mean about motor activities and spelling performance?

Section 17.4

8. You have read about the Ekman and O'Sullivan (1991) study on what people are best at detecting a liar. The study speculates that Secret Service personnel may be better at detecting a liar because they are more attuned to body language. You are a psychologist employed by the Internal Revenue Service, which wants to train its auditors to pick up on cues when someone is lying during an audit. You think that women may be socialized to pay closer attention to body language than men do, but you think you can train both men and women to catch a liar. You randomly sample 18 men and 18 women auditors for a one-week training program. Each afternoon you measure their ability to detect liars on videotape.

   a. How many between-subjects factors do you have? How many within-subjects factors? Which factors are crossed? Nested?

   b. What is K?

   c. Compute all the df values.

   d. How would you form the F ratios for this design?

9. Clinical psychologists who want to help overweight children recognize the influence of the family. Eighteen overweight 10-year-old boys and their families agree to participate in a study. Half of the boys are given exercise instructions and a low-calorie diet. The other boys receive the same thing, but they also participate in six family therapy sessions, one every 3 months. At the age of 12, all subjects are weighed. The weights (in pounds) for the boys at ages 10 and 12 are listed in the table. Natural growth accounts for some of their weight gain. Which group gained the most? Use SAS if you desire. Interpret the outcome in terms of these variables.

	Boy	Age 10	Age 12
	1	112	123
	2	98	111
	3	127	129
	4	122	134
Control	5	102	112
	6	107	111
	7	97	109
	8	98	112
	9	126	131
	10	131	139
	11	104	114
	12	109	121
	13	98	109
Family	14	127	131
	15	103	111
	16	121	129
	17	136	145
	18	101	119

Section 17.5

10. Suppose you want to know what variables influence people's ability to estimate future values of cost of production for a small business. Participants in your study see 12 months of costs and are asked to estimate the next month's cost. Participants are randomly assigned to one of four groups formed by combining time to view the 12 months of costs (15 s or 2 min) and the average cost (high or low). All participants saw six sets of costs: three patterns (trend, random, and alternating) each combined with variance of the 12 costs (high or low). You use a total of 100 participants.

    a. Of the four factors—time, average cost, pattern, and variance of costs, which are within subjects (repeated) and which are between subjects?

    b. Based on your answer in part a, how would you characterize this repeated measures design?

       (_____ between and _____ within)

    c. Give the df for each of the following: time, average cost, pattern, variance of costs, and time by pattern interaction.

    d. Which of the factors listed in part a meet the sphericity assumption?

11. A researcher on factors that influence auditors' probability of an unqualified opinion (a good audit) wanted to investigate source reliability (four levels) and degree of informativeness (two levels). The researcher developed eight scenarios to include these factors. Thirty-five auditors read all eight scenarios presented in a random order and gave a probability estimate for each.

    a. Of the two factors—source reliability and degree of informativeness, which are within subjects (repeated) and which are between subjects?

    b. Based on your answer in part a, how would you characterize this repeated measures design?

       (_____ between and _____ within)

    c. Give the df for each of the following: subjects, source reliability, degree of informativeness, and subjects by source reliability interaction.

    d. Which of the factors listed in part a meet the sphericity assumption?

18

Nonparametric Methods: χ^2 Tests

All of the inferential statistical methods discussed so far have assumed normality associated with the population(s). Most of the tests are designed to work with data that are quantitative. Are there tests that don't assume normality of the populations? Are any tests designed to work with qualitative data? This chapter introduces nonparametric methods and examines two chi-square tests designed to work with qualitative data.

Research Example 18
18.1   Introduction to Nonparametric Methods
    Language
    Hypotheses and assumptions
    Parametric versus nonparametric
    Warnings
18.2 χ^2 Tests: Qualitative Data
    Introduction
    Two types of tests
18.3   Chi-Square Test for Goodness of Fit
    Example
    Sensitivity
    Hypotheses
    Statistic
    Distribution
    Decision rules
    Assumptions
18.4   Chi-Square Test for Contingency Tables
    Example
    Sensitivity
    Hypotheses
    Statistic
    Distribution
    Decision rules
    Assumptions
    Beyond these nonparametric procedures
18.5   Summary, Study Tips, and Computation
    Chapter summary
    Study tips
    Computation
Exercises

Research Example 18

Communication isn't always written or spoken. Many psychologists devote their careers to exploring nonverbal communication and behavior, such as body language. Willis and Briggs (1992) studied how men and women initiate physical contact in public settings. They wanted to know whether the status of a relationship (dating/engaged, and so on) determines who makes the first physical contact between a man and a woman in a public place. Does the man reach out and touch the woman first, or do women touch first? Does it matter whether the couple is married or on a first date? Willis and Briggs observed hundreds of mainly white male–female couples in restaurants, parks, theaters, and sporting events. Each couple was observed unobtrusively for 5 minutes. The observers recorded whether the woman initiated a touch with a hand, whether the man initiated a hand touch, or whether no hand touches occurred. Then one observer approached the couple and asked for a description of their relationship. Couples were categorized as engaged/dating, married/cohabiting less than a year, or married/cohabiting a year or more. Table 18.1 contains part of their results.

Willis and Briggs computed a chi-square (χ^2) test for independence of categorical variables and obtained $\chi^2 = 4.45$, $p < .05$. They concluded that men "were more likely to initiate touch in the engaged/dating and married/cohabiting for less than one year groups and women were more likely to initiate touch in the married/cohabiting for one year or more group." Another χ^2 considered whether or not touch occurred for the two types of couples mentioned here. They found that touch was more likely to occur for the couples who were newer to the relationship than for the established couples ($\chi^2 = 37.31$, $p < .001$). Willis and Briggs suggested that women might take over the initiation of touch to preserve a bond with a partner, but they also presented other possibilities: There might be an age effect because the newer couples were younger; observing hand touches doesn't provide information about whether the couples are happy; cultural and racial factors surely are involved; and men and women perceive touch as occurring for different reasons.

The kind of relationship is categorized, so the data are qualitative. This chapter introduces two χ^2 statistics for testing hypotheses about categorical variables. These statistics are called *nonparametric methods*. More nonparametric tests are presented in Chapter 19.

Table 18.1

Frequency of female-initiated and male-initiated contact in three types of couples

Type of Couple	F Initiated	M Initiated	Totals
Engaged/dating or married/cohabiting less than 1 year	60	86	146
Married/cohabiting more than 1 year	41	32	73
Totals	101	118	219

Source: Willis and Briggs (1992).

18.1   Introduction to Nonparametric Methods

For every new statistic, we have tried to show why you need it. Research Example 18 summarizes a study about relationship and touch in public settings. The researchers observed male–female couples and recorded whether a hand touch occurred and, if so, who initiated the contact. Then couples were asked to categorize their relationship—dating/engaged, and so on. There are three variables: type of relationship, which gender initiated contact (if any), and whether or not touch occurred. Could you do a two-way ANOVA on these data? When you learned the two-way ANOVA, the data were scores, such as test scores in the study technique example, and you summed the scores in various ways, squared them, and did other calculations. Can you do that for the relationship/touch data? No, because the two variables "type of relationship" and "gender of initiating person" influence touch, which is a dichotomous variable; that is, the couple either touched or did not. For any cell in the design, the numbers are frequencies: How many couples were married more than a year? How many of those couples had the first hand touch made by the woman? You end up with frequencies in each cell. The two-way ANOVA is of no use to you here. You need new statistics.

Before you learn two new statistics, let's look at some vocabulary and the motivations for the creation of these statistics and those in Chapter 19.

Language

You have learned the statistical methods appropriate for testing hypotheses about parameters. Because of the type of hypothesis they are designed to test, they are called *parametric* statistical methods. These methods also have something else in common: some normality assumption. The methods require normality of observations, differences, or, in the case of the Pearson correlation coefficient, bivariate (joint) normality. In the early 1920s, little was known about these methods' robustness or lack of robustness to nonnormality. Robustness research began in the late 1940s, and recognition of robustness emerged in behavioral science texts in the 1960s. One way that researchers tried to get around the normality assumptions was to develop methods that did not assume normality or any other particular shape of the population. Two of these methods are presented in this chapter.

As you might guess, these methods differ from the usual parametric methods in several ways, such as their hypotheses. The methods here and in Chapter 19 are all *designed* to test null hypotheses that do not make statements about parameters; rather, they make statements about entire distributions. For example, suppose there are four ways to deal with the federal deficit. You ask Democrats and Republicans to choose one. Then you look at how many Democrats and Republicans chose the first way, the second way, and so on. Do Republicans have the same distribution of frequencies as Democrats? That is, when you are looking at people's choices of ways to deal with the deficit, does it matter whether you are looking at Democrats or Republicans? Such hypotheses do not focus on any specific parameter to test, but instead deal with the entire distribution. Because the hypothesis does not concern parameters, this type of hypothesis is called *nonparametric*. Over time, **statistical methods designed to test nonparametric hypotheses** also came to be called *nonparametric*. What makes the statistic parametric or nonparametric is the type of hypothesis that the statistic is designed to test.

Statistical methods designed to test nonparametric hypotheses
The actual meaning of *nonparametric methods*

Using *nonparametric* as a label for these statistical methods is not really accurate, so some researchers have invented new labels, such as *distribution-free*. Sometimes these new labels can be just as confusing as *nonparametric,* so not much is gained. We discuss these methods using the term *nonparametric,* understanding that it means statistical procedures *designed* to test hypotheses that don't have parameters in them.

Hypotheses and Assumptions

Nonparametric hypotheses
Hypotheses that state equality of entire population distributions and do not make statements about parameters

Nonparametric hypotheses state that entire population distributions are equal or that the population distribution is equal to some standard known form. In the two-independent-sample case, a parametric hypothesis might state equality of the population means, $H_0: \mu_1 = \mu_2$. A nonparametric hypothesis would state equality of the entire population distributions:

$$H_0: \text{distribution}_1 = \text{distribution}_2$$

For example, when considering opinions on solving the federal deficit problem, you might hypothesize that the Republic distribution equals the Democratic distribution. That is, the distribution of Republican opinions is hypothesized to be the same as the distribution of Democratic opinions. This is a nonparametric hypothesis. Compare this to what you tested with a two-independent-sample *t*-test, where you compared the means of two groups. That comparison of means really focused on the central tendency of the two groups. Methods that are good for the nonparametric hypothesis (such as the chi-square tests in this chapter) detect *any* difference in the population, such as differences in any measure of central tendency, variability, skewness, kurtosis, or overall shape. If the statistical method is good at detecting any difference, usually it is not so good at detecting a specific kind of difference, such as a difference in means. The description "jack of all trades, master of none" applies to nonparametric methods that are sensitive to nonparametric hypotheses.

Some nonparametric methods are actually sensitive to parametric hypotheses, even though they were *designed* to test more general nonparametric hypotheses. In other words, some of these new methods are good at detecting more specific differences in populations, such as certain parameters of the population. This may seem confusing. An analogy is a basketball player who was recruited because of his reputation as a good all-around player, but who turns out to be a great rebounder and only average in other ways. The methods here and in Chapter 19 are *designed* to test nonparametric hypotheses. Some of these methods are good for testing nonparametric hypotheses; others are not. Those that are not good for testing nonparametric hypotheses are good at testing the more specific parametric hypotheses. For each method we'll tell you the type of hypothesis to which it is sensitive: parametric or nonparametric.

Nonparametric methods can differ from parametric methods not only on the hypothesis tested, but also on the assumptions. As you know, the statistical methods discussed so far have some normality assumption. Nonparametric inferential statistics were designed so that normality of some population(s) does not have to be assumed. These nonparametric methods *do not* make any normality assumptions. However, other assumptions remain.

All nonparametric methods given in this text assume independence. Some of the methods assume independence of observations, whereas other assume independence of pairs of observations or differences in observations. Usually this assumption is tied to random sampling and, if applicable, random assignment of participants to groups.

All nonparametric methods assume a continuous underlying distribution of the dependent variable. That is, even if you measure the dependent variable with a discrete measure, the underlying distribution is assumed to be continuous. For example, height is continuous, but you measure it with a discrete measurement, such as ranking a group of people by height. Because of this assumption, it is assumed that no two observations are equal, which means that for some methods there will be no ties among the ranks of the observations. For other methods, this assumption means that no differences should have a value of zero. Of course, in real life, tied ranks or zero differences do occur. We'll show you how to deal with these situations.

Parametric versus Nonparametric

All of the parametric statistics you've learned so far have nonparametric counterparts. How do you choose between a nonparametric method and its corresponding parametric method? For example, a nonparametric method for the two-independent-sample case is the Mann-Whitney U test. When should you use the U test instead of the two-independent-sample t-test? We give directions for choosing between parametric and nonparametric statistics for each nonparametric method. For now, let's look at four important criteria: hypothesis (sensitivity), assumptions (normality), scale of measurement of the data, and sample size.

If you want to test the more general nonparametric hypothesis about distributions, be sure to select a nonparametric method that is good for this type of hypothesis. None of the *parametric* methods in this text is good for *nonparametric* hypotheses, so use a nonparametric method if you are interested in detecting any difference in the populations. However, if you are interested in detecting differences in parameters, choose either the parametric method or a nonparametric method that is sensitive to the specific parameters of interest. For example, the Mann-Whitney U test is sensitive to differences in central tendency and could be a competitor to the two-independent-sample t-test. In this case, the choice would depend on some other criteria. Sensitivity to type of hypothesis is basically a question of power. Power also is related to the assumptions of the methods.

Because the only assumption that is relaxed for all nonparametric methods is normality, you might consider a nonparametric method if the data came from a nonnormal population. Some problems exist in this consideration, however. First, the assumption is that the *population* is normal, not the sample. A sample from a normal population can be extremely nonnormal, so you can't use the sample to tell whether the population is normal. Granted, there are tests to check for normality, but we don't recommend them. Second, for "moderate" departures from normality, the usual tests are robust, so you don't need the nonparametric method. But what is meant by *moderate*? Also, for normal populations, the usual parametric methods are more powerful than their nonparametric counterparts. But you would want to use a nonparametric method if the departure from normality is considerable. The definition of *considerable* is left to the researcher, except for the case of extreme scores. The usual parametric methods are not robust if 5% to 10% of the scores in one tail are extreme scores (outliers). Samples from such populations have a concentration, or "lump," of scores in one tail, where these scores are very large or very small compared to the other scores.

Another consideration in using nonparametric methods is the scale of measurement of the data (see Section 2.6). If the data are measured on a nominal scale (qualitative data), then a nonparametric method is the best choice. You will see that the popular chi-square (χ^2) tests are appropriate for nominal data and that there is no universally applicable parametric test. However, some research done with parametric tests (*t*-tests and ANOVA) on nominal data has shown them to perform adequately. If the data are measured on an ordinal scale (rank data), then a nonparametric method from Chapter 19 can be used. Nonparametric methods are appropriate if the data are actual ranks or are from a scale that can not be determined to be interval in nature and ranks of the data can be obtained. However, research shows that some parametric tests perform adequately for rank data.

Finally, sample size is often given as a consideration in deciding between parametric and nonparametric methods for a given situation. Some sources (for example, Bradley, 1968) suggest that nonparametric methods be used if you have unequal population variances or nonnormality with small sample sizes, especially if the *n*'s are unequal. This suggestion is based on the lack of robustness of the parametric methods in some of those circumstances (for example, unequal *n*'s). However, before the question of sample size can be settled, more research is needed that directly compares parametric and nonparametric methods when the *n*'s are small. Perhaps nonparametric methods don't work well in these circumstances either. For now, the hypotheses and assumptions seem to be more salient in deciding between parametric and nonparametric methods.

In summary, use a suitable nonparametric method in these cases:

1. The hypothesis is about entire distributions.
2. When parametric hypotheses are tested, 5% to 10% of the scores are extreme and in one tail.
3. The scale of measurement is nominal or perhaps ordinal.

Warnings

Three warnings are in order when you consider using nonparametric methods. First, just because these methods do not have a normality assumption, do not jump to the incorrect conclusion that they do not have any assumptions. All nonparametric methods have certain assumptions. You'll read about the robustness of each method.

Second, when students see that nonparametric methods relax the normality assumption, they often think that they should always use nonparametric methods. But there is often an advantage to the parametric test, and that can involve statistical power.

Finally, nonparametric methods are not meant to miraculously rescue data from a sloppy experiment. All too often people will say, "Well, I've done this wrong, and this bias exists, and such-and-such bad thing happened, so I think I'll use a nonparametric method." There is no special healing power of nonparametric methods. When the research is bad, the results are bad, regardless of the statistical method. The principle of GIGO (garbage in, garbage out) applies to all statistics, including nonparametric methods.

You should have concluded that nonparametric methods provide some potentially useful tests for your statistical repertoire. You should *not* decide to use only nonparametric methods because they are not always the best methods. Rather, they are useful techniques for some situations. In other situations, you would want to use the usual parametric tests.

Quick Quiz

Suppose you are studying the alcohol-drinking habits of college students. You want to compare men and women on binge drinking, defined as consuming at least five drinks in a row within the last 2 weeks. (a) What hypothesis do you want to test? (b) Give one reason that a nonparametric statistic might be appropriate.

Answers

(a) The distribution of binge/nonbinge drinkers among men is equal to the distribution of binge/nonbinge drinkers among women. (b) You might want to use a nonparametric statistic because you are classifying participants in two ways: by gender and by drinking habit. A nonparametric statistic is appropriate for qualitative data like these.

18.2   χ² Tests: Qualitative Data

Introduction

There are many nonparametric statistics. You've already seen the symbol χ^2 for chi-square (pronounced like "ki" as in *kite*). We introduce two chi-square tests in this chapter. Chi-square (χ^2) tests are appropriate for data that have been measured on a nominal scale. Such data do not have quantity or magnitude, so they are qualitative. They are expressed as labels or names, they possess some characteristic, or they come from participants who have been assigned to one of several categories. As an example of qualitative data that do not have quantity, consider eye color. People don't have a numerical value for their eye color; either they have brown eyes or they do not. Another way of explaining qualitative data is that participants are usually placed into one of several categories. For eye color, the categories are blue, brown, green, and so on. For each category, people either possess or do not possess the characteristic. Another example is placement in the category of political party—Republican, Democrat, or other.

Finally, qualitative data usually result in frequency counts of participants in each of the categories, such as the categories of "less than 1 year" and "1 year or longer" for number of years people have been married. In the relationship/touch study in Research Example 18, the researchers counted the frequency of couples in each of their classifications of relationship.

Here are some questions you may ask as you decide whether a χ^2 method is appropriate in a given research scenario:

1. Are the data qualitative (presence or absence of some characteristic) rather than quantitative?
2. Are participants placed into categories on some variable? In other words, is a categorical variable involved?
3. Are frequencies of participants mentioned?

Two Types of Tests

You can separate categorical data analysis into two types: goodness-of-fit problems and contingency table problems. Although this way of separating categorical data analysis may be somewhat oversimplified, it provides the framework for this chapter.

Goodness of fit
A problem that asks a question about the fit of a sampled population to some theoretical distribution

In problems of **goodness of fit,** you are asking whether the frequencies or proportions in the *K* categories of a single categorical variable fit some predetermined pattern. In other words, you have one categorical variable with *K* categories. Are the frequencies for the categories all equal? Are the frequencies such that they could have come from a normal distribution? Is the proportion for men the same as that for women? Goodness-of-fit problems deal with *one* categorical variable and are sometimes called *one-variable problems.*

Contingency table
A problem that asks a question about the independence of the two categorical variables that form a table of frequencies

For the second type of problem, you are dealing with *two* categorical variables that form a table of frequencies known as a **contingency table.** You've seen such tables in Chapter 8 on probability and in Research Example 18 on relationship and touch. You want to know whether the two categorical variables are independent, as shown by the frequencies in the table. You can ask: Are the distributions of frequencies across levels of one categorical variable the same for all levels of the second categorical variable? As you reexamine Research Example 18, you might ask whether the tendency to initiate touch is independent of the kind of relationship the person is in. Or, in the federal deficit problem, is preference for solutions to the deficit problem independent of political party?

Quick Quiz

Tell what kind of data the following scenarios contain. (a) A sample of 200 college students report their year (freshman, sophomore, and so on) and their rating (on a 1–10 scale) of how risky their behavior becomes after they have consumed alcohol. (b) A study of sudden infant deaths in New Zealand reports how many of these babies were placed on their stomachs at bedtime the night they died. (c) Researchers compare smokers and nonsmokers on their cognitive abilities by giving them an aptitude test. (d) Men's and women's preferences for action or comedy movies are compared.

Answers

(a) College year is qualitative, and ratings are a quantitative scale. (b) The study reports a frequency for babies placed on their stomachs. Sleeping position is qualitative (on the stomach or not). (c) Smoking/nonsmoking is qualitative. The aptitude test provides quantitative data. (d) Gender and movie preference are both qualitative.

18.3   Chi-Square Test for Goodness of Fit

Example

Is there a certain day of the working week that you find most stressful? Most people would name Monday as their least favorite workday because they have to set aside their hobbies to return to work. Stress can affect physical health, and some researchers have found that heart attacks are most likely to occur on a Monday. Suppose you examined a year's records for a few hospitals and found the following frequencies of heart attacks for the seven days of the week:

Sunday	Monday	Tuesday	Wednesday	Thursday	Friday	Saturday
336	512	397	378	415	354	408

Indeed, Monday has the highest frequency, but you know that all statistics have variability. You want to determine whether these frequencies are more or less equal, or within sampling variability of each other.

What clues will help you choose the correct statistic? You have one categorical variable; you're looking at whether people have a heart attack. The days of the weeks are the K categories. So the appropriate statistic is the **chi-square test for goodness of fit.**

χ^2 goodness-of-fit statistic
Statistic formed to test for significant differences between observed frequencies and frequencies that would be expected given the null hypothesis

Sensitivity

The χ^2 test for goodness of fit is sensitive to any difference in the population. The test detects differences in central tendency, variability, skewness, and so on between the observed frequencies and the frequencies expected from the hypothesis. Because of the sensitivity of the χ^2 goodness-of-fit test to any differences in the populations, it is appropriate to use it to test nonparametric hypotheses.

Hypotheses

The goodness-of-fit χ^2 tests a nonparametric hypothesis that deals with the entire distribution. The null and alternative hypotheses are:

$$H_0: \text{distribution}_{\text{pop}} = \text{distribution}_{\text{theory}}$$

$$H_1: \text{distribution}_{\text{pop}} \neq \text{distribution}_{\text{theory}}$$

(18.1)

The null hypothesis states that the population distribution from which you have sampled is equal to the distribution from some theory. Because this H_0 contains no parameters of the population, it is a nonparametric hypothesis. Any characteristic or combination of characteristics of the population distribution that differs from that for the distribution given by the theory could lead you to reject H_0. The null hypothesis in the heart attack example is that the population distribution would have equal numbers of heart attacks for each day of the week. If you reject H_0, you cannot state which characteristic of the population is different, just that the distribution is not the one stated by the theory.

Statistic

The χ^2 goodness-of-fit statistic used to test this H_0 is

$$\chi^2 = \sum \frac{(O_k - E_k)^2}{E_k}$$

(18.2)

where O_k is the observed frequency for the kth category, E_k is the expected frequency for the kth category, and the summation is over all K categories. Notice that χ^2 is large if the squared differences between the observed and expected frequencies are large relative to the expected frequency. If the observed and expected frequencies are close, then the statistic is small and you retain H_0.

The χ^2 statistic is designed to take into account the size of the original expected frequency when the difference between observed and expected frequencies is examined. Suppose you have two categories, one with $O = 20$ and $E = 10$ and the other with $O = 1010$ and $E = 1000$. Both categories have a difference of 10 between the observed and expected frequencies and a squared difference of 100. For which category is the difference of 10 more meaningful or important? The formula divides $(O - E)^2$

by E to take into account the size of the expected frequency, which shows the relative importance of each category. The first category contributes

$$\frac{(20 - 10)^2}{10} = \frac{100}{10} = 10$$

to the statistic, whereas the second category contributes

$$\frac{(1010 - 1000)^2}{1000} = \frac{100}{1000} = 0.10$$

to the statistic.

For the heart attack example, the calculation of the χ^2 statistic begins with calculation of the expected frequency for each category. Because the null hypothesis states that equal frequencies would be expected, you obtain the E_k by dividing the total observed frequency, $N = 2800$, by the number of categories, $K = 7$, to get $2800/7 = 400$. Using $E_k = 400$ for all categories gives

$$\chi^2 = \frac{(336 - 400)^2}{400} + \frac{(512 - 400)^2}{400} + \frac{(397 - 400)^2}{400} + \frac{(378 - 400)^2}{400}$$

$$+ \frac{(415 - 400)^2}{400} + \frac{(354 - 400)^2}{400} + \frac{(408 - 400)^2}{400}$$

$$= 10.24 + 31.36 + 0.0225 + 6.76 + 0.5625 + 5.29 + 0.16$$

$$= 54.395$$

Your theory won't always give equal expected frequencies. You need to derive the expected frequencies from the theory given in the literature for your research. For example, suppose you wanted to research whether newborn infants possess some characteristic proportionately for the two genders. You can't assume equal numbers of boy and girl infants in order to get expected frequencies because there are different numbers of boy and girl babies born each year. For example, there were 2,129,000 boys and 2,029,000 girls born in 1990. Thus, you could get the expected frequency for boys by multiplying 2,129,000/4,158,000 by the sample size in your study. Similarly, you could obtain the expected frequency for girls. Then you could use these expected frequencies to compute the goodness-of-fit χ^2. Using equal expected frequencies would not have been correct.

Distribution

χ^2 distributions
A family of skewed distributions with one parameter, degrees of freedom

The χ^2 goodness-of-fit statistic given in formula 18.2 has a sampling distribution that is approximately fit by a χ^2 distribution. Chi-square distributions are positively skewed with a minimum of zero, and they have one parameter, degrees of freedom. Similar to the t distributions, the **χ^2 distributions** form a family of distributions, with a unique distribution for each value of *df*. Figure 18.1 shows χ^2 distributions for *df* = 3 and *df* = 6. Each χ^2 distribution has values that range from zero to infinity and is positively

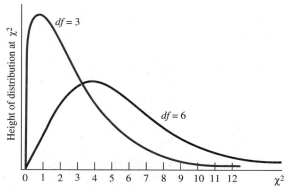

Figure 18.1
The χ^2 distributions for $df = 3$ and $df = 6$

skewed, similar to the distribution of s^2. The squaring in the statistic means that χ^2 has no negative values.

Degrees of freedom
For the χ^2 goodness-of-fit statistic, $df = K - 1$, the number of categories minus 1

The goodness-of-fit statistic is approximately distributed as χ^2 with **degrees of freedom** equal to the number of categories minus 1, or $df = K - 1$:

$$\chi^2 \text{ is distributed as a } \chi^2 \text{ distribution with } df = K - 1 \qquad (18.3)$$

if all the assumptions are met. The value of df is $K - 1$ only if all of the expected frequencies are given to you directly from the theory without estimation of any parameters, such as computing $\overline{X}$ or s^2. See Hays (1994) for other applications.

Recall the working definition of degrees of freedom: the number of independent components minus the number of parameters estimated. The reason that degrees of freedom are $K - 1$ is that the component is the frequency in a category. You have K categories each with one frequency, so you have K observations. The -1 is for the total frequency; once you fix the total frequency, only $K - 1$ of the category frequencies are free to vary. For the heart attack example, $K = 7$, so $df = 7 - 1 = 6$.

Decision Rules

You will use Table A.9 in Appendix A to look up the critical value with your chosen α—say, $\alpha = .05$—and $df = K - 1$. The χ^2 tests are all one tailed. Like a variance, the differences between the observed and expected frequencies are squared, allowing the χ^2 statistic to get larger to reflect the size of the differences. You expect the χ^2 statistic to be large when H_0 is false, so you use only the upper tail of the χ^2 distribution for the rejection values (see Figure 18.2). Your decision rule is to reject H_0 if your observed statistic is larger than or equal to the critical value, or, from a computer, to reject H_0 if the obtained probability value is less than or equal to α. With $\alpha = .05$, the critical value for the heart attack problem is $\chi^2 = 12.59$. Because you obtained $\chi^2 = 54.395$, you would reject H_0 and conclude that there are significantly unequal numbers of heart attacks on the seven days of the week.

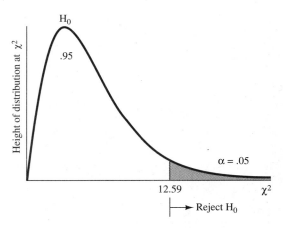

Figure 18.2
The χ^2 distribution with $df = 6$, showing critical value, rejection values, and areas

---

If you want to compare the days two at a time to see which day is significantly more risky, you could do tests of two independent proportions from Chapter 13. However, you should recognize that this is another MCP problem and that the probability of at least one Type I error needs to be controlled for all of these tests. The simplest approach is to do the tests of proportions, and for each test use an adjusted $\alpha' = \alpha/C$, where C is the number of tests. This is referred to as Dunn's or Bonferroni's procedure (Dunn, 1961). Many journals use the following format to give results: $\chi^2(6) = 54.395, p < .05$. The degrees of freedom are given in parentheses after the χ^2 symbol.

The fit of the χ^2 distribution with $df = K - 1$ to the sampling distribution of the χ^2 goodness-of-fit statistic depends on the sample size. If the expected frequency for each category is larger than or equal to 5, then the fit is adequate. For $df = 1$, this sample-size requirement is increased to $E = 10$ for each category.

Assumptions

Like nonparametric tests, the χ^2 goodness-of-fit test assumes that the observations are independent. That is, one participant being counted in one category does not influence any other participant being counted in any other category. Because of this, each participant must fit into one and only one category, and participants must not be counted twice. In the heart attack problem, every patient fits in only one category (day of week). Even with no more information about the effect of violating this assumption, you can extrapolate from other statistical tests and state that the χ^2 goodness-of-fit test is not robust to violation of the independence assumption.

Mutually exclusive and exhaustive

Each participant must fit into one and only one category, and the categories must be chosen so as to include all participants

Sometimes the assumption of independence is stated with the "one and only one category" part as a separate assumption. It is usually stated that the categories are assumed to be **mutually exclusive.** Categories must be chosen so that you can include all participants. If you decided, for some reason, to look at only weekday heart attacks, the patients who had heart attacks on the weekends wouldn't be included in the study. You need to choose your categories so that all participants are included, which is another way of saying your categories must be **exhaustive.**

Quick Quiz

You decide to see whether the months of the year have equal numbers of heart attacks. You go back through some hospitals' records and count how many heart attack patients were treated in each month last year. (a) Compute *df*. (b) Find the critical value from Table A.9.

Answers

(a) $df = K - 1 = 12$ months $- 1 = 11$. (b) For $\alpha = .05$, $\chi^2_{crit} = 19.68$.

18.4   Chi-Square Test for Contingency Tables

χ^2 test for contingency tables
Test statistic formed to test for independence of two categorical variables whose frequencies are arranged in a contingency table

The second nonparametric test we introduce is the **χ^2 test for contingency tables.** This statistic will help you find out whether two categorical variables are independent or dependent (contingent), as shown by the frequencies in the contingency table.

Example

Look at the contingency table for the relationship/touch data from Research Example 18 in Table 18.2. Couples in row 1 were engaged/dating or had been married/cohabiting less than a year. Row 2 contains the data for the couples married more than a year. Column 1 shows how many couples had the first hand touch made by the female, and column 2 shows the frequency of male-initiated touches. The researchers were interested in testing a hypothesis of independence of type of couple and who made the initial touch. Does the gender of the person who makes the first touch depend on the kind of relationship?

Notice the clues that this is a χ^2 problem. The description of the study indicates you have two categorical variables: type of couple and gender of who initiated touch. You can test a hypothesis of the independence of these two categorical variables.

Sensitivity

Like the χ^2 test for goodness of fit, the χ^2 test of independence of categorical variables is sensitive to any type of difference in the populations. For this test, you can think of the hypothesis in terms of equality of distributions across categories of one of the variables. For example, is the distribution of initial touches by women across types of couples the same as the distribution of initial touches by men? Because this test is sensitive to any type of difference in the populations, the hypothesis is nonparametric.

Table 18.2
Observed frequencies of female-initiated and male-initiated contact in three types of couples

Type of Couple	F Initiated	M Initiated	Totals
Engaged/dating or married/cohabiting less than 1 year	60	86	146
Married/cohabiting more than 1 year	41	32	73
Totals	101	118	219

Hypotheses

Here are the null and alternative hypotheses for the χ^2 test for contingency tables:

$$H_0: \text{distribution}_1 = \text{distribution}_2 = \cdots = \text{distribution}_K \tag{18.4}$$

H_1: some difference in the distributions

An optional way to state the hypotheses is:

$$H_0: \text{variable } A \text{ is independent of variable } B \tag{18.5}$$

H_1: variable A is not independent of variable B

For the example of relationship/touch, the null hypothesis is

$$H_0: \text{distribution}_{\text{male-initiated touch}} = \text{distribution}_{\text{female-initiated touch}}$$

or, for the optional way of stating H_0,

$$H_0: \text{gender of first toucher is independent of type of couple}$$

These hypotheses are nonparametric because they contain no parameters. If you reject H_0, you cannot pinpoint specific types of differences; you can say only that men and women differ across the kinds of couples. Alternatively, you can say that the gender of the initial toucher is not independent of type of couple.

Here, you do not have a theory that stipulates expected frequencies, as was the case for the goodness-of-fit χ^2. The expected frequencies are derived from the **marginal frequencies** (the row and column totals) and the idea that H_0 is true. Because of this, the actual test statistic, as well as the hypotheses, depends on the marginal frequencies of the contingency table.

Marginal frequencies
Frequencies of the rows and columns of a contingency table

Statistic

The χ^2 statistic for testing independence of categorical variables is

$$\chi^2 = \sum \frac{(O_{jk} - E_{jk})^2}{E_{jk}} \tag{18.6}$$

where O_{jk} is the observed frequency for the jkth cell, E_{jk} is the expected frequency for the jkth cell, and the summation is over all cells. Let's see how you get the values of E for each cell by using the marginal frequencies (row and column totals) in conjunction with H_0.

If the categorical variables are independent (H_0 is true), then the frequency that you would expect for any cell is simply a function of the row and column totals for that cell. For the cell that contains the frequency for female-initiated touch for a couple married more than a year, you would expect the frequency to be based on the "F initiated" column total and the "married/cohabiting more than 1 year" row total. The **expected frequency** for any cell is the product of the column and row marginal frequencies divided by the total frequency, or

Expected frequency
In contingency table problems, the product of row and column frequencies for a given cell divided by the total frequency

$$E_{jk} = \frac{(\text{column}_j \text{ total})(\text{row}_k \text{ total})}{N} \tag{18.7}$$

If you have R = number of rows and C = number of columns, you use this formula to find the expected frequency for each of the RC cells. For example, the expected frequency for the cell that contains the frequency for female-initiated and married/cohabiting more than a year is

$$E_{jk} = E_{21} = \frac{(101)(73)}{219} = 33.6667$$

because the column total for "F initiated" is 101, the row total for "married/cohabiting more than 1 year" is 73, and $N = 219$. Compute the E_{jk} for the other three cells and compare your results to those in Table 18.3. (You can check your computation of the E values by seeing whether they sum to N.)

The logic of this computation is based on the marginal frequencies and H_0 being true. If gender of the initial toucher and type of couple are independent, then you expect that a certain proportion of the 219 people will be "female/married more than a year." Specifically, the probability for "female" is $101/219 = .4612$, and the probability for "married more than a year" is $73/219 = .3333$. What is the probability of female-initiated touch *and* married more than a year? You should recognize that this question involves the multiplication (And) rule that you learned in Chapter 8 on probability. If the two events are independent, then p(female and married more than a year) $= p$(female)p(more than a year) $= (.4612)(.3333) = .1537$.

How do you find the *frequency* you would expect in that cell? You know what probability (proportion) you would expect in the cell, so multiply the probability of the joint event, $p = .1537$, by $N = 219$, $(.1537)(219) = 33.66$. Small rounding errors can occur, so the most accurate way to compute the expected frequencies is given in formula 18.7. The logic is tied to the computational formula. To find the proportion of people expected in a given cell if the two events are independent (H_0 true), use

$$p(\text{event 1})p(\text{event 2}) = \left(\frac{\text{column total}}{N}\right)\left(\frac{\text{row total}}{N}\right)$$

To find how many of the N people are expected in the cell, multiply the above proportion by N:

$$\left(\frac{\text{column total}}{N}\right)\left(\frac{\text{row total}}{N}\right) \times N = \frac{(\text{column total})(\text{row total})}{N}$$

Table 18.3
Expected frequencies of female-initiated and male-initiated contact in three types of couples

Type of Couple	F Initiated	M Initiated	Totals
Engaged/dating or married/cohabiting less than 1 year	67.3̄3̄	78.6̄6̄	146
Married/cohabiting more than 1 year	33.6̄6̄	39.3̄3̄	73
Totals	101	118	219

After you have calculated the E_{jk} for each cell, you square the difference between O_{jk} and E_{jk} and divide by E_{jk} for each cell; then sum those amounts. Be sure to use all of the digits your calculator will hold and do not round until you get your final answer. For the relationship/touch data, the computation of the χ^2 statistic gives

$$\chi^2 = \frac{(60 - 67.333333)^2}{67.333333} + \frac{(86 - 78.666667)^2}{78.666667}$$

$$+ \frac{(41 - 33.666667)^2}{33.666667} + \frac{(32 - 39.333333)^2}{39.333333}$$

$$= 0.7986797 + 0.6836157 + 1.5973595 + 1.3672315$$

$$= 4.45$$

For every new χ^2 for contingency tables, you have to compute the expected frequencies simply because the values of E are obtained from the observed marginal frequencies in the table.

Distribution

Degrees of freedom
For the contingency table χ^2 statistic, $df = (R - 1)$ $(C - 1)$, the number of rows minus 1 times the number of columns minus 1

The χ^2 statistic for testing independence of categorical variables given in formula 18.6 has a sampling distribution that is approximately fit by a χ^2 distribution with **degrees of freedom** equal to

$$df = (R - 1)(C - 1) \tag{18.8}$$

if all assumptions are met. Because the total frequency is fixed, $R - 1$ row frequencies are free to vary and $C - 1$ column frequencies are free to vary. The RC cell frequencies (the "independent components" from the working definition of degrees of freedom) have $R - 1$ row frequencies, $C - 1$ column frequencies, and the 1 total frequency subtracted to give

$$df = RC - (R - 1) - (C - 1) - 1$$

$$= RC - R + 1 - C + 1 - 1$$

$$= RC - R - C + 1$$

$$= (R - 1)(C - 1)$$

This rationale for the degrees of freedom is analogous to that given for the interaction degrees of freedom in the two-way ANOVA, where $df_{AB} = (J - 1)(K - 1)$.

For the relationship/touch example, $R = 2$ and $C = 2$, so $df = (2 - 1)(2 - 1) = (1)(1) = 1$.

Decision Rules

You test H_0 by finding the critical value for a chosen α—say, $\alpha = .05$—with $df = (R - 1)(C - 1)$ from Table A.9. The decision rule is to reject H_0 if your observed statistic is larger than or equal to the critical value, or, from a computer, to reject H_0 if the obtained probability value is less than or equal to α. For the relationship/touch example with $\alpha = .05$ and $df = 1$, the critical value is $\chi^2_{\text{crit}} = 3.84$. Because the observed χ^2 value of 4.45 exceeds the critical value, you reject H_0 and conclude that the gender of the person who makes the initial touch depends on the type of couple. As for the goodness-of-fit χ^2, journals use the following form to report these results: $\chi^2(1) = 4.45$, $p < .05$.

As you saw for the goodness-of-fit statistic, the fit of the χ^2 distribution with $df = (R - 1)(C - 1)$ depends on the sample size. If the expected frequency for each cell is larger than or equal to 5, then the fit is adequate. For 2×2 tables, where $df = 1$, this sample-size requirement is increased to $E = 10$ for each cell.

Assumptions

The N observations in the contingency table are assumed to be independent, as was the case for the goodness-of-fit χ^2 test. The categories for both variables also are assumed to be mutually exclusive and exhaustive. For the relationship/touch example, mutually exclusive means that a couple goes into only one of the two categories for type of couple. Exhaustive means that every participant has to fit in one of the categories of each variable. Researchers sometimes have to make decisions about how to classify participants. A couple could be engaged but cohabiting for more than a year. The researchers would decide how to classify the couple, but they could not count the couple twice, once in each category.

Quick Quiz

Suppose you replicated the relationship/touch study, except you classified couples as dating, engaged, married/cohabiting less than a year, or married/cohabiting a year or longer. You observed the couples and recorded whether the man or woman made the first touch, or if no touch was made during the 5-min observation period. (a) These data could be placed in a _____ $\times$ _____ _____ table. (b) What are the df? (c) What is χ^2_{crit}?

Answers

(a) 4×3 contingency table. (b) $df = (R - 1)(C - 1) = (4 - 1)(3 - 1) = 6$. (c) For $\alpha = .05$, $\chi^2_{crit} = 12.59$.

Beyond These Nonparametric Procedures

If you think about what you learned in Chapter 16 on the two-way ANOVA, you might be able to come up with some ideas for extensions on the χ^2 for contingency tables. It is possible to have three-way and even higher-order contingency tables. These analyses, however, are difficult, and the simpler two-way tables often answer the questions posed by researchers. See Wickens (1989) for excellent coverage of higher-order contingency table problems.

This chapter opened with some general statements about nonparametric statistics, which test hypotheses about distributions and not individual parameters. You might have noticed the mention of ranked data. You'll learn some statistics for use with ranked data in Chapter 19.

18.5   Summary, Study Tips, and Computation

Chapter Summary

Nonparametric procedures are test statistics designed to test hypotheses that have no parameters in them. Some of these procedures are good for nonparametric hypotheses because they detect any type of difference, whereas others are good for parametric hypotheses. Most of these methods were designed to relax the normality assumption. All nonparametric methods assume independence and continuity of the underlying distribution. Another issue on which to compare nonparametric and classical (parametric) statistical methods is scale of measurement.

For qualitative data (nominal scale), the χ^2 tests for goodness of fit and contingency tables were introduced. Both test nonparametric hypotheses and are sensitive to any difference in the distributions. Both are distributed as the χ^2 distribution with degrees of freedom unique to each test.

Key terms used in this chapter are:

Nonparametric	Mutually exclusive
Underlying distribution	Exhaustive
χ^2 test for goodness of fit	χ^2 tests for contingency
Observed frequency	tables
Expected frequency	Marginal frequencies
χ^2 distribution	

The statistical tests introduced in this chapter are summarized in Table 18.4, which shows the situation where the statistic would be used, the name of the statistic, and the theoretical reference distribution. For decision rules, assumptions, and any restrictions on the use of each procedure, refer to the section where it was presented.

Study Tips

Many people find χ^2 computations to be fairly straightforward, but the hypothesis being tested is harder to grasp. You might try this little test: Go around and ask about 30 friends, relatives, or classmates whether they prefer vanilla, chocolate, or strawberry ice cream (or any other three flavors). Keep track of the number of men and women in each category of ice cream. Now, why is χ^2 well suited for this situation? Because the data are categorical. You could to a χ^2 test for goodness of fit, ignoring the gender of your participants, or you could do a χ^2 for contingency tables, using both variables. Now, think about what kind of question you might answer with your data. Perhaps you are looking for whether ice cream preference depends on gender. Is the distribution of preferences for men the same as the distribution of preferences for women? Calculate χ^2 for your data and test your hypothesis. Learn by doing, and you'll remember the information on χ^2 better than if you just passively read and tried to memorize terms.

Computation

SAS contains procedures or statements to compute the contingency table χ^2. Also, SPSS has various commands that compute a χ^2 statistic. Examples are given here. However, because of the simplicity inherent in the nonparametric methods presented in this chapter, it may be more difficult to do them on the computer than to do them by hand. For large contingency tables, the chore of computing the expected frequencies can be better done by a computer. Thus, the computer offers mainly the accuracy advantage, which is, of course, limited to the accuracy of the input.

SAS Example

(SAS system's lines)

```
DATA CHI;
INPUT RESP$ VRBCOND$ @@;
```
(inputs the response to the question about seeing broken glass and verb condition "smashed or hit" for each participant from Research Example 13)

```
CARDS;
Y S Y S Y S Y S Y S Y S Y S Y S Y S Y S Y S Y S Y S Y S Y S
Y H Y H Y H Y H Y H Y H Y H Y C Y C Y C Y C Y C Y C N S N S N S
N S N S N S N S N S N S N S N S N S N S N S N S N S N S N S N S
N S N S N S N S N S N S N S N S N S N S N S N S N S N S N S N H
N H N H N H N H N H N H N H N H N H N H N H N H N H N H N H N H
N H N H N H N H N H N H N H N H N H N H N H N H N H N H N H N H
N H N H N H N H N H N H N H N H N H N H N H N C N C N C N C N C
N C N C N C N C N C N C N C N C N C N C N C N C N C N C N C N C
N C N C N C N C N C N C N C N C N C N C N C N C N C N C N C N C
N C N C N C N C N C
PROC PRINT;
PROC FREQ;
```
(PROC FREQ asks for the frequency procedure to count the frequencies for the tables requested in the next line. TABLES asks for a frequency table of RESP by VRBCOND, giving the expected frequencies for each cell, the χ^2 statistic, but not giving percentages for the cells, rows, and columns.)

```
TABLES RESP*VRBCOND/EXPECTED CHISQ NOPERCENT NOROW NOCOL;
TITLE 'CHISQUARE FOR BROKEN GLASS';
```
(system's line)

```
         CHISQUARE FOR BROKEN GLASS

              TABLE OF RESP BY VRBCOND ①

      RESP ②          VRBCOND ④

      FREQUENCY±
      EXPECTED ±C       ±H ⑤      ±S        ±   TOTAL
      ---------+---------+--------+--------+
   ③ N         ±  ⑥ 44 ±      43 ±     34 ±    121
              ±  ⑦ 40.3 ±    40.3 ±   40.3 ±
      ---------+---------+--------+--------+
      Y         ±     6 ±       7 ±     16 ±     29
              ±     9.7 ±    9.7 ±    9.7 ±
      ---------+---------+--------+--------+
      TOTAL        50        50        50       150

              STATISTICS FOR 2-WAY TABLES

CHI-SQUARE                  7.780 ⑧  DF= 2 ⑨  PROB=0.0204 ⑩
PHI                         0.228
CONTINGENCY COEFFICIENT     0.222
CRAMER'S V                  0.228
LIKELIHOOD RATIO CHISQUARE  7.430     DF= 2     PROB=0.0244
```

Figure 18.3
SAS output from PROC FREQ, χ^2

For PROC FREQ, the SAS output in Figure 18.3 gives the following:

1. This is a contingency table of the categorical variables RESP and VRBCOND.
2. RESP is given as the variable for the vertical axis.
3. The values for RESP are Y and N, which stand for yes and no.
4. VRBCOND is given as the variable for the horizontal axis.
5. The values for VRBCOND are C (control), H (hit), and S (smashed).
6. For each combination of values of the variables (each cell), the observed frequency is given.
7. For each cell, the expected frequency is given.
8. One of the many statistics is χ^2.
9. $df = (R - 1)(C - 1)$.
10. This is the probability of getting a χ^2 as large as or larger than the observed χ^2.

SPSS Example

(SPSS system's lines)
```
SET WIDTH 80
DATA LIST FREE/RESP (A) BY VRBCOND (A)      (The two variables are being read as qualitative variables, and SPSS uses the
                                             A to show this and that there is only one character in the values for response
                                             and verb condition.)

BEGIN DATA
Y S Y S Y S Y S Y S Y S Y S Y S Y S Y S Y S Y S Y S Y S Y S Y S
Y H Y H Y H Y H Y H Y H Y C Y C Y C Y C Y C Y C Y C N S N S N S
N S N S N S N S N S N S N S N S N S N S N S N S N S N S N S N S
N S N S N S N S N S N S N S N S N S N S N S N S N S N S N S N H
N H N H N H N H N H N H N H N H N H N H N H N H N H N H N H N H
N H N H N H N H N H N H N H N H N H N H N H N H N H N H N H N H
N H N H N H N H N H N H N H N H N H N H N H N C N C N C N C N C
N C N C N C N C N C N C N C N C N C N C N C N C N C N C N C N C
N C N C N C N C N C N C N C N C N C N C N C N C N C N C N C N C
N C N C N C N C N C N C
END DATA
CROSSTABS TABLES=RESP BY VRBCOND/STATISTICS=CHISQ      (asks for the contingency table to be built for the two
                                                       variables and the χ² statistic to be computed)
```
(system's line)

For the command CROSSTABS, the SPSS output in Figure 18.4 gives the following:

1. This is a contingency table of the categorical variables RESP and VRBCOND.
2. RESP is given as the variable for the vertical axis.
3. The values for RESP are N and Y, which stand for no and yes.
4. VRBCOND is given as the variable for the horizontal axis.
5. The values for VRBCOND are C (control), H (hit), and S (smashed).
6. For each combination of values of the variables (each cell), the observed frequency is given.
7. One of the statistics is χ^2.
8. $df = (R - 1)(C - 1)$.
9. This is the probability of getting a χ^2 as large as or larger than the observed χ^2.

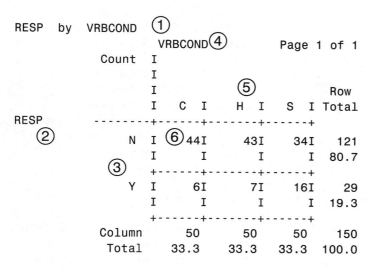

```
RESP  by  VRBCOND  ①
                 VRBCOND④                Page 1 of 1
           Count  I
                  I
                  I            ⑤            Row
                  I  C  I   H  I   S  I  Total
RESP          ----------+-------+------+
   ②           N  I ⑥44I    43I    34I    121
                  I     I      I      I   80.7
       ③          +------+-------+------+
               Y  I    6I     7I    16I     29
                  I     I      I      I   19.3
                  +------+-------+------+
          Column     50     50     50    150
          Total    33.3   33.3   33.3  100.0
```

Chi-Square	Value	DF	Significance
Pearson	⑦7.77999	2⑧	.02045⑨
Likelihood Ratio	7.43030	2	.02435

Minimum Expected Frequency -   9.667

Number of Missing Observations: 0

Figure 18.4
SPSS output for CROSSTABS

Exercises

Sections 18.1 and 18.2

1. In your own words, give the true meaning of *nonparametric*.
2. On the issue of sensitivity, for what type of hypothesis are the χ^2 tests sensitive? Can they detect mean differences? Variance differences? Any difference?

Grade	Frequency
A	140
B	300
C	550
D	220
F	90
	1300

Section 18.3

3. In Number 2 of the Chapter 8 exercises, you saw this table for the grades earned by the 1300 students enrolled in an introductory psychology course one semester.
   a. For a χ^2 test for goodness of fit, what is K?
   b. Compute *df*.
   c. Find χ^2_{crit}, using $\alpha = .05$.
   d. If you thought that grades should be even—that is,

the same number of A's, B's, and so on—how would you compute E_k?
   e. Complete the χ^2 computation and test your hypothesis. What conclusion would you draw?
4. Suppose you think there are more property crimes on the weekend than on weekdays. You decide to count the numbers of burglaries, acts of vandalism and car theft reported to your city's police

department for one week. You find 152 crimes that meet your criteria. You think the numbers of crimes won't be equal for the seven days of the week.

   a. Why might you be able to use χ^2 for goodness of fit?

   b. If you use χ^2 for goodness of fit, what are your *df* and χ^2_{crit} for $\alpha = .05$?

   c. What is H_0?

   d. Calculate E_k.

5. Gilliland and Andress (1981) checked the frequencies of incomplete grades in the introductory psychology course for a group of college students in their caffeine study (see Exercise 12 in Chapter 16). The total number of incompletes was 42 for that semester in that course. They categorized students into four groups on caffeine consumption and hypothesized equal frequencies of incompletes for the null hypothesis.

   a. What is the expected frequency of incompletes for each of the four groups?

   b. If the observed frequencies of incompletes are 8, 4, 16, and 14 for the abstainers, low, moderate, and high groups, respectively, what is the value of the goodness-of-fit χ^2?

   c. Would you reject the hypothesis that the population of incompletes is uniformly distributed across caffeine consumption categories?

6. Suppose someone has a hypothesis that the "Transylvania effect" of the full moon is related to incidence of drug overdose (see Sharfman, 1980). A search of medical files at a hospital yielded 1182 drug overdose cases that included the date. The full-moon phase was based on the actual dates of the full moon plus or minus 2 days, yielding 75 full-moon days and 381 non-full-moon days (total number of days was 456 for the period investigated). The observed frequency of drug overdose was 196 during full-moon days and 986 during non-full-moon days.

   a. How do you get the expected frequencies, and what are their values?

   b. What is the value of the goodness-of-fit χ^2? What is your decision?

7. Lester (1988) was interested in a "Friday the 13th" effect on suicides. Do more people commit suicide on Friday the 13th than on other Fridays? He obtained data for 1972–1982 for Friday the 6th (1403), Friday the 13th (1374), Friday the 20th (1317), and Friday the 27th (1294).

   a. How would you obtain the *E*'s for this data set?

   b. Compute the goodness-of-fit χ^2 and write up the results as you would for a journal article.

8. The table of tobacco use by gender and geographic location from Research Example 8 is given here. Before you go on to the questions, think of what questions you might want to ask that could be answered from these data.

Percent of tobacco use in persons 20 or older, by gender and geographic location

	Men							Women		
	None	*Cigarette*	*Snuff*	*Chewing Tobacco*	*Cigar*	*Pipe*	*At Least One Tobacco Product*	*None*	*Cigarette*	*At Least One Tobacco Product*
United States (105,225)	60.32	32.66	1.84	3.95	2.14	2.40	39.67	73.41	25.81	26.59
Northeast (26,186)	63.12	31.00	0.94	1.48	3.15	2.57	36.89	74.00	25.77	26.01
New England (9,434)	64.34	30.25	0.42	0.74	3.67	2.79	35.66	72.25	27.58	27.75
Middle Atlantic (16,752)	62.71	31.26	1.11	1.73	2.98	2.49	37.30	74.59	25.16	25.40
North Central (26,154)	60.45	32.20	2.07	3.43	2.29	3.01	39.55	72.54	27.33	27.46
East North Central (16,388)	60.07	32.83	1.70	2.90	2.53	3.20	39.94	71.31	28.55	28.70
West North Central (9,766)	61.34	30.70	2.95	4.69	1.72	2.54	38.66	75.40	24.51	24.60
South (31,646)	55.44	36.04	2.48	6.22	1.89	2.17	44.56	72.11	26.03	27.89
South Atlantic (18,014)	56.53	35.89	1.64	5.35	2.12	2.23	43.46	71.79	26.19	28.20
East South Central (4,985)	51.49	37.33	2.57	9.58	1.65	2.12	48.51	71.77	25.95	28.22
West South Central (8,647)	55.99	35.54	3.82	5.65	1.66	2.11	44.01	72.84	25.82	27.16
West (21,239)	65.57	29.19	1.41	3.34	1.29	1.82	34.43	76.28	23.47	23.72
Mountain (8,854)	62.20	29.92	2.36	5.61	1.46	2.04	37.81	75.44	24.27	24.57
Pacific (12,385)	66.81	28.92	1.05	2.51	1.23	1.73	33.18	76.58	23.18	23.42

Note: Percentages are based on the number of men and women participants within the individual geographic categories.
Source: Shopland, Niemcryk, and Marconi (1992).

Region	N	O = Observed Frequency	E = Expected Frequency
NE	26,186	9,661	10,307.66567
NC	26,154	10,344	10,295.06942
S	31,646	14,102	12,456.90017
W	21,239	7,313	8,360.36474
United States	105,225	41,420	41,420

a. Was one of your questions about the variation from one geographic region to another? Is this variability significant? Here is one way to answer this question from the data. First, for the men, obtain observed frequencies for the four major regions, Northeast (NE), North Central (NC), South (S), and West (W), by multiplying the proportion of at least one tobacco use by the number in the region (in parentheses). You should get the observed frequencies (rounded up for any decimal part) shown in the table at the top of the page.

b. How would you get expected frequencies if a null hypothesis of proportional use in geographic regions is true? Think about this before you go on. Divide the N for each region by the total, 105,225, and multiply that proportion by the total of the O's, 41,420. Check your answers with the E's given in the table. These E's should make some sense to you; for example, the 12,456 for the South is logically the highest frequency because the N for the South is the highest.

c. Compute the goodness-of-fit χ^2 and test your hypothesis of proportional use of at least one tobacco product among these four regions.

d. Think of other interesting questions from the data. Use what you know about statistics to answer them.

Section 18.4

9. You have surveyed 100 people for their opinions of the performance of the mayor of your hometown (OK, not OK) and recorded their political party affiliation (Republican, Democrat, other). You obtained the frequencies listed in the table. Test the independence of party and opinion ($\alpha = .05$).

	Party			
Opinion	Democrat	Republican	Other	Totals
OK	45	7	10	62
Not OK	15	13	10	38
Totals	60	20	20	100

10. Research Example 13 gave results for a study by Loftus and Palmer (1974) in which students were shown a short film of a car accident and asked whether they saw any broken glass after the two cars *hit* or *smashed* into each other. The researchers wanted to determine whether the wording of the question would influence recall of the presence or absence of glass, when in truth there was no broken glass. Part of their results are given in the table.

Frequencies for Verb and Response to "Did you see any broken glass?"

	Verb		
Response	Smashed	Hit	Totals
Yes	16	7	23
No	34	43	77
Totals	50	50	100

a. Why might a χ^2 for contingency tables be an appropriate statistic?

b. Compute *df* and find χ^2_{crit}, $\alpha = .05$.

c. What hypothesis are you testing?

d. Compute the four E_{jk} values.

e. Complete the χ^2 computation and test your hypothesis.

f. What conclusion would you draw about this study?

11. Test the hypothesis of independence of handedness (right or left) and grade (A, B, C, D, F) in statistics with the data in the table (use $\alpha = .05$).

	Grade				
Handedness	A	B	C	D	F
Right	8	13	23	13	8
Left	12	12	17	7	2

12. The data given here are from an example in Number 5 of the Chapter 8 exercises. They are the frequencies of payoff by two different slot machines.

	Machine A	Machine B
Paid	23	11
Did not pay	271	339

   a. What hypothesis could you test?
   b. Calculate χ^2 for contingency tables and test your hypothesis at the $\alpha = .05$ level. Does it matter which slot machine you use?

13. Looking again to an example you saw in Number 7 of the Chapter 8 exercises, suppose you have these frequencies for grades and majors in a statistics class.

		Major		
Grade	Math	Psychology	Pharmacy	Total
A	5	5	1	11
B	7	9	9	25
C	12	15	15	42
D	3	10	10	23
F	1	0	5	6
Total	28	39	40	107

   a. What are R, C, and df?
   b. What hypothesis might you test?
   c. Find χ^2_{crit} for $\alpha = .05$.
   d. Compute χ^2 for contingency tables and test your hypothesis. What is your conclusion?

14. The example of a developmental psychologist interested in gender role development was given in Number 9 of the Chapter 8 exercises. This researcher decided to study toy selection as a function of the gender of children. These frequencies were observed.

	M	F	Total
Truck	35	25	60
Doll	15	25	40
Total	50	50	100

   a. Find χ^2_{crit}, with $\alpha = .05$.
   b. What hypothesis might you test?
   c. Calculate χ^2 and test your hypothesis.

15. This table was used in Table 8.2 with the juror example. The question being asked is, Does receiving an award in a civil suit depend on the authoritarianism of the jurors? Compute χ^2 and answer this question.

Jurors classified as to award and authoritarianism

	Authoritarian	Egalitarian	Totals
Gave an award	18	13	31
Gave no award	2	15	17
Totals	20	28	48

16. In Research Example 18 on relationship/touch, you read that Willis and Briggs (1992) looked at whether or not touch occurred for two types of couples. They found that touch was more likely to occur for couples who were engaged/dating or married/cohabiting for less than a year, compared with couples who had been married/cohabiting for more than a year. Their data are presented in the table. Compute χ^2 and verify their results ($\chi^2 = 37.31$, $p < .001$).

Type of Couple	Touch	No Touch	Totals
Engaged/Dating or Married/ Cohabiting less than 1 year	146	110	256
Married/Cohabiting more than 1 year	73	171	244
Totals	219	281	500

Source: Willis and Briggs (1992).

19

Nonparametric Methods: Rank Tests

Chapter 18 presented chi-square tests, which are nonparametric procedures appropriate for qualitative data and which don't assume normality. There also are nonparametric procedures for use with quantitative data. For the tests in this chapter, you can rank quantitative data, or some function of the data, and use the ranks in the statistic, also without having to assume normality.

Research Example 19
19.1 Rank Tests: General Comments
    Common characteristics
    Power
    Sensitivity
19.2 Mann-Whitney U Test: Two Independent Samples
    Example
    Hypotheses
    Statistic
    Distribution
19.3 Wilcoxon Test: Two Dependent Samples
    Example
    Hypotheses
    Statistic
    Distribution
19.4 Kruskal-Wallis Test: J Independent Samples
    Example
    Hypotheses
    Statistic
    Distribution
19.5 Friedman Test: J Dependent Samples
    Example
    Hypotheses
    Statistic
    Distribution
19.6 Spearman Correlation Coefficient
    Definition of Monotonic
    Example
    Hypotheses
    Statistic
    Distribution
    Beyond these statistics

19.7 Summary, Study Tips, and Computation
Chapter summary
Study tips
Computation
Exercises

Research Example 19

Perhaps you have played the game "Dungeons and Dragons," which involves adopting an alter ego in a medieval setting. In the game of D&D, you roll dice to take on characteristics such as strength and intelligence and gain other characteristics (experience, wealth, power) as you advance in levels of playing.

Some people have been concerned about possible harmful effects of playing this game. Detachment and alienation from friends and family are criticisms of D&D players over the years. Others claim that these characteristics increase as commitment to the game increases. DeRenard and Kline (1990) reviewed these issues and provided some empirical evidence regarding these claims. They recruited 35 D&D players from a campus role-playing club and 35 nonplayers from a general psychology class. All students were given a questionnaire that included gender, age, D&D information (number of years played, frequency of playing, level achieved, amount of money spent on game materials, and so on), a scale that measured various types of alienation including meaninglessness, and some other scales and filler items.

DeRenard and Kline performed several tests of differences between the two groups, but only differences in cultural estrangement (part of the alienation scale) were significant in the predicted direction. Looking only at the responses from the D&D players, the researchers calculated several Spearman correlation coefficients relating measures of commitment to D&D and measures of alienation. They found that the amount of money spent on the game was significantly related to feelings of general alienation ($r_S = .47$, $p < .01$) and feelings of meaninglessness ($r_S = .61$, $p < .01$). They also found that feelings of meaninglessness increased as the frequency of playing increased ($r_S = .42$, $p < .01$) and as higher levels of play were achieved ($r_S = .45$, $p < .01$). These findings support the proposition that alienation increases as commitment to the game increases. The researchers hasten to point out lack of causal relationships and call for more research on the effects of playing this game, perhaps comparing D&D players to people who exhibit intense commitment to other recreational activities.

In this chapter you'll learn more nonparametric statistics, such as the Spearman correlation coefficient r_s, which is the nonparametric counterpart to the Pearson correlation coefficient r. The nonparametric statistics in this chapter involve ranking the data, or some function of the data, and then performing an analysis on the ranks. You will see that in some situations, these procedures are preferable to classic (parametric) statistics.

19.1   Rank Tests: General Comments

In Chapter 18 you learned two χ^2 tests. Both involved frequencies in categories, such as the number of married men who initiated touch. Alternatives to the χ^2 tests do not share the uniform quality of the χ^2 tests for contingency tables and goodness of fit. So research supports the common practice of using χ^2 tests when data are qualitative.

When you shift your attention to quantitative data, you can choose between classic (parametric) tests and the newer nonparametric tests. The introduction to Chapter 18 gave some general guidelines on choosing a statistical method based on hypotheses (sensitivity), assumptions, and scale of measurement of the data. You were advised to use nonparametric methods if the hypothesis to be tested is the more general nonparametric hypothesis about entire distributions (χ^2 tests), if the departure from normality is considerable, or if the scale of measurement is nominal, or perhaps ordinal. Among the nonparametric methods, the rank methods in this chapter are not only the most popular but also the most carefully researched.

Common Characteristics

Sum of ranks
Sum of the ranks of observations or differences

The methods covered in this chapter have the common characteristic of being based on the **sum of ranks.** Each method asks you to substitute ranks for observations (or differences in observations) and then find one or more rank sums in the computation of the statistic. That is, if you have three scores, 91, 78, and 88, they can be ranked 3, 1, and 2, respectively, and the ranks add up to 6.

Tied ranks
If two or more scores have the same value, the average of the ranks is given to each score

Rank methods also share the common assumptions of independence and a continuous underlying distribution. A continuous underlying distribution implies that all observations are unique, so you assume there are no tied ranks. In practice, **tied ranks** occur frequently, especially in data from ordinal scales of measurement. You solve the problem by averaging the ranks of the equal scores to get the rank of each score. For example, if you have two values of $X = 47$ and the ranks would have been 11 and 12, you use $(11 + 12)/2 = 11.5$ as the rank for both values of 47.

The rank tests for differences in central tendency (analogous to the two-independent-sample t and ANOVAs) also assume the populations have identical shapes, which implies an assumption of equal variances (explained later). Another common characteristic is simplicity. Methods based on rank sums are relatively easy to compute. However, for large sample sizes, ranking can become difficult, especially if the data have a large number of ties. Of course, using computers can make it easier.

The final two common characteristics of rank tests are power and sensitivity. Because these areas are quite important, we discuss them separately.

Power

The best way to talk about the power of rank tests is to compare it to the power of the corresponding classic (parametric) tests. For example, how does the power of the Mann-Whitney U test compare with the power of the two-independent-sample t-test? This comparison of the powers of two statistical tests is called *power efficiency*. Tech-

Power efficiency
Ratio of the sample sizes from two tests necessary for the tests to have the same power

nically, **power efficiency** is the ratio of the sample sizes of the two tests necessary for them to achieve the same power. Suppose the two-independent-sample t-test has power $= .90$ for some alternative hypothesis with $N = 96$. For the Mann-Whitney U test to have power $= .90$ for the same alternative, you would have to use $N = 100$. Then the power efficiency is $96/100 = .96$, or 96% efficiency for the U test. Usually the sample size for the nonparametric test is put in the denominator of the power efficiency. Power efficiency varies as a function of sample size and type of population sampled. Some general indication of the power efficiency is given for the rank tests. Fortunately, the rank tests have their power characteristics in common, so you need to examine the question of relative power only once.

If the populations are normally distributed, the rank tests are less powerful than their parametric counterparts. With the normality assumption met, the *t*-tests and ANOVA are the most powerful tests available. However, the power of the rank tests is close to that of these classic tests, even for normal populations. For very large samples (technically, as sample size approaches infinity) from normal populations, the power efficiency of the rank tests that are comparable to the classic tests on means is .955. The power efficiency is .912 for the rank correlation, Spearman's r_S, relative to the Pearson *r* for very large samples. For smaller samples from normal populations, the power efficiency is somewhat smaller but close to that given for very large samples.

The minimum power efficiency for rank tests for very large samples is .864, with values larger than one for some distributions. For a uniform (rectangular) distribution, the power efficiency is 1.00, whereas it is 1.50 for a long-tailed, symmetric, peaked distribution called the double exponential. These values of power efficiency that are larger than one indicate that for very large sample sizes, the rank tests can be more powerful than the classic tests. Research by Blair and Higgins (1980) showed that for reasonable-sized samples (from $n_1 = 3$ and $n_2 = 9$ up to $n_1 = n_2 = 54$), the Mann-Whitney *U* test could be much more powerful than the two-independent-sample *t*-test if the populations sampled had 5% to 10% of the scores in one tail as extreme scores. As indicated earlier, such considerable departure from normality in the populations would lead you to select a nonparametric method.

Quick Quiz

Suppose a certain nonparametric statistic has a relative efficiency of 1.05. If you used 100 participants for the nonparametric test, how many would you need if you wanted to use the corresponding parametric statistic and get the same power?

Answer

You would need 105 participants to obtain the same power as you would get with 100 for the nonparametric statistic.

Sensitivity

Some nonparametric tests, such as the χ^2 tests, are sensitive to any differences and are useful to test the more general nonparametric hypotheses. Other nonparametric tests are sensitive to differences in a specific parameter and are useful to test a parametric hypothesis. Even though these nonparametric tests were designed to test nonparametric hypotheses, they are sensitive to specific parametric differences.

The rank tests are this last type. They are sensitive to differences in location (central tendency) of otherwise identical populations. To rephrase, these rank tests are sensitive to differences in medians, or means if the populations are symmetric. Of course, you never really know whether the populations are symmetric, so effectively the rank tests are tests of hypotheses of equal population medians. The meaning of "otherwise identical populations" is that the rank tests are not really very sensitive to other types of differences in the populations.

This also implies an assumption of equal variances for these rank tests. Consider this argument: If you want to use the rank tests to test hypotheses about equal measures of central tendency, do you want unequal variances to cause your test to reject? No, you want only unequal medians to cause the rank test to reject, so you need to assume that the variances are equal. Now we question the robustness of the rank tests to violation of the equal-variance assumption. They are similar to the classic tests in their robustness or lack of robustness to violation of the assumption of equal variances. Except for the Spearman correlation, the rank tests in this chapter fit this pattern of sensitivity to median differences. All except the Spearman and Wilcoxon tests have an equal-variance assumption. The sensitivity of the Spearman correlation is discussed separately when that statistic is covered.

The following sections explain nonparametric procedures that might be useful in place of some classic statistics you've already learned. Remember that they all have in common the characteristics of computing sums of ranks using the average rank to resolve tied scores, simplicity, power efficiency, and, except for the Spearman correlation, sensitivity to median differences. All except Spearman and Wilcoxon include an implicit assumption of equal variances. We now explain what each test does that is unique.

19.2   Mann-Whitney *U* Test: Two Independent Samples

Example

Let's return to an example you've seen before, the impact of language on memory for details (see Research Example 13 and Exercise 9 from Chapter 13). We'll use this example to illustrate a nonparametric competitor to the two-independent-sample *t*-test. The simulated data in Table 19.1 are speed estimates from two groups asked how fast cars in a video were going when they *smashed* or *hit* into each other.

Hypotheses

Mann-Whitney *U* test
A rank test for two
independent samples

When you have two independent samples and want to test hypotheses about equal medians, the **Mann-Whitney *U* test** is the appropriate rank test (Mann & Whitney, 1947). Other rank methods have been developed for the two-independent-sample case, but the *U* is the best known of these statistics. The null hypothesis is

$$H_0: \text{population median}_1 = \text{population median}_2 \tag{19.1}$$

and the nondirectional alternative hypothesis is

$$H_1: \text{population median}_1 \neq \text{population median}_2$$

Directional hypotheses also can be tested with the Mann-Whitney *U* test, as is demonstrated shortly. If the populations are symmetric, these hypotheses in effect become hypotheses about means and medians in the populations.

Statistic

Here is how to conduct the *U* test:

1. Combine all the observations from both samples, and rank all the data from 1 for the smallest score to *N* for the largest score. Resolve all tied ranks, using the average of

Table 19.1
Speed estimates

Smashed	Hit
12	14
10	5
10	7
7	11
8	7
16	4
16	6
9	8
9	11
8	7

the ranks for the tied scores. For example, the three values of 8 get the average of ranks 8, 9, and 10, or average rank = 9. The two values of 10 get average rank = 13.5. Now group the ranks by the original two samples.

2. Compute the rank sums T_1 and T_2, where T_1 = sum of ranks for sample 1 and T_2 = sum of ranks for sample 2.

3. Compute the values of U_1 and U_2:

$$U_1 = n_1 n_2 + \frac{n_1(n_1 + 1)}{2} - T_1$$

$$U_2 = n_1 n_2 + \frac{n_2(n_2 + 1)}{2} - T_2$$

(19.2)

where n_1 is the size of sample 1 and n_2 is the size of sample 2. Then we choose U to be:

$$U = \text{the smaller of } U_1 \text{ or } U_2$$

A computational check is available from a formula that shows the relationship between U_1 and U_2, which is

$$U_1 + U_2 = n_1 n_2$$

The computations necessary to get U for the speed estimates data are given in Table 19.2.

Table 19.2
Speed estimates

Smashed	Rank	Hit	Rank	
12	17	14	18	
10	13.5	5	2	$n_1 = n_2 = 10$
10	13.5	7	5.5	$N = n_1 + n_2 = 20$
7	5.5	11	15.5	$U_{crit} = 23$ (from Table A.10)
8	9	7	5.5	
16	19.5	4	1	
16	19.5	6	3	
9	11.5	8	9	
9	11.5	11	15.5	
8	9	7	5.5	
	129.5		80.5	

$$U_1 = n_1 n_2 + \frac{n_1(n_1 + 1)}{2} - T_1 = (10)(10) + \frac{(10)(11)}{2} - 129.5$$

$$= 100 + 55 - 129.5 = 25.5$$

$$U_2 = n_1 n_2 + \frac{n_2(n_2 + 1)}{2} - T_2 = (10)(10) + \frac{(10)(11)}{2} - 80.5$$

$$= 100 + 55 - 80.5 = 74.5$$

$U = 25.5$; because $U = 25.5 > 23$, retain H_0.

Distribution

The sampling distribution of U is discrete and symmetric. For larger sample sizes (n_1 or n_2 larger than 20), the sampling distribution of U can be approximated by a normal distribution. For small samples, Table A.10 in Appendix A gives the critical values of U necessary to test hypotheses. Critical values are obtained from Table A.10 by entering the table in the row indicated by n_1 and the column indicated by n_2 for your chosen value of α. From the computations in Table 19.2, you would conclude that the language used to describe the accident does not make a difference in the population medians of estimates of speed.

Quick Quiz

If you have 15 participants in each group and you choose $\alpha = .05$ for a two-tailed test, find the U critical value in Table A.10.

Answer

64

You can test the nondirectional hypothesis with a two-tailed test by rejecting H_0 if U (the smaller of U_1 and U_2) is less than or equal to the critical value. It is unusual for a test to work with low values of a statistic, so be careful about this when you do the Mann-Whitney U test. Let's step through the logic of the low values of the statistic: If you have low scores in one group and high scores in the other group, then the higher ranks will be in the second group. The sum of the ranks for the second group will be large, leading to your obtained U from the second group being the smaller of the two. Then you choose the smaller of the two values of U to compare to a critical value. If your observed U is extreme enough (smaller than your critical value), then you reject H_0.

Directional hypotheses may be tested with one-tailed tests, which are simple to perform if you think through the consequences of the alternative hypothesis. Suppose you have an alternative hypothesis that says "median$_1$ > median$_2$." In general, then, the first sample should have scores that are larger than those for the second sample. The first sample should have larger ranks than those for the second sample, and T_1 should be larger than T_2. If T_1 is large, then U_1 is small. So you reject H_0 if U_1 is less than the critical value. For these one-tailed tests, you do not use the value of U, but you use U_1 or U_2, whichever corresponds to your alternative hypothesis.

For n_1 or n_2 larger than 20, a large-sample form of the U test is needed because Table A.10 is limited to 20 observations per group. This large-sample test uses the fact that as sample size increases, the sampling distribution of U approaches a normal distribution. It also uses the familiar z formula with a mean of $n_1 n_2/2$ and a standard deviation of $\sqrt{n_1 n_2(N + 1)/12}$. The form of the large-sample test statistic for U is

$$z = \frac{U - \dfrac{n_1 n_2}{2}}{\sqrt{\dfrac{n_1 n_2(N + 1)}{12}}} \tag{19.3}$$

where $N = n_1 + n_2$. The statistic z is approximately normally distributed and can be referred to critical values from the standard normal distribution in Table A.2.

Two-tailed or one-tailed tests can be done by using critical values at the appropriate $\alpha/2$ or α, respectively.

To illustrate the large-sample formula, let's use another example you've seen several times, the exam stress study (see Chapter 1, Research Example 11, and Chapter 13 for the two-independent-sample t). DasGupta (1992) randomly assigned 30 students to one of two conditions that were different with respect to the perceived control over a test-taking situation. The perceived-control (PC) students submitted written questions for a test, believing the questions might be used on the test. The no-control (NC) students also submitted questions, but they thought this task would help them study for the test. The actual test contained questions that were similar to 82% of the questions from the PC group and 87% of the NC group. One of the dependent variables was the number of symptoms indicated on a form of the *Stress Self-Assessment Checklist* (SSAC) (Neidhardt, Weinstein & Conry, 1985). Would perception of control make any difference in exam stress?

The data from Table 13.1, when ranked, give a value for U of 266.5. For a two-tailed test with nondirectional H_1 and $\alpha = .05$, the critical values from Table A2 are ± 1.96. Calculation of z gives

$$z = \frac{266.5 - (30)(30)/2}{\sqrt{(30)(30)(60 + 1)/12}} = \frac{266.5 - 450}{67.6387} = -2.71$$

Because -2.71 is less than -1.96, you would reject H_0 and conclude that the population medians were unequal. This result agrees with the result obtained by using the two-independent-sample t-test (see Table 13.2).

Quick Quiz

Suppose you want to know whether light from halogen lamps helps counteract depression among people who have seasonal affective disorder (SAD). You have two groups, with ten people spending time in a room with normal light bulbs and ten people in a room with halogen lights. You rank the depression scores for all 20 people and compute $U_1 = 52$ and $U_2 = 48$. Is there a significant difference in the groups?

Answer

With ten participants in each group, the U critical value from Table A.10 when $\alpha = .05$ is 23, and $U = 48$, the lesser of U_1 and U_2. Because U is greater than the critical value, you retain H_0 and conclude that the groups are not significantly different.

19.3   Wilcoxon Test: Two Dependent Samples

Example

Let's look at a nonparametric competitor to the two-dependent-sample t-test. In Chapter 13 you examined the study by Als, Tronick, Lester, and Brazelton (1979) that provided normative data on the Brazelton Neonatal Behavior Assessment Scale (BNBAS). The researchers collected data for most of the first 10 days of the lives of 54 healthy full-term white newborn babies and found statistically significant improvement. You computed a two-dependent-sample t-test on data from a replication study with another type of infant—full-term but small babies (Table 13.3). Simulated data for 15 babies on only days 1 and 10 are listed in Table 19.3.

You recognize this as a two-dependent-sample case: two measurements on the same set of babies. The two-dependent-sample case also can be identified when a researcher matches participants on some extraneous variable and then randomly assigns one member of the pair to one group and the other member to the second group. You also have a two-dependent-sample case when you use naturally occurring pairs, such as married couples, and compare them on a dependent variable such as opinion of the husband's commitment to the relationship. A nonparametric test appropriate for the two-dependent-sample case is the **Wilcoxon matched-pairs signed-ranks test.**

Wilcoxon matched-pairs signed-ranks test
A rank test for two dependent samples

Hypotheses

Recall the null hypothesis for the two-independent-sample t-test, H_0: $\mu_1 = \mu_2$. For the two-dependent-sample t, the hypothesis was identical, except the means were correlated. You have a similar situation here for the nonparametric counterparts to those t-tests. The hypotheses for the Wilcoxon matched-pairs signed-ranks test are exactly the same as those for the Mann-Whitney U test, except that the two medians are related. The null hypothesis is equality of medians in the population, except that there is a correlation between the scores in the two samples and between the two sample medians. The title of the test (matched-pairs signed-ranks) tells not only the design (matched pairs) but also something about how the statistic is computed (signed ranks).

Statistic

The Wilcoxon matched-pairs signed-ranks statistic is quite simple. The following sequence of steps leads to calculation of a correct value of the statistic.

1. Obtain all differences $d = X_2 - X_1$, just as for the two-dependent-sample t-test. Eliminate all differences that have a value of zero. The number of nonzero differences is K.
2. Working only with the K nonzero differences, obtain the absolute values of the d's.
3. Rank the absolute values of the differences. Ranks are from 1 for the smallest absolute difference to K for the largest absolute difference. Resolve all tied ranks, using the average of the ranks for the absolute differences that are tied.
4. For the differences that have a minus sign, sum their ranks and call it T_-. For the differences that have a plus sign, sum their ranks and call it T_+. Let T be the smaller of T_+ or T_-. So T is the test statistic.

The Wilcoxon statistic uses a rank sum directly as the statistic.

Table 19.3
Orientation to face and voice for 15 full-term but small babies

Baby	$X_1 = Day\ 1$	$X_2 = Day\ 10$
1	6	7
2	5	7
3	3	6
4	8	8
5	6	8
6	6	8
7	6	8
8	7	8
9	8	6
10	5	7
11	6	7
12	7	7
13	5	7
14	6	8
15	4	6

Distribution

As was the case for the Mann-Whitney U test, the sampling distribution of T is discrete and symmetric. For larger sample sizes (K larger than 50), the sampling distribution of T can be approximated by a normal distribution. For small samples, Table A.11 in Appendix A gives the critical values of T necessary to test hypotheses. Critical values are obtained from Table A.11 by entering the table in the row indicated by K, the number of nonzero differences, and the column for your chosen value of α.

The nondirectional hypothesis may be tested with a two-tailed test by rejecting H_0 if T (the smaller value of T_+ or T_-) is less than or equal to the critical value. As in the Mann-Whitney U test, you reject the H_0 of equal population medians if the statistic is

Table 19.4
Orientation to face and voice for 15 full-term but small babies

Baby	$X_1 = Day\ 1$	$X_2 = Day\ 10$	$d = X_2 - X_1$	$|d|$	Rank of $|d|$
1	6	7	1	1	2
2	5	7	2	2	8
3	3	6	3	3	13
4	8	8	0	0	No rank
5	6	8	2	2	8
6	6	8	2	2	8
7	6	8	2	2	8
8	7	8	1	1	2
9	8	6	−2	2	8
10	5	7	2	2	8
11	6	7	1	1	2
12	7	7	0	0	No rank
13	5	7	2	2	8
14	6	8	2	2	8
15	4	6	2	2	8

$\alpha = .05$
K = number of nonzero differences = 13
$T_{crit} = 17$
$T_- = 8$
$T_+ = 83$, so $T = 8 < 17$; reject H_0.

smaller than (or equal to) the critical value. In the Brazelton example (Table 19.4), $T = 8$ is less than the critical value from Table A.11 for $K = 13$, $T_{crit} = 17$. So you reject H_0 of equal population medians, which is consistent with the results for the two-dependent-sample t-test. Rejecting this null hypothesis means that there is statistically significant improvement in orientation to face and voice over the first 10 days for full-term but small babies.

Quick Quiz

You have decided to run another study on the effect of light sources on depression scores for people who have seasonal affective disorder. You have 24 people, and you pair them on their initial depression scores. Half of the participants are in the normal light bulb condition and half are exposed to halogen lights. When you measure the participants' depression levels at the end of the study, you have only nine nonzero differences. You want to test a nondirectional hypothesis. (a) For $\alpha = .05$ and a two-tailed test, what is the critical value? (b) If X_1 corresponds with the halogen group and your d's are formed by taking $X_2 - X_1$, then a negative d means that the normal-light

participant had a _____ depression score than his or her counterpart in the halogen group. (c) If $T_- = 10.5$ and $T_+ = 34.5$, what is your decision about H_0? (d) What does your decision mean in terms of this study?

Answers

exposed to different light sources when initial depression scores are taken into account.

critical value. (d) There is no significant difference in the depression levels of the groups

the than greater is (T_+) and T_- of lesser (the $10.5 = T$ because H_0 Retain (c) lower (b) 5 (a)

Directional hypotheses may be tested with one-tailed tests, but you need to think through the consequences of the hypotheses. If the alternative hypothesis is "median₁ > median₂," then you would generally expect the scores from the first sample to be larger than those from the second sample. Because you form the differences as $d = X_2 - X_1$, you would expect the differences to be negative if the alternative hypothesis were true. Then you would expect T_- to be large and T_+ to be small, so you would refer T_+ to the critical value. H_0 would be rejected if T_+ were less than or equal to the tabled critical value. For these one-tailed tests, you do not use T; you use T_+ or T_-, whichever is appropriate.

For K larger than 50, a large-sample form of the Wilcoxon test is needed because the use of Table A.11 is limited to $K \le 50$. This large-sample test makes use of the large-sample normality of the sampling distribution of T. It also uses the familiar z statistic with mean equal to $K(K + 1)/4$ and standard deviation equal to $\sqrt{K(K + 1)(2K + 1)/24}$. The statistic is given as

Table 19.5
Liar data: Influence of occupation on deception accuracy scores (percent correct)

$$z = \frac{T - \dfrac{K(K + 1)}{4}}{\sqrt{\dfrac{K(K + 1)(2K + 1)}{24}}} \tag{19.4}$$

The statistic z is approximately normally distributed and can be referred to critical values from the standard normal distribution in Table A.2. Two-tailed or one-tailed tests can be done by using critical values at the appropriate $\alpha/2$ or α, respectively.

Suppose a researcher has a before-and-after design with 55 students who are suffering from exam stress. She wants to see whether their stress scores will change as a result of going through a 2-h session on meditation techniques. She measures the students' stress before an exam, the students go through the training, and then their stress levels are measured a few days later before they take another exam. After the difference scores are obtained (posttraining exam stress minus pretraining stress), there are 52 nonzero differences. The smaller rank sum is 570. To test the hypothesis of equal population medians, using $\alpha = .05$ and a nondirectional hypothesis, you would calculate

$$z = \frac{570 - 52(53)/4}{\sqrt{52(53)(105)/24}} = \frac{570 - 689}{109.81} = -1.08$$

Because -1.08 is not less than -1.96, the researcher would retain H_0 and conclude that the population medians are equal. She would conclude that training does not influence exam stress.

Secret Service	Judges	Psychiatrists
60	50	60
60	60	90
70	50	60
50	60	70
70	70	60
60	50	50
70	60	50
70	50	50
60	40	60
60	70	70
40	50	60
80	70	60
70	40	60
90	90	50
80	50	70
60	60	30
80	40	60
90	60	50
50	60	60
40	40	60
50	50	40
40	50	60
50	40	70
70	70	40
70	70	50
70	50	50
60	50	60
60	70	60
70	60	60
60	50	50
80	80	40
60	70	80
80	70	60
50	50	40
60	30	80

19.4 Kruskal-Wallis Test: *J* Independent Samples

Example

Let's return to the liar data introduced in Chapter 2 and covered in Chapter 14. You would like to find out whether judges, psychiatrists, and Secret Service personnel differ in their ability to detect a liar. People in each career group are shown 1-min videotape segments of ten individuals telling how they felt about a film. The participants then are asked to indicate whether the person in the videotape was telling the truth. The score for each participant is the deception accuracy score, which is the percentage of correct responses given that exactly five of the ten videotaped people were lying. Simulated data for this study are given in Table 19.5.

Kruskal-Wallis *H* test

A rank test for two or more independent samples

You should be able to identify this example as a *J*-independent-sample situation. A nonparametric competitor to the one-way ANOVA for this case is the **Kruskal-Wallis *H* test.**

Hypotheses

Like the Mann-Whitney *U* test and the Wilcoxon test, the Kruskal-Wallis *H* test is sensitive to median differences in the populations. The one-way ANOVA *F* test can be considered an extension or generalization of the two-independent-sample *t*-test; similarly, the Kruskal-Wallis *H* statistic can be considered an extension or generalization of the Mann-Whitney *U* test. The null hypothesis is

$$H_0: \text{population median}_1 = \text{population median}_2 \tag{19.5}$$

$$= \cdots = \text{population median}_J$$

and the nondirectional alternative hypothesis is

$$H_1: \text{some population medians are unequal}$$

Similar to the one-way ANOVA, the Kruskal-Wallis statistic gives a one-tailed test that is sensitive to only nondirectional alternative hypotheses.

Statistic

Here is how to conduct the *H* test:

1. Combine all the observations from the *J* samples (groups), and rank all the data from 1 for the smallest score to *N* = total sample size for the largest score. Resolve all tied ranks, using the average of the ranks for the tied scores. Now arrange the ranks by the original *J* groups.
2. Compute the rank sum for each group, T_j = sum of ranks for group *j*.
3. Compute the value of the Kruskal-Wallis *H*, using

$$H = \frac{12}{N(N+1)} \sum_j \frac{T_j^2}{n_j} - 3(N+1) \tag{19.6}$$

where $N = \sum n_j$ is the total sample size and T_j is the rank sum for the *j*th group.

There is a strong relationship between *H* and the Mann-Whitney *U* because both these statistics are nonparametric methods, both are used for independent samples, both have the same sensitivity and power, and both have the same assumptions. There also is a clear connection between *H* and the one-way ANOVA *F* test. Both are used for *J* independent samples (groups), both are sensitive to central tendency differences, and both are some function of squared sums for the groups. The overall relationship is so strong that some sources refer to *H* as the "analysis of variance by ranks."

If there are many tied ranks, most sources recommend a modification to formula 19.6 to avoid having a conservative test. If you let t_s be the number of observations that are tied at rank *s*, then you can get a statistic corrected for ties, *H**:

$$H^* = \frac{H}{1 - \frac{1}{N^3 - N} \sum_s (t_s^3 - t_s)} \tag{19.7}$$

At every rank, you find t_s. For example, in the Table 19.5 data, two scores of 30 are tied at the lowest rank, so they get 1.5 for the rank, and $t_s = 2$. There are 12 scores of 40 tied at rank 8.5, so $t_s = 12$. If you continue on for all of the tied scores, the value of $H^* = 6.59$, which is larger than $H = 6.23$.

Distribution

The sampling distribution for H was given by Kruskal and Wallis (1952) for small samples. However, the large-sample approximation to the sampling distribution is simple to use and adequate for all but the very smallest sample sizes. The large-sample test is given by:

$$H \text{ is distributed as } \chi^2 \text{ with } df = J - 1 \tag{19.8}$$

The degrees of freedom for H are the same as the degrees of freedom for the SS_B from the one-way ANOVA—the number of groups minus 1. Critical values for the χ^2 distribution are listed in Table A.9 for the chosen value of α and $df = J - 1$. You should reject the H_0 of equality of medians if the observed H exceeds or is equal to the critical value of χ^2. Just as you saw in the one-way ANOVA, rejecting the null hypothesis tells that the groups are different in some way; it doesn't tell which group is significantly different from the others. Multiple comparison methods are available for further analysis of medians following the Kruskal-Wallis test (see Toothaker, 1991).

For the data in Table 19.6, we find $H = 6.23$. Because $H = 6.23$ is larger than $\chi^2_{crit} = 5.99$, you reject H_0 of equal population medians. You would conclude that there is a significant difference in the liar-catching ability of judges, psychiatrists, and Secret Service personnel, but without multiple comparisons, you cannot say which group is best. This agrees with the decision you reached using the one-way ANOVA to test the hypothesis of equal population means in Table 14.8.

Quick Quiz

You want to compare the extroversion scores of several groups of performing artists—actors, dancers, singers, and musicians. (a) For $\alpha = .05$, what is the critical value for the Kruskal-Wallis test? (b) If you obtain $H = 8.02$, what is your decision about H_0? (c) What does that tell about the extroversion scores of performing artists?

Answers

(a) $df = J - 1 = 4 - 1 = 3$, so from Table A.9 the critical value is 7.82. (b) Reject H_0. (c) There is some difference in the median extroversion scores for the groups of performing artists, but without multiple comparisons you cannot say which groups are significantly different from each other.

19.5 Friedman Test: J Dependent Samples

Friedman test

A rank test for two or more dependent samples

The Kruskal-Wallis H test is appropriate for only independent samples. Sometimes researchers have dependent samples and want to use a nonparametric test. For two dependent samples, you already have the Wilcoxon test. The extension of the Wilcoxon test for more than two dependent samples is the **Friedman test,** sometimes referred to as a "two-way analysis of variance by ranks" (Friedman, 1937). When there are J dependent samples each with K observations, the Friedman test might be appropriate.

Table 19.6
Liar data: Influence of occupation on deception accuracy scores (percent correct)

Secret Service	Rank	Judges	Rank	Psychiatrists	Rank	
60	56	50	27	60	56	
60	56	60	56	90	103.5	$n_1 = n_2 = n_3 = 35$
70	83	50	27	60	56	
50	27	60	56	70	83	$J = 3$
70	83	70	83	60	56	
60	56	50	27	50	27	$df = J - 1 = 2$
70	83	60	56	50	27	
70	83	50	27	50	27	$N = \Sigma n = 105$
60	56	40	8.5	60	56	
60	56	70	83	70	83	
40	8.5	50	27	60	56	
80	97.5	70	83	60	56	
70	83	40	8.5	60	56	
90	103.5	90	103.5	50	27	
80	97.5	50	27	70	83	
60	56	60	56	30	1.5	
80	97.5	40	8.5	60	56	
90	103.5	60	56	50	27	
50	27	60	56	60	56	
40	8.5	40	8.5	60	56	
50	27	50	27	40	8.5	
40	8.5	50	27	60	56	
50	27	40	8.5	70	83	
70	83	70	83	40	8.5	
70	83	70	83	50	27	
70	83	50	27	50	27	
60	56	50	27	60	56	
60	56	70	83	60	56	
70	83	60	56	60	56	
60	56	50	27	50	27	
80	97.5	80	97.5	40	8.5	
60	56	70	83	80	97.5	
80	97.5	70	83	60	56	
50	27	50	27	40	8.5	
60	56	30	1.5	80	97.5	
T_j	2218		1625		1722	

$$H = \frac{12}{N(N+1)} \Sigma_j \frac{T_j^2}{n_j} - 3(N+1)$$

$$= \frac{12}{105(106)} \left(\frac{2218^2 + 1625^2 + 1722^2}{35} \right) - 3(106)$$

$$= 6.23$$

$$\chi^2_{crit} = 5.99$$

Because $H = 6.23 > 5.99$, reject H_0.

The relationships among the J samples may come from matching J participants in each of K sets; or they may come from J measurements on the same K participants on the dependent variable, which is analogous to a simple repeated measures design.

Table 19.7
Simple repeated measures design

Participant	Alone	Present	Watching
1	15	14	11
2	14	11	6
3	15	17	13
4	12	11	8
5	9	10	6
6	15	12	8
7	17	19	15
8	20	17	9
9	19	15	10
10	13	10	9

Example

Consider the simple repeated measures design from Chapter 17. We gave the example of performance on a difficult task being affected by the presence and activity of another person. The three conditions were working alone, working with someone present but not watching, and working with someone watching. The researchers chose to use each participant as his or her own control and to use the experimental factor as a repeated factor. All participants were measured under all three conditions: alone, present, and watching. The order of conditions was randomly assigned to each of ten participants. Fictitious data for this example are given in Table 19.7.

Hypotheses

The variable that establishes the J samples is called the *treatment variable*. The Friedman test is sensitive to median differences in the J populations represented by the J levels of the treatment variable (samples). The hypotheses are identical to those for the Kruskal-Wallis test except that the J medians are correlated.

Statistic

Here are the steps to conduct the Friedman test:

1. Rank the J observations within each of the K sets from 1 for the smallest observation to J for the largest observation. That is, rank the observations within the matched set across all levels of the treatment variable. Resolve all tied ranks, using the average of the ranks for the tied observations.
2. Sum the ranks within a treatment level (sample), obtaining T_j = sum of the ranks for sample j.
3. Compute the Friedman statistic χ:

$$\chi = \frac{12}{KJ(J+1)} \Sigma_j T_j^2 - 3K(J+1) \tag{19.9}$$

The J indicates the number of levels of the treatment variable, and K is the number of observations in each level of the treatment variable or the number of sets of matched

Table 19.8

Simple repeated measures design

Participant	Alone	Rank	Present	Rank	Watching	Rank	
1	15	3	14	2	11	1	$K = 10$
2	14	3	11	2	6	1	$J = 3$
3	15	2	17	3	13	1	
4	12	3	11	2	8	1	
5	9	2	10	3	6	1	$df = J - 1 = 3 - 1 = 2$
6	15	3	12	2	8	1	
7	17	2	19	3	15	1	
8	20	3	17	2	9	1	
9	19	3	15	2	10	1	
10	13	3	10	2	9	1	
T_j		27		23		10	

$$\chi = \frac{12}{KJ(J + 1)} \Sigma_j T_j^2 - 3K(J + 1)$$

$$= \frac{12}{10(3)(4)}(1358) - 3(10)(4)$$

$$= 15.8$$

$\chi = 15.8$, $\chi_{crit}^2 = 5.99$, and $15.8 > 5.99$; reject H_0.

subjects. In Table 19.7 there are ten sets of matched subjects. (We call them *sets* of matched subjects instead of matched pairs because now you are matching across more than two groups.) When you have three levels of the treatment variable, the only ranks assigned are 1, 2, and 3. Within the matched set, the data are ranked. This is different from how the data were ranked in the Kruskal-Wallis test.

Distribution

As for the Kruskal-Wallis H, only the large-sample approximation to the sampling distribution of χ is given here. The large-sample distribution of χ is given as:

χ is distributed as the χ^2 distribution with $df = J - 1$ (19.10)

The critical value is found in Table A.9 given $df = J - 1$ and the chosen α. Reject the H_0 of equality of medians if χ exceeds or equals the critical value.

For the data in Table 19.7, $\chi = 15.8$, $df = J - 1 = 3 - 1 = 2$ and $\chi_{crit}^2 = 5.99$, so you reject H_0 of equal population medians (see Table 19.8). You would conclude that there are significant differences in performance as a function of the presence and activity of another person. This agrees with the decision reached on the hypothesis of equality of population means by using the simple repeated measures ANOVA F test in Table 17.1.

Quick Quiz

Suppose you replicate the study in Research Example 17, where running speed was measured when people were jogging alone, jogging with someone present but not watching, and jogging with someone watching. Each of the

30 runners in your study is measured three times. (a) Find the critical value for the Friedman test. Use $\alpha = .05$. (b) If you obtain $\chi = 9.92$, what is your decision about H_0? (c) What does your decision mean about the running speeds?

Answers

(a) 5.99 (b) Reject H_0. (c) Running speed depends on whether the people are running alone, with someone present, or with someone watching. Without doing multiple comparisons, you cannot say whether running speed is significantly faster in one group or another.

19.6   Spearman Correlation Coefficient

Monotonic relationship

When an increase in X is accompanied by a corresponding increase (decrease) in Y, there is an increasing (decreasing) monotonic relationship between X and Y

The Pearson r from Chapter 6 is appropriate for testing hypotheses about the linear relationship between two variables (see also Chapter 12). Now you'll learn a nonparametric test that originally was derived to test a broader hypothesis about a **monotonic relationship** between two variables.

Definition of Monotonic

A *monotonic* relationship is best defined as follows:

1. If the value of Y increases as the value of X increases, you have an increasing monotonic relationship.
2. If the value of Y decreases as the value of X increases, you have a decreasing monotonic relationship.

Figure 19.1 shows three examples of monotonic relationships as well as one example of a nonmonotonic relationship. The relationships shown in parts (*a*) and (*b*) are both increasing monotonic relationships, whereas part (*c*) illustrates a decreasing monotonic relationship. The relationship in part (*d*) is not monotonic because Y increases for small values of X and decreases for large values of X. Any linear relationship is monotonic, but not all monotonic relationships are linear. Monotonic is a broader concept than linear, and it includes linear.

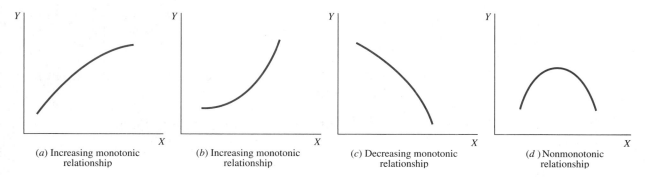

(*a*) Increasing monotonic relationship (*b*) Increasing monotonic relationship (*c*) Decreasing monotonic relationship (*d*) Nonmonotonic relationship

Figure 19.1
Monotonic and nonmonotonic relationships

Spearman r_S
A rank test for a monotonic relationship between two variables

The nonparametric counterpart to the Pearson r is the **Spearman r_S,** which tests a hypothesis of no association between two variables. The Spearman correlation coefficient actually is a Pearson r computed on the ranks. Why use Spearman? It has the advantage of being sensitive to a broader spectrum of relationships than the Pearson r. The disadvantage, however, is that when the statistic is significant, you can say only that the relationship is monotonically increasing or decreasing. You cannot be as specific as saying the relationship is linear.

Example

In Chapter 6 one of the SAS examples used a data set that contained baby lengths and adult heights for a group of college students. Most of these pairs of scores also were identified by the gender of the student. You examined the degree of linear relationship between baby length and adult height. Now you'll examine these data for the men for any possible monotonic relationship. Table 19.9 contains the original data.

Hypotheses

The null hypothesis tested by the Spearman statistic is no monotonic relationship or no association (not the same as independence):

$$H_0: \text{ no association between } X \text{ and } Y \tag{19.11}$$

The alternative hypothesis is

$$H_1: \text{ monotonic relationship between } X \text{ and } Y$$

The Spearman correlation coefficient is appropriate for ranks of original raw observations or for original data that are actually ranks. Suppose someone wanted to test a hypothesis of no association between the rankings of ten paintings from two different judges of an art contest. The original scores would be ranks, and the Spearman correlation coefficient could be used.

Table 19.9
Baby length and adult height (in inches) for $N = 11$ college men

Student	Baby	Adult
1	18.0	69.0
2	20.0	69.0
3	21.0	71.0
4	20.5	70.0
5	21.0	71.0
6	20.0	70.0
7	20.5	73.0
8	19.0	66.0
9	21.0	72.0
10	19.5	69.5
11	20.5	67.0

Statistic

Although r_S could be computed by plugging the ranks into the formula for the Pearson r, sometimes you can use a simpler computational formula. Computation of r_S is done in the following steps:

1. Rank X from 1 (lowest score) to N (highest score), and then separately rank Y from 1 to N. Resolve all tied ranks by using the average of the ranks for the tied observations.
2. Obtain $D_i = \text{rank of } X - \text{rank of } Y$ for all pairs for i from 1 to N.
3. Compute r_S as

$$r_S = 1 - \frac{6\Sigma_i D_i^2}{N(N^2 - 1)} \tag{19.12}$$

If there are tied ranks, some sources recommend that you ignore steps 2 and 3 and use the computational formula for the Pearson r (formula 6.2) on the ranks to compute r_S. Calculation of r_S from Table 19.9 gives $r_S = .7182$ by using the special formula 19.12 and $r_S = .7104$ by using Pearson's r (formula 6.2). Because r_S is actually a Pearson r computed on the ranks of the observations, you can expect the same range of values: $-1.00 \leq r_S \leq 1.00$.

Distribution

For N between 5 and 30, the sampling distribution of r_S has the critical values listed in Table A.12. The value of N establishes the correct row, and your choice of α gives the correct column of Table A.12. If r_S is greater than or equal to the tabled value, then r_S is significant at the chosen α level. Again, a significant r_S does not indicate a significant linear relationship, but rather indicates that a hypothesis of zero monotonic association should be rejected.

For the data on male baby length and adult height, you reject H_0 of no monotonic relationship (see Table 19.10). You reject H_0 because $r_S = .7182$ (or .7104, depending on whether you use the special formula or Pearson's formula) is larger than .618, the two-tailed critical value for $\alpha = .05$. A computer program showed that the p-value for r_S was .007. Pearson's r on the original observations gave $r = .5437$, $p = .0838$. Why was r_S significant and r not significant? It is because r_S tests for monotonic relationships, whereas r is sensitive to only linear relationships.

Table 19.10
Baby length and adult height for $N = 11$ college men

Student	Baby	Baby Rank	Adult	Adult Rank	D = baby rank − adult rank	D^2
1	18.0	1	69.0	3.5	−2.5	6.25
2	20.0	4.5	69.0	3.5	1.0	1.00
3	21.0	10	71.0	8.5	1.5	2.25
4	20.5	7	70.0	6.5	0.5	0.25
5	21.0	10	71.0	8.5	1.5	2.25
6	20.0	4.5	70.0	6.5	−2.0	4.00
7	20.5	7	73.0	11	−4.0	16.00
8	19.0	2	66.0	1	1.0	1.00
9	21.0	10	72.0	10	0	0
10	19.5	3	69.5	5	−2.0	4.00
11	20.5	7	67.0	2	5.0	25.00
						62.00

$$r_S = 1 - \frac{6\Sigma_i D_i^2}{N(N^2 - 1)} = 1 - \frac{6(62)}{11(11^2 - 1)} = 1 - \frac{372}{1320}$$

$$= 1 - .2818 = .7182$$

$$r_{crit} = .618$$

Because $r_S = .7182 > r_{crit} = .618$, reject H_0.

Quick Quiz

You have run a study to look at the relationship between dental anxiety and general anxiety. You suspect that dental anxiety is situation specific and will not be related to scores on a scale that measures generalized anxiety. You have 28 volunteers who were patients at a dentist's office in your hometown. You compute $r_S = .1824$. What conclusion can you draw?

Answer

For $\alpha = .05$, the two-tailed critical value from Table A.12 is $\pm.375$. Because your obtained r_S does not exceed the critical value, retain H_0 and conclude that there is no monotonic relationship between dental anxiety and general anxiety.

For samples larger than 30 pairs of scores, Table A.12 cannot be used. For large samples, the value of r_S may be used to test the hypothesis of no association by using

$$z = \frac{r_S - 0}{1/\sqrt{N-1}} = r_S\sqrt{N-1} \tag{19.13}$$

The statistic z is approximately distributed as the standard normal distribution and can be referred to critical values from Table A.2. Two-tailed or one-tailed tests can be done by using critical values with the appropriate $\alpha/2$ or α, respectively.

If a researcher had computed $r_S = .70$ on $N = 37$ pairs of scores, then the test statistic would be

$$z = .70\sqrt{36} = .70(6) = 4.2$$

If the researcher had wanted to do a two-tailed test with $\alpha = .05$, then the critical values would have been ±1.96. Because $z = 4.2$ is larger than 1.96, you would reject H_0.

Beyond These Statistics

We've covered only a few nonparametric statistical methods. Entire texts have been written about these methods, such as Siegel and Castellan (1988), the excellent but out-of-print book by Marascuilo and McSweeney (1977), and Gibbons (1993). Some of these additional statistics are based on ranks, but a substantial number of procedures are based on other techniques to circumvent the normality assumption. If you are interested in using nonparametric statistics, be sure they are well suited for testing the kinds of hypotheses that will answer your research questions.

19.7   Summary, Study Tips, and Computation

Chapter Summary

Rank tests can be used on ordinal or higher data to test parametric hypotheses. Except for the Spearman test, they are sensitive to differences in population medians. We discussed these rank tests: Mann-Whitney U (two independent samples), Wilcoxon T (two dependent samples), Kruskal-Wallis H (J independent samples), Friedman χ (J related samples), and Spearman r_S (monotonic relationships). Common issues for all rank tests are assumptions, the problem of tied ranks, simplicity, power, and sensitivity.

Table 19.11

Situation	Statistic	Distribution
Two independent samples H_0: population median$_1$ = population median$_2$	Mann-Whitney U	Table A.10
Two dependent samples H_0: population median$_1$ = population median$_2$	Wilcoxon T	Table A.11
J independent samples H_0: population median$_1$ = population median$_2$ = $\cdots$ = population median$_J$	Kruskal-Wallis H	χ^2 with $df = J - 1$
J dependent samples H_0: population median$_1$ = population median$_2$ = $\cdots$ = population median$_J$	Friedman χ	χ^2 with $df = J - 1$
One sample Two variables, X and Y H_0: no association between X and Y	Spearman r_S	Table A.12

Key terms used in this chapter are:

Rank tests   Kruskal-Wallis H
Tied ranks   Friedman χ
Power efficiency   Spearman r_S
Mann-Whitney U Monotonic relationship
Wilcoxon T Association

The statistical tests introduced in this chapter are summarized in Table 19.11, which shows the situation where the statistic would be used, the name of the statistic, and the theoretical reference distribution. For decision rules, assumptions, and any restrictions on the use of each procedure, refer to the section where it was presented.

Study Tips

Each statistic in this chapter has a corresponding parametric test, so be sure you know them. For instance, Mann-Whitney U has the two-independent-sample t as its counterpart. These connections help you remember the situation in which you would use these nonparametric tests. When ranking tied scores, be careful about the ranking process because it is easy to miss one of the ranks. Two hints to be sure that you have ranked correctly are that the top rank must equal the total sample size (or number of nonzero d's) and the sum of the ranks from 1 to N is $N(N + 1)/2$.

Computation

Most of the methods given in this chapter can be done in SAS or SPSS. Examples are given here. However, because of the simplicity inherent in the nonparametric methods presented in this chapter, it may be more difficult to do them on the computer than by hand. The computer offers only the accuracy advantage, which is, of course, limited to the accuracy of the input.

SAS Examples

(SAS system's lines)

```
DATA X;
INPUT GROUP$ N;    (allows you to input different sample sizes if necessary; data here are from the "detection of a liar" study)
DO I=1 TO N;
INPUT Y@@;
OUTPUT;
END;
```

```
CARDS;
SECRSER 35
60 60 70 50 70 60 70 70 60 60 40 80 70 90 80 60 80 90 50 40 50 40
50 70 70 70 60 60 70 60 80 60 80 50 60
JUDGES 35
50 60 50 60 70 50 60 50 40 70 50 70 40 90 50 60 40 60 60 40 50 50
40 70 70 50 50 70 60 50 80 70 70 50 30
PSYCHIAT 35
60 90 60 70 60 50 50 50 60 70 60 60 60 50 70 30 60 50 60 60 40 60
70 40 50 50 60 60 60 50 40 80 60 40 80
PROC PRINT;
PROC NPAR1WAY WILCOXON;    (asks for the Kruskal-Wallis by asking for the one-way analysis to be done on Wilcoxon scores,
                            which is what SAS calls ranks)

CLASS GROUP;
```
(system's line)

The SAS System

N P A R 1 W A Y   P R O C E D U R E

Wilcoxon Scores (Rank Sums) for Variable Y
Classified by Variable GROUP

① GROUP	N	② Sum of Scores	Expected Under H0	Std Dev Under H0	Mean Score
SECRSER	35	2218.0	1855.0	143.049716	63.3714286
JUDGES	35	1625.0	1855.0	143.049716	46.4285714
PSYCHIAT	35	1722.0	1855.0	143.049716	49.2000000

Average Scores were used for Ties

Kruskal-Wallis Test (Chi-Square Approximation)
CHISQ= 6.5926 ③   DF= 2   Prob > CHISQ= 0.0370

Figure 19.2
SAS output from NPAR1WAY

For PROC NPAR1WAY, the SAS output in Figure 19.2 shows the following:

1. A listing of the levels of the independent variable, here called GROUP
2. The sum of the scores (ranks for this example) for each group
3. The value of χ^2 corrected for ties

(SAS system's lines)
```
DATA X;
INPUT BABY ADULT SEX$;    (data are baby length, adult height, and gender for only the male students from Chapter 6,
                           SAS examples)
```

```
DROP SEX;
CARDS;
18.0 69.0 M
20.0 69.0 M
21.0 71.0 M
20.5 70.0 M
21.0 71.0 M
20.0 70.0 M
20.5 73.0 M
19.0 66.0 M
21.0 72.0 M
19.5 69.5 M
20.5 67.0 M
PROC PRINT;
PROC CORR SPEARMAN;
```
(The Spearman correlation coefficient is an option of PROC CORR; just place the word SPEARMAN after a blank in the PROC CORR statement.)
```
TITLE 'SPEARMAN CORRELATION MALE BABY ADULT';
```
(system's line)

SPEARMAN CORRELATION BABY ADULT

VARIABLE①	N	MEAN	STD DEV	MEDIAN	MINIMUM	MAXIMUM
BABY	11	20.09090909	0.94387981	20.50000000	18.00000000	21.00000000
ADULT	11	69.77272727	2.04161255	70.00000000	66.00000000	73.00000000

SPEARMAN CORRELATION COEFFICIENTS / PROB > |R| UNDER HO:RHO=0 / N = 11

	BABY	ADULT
BABY	1.00000	0.71035②
	0.0000	0.0143③
ADULT	0.71035	1.00000
	0.0143	0.0000

Figure 19.3
SAS output from PROC CORR, Spearman correlation coefficient

For PROC CORR, the SAS output in Figure 19.3 gives the following:

1. Descriptive statistics are given for each variable, including N.
2. The value of the Spearman $r_S = .71035$.
3. The two-tailed probability is .0143.

SPSS Example

(SPSS system's lines)

```
SET WIDTH 80
DATA LIST FREE/BABY ADULT
BEGIN DATA
18 69 20 69 21 71 20.5 70 21 71 20 70 20.5 73 19 66 21 72
19.5 69.5 20.5 67
END DATA
NONPAR CORR VARIABLES=BABY ADULT
FINISH
```

(system's line)

```
- - -  S P E A R M A N   C O R R E L A T I O N   C O E F F I C I E N T S  - - -

ADULT          .7104①
          N(   11)②
          SIG .007③


             BABY

''  .  '' IS PRINTED IF A COEFFICIENT CANNOT BE COMPUTED.
```

Figure 19.4
SPSS output for NONPAR CORR

For the command NONPAR CORR, the SPSS output in Figure 19.4 gives the following:

1. The value of the Spearman r_S = .7104.
2. The sample size N = 11.
3. The one-tailed probability = .007, which is the default for this command.

Exercises

Section 19.1

1. For each of the following methods, give the type of alternative hypothesis to which the statistic is sensitive.
   a. Mann-Whitney U
   b. Spearman r_S
   c. Wilcoxon T

Section 19.2

2. Suppose you decide to research how satisfied personal-computer owners are with their word-processing programs. You find ten owners of brand X computers, five of whom purchased the Word-Whiz program and five of whom purchased the Talk-Text program. They volunteered to fill out your

questionnaire and responded with the scores shown in the table for overall satisfaction (scale ranged from 1 to 7). Compute the Mann-Whitney U for these data and decide whether you would reject the H_0 of equal population medians for overall satisfaction.

Word-Whiz	Talk-Text
7	3
7	2
4	5
5	1
6	2

3. Suppose a researcher did a study to compare the worries of boys and girls aged 11. Using a numerical scale ranging from 1 ("never") to 5 ("always"), the researcher asked the children to respond to a number of questions about worries (for example, failing a test, talking too much, my mother getting sick). Worry scores were obtained for several general categories in order to test a hypothesis of no gender differences in averages for each category. What nonparametric test would you use to test a hypothesis of no gender difference in the medians for the category of family worries?

4. Brumback, Jackoway, and Weinberg (1980) studied the relationship between depression and intelligence test scores. Children who had school problems and were subsequently referred for educational assessment were diagnosed as depressed or not depressed according to previously established criteria (primarily commonly agreed-on symptoms). Scores on the full-scale IQ measurements for depressed and nondepressed children are given here (simulated data are based on Brumback, Jackoway & Weinberg, 1980):

Depressed	100 118 91 127 96 103 108 86 90 118
Nondepressed	81 105 118 119 118 111 106 85 115 106

With $\alpha = .05$, use these data to test the hypothesis that median IQ scores are equal for depressed and nondepressed children.

5. Suppose a smoking reduction clinic allowed clients to select which type of treatment they would take. Here are the data for ten participants in each of two treatments (scores are the numbers of cigarettes per week reduced since the start of the program):

Treatment A	10	17	13	20	21	14	19	19	21	29
Treatment B	11	13	12	9	17	28	15	17	13	14

   a. What nonparametric test statistic is appropriate? Explain.
   b. Use your choice in part a to test a hypothesis of no difference in medians ($\alpha = .05$).
   c. Can you conclude that the treatments are different in effectiveness of reducing smoking?
   d. Is this a true experiment? What are some possible extraneous variables? Have they been controlled? Could confounding exist?

6. Use the data in the table for women alcoholics and nonalcoholics on the Tactual Performance Test (see Exercise 22 in Chapter 1).

Alcoholics					Nonalcoholics				
34	28	26	28	19	15	13	27	12	15
26	14	10	1	10	2	9	28	18	15
18	33	21	30	20	23	23	12	18	31
26	43	33	25	14	7	8	4	14	15
9	50	24	27	7	18	16	28	6	15

Source: Simulated data based on Silberstein and Parsons (1981).

   a. What nonparametric test statistic is appropriate? Explain.
   b. Use your choice in part a to test a hypothesis of equal medians with $\alpha = .05$.

Section 19.3

7. If the research described in Exercise 3 used brother–sister pairs to control for family variables (socioeconomic status, single-parent families, and so on), what nonparametric test would you use to test the same hypothesis as in Exercise 3?

8. In a study on attraction, suppose people were asked to rate pictures of females taken before orthodontic treatment (braces). Participants rated the females in the pictures on a number of variables. Two weeks later the participants returned to rate another set of pictures of the same females after orthodontic treatment. The females in both pictures had their mouths closed and teeth not showing. Ratings of intelligence are given in the table. Test the hypothesis that there is no change in perceived intelligence.

Pair	Prerating	Postrating
1	113	115
2	105	117
3	120	125
4	119	117
5	104	107
6	100	105
7	111	110
8	130	125
9	119	121
10	127	130
11	111	110
12	115	117
13	107	113
14	102	105

9. A fertilizer is to be tested for its percentage of nitrogen. Tests will be done by the producing company and a state laboratory. Samples of the fertilizer are taken from the most recent batch. Each sample is ground into a powder and divided into two equal parts, and the parts are randomly assigned to the two laboratories. The results are listed in the table.

Sample	Company	State
1	10.10	10.02
2	9.92	9.90
3	10.83	10.59
4	9.34	9.71
5	10.04	9.92
6	10.29	10.11
7	10.07	10.06

a. What nonparametric test statistic is appropriate? Explain.
b. Use your choice in part a to test a hypothesis that the laboratories have the same average results ($\alpha = .05$).

10. Participants in a weight loss experiment are first paired by gender, age, weight, and body type and then within each pair are randomly assigned to one of two treatments. The data in the table are for ten pairs of participants (data are the pounds lost since the start of the program).

Pair	1	2	3	4	5	6	7	8	9	10
Treatment A	5	7	20	13	11	9	8	19	16	15
Treatment B	4	6	18	14	12	10	7	16	13	10

a. What is the correct nonparametric test statistic? Explain.
b. Use your choice in part a to test a hypothesis of equal medians ($\alpha = .05$).
c. Can you conclude that the treatments are different in effectiveness of weight reduction?
d. Is this a true experiment? What are some possible extraneous variables? Have they been controlled? Could confounding exist?

11. From Research Example 11 suppose you have the data in the table for the three sickle-cell anemia patients. They were measured before the butyrate treatment started and after 3 weeks of daily intravenous doses of a butyrate solution. The research laboratory examination of a slide of blood gives a measurement that is a count of the number of sickle cells in 50 fields of 50 cells.

Subject	1	2	3
Before treatment	776	547	932
After treatment	43	21	49

a. What is the correct nonparametric test statistic? Explain.
b. Use your choice in part a to test a hypothesis of equal medians ($\alpha = .05$).
c. Can you conclude that the butyrate treatment is effective? What concern does the small sample size give you?

Section 19.4
12. Suppose a group of nonexercisers who wanted to lose weight and volunteered for an exercise program were all put through a general conditioning program for 6 months. Then they were randomly assigned to one of three groups: continue with the general exercise program, increase amount of exercise, or stop exercising ("not enough instructors, wait for others to finish"). At the end of 6 weeks, a mood state inventory found the "vigor" scores shown in the table: Compute the Kruskal-Wallis H for these data.

No Exercise	General Exercise	Increased Exercise
10	20	21
11	19	23
12	24	27
9	17	30

Would you reject H_0 of equal population medians ($\alpha = .05$)?

13. A study was concerned with the effects of instructions to young children and their subsequent attempts to help another child (apparently) in distress (based on Staub, 1970). Forty-two first-grade students were randomly assigned to one of three groups. The first group was indirect responsibility (IR), where students were informed that another child was alone in an adjoining room and had been warned not to climb up on a chair. The second group was direct responsibility (DR1), where students were told the same story as in IR and also that they were being left in charge and to take care of anything that happened. Students were given a simple task, and the researcher left the room. Students then heard a loud crash from the adjoining room followed by a minute of crying and sobbing. Students in the third group (DR2) had the same instructions as the DR1 group, but the sounds of distress also included calls for help. Ratings from 1 (no help) to 5 (went to adjoining room) were given to each student from behind a one-way mirror. Using $\alpha = .05$, test the hypothesis of equal population medians of the three conditions.

IR	DR1	DR2
3	5	4
4	4	4
2	5	3
1	3	4
1	4	5
2	5	4
1	5	5
2	5	5
3	5	3
3	4	2
2	3	3
1	1	2
1	4	4
2	3	1

Section 19.5

14. Suppose a panel of ten students read and ranked four statistics texts. Test the hypothesis of equal medians for the rankings of the five texts, using the Friedman χ with $\alpha = .05$.

Student	Text 1	Text 2	Text 3	Text 4
1	3	4	1	2
2	4	1	2	3
3	2	3	4	1
4	4	2	1	3
5	3	2	4	1
6	4	3	2	1
7	4	2	3	1
8	3	4	2	1
9	3	2	1	4
10	2	4	1	3

15. A researcher wanted to see whether different types of motor activity in training children on words result in different spelling abilities. Each child was shown a word printed on a 3×5 card, the researcher named the word and asked the child to repeat it, and then the child was asked to reproduce the word by one of three activities. The three motor activities were handwriting, typing the word on a computer keyboard, or using letter tiles (plastic tiles with two sets of the alphabet). Training was over 4 days, and ten short words were used in each of the three training activities (a total of 30 words), with random order of training. Each child received all three training activities. There were 12 first-grade students. A spelling test was given on the fifth day. The numbers of correct words recorded for each of the training activities are listed in the table. Use the appropriate nonparametric test statistic to test the hypothesis that the different motor activities result in the same spelling performance ($\alpha = .05$).

Student	Writing	Computer	Tiles
1	3	2	1
2	5	3	2
3	3	1	2
4	2	1	1
5	1	1	1
6	6	3	2
7	2	2	1
8	3	2	3
9	2	1	0
10	4	3	1
11	4	2	1
12	3	1	3

Section 19.6

16. Locus of control refers to the placement of control of reinforcement in one's world. Internal control refers to the belief that events are dependent on a person's own behavior, whereas external control refers to the belief that events are not entirely dependent on personal behavior but are the result of some outside influence (others, luck, and so on). Rotter (1966) developed the I/E (internal/external) scale to measure locus of control where high scores show internal control and low scores show external control. Suppose a researcher asked students to answer the questions in this scale as they thought a hypothetical "other student at their university" might answer them. Also suppose that 6 months earlier these same students had answered the questions in the scale for themselves. The data in the table were collected. Compute r_S. Do these two variables show a monotonic relationship ($\alpha = .05$)?

Student	A	B	C	D	E	F	G	H
I/E (self)	14	17	25	11	9	17	19	20
I/E attributed to other	18	17	22	19	10	18	18	16

17. You have completed a study of preschoolers' aggressiveness and television watching habits. Parents of ten preschoolers have kept a diary of how much time their child watched television for one week. During the same week, you and a coresearcher watched the ten children through a mirrored glass at their pre-

school and calculated an aggression score for each child. The score was the number of times the child pushed another child or otherwise acted aggressively. The results from your study are given in the table (X = number of hours of television watched, Y = aggression score, Child = number used to identify each child).

Child	1	2	3	4	5	6	7	8	9	10
X	26	28	24	18	19	36	12	21	28	33
Y	4	2	0	5	5	4	6	3	2	0

a. Draw a scatterplot of the data.
b. Compute r_S.
c. Would you reject the hypothesis of no association between hours of TV watched and aggression?

18. The following data are scores from 15 students on Y (ACT composites) and X (number of semester hours of science courses taken in 3 years of high school):

Student	1	2	3	4	5	6	7	8	9	10	11	12	13	14	15
Y		23	27	30	19	18	21	17	21	27	29	25	22	26	25	24
X		15	18	18	12	9	9	6	12	15	12	12	12	15	12	18

a. Form a scatterplot with Y as the vertical axis and X as the horizontal axis.
b. Compute r_S.
c. Do these two variables show a monotonic relationship ($\alpha = .05$)?

20

Review and Choice
of Statistical Method

You've learned several
statistical tests in this text.
Now you get to practice
choosing from among
them. When do you use
a two-dependent-sample
t-test instead of the test of
correlation, *r*? We present
several research scenarios
so you can learn to look
for clues about which
statistic is correct
for each situation.

Research Example 20
20.1 Introduction
20.2 Overview of Statistical Procedures
 Tests of hypotheses about means
 Tests of hypotheses about medians
 Tests of hypotheses about correlations
 Other tests
20.3 Choice of Statistic
 Key questions
 Key words
 More scenarios
20.4 Beyond These Statistics
 Exercises

Research Example 20

Most undergraduates have only a vague idea of what is meant by a "scientific journal article." We think it would be valuable for you to see how statistics and research design are discussed in an actual journal article. So go to your library and find the journal *Personality and Individual Differences*. (If your library doesn't have this journal, check with a psychology professor, who might subscribe to it.) Find the article "*In Vivo* Brain Size, Head Perimeter, and Intelligence in a Sample of Healthy Adult Females" by Wickett, Vernon, and Lee (1994, Vol. 16, No. 6, pp. 831–838). Read it and make notes of concepts you have learned in this text. If you can't find the article at your school, write to one of the authors for a reprint:

 Philip A. Vernon
 Department of Psychology
 University of Western Ontario
 London, Ontario
 N6A 5C2, Canada

As you read the article, did you think how much of it would have been difficult to understand before you took your statistics course? Here are some concepts you may have noticed in the article. (All page references are to the journal article, not this text.)

On the first page, the authors say that in previous studies, 39 samples with a total $N = 51,931$ had small positive correlations between head size and IQ. "The n-weighted mean" refers to an average of those correlations, with each sample size taken into account in the average. The article says this weighted average of $r = .194$ "may be considered the population value for the relationship between external head size and IQ." You learned about population values, or parameters, in Chapter 1. The authors then say there are many sources of error in these head measurements as estimates of brain size. In other words, the proportion of variability in IQ that's explained by head size is small ($r^2 = .0376$), so most of the variance is unexplained.

In Chapter 6 you read about how correlation coefficients can be inflated if you combine data from subjects on extremes of a scale. On page 832 the article says that in one study, high and average IQ subjects underwent magnetic resonance imaging (MRI) measurements of brain size, leading to "a significant $r = .51$." The authors say this resulted in an "overextended range," and a computation was done to correct for the range problem. In the method section on page 833, you probably noted how the participants were selected—not randomly, but methodically. Newspaper ads solicited paid volunteers, who were chosen according to some medical criteria. You may wonder why claustrophobics were excluded; during an MRI, patients lie on a table enclosed in a metal cylinder. The table inches through the cylinder while loud banging noises are all around the patient, which would be miserable for a claustrophobic. Why were all participants women and right handed? The researchers were controlling those two extraneous variables by making all participants constant on those variables (see Chapter 2). At the bottom of page 833, the authors give the interrater reliability as $r = .995$. In Chapter 6 we defined reliability as consistency in measurement, and these researchers wanted to be sure two raters were consistent. Other kinds of reliabilities are discussed on page 834.

In Chapter 4 you learned descriptive statistics for measuring central tendency and variability, and these are the first summary measures given in the results section of this paper (SD = standard deviation). The authors write, "the key finding from this study is that overall MR-measured brain volume correlated $r = .395$ ($P < .05$) with full-scale IQ, indicating that, within a population, as brain size increases so does intelligence."

Study the article's Table 2, which gives the main results of the study. The significant r's are labeled, and the p-values are "all two tailed," which means the researchers' hypotheses were nondirectional (Chapter 10). The interesting yet nonsignificant results discussed in the article are labeled "NS." The article also includes a scatterplot, which you learned about in Chapter 3 and used in Chapter 6. You also probably noted a statistic that you didn't learn in this text: Hotelling's t, a multivariate statistic. Whenever the article mentions that a correlation is corrected for a variable, such as body size, it means multiple regression is involved (Chapter 7). "It would appear that the size of the brain is largely independent of the size of the body," the authors say on page 836. You studied the concept of independence in connection with random sampling (Chapter 2) and probability (Chapter 8); does the statement about independence here make sense? Reread this section: "It is clear that body size is not a hypothetical third factor accounting for the correlation between brain size and IQ, but this of course does not rule out there being another, as yet unidentified, third factor accounting for the relationship." Chapter 6: *Lurking variables! Correlation does not imply causation!*

The article concludes with a discussion of "future directions for research into the relationship between brain size and intelligence. . . ." You know that the scientific method is cyclical (Chapter 2), with each study answering some questions and posing new ones. For instance, one question posed by the authors is *why* brain volume is related to IQ. Will you be the future researcher to find the answer to this question? If so, we hope this text has given you a solid foundation on which to build your research and data analysis.

20.1 Introduction

Do you feel as if you've been on a long journey through "statistics land"? When you pause at this point of your statistics course and look back, you realize how much you have learned. You also may be scared at how much you've forgotten. If so, perhaps this review chapter will help you recall some information.

You have considered some aspects of research and research design, including where statistics fit into the overall picture of scientific methods. Types of variables, types of relationships between variables, types of research, and issues about the data themselves were topics you explored. You learned about pictorial descriptions of data using histograms, stem and leaf displays, and others. You also learned how to use statistics to describe the central tendency and variability of data. These go together as a package that lets you get familiar with your data, exploring what your data had to tell, giving hints about the answers to your questions.

Then came inferential statistics: sampling variability of statistics, sampling distributions of statistics, and the use of probability to make decisions about hypotheses based on your statistics. These basic topics and the formalities of hypothesis testing are crucial to your understanding of how to use any particular statistical procedure. These topics gave you the "why" behind the "how" for all the rest of the inferential statistics you have learned. Now you have some tools for the confirmatory phase of data analysis: You can go beyond describing the data to using statistics to make decisions. You have a start on what one statistician calls a "bag of tricks." You have put several statistical tricks into your bag, and you ought to feel somewhat comfortable to pull them out and use them on real data from real research.

Answer: Never.

The point of this chapter is to give you some clues to look for when you are deciding which statistic to use for a given research scenario. What clue will tell you whether to use a one-way ANOVA or a simple repeated measures design? The examples in this chapter could be considered Quick Quizzes, and the hints you'll learn are like Study Tips, so those features are not presented formally in this chapter. Now let's review the inferential methods you have learned.

20.2   Overview of Statistical Procedures

In the Study Tips for Chapter 12, you were advised to start a chart that combines the four topics situation/hypotheses, test statistic, distribution/decision rules, and assumptions for the statistics you have learned. As you went on to other chapters, you should have added to your chart. By now, you may have had to go to another sheet of paper to include all of the statistical procedures you have learned.

You may or may not have included in your chart the confidence intervals used to estimate parameters. Because these are inferential procedures, we will review them here. These intervals can be used not only to get an interval estimate of the true value of the parameter, but also to test hypotheses about the parameters estimated. Two confidence intervals were given for the population mean, μ. The first uses a critical value from the standard normal distribution and a given value of the population standard deviation, σ. Because of these characteristics, the width of the interval is constant and cannot change from sample to sample. The second confidence interval for μ uses a critical value from a t distribution with $df = N - 1$ and estimates σ with s. Because of these characteristics, the width of the interval is variable and can change from sample to sample. In both intervals, $\overline{X}$ gives the center of the interval, and the width of the interval is influenced by N, variability (σ or s), and the degree of confidence you desire.

Confidence intervals also were given for the difference between two means and for scores predicted from a simple linear regression equation.

To review all of the statistical tests, we group them by type of hypothesis. First are tests of hypotheses about means, which range from one-sample tests up to complex ANOVA designs.

Tests of Hypotheses about Means

All these tests have assumptions of independence and normality of some population. Except for the one-sample tests and the two-dependent-sample t-test, they all assume equal variances.

One-Sample Tests.   You learned two one-sample tests of a hypothesis about a single population mean: $z_{\overline{X}}$ (Chapters 9–11) and the one-sample t (Chapter 12). These two tests have similar assumptions and hypotheses, but they differ in statistic, distribution, and knowledge of σ^2 (known for $z_{\overline{X}}$ and unknown for t).

Two-Sample Tests.   There are three two-sample t-tests (Chapter 13) of a hypothesis of equality of two means: for two independent samples ($n_1 = n_2 \geq 15$), for two dependent samples, and the AWS test (two independent samples but unequal n's or equal n's less than 15). These tests are similar in hypothesis and distribution (t distribution with different df) but different in statistic, situation, and assumptions.

***J*-Sample Test.**   The one-way ANOVA (Chapter 14) tests a hypothesis of equality of $J \geq 2$ independent means with an F statistic and distribution. It has the same assumptions as the two-independent-sample t-test, but different robustness.

MCPs.   In order to determine which pairs of means are significantly different, MCPs are used. There are tests (Chapter 15) due to Tukey, Fisher-Hayter, Ryan, and Games-Howell (for unequal n's). They test hypotheses of equality of two means at a time for all pairwise comparisons.

Two-Way ANOVA and Repeated Measures Designs.   Further complexity in tests of hypotheses about means with two or more variables and two or more means for each variable need the two-way ANOVA (Chapter 16) and repeated measures designs (Chapter 17). The tests are F ratios that have F distributions if all assumptions are met and the specific hypothesis is true. F tests for interaction are important and make the statistics and their interpretation even more involved. All within-subjects F tests in repeated measures designs have the additional assumption of sphericity.

Tests of Hypotheses about Medians

All these tests assume independence and underlying continuity of the distributions of the dependent variable. They were introduced in Chapter 19, and, except for the Wilcoxon test, they all implicitly assume equal variances.

Two-Sample Tests.   The Mann-Whitney U is appropriate for two independent samples if you want to test for equal population medians. It is a rank test, ranking all observations from both samples together and basing the U statistic on the sum of the ranks from one of the samples. Ties in the scores are resolved using the average rank solution. The Wilcoxon test is appropriate for two dependent samples, but it ranks the absolute values of the d's. Zero differences are not ranked, and tied values are given the average rank.

***J*-Sample Test.**   The Kruskal-Wallis test is the rank test that is analogous to the one-way ANOVA. You rank all of the observations from the J independent samples together and get the sums of the ranks for each sample. The statistic has an approximate distribution of χ^2 with $df = J - 1$.

***J* Dependent Samples.**   The Friedman test is appropriate for testing equal medians when you have J dependent samples with K observations in each. It is analogous to the simple repeated measures ANOVA. Observations are ranked from 1 to J within each of the K sets of observations. The statistic is based on the sum of the ranks in each of the J samples and has an approximate χ^2 distribution with $df = J - 1$.

Tests of Hypotheses about Correlations

Linear Relationship, One Predictor.   There are equivalent tests about regression coefficients, but we have chosen in this text to emphasize the correlation tests. For the one-predictor setting, the test statistic is the Pearson r (Chapter 12). Assumptions are independence of X, Y pairs (or participants) and bivariate normality.

Monotonic Relationship, One Predictor.   The nonparametric test for correlation is sensitive to more types of relationships than is the Pearson correlation. The Spearman r_s (Chapter 19) detects monotonic relationships between two variables. This test has the general rank test assumptions of independence (of X, Y pairs or participants) and continuous underlying distributions for the two variables.

Other Tests

About Proportions.   There is a one-sample test of a hypothesis about a proportion (Chapter 12) and a two-independent-sample test of a hypothesis of equality of population proportions (Chapter 13). Both of these test statistics are z's and have the standard normal distribution as a large-sample approximate distribution.

About Distributions.   The statistical tests that are good at detecting any difference in distributions are the χ^2 tests (Chapter 18). Both tests are approximately distributed as χ^2. The goodness-of-fit χ^2 test is used to test for a population distribution that differs from a distribution expected from theory, and typically has $df = K - 1$. The χ^2 test for contingency tables is used to test for independence of categorical variables and has $df = (R - 1)(C - 1)$.

20.3   Choice of Statistic

In real-world applications of statistics, you need to correctly choose when to use a given statistic from the list. Being able to read or listen to a research scenario and determine the correct statistic is considered by some to be an art. Others think such ability is science. Still others recognize the role of experience in such tasks. Art, science, and experience all come to bear in choosing the correct statistic. We will try to take some of the mystery out of it, but you must practice to build up your experience. Think about the following questions, which you should ask as you try to figure out which statistic is appropriate in a certain research situation.

Key Questions

When you try to choose the correct statistic, you need to answer several questions:

1. How many variables are there?
2. What are the variables? For the independent/predictor variable: How many levels are there (this gives the number of groups)?
3. How are the variable(s) measured? Are they quantitative? Qualitative?
4. What is the research question? The hypothesis? Is it about means or differences in means? Is it about the relationship between two variables?
5. How many groups of participants (or scores) are there (see question 2)?
6. Does each group have an equal number of participants? (If you have total $N = 41$ participants, then there cannot be equal numbers in two independent groups, which tells you to use the AWS statistic instead of the two-independent-sample t. Remember that the robustness of the one-way ANOVA is helped by equal n's and that the two-way ANOVA as presented in this text requires equal n's.)
7. Is σ (σ^2) known? (If the dependent variable or criterion variable is a standardized test, knowing σ^2 will determine the choice between $z_{\bar{X}}$ and the one-sample t.)

8. Is there any indication of about 5% of the scores being outliers? (If so, then one of the nonparametric methods may be justified. Another hint is an interest in median differences or ordinal level data. Remember that the Spearman r_S looks for broader relationships than linear.)

Let's see how the answers to some of these questions, indicated by the number in parentheses, combine to point to a specific test. For example, if there are two variables (1), they are both measured quantitatively (3), and the question/hypothesis is about the degree of linear relationship between the two variables (4), then the statistic is likely to be r.
    Read the following scenario and see if you think r fits:

A researcher wants to see whether there is any relationship between parenting-skills scores for mothers and the blood sugar levels of their diabetic children. The blood sugar test gives scores from 65 to 120 if the person had fasted before the test. The sample had 30 families in it.

Notice the word *relationship,* which you should connect with the statistic r. The correlation coefficient, as you know, measures linear relationship. If the mothers' scores on a parenting-skills test are strongly and linearly related to blood sugar levels, then r should reflect this linear relationship.
    For another example, if there are two variables (1), but one of them is measured qualitatively and defines two groups (3 and 2), and the question/hypothesis is about differences in group means (4) on the quantitative variable, then the statistic is most likely to be the two-independent-sample t. However, remember about the sample sizes (6) and that they need to be equal and 15 or larger.
    Read the following scenario and see if you think the two-independent-sample t fits:

Based on previous research and sound theoretical considerations, an experimental psychologist believes that memory for pictures is superior to memory for words. Thirty-six students from an introductory psychology class were randomly assigned to two groups (18 each). Eighteen students viewed 30 slides with nouns printed on them, and another group of 18 students viewed 30 slides with actual pictures of the same nouns. Each slide contained either one noun or one picture and was viewed for 4 s. After viewing the slides, the students were given a recall test, and the numbers of correctly remembered items were recorded.

The researcher created two independent groups by randomly assigning students to one of the two conditions. Each student's score was the number of correctly recalled items. Can you see why this is not the two-dependent-sample t? There is nothing that pairs the students.
    At this point, a good exercise would be for you to think through how the eight questions are answered for each of the statistics in this text. Group them by the hypothesis tested, and your task will be easier than it first appears. We will do two of the most common tests for you. You will benefit most if you complete this exercise for the remaining statistics.
    For the two-dependent-sample $t,$ there are three variables (1 and 2): the variable (perhaps independent) that formed the two samples (or two measures for the repeated measures way of getting pairs), the dependent variable, and the variable that formed the pairs. The dependent variable is measured quantitatively, the independent variable

may be quantitative or qualitative but it gives two groups (5), and the pairing variable may be either (3). The research question must be about differences in the groups, leading to differences in two means for the hypothesis (4). In most settings, σ^2 is unknown (7). You have equal n's in each group because of the pairing (6). As long as the difference question is not about medians, the data are not clearly ordinal, and there is no indication of a cluster of outliers, then a nonparametric test is not indicated (8).

Read the following scenario to see how it fits the two-dependent-sample t:

> The manager of the cosmetics section of a large department store wants to determine whether newspaper advertising really does affect sales. For her experiment, she randomly selects 15 items currently in stock. She establishes a baseline for the 15 items by pricing them at their usual competitive values, and she records the quantity of each item sold during a 1-week period. Then, without changing the prices, she places a large ad in the newspaper, advertising the 15 items. Again, she records the quantity sold during a 1-week period.

The two groups are formed by time, before and after the ad's publication. The dependent variable is the number of items sold in a week. The pairs are formed by measuring the number sold for the same 15 items. So each item is like a subject being measured twice.

For the χ^2 test for contingency tables, there are variables (1 and 2). They are two categorical variables (3) and you have frequencies for each combination of these variables. The question (4) is about the relationship between the two variables or perhaps about differences between the levels of one of the variables (usually expressed as "differences in _____," where _____ is the other variable). The number of groups (5) depends on the number of levels of each of the two variables.

Read the following scenario to see how it fits the χ^2 test for contingency tables:

> A study was conducted to determine whether big-city and small-town dwellers differ in their helpfulness to strangers. The investigators rang the doorbells of strangers who lived in New York City and in small towns in the vicinity. They explained that they had misplaced the address of a friend who lived in the neighborhood and asked to use the phone. The researchers counted the number of individuals who admitted or did not admit the strangers (the investigators) into their homes.

Here the researchers are not quantifying "big" and "small" towns. The size of town is categorized. Similarly, being let into a home or not being allowed to enter is categorical. Frequencies were tabulated for each combination of city size and entry to the home.

Key Words

Now let's examine some key words that will help you choose the correct statistical procedure.

1. If you see the word **paired** (or **matched**) with regard to study participants, then the most likely test is the two-dependent-sample t. However, make sure it is the participants who are paired on some extraneous variable and then compared between the members of the pairs.

2. If you see a question about degree of **relationship (correlation, prediction)**, then the most likely test is r or the χ^2 test for contingency tables.

3. If you see the word **difference** with respect to two groups or conditions, then candidates are the three different two-sample t-tests, the ANOVAs, the nonparametric equivalent tests, and possibly the χ^2 test for contingency tables. The word **equal** expressed in the null hypothesis could indicate the same tests.

4. If a difference from a **standard** average numeric value is indicated, then the likely test is $z_{\bar{x}}$ or the one-sample t. The answer to key question 7 makes the choice between these two tests.

5. If you see the word **frequency** or **categorical,** then χ^2 is indicated. The answers to key questions 1–4 decide between the goodness-of-fit test and the test for contingency tables.

More Scenarios

Now let's work through some simple scenarios to give you more practice. After you read each one, try to choose the correct statistic before you read ahead. Use the key questions and key words to help you. Then we'll tell you our choice and why.

Scenario A: On the basis of her newly developed technique, a student believes she can reduce the amount of time patients with schizophrenia spend in an institution. As director of training at a nearby institution, you agree to let her try her method on 20 schizophrenic patients randomly selected from your institution. For the 40-year history of your institution, the mean duration that schizophrenic patients stay is 85 weeks, with a standard deviation of 15 weeks. The lengths of stays are normally distributed. The results of the experiment show that the patients treated by the student stay a mean duration of 78 weeks.

We chose $z_{\bar{x}}$ because there is only one sample/group, and it is compared to all of the schizophrenic patients who had ever been at the institution (the population). Time is the dependent variable, and treatment is the independent variable. The σ is given as 15 weeks. If the "15 weeks" had been identified with the 20 patients in the sample, then the one-sample t would be best. When you see the words *variance* or *standard deviation,* ask yourself whether those values come from the *sample.* If so, they are statistics, not parameters. If the variance or standard deviation comes from years of experience with the variable, it's more likely to be a parameter.

Scenario B: Because of rampant inflation, the government is considering imposing wage and price controls. A government economist interested in determining whether there is a relationship between occupation and attitude toward wage and price controls classifies occupations into labor, business, or professional. Then he measures attitude as either for or against control. The data show for each occupation the number of individuals in the sample who were for or against the controls.

We chose the χ^2 test for contingency tables because of two variables (occupation and attitude, both categorical variables) and the key words *relationship* and *number of individuals.*

Scenario C: An educator wants to determine whether early exposure to school affects IQ. He enlists the aid of the parents of 12 pairs of preschool-age identical twins who agree to let their twins participate in his experiment. One member of each twin pair is enrolled in preschool for 2 years, while the other member of each pair remains at home. At the end of the 2 years, the IQs of all the children are measured.

This scenario is obviously contrived, but it illustrates one of the three ways of pairing participants (naturally occurring pairs) for the two-dependent-sample *t.* Two groups (school, no school), IQ as a quantitative dependent variable, and an implied question about differences help make the choice.

Scenario D: As the principal of a private high school, you are interested in finding out how the training in mathematics at your school compares with that of other public schools in your area. For the last 15 years, the public schools have given all graduating seniors a mathematics proficiency test. You choose a high school of about the same size as yours and in an area similar to yours. You get the cooperation of the principal, and he tells you that the mean for the 49 seniors from his school is 78, with a standard deviation of 11.1. You give all graduating seniors in your school the same mathematics proficiency test. Your results show a distribution of 49 scores, with a mean of 83 and a standard deviation of 12.2.

Here we have a situation for the two-independent-sample *t.* There are 49 seniors from each of the two schools, and the dependent variable is quantitative. A difference hypothesis is implied.

Scenario E: Folklore has it that there is an inverse relationship between mathematical and artistic ability. A psychologist decides to determine whether there is anything to this notion. She randomly samples 15 undergraduates and gives them tests that measure these two abilities. Both tests result in scores that range from 1 to 100.

She would want to use *r.* There are two numerical variables, and the key word *relationship* is used.

Scenario F: A researcher believes that in recent years women have been getting taller. She knows that 10 years ago the average height of young adult women living in her city was 63 in. Height is approximately normally distributed in the population, but the standard deviation is unknown. She randomly samples nine young adult women who reside in her city and measure their heights. The mean is 64.25 in. and the standard deviation is 2.55 in.

Did you decide on the one-sample *t?* Clues are the comparison to an average for a large collection of scores, one sample, and the standard deviation known for the sample but not for the population.

Scenario G: A psychologist is interested in determining whether immediate memory capacity is affected by sleep loss. Immediate memory is defined as the amount of material that can be remembered immediately after it is presented. Forty-eight students are randomly selected from an introductory psychology class and randomly assigned to three groups of 16 students each. One of the groups is sleep-deprived for 24 h before the material is presented. All students in the second group receive the normal amount of sleep (7–8 h). The students in the third group are allowed to sleep for 7–8 h but are awakened every hour. The material consists of a series of slides, with each slide containing nine letters in a 3×3 array. Each slide is presented for a short time (50 ms), and then the student must recall as many numbers as possible. The dependent variable is recorded as the number of letters correctly recalled.

The correct statistic is the one-way ANOVA, followed by some MCP. There are three groups, a numerical dependent variable, and an implied question about differences.

Scenario H: A nurse was hired by a government ecology agency to investigate the impact of a lead smelter on the level of lead in the blood of children who live near the smelter. Ten children were chosen at random from those living near the smelter. For comparison, seven children were randomly selected from those who lived in the same community but in an area relatively free from possible lead pollution. Blood samples were taken from the children and lead levels determined.

This is a tough one because you have to remember the conditions for the use of the two-independent-sample t-test and the AWS test. The sample sizes are small and unequal (6), so you should use the AWS test. Nothing is mentioned about pairing the children, and there are two groups, a quantitative dependent variable, and an implied question of difference.

Scenario I: An experimenter wants to test the recovery of patients from depression. He has two types of treatment, counseling and drugs, and wants to combine them to form four groups: no treatment, counseling only, drugs only, and drugs plus counseling. His dependent measure is number of symptoms after 8 weeks.

This is an example of a two-way ANOVA. The different types of treatment make up the two factors, counseling and drugs. The levels for each are presence or absence of the treatment. The dependent variable is quantitative. What if he had wanted to track the number of symptoms over the 8-week period by getting a count of the number of symptoms every week? Then this would be a repeated measures design with eight levels of time, the repeated factor.

Scenario J: Is willingness to buy a new toothpaste the same for both genders? Fifty men and 50 women were asked whether they would buy the product after seeing a brief commercial.

Because the participants respond with yes or no to being willing to buy the toothpaste, you can compute the proportion of yes answers out of 50 for each gender. Then the statistic is the test for two independent proportions. An alternative statistic is the χ^2 test for contingency tables.

Scenario K: At your school, the proportion of freshmen who fail English composition has been fairly steady for the last 10 years at .21. You have developed a new teaching technique for this course, and you hope it will decrease the rate of failure. You have tried the new technique with 210 students and there are 25 failures.

Here the test is the one-sample test of a proportion. A test of a hypothesis about a mean is not correct because you are interested in the failure rate. You have data in the form of 25 failures out of the 210 students who got the new technique.

Scenario L: You wonder whether there are seasonal fluctuations in the numbers of babies born in your state. You can check state records for the numbers of live births by month for the past year, and you believe that the numbers won't be equal.

The 12 months form the categories, and you can get observed frequencies for each. The expected frequencies would come from the null hypothesis (opposite of your belief of unequal frequencies) of equal frequencies. Simply take the total for the year and divide by 12. You have a goodness-of-fit χ^2.

20.4   Beyond These Statistics

The purpose of this text has been to introduce statistical procedures used by scientists in disciplines that are considered applied. In meeting this purpose, the scope of the statistics has been limited. Most of your attention has focused on learning basic procedures to implement the concepts of data analysis: exploration/description and confirmation/inference. Many more statistical procedures can be learned in more advanced courses. Some of these statistical procedures are much more complex than those in this text, many of them *requiring* computer analysis. Examples are multivariate ANOVA, logistic regression, canonical correlation, tests for three-way and higher-order contingency tables, multidimensional scaling, and factor analysis. These words don't mean much to you now, but they might be useful tools in the future. These statistical methods have the same conceptual basis as those you have learned in this text. You should have an excellent foundation on which to build, and we hope you have *learned how to learn* about statistics. Maybe you have even found the topic interesting enough to want to take more statistics courses. Regardless of whether you continue to study statistics, we wish you well in using statistics and understanding research in your daily life and further academic career.

Exercises

We have grouped these exercises into two sets.

Instructions for Set A: The research scenarios in Set A have several hints, which should make them a bit easier than Set B. For Set A, answer these four questions for each exercise: (a) What is the hypothesis being tested? (b) What key questions or key words are in the scenario? (c) What inferential statistical method is appro-

priate? (d) Why are some other statistics inappropriate? Set A contains one scenario for each statistic method given in this text.

Instructions for Set B: You get fewer hints in these scenarios. Also, the same statistic may apply to more than one scenario. There may not be a scenario for every statistic you've learned, so a process of elimination won't help you answer the question, What inferential statistical method is appropriate? Try to find the reasons that some other statistics are inappropriate.

Set A

1. What is the relationship between age (in months) when talking starts and later adult vocabulary?

2. The national average on the Graduate Record Exam (GRE) is 1200 and the standard deviation is 100. This year's graduates from your university average 1250 ($N = 500$). Do these graduates score significantly higher than the national average?

3. Senate hearings were held in 1994 at the Fernald State School in Waltham, Massachusetts, to investigate human radiation experiments conducted in the late 1940s and early 1950s. Government researchers at that time didn't tell parents or students of the school for mentally handicapped children that the "nutrition studies" involved oatmeal laced with a radioactive substance. Suppose you are part of a team of investigators trying to find out whether the people who ate the oatmeal now have higher rates of cancer. You have tracked down 28 people who were part of the "Science Club," which is what the experimental group was called, and 17 of them have been treated for some form of abdominal cancer. You find 35 people who also were in the school but didn't eat the oatmeal, and 9 of them have undergone treatment for abdominal tumors.

4. Suppose 50 depressed adults are matched on age, gender, and severity of symptoms. Then they are randomly assigned to one of two different forms of treatment (25 in each treatment group): drugs alone or drugs plus counseling. After 2 weeks of treatment, they are measured on number of symptoms to see whether there are significant differences in the two treatments. It is known that severely depressed patients don't respond to these treatments very quickly, and you expect a cluster of about 5% of the scores to be rather large and different from the other scores.

5. Is there any difference among the reading scores of second-grade pupils in three elementary schools?

6. A medical researcher wants to see whether there is any relationship between smoking behavior and presence/absence of persistent coughing. Of 54 smokers (regular smokers for 2 or more years), 27 reported persistent coughing; of 54 nonsmokers, only 13 reported coughing.

7. Members of a graduate program's admissions committee are concerned about providing equal opportunity for both genders. They know that equal numbers of men and women are applying to their program, but they want to answer the question about the proportion of women being .50 for those students admitted this last year.

8. A sports physiologist believes that drinking Gatorade plus water (in equal parts) is more effective than drinking straight Gatorade or plain water in relieving fatigue after strenuous exercise. Type of exercise is also a concern, so both runners and swimmers are recruited. The dependent variable is a numerical measure of fatigue 10 min after strenuous exercise. A total of 30 swimmers and 30 runners participate and are randomly assigned to treatments within type of exercise.

9. A teacher wants to know whether frequent exams lead to higher final exam scores. However, distributions of final exam scores are known to be negatively skewed, with a cluster of failing grades (about 5% of the students) well below the next closest scores. He teaches two sections of introductory sociology, each with 30 students. He gives Section 1 six exams plus a final exam. Section 2 takes three exams plus a final exam.

10. You are doing a study of body temperature, and you want to find out whether temperature differs depending on the day of the week. You obtain 50 volunteers and take their temperatures at noon every day for 7 days.

11. Your latest study compares men's and women's body temperatures. You measure 35 men's and 35 women's temperatures daily for a week.

12. Fifty people are measured on both self-esteem and locus of control to see whether there is a significant association between these variables. You are interested in detecting more than just a linear relationship because you think there may be a ceiling effect on self-esteem. Numerical scores are available for each variable.

13. You think people are abstaining more from alcohol than they used to. You find frequencies of abstaining from surveys done in 1977, 1982, 1988, and 1994 by college students in the Midwest. Are the rates of abstention the same?

14. You want to find out whether knowing a depressed person's music preferences could help a counseling psychologist in treatment. You ask clients at a community mental health clinic to participate in your

study. Sixty-two people complete your survey, which includes a measure of depression and knowledge (number recognized) of currently popular songs on the country music charts. Does knowledge of current country music explain any variability in depression scores after you have accounted for age and a numerical score for general physical health?

15. You are conducting an experiment to learn the effect of task difficulty on compliance in people who would answer a ringing pay phone. Participants are randomly assigned to one of two levels of difficulty of task (easy, hard), with 20 in each group. The easy task is to read to the phone caller the name of a street from a plainly visible street sign. The difficult task is to agree to go seven blocks away to a small grocery store and give a message to one of the clerks (the store has no phone). A rating of compliance from 1 to 5 is the dependent variable.

16. A psychologist believes that high stress reduces long-term memory relative to low stress. She randomly assigned ten people to a high-stress condition (a group of peers would be allowed to see how they performed). The other ten people were in a low-stress condition (only the researcher would know how they performed). Each participant then learned a list of 50 nonsense syllables on which they were tested 1 h later.

17. Is there a difference in total points earned in an introductory psychology class between students taught by method X and those taught by method Y? The two groups of students were paired on the basis of intelligence and then randomly assigned to one of the two methods.

18. To estimate the average life of his 100-watt light bulbs, the manufacturer randomly samples 87 light bulbs and keeps them lit until they burn out. The sample has a mean life of 211 h and a standard deviation of 7 h. For the past 5 years, the mean life of 100-watt light bulbs has been known to be 202 h.

19. Suppose you do a study like that done on the effects of smoking in Research Example 14. You have three groups, with 21 people in each group. Nonsmokers (NS) were participants who had never smoked regularly and did not smoke at the time of the research. Smokers claimed to have smoked at least one pack of cigarettes per day during the last year. Smokers were randomly assigned to one of two groups: those who had just actively smoked (AS) and those who were deprived of smoking for 3 h (DS). In the 6 min before the study started, the AS smokers were pro-

vided with a cigarette with 1.2 mg of nicotine and were "requested to inhale normally every 25 seconds and hold that puff for 5 seconds, for a total of 12 puffs." All subjects sat alone in a waiting room for 6 min before the study, and the NS and DS participants "sham smoked" an imaginary cigarette, so their experience was as similar as possible to the AS group's experience. You have them participate in a driving simulation. About 5% of the participants evidently had little or no actual driving experience because they had many more accidents than the others.

20. Now you want to see whether there is a dose effect for smoking: Do the number of accidents on the simulator differ for different amounts of time spent smoking? You use 20 smokers and have them smoke for 2 min, 4 min, 6 min, and 8 min, with each smoking session followed by a turn on the simulator. The order of the sessions is randomly assigned to each smoker. You are interested in differences in the median numbers of accidents because of the potential effect of outliers on the means.

Set B

21. Hometown, USA, has implemented a new kind of public school schedule. Instead of a 3-month summer vacation, students in Hometown schools have four 3-week breaks scattered throughout the year. The school board thinks the shorter breaks and year-round teaching will prevent students from forgetting what they have learned, and that this will lead to higher scores on achievement tests. Do Hometown High School seniors have higher achievement scores than those in a similar school in a town with a traditional summer vacation?

22. A psychology department requires its seniors to take a standardized psychology test before they graduate. You want to know whether the scores of this year's 112 seniors differ, on the average, from the national norm. The norms include $\mu = 32.1$, but σ^2 is unknown.

23. Researchers want to know whether calcium and vitamin D ingested together will help elderly women suffer fewer hip fractures. The medical experts running the study think women will have stronger joints if they take the two substances together. Hip fractures occur at low rates, so the researchers know they will have to run a large study. A team of doctors organizes the study and recruits 3,000 women to participate. The women know they are participating in

a study of bone strength among the elderly, but they don't know whether they will receive a placebo or an active ingredient in their daily pill. Half of the women take 1.2 g of calcium and 800 international units of vitamin D daily for 18 months, while the other women receive an identical-appearing placebo. At the end of the period, the doctors report that 87 women in the control group and 31 in the treatment group had fractured a hip.

24. Thirty obese women were put on a calorie-restricted diet as part of a study of weight loss efficiency. Half of the women ate 70% of their normal intake, and the other half ate 40% of their normal calories. For each woman, the researchers calculated a deficit-efficiency factor, which is a ratio of the amount of weight loss to the amount of deprivation. A higher number means more efficient weight loss. It is known that for this dependent variable, about 5% of the scores on the deficit-efficiency factor cluster at the high end of the scale, considerably above the next closest scores. Which group's weight loss was more efficient?

25. You decide to run a study on weight loss, and you want to know whether counseling has any effect, in addition to either diet or exercise, on people's weight. Ninety women are signed up for the program. You randomly assign them to either a 40%-of-normal-calorie diet or a supervised moderate exercise treatment. You also randomly assign them to one of three counseling groups: a group therapy session to be held when they report for their weekly weigh-in, a waiting room condition with other women in the same waiting room, or a solitary waiting room condition. You are not interested in their weekly fluctuations in weight. You will focus on weight at the end of the study.

26. An exercise physiologist who works with people at a large retirement center wants to find out whether strengthening exercises will help senior citizens improve their balance and, as a result, reduce their tendency to fall. The physiologist has 21 volunteers for the preliminary study, in which one group will do flexibility exercises for an hour 3 days a week, while another group will do t'ai chi, take a 20-min walk, and do leg presses on a weight machine 3 days a week. The dependent variable is a measure of sway while the participant stands on one foot. Will the flexibility group have better sway scores than the diverse-training group?

27. After studying the results of the sway study in Exercise 26, the exercise physiologist decides that some people naturally swayed less and she should have measured the reduction in sway. She recruits a new group of 40, measures everyone's sway, and then randomly assigns them to the flexibility training or the diverse exercise. After a month, she checks everyone's improvement.

28. The exercise physiologist wants to find out which kind of exercise is best for improving older people's balance. She obtains permission to recruit volunteers at a community senior citizens center. Forty-eight people signed up for the study. She randomly assigns them to either a 20-min walk, t'ai chi exercises, or leg presses on the weight machine three times a week. Which group shows the most reduction in sway?

29. Can calcium consumption during the teen years affect whether a woman develops osteoporosis, which causes brittle bones in older women? Researchers find 94 teenage girls who already consume about 80% of the recommended daily allowance of calcium and measure their bone density. Half of the girls take a placebo and half take 354 mg of calcium every day for 18 months. Does one group have a greater increase in bone density?

30. You are a city manager with a potential problem of using up your landfill site for garbage in the next decade. You study many other cities; some of them are about the size of your city, while others are bigger—up to 25% larger. Some cities have many industries, some have a high proportion of people with high socioeconomic status, and some don't pick up grass clippings. You are looking for variables that affect the size of landfill needed. You want to know whether the variables of size of landfill and number of people serviced are related when all these other variables are taken into account.

31. You are a medical researcher wondering whether the widely used number of 98.6°F is truly the average adult human temperature (the standard deviation is unknown). You recruit 200 healthy adults and take their temperatures one afternoon, using sterilized electronic thermometers.

32. A professor of religious studies is interested in finding out whether there is a relationship between church attendance and educational level. Data are collected on a sample of individuals who completed only high school and on another group who received a college education. Each person is asked whether he or she attends church regularly.

33. The owner of a large factory is considering hiring part-time employees to fill jobs previously staffed with full-time workers. However, he wonders whether doing so will affect productivity. He conducts an experiment to evaluate the idea before implementing it factorywide. Six full-time job openings from the parts manufacturing division of the company are each filled with two employees hired to work half-time. The output of these six half-time pairs is compared with the output of a randomly selected sample of six full-time employees from the same division. All employees in the experiment are engaged in manufacturing the same parts. The numbers of parts produced per day by the half-time pairs and full-time workers are recorded for 20 days. The total number of parts produced is the dependent variable.

34. Do low-fat foods indeed have low fat content? Because the government allows fat content to be 20% higher than the amount stated on the label, you suspect that about half of low-fat products will indeed have more than the fat content stated on the package. From a grocery store chain, you get a list of products that are advertised as low fat. You randomly sample 30 products from the list and buy one of each item. A laboratory determines what percentage of each product's calories come from fat. You compare that figure to the percentage on the label and determine that 43% of the products have more than the stated level.

35. Performing artists take financial and personal risks when they devote themselves to their art. Do actors, dancers, musicians, and singers differ from other people in their willingness to take risks? You get 15 people in each of these groups and measure risk-taking with a scale that has scores from 1 to 50.

36. After looking at performing artists' risk-taking, you want to know whether gender has an impact. You find ten men and ten women in each of the four career groups and measure risk-taking.

37. It has been claimed that the number of points earned on the final exam in your statistics course predicts the number of points earned in a certain senior-level course in your department.

38. An educational psychologist has reason to believe that children who have poor deductive reasoning skill can improve during a 2-month special education program. The dependent variable is a standard test of deductive reasoning that yields scores from 1 to 50. Is there any gain in deductive reasoning?

39. A gasoline manufacturer believes that a new additive will result in more miles per gallon. A large number of mileage measurements on the gasoline without the additive have been made by the company under rigorously controlled conditions. The records show a mean of 24.7 miles per gallon and a standard deviation of 4.8. Tests are conducted on a sample of 25 cars using the gasoline plus the additive. The sample mean is 26.7 miles per gallon.

40. Dr. Toothaker has been teaching statistics for more than 26 years. His records show that the overall mean for his final exam scores is 82, with a standard deviation of 10. He believes that this year's class is superior to his previous classes. The mean final exam score for this year's class of 64 students is 87.

41. Do adolescent children of divorced families with mother custody differ in self-esteem from those of intact families? High school students were asked about their family status along with other demographic questions. They then answered questions in a self-esteem measure. There were 31 from intact families and 24 from divorced families with mother custody.

42. Does systematic desensitization reduce racial prejudice? You investigate 32 college students who are participating in a class on racial issues. Part of the course requirements are to meet 1 h a week with a qualified clinician who leads a group using desensitization methods. Measures of racial prejudice are taken every week for 12 weeks.

Appendix A
Tables

Table A.1
Random numbers

```
56  25  08  71  14    07  38  35  10  71    80  77  78  58  79    17  56  95  18  56    02  88  70  79  63
44  16  00  32  06    25  43  17  89  14    65  61  35  37  73    08  73  57  41  31    11  04  24  48  23
46  55  22  28  86    86  49  07  43  00    10  96  69  44  70    33  36  30  17  50    39  96  58  96  56
40  16  91  19  95    95  22  11  42  89    90  35  59  91  85    79  07  79  19  98    61  83  26  96  93
16  60  63  96  40    35  81  60  94  67    33  41  83  60  46    89  96  03  67  41    34  64  47  95  23

31  36  67  14  48    05  69  04  52  55    50  46  89  85  11    04  90  10  78  67    13  39  01  24  18
43  99  74  07  26    88  82  62  89  91    06  08  29  65  06    27  04  05  02  91    58  58  31  64  80
43  66  11  90  82    43  63  71  54  78    30  67  06  48  78    61  43  48  85  24    30  22  74  71  30
90  08  73  69  55    01  12  52  18  63    45  14  47  64  08    13  48  79  93  14    95  23  72  14  07
62  88  57  00  61    38  17  90  36  20    84  03  57  28  54    17  73  52  50  02    17  27  71  46  84

53  71  33  45  55    55  95  37  01  94    84  05  04  36  92    45  46  56  50  06    39  44  97  02  92
19  32  62  07  89    94  97  81  73  31    78  41  97  04  77    85  62  87  48  21    54  20  66  77  69
90  42  50  72  23    91  34  84  54  86    52  71  08  24  02    98  33  13  56  19    46  24  93  55  77
58  97  67  25  47    07  31  79  13  42    70  03  33  36  04    93  27  55  90  24    12  73  01  48  49
18  45  83  87  03    97  52  18  34  40    78  17  32  32  21    74  26  47  17  60    71  38  51  48  85

76  90  15  97  89    17  61  48  76  91    22  45  19  39  54    02  49  58  85  78    50  46  62  63  04
62  79  39  14  03    29  04  88  93  20    03  27  59  94  35    68  79  71  17  18    98  40  72  54  55
01  44  82  51  49    22  53  83  81  55    22  22  71  52  91    35  00  09  83  13    93  15  03  49  70
96  06  53  52  67    71  68  70  44  38    13  05  05  32  21    21  65  10  50  74    92  49  42  07  62
22  88  68  01  80    73  96  49  00  05    10  42  87  25  98    54  25  78  03  99    78  00  57  60  29

61  40  44  92  18    82  24  27  82  27    18  00  27  25  87    17  38  29  46  25    14  69  95  97  57
37  85  79  67  31    04  77  65  92  65    55  16  32  20  39    76  50  67  40  22    32  54  92  21  18
22  21  76  99  66    65  35  97  96  15    13  16  05  31  14    46  36  07  33  94    21  98  51  57  82
04  35  64  21  02    64  35  06  95  94    78  33  67  67  05    83  22  04  20  12    75  29  27  18  49
72  13  35  40  63    52  37  14  67  21    84  06  75  97  98    89  54  75  59  94    15  89  64  64  98

63  54  41  32  82    06  94  05  22  00    53  51  78  51  58    51  39  47  41  77    42  43  69  14  72
74  20  78  73  40    20  56  18  28  61    05  42  55  72  54    24  20  86  58  85    06  17  64  76  00
77  85  69  55  06    96  84  15  64  82    15  71  49  12  31    06  42  66  49  31    16  96  18  74  63
46  50  03  55  68    48  09  27  87  36    32  32  73  00  70    85  10  24  43  48    60  94  66  18  93
45  09  42  62  18    52  86  56  49  55    33  84  74  19  47    83  89  92  31  06    60  99  73  27  72

16  90  04  20  57    40  44  88  47  15    86  55  39  33  14    94  69  92  86  20    78  05  91  30  52
78  25  60  82  94    25  66  50  02  93    37  72  70  24  42    55  55  65  35  98    39  52  61  73  16
30  08  62  31  90    82  77  01  37  71    60  80  53  31  15    70  72  22  72  37    23  59  46  67  63
60  77  80  68  41    96  62  06  98  27    18  62  15  42  83    46  94  57  01  75    29  86  62  61  84
16  11  97  55  11    25  38  07  42  79    46  75  45  58  17    19  61  96  07  42    90  81  97  66  46

66  04  34  78  75    40  27  81  04  94    82  43  12  95  51    48  67  74  83  32    59  06  01  42  59
55  28  00  58  07    80  01  30  87  38    81  92  70  95  21    25  14  80  51  62    58  13  31  82  79
85  15  47  65  60    21  75  81  40  03    97  08  26  14  57    63  96  83  36  94    18  11  89  34  67
59  26  69  84  77    89  57  36  54  43    55  90  28  69  47    18  49  97  76  64    18  09  66  14  73
57  97  50  10  27    30  88  14  71  57    37  85  22  76  37    40  21  82  83  12    06  95  15  05  00

69  82  43  45  81    18  55  54  76  90    89  87  09  10  06    08  28  89  02  23    02  27  76  10  22
98  84  47  33  55    38  11  98  12  98    77  93  94  44  30    61  79  88  97  27    02  18  68  27  92
08  41  80  44  13    90  26  26  23  03    04  12  80  35  53    13  63  49  23  39    90  38  19  44  08
46  13  33  64  81    70  57  42  78  93    21  91  05  19  86    90  68  57  15  34    98  67  47  41  01
77  74  09  68  15    19  95  02  82  58    18  42  05  32  87    68  26  59  14  20    02  37  14  94  38
```

Table A.1 was created by the authors.

Table A.2
Areas for the standard normal distribution

1	2	3		1	2	3		1	2	3
0.00	.0000	.5000		0.40	.1554	.3446		0.80	.2881	.2119
0.01	.0040	.4960		0.41	.1591	.3409		0.81	.2910	.2090
0.02	.0080	.4920		0.42	.1628	.3372		0.82	.2939	.2061
0.03	.0120	.4880		0.43	.1664	.3336		0.83	.2967	.2033
0.04	.0160	.4840		0.44	.1700	.3300		0.84	.2995	.2005
0.05	.0199	.4801		0.45	.1736	.3264		0.85	.3023	.1977
0.06	.0239	.4761		0.46	.1772	.3228		0.86	.3051	.1949
0.07	.0279	.4721		0.47	.1808	.3192		0.87	.3078	.1922
0.08	.0319	.4681		0.48	.1844	.3156		0.88	.3106	.1894
0.09	.0359	.4641		0.49	.1879	.3121		0.89	.3133	.1867
0.10	.0398	.4602		0.50	.1915	.3085		0.90	.3159	.1841
0.11	.0438	.4562		0.51	.1950	.3050		0.91	.3186	.1814
0.12	.0478	.4522		0.52	.1985	.3015		0.92	.3212	.1788
0.13	.0517	.4483		0.53	.2019	.2981		0.93	.3238	.1762
0.14	.0557	.4443		0.54	.2054	.2946		0.94	.3264	.1736
0.15	.0596	.4404		0.55	.2088	.2912		0.95	.3289	.1711
0.16	.0636	.4364		0.56	.2123	.2877		0.96	.3315	.1685
0.17	.0675	.4325		0.57	.2157	.2843		0.97	.3340	.1660
0.18	.0714	.4286		0.58	.2190	.2810		0.98	.3365	.1635
0.19	.0753	.4247		0.59	.2224	.2776		0.99	.3389	.1611
0.20	.0793	.4207		0.60	.2257	.2743		1.00	.3413	.1587
0.21	.0832	.4168		0.61	.2291	.2709		1.01	.3438	.1562
0.22	.0871	.4129		0.62	.2324	.2676		1.02	.3461	.1539
0.23	.0910	.4090		0.63	.2357	.2643		1.03	.3485	.1515
0.24	.0948	.4052		0.64	.2389	.2611		1.04	.3508	.1492
0.25	.0987	.4013		0.65	.2422	.2578		1.05	.3531	.1469
0.26	.1026	.3974		0.66	.2454	.2546		1.06	.3554	.1446
0.27	.1064	.3936		0.67	.2486	.2514		1.07	.3577	.1423
0.28	.1103	.3897		0.68	.2517	.2483		1.08	.3599	.1401
0.29	.1141	.3859		0.69	.2549	.2451		1.09	.3621	.1379
0.30	.1179	.3821		0.70	.2580	.2420		1.10	.3643	.1357
0.31	.1217	.3783		0.71	.2611	.2389		1.11	.3665	.1335
0.32	.1255	.3745		0.72	.2642	.2358		1.12	.3686	.1314
0.33	.1293	.3707		0.73	.2673	.2327		1.13	.3708	.1292
0.34	.1331	.3669		0.74	.2704	.2296		1.14	.3729	.1271
0.35	.1368	.3632		0.75	.2734	.2266		1.15	.3749	.1251
0.36	.1406	.3594		0.76	.2764	.2236		1.16	.3770	.1230
0.37	.1443	.3557		0.77	.2794	.2206		1.17	.3790	.1210
0.38	.1480	.3520		0.78	.2823	.2177		1.18	.3810	.1190
0.39	.1517	.3483		0.79	.2852	.2148		1.19	.3830	.1170

Table A.2 was computed by the authors.

Table A.2 (continued)

1	2	3	1	2	3	1	2	3
z or −z			z or −z			z or −z		

z			z			z		
1.20	.3849	.1151	1.60	.4452	.0548	2.00	.4772	.0228
1.21	.3869	.1131	1.61	.4463	.0537	2.01	.4778	.0222
1.22	.3888	.1112	1.62	.4474	.0526	2.02	.4783	.0217
1.23	.3907	.1093	1.63	.4484	.0516	2.03	.4788	.0212
1.24	.3925	.1075	1.64	.4495	.0505	2.04	.4793	.0207
1.25	.3944	.1056	1.65	.4505	.0495	2.05	.4798	.0202
1.26	.3962	.1038	1.66	.4515	.0485	2.06	.4803	.0197
1.27	.3980	.1020	1.67	.4525	.0475	2.07	.4808	.0192
1.28	.3997	.1003	1.68	.4535	.0465	2.08	.4812	.0188
1.29	.4015	.0985	1.69	.4545	.0455	2.09	.4817	.0183
1.30	.4032	.0968	1.70	.4554	.0446	2.10	.4821	.0179
1.31	.4049	.0951	1.71	.4564	.0436	2.11	.4826	.0174
1.32	.4066	.0934	1.72	.4573	.0427	2.12	.4830	.0170
1.33	.4082	.0918	1.73	.4582	.0418	2.13	.4834	.0166
1.34	.4099	.0901	1.74	.4591	.0409	2.14	.4838	.0162
1.35	.4115	.0885	1.75	.4599	.0401	2.15	.4842	.0158
1.36	.4131	.0869	1.76	.4608	.0392	2.16	.4846	.0154
1.37	.4147	.0853	1.77	.4616	.0384	2.17	.4850	.0150
1.38	.4162	.0838	1.78	.4625	.0375	2.18	.4854	.0146
1.39	.4177	.0823	1.79	.4633	.0367	2.19	.4857	.0143
1.40	.4192	.0808	1.80	.4641	.0359	2.20	.4861	.0139
1.41	.4207	.0793	1.81	.4649	.0351	2.21	.4864	.0136
1.42	.4222	.0778	1.82	.4656	.0344	2.22	.4868	.0132
1.43	.4236	.0764	1.83	.4664	.0336	2.23	.4871	.0129
1.44	.4251	.0749	1.84	.4671	.0329	2.24	.4875	.0125
1.45	.4265	.0735	1.85	.4678	.0322	2.25	.4878	.0122
1.46	.4279	.0721	1.86	.4686	.0314	2.26	.4881	.0119
1.47	.4292	.0708	1.87	.4693	.0307	2.27	.4884	.0116
1.48	.4306	.0694	1.88	.4699	.0301	2.28	.4887	.0113
1.49	.4319	.0681	1.89	.4706	.0294	2.29	.4890	.0110
1.50	.4332	.0668	1.90	.4713	.0287	2.30	.4893	.0107
1.51	.4345	.0655	1.91	.4719	.0281	2.31	.4896	.0104
1.52	.4357	.0643	1.92	.4726	.0274	2.32	.4898	.0102
1.53	.4370	.0630	1.93	.4732	.0268	2.33	.4901	.0099
1.54	.4382	.0618	1.94	.4738	.0262	2.34	.4904	.0096
1.55	.4394	.0606	1.95	.4744	.0256	2.35	.4906	.0094
1.56	.4406	.0594	1.96	.4750	.0250	2.36	.4909	.0091
1.57	.4418	.0582	1.97	.4756	.0244	2.37	.4911	.0089
1.58	.4429	.0571	1.98	.4761	.0239	2.38	.4913	.0087
1.59	.4441	.0559	1.99	.4767	.0233	2.39	.4916	.0084

(continued)

Table A.2 (continued)

1	2	3	1	2	3	1	2	3

z or −z			z or −z			z or −z		
2.40	.4918	.0082	2.72	.4967	.0033	3.04	.4988	.0012
2.41	.4920	.0080	2.73	.4968	.0032	3.05	.4989	.0011
2.42	.4922	.0078	2.74	.4969	.0031	3.06	.4989	.0011
2.43	.4925	.0075	2.75	.4970	.0030	3.07	.4989	.0011
2.44	.4927	.0073	2.76	.4971	.0029	3.08	.4990	.0010
2.45	.4929	.0071	2.77	.4972	.0028	3.09	.4990	.0010
2.46	.4931	.0069	2.78	.4973	.0027	3.10	.4990	.0010
2.47	.4932	.0068	2.79	.4974	.0026	3.11	.4991	.0009
2.48	.4934	.0066	2.80	.4974	.0026	3.12	.4991	.0009
2.49	.4936	.0064	2.81	.4975	.0025	3.13	.4991	.0009
2.50	.4938	.0062	2.82	.4976	.0024	3.14	.4992	.0008
2.51	.4940	.0060	2.83	.4977	.0023	3.15	.4992	.0008
2.52	.4941	.0059	2.84	.4977	.0023	3.16	.4992	.0008
2.53	.4943	.0057	2.85	.4978	.0022	3.17	.4992	.0008
2.54	.4945	.0055	2.86	.4979	.0021	3.18	.4993	.0007
2.55	.4946	.0054	2.87	.4979	.0021	3.19	.4993	.0007
2.56	.4948	.0052	2.88	.4980	.0020	3.20	.4993	.0007
2.57	.4949	.0051	2.89	.4981	.0019	3.21	.4993	.0007
2.58	.4951	.0049	2.90	.4981	.0019	3.22	.4994	.0006
2.59	.4952	.0048	2.91	.4982	.0018	3.23	.4994	.0006
2.60	.4953	.0047	2.92	.4982	.0018	3.24	.4994	.0006
2.61	.4955	.0045	2.93	.4983	.0017	3.25	.4994	.0006
2.62	.4956	.0044	2.94	.4984	.0016	3.30	.49952	.00048
2.63	.4957	.0043	2.95	.4984	.0016	3.35	.49960	.00040
2.64	.4959	.0041	2.96	.4985	.0015	3.40	.49966	.00034
2.65	.4960	.0040	2.97	.4985	.0015	3.45	.49972	.00028
2.66	.4961	.0039	2.98	.4986	.0014	3.50	.49977	.00023
2.67	.4962	.0038	2.99	.4986	.0014	3.60	.49984	.00016
2.68	.4963	.0037	3.00	.4987	.0013	3.70	.49989	.00011
2.69	.4964	.0036	3.01	.4987	.0013	3.80	.49993	.00007
2.70	.4965	.0035	3.02	.4987	.0013	3.90	.49995	.00005
2.71	.4966	.0034	3.03	.4988	.0012	4.00	.49997	.00003

Table A.3
Binomial probabilities

N	r	.01	.05	.10	.15	.20	.25	.30	1/3	.35	.40	.45	.50	r
2	0	.9801	.9025	.8100	.7225	.6400	.5625	.4900	.4444	.4225	.3600	.3025	.2500	0
	1	.0198	.0950	.1800	.2550	.3200	.3750	.4200	.4444	.4550	.4800	.4950	.5000	1
	2	.0001	.0025	.0100	.0225	.0400	.0625	.0900	.1111	.1225	.1600	.2025	.2500	2
3	0	.9703	.8574	.7290	.6141	.5120	.4219	.3430	.2963	.2746	.2160	.1664	.1250	0
	1	.0294	.1354	.2430	.3251	.3840	.4219	.4410	.4444	.4436	.4320	.4084	.3750	1
	2	.0003	.0071	.0270	.0574	.0960	.1406	.1890	.2222	.2389	.2880	.3341	.3750	2
	3	.0000	.0001	.0010	.0034	.0080	.0156	.0270	.0370	.0429	.0640	.0911	.1250	3
4	0	.9606	.8145	.6561	.5220	.4096	.3164	.2401	.1975	.1785	.1296	.0915	.0625	0
	1	.0388	.1715	.2916	.3685	.4096	.4219	.4116	.3951	.3845	.3456	.2995	.2500	1
	2	.0006	.0135	.0486	.0975	.1536	.2109	.2646	.2963	.3105	.3456	.3675	.3750	2
	3	.0000	.0005	.0036	.0115	.0256	.0469	.0756	.0988	.1115	.1536	.2005	.2500	3
	4	.0000	.0000	.0001	.0005	.0016	.0039	.0081	.0123	.0150	.0256	.0410	.0625	4
5	0	.9510	.7738	.5905	.4437	.3277	.2373	.1681	.1317	.1160	.0778	.0503	.0313	0
	1	.0480	.2036	.3280	.3915	.4096	.3955	.3601	.3292	.3124	.2592	.2059	.1563	1
	2	.0010	.0214	.0729	.1382	.2048	.2637	.3087	.3292	.3364	.3456	.3369	.3125	2
	3	.0000	.0011	.0081	.0244	.0512	.0879	.1323	.1646	.1811	.2304	.2757	.3125	3
	4	.0000	.0000	.0005	.0022	.0064	.0146	.0284	.0412	.0488	.0768	.1128	.1563	4
	5	.0000	.0000	.0000	.0001	.0003	.0010	.0024	.0041	.0053	.0102	.0185	.0313	5
6	0	.9415	.7351	.5314	.3771	.2621	.1780	.1176	.0878	.0754	.0467	.0277	.0156	0
	1	.0571	.2321	.3543	.3993	.3932	.3560	.3025	.2634	.2437	.1866	.1359	.0938	1
	2	.0014	.0305	.0984	.1762	.2458	.2966	.3241	.3292	.3280	.3110	.2780	.2344	2
	3	.0000	.0021	.0146	.0415	.0819	.1318	.1852	.2195	.2355	.2765	.3032	.3125	3
	4	.0000	.0001	.0012	.0055	.0154	.0330	.0595	.0823	.0951	.1382	.1861	.2344	4
	5	.0000	.0000	.0001	.0004	.0015	.0044	.0102	.0165	.0205	.0369	.0609	.0938	5
	6	.0000	.0000	.0000	.0000	.0001	.0002	.0007	.0014	.0018	.0041	.0083	.0156	6
7	0	.9321	.6983	.4783	.3206	.2097	.1335	.0824	.0585	.0490	.0280	.0152	.0078	0
	1	.0659	.2573	.3720	.3960	.3670	.3115	.2471	.2048	.1848	.1306	.0872	.0547	1
	2	.0020	.0406	.1240	.2097	.2753	.3115	.3177	.3073	.2985	.2613	.2140	.1641	2
	3	.0000	.0036	.0230	.0617	.1147	.1730	.2269	.2561	.2679	.2903	.2918	.2734	3
	4	.0000	.0002	.0026	.0109	.0287	.0577	.0972	.1280	.1442	.1935	.2388	.2734	4
	5	.0000	.0000	.0002	.0012	.0043	.0115	.0250	.0384	.0466	.0774	.1172	.1641	5
	6	.0000	.0000	.0000	.0001	.0004	.0013	.0036	.0064	.0084	.0172	.0320	.0547	6
	7	.0000	.0000	.0000	.0000	.0000	.0001	.0002	.0005	.0006	.0016	.0037	.0078	7
8	0	.9227	.6634	.4305	.2725	.1678	.1001	.0576	.0390	.0319	.0168	.0084	.0039	0
	1	.0746	.2793	.3826	.3847	.3355	.2670	.1977	.1561	.1373	.0896	.0548	.0313	1
	2	.0026	.0515	.1488	.2376	.2936	.3115	.2965	.2731	.2587	.2090	.1569	.1094	2
	3	.0001	.0054	.0331	.0839	.1468	.2076	.2541	.2731	.2786	.2787	.2568	.2188	3
	4	.0000	.0004	.0046	.0185	.0459	.0865	.1361	.1707	.1875	.2322	.2627	.2734	4
	5	.0000	.0000	.0004	.0026	.0092	.0231	.0467	.0683	.0808	.1239	.1719	.2188	5
	6	.0000	.0000	.0000	.0002	.0011	.0038	.0100	.0171	.0217	.0413	.0703	.1094	6
	7	.0000	.0000	.0000	.0000	.0001	.0004	.0012	.0024	.0033	.0079	.0164	.0313	7
	8	.0000	.0000	.0000	.0000	.0000	.0000	.0001	.0002	.0002	.0007	.0017	.0039	8
9	0	.9135	.6302	.3874	.2316	.1342	.0751	.0404	.0260	.0207	.0101	.0046	.0020	0
	1	.0830	.2985	.3874	.3679	.3020	.2253	.1556	.1171	.1004	.0605	.0339	.0176	1
	2	.0034	.0629	.1722	.2597	.3020	.3003	.2668	.2341	.2162	.1612	.1110	.0703	2
	3	.0001	.0077	.0446	.1069	.1762	.2336	.2668	.2731	.2716	.2508	.2119	.1641	3
	4	.0000	.0006	.0074	.0283	.0661	.1168	.1715	.2048	.2194	.2508	.2600	.2461	4
	5	.0000	.0000	.0008	.0050	.0165	.0389	.0735	.1024	.1181	.1672	.2128	.2461	5
	6	.0000	.0000	.0001	.0006	.0028	.0087	.0210	.0341	.0424	.0743	.1160	.1641	6
	7	.0000	.0000	.0000	.0000	.0003	.0012	.0039	.0073	.0098	.0212	.0407	.0703	7
	8	.0000	.0000	.0000	.0000	.0000	.0001	.0004	.0009	.0013	.0035	.0083	.0176	8
	9	.0000	.0000	.0000	.0000	.0000	.0000	.0000	.0001	.0001	.0003	.0008	.0020	9
10	0	.9044	.5987	.3487	.1969	.1074	.0563	.0282	.0173	.0135	.0060	.0025	.0010	0
	1	.0914	.3151	.3874	.3474	.2684	.1877	.1211	.0867	.0725	.0403	.0207	.0098	1
	2	.0042	.0746	.1937	.2759	.3020	.2816	.2335	.1951	.1757	.1209	.0763	.0439	2
	3	.0001	.0105	.0574	.1298	.2013	.2503	.2668	.2601	.2522	.2150	.1665	.1172	3
	4	.0000	.0010	.0112	.0401	.0881	.1460	.2001	.2276	.2377	.2508	.2384	.2051	4
	5	.0000	.0001	.0015	.0085	.0264	.0584	.1029	.1366	.1536	.2007	.2340	.2461	5
	6	.0000	.0000	.0001	.0012	.0055	.0162	.0368	.0569	.0689	.1115	.1596	.2051	6
	7	.0000	.0000	.0000	.0001	.0008	.0031	.0090	.0163	.0212	.0425	.0746	.1172	7
	8	.0000	.0000	.0000	.0000	.0001	.0004	.0014	.0030	.0043	.0106	.0229	.0439	8
	9	.0000	.0000	.0000	.0000	.0000	.0000	.0001	.0003	.0005	.0016	.0042	.0098	9
	10	.0000	.0000	.0000	.0000	.0000	.0000	.0000	.0000	.0000	.0001	.0003	.0010	10

Table A.3 was computed by the authors.

[a]For values of $p > .50$, enter table for $q = 1 - p$ in place of p and $N - r$ in place of r.

T-table   - 8.63

Table A.4
Critical values for *t* distributions

df	α for Two-Tailed Test					
	.20	.10	.05	.02	.01	.001
	α for One-Tailed Test					
	.10	.05	.025	.01	.005	.0005
1	3.078	6.314	12.706	31.821	63.657	639.619
2	1.886	2.920	4.303	6.965	9.925	31.599
3	1.638	2.353	3.182	4.541	5.841	12.924
4	1.533	2.132	2.776	3.747	4.604	8.610
5	1.476	2.015	2.571	3.365	4.032	6.869
6	1.440	1.943	2.447	3.143	3.707	5.959
7	1.415	1.895	2.365	2.998	3.499	5.408
8	1.397	1.860	2.306	2.896	3.355	5.041
9	1.383	1.833	2.262	2.821	3.250	4.781
10	1.372	1.812	2.228	2.764	3.169	4.587
11	1.363	1.796	2.201	2.718	3.106	4.437
12	1.356	1.782	2.179	2.681	3.055	4.318
13	1.350	1.771	2.160	2.650	3.012	4.221
14	1.345	1.761	2.145	2.624	2.977	4.140
15	1.341	1.753	2.131	2.602	2.947	4.073
16	1.337	1.746	2.120	2.583	2.921	4.015
17	1.333	1.740	2.110	2.567	2.898	3.965
18	1.330	1.734	2.101	2.552	2.878	3.922
19	1.328	1.729	2.093	2.539	2.861	3.883
20	1.325	1.725	2.086	2.528	2.845	3.850
21	1.323	1.721	2.080	2.518	2.831	3.819
22	1.321	1.717	2.074	2.508	2.819	3.792
23	1.319	1.714	2.069	2.500	2.807	3.768
24	1.318	1.711	2.064	2.492	2.797	3.745
25	1.316	1.708	2.060	2.485	2.787	3.725
26	1.315	1.706	2.056	2.479	2.779	3.707
27	1.314	1.703	2.052	2.473	2.771	3.690
28	1.313	1.701	2.048	2.467	2.763	3.674
29	1.311	1.699	2.045	2.462	2.756	3.659
30	1.310	1.697	2.042	2.457	2.750	3.646
35	1.306	1.690	2.030	2.438	2.724	3.591
40	1.303	1.684	2.021	2.423	2.704	3.551
45	1.301	1.679	2.014	2.412	2.690	3.520
50	1.299	1.676	2.009	2.403	2.678	3.496
55	1.297	1.673	2.004	2.396	2.668	3.476
60	1.296	1.671	2.000	2.390	2.660	3.460
70	1.294	1.667	1.994	2.381	2.648	3.435
80	1.292	1.664	1.990	2.374	2.639	3.416
90	1.291	1.662	1.987	2.368	2.632	3.402
120	1.289	1.658	1.980	2.358	2.617	3.373
∞	1.282	1.645	1.960	2.326	2.576	3.291

Table A.4 was computed by the authors.
Interpolation with respect to *df* should be done linearly in 1/*df*.

Table A.5
Critical values for Pearson's *r*

	Levels of Significance for a One-Tailed Test					Levels of Significance for a One-Tailed Test			
df	*.05*	*.025*	*.01*	*.005*	*df*	*.05*	*.025*	*.01*	*.005*
	Levels of Significance for a Two-Tailed Test					Levels of Significance for a Two-Tailed Test			
df	*.10*	*.05*	*.02*	*.01*	*df*	*.10*	*.05*	*.02*	*.01*
1	.9877	.9969	.9995	.9999	25	.323	.381	.445	.487
2	.900	.950	.980	.990	26	.317	.374	.437	.479
3	.805	.878	.934	.959	27	.311	.367	.430	.471
4	.729	.811	.882	.917	28	.306	.361	.423	.463
5	.669	.754	.833	.875	29	.301	.355	.416	.456
6	.621	.707	.789	.834	30	.296	.349	.409	.449
7	.582	.666	.750	.798	35	.275	.325	.381	.418
8	.549	.632	.715	.765	40	.257	.304	.358	.393
9	.521	.602	.685	.735	45	.243	.288	.338	.372
10	.497	.576	.658	.708	50	.231	.273	.322	.354
11	.476	.553	.634	.684	55	.220	.261	.307	.339
12	.458	.532	.612	.661	60	.211	.250	.295	.325
13	.441	.514	.592	.641	70	.195	.232	.274	.302
14	.426	.497	.574	.623	80	.183	.217	.257	.283
15	.412	.482	.558	.606	90	.173	.205	.242	.267
16	.400	.468	.543	.590	100	.164	.195	.230	.254
17	.389	.456	.529	.575	120	.150	.178	.210	.232
18	.378	.444	.516	.561	150	.134	.159	.189	.208
19	.369	.433	.503	.549	200	.116	.138	.164	.181
20	.360	.423	.492	.537	300	.095	.113	.134	.148
21	.352	.413	.482	.526	400	.082	.098	.116	.128
22	.344	.404	.472	.515	500	.073	.088	.104	.115
23	.337	.396	.462	.505	700	.062	.074	.088	.097
24	.330	.388	.453	.496	1000	.052	.062	.073	.081

Table A.5 was computed by the authors.
Interpolation with respect to *df* should be done linearly in 1/*df*.

Table A.6
Critical values for F distributions

Denominator df	α							Numerator df								
		1	2	3	4	5	6	7	8	9	10	11	12	14	16	20
1	.05	161	200	216	225	230	234	237	239	241	242	243	244	245	246	248
	.01	4052	4999	5403	5625	5764	5859	5928	5981	6022	6056	6083	6106	6143	6170	6209
2	.05	18.51	19.00	19.16	19.25	19.30	19.33	19.35	19.37	19.38	19.40	19.40	19.41	19.42	19.43	19.45
	.01	98.50	99.00	99.17	99.25	99.30	99.33	99.36	99.37	99.39	99.40	99.41	99.42	99.43	99.44	99.45
3	.05	10.13	9.55	9.28	9.12	9.01	8.94	8.89	8.85	8.81	8.79	8.76	8.74	8.71	8.69	8.66
	.01	34.12	30.82	29.46	28.71	28.24	27.91	27.67	27.49	27.35	27.23	27.13	27.05	26.92	26.83	26.69
4	.05	7.71	6.94	6.59	6.39	6.26	6.16	6.09	6.04	6.00	5.96	5.94	5.91	5.87	5.84	5.80
	.01	21.20	18.00	16.69	15.98	15.52	15.21	14.98	14.80	14.66	14.55	14.45	14.37	14.25	14.15	14.02
5	.05	6.61	5.79	5.41	5.19	5.05	4.95	4.88	4.82	4.77	4.74	4.70	4.68	4.64	4.60	4.56
	.01	16.26	13.27	12.06	11.39	10.97	10.67	10.46	10.29	10.16	10.05	9.96	9.89	9.77	9.68	9.55
6	.05	5.99	5.14	4.76	4.53	4.39	4.28	4.21	4.15	4.10	4.06	4.03	4.00	3.96	3.92	3.87
	.01	13.75	10.92	9.78	9.15	8.75	8.47	8.26	8.10	7.98	7.87	7.79	7.72	7.60	7.52	7.40
7	.05	5.59	4.74	4.35	4.12	3.97	3.87	3.79	3.73	3.68	3.64	3.60	3.57	3.53	3.49	3.44
	.01	12.25	9.55	8.45	7.85	7.46	7.19	6.99	6.84	6.72	6.62	6.54	6.47	6.36	6.28	6.16
8	.05	5.32	4.46	4.07	3.84	3.69	3.58	3.50	3.44	3.39	3.35	3.31	3.28	3.24	3.20	3.15
	.01	11.26	8.65	7.59	7.01	6.63	6.37	6.18	6.03	5.91	5.81	5.73	5.67	5.56	5.48	5.36
9	.05	5.12	4.26	3.86	3.63	3.48	3.37	3.29	3.23	3.18	3.14	3.10	3.07	3.03	2.99	2.94
	.01	10.56	8.02	6.99	6.42	6.06	5.80	5.61	5.47	5.35	5.26	5.18	5.11	5.01	4.92	4.81
10	.05	4.96	4.10	3.71	3.48	3.33	3.22	3.14	3.07	3.02	2.98	2.94	2.91	2.86	2.83	2.77
	.01	10.04	7.56	6.55	5.99	5.64	5.39	5.20	5.06	4.94	4.85	4.77	4.71	4.60	4.52	4.41
11	.05	4.84	3.98	3.59	3.36	3.20	3.09	3.01	2.95	2.90	2.85	2.82	2.79	2.74	2.70	2.65
	.01	9.65	7.21	6.22	5.67	5.32	5.07	4.89	4.74	4.63	4.54	4.46	4.40	4.29	4.21	4.10
12	.05	4.75	3.89	3.49	3.26	3.11	3.00	2.91	2.85	2.80	2.75	2.72	2.69	2.64	2.60	2.54
	.01	9.33	6.93	5.95	5.41	5.06	4.82	4.64	4.50	4.39	4.30	4.22	4.16	4.05	3.97	3.86
13	.05	4.67	3.81	3.41	3.18	3.03	2.92	2.83	2.77	2.71	2.67	2.63	2.60	2.55	2.51	2.46
	.01	9.07	6.70	5.74	5.21	4.86	4.62	4.44	4.30	4.19	4.10	4.02	3.96	3.86	3.78	3.66
14	.05	4.60	3.74	3.34	3.11	2.96	2.85	2.76	2.70	2.65	2.60	2.57	2.53	2.48	2.44	2.39
	.01	8.86	6.51	5.56	5.04	4.69	4.46	4.28	4.14	4.03	3.94	3.86	3.80	3.70	3.62	3.51
15	.05	4.54	3.68	3.29	3.06	2.90	2.79	2.71	2.64	2.59	2.54	2.51	2.48	2.42	2.38	2.33
	.01	8.68	6.36	5.42	4.89	4.56	4.32	4.14	4.00	3.89	3.80	3.73	3.67	3.56	3.49	3.37
16	.05	4.49	3.63	3.24	3.01	2.85	2.74	2.66	2.59	2.54	2.49	2.46	2.42	2.37	2.33	2.28
	.01	8.53	6.23	5.29	4.77	4.44	4.20	4.03	3.89	3.78	3.69	3.62	3.55	3.45	3.37	3.26
17	.05	4.45	3.59	3.20	2.96	2.81	2.70	2.61	2.55	2.49	2.45	2.41	2.38	2.33	2.29	2.23
	.01	8.40	6.11	5.18	4.67	4.34	4.10	3.93	3.79	3.68	3.59	3.52	3.46	3.35	3.27	3.16
18	.05	4.41	3.55	3.16	2.93	2.77	2.66	2.58	2.51	2.46	2.41	2.37	2.34	2.29	2.25	2.19
	.01	8.29	6.01	5.09	4.58	4.25	4.01	3.84	3.71	3.60	3.51	3.43	3.37	3.27	3.19	3.08
19	.05	4.38	3.52	3.13	2.90	2.74	2.63	2.54	2.48	2.42	2.38	2.34	2.31	2.26	2.21	2.16
	.01	8.18	5.93	5.01	4.50	4.17	3.94	3.77	3.63	3.52	3.43	3.36	3.30	3.19	3.12	3.00
20	.05	4.35	3.49	3.10	2.87	2.71	2.60	2.51	2.45	2.39	2.35	2.31	2.28	2.22	2.18	2.12
	.01	8.10	5.85	4.94	4.43	4.10	3.87	3.70	3.56	3.46	3.37	3.29	3.23	3.13	3.05	2.94
21	.05	4.32	3.47	3.07	2.84	2.68	2.57	2.49	2.42	2.37	2.32	2.28	2.25	2.20	2.16	2.10
	.01	8.02	5.78	4.87	4.37	4.04	3.81	3.64	3.51	3.40	3.31	3.24	3.17	3.07	2.99	2.88
22	.05	4.30	3.44	3.05	2.82	2.66	2.55	2.46	2.40	2.34	2.30	2.26	2.23	2.17	2.13	2.07
	.01	7.95	5.72	4.82	4.31	3.99	3.76	3.59	3.45	3.35	3.26	3.18	3.12	3.02	2.94	2.83
23	.05	4.28	3.42	3.03	2.80	2.64	2.53	2.44	2.37	2.32	2.27	2.24	2.20	2.15	2.11	2.05
	.01	7.88	5.66	4.76	4.26	3.94	3.71	3.54	3.41	3.30	3.21	3.14	3.07	2.97	2.89	2.78
24	.05	4.26	3.40	3.01	2.78	2.62	2.51	2.42	2.36	2.30	2.25	2.22	2.18	2.13	2.09	2.03
	.01	7.82	5.61	4.72	4.22	3.90	3.67	3.50	3.36	3.26	3.17	3.09	3.03	2.93	2.85	2.74
25	.05	4.24	3.39	2.99	2.76	2.60	2.49	2.40	2.34	2.28	2.24	2.20	2.16	2.11	2.07	2.01
	.01	7.77	5.57	4.68	4.18	3.85	3.63	3.46	3.32	3.22	3.13	3.06	2.99	2.89	2.81	2.70

Table A.6 was computed by the authors.
Interpolation with respect to df should be done linearly in $1/df$.

(continued)

Table A.6 (continued)

Denominator df	α	Numerator df 1	2	3	4	5	6	7	8	9	10	11	12	14	16	20
26	.05	4.23	3.37	2.98	2.74	2.59	2.47	2.39	2.32	2.27	2.22	2.18	2.15	2.09	2.05	1.99
	.01	7.72	5.53	4.64	4.14	3.82	3.59	3.42	3.29	3.18	3.09	3.02	2.96	2.86	2.78	2.66
27	.05	4.21	3.35	2.96	2.73	2.57	2.46	2.37	2.31	2.25	2.20	2.17	2.13	2.08	2.04	1.97
	.01	7.68	5.49	4.60	4.11	3.78	3.56	3.39	3.26	3.15	3.06	2.99	2.93	2.82	2.75	2.63
28	.05	4.20	3.34	2.95	2.71	2.56	2.45	2.36	2.29	2.24	2.19	2.15	2.12	2.06	2.02	1.96
	.01	7.64	5.45	4.57	4.07	3.75	3.53	3.36	3.23	3.12	3.03	2.96	2.90	2.79	2.72	2.60
29	.05	4.18	3.33	2.93	2.70	2.55	2.43	2.35	2.28	2.22	2.18	2.14	2.10	2.05	2.01	1.94
	.01	7.60	5.42	4.54	4.04	3.73	3.50	3.33	3.20	3.09	3.00	2.93	2.87	2.77	2.69	2.57
30	.05	4.17	3.32	2.92	2.69	2.53	2.42	2.33	2.27	2.21	2.16	2.13	2.09	2.04	1.99	1.93
	.01	7.56	5.39	4.51	4.02	3.70	3.47	3.30	3.17	3.07	2.98	2.91	2.84	2.74	2.66	2.55
32	.05	4.15	3.29	2.90	2.67	2.51	2.40	2.31	2.24	2.19	2.14	2.10	2.07	2.01	1.97	1.91
	.01	7.50	5.34	4.46	3.97	3.65	3.43	3.26	3.13	3.02	2.93	2.86	2.80	2.70	2.62	2.50
34	.05	4.13	3.28	2.88	2.65	2.49	2.38	2.29	2.23	2.17	2.12	2.08	2.05	1.99	1.95	1.89
	.01	7.44	5.29	4.42	3.93	3.61	3.39	3.22	3.09	2.98	2.89	2.82	2.76	2.66	2.58	2.46
36	.05	4.11	3.26	2.87	2.63	2.48	2.36	2.28	2.21	2.15	2.11	2.07	2.03	1.98	1.93	1.87
	.01	7.40	5.25	4.38	3.89	3.57	3.35	3.18	3.05	2.95	2.86	2.79	2.72	2.62	2.54	2.43
38	.05	4.10	3.24	2.85	2.62	2.46	2.35	2.26	2.19	2.14	2.09	2.05	2.02	1.96	1.92	1.85
	.01	7.35	5.21	4.34	3.86	3.54	3.32	3.15	3.02	2.92	2.83	2.75	2.69	2.59	2.51	2.40
40	.05	4.08	3.23	2.84	2.61	2.45	2.34	2.25	2.18	2.12	2.08	2.04	2.00	1.95	1.90	1.84
	.01	7.31	5.18	4.31	3.83	3.51	3.29	3.12	2.99	2.89	2.80	2.73	2.66	2.56	2.48	2.37
42	.05	4.07	3.22	2.83	2.59	2.44	2.32	2.24	2.17	2.11	2.06	2.03	1.99	1.94	1.89	1.83
	.01	7.28	5.15	4.29	3.80	3.49	3.27	3.10	2.97	2.86	2.78	2.70	2.64	2.54	2.46	2.34
44	.05	4.06	3.21	2.82	2.58	2.43	2.31	2.23	2.16	2.10	2.05	2.01	1.98	1.92	1.88	1.81
	.01	7.25	5.12	4.26	3.78	3.47	3.24	3.08	2.95	2.84	2.75	2.68	2.62	2.52	2.44	2.32
46	.05	4.05	3.20	2.81	2.57	2.42	2.30	2.22	2.15	2.09	2.04	2.00	1.97	1.91	1.87	1.80
	.01	7.22	5.10	4.24	3.76	3.44	3.22	3.06	2.93	2.82	2.73	2.66	2.60	2.50	2.42	2.30
48	.05	4.04	3.19	2.80	2.57	2.41	2.29	2.21	2.14	2.08	2.03	1.99	1.96	1.90	1.86	1.79
	.01	7.19	5.08	4.22	3.74	3.43	3.20	3.04	2.91	2.80	2.71	2.64	2.58	2.48	2.40	2.28
50	.05	4.03	3.18	2.79	2.56	2.40	2.29	2.20	2.13	2.07	2.03	1.99	1.95	1.89	1.85	1.78
	.01	7.17	5.06	4.20	3.72	3.41	3.19	3.02	2.89	2.78	2.70	2.63	2.56	2.46	2.38	2.27
55	.05	4.02	3.16	2.77	2.54	2.38	2.27	2.18	2.11	2.06	2.01	1.97	1.93	1.88	1.83	1.76
	.01	7.12	5.01	4.16	3.68	3.37	3.15	2.98	2.85	2.75	2.66	2.59	2.53	2.42	2.34	2.23
60	.05	4.00	3.15	2.76	2.53	2.37	2.25	2.17	2.10	2.04	1.99	1.95	1.92	1.86	1.82	1.75
	.01	7.08	4.98	4.13	3.65	3.34	3.12	2.95	2.82	2.72	2.63	2.56	2.50	2.39	2.31	2.20
65	.05	3.99	3.14	2.75	2.51	2.36	2.24	2.15	2.08	2.03	1.98	1.94	1.90	1.85	1.80	1.73
	.01	7.04	4.95	4.10	3.62	3.31	3.09	2.93	2.80	2.69	2.61	2.53	2.47	2.37	2.29	2.17
70	.05	3.98	3.13	2.74	2.50	2.35	2.23	2.14	2.07	2.02	1.97	1.93	1.89	1.84	1.79	1.72
	.01	7.01	4.92	4.07	3.60	3.29	3.07	2.91	2.78	2.67	2.59	2.51	2.45	2.35	2.27	2.15
80	.05	3.96	3.11	2.72	2.49	2.33	2.21	2.13	2.06	2.00	1.95	1.91	1.88	1.82	1.77	1.70
	.01	6.96	4.88	4.04	3.56	3.26	3.04	2.87	2.74	2.64	2.55	2.48	2.42	2.31	2.23	2.12
100	.05	3.94	3.09	2.70	2.46	2.31	2.19	2.10	2.03	1.97	1.93	1.89	1.85	1.79	1.75	1.68
	.01	6.90	4.82	3.98	3.51	3.21	2.99	2.82	2.69	2.59	2.50	2.43	2.37	2.27	2.19	2.07
125	.05	3.92	3.07	2.68	2.44	2.29	2.17	2.08	2.01	1.96	1.91	1.87	1.83	1.77	1.73	1.66
	.01	6.84	4.78	3.94	3.47	3.17	2.95	2.79	2.66	2.55	2.47	2.39	2.33	2.23	2.15	2.03
150	.05	3.90	3.06	2.66	2.43	2.27	2.16	2.07	2.00	1.94	1.89	1.85	1.82	1.76	1.71	1.64
	.01	6.81	4.75	3.91	3.45	3.14	2.92	2.76	2.63	2.53	2.44	2.37	2.31	2.20	2.12	2.00
200	.05	3.89	3.04	2.65	2.42	2.26	2.14	2.06	1.98	1.93	1.88	1.84	1.80	1.74	1.69	1.62
	.01	6.76	4.71	3.88	3.41	3.11	2.89	2.73	2.60	2.50	2.41	2.34	2.27	2.17	2.09	1.97
400	.05	3.86	3.02	2.63	2.39	2.24	2.12	2.03	1.96	1.90	1.85	1.81	1.78	1.72	1.67	1.60
	.01	6.70	4.66	3.83	3.37	3.06	2.85	2.68	2.56	2.45	2.37	2.29	2.23	2.13	2.05	1.92
1000	.05	3.85	3.00	2.61	2.38	2.22	2.11	2.02	1.95	1.89	1.84	1.80	1.76	1.70	1.65	1.58
	.01	6.66	4.63	3.80	3.34	3.04	2.82	2.66	2.53	2.43	2.34	2.27	2.20	2.10	2.02	1.90
∞	.05	3.84	3.00	2.60	2.37	2.21	2.10	2.01	1.94	1.88	1.83	1.79	1.75	1.69	1.64	1.57
	.01	6.63	4.61	3.78	3.32	3.02	2.80	2.64	2.51	2.41	2.32	2.25	2.18	2.08	2.00	1.88

Table A.7
Critical values for Studentized Range distributions

df_w	α	2	3	4	5	6	7	8	9	10
					$J = Number\ of\ Groups$					
5	.05	3.64	4.60	5.22	5.67	6.03	6.33	6.58	6.80	6.99
	.01	5.70	6.98	7.80	8.42	8.91	9.32	9.67	9.97	10.24
6	.05	3.46	4.34	4.90	5.31	5.63	5.89	6.12	6.32	6.49
	.01	5.24	6.33	7.03	7.56	7.97	8.32	8.61	8.87	9.10
7	.05	3.34	4.16	4.68	5.06	5.36	5.61	5.82	6.00	6.16
	.01	4.95	5.92	6.54	7.01	7.37	7.68	7.94	8.17	8.37
8	.05	3.26	4.04	4.53	4.89	5.17	5.40	5.60	5.77	5.92
	.01	4.75	5.64	6.20	6.62	6.96	7.24	7.47	7.68	7.86
9	.05	3.20	3.95	4.42	4.76	5.02	5.24	5.43	5.60	5.74
	.01	4.60	5.43	5.96	6.35	6.66	6.91	7.13	7.33	7.49
10	.05	3.15	3.88	4.33	4.65	4.91	5.12	5.30	5.46	5.60
	.01	4.48	5.27	5.77	6.14	6.43	6.67	6.87	7.05	7.21
11	.05	3.11	3.82	4.26	4.57	4.82	5.03	5.20	5.35	5.49
	.01	4.39	5.15	5.62	5.97	6.25	6.48	6.67	6.84	6.99
12	.05	3.08	3.77	4.20	4.51	4.75	4.95	5.12	5.27	5.40
	.01	4.32	5.05	5.50	5.84	6.10	6.32	6.51	6.67	6.81
13	.05	3.06	3.73	4.15	4.45	4.69	4.88	5.05	5.19	5.32
	.01	4.26	4.96	5.40	5.73	5.98	6.19	6.37	6.53	6.67
14	.05	3.03	3.70	4.11	4.41	4.64	4.83	4.99	5.13	5.25
	.01	4.21	4.89	5.32	5.63	5.88	6.08	6.26	6.41	6.54
15	.05	3.01	3.67	4.08	4.37	4.60	4.78	4.94	5.08	5.20
	.01	4.17	4.84	5.25	5.56	5.80	5.99	6.16	6.31	6.44
16	.05	3.00	3.65	4.05	4.33	4.56	4.74	4.90	5.03	5.15
	.01	4.13	4.79	5.19	5.49	5.72	5.92	6.08	6.22	6.35
17	.05	2.98	3.63	4.02	4.30	4.52	4.71	4.86	4.99	5.11
	.01	4.10	4.74	5.14	5.43	5.66	5.85	6.01	6.15	6.27
18	.05	2.97	3.61	4.00	4.28	4.49	4.67	4.82	4.96	5.07
	.01	4.07	4.70	5.09	5.38	5.60	5.79	5.94	6.08	6.20
19	.05	2.96	3.59	3.98	4.25	4.47	4.65	4.79	4.92	5.04
	.01	4.05	4.67	5.05	5.33	5.55	5.73	5.89	6.02	6.14
20	.05	2.95	3.58	3.96	4.23	4.45	4.62	4.77	4.90	5.01
	.01	4.02	4.64	5.02	5.29	5.51	5.69	5.84	5.97	6.09
24	.05	2.92	3.53	3.90	4.17	4.37	4.54	4.68	4.81	4.92
	.01	3.96	4.55	4.91	5.17	5.37	5.54	5.69	5.81	5.92
30	.05	2.89	3.49	3.84	4.10	4.30	4.46	4.60	4.72	4.83
	.01	3.89	4.45	4.80	5.05	5.24	5.40	5.54	5.65	5.76
40	.05	2.86	3.44	3.79	4.04	4.23	4.39	4.52	4.63	4.74
	.01	3.82	4.37	4.70	4.93	5.11	5.26	5.39	5.50	5.60
60	.05	2.83	3.40	3.74	3.98	4.16	4.31	4.44	4.55	4.65
	.01	3.76	4.28	4.59	4.82	4.99	5.13	5.25	5.36	5.45
120	.05	2.80	3.36	3.69	3.92	4.10	4.24	4.36	4.48	4.56
	.01	3.70	4.20	4.50	4.71	4.87	5.01	5.12	5.21	5.30
∞	.05	2.77	3.31	3.63	3.86	4.03	4.17	4.29	4.39	4.47
	.01	3.64	4.12	4.40	4.60	4.76	4.88	4.99	5.08	5.16

Source: Pearson and Hartley (1966).
Interpolation with respect to df should be done linearly in $1/df$.

Table A.8
Critical values for the Dunn Multiple Comparison Procedure

Denominator df	α	\multicolumn{17}{c}{Number of Comparisons (C)}																
		2	3	4	5	6	7	8	9	10	11	12	13	14	16	18	20	100
5	.05	3.16	3.53	3.81	4.03	4.22	4.38	4.53	4.66	4.77	4.88	4.98	5.08	5.16	5.33	5.47	5.60	7.98
	.01	4.77	5.25	5.60	5.89	6.14	6.35	6.54	6.71	6.87	7.01	7.15	7.27	7.39	7.60	7.80	7.98	11.18
7	.05	2.84	3.13	3.34	3.50	3.64	3.75	3.86	3.95	4.03	4.10	4.17	4.24	4.30	4.41	4.51	4.59	6.08
	.01	4.03	4.36	4.59	4.79	4.94	5.08	5.20	5.31	5.41	5.50	5.58	5.66	5.73	5.86	5.98	6.08	7.88
10	.05	2.63	2.87	3.04	3.17	3.28	3.37	3.45	3.52	3.58	3.64	3.69	3.74	3.79	3.87	3.94	4.00	5.05
	.01	3.58	3.83	4.00	4.14	4.26	4.36	4.44	4.52	4.59	4.65	4.71	4.76	4.81	4.90	4.98	5.05	6.21
12	.05	2.56	2.78	2.93	3.05	3.15	3.24	3.31	3.37	3.43	3.48	3.53	3.57	3.61	3.68	3.75	3.81	4.72
	.01	3.43	3.65	3.81	3.93	4.03	4.12	4.19	4.26	4.32	4.37	4.42	4.47	4.51	4.59	4.66	4.72	5.69
15	.05	2.49	2.69	2.84	2.95	3.04	3.11	3.18	3.23	3.29	3.33	3.37	3.41	3.45	3.52	3.57	3.62	4.42
	.01	3.29	3.48	3.62	3.73	3.82	3.90	3.96	4.02	4.07	4.12	4.16	4.20	4.24	4.31	4.36	4.42	5.24
16	.05	2.47	2.67	2.81	2.92	3.01	3.08	3.15	3.20	3.25	3.30	3.34	3.38	3.41	3.47	3.53	3.58	4.35
	.01	3.25	3.44	3.58	3.69	3.77	3.85	3.91	3.96	4.01	4.06	4.10	4.14	4.18	4.24	4.30	4.35	5.13
17	.05	2.46	2.65	2.79	2.90	2.98	3.06	3.12	3.17	3.22	3.27	3.31	3.34	3.38	3.44	3.49	3.54	4.29
	.01	3.22	3.41	3.54	3.65	3.73	3.80	3.86	3.92	3.97	4.01	4.05	4.09	4.12	4.18	4.24	4.29	5.04
18	.05	2.45	2.64	2.77	2.88	2.96	3.03	3.09	3.15	3.20	3.24	3.28	3.32	3.35	3.41	3.46	3.51	4.23
	.01	3.20	3.38	3.51	3.61	3.69	3.76	3.82	3.87	3.92	3.96	4.00	4.04	4.07	4.13	4.19	4.23	4.97
19	.05	2.43	2.63	2.76	2.86	2.94	3.01	3.07	3.13	3.17	3.22	3.25	3.29	3.32	3.38	3.43	3.48	4.19
	.01	3.17	3.35	3.48	3.58	3.66	3.73	3.79	3.84	3.88	3.93	3.96	4.00	4.03	4.09	4.14	4.19	4.90
20	.05	2.42	2.61	2.74	2.85	2.93	3.00	3.06	3.11	3.15	3.20	3.23	3.27	3.30	3.36	3.41	3.46	4.15
	.01	3.15	3.33	3.46	3.55	3.63	3.70	3.75	3.80	3.85	3.89	3.93	3.96	3.99	4.05	4.10	4.15	4.84
21	.05	2.41	2.60	2.73	2.83	2.91	2.98	3.04	3.09	3.14	3.18	3.21	3.25	3.28	3.34	3.39	3.43	4.11
	.01	3.14	3.31	3.43	3.53	3.60	3.67	3.73	3.78	3.82	3.86	3.90	3.93	3.96	4.02	4.07	4.11	4.78
22	.05	2.41	2.59	2.72	2.82	2.90	2.97	3.02	3.07	3.12	3.16	3.20	3.23	3.26	3.32	3.37	3.41	4.08
	.01	3.12	3.29	3.41	3.50	3.58	3.64	3.70	3.75	3.79	3.83	3.87	3.90	3.93	3.99	4.03	4.08	4.74
23	.05	2.40	2.58	2.71	2.81	2.89	2.95	3.01	3.06	3.10	3.14	3.18	3.21	3.25	3.30	3.35	3.39	4.05
	.01	3.10	3.27	3.39	3.48	3.56	3.62	3.68	3.72	3.77	3.81	3.84	3.87	3.90	3.96	4.01	4.05	4.69
24	.05	2.39	2.57	2.70	2.80	2.88	2.94	3.00	3.05	3.09	3.13	3.17	3.20	3.23	3.28	3.33	3.38	4.02
	.01	3.09	3.26	3.38	3.47	3.54	3.60	3.66	3.70	3.75	3.78	3.82	3.85	3.88	3.93	3.98	4.02	4.65
25	.05	2.38	2.57	2.69	2.79	2.86	2.93	2.99	3.03	3.08	3.12	3.15	3.19	3.22	3.27	3.32	3.36	4.00
	.01	3.08	3.24	3.36	3.45	3.52	3.58	3.64	3.68	3.73	3.76	3.80	3.83	3.86	3.91	3.96	4.00	4.62
26	.05	2.38	2.56	2.68	2.78	2.86	2.92	2.98	3.02	3.07	3.11	3.14	3.17	3.20	3.26	3.30	3.35	3.97
	.01	3.07	3.23	3.35	3.43	3.51	3.57	3.62	3.67	3.71	3.74	3.78	3.81	3.84	3.89	3.93	3.97	4.59
27	.05	2.37	2.55	2.68	2.77	2.85	2.91	2.97	3.01	3.06	3.10	3.13	3.16	3.19	3.25	3.29	3.33	3.95
	.01	3.06	3.22	3.33	3.42	3.49	3.55	3.60	3.65	3.69	3.73	3.76	3.79	3.82	3.87	3.91	3.95	4.56
28	.05	2.37	2.55	2.67	2.76	2.84	2.90	2.96	3.00	3.05	3.09	3.12	3.15	3.18	3.23	3.28	3.32	3.94
	.01	3.05	3.21	3.32	3.41	3.48	3.54	3.59	3.63	3.67	3.71	3.74	3.77	3.80	3.85	3.90	3.94	4.53
29	.05	2.36	2.54	2.66	2.76	2.83	2.89	2.95	3.00	3.04	3.08	3.11	3.14	3.17	3.22	3.27	3.31	3.92
	.01	3.04	3.20	3.31	3.40	3.47	3.52	3.58	3.62	3.66	3.70	3.73	3.76	3.79	3.84	3.88	3.92	4.51
30	.05	2.36	2.54	2.66	2.75	2.82	2.89	2.94	2.99	3.03	3.07	3.10	3.13	3.16	3.21	3.26	3.30	3.90
	.01	3.03	3.19	3.30	3.39	3.45	3.51	3.56	3.61	3.65	3.68	3.71	3.74	3.77	3.82	3.86	3.90	4.48
40	.05	2.33	2.50	2.62	2.70	2.78	2.84	2.89	2.93	2.97	3.01	3.04	3.07	3.10	3.15	3.19	3.23	3.79
	.01	2.97	3.12	3.23	3.31	3.37	3.43	3.47	3.51	3.55	3.58	3.61	3.64	3.67	3.71	3.75	3.79	4.32
50	.05	2.31	2.48	2.59	2.68	2.75	2.81	2.85	2.90	2.94	2.97	3.00	3.03	3.06	3.11	3.15	3.18	3.72
	.01	2.94	3.08	3.18	3.26	3.32	3.38	3.42	3.46	3.50	3.53	3.56	3.58	3.61	3.65	3.69	3.72	4.23
60	.05	2.30	2.46	2.58	2.66	2.73	2.79	2.83	2.88	2.91	2.95	2.98	3.01	3.03	3.08	3.12	3.16	3.68
	.01	2.91	3.06	3.16	3.23	3.29	3.34	3.39	3.43	3.46	3.49	3.52	3.54	3.57	3.61	3.65	3.68	4.17
70	.05	2.29	2.45	2.56	2.65	2.72	2.77	2.82	2.86	2.90	2.93	2.96	2.99	3.02	3.06	3.10	3.14	3.65
	.01	2.90	3.04	3.14	3.21	3.27	3.32	3.36	3.40	3.44	3.47	3.49	3.52	3.54	3.58	3.62	3.65	4.13
80	.05	2.28	2.45	2.56	2.64	2.71	2.76	2.81	2.85	2.89	2.92	2.95	2.98	3.00	3.05	3.09	3.12	3.63
	.01	2.89	3.03	3.12	3.20	3.25	3.30	3.35	3.38	3.42	3.45	3.47	3.50	3.52	3.56	3.60	3.63	4.10
100	.05	2.28	2.43	2.54	2.63	2.69	2.75	2.79	2.83	2.87	2.90	2.93	2.96	2.98	3.03	3.07	3.10	3.60
	.01	2.87	3.01	3.10	3.17	3.23	3.28	3.32	3.36	3.39	3.42	3.45	3.47	3.49	3.53	3.57	3.60	4.05
150	.05	2.26	2.42	2.53	2.61	2.67	2.73	2.77	2.81	2.85	2.88	2.91	2.94	2.96	3.00	3.04	3.08	3.56
	.01	2.85	2.98	3.08	3.15	3.20	3.25	3.29	3.33	3.36	3.38	3.41	3.43	3.46	3.49	3.53	3.56	4.00
400	.05	2.25	2.40	2.51	2.59	2.65	2.70	2.75	2.79	2.82	2.85	2.88	2.91	2.93	2.97	3.01	3.04	3.51
	.01	2.82	2.95	3.04	3.11	3.17	3.21	3.25	3.28	3.32	3.34	3.37	3.39	3.41	3.45	3.48	3.51	3.93
∞	.05	2.24	2.39	2.50	2.58	2.64	2.69	2.73	2.77	2.81	2.84	2.87	2.89	2.91	2.96	2.99	3.02	3.48
	.01	2.81	2.94	3.02	3.09	3.14	3.19	3.23	3.26	3.29	3.32	3.34	3.36	3.38	3.42	3.45	3.48	3.89

Table A.8 was computed by the authors.

Interpolation with respect to *df* should be done linearly in $1/df$; with respect to *C*, it should be done linearly in log *C*.

Table A.9
Critical values for χ^2 distributions

df	α for One-Tailed Test			
	.10	.05	.01	.001
1	2.71	3.84	6.63	10.83
2	4.61	5.99	9.21	13.82
3	6.25	7.81	11.34	16.27
4	7.78	9.49	13.28	18.47
5	9.24	11.07	15.09	20.52
6	10.64	12.59	16.81	22.46
7	12.02	14.07	18.48	24.32
8	13.36	15.51	20.09	26.12
9	14.68	16.92	21.67	27.88
10	15.99	18.31	23.21	29.59
11	17.28	19.68	24.72	31.26
12	18.55	21.03	26.22	32.91
13	19.81	22.36	27.69	34.53
14	21.06	23.68	29.14	36.12
15	22.31	25.00	30.58	37.70
16	23.54	26.30	32.00	39.25
17	24.77	27.59	33.41	40.79
18	25.99	28.87	34.81	42.31
19	27.20	30.14	36.19	43.82
20	28.41	31.41	37.57	45.31
21	29.62	32.67	38.93	46.80
22	30.81	33.92	40.29	48.27
23	32.01	35.17	41.64	49.73
24	33.20	36.42	42.98	51.18
25	34.38	37.65	44.31	52.62
26	35.56	38.89	45.64	54.05
27	36.74	40.11	46.96	55.48
28	37.92	41.34	48.28	56.89
29	39.09	42.56	49.59	58.30
30	40.26	43.77	50.89	59.70
40	51.81	55.76	63.69	73.40
50	63.17	67.50	76.15	86.66
60	74.40	79.08	88.38	99.61
70	85.53	90.53	100.43	112.32

Table A.9 was computed by the authors.
Interpolation with respect to *df* should be done linearly in 1/*df*.

Table A.10
Critical values for the Mann-Whitney U[a]

n_2										n_1										
	1	*2*	*3*	*4*	*5*	*6*	*7*	*8*	*9*	*10*	*11*	*12*	*13*	*14*	*15*	*16*	*17*	*18*	*19*	*20*
1	—[b]	—	—	—	—	—	—	—	—	—	—	—	—	—	—	—	—	—	0	0
	—	—	—	—	—	—	—	—	—	—	—	—	—	—	—	—	—	—	—	—
2	—	—	—	—	0	0	0	1	1	1	1	2	2	2	3	3	3	4	4	4
	—	—	—	—	—	—	—	**0**	**0**	**0**	**0**	**1**	**1**	**1**	**1**	**1**	**2**	**2**	**2**	**2**
3	—	—	0	0	1	2	2	3	3	4	5	5	6	7	7	8	9	9	10	11
	—	—	—	—	**0**	**1**	**1**	**2**	**2**	**3**	**3**	**4**	**4**	**5**	**5**	**6**	**6**	**7**	**7**	**8**
4	—	—	0	1	2	3	4	5	6	7	8	9	10	11	12	14	15	16	17	18
	—	—	—	**0**	**1**	**2**	**3**	**4**	**4**	**5**	**6**	**7**	**8**	**9**	**10**	**11**	**11**	**12**	**13**	**13**
5	—	0	1	2	4	5	6	8	9	11	12	13	15	16	18	19	20	22	23	25
	—	—	**0**	**1**	**2**	**3**	**5**	**6**	**7**	**8**	**9**	**11**	**12**	**13**	**14**	**15**	**17**	**18**	**19**	**20**
6	—	0	2	3	5	7	8	10	12	14	16	17	19	21	23	25	26	28	30	32
	—	—	**1**	**2**	**3**	**5**	**6**	**8**	**10**	**11**	**13**	**14**	**16**	**17**	**19**	**21**	**22**	**24**	**25**	**27**
7	—	0	2	4	6	8	11	13	15	17	19	21	24	26	28	30	33	35	37	39
	—	—	**1**	**3**	**5**	**6**	**8**	**10**	**12**	**14**	**16**	**18**	**20**	**22**	**24**	**26**	**28**	**30**	**32**	**34**
8	—	1	3	5	8	10	13	15	18	20	23	26	28	31	33	36	39	41	44	47
	—	**0**	**2**	**4**	**6**	**8**	**10**	**13**	**15**	**17**	**19**	**22**	**24**	**26**	**29**	**31**	**34**	**36**	**38**	**41**
9	—	1	3	6	9	12	15	18	21	24	27	30	33	36	39	42	45	48	51	54
	—	**0**	**2**	**4**	**7**	**10**	**12**	**15**	**17**	**20**	**23**	**26**	**28**	**31**	**34**	**37**	**39**	**42**	**45**	**48**
10	—	1	4	7	11	14	17	20	24	27	31	34	37	41	44	48	51	55	58	62
	—	**0**	**3**	**5**	**8**	**11**	**14**	**17**	**20**	**23**	**26**	**29**	**33**	**36**	**39**	**42**	**45**	**48**	**52**	**55**
11	—	1	5	8	12	16	19	23	27	31	34	38	42	46	50	54	57	61	65	69
	—	**0**	**3**	**6**	**9**	**13**	**16**	**19**	**23**	**26**	**30**	**33**	**37**	**40**	**44**	**47**	**51**	**55**	**58**	**62**
12	—	2	5	9	13	17	21	26	30	34	38	42	47	51	55	60	64	68	72	77
	—	**1**	**4**	**7**	**11**	**14**	**18**	**22**	**26**	**29**	**33**	**37**	**41**	**45**	**49**	**53**	**57**	**61**	**65**	**69**
13	—	2	6	10	15	19	24	28	33	37	42	47	51	56	61	65	70	75	80	84
	—	**1**	**4**	**8**	**12**	**16**	**20**	**24**	**28**	**33**	**37**	**41**	**45**	**50**	**54**	**59**	**63**	**67**	**72**	**76**
14	—	2	7	11	16	21	26	31	36	41	46	51	56	61	66	71	77	82	87	92
	—	**1**	**5**	**9**	**13**	**17**	**22**	**26**	**31**	**36**	**40**	**45**	**50**	**55**	**59**	**64**	**67**	**74**	**78**	**83**
15	—	3	7	12	18	23	28	33	39	44	50	55	61	66	72	77	83	88	94	100
	—	**1**	**5**	**10**	**14**	**19**	**24**	**29**	**34**	**39**	**44**	**49**	**54**	**59**	**64**	**70**	**75**	**80**	**85**	**90**
16	—	3	8	14	19	25	30	36	42	48	54	60	65	71	77	83	89	95	101	107
	—	**1**	**6**	**11**	**15**	**21**	**26**	**31**	**37**	**42**	**47**	**53**	**59**	**64**	**70**	**75**	**81**	**86**	**92**	**98**
17	—	3	9	15	20	26	33	39	45	51	57	64	70	77	83	89	96	102	109	115
	—	**2**	**6**	**11**	**17**	**22**	**28**	**34**	**39**	**45**	**51**	**57**	**63**	**67**	**75**	**81**	**87**	**93**	**99**	**105**
18	—	4	9	16	22	28	35	41	48	55	61	68	75	82	88	95	102	109	116	123
	—	**2**	**7**	**12**	**18**	**24**	**30**	**36**	**42**	**48**	**55**	**61**	**67**	**74**	**80**	**86**	**93**	**99**	**106**	**112**
19	0	4	10	17	23	30	37	44	51	58	65	72	80	87	94	101	109	116	123	130
	—	**2**	**7**	**13**	**19**	**25**	**32**	**38**	**45**	**52**	**58**	**65**	**72**	**78**	**85**	**92**	**99**	**106**	**113**	**119**
20	0	4	11	18	25	32	39	47	54	62	69	77	84	92	100	107	115	123	130	138
	—	**2**	**8**	**13**	**20**	**27**	**34**	**41**	**48**	**55**	**62**	**69**	**76**	**83**	**90**	**98**	**105**	**112**	**119**	**127**

Source: Kirk (1984).

[a]For a one-tailed test at $\alpha = .05$ (light type) and $\alpha = .025$ (bold type) and for a two-tailed test at $\alpha = .10$ (light type) and $\alpha = .05$ (bold type).
[b]Dashes in the body of the table indicate that no decision is possible at the given α.

(continued)

Table A.10 (continued)

	n_1																			
n_2	1	2	3	4	5	6	7	8	9	10	11	12	13	14	15	16	17	18	19	20
1	—[b]	—	—	—	—	—	—	—	—	—	—	—	—	—	—	—	—	—	—	—
2	—	—	—	—	—	—	—	—	—	—	—	—	0	0	0	0	0	0	1	1
	—	—	—	—	—	—	—	—	—	—	—	—	—	—	—	—	—	—	**0**	**0**
3	—	—	—	—	—	—	0	0	1	1	1	2	2	2	3	3	4	4	4	5
	—	—	—	—	—	—	—	—	**0**	**0**	**0**	**1**	**1**	**1**	**2**	**2**	**2**	**2**	**3**	**3**
4	—	—	—	—	0	1	1	2	3	3	4	5	5	6	7	7	8	9	9	10
	—	—	—	—	—	**0**	**0**	**1**	**1**	**2**	**2**	**3**	**3**	**4**	**5**	**5**	**6**	**6**	**7**	**8**
5	—	—	—	0	1	2	3	4	5	6	7	8	9	10	11	12	13	14	15	16
	—	—	—	—	**0**	**1**	**1**	**2**	**3**	**4**	**5**	**6**	**7**	**7**	**8**	**9**	**10**	**11**	**12**	**13**
6	—	—	—	1	2	3	4	6	7	8	9	11	12	13	15	16	18	19	20	22
	—	—	—	**0**	**1**	**2**	**3**	**4**	**5**	**6**	**7**	**9**	**10**	**11**	**12**	**13**	**15**	**16**	**17**	**18**
7	—	—	0	1	3	4	6	7	9	11	12	14	16	17	19	21	23	24	26	28
	—	—	—	**0**	**1**	**3**	**4**	**6**	**7**	**9**	**10**	**12**	**13**	**15**	**16**	**18**	**19**	**21**	**22**	**24**
8	—	—	0	2	4	6	7	9	11	13	15	17	20	22	24	26	28	30	32	34
	—	—	—	**1**	**2**	**4**	**6**	**7**	**9**	**11**	**13**	**15**	**17**	**18**	**20**	**22**	**24**	**26**	**28**	**30**
9	—	—	1	3	5	7	9	11	14	16	18	21	23	26	28	31	33	36	38	40
	—	—	**0**	**1**	**3**	**5**	**7**	**9**	**11**	**13**	**16**	**18**	**20**	**22**	**24**	**27**	**29**	**31**	**33**	**36**
10	—	—	1	3	6	8	11	13	16	19	22	24	27	30	33	36	38	41	44	47
	—	—	**0**	**2**	**4**	**6**	**9**	**11**	**13**	**16**	**18**	**21**	**24**	**26**	**29**	**31**	**34**	**37**	**39**	**42**
11	—	—	1	4	7	9	12	15	18	22	25	28	31	34	37	41	44	47	50	53
	—	—	**0**	**2**	**5**	**7**	**10**	**13**	**16**	**18**	**21**	**24**	**27**	**30**	**33**	**36**	**39**	**42**	**45**	**48**
12	—	—	2	5	8	11	14	17	21	24	28	31	35	38	42	46	49	53	56	60
	—	—	**1**	**3**	**6**	**9**	**12**	**15**	**18**	**21**	**24**	**27**	**31**	**34**	**37**	**41**	**44**	**47**	**51**	**54**
13	—	0	2	5	9	12	16	20	23	27	31	35	39	43	47	51	55	59	63	67
	—	—	**1**	**3**	**7**	**10**	**13**	**17**	**20**	**24**	**27**	**31**	**34**	**38**	**42**	**45**	**49**	**53**	**56**	**60**
14	—	0	2	6	10	13	17	22	26	30	34	38	43	47	51	56	60	65	69	73
	—	—	**1**	**4**	**7**	**11**	**15**	**18**	**22**	**26**	**30**	**34**	**38**	**42**	**46**	**50**	**54**	**58**	**63**	**67**
15	—	0	3	7	11	15	19	24	28	33	37	42	47	51	56	61	66	70	75	80
	—	—	**2**	**5**	**8**	**12**	**16**	**20**	**24**	**29**	**33**	**37**	**42**	**46**	**51**	**55**	**60**	**64**	**69**	**73**
16	—	0	3	7	12	16	21	26	31	36	41	46	51	56	61	66	71	76	82	87
	—	—	**2**	**5**	**9**	**13**	**18**	**22**	**27**	**31**	**36**	**41**	**45**	**50**	**55**	**60**	**65**	**70**	**74**	**79**
17	—	0	4	8	13	18	23	28	33	38	44	49	55	60	66	71	77	82	88	93
	—	—	**2**	**6**	**10**	**15**	**19**	**24**	**29**	**34**	**39**	**44**	**49**	**54**	**60**	**65**	**70**	**75**	**81**	**86**
18	—	0	4	9	14	19	24	30	36	41	47	53	59	65	70	76	82	88	94	100
	—	—	**2**	**6**	**11**	**16**	**21**	**26**	**31**	**37**	**42**	**47**	**53**	**58**	**64**	**70**	**75**	**81**	**87**	**92**
19	—	1	4	9	15	20	26	32	38	44	50	56	63	69	75	82	88	94	101	107
	—	**0**	**3**	**7**	**12**	**17**	**22**	**28**	**33**	**39**	**45**	**51**	**56**	**63**	**69**	**74**	**81**	**87**	**93**	**99**
20	—	1	5	10	16	22	28	34	40	47	53	60	67	73	80	87	93	100	107	114
	—	**0**	**3**	**8**	**13**	**18**	**24**	**30**	**36**	**42**	**48**	**54**	**60**	**67**	**73**	**79**	**86**	**92**	**99**	**105**

[a]For a one-tailed test at $\alpha = .01$ (light type) and $\alpha = .005$ (bold type) and for a two-tailed test at $\alpha = .02$ (light type) and $\alpha = .01$ (bold type).

[b]Dashes in the body of the table indicate that no decision is possible at the given α.

Table A.11
Critical values for the Wilcoxon *T*

	Levels of Significance for a One-Tailed Test					Levels of Significance for a One-Tailed Test			
n	.05	.025	.01	.005	*n*	.05	.025	.01	.005
	Levels of Significance for a Two-Tailed Test					Levels of Significance for a Two-Tailed Test			
n	.10	.05	.02	.01	*n*	.10	.05	.02	.01
5	0	–	–	–	28	130	116	101	91
6	2	0	–	–	29	140	126	110	100
7	3	2	0	–	30	151	137	120	109
8	5	3	1	0	31	163	147	130	118
9	8	5	3	1	32	175	159	140	128
10	10	8	5	3	33	187	170	151	138
11	13	10	7	5	34	200	182	162	148
12	17	13	9	7	35	213	195	173	159
13	21	17	12	9	36	227	208	185	171
14	25	21	15	12	37	241	221	198	182
15	30	25	19	15	38	256	235	211	194
16	35	29	23	19	39	271	249	224	207
17	41	34	27	23	40	286	264	238	220
18	47	40	32	27	41	302	279	252	233
19	53	46	37	32	42	319	294	266	247
20	60	52	43	37	43	336	310	281	261
21	67	58	49	42	44	353	327	296	276
22	75	65	55	48	45	371	343	312	291
23	83	73	62	54	46	389	361	328	307
24	91	81	69	61	47	407	378	345	322
25	100	89	76	68	48	426	396	362	339
26	110	98	84	75	49	446	415	379	355
27	119	107	92	83	50	466	434	397	373

Source: Kirk (1984).

Table A.12

Critical values for the Spearman r_S

			Levels of Significance for a One-Tailed Test					
.25	*.10*	*.05*	*.025*	*.01*	*.005*	*.0025*	*.001*	*.0005*
			Levels of Significance for a Two-Tailed Test					
N	*.50*	*.20*	*.10*	*.05*	*.02*	*.01*	*.005*	*.002*	*.001*
5	.500	.800	.900	1.000	1.000				
6	.371	.657	.829	.886	.943	1.000	1.000		
7	.321	.571	.714	.786	.893	.929	.964	1.000	1.000
8	.310	.524	.643	.738	.833	.881	.905	.952	.976
9	.267	.483	.600	.700	.783	.833	.867	.917	.933
10	.248	.455	.564	.648	.745	.794	.830	.879	.903
11	.236	.427	.536	.618	.709	.755	.800	.845	.873
12	.224	.406	.503	.587	.671	.727	.776	.825	.860
13	.209	.385	.484	.560	.648	.703	.747	.802	.835
14	.200	.367	.464	.538	.622	.675	.723	.776	.811
15	.189	.354	.443	.521	.604	.654	.700	.754	.786
16	.182	.341	.429	.503	.582	.635	.679	.732	.765
17	.176	.328	.414	.485	.566	.615	.662	.713	.748
18	.170	.317	.401	.472	.550	.600	.643	.695	.728
19	.165	.309	.391	.460	.535	.584	.628	.677	.712
20	.161	.299	.380	.447	.520	.570	.612	.662	.696
21	.156	.292	.370	.435	.508	.556	.599	.648	.681
22	.152	.284	.361	.425	.496	.544	.586	.634	.667
23	.148	.278	.353	.415	.486	.532	.573	.622	.654
24	.144	.271	.344	.406	.476	.521	.562	.610	.642
25	.142	.265	.337	.398	.466	.511	.551	.598	.630
26	.138	.259	.331	.390	.457	.501	.541	.587	.619
27	.136	.255	.324	.382	.448	.491	.531	.577	.608
28	.133	.250	.317	.375	.440	.483	.522	.567	.598
29	.130	.245	.312	.368	.433	.475	.513	.558	.589
30	.128	.240	.306	.362	.425	.467	.504	.549	.580
31	.126	.236	.301	.356	.418	.459	.496	.541	.571
32	.124	.232	.296	.350	.412	.452	.489	.533	.563
33	.121	.229	.291	.345	.405	.446	.482	.525	.554
34	.120	.225	.287	.340	.399	.439	.475	.517	.547
35	.118	.222	.283	.335	.394	.433	.468	.510	.539
36	.116	.219	.279	.330	.388	.427	.462	.504	.533
37	.114	.216	.275	.325	.383	.421	.456	.497	.526
38	.113	.212	.271	.321	.378	.415	.450	.491	.519
39	.111	.210	.267	.317	.373	.410	.444	.485	.513
40	.110	.207	.264	.313	.368	.405	.439	.479	.507
41	.108	.204	.261	.309	.364	.400	.433	.473	.501
42	.107	.202	.257	.305	.359	.395	.428	.468	.495
43	.105	.199	.254	.301	.355	.391	.423	.463	.490
44	.104	.197	.251	.298	.351	.386	.419	.458	.484
45	.103	.194	.248	.294	.347	.382	.414	.453	.479
46	.102	.192	.246	.291	.343	.378	.410	.448	.474
47	.101	.190	.243	.288	.340	.374	.405	.443	.469
48	.100	.188	.240	.285	.336	.370	.401	.439	.465
49	.098	.186	.238	.282	.333	.366	.397	.434	.460
50	.097	.184	.235	.279	.329	.363	.393	.430	.456
60	.089	.168	.214	.255	.300	.331	.360	.394	.418
70	.082	.155	.198	.235	.278	.307	.333	.365	.388
80	.076	.145	.185	.220	.260	.287	.312	.342	.363
90	.072	.136	.174	.207	.245	.271	.294	.323	.343
100	.068	.129	.165	.197	.233	.257	.279	.307	.326

Source: Zar (1972).

Appendix B
Review of Basic Mathematics

Part 1: Self-Quiz

The following problems are grouped according to the section in this appendix where you can review the procedure being tested. Do the odd-numbered problems as a pretest and check the answers at the end of this appendix. Complete this appendix to learn why you missed any problems, and then do the even-numbered problems as a posttest.

Part 2. **1.** T or F: $(6)(3) = 18$ **2.** T or F: $9/3 = 6$ **3.** T or F: $6 < 3$ **4.** T or F: $3.5 \geq 6$ **5.** T or F: $|6| = -6$

6. T or F: $|-1| = 1$ **7.** $7 \pm 2 = $ ____   **8.** $2 \pm 12 = $ ____

Part 3. **9.** $7.5 - 3.7 = $ ____   **10.** $-12.1 + 14 = $ ____   **11.** $2.7 \times 9.1 = $ ____   **12.** $0.1 \times 100 = $ ____

13. $0.12/0.3 = $ ____   **14.** $14.6/0.7 = $ ____

Part 4. **15.** $7/8 + 4/3 = $ ____   **16.** $12/11 - 1/2 = $ ____   **17.** $(25/3)(16/21) = $ ____

18. $(7/8)(41/3) = $ ____   **19.** $(4/3)/(2/9) = $ ____   **20.** $(9/13)/(6/7) = $ ____   **21.** If you have 12 quarters, 9 dimes, 2 nickels, and a penny, what proportion of the *number* of coins are dimes? What percentage are dimes?   **22.** If you have 48 colas in a cooler and 9 of them are diet drinks, what proportion of them are diet drinks? What percentage?   **23.** If you are paying your kid brother 15% of you earnings for helping you mow lawns, how much will he get if you make $320?

24. Find 17% of 170.   **25.** $7^4 = $ ____   **26.** $4^7 = $ ____   **27.** $\sqrt{36} = $ ____   **28.** $\sqrt{49} = $ ____

29. $36^2 = $ ____   **30.** $49^2 = $ ____

Part 5. **31.** $-6 - 7 + 3 = $ ____   **32.** $-12 - 1 + 4 = $ ____   **33.** $-6 - (-7 + 3) = $ ____

34. $-12 - (-1 + 4) = $ ____   **35.** $(-6)(-7)(3) = $ ____   **36.** $(-12)(-3)(-1) = $ ____   **37.** $-6/-3.5 = $ ____

38. $-3.5/6 = $ ____

Part 6. **39.**

$$\frac{(6)(4^2 - 9) + (12 - 4^3)(9)}{\sqrt{14(112 - 7^2)}} = \underline{\quad}$$

40.

$$\frac{(9^2 - 4)(3) - (4^3 - 12)}{\sqrt{(9)(7^2 - 3)}} = \underline{\quad}$$

Part 7.   41. Simplify: $(X - Y)(2X + 4Y)$ **42.** Simplify: $(4X + 4Y)(3X - 2Y)$ **43.** If X can equal $0, -1, -2$, or -3, what values can Y have if $Y = -2X + 4$?   **44.** If X can equal $4, 5, 6$, or 7, what values can Y have if $Y = 6X - 9$?
45. If $Y = \sqrt{(2X + 4)/7}$ and $Y^2 = 9$, find X.   **46.** If $Y = \sqrt{(4X - 7)/9}$ and $Y = 2$, find X.

Part 2:   Symbols

Symbol	Meaning	Examples
=	equals	$X = Y$; $3 = 3$
≠	does not equal	$X \neq Y$; $3 \neq 5$
+	plus (addition)	$X + Y = Z$; $4 + 3 = 7$
−	minus (subtraction)	$X - Y = Z$; $4 - 3 = 1$
( )( ) or ×	times (multiplication)	$(X)(Y) = XY^a$; $(3)(4) = 3 \times 4 = 12$
÷ or /	divided by (division)	$X/Y = X \div Y$; $3/4 = 3 \div 4 = 0.75$
( )²	squared	X^2; $2^2 = 2 \times 2 = 4$
√	square root of	$\sqrt{X}$; $\sqrt{4} = 2$
>	is greater than	$X > Y$; $5 > 4$
<	is less than	$X < Y$; $4 < 5$
≥	is greater than or equal to	$X \geq Y$; $z \geq 1.645$
≤	is less than or equal to	$X \leq Y$; $z \leq -1.645$
| |	absolute value of (ignore negative signs)	$\|X\|$; $\|-3\| = 3$
±	plus or minus	$X \pm 7.5$; 3 ± 1 gives $(3 + 1) = 4$ and $(3 - 1) = 2$

[a]Multiplication is indicated when two symbols are shown next to each other with no multiplication sign or parentheses.

Part 3:   Decimals

Addition and Subtraction of Decimals.   Line up the decimal points vertically, and then add or subtract.

$3.2 + 4$:
```
  3.2
+4.0
─────
  7.2
```

$0.93 + 5.7$:
```
 0.93
+5.70
─────
 6.63
```

$5 - 0.72$:
```
 5.00
-0.72
─────
 4.28
```

$4.39 - 2$:
```
 4.39
-2.00
─────
 2.39
```

Multiplication of Decimals.   How many numbers should follow the decimal point in your answer? (That is, how many decimal places should there be?) The number of decimal places in your answer equals the sum of the number of decimal places in the two numbers being multiplied.

1.3×0.5:
```
  1.3
×0.5
─────
 0.65
```

7×0.6:
```
   7
×0.6
─────
  4.2
```

0.09×0.4:
```
  0.09
×0.4
──────
 0.036
```

1.05×0.5:
```
  1.05
×0.5
──────
 0.525
```

Division of Decimals.   You can convert decimal numbers to whole numbers and then do the division. Suppose you want to divide 0.65 by 0.5. You may write this expression as a fraction. A fraction's value is unchanged when it is multiplied by 1. A way to write 1 is 100/100. Multiplying the fraction by 100/100 does not change its value but converts each piece to a whole number:

$$\frac{0.65}{0.5} \times \frac{100}{100} = \frac{65}{50} = 1.3$$

To decide whether to use 10/10, 100/100, 1000/1000, and so on, choose the number with the most decimal places. You need to have as many zeros as you have decimal places.

$$\frac{4.2}{7} \times \frac{10}{10} = \frac{42}{70} = 0.6 \qquad \frac{0.525}{1.05} \times \frac{1000}{1000} = \frac{525}{1050} = 0.5$$

Part 4:   Fractions, Proportions, Percentages, and Exponents

Fractions.   You may feel more comfortable working with fractions if you convert each one to a decimal and then do the math. If you keep the fractions, when do you need a common denominator? When adding or subtracting. If two fractions have the same denominator, you can add or subtract the numerators and leave the denominator alone. Remember, the value of a fraction isn't changed when it is multiplied by 1. To add or subtract two fractions that have different denominators, the easiest way to find a common denominator is to multiply each fraction by a version of 1 from the other fraction:

$$\frac{1}{4} + \frac{1}{2} = \left(\frac{1}{4}\right)\left(\frac{2}{2}\right) + \left(\frac{1}{2}\right)\left(\frac{4}{4}\right) = \frac{2}{8} + \frac{4}{8} = \frac{6}{8} = 0.75$$

$$\frac{1}{2} - \frac{3}{8} = \left(\frac{1}{2}\right)\left(\frac{8}{8}\right) - \left(\frac{3}{8}\right)\left(\frac{2}{2}\right) = \frac{8}{16} - \frac{6}{16} = \frac{2}{16} = 0.125$$

Sometimes only one of the fractions needs to be multiplied by a value of 1. In the last equation, you could have multiplied 1/2 by 4/4 to get 4/8. Then the answer would be 1/8 = 0.125.

To multiply fractions, convert them to decimals and multiply; or multiply the two numerators to get the new numerator, and multiply the two denominators to get the new denominator.

$$\left(\frac{1}{2}\right)\left(\frac{1}{4}\right) = (0.5)(0.25) = 0.125$$

$$\left(\frac{3}{10}\right)\left(\frac{2}{4}\right) = \frac{6}{40} = 0.15$$

To divide fractions, remember which one is being divided into the other. (That is, remember which fraction is the denominator of the whole problem.) The easiest way to find an answer is to invert the denominator of your problem and multiply the two fractions.

$$\frac{1/2}{1/4} = \left(\frac{1}{2}\right)\left(\frac{4}{1}\right) = \frac{4}{2} = 2$$

$$\frac{3/4}{1/2} = \left(\frac{3}{4}\right)\left(\frac{2}{1}\right) = \frac{6}{4} = 1.5$$

Or you could convert each number to a decimal and divide, which in the last example gives 0.75/0.5 = 1.5.

Proportions and Percentages.   A proportion is a fraction, a part of a whole, and is usually expressed as a decimal. A percentage is a proportion times 100. To get from a percentage to a proportion, divide by 100.

If you have $550 in the bank and you spend $66 on groceries, what proportion of your money have you spent on food? The answer is $66/550 = .12$. What percentage of your money did you spend on food? The answer is $.12 \times 100 = 12\%$.

If you are on a budget of $1500 per month and you don't want to spend more than 40% of your budget on rent, what is the highest rent you should consider? To find the answer, you can convert 40% to a proportion by dividing by 100: $40/100 = .40$. This is the fraction of your budget that would go toward rent. Multiply your total budget by .40 to get $600.

If you survey 500 freshmen at your school and find that 150 of them have season tickets to the football games, what proportion of them have tickets? You calculate $150/500 = .3$.

If 3% of the 3,800,500 residents of a city use the public transportation system every day, how many people does this represent? Convert the percentage to a proportion, and then multiply by the population: $(3/100)(3,800,500) = (.03)(3,800,500) = 114,015$.

Exponents.   An exponent is a superscript on a number that tells you how many times to multiply the number by itself. So 3^3 means $3 \times 3 \times 3 = 27$, and 4^6 means 4 times itself six times, or 4096. This kind of multiplication is also referred to as raising a number to a *power*. So 4^6 is sometimes called "4 raised to the sixth power."

$$5^3 = (5)(5)(5) = 125$$

$$2^4 = (2)(2)(2)(2) = 16$$

$$164^1 = 164$$

The most common powers in statistics are *squares* and *square roots*. Squaring a number means raising the number to the power of 2—that is, just multiplying the number by itself. So $5^2 = (5)(5) = 25$.

Finding a square root of a number is like working backward from squaring. If you want to find the square root of 25, or $\sqrt{25}$, then you want to know, What number, when multiplied by itself, gives you 25? The answer here is easy: 5. So 5 is the square root of 25, which can be written as $\sqrt{25} = 5$. Most square roots are much harder to find, such as $\sqrt{26}$, which is why you should make sure your calculator has a button that gives you square roots. Even calculators that cost only a few dollars have this feature. By the way, taking the square root of a number is the same as raising it to the power of ½, so $\sqrt{25} = 25^{1/2} = 5$.

Part 5:   Working with Negative Numbers

Addition of Negative Numbers.   If you have several negative numbers to add together, then add the numbers and put a negative sign in front of your answer.

$$(-3) + (-5) + (-9) + (-1) = -18$$

Addition of Positive and Negative Numbers.   If you need to add (that is, to sum) positive and negative numbers, first sum the negative numbers, and then add up the positive numbers. Put first the positive sum on a line, then a plus sign, then the negative number. The negative sign turns this addition problem into a subtraction.

$$(-3) + (9) + (-1) + (5) = [(-3) + (-1)] + [9 + 5]$$
$$= (-4) + 14 = 14 + (-4)$$
$$= 14 - 4 = 10$$

Here is an example in which the final answer is negative:

$$(-23) + (9) + (-5) + (7) = [(-23) + (-5)] + [9 + 7]$$
$$= (-28) + 16 = 16 + (-28)$$
$$= 16 - 28 = -12$$

Subtraction of Negative Numbers.   If you are subtracting a negative, think of the two negative signs as creating a plus sign. Change the sign of the negative number to be subtracted and add:

$$4 - (-3) = 4 + 3 = 7 \qquad -5 - (-2) = -5 + 2 = -3$$

Multiplication and Division of Negative Numbers.   If you have an even number of negative signs, then your answer is positive. If you have an odd number of negative signs, then your answer is negative.

$$(-4)(-3) = 12 \qquad (-4)(3) = -12 \qquad \frac{12}{-3} = -4 \qquad \frac{-12}{-4} = 3$$

$$\frac{(-2)(-4)(12)(-3)}{(-9)(-6)} = \frac{(8)(12)(-3)}{54} = \frac{(96)(-3)}{54}$$

$$= \frac{-288}{54} = -5.3333$$

Were you able to predict that the last answer would be a negative number? There were five negative signs in the problem.

Part 6: Order of Operations

When you have a large formula with parentheses, square roots, and other symbols, where do you begin? Start with the innermost parentheses and work outward. Simply convert insides of parentheses to single numbers. Treat numerators and denominators separately, and don't divide until you get a single number on top and on bottom.

$$[6(4 + 5) - (9 \times 7)] = [6(9) - 63] = 54 - 63 = -9$$

To remember what to do first in a big formula, you might use the mnemonic device, "*Please Excuse My Dear Aunt Sally.*" This tells you to start with the innermost *p*arentheses. Next, simplify any number that has an *e*xponent, like a number being squared. Then do *m*ultiplication and *d*ivision, with the *a*ddition and *s*ubtraction being last.

$$10[3 - (6 - 2^2)^2] = 10[3 - (6 - 4)^2] = 10[3 - 2^2]$$

$$= 10[3 - 4] = 10(-1) = -10$$

$$\frac{(2 + 3)^2 + (4 + 1)^2 + (7 + 1)^2}{2} = \frac{5^2 + 5^2 + 8^2}{2} = \frac{25 + 25 + 64}{2}$$

$$= \frac{114}{2} = 57$$

Everything under the square root sign must be simplified to one number, and then you take the square root of that number. The square root of $\{3 + 6 + 8\}$ is not the same as $\sqrt{3} + \sqrt{6} + \sqrt{8}$. Treat a square root symbol like parentheses, and do everything before you apply the square root.

$$\sqrt{\frac{3(42) - (1 + 4 + 5)^2}{3^2}} = \sqrt{\frac{3(42) - 10^2}{3^2}} = \sqrt{\frac{126 - 100}{9}} = \sqrt{\frac{26}{9}}$$

$$= \sqrt{2.8888888} = 1.6996731 \cong 1.70$$

What if you have a negative sign in front of parentheses? You can simplify the expression inside the parentheses and then apply the negative sign, or you can distribute the negative sign to each number inside the parentheses.

$$\left(\frac{52^2}{14-9}\right) - \left[8 - 6 + \left(\frac{18}{4^2}\right)\right] = \left(\frac{52^2}{5}\right) - \left[8 - 6 + \left(\frac{18}{16}\right)\right]$$

$$= \left(\frac{2704}{5}\right) - [8 - 6 + 1.125]$$

$$= 540.8 - 3.125 = 537.675$$

The last line of this example also could be worked this way:

$$540.8 - 8 + 6 - 1.125 = (540.8 - 8) + 6 - 1.125$$

$$= (532.8 + 6) - 1.125$$

$$= 538.8 - 1.125 = 537.675$$

Part 7: Algebraic Manipulation

The FOIL rule.   How do you simplify an algebraic expression such as $(X + Y)(2X + 4Y)$? Notice that two things are being multiplied. The first thing is $X + Y$, and the second is $2X + 4Y$. To handle multiplication like this, you can use the mnemonic device FOIL: Multiply the *f*irst terms, then the *o*utside terms, next the *i*nside terms, and finally the *l*ast terms. The four resulting terms are added or subtracted, depending on the signs involved in the FOIL steps. In this example, every term is positive, so each of the four terms is added in the final answer.

*F*irst: X times $2X = (X)(2)(X) = 2X^2$

*O*utside: X times $4Y = (X)(4)(Y) = 4XY$

*I*nside: Y times $2X = (Y)(2)(X) = 2XY$

*L*ast: Y times $4Y = (Y)(4)(Y) = 4Y^2$

The answer is the sum of these four terms:

$$(X + Y)(2X + 4Y) = 2X^2 + 4XY + 2XY + 4Y^2 = 2X^2 + 6XY + 4Y^2$$

You can add together the terms with the same X or Y combination. The term $4XY$ means you have four "somethings" called XY. The term $2XY$ means you have two more of the "somethings" called XY. Add them together for $6XY$. But you can't simplify the final answer any further without knowing what the X and the Y stand for.
   Can you simplify this expression?

$$2X - 4X^2 + 5XY - 91Y^2 + 8 - X^2$$

The only terms that can be combined are the second and last terms. The $-4X^2$ can be added to $-X^2$ to get $-5X^2$.

Defining Y in terms of X.   Sometimes one symbol is defined in terms of another, such as $Y = 4X - 6$. Suppose X can equal the whole numbers between 4 and 8, inclusive. That means Y can have five different values:

If X equals	then Y equals
4	$4(4) - 6 = 10$
5	$4(5) - 6 = 14$
6	$4(6) - 6 = 18$
7	$4(7) - 6 = 22$
8	$4(8) - 6 = 26$

These values of X and Y are linked; Y depends on the value of X. These pairs of numbers sometimes are plotted on a coordinate system, where the number line for the X values is a horizontal axis and the number line for the Y values is a vertical axis.

Working Backward to Solve for X.   Sometimes you may know the value of Y but not X. If $Y = 2X + 12$ and you know $Y = 6$, then you have to work backward to get X:

$$6 = 2X + 12$$

First, subtract 12 from both sides of the equation:

$$6 - 12 = 2X + 12 - 12$$
$$-6 = 2X$$

Then divide both sides of the equation by 2, which isolates X and gives you its value:

$$\frac{-6}{2} = \frac{2X}{2}$$
$$-3 = X$$

To check your work, plug $X = -3$ into the equation $Y = 2X + 12$. You should get $Y = 6$.

Square roots.   What if you have a square root symbol over the expression that contains the X you are trying to isolate? Let's say that $Y = 9$ and you are given the following equation:

$$Y = \sqrt{\frac{7X - 14}{3}}$$

First, put the 9 where the Y is supposed to be. Then, to get rid of the square root sign, square both sides of the equation. A square root of "something," when multiplied by itself, gives you the "something":

$$(9)(9) = \sqrt{\frac{7X - 14}{3}} \sqrt{\frac{7X - 14}{3}}$$
$$81 = \frac{7X + 14}{3}$$

Now you can multiply both sides by 3, then add 14 to both sides, and then divide both sides by 7. You should get $X = 36.7143$ (rounded).

Answers to Self-Quiz

All answers are rounded to four decimal places.
1. T   2. F   3. F   4. F   5. F   6. T   7. 5 and 9   8. -10 and 14   9. 3.8   10. 1.9
11. 24.57   12. 10   13. 0.4   14. 20.8571   15. 53/24 or 2.2083   16. 13/22 or 0.5909   17. 400/63 or 6.3492   18. 287/24 or 11.9583   19. 6   20. 63/78 or 0.8077   21. 9/24 or .375; 37.5%   22. 9/48 or .1875; 18.75%   23. $48   24. 28.9   25. 2401   26. 16,384   27. 6   28. 7   29. 1296   30. 2401
31. -10 32. -9 33. -2 34. -15 35. 126   36. -36 37. 1.7143   38. -0.5833
39. $-426/\sqrt{882}$ or -14.3442 40. $179/\sqrt{414}$ or 8.7974   41. $2X^2 + 2XY - 4Y^2$ 42. $12X^2 + 4XY - 8Y^2$
43. 4, 6, 8, and 10, respectively   44. 15, 21, 27, and 33, respectively   45. 59/2 or 29.5   46. 43/4 or 10.75

Answers to Selected Exercises

Chapter 1

1. (*a*) You might attract only people who are interested in or concerned about the effect of caffeine, not all segments of the population who use products that contain caffeine. Also, having participants list the effects of caffeine might make them overlook some important effects not commonly associated with caffeine. (*b*) In the volunteer study, you do not have the ability to manipulate when the participants consume caffeine, so the symptoms may be a result of something other than caffeine.

2. First, some data would be reports by the arresting officers, results of blood or breath tests, results of a "walk-the-line" test, and reports of open containers in the car. Second, some statistics cited on drinking and driving might be percentage of accidents that are alcohol related, average number of deaths per day in alcohol-related accidents, and average cost of repair in alcohol-related accidents.

3. (*a*) Data could be job location, whether or not you will travel on the job, and what the boss is like. (*b*) Some statistics are salary, growth indicators of the company, benefits, retirement package, and insurance package. (*c*) Risks in taking the job offer include getting a better offer in the near future, the company going under soon, the company downsizing soon, and finding out you don't like the job. Risks in not taking the job include receiving no other offer with the side effects of unemployment or living with in-laws.

4. Statistics from Box 1.1 include the "average of three and one-half" servings of fruits or vegetables daily, "23 percent of all adults eat five or more servings a day," and the "half a serving less per day" effect of less education. You could cite just about any number in the article that summarized some variable for a group of people, such as any percentage or any average.

5. Statistics from Box 1.2 include the "more than 70 percent" reported early in the article and the actual 73% who reportedly said the Dodge was better than their car.

6. (*a*) You might list food/nutrition, car purchase, or purchase of electronics. (*b*) Experimental psychology, research methods in your field, graduate statistics, an applied course that examines the results of research.

7. (*a*) Statistics from DasGupta (1992) were the percentages of questions on the actual test that were similar to those submitted by the students (82% for PC and 87% for NC), the average numbers of symptoms (12.50 for NC and 10.00 for PC), the *t* on the number of symptoms (value of 3.28), and the *t* on the frequency of stress (value of 1.46). (*b*) These statistics were used to draw the conclusions that perceived control over the test-taking situation resulted in significantly fewer symptoms, but not significantly less stress or better performance. (*c*) Because random sampling most likely was not used, there may be biases caused by the type of person in the research: college student in an introductory psychology class at that university. Random assignment of participants to groups helps control differential biases between the two groups (for example, all females in one class). Because the participants did

not know what the researcher was studying (test anxiety and how it is affected by perceived control over the test), most likely that is not an issue in this study.

8. Samples can be obtained because they are small and usually close to the researcher, like Ornish's heart patients, who were only a subset of all the people with heart problems in the United States that year. The researchers computed statistics to infer to parameters (unobtainable numerical characteristics of populations), such as the average reduction in cholesterol levels. They also wanted to describe the sample with the statistics.

9. All college students in the present and future who will take a statistics class.

10. College students in the broadest definition, possibly narrowed by type of college, area of the country, gender, and so on.

11. (*a*) In this case, I might know something about the population of 100, but not about the broader population of all college students to whom the researchers likely want to infer. In any case, I could examine the sample for gender ratio, average age, caffeine habit, or hours of work per week. Hypotheses might compare college students to other age groups. (*b*) Your friend is wrong. Choosing every fifth person gives an arbitrary sample but not a random sample because selection is not independent. Some researchers consider a systematic sample like this to be random if the starting point is randomly chosen. However, such systematic sampling with a random starting point falls short of fitting the definition of independent selection given for random sampling. (*c*) See Box 1.3.

12. (*a*) All U.S. residents aged 18 and over. (*b*) The 1800 people selected and interviewed. (*c*) That some similar percentage in the population support Candidate X. (*d*) A statistic. (*e*) The researchers can't select all people 18 and over; 1800 was likely computed to be the size necessary for their type of sampling. (*f*) No; the population would be all U.S. residents whose numbers are listed in the phone book. (See answer for Exercise 11b.)

13. (*a*) Those households with telephone numbers in the directory who are willing to participate. (*b*) No. (*c*) No, because they wish to sample from all people who watch TV. (*d*) The 1200 households actually selected. (*e*) Further restricts the population to listed numbers; brings in a bias by excluding the unlisted numbers.

14. Not all TV-owning families have telephones; unlisted numbers restrict the population; poor people are less likely to have telephones; recent Latino immigrants are less likely to own telephones and TVs but may have high interest in the program.

15. Blooper did not randomly sample the population. Usually only those with very strong feelings write to their congressman about an issue.

16. Similar to those of Exercise 15. The participants select themselves into the sample and may feel strongly about the issue; they are not randomly selected.

17. (*a*) Statistic. (*b*) Parameter. (*c*) 57% is a parameter; 59% is a statistic. (*d*) 22 is a statistic; 20 is a parameter.

18. (*a*) The sample is babies up to one year of age in Avon County. The population is similar-aged babies in England (or perhaps even in countries like England). (*b*) A statistic; a parameter.

19. (*a*) All adults in the United States; the 105,225 adults surveyed. (*b*) 27.9% of Southern females are tobacco users. (*c*) An inferential statistic.

20. (*a*) There are no population differences in the ability to catch a liar. (*b*) Current and future Secret Service personnel, judges, and psychiatrists.

21. (*a*) Be reduced. (*b*) Be increased. (*c*) Be increased. (*d*) It depends on the numbers in each category of disease, but it might all even out. (*e*) They might be more likely to follow directions exactly as given and to be more faithful to continue in the study; they are more educated. In the aspirin study, the researchers found fewer heart attacks but more hemorrhages in the brain and more ulcers for those who took an aspirin a day. The overall incidence of deaths from all causes was about the same for the two groups. An over-40 male should contact his doctor before taking one aspirin per day.

22. (*a*) Means and differences in means. (*b*) Yes; yes; no. (*c*) Yes.

23. (*a*) They should have used inferential statistical procedures to see whether the differences discussed, based on the descriptive statistics given in the article, were significant. (*b*) The sample is described as "2837 Americans over age 18." All such Americans are the population. (*c*) They really mean "studies of samples around the world" because they could not have measured everyone in all the populations. (*d*) The overall hypothesis that the researchers tested was most likely that there was no relationship between fruit and vegetable consumption and cancer. Of course, there were many subhypotheses about the consumption of fruits and vegetables and related factors.

24. (*a*) Even though the difference is slight (4%), there might be some differential self-selection in the two groups, so we can infer only to those people who would have agreed to participate after they knew the treatment. (*b*) From a pure statistics standpoint, it would have been better than the way they did the study, but it might have had compliance problems in that some participants may not have wanted to be in their randomly assigned group and really would have wanted to participate only if they were in a certain group.

25. (*a*) All fourth-, eighth-, and twelfth-graders who took the test; all such students in the United States (present and future) (*b*) All fourth-, eighth-, and twelfth-graders who took the test; all such students in that country (present and future) (*c*) A higher percentage of U.S. children are in school than in other countries, where some selection excludes children from progressing through higher grades (or there is no compulsory education).

Chapter 2

1. (*a*) Absolute (*b*) Comparative (*c*) Comparative (*d*) Absolute (*e*) Comparative

2. Step 1: Other treatments for heart disease are invasive, such as bypass surgery, and current "wait" strategies rarely improve the patient's symptoms. Will a radical fat-reducing diet plus stress reduction plus mild supervised exercise plus stopping smoking be better than current "wait" strategies? Step 2: One hypothesis says there will be no difference between patients in the comparison and life-style/heart groups, whereas the other hypothesis says that there will be differences in many factors, such as cholesterol reduction. Step 3: If the life-style/heart treatment is effective, then that group will have fewer symptoms and greater reduction in cholesterol levels. If the new treatment is not effective, then there will be no real differences in the two groups in the number of symptoms or cholesterol level reduction. Step 4: They used 94 subjects, 48 of whom agreed to be in the study; they participated for one year; many measures were taken; statistics were computed on the measures; hypotheses were tested. Step 5: The conclusion was that subjects in the life-style/heart group improved on almost every measure.

3. (*a*) No, this does not prove a causal relationship between taking algebra and getting higher grades in statistics. Because students came to the statistics course with their own math backgrounds and the professor did not manipulate math background (nor were students randomly assigned to the levels of math background), there is only a predictive relationship. The professor cannot make cause-and-effect statements from this observational research. She needs a true experiment before she can claim "cause." (*b*) Possible extraneous variables are age/class/experience (other than algebra) of the students, overall ability of the students, better math ability (different from experience), previous exposure to statistics, gender, and attitude toward mathematical subjects. None of these is controlled. (*c*) A predictor variable (*d*) A criterion variable

4. No; amount of affection shown, income, age of parents, spacing of children, number of children, religious orientation of family, cultural background, and others

5. (*a*) Yes (*b*) Presence or absence of vitamin C (*c*) Presence or absence of a cold (*d*) Age of subjects, gender of subjects, overall health of subjects, home climate conditions (heat, humidity, and so on), amount of exposure to other people with colds; yes; by randomizing subjects to the two groups (*e*) The 200 subjects; all adults (*f*) The percentage who had not had a cold

6. (*a*) Was the class divided by random assignment? (*b*) Teaching method; statistics knowledge, or the change in it

7. (*a*) Observational research (*b*) No, because this is not a true experiment. (*c*) Cultural expectations, training, and others

8. (*a*) If the caffeine/no caffeine conditions were randomly assigned to the people, then it would be a true experiment. (*b*) Caffeine (*c*) Randomization of subjects to groups, if present (*d*) There were likely several, such as the number of headaches.

9. (*a*) True experiment (*b*) Treatment for heart problems (*c*) Randomization of subjects to groups (*d*) One was reduction in cholesterol levels

10. (*a*) True experiment (*b*) Perceived control (present or absent) over the testing situation (*c*) Randomization of students to the two classes (*d*) Number of stress symptoms, average stress frequency rating, and performance on the test

11. (*a*) Observational research (*b*) No, because alcoholism was not manipulated by the researchers. (*c*) Education, economic level, age, alcoholism in parents, other disease, and others (*d*) All females

12. (*a*) Observational research, because the placement of babies on their stomachs or backs was not manipulated by the researchers (*b*) Stomach or back placement of babies (*c*) The infants lived in the same county in England (other controls were instituted in the study, but not in the Chapter 1 description of it). (*d*) SIDS rates

13. (*a*) It is neither. (*b*) Quasiexperimental design

14. (*a*) How the paper was prepared or presented to the grader (typed, neat handwriting, and so on) (*b*) No (*c*) The content of the paper was held constant because the same paper was prepared four ways; no other control. (*d*) No (*e*) Quasiexperiment

15. (*a*) Yes, both randomization of subjects to groups and manipulation of an independent variable were present. (*b*) Age, health background, and so on were controlled by randomization of subjects to groups. (*c*) External validity has some weaknesses because the research used doctors as subjects. Would other males of different educational background, economic status, amount of stress, and so on give the same results? Would they have the same level of compliance with the instructions to the two groups? Perhaps the results apply to only doctors or others like doctors.

16. (*a*) Absolute; comparative (*b*) Random assignment; yes (*c*) Yes; external validity

17. (*a*) All children; yes, because we were all children once. (*b*) The 400,000 school children (*c*) The vaccine was effective, and these results were not due only to chance. (*d*) There are tremendous year-to-year fluctuations in the polio rate. (*e*) The no-consent group had a lower rate than the control group (48 vs. 70 per 100,000), confirming the lower consent rate/lower income/lower polio rate connection.

18. (*a*) Wind is from the north, jersey number 52, events (*b*) Place of finish (*c*) Temperature (*d*) Wind speed, time of the race, number of hurdles (*e*) Discrete are jersey number, events, place of finish, number of hurdles; continuous are compass degrees, temperature, wind speed, time of the race.

19. (*a*) Ratio (*b*) Nominal (*c*) Ordinal (*d*) Ratio (*e*) Nominal (*f*) Interval (*g*) Ordinal

20. (*a*) Observational research (*b*) Predictive (*c*) Quantitative (*d*) Ordinal

21. (*a*) Discrete, qualitative, nominal (*b*) Discrete, qualitative, nominal (*c*) It depends on how it is measured (most likely discrete), qualitative, nominal (*d*) Continuous, qualitative in the way color is described by most people (for example, not using the chromatic scale that is quantitative), nominal (*e*) Discrete, quantitative, ordinal (*f*) Discrete, quantitative, ordinal (*g*) Continuous, quantitative, ordinal (*h*) Continuous, quantitative, ordinal (*i*) Discrete, quantitative, ratio (*j*) Discrete, quantitative, ratio (*k*) Continuous, quantitative, ratio (*l*) Continuous, quantitative, ratio

22. (*a*) Quantitative, ratio (*b*) Qualitative, nominal

23. (*a*) True experiment (*b*) Dependent variable; quantitative (*c*) Nominal (*d*) Gender of child, economic background of child, gender of researcher, and others

24. (*a*) Observational research (*b*) Perhaps a more agrarian and less industrialized country would both eat more fruits and vegetables and be less exposed to carcinogens. (*c*) Number of fruits and vegetables consumed is the predictor variable in the relationship between such consumption and cancer rates, but it is the criterion variable in studies on what factors influence such consumption. Number of fruits and vegetables consumed is quantitative and measured on a ratio scale. (*d*) Cancer rate is the criterion variable in the relationship between fruit and vegetable consumption and cancer rates. Cancer rate is quantitative at the level of city/state/country but qualitative at the level of the individual. The scale of measurement of cancer rate is ratio at the level of city/state/country but nominal at the level of the individual.

Chapter 3

1. (*a*) Both frequency distributions and stem and leaf displays are fairly simple, but the edge goes to the stem and leaf displays for thoroughness and accuracy. This is largely because they represent each score (you can reproduce the data from the display), whereas the frequency distribution "hides" the individual scores. (*b*) This comparison also favors stem and leaf displays, with the same disadvantages for the histogram as for frequency distributions in part a. (*c*) Both are simple and about the same on accuracy. The slight edge on thoroughness goes to the histogram because it is more of a picture of the data; that is, the visual appeal is greater than for a frequency distribution.

2. (*a*) Eight intervals (interval width of 2) or 15 intervals (interval width of 1) result in suitable frequency distributions. Scores range from 5 to 15 for perceived control and 7 to 19 for no control. The number of anxiety symptoms are more evenly distributed and higher for no control, with perceived control having scores in two groups from 11 to 15 and a lower group from 5 to 9.

3. (*a*) Seven intervals with an interval width of 10 result in a suitable frequency distribution. Scores range from 40 to 90 for Secret Service personnel and 30 to 90 for judges and psychiatrists. The distribution for the Secret Service group seems higher than the other two, with more 70–90 scores and fewer low scores (no 30s and fewer 40–50s).

4. (*c*) If you choose stems from 2.3 to 3.8 in increments of 0.1, you will be able to include all of the GPAs for both psychology and engineering majors. It appears that the spread of the psychology GPAs is larger and that there are a few more moderately high GPAs for psychology majors.

Psych.	Stem	Eng.
7	38	7
	37	
9	36	
75	35	
5	34	5
4	33	
90	32	
21	31	123
2	30	47
777	29	69
9	28	
321	27	668
773	26	9
	25	
5	24	
31	23	

5. (*c*) Choosing stems from 5 to 19 in increments of 1 will include the values from both perceived-control and no-control groups, but it gives only 0s for leaves. It appears that the no-control group has more anxiety symptoms.

Perceived control	Stem	No control
	19	0
	18	
	17	00
	16	00
00	15	00
	14	0000
000	13	0000
0000000	12	00
000000	11	0000000
	10	0
0	9	000
00	8	
00000	7	00
0	6	
000	5	

6. (*c*) The range of possible numbers limits you to choosing stems of 3 to 9 in increments of 1, with leaves of 0. It appears that the deception accuracy scores for judges are lower than those for Secret Service personnel.

Secret Service	Stem	Judges
00	9	0
00000	8	0
000000000	7	00000000
0000000000	6	0000000
00000	5	000000000000
000	4	00000
	3	0

7. The bar graph in part a has 9 as the frequency for males and 5 for females. The bar graph in part b has $9/11 = .82$ as the proportion of males over 67 in. and $5/24 = .21$ as the proportion of females over 67 in. If you concluded from the bar graph of frequency that the number of females over 67 in. was slightly more than 50% of that for males (5 as compared to 9), you would adjust that to be slightly over 25% (.21 as compared to .82) when the relative sizes of the two groups are taken into account.

11. (*a*) The frequencies of GPAs of 3.0 or higher are 3 for undecided, 7 for engineering, and 11 for psychology. Dividing each of these by the total 21 gives percentages of 14.3, 33.3, and 52.4, respectively. The pie is divided into three segments, with these percentages of the total circle representing each of the majors. If you want to get very precise on drawing the segments in the circle, you can translate these percentages to degrees of the circle by taking the proportions times 360—that is, 51.48 degrees, 119.88 degrees, and 188.64 degrees, respectively. Now you can use a protractor to accurately divide the circle into the three segments with those degrees. (*b*) The numbers of students with GPAs less than 3.0 are 2 for undecided (9.5% or 34.2 degrees), 6 for engineering (28.6% or 102.96 degrees), and 13 for psychology (61.9% or 222.84 degrees). (*c*) The two pie charts are fairly similar, showing that GPAs of 3.0 and over are distributed among the three majors in a manner similar to that for GPAs under 3.0.

12. (*a*) For the baseline data, ≤ 50 has 5 (5.6% or 20 degrees), 50–60 has 31 (34.4% or 124 degrees), and ≥ 60 has 54 (60% or 216 degrees). (*b*) For the posting data, ≤ 50 has 15 (16.7% or 60 degrees), 50–60 has 48 (53.3% or 192 degrees), and ≥ 60 has 27 (30% or 108 degrees).

13. (*d*) It appears that males generally have greater adult heights, which shifts that plot up from the female plot. This shift makes the relationship between baby length and adult height appear to be less for the combined groups than for males or females separately.

14. A frequency distribution could be used with month as the interval, giving 12 intervals. Any other interval might give too few intervals, like quarter with 4, or too many, like day with 365. A histogram would show the same information with month as the interval for the bars and the height of the bar showing the frequency born in a given month. A pie chart might

help emphasize any differences in percentages born in, say, a different quarter (month would give 12 pieces of the pie, perhaps too many).

15. (*a*) The sample is implied to be some group of people who can read, so junior high age or older. The population is likely all people of a similar description as the sample. So if adults were used in the sample, the population would be all adults. (*b*) This is a true experiment because the subjects are randomly assigned to a percent of similarity and because the percent of similarity is manipulated by the researcher. (*c*) Percent of similarity is an independent variable because it is manipulated by the researcher. (*d*) The IJS score is the dependent variable because it is measured by the researcher, and the researcher wants to know the effect of the percent of similarity on the IJS score. (*e*) IJS scores are measured on an ordinal or higher scale, depending on how the ratings are taken.

17. (*a*) Positively skewed (*b*) Positively skewed (*c*) Negatively skewed (*d*) Close to symmetric unless the school policy of having students repeat a grade has placed some older students in the third grade; then the direction of skew would depend on how many of these older students were present. (*e*) Negatively skewed

Chapter 4

1. $\Sigma X = 7$, $(\Sigma X)^2 = 49$, $\Sigma X^2 = 19$
2. $\Sigma X = 113$, $(\Sigma X)^2 = 12{,}769$, $\Sigma X^2 = 1477$
3. Mode $= 9$, median $= 9$, $\overline{X} = 19.125$. Median is best because $\overline{X}$ is influenced too much by 81.
4. The mode is the only central tendency measure that can be obtained.
5. The $\overline{X}$ and X_{50} for both males and females are 3 (mode is 3 for females and 1 and 5 for males), but the data in the samples are very different. Measures of variability are needed, too.
6. Only the mode could be used to show the most popular fruits and vegetables.
7. The mean takes into account every punt distance and treats them equally, but it is influenced by extremes such as the very longest punt (he had a fantastic punt with the wind behind him) or the very shortest punt (he "shanked it" while punting into the wind). The median ignores all of the data except the one or two middle punt distances and thus is not influenced by very long or very short punts. The mode shows only which distance is the most frequent and might be very misleading as a measure of central tendency, especially if there were a small number of punts. It would be best to report both the mean and median.
8. $\overline{X} = 767.5/11 = 69.7727$
9. (*a*) The mode, which is the interval 67.0–68.4 (or the mode can be taken to be the midpoint of the interval, 67.75) (*b*) X_{50} is between the intervals 64.0–65.4 and 65.5–66.9, so the best value is the real limit 65.45.
10. (*a*) Median (*b*) Mean (*c*) Mean (*d*) Mode
11. (*a*) Mean (*b*) Mode (*c*) Mean (if you desire to reflect the total given) or median (*d*) Median
12. (*a*) Median (*b*) The values of your speed should be fairly close to 65 mph (or have small variability), whereas the speeds for the truck will be quite a bit slower than 65 mph up the hills and quite a bit faster than 65 mph down the hills (or have high variability).
13. He or she ignored variability and likely drowned in an 8-ft hole.
14. Range $= 3 - 1 = 2$; $\overset{*}{s}{}^2 = 0.89$; $\overset{*}{s} = 0.94$
15. Data set 1: range $= 30 - 10 = 20$, $\overset{*}{s} = 8.51$; data set 2: range $= 35 - 10 = 25$, $\overset{*}{s} = 8.02$. Range is a function of only two scores (high and low); standard deviation takes into account all scores. The scores other than high and low (11, 20, 29) in Data set 1 are more variable from the mean (20) than are the scores 19, 20, and 21 in Data set 2, even though the range is slightly larger in Data set 2.
16. (*a*) For Set A, $\overline{X} = 4.2$, $\overset{*}{s} = 1.72$; for Set B, $\overline{X} = 104.2$, $\overset{*}{s} = 1.72$; for Set C, $\overline{X} = 42$, $\overset{*}{s} = 17.20$. Yes; by adding 100 (*b*) No (*c*) Yes; by multiplying by 10; yes; by multiplying by 10 (*d*) $X_{50} = 4$ for Set A, $X_{50} = 104$ for Set B (*e*) Range $= 5$ for Set A, Range $= 50$ for Set C
17. For the perceived-control group, $\overline{X} = 10$, $\overset{*}{s}{}^2 = 8.53$, $\overset{*}{s} = 2.92$, $X_{50} = 11$, and range $= 10$. For the no-control group, $\overline{X} = 12.5$, $\overset{*}{s}{}^2 = 8.32$, $\overset{*}{s} = 2.88$, $X_{50} = 12.5$, and range $= 12$.
18. For Secret Service personnel, $\overline{X} = 64$, $\overset{*}{s}{}^2 = 166.86$, $\overset{*}{s} = 12.92$, $X_{50} = 60$, and range $= 50$.

For judges, $\overline{X} = 56.57$, $\overset{*2}{s} = 165.39$, $\overset{*}{s} = 12.86$, $X_{50} = 50$, and range = 60. For psychiatrists, $\overline{X} = 57.71$, $\overset{*2}{s} = 149.06$, $\overset{*}{s} = 12.21$, $X_{50} = 60$, and range = 60.

19. (a) (0,2) has the greatest variance. (b) (0,0) or (1,1) or (2,2) has the smallest variance; $\overset{*2}{s} = 0$.

20. For spaced, $\overline{X} = 29.1$, $\overset{*2}{s} = 8.09$, $\overset{*}{s} = 2.84$. For massed, $\overline{X} = 11$, $\overset{*2}{s} = 8.80$, $\overset{*}{s} = 2.97$.

21. 3 min 10 s

22. 31.07 mph

23. The five-number summary for the perceived-control group is:

5 7 11 12 15
 2 4 1 3
  6 5 4

The five-number summary for the no-control group is:

7 11   12.5   14 19
 4   1.5   1.5   5
  5.5   3   6.5

The box plot for the no-control group should show that 19 is an outlier.

24. The five-number summary for the Secret Service personnel is:

40 60 60 70 90
  20 0 10 20
    20 10 30

The five-number summary for the judges is:

30 50 50 70 90
  20 0 20 20
    20 20 40

For the psychiatrists:

30 50 60 60 90
  20 10 0 30
    30 10 30

You should have observed outliers for psychiatrists of 30, 80, 80, and 90, and for Secret Service personnel of 40 and 90.

Chapter 5

1. (a) $z = (90 - 79.5)/6$ (b) $z = (90 - 83)/7$

2. "Joe, a z score is supposed to be something minus its mean divided by its standard deviation, not its variance."

3. (a) IQ = 130 (b) $z = 1.53$

4. $z = (26 - 19)/2 = 3.5$

5. $z = (12 - 10.0)/2.9212 = 0.6847$

6. (a) $\overline{X} = 63$ (b) $\overset{*2}{s} = 41$ (c) $z = (60 - 63)/6.4031 = -0.4685$ (d) 0 (e) 1

7. (a) $\overline{X} = 89$, $\overset{*}{s} = 4.3716$

(b)

Class Grades	z
91	0.4575
93	0.9150
90	0.2287
89	0
90	0.2287
90	0.2287
77	-2.7450
90	0.2287
91	0.4575

(c) Mean = 0, variance = 1

8. (*a*) The shape is the same as the shape of the distribution of the raw scores on the subscale of the personality test. (*b*) 0 (*c*) 1 (*d*) No, because the distribution may be, say, positively skewed, and then less than 50% of the z scores are above the mean of 0 because the mean (of 0) is higher than the median, which has 50% of the scores above it.

9. (*a*) .0495 (*b*) .8907 (*c*) .025 (*d*) .9987 (*e*) .025 (*f*) .0049 (*g*) .0099 (*h*) .3821 (*i*) .7088 (*j*) .9564 (*k*) .901 (*l*) .796 (*m*) .4641 + .4115 = .8756 (*n*) .4656 − .1628 = .3028 (*o*) .4974 − .3665 = .1309 (*p*) .4236 − .0753 = .3483 (*q*) .0049 + .0049 = .0098

10. (*a*) −0.44 (*b*) −0.88 (*c*) 1.13

11. (*a*) 2.28% (*b*) 15.87% (*c*) 25.14% (*d*) 119.2

12. (*a*) 24 h × 296 days = 7104 h, z = (7104 − 9000)/500 = −3.792, percent below −3.80 is .01%. (*b*) How long did it sit on the shelf before you bought it?

13. The percent between z = −1.1 and z = 0.2 is .4436.

14. (*b*) $\overline{X}$ = 49.9667 (*c*) $\overset{*}{s}{}^2$ = 96.2989 (*d*) The difference between $\overline{X}$ and μ is very small, 0.0333, well within sampling variability. (*e*) The difference between $\overset{*}{s}{}^2$ and σ^2 is 3.7011, but much of this is because $\overset{*}{s}{}^2$ is not a good estimate of σ^2. If we use $s^2 = \overset{*}{s}{}^2 [N/(N − 1)] = 99.6195$, we get an estimate that is much closer to σ^2. (*f*) The skewness is negative; the distribution is lumpy and discrete, and 24 may be an outlier. (*g*) The sample distribution is clearly not normal. The normal shape is how the population is described, not the sample. Samples from normally distributed populations can be shaped like this one. (*h*) These are routine differences between samples and populations.

15. (*a*) 0.38% (*b*) 81.64%

16. (*a*) .0918 (*b*) The proportion would increase.

17. (*a*) .6826 (*b*) .0228 (*c*) Yes, because only a .00003 proportion of the parts would be this long if μ = 2 and σ = 0.05. (*d*) 1.9665 and 2.0335

18. 45

19. (*a*) 47.22 (*b*) 15.28

20. (*a*) 67.275 (*b*) 63.45

21. (*a*) 37.36 (*b*) 4.01% (*c*) 29.4 and 38.6 (*d*) 37.36

22. (*a*) 47, z = 0.38 (*b*) 54, z = 1.01, z = 0.30

23. (*a*) z scores are normally distributed only if the original X values are normally distributed. (*b*) The mean of a set of z scores is always 0, so this mean is wrong, or the calculation of the original z scores is wrong. (*c*) The variance of a set of z scores is 0 only if all scores are the same (perhaps they switched the mean in part b and the variance in part c). (*d*) 20% of the scores in a normal distribution would lie above z = 0.84, or only 15.87% of the distribution would lie above z = 1.00. Thus, it is likely that their claim to normality for IQUQ is not accurate.

Chapter 6

1. (*a*) Sale of cold drinks and temperature; sale of umbrellas and inches of rain; attendance and quality of opponent; attendance and quality of home team; sale of any item and attendance; quality of opponent and sale of any item; quality of home team and sale of any item (*b*) Sale of hot drinks and temperature; inches of rain and attendance; inches of rain and sale of cold drinks or peanuts (*c*) Sale of peanuts and temperature; temperature and quality of home team and opponent (*d*) Temperature and attendance (if temperatures are extreme)

2. (*a*) Yes (*b*) Negatively related

3. (*a*) Zero (*b*) Positive (*c*) Negative (*d*) Negative (*e*) Zero (*f*) Positive (*g*) Positive

4. (*a*) There is a slight tendency for shyness to increase as mother's acceptance decreases. (*b*) r^2 = .1024, so 10.24% of the variability of shyness is explained by a linear relationship with mother's acceptance.

5. (*a*) r^2 = .2025, so the percentage is 20.25%. Age, family situation/problems, number of years at the current job, relationships with coworkers and boss (*c*) This is an accurate statement because correlation does not imply causation.

6. (*a*) $\overline{X}$, $\overset{*}{s}{}^2$, s^2, median position, percentile rank (*b*) $\overline{X}$, $\overset{*}{s}{}^2$, s^2 (*c*) None (*d*) $\overset{*}{s}{}^2$, s^2 (*e*) None (*f*) $\overset{*}{s}{}^2$, s^2 (*g*) None (*h*) $\overset{*}{s}{}^2$, s^2 (*i*) None (*j*) z (*k*) None

7. (*b.*) $(\Sigma X)^2 = (38)^2 = 1444$; $(\Sigma Y)^2 = (100)^2 = 10{,}000$ (*c*) $\Sigma X^2 = 338$; $\Sigma Y^2 = 2010$ (*d*) $N = 5$
 (*e*) $\Sigma XY = 757$

8. (*a*) X represents country music airtime, Y represents suicide rates. (*b*) $r = 5/\sqrt{(50)(106)} = .0687$ (*c*) It appears that there is a very small linear relationship, or perhaps no linear relationship.

9. (*b.*) 24.5; 3.1 (*d*) 47.25; 3.89 (*f*) $N = 10$, $\Sigma XY = 680$ (*g*) $r = -.5864$ (*h*) Bandura might have predicted a positive relationship, but we found a negative r. This means that as the amount of television viewing increases, there is a tendency for aggressiveness among pre-schoolers to decrease. (*i*) You might design a study that counts the number of hours of television watched for Barney and non-Barney shows to investigate whether Barney is having an effect on children.

10. (*a*) Means for self and other are 16.5 and 17.25, respectively. Standard deviations for self and other are 4.7958 and 3.1918, respectively. (*c*) $r = .66$; yes, self and other I/E have a moderate positive linear relationship with about 43.56% of the variability of other ratings explained by self ratings.

11. (*a*) $r = .88$ (*b*) $r = .14$. It should be surprising that a change in one score can change r this much; however, the sample size is small and the change in the score is from one of the lowest values to one of the highest values.

12. A value of $r = .11$ shows that there is only a small linear relationship between X and Y, with 1.21% of the variability explained. However, the relationship could be quite strong and be nonlinear.

13. $r = -.4$ shows the strongest linear relationship because $r^2 = .16$ is the largest percentage of variance explained.

14. (*b*) The r is negative and moderate—say, about $-.6$. (*c*) $r = -.87$ (*d*) The value of r would become positive ($r = .93$). (*e*) $r = -.77$, so one pair of scores can radically influence r with this small a sample size, changing the size or even the sign of r.

15. When only the ten selected people are used in the second correlation, the range of the original scores is restricted (attenuated). Such restriction of range and lower variability of the ten people hired can have a major impact on correlation.

16. Correlation does not imply causation; maybe some third variable—say, number of hours in courses or number of hours working—influences both sleep hours and miles run. Also, only 6.25% of the variability in miles run is explained by sleep hours, so sleep hours is only a weak influence, even if causal, on miles run.

17. (*a*) $r = 1.00$ (*b*) $r = 1.00$ (*c*) $r = -1.00$ (*d*) r will be -1 or $+1$ or undefined. (*e*) No, because r is undefined; -1 or $+1$ unless there is zero variability for one of the two variables.

18. (*b*) $r = -.67$ (*c*) $r = -.88$ (*d*) $r = .98$ (*e*) Negatively related; other variables enter the picture in 1974; gas shortage, changes to smaller cars, better gas mileage in newer cars

Chapter 7

1. You would not want to use linear regression because it appears that caffeine intake and amount of studying have a curvilinear relationship.

2. $205

3. (*a*) $Y' = 2X + 10$ (*b*) 20 (*c*) -1

4. (*b*) $Y' = 0.52X - 1.243$ (*c*) r is positive, which means that as waiting room time increased, generally dental anxiety increased.

5. (*b*) $r = -.14$ (*c*) $b = -0.06$ and $a = 20.46$, $Y' = -0.06X + 20.46$

6. (*a*) X is the amount of country music airtime and Y is the suicide rate. (*b*) $b = 0.10$ and $a = 13.2$

7. (*a*) Means for self and other are 16.5 and 17.25, respectively. Standard deviations for self and other are 4.7958 and 3.1918, respectively. (*c*) $b = 0.44$ and $a = 9.99$, $Y' = 0.44X + 9.99$; they are positively related.

8. (*b*) $r = -.59$ (*c*) $b = -0.17$ and $a = 7.22$, $Y' = -0.17X + 7.22$ (*e*) $Y' = 4.53$ (*f*) -0.53

9. (*a*) $b = 0.39$ and $a = 0.97$, $Y' = 0.39X + 0.97$ (*b*) $b = 0.06$ and $a = 3.15$, $Y' = 0.06X +$

3.15. The change in the regression line is not a surprise when you realize the impact of a single score on regression with a small sample size.

10. (c) $b = -0.22$ and $a = 13.14$, $Y' = -0.22X + 13.14$. (d) $b = 0.69$ and $a = -2.75$, $Y' = 0.69X - 2.75$ (e) $b = -0.59$ and $a = 19.78$, $Y' = -0.59X + 19.78$. The single pair of scores has a considerable impact on the regression line, changing it from negative slope to positive, but a larger sample size would moderate this impact.

11. (b) $b = -0.06$ and $a = 17.75$, $Y' = -0.06X + 17.75$ (c) $b = -0.08$ and $a = 19.00$, $Y' = -0.08X + 19.00$ (d) $b = 0.43$ and $a = -10.79$, $Y' = 0.43X - 10.79$ (e) Negatively; other variables enter the picture in 1974; gas shortage, changes to smaller cars, better gas mileage in newer cars

12. (a) $b = 21.93$ and $a = 30,562$, $Y' = 21.93X + 30,562$ (c) You should find $\Sigma e = 0$ within rounding error. (d) \$96,361

13. (a) $b = 25.25$ and $a = -31.01$, $Y' = 25.25X - 31.01$ (b) $r = .57$, $s_{Y \cdot X} = 7.78$ (c) $r^2 = .33$, so 33% of the variability in DRG is accounted for by CIG. (d) Because DRG is the frequency of illicit drug use, the large number of zeros is because many students don't use drugs. However, for any student with a CIG score higher than 1.228, you would predict greater than zero drug use. Obviously the ability to predict drug use for any given student is not perfect; you have accounted for 33% of the variability in drug use, not all of it.

14. (a) $\overline{Y} = 122.8$, $\overline{X} = 123.2$, $s_X^{*2} = 104.16$, $s_Y^{*2} = 73.36$ (b) $r = .68$ (c) $b = 0.57$ and $a = 52.02$ (d) For pair A, $Y' = 120.39$, $Y - Y' = -10.39$. (e) Σe should be zero within rounding error. (f) No, for pair D, the absolute value of $e = Y - Y'$ is larger; $\Sigma e^2 = 194.91$, $\Sigma(Y - \overline{Y})^2 = 366.8$; the least-squares criterion (g) $\overline{Y}'$ should equal $\overline{Y} = 122.8$ within rounding error. (h) Y' for $\overline{X}$ should equal $\overline{Y}$ within rounding error. (i) $s_{Y \cdot X} = 8.06$

15. (b) $b = 0.81$ and $a = 13.07$ (c) $r = .73$, $100r^2 = 53\%$ (d) $s_{Y \cdot X} = 2.79$ is smaller than $s_Y^* = 3.79$ due to variance explained by linear regression.

16. (a) $Y' = -0.53X + 75.81$ (b) 66.25

17. (a) $Y' = -0.29X + 17.51$ (b) -14.05, or more practically zero (c) $s_{Y \cdot X} = 1.94$ (d) Limits of -17.86 to -10.24; for someone with 110 min of exercise per week, we are 95% confident that the number of visits to physicians per year is in this interval, still practically zero.

18. (a) $Y' = 2.52X - 137.46$ (b) 139.99% (c) $s_{Y \cdot X} = 22.79$ (d) Limits of 95.32 to 184.66; for someone who spends 110 min studying, we are 95% confident that his or her quiz percentage will be in this interval, or more practically we predict an A with 95% confidence.

19. (a) $Y' = 0.65X + 51.46$ (b) 122.52 (c) $s_{Y \cdot X} = 16.43$ (d) 90.33 to 154.71; for someone whose mother's IQ is 110, we are 95% confident that her IQ score is in this interval.

20.

	Explained by Work Hours	Not Explained by Work Hours	Total
Proportion of Variance in Study Hours	.27	.73	1.00
Amount of Variance in Study Hours	7.06	19.06	26.12

21. (a) 538 (b) Limits of 400.8 to 675.2 (c) The confidence interval says you can get 600 or higher, but the predicted score of 538 says that not much improvement is predicted on the average. Remember that there is considerable individual variability, and the improvement depends on you and how you prepare for the test.

22. The equation with the smallest MS_e (5.9) has X_1 and X_2 as predictors. This means that the most parsimonious equation has number of hours of TV watched and number of children in the family as predictors of aggression (but only 39% of the variability in aggression is explained by this equation). Generally, as either of these variables increases, aggression increases.

23. (a) Predictor variables are the 12 factors that are rated on their importance to the decision to intervene, with the criterion variable being willingness to intervene. (b) These three

variables explain 28.5% of the variability in willingness to intervene, leaving 71.5% unexplained. (*c*) Look for the equation with the smallest MS_e because it gets the best balance between the variability explained and the number of predictors. (It appears that not much is gained over the three variables in part b by adding the other nine variables—only 2.7%.)

24. You should get a multiple R^2 of .5617 for both variables, showing an increase from the .0529 for baby length alone, which indicates the importance of gender as a predictor.

25. (*c*) The most parsimonious equation is the six-predictor equation with R^2 = .90377 and predictors of M, K, G, I, S, and HW. Only slightly worse is the five-predictor equation with R^2 = .89630 and the first five predictors above (not HW). The best prediction equation is MS' = 7.8179 − 0.2579M + 0.1143K + 0.2686G + 0.1283I + 2.7700S + 0.8028HW.

Chapter 8

1. (*a*) A consumer magazine might give probabilities for repairs of different components of cars, and you could choose the model with the lowest probabilities. (*b*) Empirical probabilities (*c*) Many people will tell the salesman what he wants to hear. Also, if they were not satisfied, they would likely go somewhere else to buy a car. This sample is not randomly selected.

2. (*a*) Grades A, B, C, D, F (*b*) Any grade—say, B (*c*) Grade C or lower (*d*) $p(A)$ = .11 (*e*) .34; addition (Or) rule (*f*) Yes

3. (*a*) 4/52 = .08 (*b*) 13/52 = .25 (*c*) 1/52 = .02 (*d*) .31

4. (*a*) .44; .17 (*b*) .44 + .20 = .64 (*c*) .20(50) = 10 (*d*) (.20)(.20) = .04 (*e*) Empirical

5. No, $p(\text{paid}|A)$ = .078, which is not equal to $p(\text{paid})$ = .053 [or $p(\text{paid}|B)$ = .031 is not equal to .053].

6. (*a*) .20 + .30 = .50 (*b*) 1.00 − .50 = .50

7. (*a*) .047; .093 (*b*) .103 (*c*) .128 (*d*) a is joint, b is marginal, c is conditional.

8. Set 3 is not a true set of probabilities because the probabilities total to more than 1.00; set 4 is not a true set of probabilities because the probabilities total to less than 1.00; set 5 is not a true set of probabilities because none of these entries is a probability.

9. (*a*) .60 (*b*) .70 (*c*) .50 (*d*) No, .70 = $p(\text{truck}|\text{male})$ ≠ $p(\text{truck})$ = .60 (*e*) .35, $p(\text{truck and male})$ = $p(\text{truck}|\text{male})p(\text{male})$ = (.70)(.50) = .35

10. (*b.*) .4299 ≠ .3967 because some people use more than one tobacco product, so they are counted twice or more in the .4299 probability. (*c*) $p(\text{cigarette and snuff})$, $p(\text{cigarette and chewing tobacco})$, and so on—that is, all of the tobacco products taken two at a time, then all taken three at a time, then four at a time, and finally all five.

11. (*a*) The 500 couples (*b*) One of the engaged/dating couples with the male-initiated touch (*c*) Male-initiated touch (*d*) 1/500 = .002 (*e*) 118/500 = .236 (*f*) $p(\text{male}|\text{married/cohabiting one year or more})$ (*g*) .131 (*h*) .236 ≠ .308; independence. (*i*) Multiplication (And) rule (*j*) (101/500)(41/101) = .082 (*k*) Addition (Or) rule (*l*) (118/500) + (227/500) − (70/500) = .55 (*m*) Zero; mutually exclusive

12. (*a*) With replacement (*b*) With (*c*) Without (*d*) Without

13. $p(z \geq 2.5)$ = .0062

14. (*a*) 1/6 = .17 (*b*) Multiplication (And) rule; (1/6)(1/6) = .028 (*c*) 2 + 2, 1 + 3, 3 + 1 (*d*) Addition (Or) rule; 3(1/36) = .083 (*e*) $p(2)$ = 1/36, $p(3)$ = 2/36, $p(4)$ = 3/36, $p(5)$ = 4/36, $p(6)$ = 5/36, $p(7)$ = 6/36, $p(8)$ = 5/36, $p(9)$ = 4/36, $p(10)$ = 3/36, $p(11)$ = 2/36, $p(12)$ = 1/36, sum = 36/36 = 1.00

15. $p(X \leq 2)$ = .52559

16. p = .0036 + .0001 = .0037, p = .3456 + .1296 = .4752

Chapter 9

1. No, because students are randomly sampled from volunteers.

2. The random sample is from the population of volunteers from introductory psychology, but the researcher could make the judgment that the sample is from the population of "all students . . ."; the population depends on the target of the researcher's inferences. Yes, because

the researcher could make the judgment that the volunteers from this university are similar to all U.S. college students enrolled in a similar course.

3. Answers are in this order: population distribution, sample distribution, and sampling distribution of $\overline{X}$. (*a*) X, $\overline{X}$, X (*b*) Unknown, known but not a standard shape, approaches normal as N approaches infinity (*c*) μ, $\overline{X}$, μ (*d*) σ^2, $\overset{*}{s}^2$, σ^2/N (*e*) Cannot obtain, can obtain, cannot obtain

4. (*a*) Small, obtainable, real (*b*) Large, unobtainable, hypothetical (*c*) Large, unobtainable, hypothetical (*d*) Small, obtainable, real

5. (*b*) Values of $\overline{X}$ and their frequencies: 5 (1), 5.5 (2), 6 (3), 6.5 (4), 7 (3), 7.5 (2), 8 (1) (*d*) $\mu = 6.5$ (*e*) $\sigma^2/N = 1.25/2 = 0.625$ (*f*) Normal; it is symmetric, unimodal, higher in the middle and lower in the tails but not normal.

6. $\mu_{\overline{X}} = 7.5$, $\sigma_{\overline{X}}^2 = 1.34/31 = 0.04$, shape will be normal.

7. $\mu_{\overline{X}} = 20$, $\sigma_{\overline{X}}^2 = 3.7/84 = 0.04$, shape will be normal.

8. (*a*) 100 (*b*) 225/25 = 9 (*c*) $z_{\overline{X}} = (115 - 100)/(15/5) = 15/3 = 5$ (*d*) $p(z_{\overline{X}} \geq 5) < .00003$; yes

9. Gets smaller (cannot obtain from Table A.2); gets larger (.0013); only the probability based on $N = 100$ would not be questionable.

10. $p(\overline{X} \geq 18) = p(z_{\overline{X}} \geq 1.33) = .0918$; normality and independence (random sampling) of the number of defects; no, because .0918 is not small, so an average of 18 defects in four cars is not unusual if $\mu = 16$ and $\sigma = 3$.

11. $p(\overline{X} \geq 18) = p(z_{\overline{X}} \geq 2.00) = .0228$; yes, because .0228 is small. The difference is due to the larger N (9 here but only 4 in Exercise 10), even though $\overline{X} = 18$ in both cases.

12. $p(\overline{X} \geq 27.8) = p(z_{\overline{X}} \geq 2.24) = .0125$

13. No, there are other definitions of "good" estimates (such as least-squares estimates); no; yes; no, only to $\overline{X}$

14. False; an unbiased statistic has a mean (mean of its sampling distribution) equal to the parameter, but this is no guarantee about any given statistic.

15. A shorter confidence interval will result from a, b, and f.

16. 108.95 to 115.05; it is a range of values that we are 95% confident includes the value of μ, or that 95% of such intervals would include the value of μ. I am 95% confident that 108.95 to 115.05 includes the value of μ.

17. (*a*) 1.95 (*b*) 1.96 (*c*) 84.24 to 91.90 (*d*) No (*e*) A likely range of values for the population mean of the IQs of deaf children is from 84.24 to 91.90, which does not include the mean IQ of the hearing population, 100.

18. (*a*) 1.98 (*b*) 0.066 (*c*) 1.96 (*d*) 1.85 to 2.11 (*e*) No (*f*) A likely range of values for the population mean of the times to answer for hypertensives is from 1.85 to 2.11 s, which does not include the mean of the normal population, 1.35 s.

19. (*a*) $\mu_{\overline{X}} = 4.06$, $\sigma_{\overline{X}}^2 = 0.0027$, shape should be approximately normal because of the Central Limit Theorem and the fact that $N = 63$ is fairly large. (*b*) -4.07 (*c*) $p(z_{\overline{X}} \leq -4.07) < .00003$; yes (*d*) 1.96 (*e*) 3.75 to 3.95 (*f*) No (*g*) A likely range of values for the population mean of the pain intensity for participants instructed to focus on the pain is from 3.75 to 3.95, which does not include the mean of the population with the usual instructions, 4.06.

Chapter 10

1. (*a*) The exploratory phase includes the original description with a graph of responses according to month. The subsequent graphs of each month from ages 13 to 23 may also fit in EDA, but they confirm a speculative reason for the high frequencies in summer months. (*b*) They start toward confirming when they examine age as a reason for the high frequencies in summer months. (*c*) There is not a second study nor is there any mention of testing theories.

2. (*a*) If country music does not influence depression, then the average depression score for people in the study should be similar to the norm. (*b*) The "if" part: Country music does not influence depression. (*c*) That the "if" part is true, so country music does not influence depression.

3. (*a*) The null hypothesis is H_0: $\mu = 22.55$ and the alternative is H_1: $\mu \neq 22.55$. (*b*) H_0 (*c*) Inhibition among singers is lower than the norms for nonsingers.

4. Identify problem: Your beliefs about gender, age, and dental anxiety identify the problem. Formulate hypotheses: The hypotheses are H_0: $\mu \geq 7.5$ and H_1: $\mu < 7.5$. Design and run the study: Collect dental anxiety data for women over age 25. Test hypotheses: Compute the sample mean of the dental anxiety scores for your sample; then use $\mu = 7.5$ and $\sigma^2 = 1.34$ along with N and $\overline{X}$ to compute $z_{\overline{X}}$, and finally use $z_{\overline{X}}$ to test the null hypothesis. Draw conclusions: If $z_{\overline{X}}$ is significant and you reject H_0, then conclude that women over 25 have less dental anxiety than average; if not, then conclude that women over 25 have average dental anxiety.

5. (a) H_0: $\mu \geq 7.5$ and H_1: $\mu < 7.5$; the lower or left tail (b) H_0: $\mu \leq 100$ and H_1: $\mu > 100$; the upper or right tail (c) H_0: $\mu = 100$ and H_1: $\mu \neq 100$; both tails (d) H_0: $\mu = 20$ and H_1: $\mu \neq 20$; both tails

6. (a) H_0: $\mu = 3.10$ and H_1: $\mu \neq 3.10$; both tails (b) H_0: $\mu = 6.70$ and H_1: $\mu \neq 6.70$; both tails (c) For engineering students, H_0: $\mu \leq 12.10$ and H_1: $\mu > 12.10$; the upper or right tail (d) For female faculty, H_0: $\mu \geq 43,750$ and H_1: $\mu < 43,750$; the lower or left tail

7. .025; .005

8. (a) $z_{crit} = 1.645$; $z \geq 1.645$ (b) $z_{crit} = 2.33$; $z \geq 2.33$; these rejection values are values of statistics and $\alpha = .01$ is a probability. (c) $z_{crit} = -1.645$; because you are looking for extreme values in the left tail, not in the middle of the distribution (d) $z_{crit} = -2.33$; $z \leq -2.33$ (e) $z_{crit} = \pm 1.96$; $z \geq 1.96$ and $z \leq -1.96$ (f) $z_{crit} = \pm 2.58$; $z \geq 2.58$ and $z \leq -2.58$

9. (a) H_0: $\mu = 100$ and H_1: $\mu \neq 100$ (b) $z_{crit} = \pm 1.96$ (c) $z_{\overline{X}} = -6.11$ (d) $-6.11 < -1.96$, so reject H_0, the performance by these deaf children is significantly different from that for hearing children. (e) The performance on the regular IQ test was so low that it is unlikely that deaf children have the same average IQ score on this IQ test as hearing children.

10. H_0: $\mu \geq 100$ and H_1: $\mu < 100$, so $z_{crit} = -2.33$ for $\alpha = .01$. Because $-6.11 < -2.33$, we still reject H_0 and conclude that deaf children have lower IQ scores.

11. (a) H_0: $\mu \geq 4.06$ and H_1: $\mu < 4.06$ (b) $z_{crit} = -1.645$ (c) $z_{\overline{X}} = -4.07$ (d) $-4.07 < -1.645$, so reject H_0, the average pain intensity is significantly lower than for the standard instructions. (e) The ratings of pain intensity when students are told to focus on the pain are lower than those when students are told to ignore the pain.

12. (a) H_0: $\mu \leq .85$ and H_1: $\mu > .85$ (b) $z_{crit} = 1.645$ (c) $z_{\overline{X}} = -2.29$ (d) $-2.29 < 1.645$, so retain H_0, the average proportion of memories is not significantly higher than that for everyday memories.

13. (a) H_0: $\mu \leq 34$ and H_1: $\mu > 34$ (b) $z_{crit} = 1.645$ (c) $z_{\overline{X}} = 20.46$ (d) $20.46 > 1.645$, so reject H_0, the average level of HDL is significantly higher than the average HDL for this age women. (e) This was not a controlled study with randomization of subjects to a combination of the two drugs or to a placebo; rather, the women had gone to their doctors who had then prescribed for them the combination of drugs. Maybe the women also dieted.

14. $z_{\overline{X}} = -1.84 < -1.65$, so reject H_0.

15. $z_{\overline{X}} = -1.84 > -1.96$, so retain H_0. Exercise 14 used a one-tailed test, which is more powerful than the two-tailed test here.

16. For all of these, if you get the p-value from SAS or another canned package, you must divide the p-value by 2 if your hypotheses are directional to get a one-tailed probability. For Exercise 11, reject H_0 if the one-tailed probability $\leq \alpha = .05$ and if the pain intensity was lower than for the standard instructions (in agreement with the alternative hypothesis). For Exercise 12, reject H_0 if the one-tailed probability $\leq \alpha = .05$ and if the proportion of details remembered was higher than for everyday memories (in agreement with the alternative hypothesis). For Exercise 13, reject H_0 if the one-tailed probability $\leq \alpha = .05$ and if the level of HDL was higher than average for women of that age (in agreement with the alternative hypothesis).

17. Reject H_0 if the two-tailed p-value $\leq .01$.

18. (a) H_0: $\mu \leq 1.35$ and H_1: $\mu > 1.35$ (b) $z_{\overline{X}} = 9.49$, and the one-tailed p-value $< .00003$ (the p-value for $z = 4.00$). (c) $.00003 < .05$, so reject H_0.

19. H_0: $\mu \leq 50$ and H_1: $\mu > 50$, $z_{\overline{X}} = 1.93$, $z_{crit} = 1.645$, so reject H_0. It is likely that the psychologist is wrong and you are right.

20. Both probabilities are less than $\alpha = .05$, so both results are significant (if both alternative hypotheses were nondirectional). "Significance" is not relative; you either have it or you don't, so both results were significant, and the other result is not necessarily better than that of your friend.

Chapter 11

1. (*a*) This is not a true experiment, and causal statements can be made only from a true experiment. (*b*) It seems like a little difference in height. (*c*) Large N of 15,028; perhaps people at banks, shopping areas, and exhibitions are more homogeneous than the general population and have lower variance.
2. (*a*) A Type I error would be saying someone had lied when he or she had not. A Type II error would be not to identify a real liar as a liar. (*b*) You could be making a Type I error. You couldn't make a Type II error. You might lose the person's friendship. (*c*) A Type I error of falsely rejecting
3. (*a*) No (*b*) The decisions to reject and retain are mutually exclusive, so you cannot make both decisions at the same time.
4. Only Type I errors; .01
5. (*a*) No (*b*) μ cannot be two different numbers. (*c*) See Chapter 10, Exercise 13, answers above. (*d*) Made a Type I error; made a correct decision (*e*) Used $\alpha = .05$ (*f*) No
6. (*a*) No (*b*) μ cannot be two different numbers. (*c*) See Chapter 10, Exercise 12, answers above. (*d*) Made a correct decision; made a Type II error (*e*) Used a moderate-sized sample (*f*) No
7. (*a*) A Type I error would be not to make the loan when they should; a Type II error would be to make the loan when they should not. (*b*) The cost of a Type I error is loss of interest on a loan that would have been repaid; the cost of a Type II error is the money lost on a defaulted loan.
8. (*a*) A Type I error would be to say the setting has shifted when it hasn't. A Type II error would be to say the setting has not shifted when it has. (*b*) The cost of a Type I error would be the time lost to shut down the plant to adjust the setting (lost productivity); the cost of a Type II error would be the expense of recalling defective parts.
9. Power is the ability to see whether the mean IQ for deaf children is different from 100, the probability of rejecting H_0: $\mu = 100$.
10. 180
11. α; 1.0
12. 0; 1.0
13. .80
14. Essentially zero
15. (*a*) Increased power from a larger sample size might have found conclusions i and iii to hold for both social groups. (*b*) Conclusion ii would not change with an increase in sample size because both social groups are already better than the control group. (*c*) Rigor or standardization of the exercise program might increase power because of bigger differences; increased power might also result from improvement in the measure of aerobic fitness (the variance might be lower).
16. (*a*) $z_{\bar{x}} = 1.36$, one-tailed *p*-value $= .0869$ (*b*) $z_{\bar{x}} = 1.66$, one-tailed *p*-value $= .0485$ (*c*) $z_{\bar{x}} = 3.46$, one-tailed *p*-value $= .0003$ (for $z = 3.45$) (*d*) Because the *p*-values decrease with increasing N, the likelihood of rejection increases (for $\alpha = .05$ did not reject for 12, barely rejected for 18, and rejected with 78).
17. (*a*) Yes, larger N (*b*) No, smaller N (*c*) No, the directional hypothesis is wrong about predicting direction. (*d*) Yes, the directional hypothesis is right about predicting direction. (*e*) No, smaller α (*f*) Yes, smaller σ^2
18. (*a*) $z_{\bar{x}} = -4.07$, one-tailed *p*-value $< .00003$ (The *p*-value for $z = -4.00$) (*b*) $z_{\bar{x}} = -1.62$, one-tailed *p*-value $= .0526$, so the smaller N gave lower power because, for $\alpha = .05$, we

could reject with 63 but not with 10. (*c*) $z_{\bar{X}} = 4.07$, one-tailed *p*-value $<$ .00003 (the *p*-value for $z = 4.00$), but you retain H_0 because the direction of the result does not agree with the prediction of H_1.

19. Increase *N*, decrease σ^2, increase α, or switch to directional hypotheses. Yes, if I judged that .1 (only one-tenth of 1%) was so small that I would not want to detect it as a significant difference.

20. (*a*) Observational research (*b*) Criterion variable (*c*) Predictor variable (*d*) H_0: $\mu \leq 22.59$ and H_1: $\mu \leq 22.59$ (*e*) $z_{\text{crit}} = 1.645$ (*f, g*) For actors, $z_{\bar{X}} = -0.22$, so retain H_0; for dancers, $z_{\bar{X}} = 2.01$, so reject H_0; for musicians, $z_{\bar{X}} = 3.38$, so reject H_0; for singers, $z_{\bar{X}} = 1.59$, so retain H_0. (*h*) A Type I error could have been made for dancers and musicians; a Type II error could have been made for actors and singers. (*i*) The test for musicians probably had the most power because it had the largest sample size. (*j*) The tests on actors and singers might need increased power: increase sample size and increase α are about the only two options open.

21. (*a*) Actors and dancers: H_0: $\mu \geq 13.16$ and H_1: $\mu < 13.16$. Musicians: H_0: $\mu \leq 13.16$ and H_1: $\mu > 13.16$. Singers: H_0: $\mu = 13.16$ and H_1: $\mu \neq 13.16$. (*b*) Actors and dancers, $z_{\text{crit}} = -1.645$; musicians, $z_{\text{crit}} = 1.645$; singers, $z_{\text{crit}} = \pm 1.96$ (*c*) That for musicians because the sample size is large, 65 (*d, e*) For actors, $z_{\bar{X}} = 1.46$, so retain H_0. For dancers, $z_{\bar{X}} = 2.66$, so retain H_0. For musicians, $z_{\bar{X}} = 4.97$, so reject H_0. For singers, $z_{\bar{X}} = 2.74$, so reject H_0. (*f*) The tests for actors and dancers because the direction of H_1 did not agree with the direction of the results. (*g*) You would be tempted to make the alternative agree with the results.

22. (*a*) Observational research (*b*) Intervention is the criterion variable; the other two are predictor variables. (*c*) The sample size of 388 (*d*) Perhaps, but the criterion variable is only qualitative and might need the larger sample size to detect differences. Also, this is relatively new research, so higher power may be needed because extraneous variables may not be controlled.

23. (*a*) H_0: $\mu \leq 17.9$, H_1: $\mu > 17.9$, $\mu_0 = 17.9$, $\mu_1 = 22$ (*b*) From Table A.2, $p(z \geq -1.04) = .8508$. (*c*) 35.34, or 36 (*d*) Yes (*e*) i) 1.645; 20.20 ii) -1.28 iii) $p(z \geq -1.28) = .8997$ from Table A.2. Yes, because 42 is larger than 36, so I expect the power to be greater than .85.

Chapter 12

1. (*a*) 17 (*b*) 60 (*c*) -1.740 (*d*) ± 2.021 (*e*) ± 3.055 (*f*) 1.725 (*g*) -1.771
2. (*a*) 6 (*b*) 5 (*c*) ± 2.571 (*d*) $\bar{X} = 21.5$, $s = 1.87$, $t = 3.27$ (*e*) $t = 3.27 > t_{\text{crit}} = 2.571$, so reject H_0. (*f*) The average SA score for college men differs from 19.
3. (*a*) H_0: $\mu \leq .85$ and H_1: $\mu > .85$ (*b*) 21 (*c*) 1.721 (*d*) $\bar{X} = .83$, $s = 0.0555$, $t = -1.65$ (*e*) Retain H_0 because the observed *t* is negative and not in agreement with H_1. (*f*) The researcher was wrong in his prediction; they didn't remember more, but less.
4. (*a*) H_0: $\mu \leq 1.35$ and H_1: $\mu > 1.35$ (*b*) 11 (*c*) 1.796 (*d*) $\bar{X} = 1.98$, $s = 0.80$, $t = 2.72$ (*e*) Reject H_0, $2.72 > 1.796$. (*f*) People with hypertension do answer more slowly (more seconds).
5. (*a*) $t = -4.14 < -2.821$, so reject H_0. (*b*) We assume that the observations came from a normal population and are independent (randomly sampled).
6. $t = 1.41 < 1.753$, so retain H_0. (*b*) $t = 3.51 > 1.662$ (t_{crit} with $df = 90$), so reject H_0. (*c*) Perhaps; I don't know enough about this test to make a good judgment. Larger sample size gives higher power.
7. (*a*) 6.72 to 6.94 (*b*) I am 95% confident that 6.72 to 6.94 includes the true value of μ. (*c*) Yes, because the setting, 6.70, is not in the interval.
8. (*a*) 19.54 to 23.46 (*b*) I am 95% confident that 19.54 to 23.46 includes the true value of μ. (*c*) Wider; the critical values are larger. (*d*) As I increase the degree of confidence, my computed confidence interval will get wider.
9. (*a*) 0.87 to 2.93 (*b*) No; no (*c*) 1.10 to 2.70; yes (2.70 is rounded from 2.697); yes (*d*) Reducing variance makes confidence intervals narrower.
10. (*a*) 83.42 to 92.72 (*b*) Yes (*c*) The total IQ score of deaf children is not 100.
11. (*a*) 16 (*b*) 60 (*c*) $-.389$ (*d*) $\pm .304$ (*e*) $\pm .684$ (*f*) .369 (*g*) $-.458$

12. (*a*) .441 (*b*) Retain H_0. (*c*) Self-acceptance and locus of control are not significantly related.
13. (*a*) $r = .59$ (*b*) 6 (*c*) .622 (*d*) Retain H_0. There is not a significant linear relationship between father and son IQs.
14. (*a*) .99 (*b*) 9 (*c*) $-.521$ (*d*) Reject H_0. There is a significant negative linear relationship between age and the body's ability to repair itself.
15. $r = -.67$, $< -.632$, reject H_0. Thus, there is a significant negative relationship between speed and miles per gallon. For the first five pairs, it appears that there is a strong negative relationship. For the last five pairs, it appears that there is a weak positive relationship, but neither X nor Y has much variability.
16. (*a*) Yes (*b*) $P = .65$, $z_P = 10.93$ (*c*) Yes, because $10.93 > 1.645$ (*d*) Observational research
17. (*a*) .109 (*b*) No; we need 40 but have only 32. (*c*) We can compute the *p*-value using binomial computations. (*d*) For example, $p(f = 1) = 8.78\text{E}-15$.
18. No, because $z_P = 1.41 < 1.645$. Yes, because $z_P = 1.70 > 1.645$
19. Yes, because $z_P = 2.21 > 1.645$
20. Yes, because $z_P = 2.81 > 1.645$
21. (*a*) One-sample t (*b*) r (*c*) r (*d*) r (*e*) One-sample t (*f*) Test of proportion (*g*) Test of proportion (*h*) Test of proportion (*i*) Confidence interval

Chapter 13

1. One-sample case uses only one sample, compares $\overline{X}$ to μ (μ must be given in H_0); two-sample case uses two samples, compares $\overline{X}_1 - \overline{X}_2$ to zero.
2. $t = 2.45 > 2.042$, so reject H_0 and conclude that there is a significant difference between the experimental and traditional methods.
3. (*a*) $t = 1.99 > 1.980$, so reject H_0 and conclude that there is a significant difference between boys and girls on family worries. (*b*) $\eta^2 = .032$ and $\omega^2 = .024$; about 2% to 3%.
4. (*a*) The AWS test, because the sample sizes are not 15 or larger (*b*) Retain H_0 because $t' = 0.44 < 2.101$. No, this is not a true experiment.
5. (*a*) The AWS test, because the sample sizes are not equal (*b*) $t' = 1.81 < 1.990$ (use $df = 80$ in place of 86), so retain H_0.
6. (*a*) Test H_0: $\mu_S \leq \mu_H$. Yes, reject H_0 because $t' = 1.78 > 1.734$ (AWS $df = 17.98$ rounds to 18). (*b*) Yes (*c*) $\eta^2 = .1490$ and $\omega^2 = .0971$; about 9.7% to 14.9%
7. 0.92 to 10.08
8. (*a*) -0.14 to 1.00 (*b*) If zero is contained in the interval, retain H_0. (*c*) No, here we retain, whereas there we rejected. (*d*) This is because in Exercise 6 we used $\alpha = .05$, whereas here we used a 99% confidence interval, which is equivalent to using $\alpha = .01$.
9. $t = 3.31$, so reject H_0 because $3.31 > 2.000$.
11. $t = 2.22$, so reject H_0 because $2.22 > 2.160$.
12. (*a*) H_0: $\mu_1 - \mu_2 = 0$ (*b*) Two groups (*c*) The participants are independent both between and within groups (random assignment to groups is preferred). (*d*) We assume normality of observations, independence of observations within groups, and equal variances between groups. We need $n_1 = n_2 \geq 15$ so that the t is robust to unequal variances, and we should be sure that we have independent observations (no obvious dependency).
13. (*a*) H_0: $\mu_1 - \mu_2 = 0$ (*b*) Two groups (*c*) The participants are independent both between and within groups (random assignment to groups is preferred). (*d*) We assume normality of observations and independence of observations within groups. We don't need equal sample sizes, but the observations should be independent.
14. (*a*) H_0: $\mu_1 - \mu_2 = 0$ (*b*) Two groups of scores that are related between groups (*c*) Scores are from two measures taken on each participant, naturally occurring pairs, or two participants who have been matched (paired) on some extraneous variable. (*d*) We assume pairs of scores (or d's) are independent and normally distributed. (*d*) Independence must be met.
15. The denominator of the two-dependent-sample t should be smaller, making it easier to reject H_0. No, the critical value for the two-dependent-sample t is larger, making it harder to reject H_0.

16. (*a*) The before and after groups of scores for the high-anxiety participants (*b*) Two-dependent-sample t (*c*) It stands for *p*-value and, because it is more than .05, the results are nonsignificant (NS).

17. (*a*) Two-independent-sample t because the sample sizes are equal and larger than 15 (*b*) $t = 2.68 > 2.014$ (for $df = 45$ instead of 48), so reject H_0.

18. (*a*) The AWS t' because the sample sizes are not equal (*b*) $t' = 2.78 > 2.021$ (for $df = 40$ instead of 42.3), so reject H_0.

19. Two-dependent-sample t because the scores are paired by batch (*b*) $t = 0.53 < 2.447$, so retain H_0.

20. (*a*) Two-independent-sample t because the sample sizes are equal and 15, and there is no obvious dependency (and no pairing) (*b*) $t = 0.47 < 1.701$ (one-tailed test looking for increase), so retain H_0 and conclude that the new material did not increase the weight of the final product.

21. (*a*) AWS t' because the sample sizes are less than 15 (and there is no pairing) (*b*) $t' = 1.45 < 2.101$, so retain H_0. (*c*) No, we cannot conclude that there are any significant differences in the treatments in effectiveness in reducing smoking. (*d*) No, because the participants self-selected into the treatments. Any subject variables could be uncontrolled extraneous variables and potentially confounded with the treatments.

22. (*a*) Two-dependent-sample t because participants were paired (*b*) $t = 2.05 < 2.262$, so retain H_0. (*c*) We cannot conclude that the treatments are different in effectiveness of weight reduction. (*d*) Yes, because the participants were randomly assigned to the treatments. Possible extraneous variables are starting weight, gender, age, body type, and any number of other possible differences (for example, personality type or childhood treatment by parents). The first four are controlled by pairing, others by random assignment within pairs, so there should be no confounding.

23. (*a*) Two-dependent-sample t because there are two measurements on each participant (*b*) $t = 6.90 > 4.303$, so reject H_0. (*c*) Yes; the small sample size is a concern only with respect to generalizing to other participants, not with respect to statistical significance.

24. (*a*) .44 (*b*) $z_{P_1 - P_2} = 2.85$ (*c*) $2.85 > 1.96$, so reject H_0.

25. $z_{P_1 - P_2} = 8.19 > 1.96$, so reject H_0.

26. $z_{P_1 - P_2} = 6.91 > 1.96$, so reject H_0 (this difference is significant).

27. $z_{P_1 - P_2} = 0.03 < 1.96$, so retain H_0 (this difference is not significant).

28. (*a*) $z_{P_1 - P_2} = 6.11 > 1.96$, so reject H_0 (this difference is significant). (*b*) For I versus II, $z_{P_1 - P_2} = 2.20 > 1.96$, so reject H_0 (this difference is significant); for I versus III, $z_{P_1 - P_2} = 1.63 < 1.96$, so retain H_0 (this difference is not significant); for I versus IV, $z_{P_1 - P_2} = 0.88 < 1.96$, so retain H_0 (this difference is not significant); for I versus V, $z_{P_1 - P_2} = 3.42 > 1.96$, so reject H_0 (this difference is significant). (*c*) $z_{P_1 - P_2} = 10.06 > 1.96$, so reject H_0 (this difference is significant).

Chapter 14

1. (*a*) 42 (*b*) 14 (*c*) 3 (*d*) The 13th score in the second group
2. (*a*) 45 (*b*) 9 (*c*) 5 (*d*) The eighth score in the fourth group
3. (*a*) 2, 60 (*b*) 1, 6 (*c*) 3, 16 (*d*) 2, 24
4. 4 and 5
5. (*a*) 3.15 (*b*) 5.99 (*c*) 3.24 (*d*) 2.69
6. (*a*) 4.13 (*b*) 5.39 (*c*) 8.53 (*d*) 3.72
7. Use 2.49 for $df_B = 4$ and $df_W = 80$.
8. See Section 14.2 on the logic of ANOVA.
9. (*a*) You need to know s^2_{pooled} to be able to form the F; only then can you test H_0. (*b*) $F = 1.12 < 3.32$, so retain H_0. (*c*) $F = 7.27 > 3.32$, so reject H_0.
10. (*a*) $F = 2.44 < 3.24$, so retain H_0. (*b*) $F = 4.87 > 2.87$, so reject H_0. (*c*) $F = 4.87 > 3.24$, so reject H_0. (*d*) $F = 9.74 > 2.87$, so reject H_0. (*e*) Increasing n increases power, and reducing variance increases power; yes.

11. (*a*)

Source	SS	df	MS	F
Between	20	2	10	5
Within	54	27	2	
Total	74	29		

(*b*)

Source	SS	df	MS	F
Between	24	3	8	2
Within	160	40	4	
Total	184	43		

12. (*a*) Means for no exercise, 10.5, general exercise, 20, increased exercise, 25.25. Grand mean, 18.58; grand median, 19.5. (*b*, *c*) $F = 25.23$ (*d*) The ANOVA obtains a variance based on the means of the exercise groups and compares it to a variance based on the vigor scores within the groups. The F led us to reject the null hypothesis of equal vigor means for the three exercise groups, which says that the variance based on the means is larger than the variance based on the vigor scores, so we say that the population means on vigor for the three groups are not equal.

13. (*a*) Groups DR1 and DR2 have negative skewness; group IR has positive skewness; averages in order from largest to smallest are DR1, DR2, and IR. (*b*) $F = 11.95 > 3.25$ (*df* of 2, 38), so reject H_0.

14. (*a*) $F = 10.76 > 4.02$ (*df* of 1, 55) (*b*) $t^2 = (-3.28)^2 = 10.76$; yes; yes

15. $\eta^2 = .85$ and $\omega^2 = .80$

16. $\eta^2 = .38$ and $\omega^2 = .34$

17. (*b*, *c*) Results on the number of correct responses include means (standard deviations) of 12.73 (2.63) for children, 12.47 (2.47) for the neural network model, and 10.27 (2.43) for the stages model. These means were significantly different, $F_{2, 42} = 4.35$, $p = .0192$, but accounted for only 13% to 17% of the variability in number of correct responses ($\omega^2 = .13$ and $\eta^2 = .17$).

18. (*b*, *c*) Results on attraction/IJS scores include means (standard deviations) of 8.08 (2.69) for low competence, 8.96 (2.60) for medium competence, and 9.54 (2.15) for high competence. These means were not significantly different, $F_{2, 69} = 2.09$, $p = .1314$, and accounted for only 3% to 6% of the variability in attraction/IJS scores ($\omega^2 = .029$ and $\eta^2 = .057$).

19. (*b*, *c*) Results on the Beck Depression Inventory (BDI) include means (standard deviations) of 5.8 (2.39) for the exercise group, 5.9 (3.90) for those with social contact, and 8 (2.05) for those on the waiting list. These means were not significantly different, $F_{2, 27} = 1.84$, $p = .1782$, and accounted for only 5% to 12% of the variability in BDI scores ($\omega^2 = .05$ and $\eta^2 = .12$).

Chapter 15

1. (*a*) Planned comparisons are also called a priori comparisons. (*b*) Controlling α per comparison gives the highest power. (*c*) The overall ANOVA F tells only that there are some differences in the means somewhere.

2. (*a*) .1855 (*b*) .0585 (*c*) .5367 (*d*) Use α control per comparison because of the phrase "for each" in parts a–c.

3. (*a*) 10 (*b*) 3 (*c*) 15

4. (*a*) .0127 (*b*) .0017 (*c*) .0034 (*d*) Use α control familywise because we are computing α' so that the total α is .05 (or .01).

5. (*a*) 2.29 (*b*) 1.29 (*c*) 3.55 (*d*) 3.48

6. (*a*) 3.23 (*b*) $3.23/\sqrt{2} = 2.29$

7. (*a*) None are significantly different because the F didn't reject. (*b*) Means 1 versus 4 and 2 versus 4 are significantly different using $df = 30$. (*c*) Means 1 versus 4 and 2 versus 4 are significantly different using $df = 16$. (*d*) Means 1 versus 4, 2 versus 4, and 3 versus 4 are

significantly different using $df = 30$. (e) As n increases and σ^2 decreases, the power of MCPs increases; yes.

8. (a) Increased exercise gave the highest sample mean on vigor, but the Tukey shows that increased exercise is significantly better than only no exercise. (General exercise is also significantly better than no exercise.) (b) No, the Fisher-Hayter also finds that increased exercise is significantly better than general exercise ($t = 2.49 > 3.20/\sqrt{2} = 2.26$).

9. Participants gave the highest degree of help in DR1, but the Tukey shows that DR1 is only significantly different from IR. (DR2 is also significantly different from IR.)

10. (a) Only the children versus stages is significantly different using Tukey; Fisher-Hayter and Ryan also find network versus stages significantly different. (b) Results on number of correct responses include means (standard deviations) of 12.73 (2.63) for children, 12.47 (2.47) for the neural network model, and 10.27 (2.43) for the stages model. These means were significantly different, $F_{2,42} = 4.35, p = .0192$, with the Fisher-Hayter MCP showing both children and the network model performing significantly better than the stages model. (c) The significant F says only that significant differences exist without telling where.

11. The largest difference, high versus low, gives $t = 2.03 < 2.40$ (for $df = 60$). Other t's are even smaller, so the results agree with the nonsignificant F of the overall ANOVA.

12. Students gave the highest degree of help in DR2, but the Games-Howell MCP shows that DR2 is significantly different from only IR. (DR1 is also significantly different from IR.) The significant differences are the same, but the order of the means is changed, with DR2 having the highest mean.

14. (a) $c_1 = 1, c_2 = 0, c_3 = 0, c_4 = -1, c_5 = 0$ (b) $c_1 = \frac{1}{2}, c_2 = \frac{1}{2}, c_3 = 0, c_4 = -1, c_5 = 0$ (c) $c_1 = 0, c_2 = \frac{1}{2}, c_3 = \frac{1}{2}, c_4 = -\frac{1}{2}, c_5 = -\frac{1}{2}$ (d) $c_1 = \frac{1}{4}, c_2 = \frac{1}{4}, c_3 = \frac{1}{4}, c_4 = \frac{1}{4}, c_5 = -1$

15. Orthogonal pairs are a–d and b–d.

16. Comparison 1: $c_1 = 1, c_2 = -1, c_3 = 0, c_4 = 0, c_5 = 0$
Comparison 2: $c_1 = \frac{1}{2}, c_2 = \frac{1}{2}, c_3 = -1, c_4 = 0, c_5 = 0$
Comparison 3: $c_1 = \frac{1}{3}, c_2 = \frac{1}{3}, c_3 = \frac{1}{3}, c_4 = -1, c_5 = 0$
Comparison 4: $c_1 = \frac{1}{4}, c_2 = \frac{1}{4}, c_3 = \frac{1}{4}, c_4 = \frac{1}{4}, c_5 = -1$

Chapter 16

1. (a) Study technique and cognitive style with four and two levels, respectively (b) Study technique has levels of no notes, student notes, outline frame, and complete outline. Cognitive style has levels of field independence and field dependence. (c) Interaction would be present if the differences for study technique were not consistent for both levels of cognitive style; maybe no notes would be low for field independence but both no notes and student notes would be low for field dependence.

2. (a) A and B (b) A and interaction (c) A and B (d) A, B, and interaction

3. (a) B and interaction (b) A, B, and interaction (c) B and interaction

4. (a)

	B_1	B_2	B_3
A_1	10	10	10
A_2	5	5	5

(b)

	B_1	B_2	B_3
A_1	10	15	20
A_2	5	10	15

(c)

	B_1	B_2	B_3
A_1	10	15	5
A_2	20	15	25

5. Fewer participants needed, greater generalizability, and ability to detect interaction. It would have taken 80 participants instead of 40; they can generalize the impact of "hurry" over the different types of messages; if "hurry" and types of messages had uniquely combined, they could have detected it.

6. X_{121} is the first subject in the cell formed by the second level of A and the first level of B; X_{321} is the third subject in the cell formed by the second level of A and the first level of B; X_{ijk} is the ith subject in the cell formed by the jth level of A and the kth level of B; $\overline{X}_k$ is the main effect mean for the kth level of B; and $\overline{X}_{jk}$ is the cell mean for the cell formed by the jth level of A and the kth level of B.

7. $df_A = 1$, $df_{AB} = 2$, and $df_W = 54$

8. (a)

Source	SS	df	MS	F
A	120	3	40	2
B	400	2	200	10
AB	60	6	10	0.5
Within	2400	120	20	
Total	2980	131		

(b) B; methods of teaching reading are significantly different, but grades and interaction are not significant.

9.

Source	SS	df	MS	F
A	200	2	100	5
B	80	2	40	2
AB	800	4	200	10
Within	720	36	20	
Total	1800	44		

10. Girls and boys differ significantly in number of correct items, methods 1 and 2 are likewise different, and girls and boys may differ in which method is best.

11. For A, $\omega^2 = .02$ and $\eta^2 = .04$. For B, $\omega^2 = .12$ and $\eta^2 = .13$. For AB, $\omega^2 = 0$ and $\eta^2 = .02$.

12. (a) Caffeine consumption and gender with four and two levels, respectively (b) $df_A = 3$, $df_B = 1$, $df_{AB} = 3$, and $df_W = 152$ (c) $F = 3.54 > 2.67$ (with df of 3, 150), so these means are significantly different. (d) No; trait anxiety is related to caffeine consumption. (e) You can conclude that grades are related to caffeine consumption, but not that caffeine reduction causes grades to be higher.

13. (a) For similarity, $F_{1,70} = 46.43$, $p \leq .0001$. For competence, $F_{2,69} = 2.09$, $p = .1314$. (b) For similarity, $F_{1,66} = 50.55$, $p \leq .0001$, $\omega^2 = .39$, and $\eta^2 = .40$; for competence, $F_{2,66} = 3.62$, $p = .0322$, $\omega^2 = .04$, and $\eta^2 = .06$; for interaction, $F_{2,66} = 1.48$, $p = .2347$, $\omega^2 = .01$ and $\eta^2 = .02$. (c) Significance was found for both main effects: Similarity explained 39% to 40% of the variability in attraction, $F_{1,66} = 50.55$, $p \leq .0001$, while competence explained 4% to 6%, $F_{2,66} = 3.62$, $p = .0322$. The interaction was nonsignificant, $F_{2,66} = 1.48$, $p = .2347$. (d) For similarity, both F's were significant but not equal. For competence, the F's and p's were different and only the two-way F was significant. Differences between the separate one-ways and the two-way ANOVA are due to the other sources being contained in the one-way within sums of squares, thus inflating the denominator of the one-ways (and reducing the F's).

14. (a) SAS output includes the following:
    For gender:

Level	Sample Size	Mean	Standard Deviation
Girls	30	12.4666667	2.54251211
Boys	30	12.1333333	1.30604254

For motor activity:

Level	Sample Size	Mean	Standard Deviation
Computer	20	11.4000000	0.99472292
Tiles	20	11.4000000	1.78885438
Writing	20	14.1000000	1.80350536

For gender and motor activity:

Level	Sample Size	Mean	Standard Deviation
Girls computer	10	10.9000000	0.87559504
Girls tiles	10	11.4000000	2.45854519
Girls writing	10	15.1000000	1.52388393
Boys computer	10	11.9000000	0.87559504
Boys tiles	10	11.4000000	0.84327404
Boys writing	10	13.1000000	1.52388393

(c) The effect for gender was not significant, $F_{1,54} = 0.77$, $p = .3831$. Motor activity differences were significant, $F_{2,54} = 22.55$, $p < .0001$, as was the interaction, $F = 5.41$, $p = .0072$. Percent of variability explained was: for gender, 0% to 0.7%; for motor activity, 39% to 41%; and for interaction, 8% to 10%.

15. (a) For gender:

Level	Sample Size	Mean	Standard Deviation
Women	12	22.5833333	7.70428846
Men	12	18.5833333	6.92109205

For exercise:

Level	Sample Size	Mean	Standard Deviation
General exercise	8	22.0000000	3.46410162
Increased exercise	8	27.7500000	4.59036258
No exercise	8	12.0000000	2.00000000

For gender and exercise:

Level	Sample Size	Mean	Standard Deviation
Women general exercise	4	24.0000000	2.94392029
Women increased exercise	4	30.2500000	4.03112887
Women no exercise	4	13.5000000	1.29099445
Men general exercise	4	20.0000000	2.94392029
Men increased exercise	4	25.2500000	4.03112887
Men no exercise	4	10.5000000	1.29099445

(c) The effects for gender and exercise were significant, $F_{1,18} = 10.83$, $p = .0041$, $F_{2,18} = 57.35$, $p < .0001$, but the interaction was not significant, $F = 0.23$, $p = .8002$. Percent of variability explained was: for gender, 7% to 8%; for exercise, 78% to 80%; and for interaction, 0% to 0.3%.

16. (a) For gender:

Level	Sample Size	Mean	Standard Deviation
Girls	21	2.80952381	1.32736761
Boys	21	3.52380952	1.40068011

For instructions:

Level	Sample Size	Mean	Standard Deviation
DR1	14	4.00000000	1.17669681
DR2	14	3.50000000	1.22474487
IR	14	2.00000000	0.96076892

For instructions and gender:

Level	Sample Size	Mean	Standard Deviation
Girls DR1	7	3.57142857	1.39727626
Girls DR2	7	2.85714286	1.34518542
Girls IR	7	2.00000000	0.81649658
Boys DR1	7	4.42857143	0.78679579
Boys DR2	7	4.14285714	0.69006556
Boys IR	7	2.00000000	1.15470054

(c) The effects for gender and instructions were significant, $F_{1,36} = 4.69$, $p = .0371$, $F_{2,36} = 13.27$, $p < .0001$, but the interaction was not significant, $F = 1.31$, $p = .2817$. Percent of variability explained was: for gender, 5% to 7%; for instructions, 35% to 38%; and for interaction, 0.9% to 4%.

17. (a) For age:

Level	Sample Size	Mean	Standard Deviation
Older than 70	15	6.06666667	2.65832027
70 or younger	15	7.06666667	3.28343606

For treatment:

Level	Sample Size	Mean	Standard Deviation
Exercise	10	5.80000000	2.39443800
Social contact	10	5.90000000	3.90014245
Wait list	10	8.00000000	2.05480467

For treatment and age:

Level	Sample Size	Mean	Standard Deviation
Older than 70 exercise	5	7.20000000	1.48323970
Older than 70 social contact	5	3.40000000	2.07364414
Older than 70 wait list	5	7.60000000	2.19089023
70 or younger exercise	5	4.40000000	2.40831892
70 or younger social contact	5	8.40000000	3.78153408
70 or younger wait list	5	8.40000000	2.07364414

(c) The effect for age was not significant, $F_{1,24} = 1.26$, $p = .2727$, nor was that for treatment, $F_{2,24} = 2.59$, $p = .0955$. Only interaction was significant, $F = 6.40$, $p = .0059$. Percent of variability explained was: for age, 0.6% to 3%; for treatment, 7% to 12%; and for interaction, 24% to 30%.

Chapter 17

1. (a) Two, experienced and new air traffic controllers (b) At least twice to show improvement (c) The experienced group will have high scores at the start that will not improve much, but the new group will start low and show great improvement. (d) At the end of the study, but this would have the disadvantage of not showing gain.

2. (*a*) The groups should be independent (no obvious pairing or other dependence). Yes, so if I measured them twice, I would have to use a repeated measures design. (*b*) i. Baby is crossed with month and parent present/absent but nested within group (full term or premature). Month, parent, and group are all crossed. ii. 360 iii. One (groups); two (parent and month) (*c*) Two-dependent-sample *t* or simple repeated measures design

3. (*b*.) One between-subjects factor (their car) and one within-subjects factor (cars driven)

4. (*a*) None; one within-subjects factor (instructions). Subjects is crossed with instructions; there is no nesting. (*b*) 4 (*c*) $df_T = 3$, $df_S = 33$, $df_{TS} = 99$ (*d*) $MS_T = SS_T/df_T$, $MS_{TS} = SS_{TS}/df_{TS}$, $F = MS_T/MS_{TS}$ (*e*) This would be a problem because instructions would be confounded with the test, so good performance might result from an easier test rather than reduced anxiety because of instructions.

5. (*a*) Zero between, one within (*b*) Four; $df_T = 3$, $df_S = 29$, $df_{TS} = 87$; df_T and df_{TS} (3 and 87) (*c*) It has two groups instead of one; one between, one within; group (1), subjects within groups (58), measurements (3), measurements interacting with groups (3), and measurements interacting with subjects within groups (174)

6. (*a*) $F = 4.94$, $p = .0447 < .05$, so reject H_0. (*b*) $t = 2.22$; $t = \sqrt{F}$ (or $t^2 = F$) (*c*) Orthodontic treatment causes a change in the ratings of intelligence.

7. $F = 14.000$, $p < .0001 < .05$, so reject H_0. (*b*) The different motor activities cause differences in spelling performance.

8. (*a*) One between and one within (*b*) For a 5-day workweek, $K = 5$. (*c*) $df_G = 1$, $df_{S(G)} = 34$, $df_T = 4$, $df_{TG} = 4$, $df_{TS(G)} = 136$ (*d*) $F_G = MS_G/MS_{S(G)}$, $F_T = MS_T/MS_{TS(G)}$, $F_{TG} = MS_{TG}/MS_{TS(G)}$

9. The family therapy group gained the most, but there is no significant difference in the groups, $F = 0.70$, $p = .4161$, nor is the interaction significant, $F = 0.08$, $p = .7783$. Only time, or age, gives significant differences, $F = 95.87$, $p < .0001$. Family therapy is no more effective than exercise and a low-calorie diet in weight gain or loss over a 2-year period.

10. (*a*) Pattern and variance of costs are within-subjects factors, whereas time and average cost are between-subjects factors. (*b*) Two; two (*c*) $df_{\text{time}} = 1$, $df_{\text{avg. cost}} = 1$, $df_{\text{pattern}} = 2$, $df_{\text{var. cost}} = 1$, $df_{\text{time} \times \text{pattern}} = 2$ (*d*) Pattern and variance of costs

11. (*a*) Both are within-subjects factors. (*b*) Zero; two (*c*) $df_{\text{subjects}} = 34$, $df_{\text{source rel.}} = 3$, $df_{\text{degr. inf.}} = 1$, $df_{\text{subj.} \times \text{source rel.}} = 102$ (*d*) Both source reliability and degree of informativeness

Chapter 18

1. The hypothesis does not include parameters.

2. Nonparametric hypotheses. Yes, they can detect mean, variance, or any type of difference, but they may not be powerful for a specific type of difference.

3. (*a*) 5 (*b*) 4 (*c*) 9.49 (*d*) Divide 1300 by 5 (260). (*e*) $\chi^2 = 502.31 > 9.49$, so reject H_0 and conclude that the grades are not evenly distributed.

4. (*a*) You have the frequency of crimes for each day and want to test the hypothesis that they are evenly distributed. (*b*) $df = 6$ and $\chi^2_{\text{crit}} = 12.59$ (*c*) H_0: $\text{dist}_{\text{pop}} = \text{dist}_{\text{theory}}$ (*d*) $E = 152/7 = 21.7143$

5. (*a*) $42/4 = 10.5$ (*b*) 8.67 (*c*) $\chi^2 = 8.67 > 7.82 = \chi^2$ critical value with $df = 3$ and $\alpha = .05$, so reject H_0.

6. (*a*) If there is no effect of the moon, 75/456 of the 1182 drug overdoses will occur on full-moon days and 381/456 of the 1182 drug overdoses will occur on non-full-moon days; $E_1 = (75/456)1182 = 194.41$ and $E_2 = (381/456)1182 = 987.59$. (*b*) $\chi^2 = 0.016 < 3.84 = \chi^2$ critical value with $df = 1$ and $\alpha = .05$, so retain H_0.

7. (*a*) Take one-fourth of the total ($5388/4 = 1347$). (*b*) The frequency of people who commit suicide on Friday the 13th is not significantly larger than the frequency of people who commit suicide on other Fridays; $\chi^2 = 5.62 < 7.82 = \chi^2_3$ and $\alpha = .05$.

8. (*c*) $\chi^2 = 389.27 > 7.82$, so reject H_0: tobacco use is not distributed proportionately among the four regions.

9. $\chi^2 = 11.71 > 5.99 = \chi^2$ critical value with $df = 2$ and $\alpha = .05$, so reject H_0 and conclude that party and opinion are not independent.

10. (*a*) You are interested in seeing whether there is a relationship between verb condition and whether or not students thought they saw broken glass. (*b*) $df = 1$ and $\chi^2_{\text{crit}} = 3.84$ (*c*) H_0: response is independent of verb (*d*) E's for the first row are 11.5; for the second row 38.5. (*e*) $\chi^2 = 4.57 > 3.84$, so reject H_0. (*f*) People will form different opinions about what they see depending on the verbs used to ask them questions.

11. $\chi^2 = 5.27 < 9.49 = \chi^2$ critical value with $df = 4$, so retain H_0 and conclude that handedness and grades in statistics are independent.

12. (*a*) H_0: payoff is independent of machine (*b*) $\chi^2 = 7.00 > 3.84$, so reject H_0: payoff depends on machine.

14. (*a*) 3.84 (*b*) H_0: toy selection is independent of gender (*c*) $\chi^2 = 4.17 > 3.84$, so reject H_0.

Chapter 19

1. (*a*) Parametric (mean or median differences) (*b*) Parametric (monotonic relationship) (*c*) Parametric (mean or median differences)

2. $U = 1.5 < 2 =$ critical value for $n_1 = 5$ and $n_2 = 5$ with $\alpha = .05$, so reject H_0.

3. Mann-Whitney U

4. $U = 43 > 23 =$ critical value for $n_1 = 10$ and $n_2 = 10$ with $\alpha = .05$, so retain H_0.

5. (*a*) Mann-Whitney U, because there is no mention of pairing and no obvious dependency in the data (*b*) $U = 26.5 > 23 =$ critical value for $n_1 = 10$ and $n_2 = 10$ with $\alpha = .05$, so retain H_0. (*c*) You cannot conclude that there are significant differences (in medians) between the two groups because you retained H_0. (*d*) No; any subject variable such as age, weight, years smoking, number of cigarettes smoked daily; no; yes

6. Mann-Whitney U, because there is no mention of pairing and no obvious dependency in the data (*b*) $U = 189$, but sample sizes are larger than the largest in the table (20), so compute $z = -2.40 < -1.96 =$ critical value for $\alpha = .05$, so reject H_0.

7. Wilcoxon

8. $T = 18.5 < 21 =$ critical value for $K = 14$ with $\alpha = .05$, so reject H_0.

9. (*a*) Wilcoxon, because the parts of each sample are related (*b*) $T_+ = 7 > 2$, the critical value for $K = 7$, so retain H_0.

10. (*a*) Wilcoxon, because the participants are paired (*b*) $T_+ = 10.5 > 8$, the critical value for $K = 10$, so retain H_0. (*c*) No (*d*) Yes; any participant variable such as gender, age, weight, body type, and prior amount of exercising; yes: the first four are controlled by pairing and others are controlled by randomization of participants within pairs to treatments. No

11. (*a*) Wilcoxon, because the participants are paired (*b*) $T_+ = 0$, but the table has no critical value for $K = 3$, so retain H_0. (*c*) No; two concerns: first, we can't reject H_0 because we can't do the test with this small a value of K (actually, we must retain because we can't get a critical value for $\alpha = .05$). Second, we have the usual concern about generalizing results from such a small sample size. Note that we were able to do the test with the parametric two-dependent-sample *t*-test.

12. $H = 8.77 > 5.99 = \chi^2$ critical value with $df = 2$ and $\alpha = .05$, so reject H_0.

13. $H = 15.01 > 5.99 = \chi^2$ critical value with $df = 2$ and $\alpha = .05$, so reject H_0.

14. $\chi = 5.64 < 7.82 = \chi^2$ critical value with $df = 3$ and $\alpha = .05$, so retain H_0.

15. $\chi = 11.79 > 5.99 = \chi^2$ critical value with $df = 2$ and $\alpha = .05$, so reject H_0.

16. $r_S = .315 < .738 =$ critical value of r_S with $N = 8$, so retain H_0; no.

17. (*b*) $r_S = -.621 > -.648 =$ critical value of r_S with $N = 10$, so retain H_0. (*c*) No

18. (*b*) $r_S = .728 > .521 =$ critical value of r_S with $N = 15$, so reject H_0. (*c*) Yes

Chapter 20

1. (*a*) H_0: $\rho = 0$ (*b*) Relationship (*c*) r (*d*) χ^2 is not appropriate because both variables are quantitative.

2. (*a*) H_0: $\mu \leq 1200$ (*b*) Average (*c*) $z_{\overline{x}}$ (*d*) The one-sample *t* is not appropriate because the population standard deviation is given.

3. (a) H_0: $p_{exp} \leq p_{control}$ (b) Rates (c) z for two independent proportions (d) The two-sample t's are not appropriate because the data are qualitative, not quantitative. You could use the χ^2 test for contingency tables (exp vs. control, cancer vs. none).

4. (a) H_0:median$_{drugs}$ = median$_{drugs\ plus\ coun.}$ (b) Differences (c) Wilcoxon (d) The two-dependent-sample t is not appropriate because it is not robust to the type of nonnormality evidenced by "5% of the scores. . . ."

5. (a) H_0: $\mu_1 = \mu_2 = \mu_3$ (b) Difference, three, scores (c) One-way ANOVA (d) The two-sample t's are not appropriate because of three groups, and the Kruskal-Wallis test is not indicated because there is nothing about 5% of the scores being outliers.

6. (a) H_0: independence of smoking and coughing (b) Relationship (c) χ^2 test for contingency tables (d) r is not appropriate because both variables are qualitative.

7. (a) H_0: $p = .50$ (b) Proportion (c) z for a proportion (d) Neither $z_{\bar{x}}$ nor the one-sample t is appropriate because the question is about a population proportion.

8. (a) No liquid effect; no type of exercise effect; no interaction (b) Two variables, numerical dependent variable (c) Two-way ANOVA (d) One-way ANOVA won't work because of the two variables and interaction. χ^2 for contingency tables won't work because of the numerical dependent variable.

9. (a) H_0: median$_{sec1}$ = median$_{sec2}$ (b) Two groups, 5% scores as outliers (c) Mann-Whitney U (d) The two-independent-sample t is not appropriate because it is not robust to the type of nonnormality evidenced by "5% of the. . . ."

10. (a) No day effect (b) Different, every day (c) Simple repeated measures design (d) One-way ANOVA won't work because the scores across days are related.

11. (a) No day effect; no gender effect; no interaction (b) Daily (c) Groups by trials repeated measures design (d) Simple repeated measures design won't work because there are two groups of participants.

12. (a) H_0: no association between self-esteem and locus of control (b) Association (c) r_S (d) r is not appropriate because of the interest in more than a linear relationship. χ^2 is not appropriate because the scores are quantitative.

13. (a) H_0: dist$_{1977}$ = dist$_{1982}$ = dist$_{1988}$ = dist$_{1994}$ (b) Frequencies, question about rates (c) Goodness-of-fit χ^2 (d) One-way ANOVA will not work because you don't have a numerical score for each participant, just frequencies of participants.

14. (a) No effect of knowledge of current country music on depression scores (b) Explain variability, other variables accounted for (c) Multiple regression (d) Simple regression/correlation will not work because there are other variables: age and general physical health.

15. (a) H_0: $\mu_{easy} = \mu_{hard}$ (b) Two levels, rating (c) Two-independent-sample t or one-way ANOVA (d) Two-dependent-sample t is not appropriate because there is no pairing. Rank tests are not indicated because there is nothing about 5% of the scores being outliers.

16. (a) H_0: $\mu_{high} = \mu_{low}$ (b) Two groups (c) AWS t' (d) Two-independent-sample t is not appropriate because the sample sizes are too small. Two-dependent-sample t is not appropriate because there is no pairing. Rank tests are not indicated because there is nothing about 5% of the scores being outliers.

17. (a) H_0: $\mu_X = \mu_Y$ (b) Two groups, paired (c) Two-dependent-sample t (d) Two-independent-sample t is not appropriate because the students are paired. Rank tests are not indicated because there is nothing about 5% of the scores being outliers.

18. (a) H_0: $\mu = 200$ (b) Average, mean (c) One-sample t (d) The $z_{\bar{x}}$ is not appropriate because the population standard deviation is not given.

19. (a) H_0: median$_{NS}$ = median$_{DS}$ = median$_{AS}$. (b) Three groups, 5% scores as outliers (c) Kruskal-Wallis H (d) The one-way ANOVA is not appropriate because it is not robust to the type of nonnormality evidenced by "5% of the. . . ."

20. (a) H_0: median$_2$ = median$_4$ = median$_6$ = median$_8$ (b) Multiple sessions per smoker, 5% scores as outliers (c) Friedman χ (d) The simple repeated measures design is not appropriate because it is not robust to the type of nonnormality evidenced by "5% of the. . . ."

21. Two-independent-sample t or one-way ANOVA. If the sample sizes are not equal and larger than 15, use the AWS t'.

22. One-sample t
23. Two-independent-sample test of proportions or χ^2 for contingency tables
24. Mann-Whitney U or Kruskal-Wallis H
25. Two-way ANOVA
26. AWS t'
27. Groups by trials repeated measures design or possibly two-independent-sample t on gain scores (if there is only one post measurement)
28. Groups by trials repeated measures design or possibly the one-way ANOVA on gain scores (if there is only one post measurement)
29. Groups by trials repeated measures design or possibly two-independent-sample t on gain scores (if there is only one post measurement)
30. Multiple regression
31. One-sample t
32. χ^2 test for contingency tables
33. AWS t'
34. One-sample test of a proportion
35. One-way ANOVA
36. Two-way ANOVA
37. r
38. Two-dependent-sample t or simple repeated measures design
39. $z_{\bar{x}}$
40. $z_{\bar{x}}$
41. AWS t'
42. Simple repeated measures design

References

ACHEN, C. H. (1982). *Interpreting and Using Regression* (Sage University Paper series on Quantitative Applications in the Social Sciences, 07-029). Newbury Park, CA: Sage Publications.

ADORNO, T. W., FRENKEL-BRUNSWICK, E., LEVINSON, D. J., & SANFORD, R. N. (1950). *The authoritarian personality.* New York: Harper.

AIKEN, L. S., & WEST, S. G. (1991). *Multiple regression: Testing and interpreting interactions.* Newbury Park, CA: Sage Publications.

ALS, H., TRONICK, E., LESTER, B., & BRAZELTON, T. (1979). Specific neonatal measures: Brazelton Neonatal Behavior Assessment Scale. In J. D. Osofski (Ed.), *Handbook of infant development.* New York: Wiley.

ARCURI, A. F., & LESTER, D. (1990). Moonlighting and stress on police officers. *Psychological Reports, 66,* 350.

ARNTZ, A., VAN ECK, M., & HEIJMANS, M. (1990). Predictions of dental pain: The fear of any expected evil is worse than the evil itself. *Behavior Research and Therapy, 28*(1), 29–41.

BABAD, E. Y., & WALLBOTT, H. G. (1986). The effects of social factors on emotional reactions. In K. R. Scherer, H. G. Wallbot, & A. B. Summerfield (Eds.), *Experiencing emotion: A cross-cultural study* (pp. 154–172). New York: Cambridge University Press.

BANDURA, A., ROSS, D., & ROSS, S. A. (1963). Imitation of film-mediated aggressive models. *Journal of Abnormal and Social Psychology, 66,* 3–11

BANDURA, A., & WALTERS, R. H. (1963). *The social learning of deviant behavior: A behavioristic approach to socialization.* New York: Holt, Rinehart & Winston.

BECK, A. T., & BEAMESDERFER, A. (1974). Assessment of depression: The Depression Inventory. In P. Pichot (Ed.), *Psychological measurements in psychopharmacology.* Basel, Switzerland: Karger.

BERRY, W. D., & FELDMAN, S. (1985). *Multiple Regression in Practice* (Sage University Paper series on Quantitative Applications in the Social Sciences, 07-050). Newbury Park, CA: Sage Publications.

BISHOP, G. D., ALVA, A. L., CANTU, L., & RITTIMAN, T. K. (1991). Responses to persons with AIDS: Fear of contagion or stigma? *Journal of Applied Social Psychology, 21,* 1877–1888.

BLAIR, R. C., & HIGGINS, J. J. (1980). A comparison of the power of Wilcoxon's rank-sum statistic to that of Student's *t* statistic under various nonnormal distributions. *Journal of Educational Statistics, 5*(4), 309–335.

BLUMENTHAL, J. A., MADDEN, D. J., PIERCE, T. W., SIEGEL, W. C., & APPELBAUM, M. (1993). Hypertension affects neurobehavioral functioning. *Psychosomatic Medicine, 55*(1), 44–50.

BOURNE, L. E., JR., & ARCHER, E. J. (1956). Time continuously on target as a function of distribution of practice. *Journal of Experimental Psychology, 51,* 25–33.

BOX, G. E. P. (1966). Use and abuse of regression. *Technometrics, 8*(4), 625–629.

BRADLEY, J. V. (1968). *Distribution-free statistical tests.* Englewood Cliffs, NJ: Prentice-Hall.

BRUMBACK, R. A., JACKOWAY, M. K., & WEINBERG, W. A. (1980). Relation of intelligence to childhood depression in children referred to an educational diagnostic center. *Perceptual and Motor Skills, 50,* 11–17.

CALLAHAN, C. M., & RIVARA, F. P. (1992). Urban high school youth and handguns: A school-based survey. *Journal of the American Medical Association, 267*(22), 3038–3042.

CARMAN, R., & ADAMS, W. R. (1972). *Study skills: A student's guide for survival.* New York: Wiley.

CENTERWALL, B. S. (1992). Television and violence: The scale of the problem and where to go from here. *Journal of the American Medical Association, 267*(22), 3059–3063.

COGGINS, C. J. (1984). A comparative study of locus of control in mentally retarded, emotionally disturbed, learning disabled, and normally achieving students. Unpublished doctoral dissertation, University of Oklahoma.

COHEN, J. (1977). *Statistical power analysis for the behavioral sciences,* 2d ed. New York: Academic.

COOK, T. D., & CAMPBELL, D. T. (1979). *Quasi-experimentation design and analysis issues for field settings.* Chicago: Rand McNally.

COON, D. (1980). *Introduction to psychology, exploration and application,* 2d ed. St. Paul: West.

COUNCIL REPORTS, COUNCIL ON SCIENTIFIC AFFAIRS, AMERICAN MEDICAL ASSOCIATION. (1992). Violence against women: Relevance for medical practitioners. *Journal of the American Medical Association, 267*(23), 3184–3189.

CRONIN, C. (1991). Sensation seeking among mountain climbers. *Personality and Individual Differences, 12*(6), 653–654.

DARLEY, J. M., & BATSON, C. D. (1973). From Jerusalem to Jericho: A study of situational and dispositional variables in helping behavior. *Journal of Personality and Social Psychology, 27,* 100–108.

DARLINGTON, R. B. (1990). *Regression and linear models.* New York: McGraw-Hill.

DASGUPTA, B. (1992). Perceived control and examination stress. *Journal of Human Behavior, 29*(1), 31–33.

DERENARD, L. A., & KLINE, L. M. (1990). Alienation and the game Dungeons and Dragons. *Psychological Reports, 66,* 1219–1222.

DIXON, W. J., & MASSEY, F. J., JR. (1983). *Introduction to statistical analysis,* 4th ed. New York: McGraw-Hill.

DUNCAN, D. F., & KLEIN, K. (1992). Tall smokers: A serendipitous examination of Ossorio's embodiment parameter. *Psychology, a Journal of Human Behavior, 29*(1), 27–30.

DUNN, O. J. (1961). Multiple comparisons among means. *Journal of the American Statistical Association, 56,* 52–64.

EKMAN, P., & O'SULLIVAN, M. (1991). Who can catch a liar? *American Psychologist, 46*(9), 913–920.

EREZ, M. (1980). Correlates of leadership style: Field-dependence and social intelligence versus social orientation. *Perceptual and Motor Skills, 50,* 231–238.

EYSENCK, H. J. (1967). New ways in psychotherapy. *Psychology Today, 1*(2), 39–47.

EYSENCK, H. J., & WILSON, G. D. (1991). *The Eysenck personality profiler.* London: Corporate Assessment Ltd.

EYSENCK, S. G. B., EYSENCK, H. J., & BARRETT, P. (1985). A revised version of the psychoticism scale. *Personality and Individual Differences, 6,* 21–29.

FEINGOLD, A. (1988). Cognitive gender differences are disappearing. *American Psychologist, 43,* 95–103.

FERGUSON, G. A., & TAKANE, Y. (1989). *Statistical analysis in psychology and education,* 6th ed. New York: McGraw-Hill.

FRANK, B. M. (1984). Effect of field independence-dependence and study technique on learning from a lecture. *American Educational Research Journal, 21*(3), 669–678.

FRENCH, J. W., EKSTROM, R. B., & PRICE, L. A. (1963). *Manual for kit of reference tests for cognitive factors.* Princeton, NJ: Educational Testing Service.

FRIEDMAN, M. (1937). The use of ranks to avoid the assumption of normality implied in the analysis of variance. *Journal of the American Statistical Association, 32,* 675–701.

GELLES, R. J. (1988). Violence and pregnancy: Are pregnant women at greater risk of abuse? *Journal of Marriage and the Family, 50,* 841–847.

GIBBONS, J. D. (1993). *Nonparametric Statistics: An Introduction* (Sage University Paper series on Quantitative Applications in the Social Sciences, 07-090). Newbury Park, CA: Sage Publications.

GILLILAND, K., & ANDRESS, D. (1981). Ad lib caffeine consumption, symptoms of caffeinism, and academic performance. *American Journal of Psychiatry, 138*(4), 512–514.

GIRDEN, E. R. (1992). *ANOVA repeated measures.* Newbury Park, CA: Sage Publications.

HACKWORTH, R. D. (1992). *Math anxiety reduction,* 2d ed. Clearwater, FL: H&H Publishing Company.

HADER, R. J. (1973). An improper method of randomization in experimental design. *The American Statistician, 27,* 82–84.

HAYS, W. L. (1994). *Statistics* (5th ed.). Fort Worth: Harcourt Brace College Publishers.

HAYTER, A. J. (1986). The maximum familywise error rate of Fisher's least significant difference test. *Journal of the American Statistical Association, 81,* 1000–1004.

HELMSTADTER, G. C. (1970). *Research concepts in human behavior.* New York: Appleton-Century-Crofts.

HIRSHOREN, A., HURLEY, O. L., & KAVALE, K. (1979). Psychometric characteristics of the WISC-R performance scale with deaf children. *Journal of Speech and Hearing Disorders, 44,* 73–79.

HUFF, D. (1954). *How to lie with statistics.* New York: Norton.

KIRBY, D. A. (1971). Determination of authoritarianism during the jury selection voir dire phase. Unpublished master's thesis, University of Oklahoma.

KIRK, R. E. (1995). *Experimental design: Procedures for the behavioral sciences,* 3d ed. Pacific Grove, CA: Brooks/Cole.

KRUSKAL, W. H., & WALLIS, W. A. (1952). Use of ranks in one-criterion variance analysis. *Journal of the American Statistical Association, 47,* 583–621.

LESTER, D. (1988). Personal violence (suicide and homicide) on Friday the 13th. *Psychological Reports, 63,* 433.

LEWIS-BECK, M. S. (1980). *Applied Regression: An Introduction* (Sage University Paper series on Quantitative Applications in the Social Sciences, 07-022). Newbury Park, CA: Sage Publications.

LOFTUS, E. F., & PALMER, J. C. (1974). Reconstruction of automobile destruction: An example of the interaction between language and memory. *Journal of Verbal Learning and Verbal Behavior, 13,* 585–589.

MANN, H. B., & WHITNEY, D. R. (1947). On a test of whether one of two random variables is stochastically larger than the other. *Annals of Mathematical Statistics, 18,* 50–60.

MARASCUILO, L. A., & MCSWEENEY, M. (1977). *Nonparametric and distribution-free methods for the social sciences.* Pacific Grove, CA: Brooks/Cole.

MARCHANT-HAYCOX, S. E., & WILSON, G. D. (1992). Personality and stress in performing artists. *Personality and Individual Differences, 13*(10), 1061–1068.

MARSHALL, J. C., & POWERS, J. M. (1969). Writing neatness, composition errors and essay grades. *Journal of Educational Measurement, 6,* 97–101.

MAXWELL, S. E. (1980). Pairwise multiple comparisons in repeated measures designs. *Journal of Educational Statistics, 5,* 269–287.

MCCOWN, W., & JOHNSON, J. (1991). Personality and chronic procrastination by university students during an academic examination period. *Personality and Individual Differences, 12*(5), 413–415.

MCNEIL, J. K., LEBLANC, E. M., & JOYNER, M. (1991). The effect of exercise on depressive symptoms in the moderately depressed elderly. *Psychology and Aging, 6*(3), 487–488.

MCNEMAR, Q. (1969). *Psychological statistics,* 4th ed. New York: Wiley.

MEIER, P. (1978). The biggest health experiment ever: The 1954 field trial of the Salk poliomyelitis vaccine. In J. M. Tanur et al. (Eds.), *Statistics: A guide to the unknown.* San Francisco: Holden-Day.

MILLS, J. K. (1991). Differences in locus of control between obese adult and adolescent females undergoing weight reduction. *The Journal of Psychology, 125*(2), 195–197.

MISCHEL, W., SHODA, Y., & RODRIGUEZ, M. L. (1989). Delay of gratification in children. *Science, 244,* 933–938.

MOORE, D. S., & MCCABE, G. P. (1993). *Introduction to the practice of statistics,* 2d ed. New York: Freeman.

NEIDHARDT, E. J., WEINSTEIN, M. S., & CONRY, R. F. (1985). *Managing stress.* Seattle: Self-Counsel.

NEWCOMB, M. D., RABOW, J., MONTO, M., & HERNANDEZ, A. C. R. (1991). Informal drunk driving intervention: Psychosocial correlates among young adult women and men. *Journal of Applied Social Psychology, 21*(24), 1988–2006.

NOWICKI, S., & STRICKLAND, B. R. (1973). A locus of control scale for children. *Journal of Consulting and Clinical Psychology, 40,* 148–154.

ORNISH, D., BROWN, S., SCHERWITZ, L., BILLINGS, J., ARMSTRONG, W., PORTS, T., MCLANAHAN, S., KIRKEEIDE, R., BRAND, R., GOULD, K. (1990). Can lifestyle changes reverse coronary heart disease? *Lancet, 336,* 129–133.

PERRINE, S., GINDER, G., FALLER, D., DOVER, G., IKUTA, T., WITKOWSKA, H., CAI, S., VICHINSKY, E., & OLIVIERI, N. (1993). A short-term trial of butyrate to stimulate fetal-globin-gene expression in the β-globin disorders. *The New England Journal of Medicine, 328*(2), 81–86.

PHELPS, L., & BRANYAN, B. J. (1988). Correlations among the Hiskey, K-ABC nonverbal scale, Leiter, and WISC-R performance scale with public-school deaf children. *Journal of Psychoeducational Assessment, 6,* 354–358.

PIKE. K. M., & RODIN, J. (1991). Mothers, daughters, and disordered eating. *Journal of Abnormal Psychology, 100*(2), 198–204.

RAMSEY, P. H. (1980). Exact Type I error rates for robustness of Student's *t* test with unequal variances. *Journal of Educational Statistics, 5,* 337–349.

RIDER, R. A., & DALY, J. (1991). Effects of flexibility training on enhancing spinal mobility in older women. *Journal of Sports Medicine and Physical Fitness, 31*(2), 213–217.

ROBINSON, F. P. (1941). *Effective behavior.* New York: Harper & Row.

RODGERS, J. L., HARRIS, D. F., & VICKERS, K. B. (1992). Seasonality of first coitus in the United States. *Social Biology, 39,* 1–14.

ROTTER, J. B. (1966). Generalized expectancies for internal versus external control of reinforcement. *Psychological Monographs, 80* (all no. 609).

SAMUELS, M. L., & LU, T. C. (1992). Sample size requirements for the back-of-the-envelope binomial confidence interval. *American Statistician, 46*(3), 228–231.

SCHROEDER, L. D., SJOQUIST, D. L., & STEPHAN, P. E. (1986). *Understanding Regression Analysis: An Introductory Guide* (Sage University Paper series on Quantitative Applications in the Social Sciences, 07-057). Newbury Park, CA: Sage Publications.

SCHWAB, R., & SCHWAB, E., JR. (1981). A cross-cultural comparison of marital roles. *Sociology and Social Research, 65,* 332–339.

SERLIN, R. C., & LAPSLEY, D. K. (1985). Rationality in psychological research: The good enough principle. *American Psychologist, 40,* 73–83.

SHARFMAN, M. (1980). Drug overdose and the full moon. *Perceptual and Motor Skills, 50,* 124–126.

SHODA, Y., MISCHEL, W., & PEAKE, P. K. (1990). Predicting adolescent cognitive and self-regulatory competencies from preschool delay of gratification: Identifying diagnostic conditions. *Developmental Psychology, 26*(6), 978–986.

SHOPLAND, D. R., NIEMCRYK, S. J., & MARCONI, K. M. (1992). Geographic and gender variations in total tobacco use. *American Journal of Public Health, 82*(1), 103–106.

SIEGEL, S., & CASTELLAN, N. J. (1988). *Nonparametric statistics for the behavioral sciences,* 2nd ed. New York: McGraw-Hill.

SILBERSTEIN, J. A., & PARSONS, O. A. (1981). Neuropsychological impairment in female alcoholics: Replication and extension. *Journal of Abnormal Psychology, 90,* 179–182.

SILVERMAN, K., EVANS, S. M., STRAIN, E. C., & GRIFFITHS, R. R. (1992). Withdrawal syndrome after the double-blind cessation of caffeine consumption. *New England Journal of Medicine, 327*(16), 1109–1114.

SMITH, G. M., SCHWERIN, F. T., STUBBLEFIELD, F. S., & FOGG, C. P. (1982). Licit and illicit substance use by adolescents: Psychosocial predisposition and escalatory outcome. *Contemporary Drug Problems,* Spring, pp. 75–100.

SPILICH, G. J., JUNE, L., & RENNER, J. (1992). Cigarette smoking and cognitive performance. *British Journal of Addiction, 87,* 1313–1326.

SPSS BASE SYSTEM USER'S GUIDE. (1990). Chicago: SPSS, Inc.

STACK, S., & GUNDLACH, J. (1992). The effect of country music on suicide. *Social Forces, 71*(1), 211–218.

STAUB, E. (1970). A child in distress: The effect of focusing of responsibility on children on their attempts to help. *Developmental Psychology, 2,* 152–153.

STEGER, J. A. (1971). *Reading in statistics for the behavioral scientist.* New York: Holt, Rinehart & Winston.

TERRY, W. S. (1988). Everyday forgetting: Data from a diary study. *Psychological Reports, 62,* 299–303.

TOBIAS, S. (1978). *Overcoming math anxiety.* New York: Norton.

TOOTHAKER, L. E. (1991). *Multiple comparisons for researchers.* Newbury Park, CA: Sage Publications.

TOOTHAKER, L. E. (1993). *Multiple Comparison Procedures* (Sage University Paper series on Quantitative Applications in the Social Sciences, 07-089). Newbury Park, CA: Sage Publications.

TUKEY, J. W. (1977). *Exploratory data analysis.* Reading, MA: Addison-Wesley.

U. S. BUREAU OF THE CENSUS. (1980). *Statistical Abstract of the United States.*

VAN HOUTEN, R., NAU, P., & MARINI, Z. (1980). An analysis of public posting in reducing speeding behavior on an urban highway. *Journal of Applied Behavior Analysis, 13,* 383–395.

WECHSLER, H., & ISAAC, N. (1992). 'Binge' drinkers at Massachusetts colleges. *Journal of the American Medical Association, 267*(21), 2929–2931.

WICKENS, T. D. (1989). *Multiway contingency tables analysis for the social sciences.* Hillsdale, NJ: Lawrence Erlbaum Associates.

WICKETT, J. C., VERNON, P. A., & LEE, D. L. (1994). *In vivo* brain size, head perimeter, and intelligence in a sample of healthy adult females. *Personality and Individual Differences, 16*(6), 831–838.

WIGFIELD, R. E., FLEMING, P. J., BERRY, P. J., RUDD, P. T., & GOLDING, J. (1992). Can the fall in Avon's sudden infant death rate be explained by changes in sleeping position? *British Medical Journal, 304,* 282–283.

WILCOX, R. R. (1987). *New statistical procedures for the social sciences: Modern solutions to basic problems.* Hillsdale, NJ: Lawrence Erlbaum Associates.

WILCOX, R. R., CHARLIN, V., & THOMPSON, K. (1986). New Monte Carlo results on the robustness of the ANOVA F, W and F statistics. *Communications in Statistics—Simulation and Computation, 15,* 933–944.

WILLIS, F. N., & BRIGGS, L. F. (1992). Relationship and touch in public settings. *Journal of Nonverbal Behavior, 16*(1), 55–63.

WINER, B. J., BROWN, D. R., & MICHELS, K. M. (1991). *Statistical principles in experimental design,* 3d ed. New York: McGraw-Hill.

WORRINGHAM, C. J., & MESSICK, C. J. (1983). Social facilitation of running: An unobtrusive study. *Journal of Social Psychology, 121,* 23–29.

WRATHER, D., & PADD, W. (1971). Unpublished manuscript.

ZAJONC, R. B. (1965). Social facilitation. *Science, 149,* 269–274.

ZAJONC, R. B., ADELMANN, P. K., MURPHY, S. T., & NIEDENTHAL, P. M. (1987). Convergence in the physical appearance of spouses. *Motivation and Emotion, 11*(4), 335–346.

Index

Absolute value, 662
Achen, C., 226
Adams, W., 28
Addition (Or) rule, 249
Adelmann, P., 379, 380
Adjacent values, 129
Adorno, T., 252
Aiken, L., 226
Alpha, defined, 320
Als, H., 426, 606
Alternative hypothesis. *See* Hypothesis
Alva, A., 276
Analysis of variance (ANOVA), one-way, 452
    assumptions, 469
    and *F* distribution, 468
    F ratio, 466
    and familywise α, 454, 491
    and levels, 462
    logic of, 455
    mean squares, 465
    and multiple comparisons, 474
    and multiple *t*-tests, 454
    notation, 452, 461
    and partitioning of variability, 463
    and relation to regression, 218
    and relation of *t* to *F*, 470
    and strength of association, 472
    summary table, 468
    sums of squares, 464
    variance estimates, 456
Analysis of variance, repeated measures. See
    Repeated measures ANOVA
Analysis of variance, two-way, 516
    advantages, 522
    assumptions, 530
    cells in, 516
    and *F* distribution, 529
    F ratios, 529
    factors, use of, 516
    and interaction, 516, 520, 526, 534
    and levels, 515
    logic of, 517
    main effects, 519
    mean squares (variance estimates), 527
    notation, 524
    and partitioning of variability, 525
    and strength of association, 536

Analysis of variance, two-way *(continued)*
    summary table, 532
    sums of squares, 526, 531
Analysis, unit of, 42
Andress, D., 543, 596
Apparent limits of an interval, 75
Appelbaum, M., 311
Archer, E., 136
Arcuri, A., 193, 389
Arntz, A., 69, 177, 198, 370, 447
Association, measures, 170
Assumptions, 316. *See also specific tests;*
        Analysis of variance; Chi-square tests; *r;*
        t-test

Babad, E., 515
Bandura, A., 37, 40, 41, 42, 63, 104
Bar graph, 70, 81
Barrett, P., 389
Batson, C., 514
Beamesderfer, A., 481
Beck, A., 481
Berry, W., 226, 275
Bias
    observer, 46
    in sampling, 17
    subject, 46
Biased standard deviation, 297
Binomial distribution, 257, 391
Bishop, G., 276
Bivariate normality
    assumption of, 388
Blair, R., 602
Blumenthal, J., 311
Bonferroni, 558
Bourne, L., Jr., 136
Box, G., 184
Box-plot, 128
    adjacent values in, 129
    inner fences in, 128
    outliers in, 129
    whiskers in, 129
Bradley, J., 580
Branyan, B., 270
Brazelton, T., 426, 606
Briggs, L., 267, 393
Brown, D., 226, 565
Brumback, R., 445, 623

Calculators, 60
Callahan, C., 448
Campbell, D., 54
Cantu, L., 276
Carman, R., 28
Castellan, N., 618
Causal relationship, 49
Causation, 184. *See also* Causal relationship
Cell. *See* Analysis of variance, two-way
Centerwall, B., 36
Central Limit Theorem, 283, 317
Central tendency, 90, 108
Chance, 19
Charlin, V., 470
Chi-square distribution, 584
Chi-square tests, 581
    chi-square distribution, 584
    for contingency tables, 582, 587
    contingency tables test, 587
    expected frequency, 583, 588
    goodness-of-fit test, 582
    marginal frequencies, 588
    See also Nonparametric methods
Choice of statistic, 632
    key questions, 632
    key words, 634
Coefficient of determination, 175
Coin-tossing example, 21, 251
Coggins, C., 315
Cohen, J., 360
Computer programs for statistical procedures, 61.
        See also SAS PROC; SPSS commands
Computers, 60
Conditional probability, 247, 342
Confidence coefficient, 298
Confidence interval
    for μ, 298, 381
    for $\mu_1 - \mu_2$, 425
Confidence limits, 217
Confirmatory data analysis (CDA), 309
Confounding, 44
Conry, R., 13, 411, 606
Contingency tables, 582, 587
Continuous variable, 41, 260
Control group, 43
Controlled experiment, 51
Cook, T., 54

Coon, D., 28
Correlation, defined, 170
Correlation coefficient, 170
　　Pearson's *r*. (*see* Pearson correlation
　　　coefficient)
　　population, 179
　　Spearman r_S, 615
　　tests of hypothesis about population, 383
Council Reports, 448
Criterion variable, 50
Critical values, 323. *See also specific tests*;
　　　Analysis of variance; Chi-square; *r*; *t*-test
Cronin, C., 277
Crossed, 550
Cumulative frequency distributions, 78
Cumulative relative-frequency distributions, 78
Curvilinear relationship, 174

Daly, J., 559
Darley, J., 514
Darlington, R., 226
DasGupta, B., 13, 30, 62, 63, 338, 411, 606
Data
　　defined, 7, 55
　　qualitative, 56, 581
　　quantitative, 56
Data sets
　　attraction, 100, 159, 480, 544
　　baby-length/adult-height, 54, 100, 185, 217,
　　　239, 399, 616
　　baseline and posting speeds, 75–78, 80–81, 99,
　　　256
　　dental anxiety, 69, 177, 181, 198, 208, 213, 221,
　　　227–233, 370, 384, 447
　　exam stress, 5, 13, 30, 62–63, 164, 338, 340,
　　　347, 351, 364, 411, 414, 424–425, 441–443,
　　　606
　　female alcoholic and nonalcoholic scores, 32,
　　　63, 117–118, 447, 623
　　liar, 5, 32, 53, 64, 104, 244, 272, 361, 470, 475,
　　　485, 494, 499, 506, 611, 619
Decision rules, 325. *See also specific tests*;
　　　Analysis of variance; Chi-square; *r*; *t*
Degrees of freedom
　　analysis of variance, 459, 464, 526
　　AWS *t'*, 422
　　contingency tables test, 590
　　Fisher-Hayter multiple comparison procedure,
　　　492
　　Friedman test, 611
　　Games-Howell multiple comparison procedure,
　　　498
　　goodness-of-fit test, 585
　　groups-by-trials repeated measures design, 560
　　Kruskal-Wallis test, 611
　　one-sample *t*, 373
　　r, 385
　　Ryan multiple comparison procedure, 493
　　simple repeated measures design, 555
　　Tukey multiple comparison procedure, 491
　　two-dependent-sample *t*, 429
　　two-independent-sample *t*, 414
　　working definition of, 374
Dependent variable, 43
DeRenard, L., 600

Descriptive statistics, 19. *See also* Mean; Median;
　　　Pearson correlation coefficient; Range;
　　　Regression; Standard deviation; Variance
Deviation (difference) score, 108, 113
Direct relationship, 172
Directional hypothesis, 321
Discrete variable, 41, 256
Distances, 127
Distribution
　　binomial (*see* Binomial distribution)
　　chi-square, 584
　　defined, 23
　　F, 468, 529
　　frequency (*see* Frequency distribution)
　　normal (*see* Normal distribution)
　　probability, 256
　　sampling (*see* Sampling distribution)
　　skewed, 90
　　t, 373
Dixon, W., 115
Double-blind experiment, 46
Duncan. *See* Multiple comparison procedures
Duncan, D., 361
Duncan-Waller. *See* Multiple comparison
　　　procedures
Dunn. *See* Multiple comparison procedures
Dunn, O., 586

Effect size, 349
Ekman, P., 32, 104, 244, 286, 361, 573
Ekstrom, R., 484, 516
Elementary event, 245
Equal variances, assumption of, 419, 469, 485,
　　　530, 564, 602
Error, 205, 341
　　standard, of estimate, 210
　　See also Type I error; Type II error
Error rates. *See* Multiple comparisons
Estimation, 19, 22, 292
　　biased, 294, 297
　　interval (*see* Confidence interval)
　　point, 292
　　unbiased, 293
Eta squared (η^2), 424, 473, 536
Evans, S., 14
Event, 245
Exhaustive categories, 586, 591
Experimental group, 43
Exploratory data analysis (EDA), 309
Extraneous variable, 44
Extreme scores, 114. *See also* Outliers
Eysenck, H., 43, 300, 308–309, 389
Eysenck, S., 389

F-test. *See* Analysis of variance
Factor, 516
Factorial design, 516
Feingold, A., 138
Feldman, S., 226
Fences. *See* Box-plot
Ferguson, G., 91
Fisher-Hayter. *See* Multiple comparison
　　　procedures
Five-number summary, 126
Fleming, P., 275

Fogg, C., 236
Frank, B., 516
French. J., 484, 516
Frenkel-Brunswick, E., 252
Frequency distribution, 69, 73
　　cumulative, 78
　　relative, 76
Frequency polygon, 83
Friedman, M., 611
Friedman test, 611

Games-Howell. *See* Multiple comparison
　　　procedures
Gelles, R., 310, 448
General linear model (GLM), 219
Gibbons, J., 618
Gilliland, K., 543, 596
Girden, E., 565
Golding, J., 275
Goodness of fit, test for, 582
Graph
　　bar, 70, 81
　　See also Frequency polygon; Histogram; Pie
　　　chart; Scatterplot; Stem and leaf display
Griffiths, R., 14
Gundlach, J., 168, 334, 339

H-spread, 118
Hackworth, R., 27
Hader, R., 45
Half-ranges, 118
Harris, D., 334
Hays, W., 224, 238, 585
Hayter, A., 491
Heijmans, M., 69, 177, 198, 370, 447
Helmstadter, G., 38
Hernandez, A., 364
Higgins, J., 602
Highrange, 118
Hinge, 118
　　position, 118, 126
Hirshoren, A., 270, 305, 335, 372
Histogram, 70, 82
Homoscedasticity, 218
Huff, D., 86
Hurley, O., 270, 305, 335, 372
Hypothesis
　　alternative (H_1), 319
　　defined, 24
　　directional, 320
　　nondirectional, 320
　　nonparametric, 577
　　null (H_0), 318
　　research, 314
　　scientific, 314
　　statistical, 315
Hypothesis testing, 24, 315
　　and assumptions, 316
　　confidence intervals, relation to, 383
　　and correction decisions, 341, 346
　　and critical values, 323, 325
　　and decision rules, 335
　　logic of, 329
　　and one- and two-tailed tests, 322
　　and rejection values, 324

Hypothesis testing *(continued)*
  and sampling distributions, 281, 310
  and significance level (α), 320, 326, 330
  steps, 326
  types of error in, 25, 341
  types of error in, control of, 347
  types of hypotheses in, 318–321

Independence, 247
  assumption of, 317, 378, 388, 393, 419–422,
    433, 439, 469, 485, 530, 564, 578, 586, 591,
    601
  Chi-square test of, 582, 587
Independent variable, 42
Inference, 14. *See also* Estimation; Hypothesis
  testing; Inferential statistics
Inferential statistics, 19
Inner fence, 128
Interaction, 516, 520, 526, 534
Interpolation, of critical values, 649
Interquartile range, 118
Interval estimation, 298, 381, 425
Interval scale, 58
Interval width, 75
Inverse (indirect) relationship, 172
Isaac, N., 275, 436, 448

Jackoway, M., 445, 623
Johnson, J., 282, 389
Joint probability, 248
Joyner, M., 363, 481, 546
Judgment samples, 18
June, L., 450

Kavale, K., 270, 305, 335, 372
Kirby, D., 251
Kirk, R., 565
Klein, K., 361
Kline, L., 600
Kruskal, W., 611
Kruskal-Wallis test, 611
Kurtosis, 90

Lapsley, D., 330
Least-squares criterion, 114, 207, 221
LeBlanc, E., 363, 481, 546
Lee, D., 627
Lester, B., 426, 606
Lester, D., 193, 403, 596
Level of significance, 320
Levels of factors. *See* Analysis of variance
Levinson, D., 252
Lewis-Beck, M., 226
Linear relationship, 169, 174, 200, 220
  negative, 172
  positive, 171
LISAN study method, 28
Loftus, E., 406, 425, 597
Lower hinge, 126
Lowrange, 118
Lu, T., 261, 391
Lurking variable, 184

McCabe, G., 184, 244
McCown, W., 282, 389

McNeil, J., 363, 481, 546
McNemar, Q., 439
McSweeney, M., 297
Madden, D., 311
Main effect. *See* Analysis of variance
Manipulation, 42
Mann, H., 603
Mann-Whitney U test, 603
Marascuilo, L., 297, 618
Marchant-Haycox, S., 286, 308–309, 318, 322,
  334, 345, 364
Marconi, K., 32, 242, 596
Marginal frequencies, 588
Marginal probability, 253
Marini, Z., 75
Marshall, J., 63
Massey, F., Jr., 115
Matching, 408, 430
Math anxiety, 26
Maxwell, S., 558
Mean, 7, 112
  characteristics of, 112–114
  compared to median and mode, 114
  deviation from, 113, 120
  as estimator, 292
  as estimator, unbiased, 293
  population, 116
  sampling distribution of, 282
  standard error of, 283
Mean absolute deviation, 119
Mean difference, 410, 427
Mean squares, 465, 527, 555, 561
Measurement
  scales of *(see* Scales of measurement)
  unit of, 42
Median, 110, 126
  compared to mean and mode, 114
  position, 110, 126
Median absolute deviation, 119
Meier, P., 38
Messick, C., 547–549
Michels, K., 226, 565
Midrange, 118, 127–128
Mills, J., 423
Mischel, W., 4
Mode, 109
  compared to median and mean, 114
Monotonic relationship, 615
Monto, M., 364
Moore, D., 184, 244
Multicollinearity, 222
Multiple comparisons, 485
  error rates, 487, 488
  nonsignificant by implication, 493
  orthogonal, 500, 502
  pairwise, 485–486
  statistics for, 489
  stretch size, 492
  t, 489
  weights, 501
Multiple comparison procedures, 485
  Bonferroni, 558
  Duncan, 490
  Duncan-Waller, 490
  Dunn, 490, 558

Multiple comparison procedures *(continued)*
  Fisher-Hayter, 491
  Games-Howell, 498
  Newman-Keuls, 490
  Ryan, 492
  Scheffé, 490
  Tukey HSD, 491
Multiple correlation, 222
Multiple linear regression, 220
  best equation, 224
  MS_e stopping rule, 225
  and multiple correlation, 222
  standardized regression coefficient, 221
  and standardized variables, 221
  stepwise, 225
Multiplication (And) rule, 248
Murphy, S., 379, 380
Mutually exclusive categories, 248, 586, 591

Nau, P., 75
Negative relationship, 172
Negative skew, 90
Neidhardt, E., 13, 411, 606
Nested, 550
Newcomb, M., 364
Newman-Keuls. *See* Multiple comparison
  procedures
Niedenthal, P., 379, 380
Niemcryk, S., 32, 242, 596
Nominal scale, 56
Nondirectional hypotheses, 321
Nonlinear transformation, 297
Nonparametric hypothesis, 577
Nonparametric methods
  assumptions of, 578, 586, 591, 601
  language about, 577
  versus parametric methods, 579
  reasons for using, 580
  warnings about, 580
  See also Chi-square tests; Rank tests
Nonsignificant by implication. *See* Multiple
  comparisons
Normal distributions, 144
  approximation to binomial, 261
  compared to t distribution, 373
  finding area (proportion) under, 146
  notation, 145
  parameters, 145
  and probability, 260
  role of in hypothesis testing, 317
  standard, 145
Normality, assumption of, 317, 378, 388, 419–
  422, 433, 469, 485, 530, 564, 578
  bivariate, 388
Nowicki, S., 316, 322
Null hypothesis. *See* Hypothesis

Observational research, 52
Observer bias, 46
Omega squared (ω^2), 424, 473, 536
One-tailed test, 323
One-way analysis of variance. *See* Analysis of
  variance
Operational definition, 47
Ordinal scale, 57

Ornish, D., 20, 31, 32, 42, 62, 63, 311
Orthogonal. *See* Multiple comparisons
O'Sullivan, M., 32, 104, 244, 286, 361, 573
Outlier, 129, 183

P. See Proportion, sample
p-value, 325, 330, 333
Padd, W., 481, 544
Palmer, J., 406, 425, 597
Parameters, 16. *See also* Estimation
Parsons, O., 32, 62, 63, 117
Partitioning variability, 213, 219, 460, 523
Peake, P., 4
Pearson correlation coefficient (Pearson's *r*), 170
    assumptions of, 388
    and causation, 184
    computational formula, 176
    defined, 170
    factors in using, 179–183
    and linear relationship, 170
    versus prediction, 199
    properties of, 173–176
    squared, 174
    used in testing hypotheses, 383
    See also Correlation coefficient
Percentile ranks, 154
    compared to *z* scores, 157
Perrine, S., 339
Phelps, L., 270
Pie chart, 83
Pierce, T., 311
Pike, K., 170
Placebo, 39
Planned comparisons, 505
Point estimate, 292
Pooled variance estimate, 418, 457
Population
    characteristics of, 14, 274
    defined, 14
    distribution of, 274
    mean, 116
    variance, 125
Population correlation coefficient. *See* Correlation
    coefficient
Positive linear relationship, 171
Positive skew, 90
Power, 340, 347, 601
    and α, 351
    computation of, 355
    computing sample size for, 359
    and effect size, 349
    hypotheses, 353
    relationship to β and $1 - \beta$, 348
    sample size, 350, 353
    variability, 351
Power efficiency, 601
Powers, J., 63
Predictive relationship, 49
Price, L., 484, 516
Probability
    and addition (Or) rule, 249
    and binomial distribution, 257
    conditional, 247, 342
    defined, 21, 245–246
    distribution and continuous variables, 260
    distribution and discrete variables, 256

Probability *(continued)*
    and elementary event, 238
    empirical, 246
    and event, 245
    and independence, 247
    joint, 248
    marginal, 247
    and multiplication (And) rule, 248
    and mutually exclusive categories, 248
    and normal distribution, 260
    and null hypothesis, 320, 341
    and sample space, 245
    and sampling distributions, 281
    and sampling with (without) replacement, 253
    and significance level, 320
    and statistics, 262
    subjective, 244
    theoretical, 246
    of Type I and Type II error, 341–347
Proportion
    population, 390, 389, 425
    sample, 391

Qualitative data, 56, 581
Quantitative data, 56
Quasi-experimental designs, 54

r. See Pearson's correlation coefficient
r_S. *See* Spearman correlation coefficient
Rabow, J., 364
Ramsey, P., 421
Random sampling, 17
Random variable, 276, 280
Randomizing subjects to groups (randomization),
    44, 409
Range, 118
    half-ranges, 118
    highrange, 118
    interquartile, 118
    lowrange, 118
    midrange, 118, 127–128
    restriction of, 180
Rank tests
    Friedman test, 611
    Kruskal-Wallis, 609
    Mann-Whitney *U* test, 603
    power efficiency of, 601
    sensitivity of, 602
    Spearman r_S, 615
    and sum of ranks, 601
    and tied ranks, 601
    Wilcoxon test, 606
    See also Nonparametric methods
Ratio scale, 58
Real limits, 75
Regression
    confidence limits, 217
    and correlation versus prediction, 199
    defined, 199
    error, 205
    least-squares criterion, 206
    partitioning variability, 213
    predicted score, 200
    and prediction, 200
    prediction equation, 200
    relation to ANOVA, 218

Regression *(continued)*
    relation to correlation, 215
    scatterplots, 204
    slope, 200, 207
    standard error of estimate, 210
    use of, 202
    Y-intercept, 202, 207
    See also Multiple linear regression
Reject hypothesis, 319
Rejection values, 324
Relative-frequency distribution, 76
Relative standing, 139
Reliability, 180
Renner, J., 450
Repeated measures, 408, 430
Repeated measures ANOVA
    assumptions, 564
    assumptions of robustness, 565
    assumptions of sphericity, 564
    and correlated data, 552
    and denominators of F's, 552
    designs, 549
    and estimate of error variance, 552
    groups-by-trials design, 559
    repeated factor, 549
    simple design, 553
    and subjects' variability, 553
    variability, between subjects, 550
    variability, within subjects, 550
Research
    absolute, 38
    comparative, 38
    defined, 38
    observational, 52
Research design, 35, 409
Research hypothesis, 314
Retain hypothesis, 319, 332
Rider, R., 559
Rittiman, T., 276
Rivara, F., 448
Robinson, F., 28
Robustness, 419–422, 433, 439, 469, 485, 530,
    565, 577, 586, 603
Rodgers, J., 334
Rodin, J., 170
Rodrigues, M., 4
Ross, D., 37, 40, 41, 42, 63, 104
Ross, S., 37, 40, 41, 42, 63, 104
Rotter, J., 194, 235, 316, 626
Rounding, 121, 207
Rudd, P., 275
Ryan. *See* Multiple comparison procedures

s^2. *See* Variance, unbiased
$\hat{s}^2$. *See* Variance, sample
Sample
    defined, 16
    distribution of, 276
    size of, 106, 359
Sample proportion, 391
Sample space, 245
Sample variance, 120
    characteristics of, 121
Sampling, 16, 272
    random, 17
    stratified random, 18

Sampling *(continued)*
  with replacement, 253
  without replacement, 254
Sampling distribution, 23, 273, 277
  and estimation, 292, 293
  need for, 281
  of r, 289
  of s^2, 289
  of $\hat{s}^2$, 288
  of sample proportion, 391
Sampling distribution of $\overline{X}$, 279, 282
  computing probabilities, 285–286
  mean of, 282
  shape of, 283
  standard error of, 283
  variance of, 283
Sampling distribution of $\overline{X}_1 - \overline{X}_2$, 417
  mean of, 417
  normal distribution of, 417
  variance of, 417
Sampling variability, 23, 277
Samuels, M., 261, 391
Sanford, R., 252
SAS PROC
  ANOVA, 475, 507, 539, 566
  CHART, 93
  CORR, 187, 228, 398, 621
  FREQ, 593
  MEANS, 131, 476, 507, 539
  NPAR1WAY, 620
  PLOT, 94, 186
  REG, 228
  RSQUARE, 228
  STANDARD, 159
  TTEST, 441
  UNIVARIATE, 131, 396, 442
Scale, change of, 124, 176
Scales of measurement, 56–59
  interval, 58
  nominal, 56
  ordinal, 57
  ratio, 58
Scatterplot, 83, 171, 204
Scheffé. *See* Multiple comparison procedures
Schroeder, L., 226
Schwab, E., Jr., 64
Schwab, R., 64
Schwerin, F., 236
Science, 39
Scientific hypothesis, 314
Scientific methods, 40
Serlin, R., 330
Sharfman, M., 596
Shoda, Y., 4
Shopland, D., 32, 242, 596
Siegel, W., 311, 618
Significance level (α), 320, 326, 330
  and confidence intervals, 380, 425
  effect of, on power, 351
Silberstein, J., 32, 62, 63, 117
Silverman, K., 14
Single-blind experiment, 46
Sjoquist, D., 226
Skewness, 90, 115
Slope, 200, 207
Smith, G., 236

Spearman correlation coefficient (Spearman r_S), 615
Spillich, G., 450
SPSS commands
  ANOVA, 540
  CORRELATION, 191, 399
  CROSSTABS, 594
  DESCRIPTIVES, 163
  EXAMINE, 96, 133
  FREQUENCIES, 96
  NONPAR CORR, 622
  ONEWAY, 477, 509
  PLOT, 189
  REGRESSION, 233
  T-TEST, 443–445
SQ3R study method, 28
Stack, S., 168, 334, 339
Standard deviation
  biased, 297
  characteristics of, 123
  population, 125
  sample, 123
Standard error
  of estimate, 210
  of the mean, 283
Standard normal distribution, 145
Standard scores, 139
  other, 153
  See also z scores
Statistical hypothesis, 315
Statistical packages, 61. *See also* SAS PROC; SPSS command
Statistics, 7, 14
  in research, 13
  and parameters, 16
  and probability, 262
  two areas of, 18
Staub, E., 479, 546, 625
Stephan, P., 226
Stepwise multiple regression, 225
Steger, J., 327
Stem and leaf displays, 78
  back-to-back, 80
Strain, E., 14
Stratified random sampling, 18
Strength of association, 175, 424, 473, 536
Stretch size. *See* Multiple comparisons
Strickland, B., 316, 322
Stubblefield, F., 236
Studentized range distribution, 491
  and Fisher-Hayter, 492
  and Games-Howell, 498
  and Ryan, 493
  and Tukey, 491
Subject bias, 46
Sum of squares, 120, 464, 526, 531. *See also* Analysis of variance
Summation notation, 106, 452
Summation rules, 107

T score, 153
t-statistic
  AWS t', 422
  for multiple comparisons, 489
  one-sample, 373
  for r, 386

t-statistic *(continued)*
  two-dependent-sample, 428
  two-independent-sample, 413
t-test
  one-sample, 371
  two-dependent-sample, 408, 426
  two-independent-sample, 408, 410
Takane, Y., 91
Target group, 14
Terry, W., 394
Test statistic, 314
Theoretical reference distribution, 24
Thompson, K., 470
Tobias, S., 27
Toothaker, L., 490, 536, 558, 564, 611
Treatment group, 43
Tronick, E., 426, 606
True experiment, 51
Tukey HSD. *See* Multiple comparison procedures
Tukey, J., 78
Two-sample research
  characteristics of, 407
  comparison of, 433
Two-tailed test, 323
Type I error, 342
Type II error, 342

Unbiased, property of, 293
Unbiased sample variance, 120, 294
Unit of analysis, 42
Unit of measurement, 42
Upper hinge, 126
U.S. Bureau of the Census, 100

Validity, 180
  external, 55
  internal, 54
Van Eck, M., 69, 177, 198, 370, 447
Van Houten, R., 75
Variability, 23, 90, 116
  mean absolute deviation, 119
  measures of, 117 (*see also* Range)
  median absolute deviation (MAD), 119
  standard deviation, 123
  variance, 120
Variable, 41
  continuous, 41, 260
  criterion, 50, 200
  dependent, 43
  discrete, 41, 256
  extraneous, 44
  independent, 42
  lurking, 184
  predictor, 50, 200
Variance
  explained, 213
  not explained, 213
  population, 125
  sample, 120, 121, 294
  unbiased, 120, 289, 294
Venn diagrams, 223–224
Vernon, P., 627
Vickers, K., 334

Wallbott, H., 515
Wallis, W., 611

Walters, R., 40
Wechsler, H., 275, 436, 448
Weinberg, W., 445, 623
Weinstein, M., 13, 606
West, S., 226
Whisker, 129
Whitney, D., 603
Wickens, T., 591
Wickett, J., 627
Wigfield, R., 63, 275

Wilcox, R., 470
Wilcoxon matched-pairs signed-ranks test, 606
Willis, F., 267, 393, 576, 578
Wilson, G., 300, 286, 308–309, 318, 322, 334, 345, 364
Winer, B., 226, 565
Working definition of degrees of freedom, 374.
    See also Degrees of freedom
Worringham, C., 547–549
Wrather, D., 481, 544

Y intercept, 200, 202

z scores, 140
    percentile ranks compared to, 157
    for the difference of two independent
        proportions, 437
    for the sample proportion, 391
    for $\overline{X}$, 285
$z_{\overline{X}}$ test statistic, 312
Zajonc, R., 379, 380, 547

Credits

Chapter 1: 9, Box 1.1 from *The Oklahoma Daily,* July 2, 1992. Copyright © 1992 Associated Press. Reprinted with permission. **11,** Box 1.2 from "Selling It: Shadow of a Doubt," copyright © 1992 Consumers Union of U.S., Inc., Yonkers, NY 10703-1057. Reprinted by permission from CONSUMER REPORTS, August 1992.

Chapter 3: 68, Figure 3.1 data from the Gallup Organization for SmithKline Beecham; Figure 3.2 data from the Gallup Poll for the National Cattlemen's Association. **69,** Figure 3.3 based on data from "Predictions of Dental Pain: The Fear of Any Expected Evil Is Worse Than the Evil Itself," by A. Arntz, M. van Eck, and M. Heijmans, 1990, *Behavior Research and Therapy, 28*(1), 29–41. Copyright © 1990. Used with permission of Dr. Arntz. **88,** Figure 3.15 data from the United States Census Bureau.

Chapter 4: 104, Table 4.1 from "Who Can Catch A Liar?" by P. Ekman and M. O'Sullivan, 1991, *American Psychologist, 46,* No. 9, 913–920. Copyright © 1991 American Psychological Association. Reprinted with permission. **105,** Table 4.2 from "Who Can Catch A Liar?" by P. Ekman and M. O'Sullivan, 1991, *American Psychologist, 46,* No. 9, 913–920. Copyright © 1991 American Psychological Association. Reprinted with permission.

Chapter 5: 138, Table 5.1 from "Cognitive Gender Differences Are Disappearing," by A. Feingold, 1988, *American Psychologist, 43,* 95–103. Copyright © 1988 American Psychological Association. Reprinted with permission.

Chapter 6: 178, Table 6.3 from "Predictions of Dental Pain: The Fear of Any Expected Evil Is Worse Than the Evil Itself," by A. Arntz, M. van Eck, and M. Heijmans, 1990, *Behavior Research and Therapy, 28*(1), 29–41. Copyright © 1990. Reprinted with permission of Dr. Arntz.

Chapter 7: 209, Table 7.2 from "Predictions of Dental Pain: The Fear of Any Expected Evil Is Worse Than the Evil Itself," by A. Arntz, M. van Eck, and M. Heijmans, 1990, *Behavior Research and Therapy, 28*(1), 29–41. Copyright © 1990. Reprinted with permission of Dr. Arntz.

Chapter 8: 243, Table 8.1 from "Geographic and Gender Variations in Total Tobacco Use," by D. R. Shopland, S. J. Niemcryk, and K. M. Marconi, 1992, *American Journal of Public Health, 82*(1), 103–106. Copyright © 1992 National Cancer Institute. Reprinted with permission. **261,** Table 8.7 from "Sample Size Requirements for the Back-of-the-Envelope Binomial Confidence Interval," by M. L. Samuels and T. C. Lu, 1992, *American Statistician, 46*(3), 228–231. Copyright © 1992 American Statistical Association. Reprinted with permission from the *American Statistician.* All rights reserved. **267,** table to Exercise 11 from "Relationship and Touch in Public

TO THE OWNER OF THIS BOOK:

We hope that you have found *Introductory Statistics for the Behavioral Sciences*, Second Edition, useful. So that this book can be improved in a future edition, would you take the time to complete this sheet and return it? Thank you.

School and address: _____

Department: _____

Instructor's name: _____

1. What I like most about this book is: _____

_____

_____

2. What I like least about this book is: _____

_____

_____

3. My general reaction to this book is: _____

_____

4. The name of the course in which I used this book is: _____

_____

5. Were all of the chapters of the book assigned for you to read? _____

   If not, which ones weren't? _____

6. In the space below, or on a separate sheet of paper, please write specific suggestions for improving this book and anything else you'd care to share about your experience in using the book.

_____

_____

_____

_____

_____

_____

Optional:

Your name: _____ Date: _____

May Brooks/Cole quote you, either in promotion for *Introductory Statistics for the Behavioral Sciences,* Second Edition, or in future publishing ventures?

Yes: _____ No: _____

Sincerely,

Larry E. Toothaker
Lise Miller

- -
FOLD HERE

- -
FOLD HERE

List of Major Formulas

	Formula
Median position	$(N + 1)/2$
Mean	$\bar{X} = \dfrac{\Sigma X}{N}$
Hinge position	Hinge position $= \dfrac{[\text{median position}] + 1}{2}$
Sample variance	$\overset{*}{s}{}^2 = \dfrac{\Sigma(X - \bar{X})^2}{N} = \dfrac{SS}{N} = \dfrac{N\Sigma X^2 - (\Sigma X)^2}{N^2}$
Unbiased sample variance	$s^2 = \dfrac{\Sigma(X - \bar{X})^2}{N - 1} = \dfrac{N\Sigma X^2 - (\Sigma X)^2}{N(N - 1)}$
Standard deviation	$\overset{*}{s} = \sqrt{\overset{*}{s}{}^2}$
Midrange	$UH - LH$
Lower inner fence	$LH - 1.5 \times \text{midrange}$
Upper inner fence	$UH + 1.5 \times \text{midrange}$
z score	$z = \dfrac{X - \bar{X}}{\overset{*}{s}}$
Percentile rank	$PR = \dfrac{f_\Delta(X - LL) + \Delta f_{LL}}{N\Delta}(100)$
Score with a given PR	$X = LL + \dfrac{\Delta[(PR/100)N - f_{LL}]}{f_\Delta}$
Pearson correlation coefficient	$r = \dfrac{\Sigma z_X z_Y}{N} = \dfrac{N\Sigma XY - (\Sigma X)(\Sigma Y)}{\sqrt{[N\Sigma X^2 - (\Sigma X)^2][N\Sigma Y^2 - (\Sigma Y)^2]}}$
Prediction equation	$Y' = bX + a$
Slope	$b = \dfrac{N\Sigma XY - (\Sigma X)(\Sigma Y)}{N\Sigma X^2 - (\Sigma X)^2}$
Y intercept	$a = \bar{Y} - b\bar{X}$
Standard error of estimate	$s_{Y \cdot X} = \sqrt{\dfrac{\Sigma(Y - Y')^2}{N - 2}} = \sqrt{\dfrac{N}{N - 2}}\,\overset{*}{s}\sqrt{(1 - r^2)}$
Independence of A and B	If $p(A|B) = p(A)$, then A and B are independent
Multiplication (And) rule	$p(A \text{ and } B) = p(A|B)p(B) = p(A)p(B|A)$
Addition (Or) rule	$p(A \text{ or } B) = p(A) + p(B) - p(A \text{ and } B)$
Binomial probabilities	$p(r \text{ successes}) = \dfrac{N!}{r!(N - r)!}p^r q^{N-r}$